THIS
BOOK
BELONGS TO
J.P.O.
POTTER
B.M.Sc.

PUBLICATIONS OF
THE WELLCOME HISTORICAL MEDICAL LIBRARY

(*General Editor*: F. N. L. Poynter, Ph.D.)

New Series, Volume XI

THE ORIGINS OF THE NATIONAL HEALTH SERVICE

TO MY PARENTS

C. Edgar and Hedy Lomax

SIR EDWIN CHADWICK (1800-1890)

Whose ideas and principles, while receiving little recognition from his contemporaries, are achieving fruition in the welfare state. *From an original photograph by J. & C. Watkins in The Wellcome Historical Medical Museum and Library. By courtesy of The Wellcome Trustees.*

THE ORIGINS OF THE NATIONAL HEALTH SERVICE

The Medical Services of the New Poor Law,
1834–1871

by

RUTH G. HODGKINSON, Ph.D.

LONDON

THE WELLCOME HISTORICAL MEDICAL LIBRARY

1967

Made and printed in Great Britain by
William Clowes and Sons, Limited, London and Beccles

CONTENTS

v

CONTENTS

SYNOPSIS

PART I, 1834-47

vii

Law Commissioners and British Medical Association inquiries, 1839; Poor Law Commissioners agreed to abandon tender system, 1840; proposed Bill of Provincial Medical and Surgical Association—Poor Law Commissioners too weak to enforce prohibition; Medical Order; Select Committee on Medical Relief, 1844—evidence; salaries; Select Committee, 1838; Provincial Medical and Surgical Association inquiries; various Unions compared; Medical Officers' complaints; Poor Law Commissioners; charges for non-resident sick; reasons for Medical Officers accepting low salaries; activity of Assistant Commissioners; salaries in various Unions compared; variation within a Union; effect on sick; London Medical Officers—salaries and numbers attended; assistance of Farr to Medical Officers; increase in salaries demanded—Provincial Medical and Surgical Association, Kay and other schemes; Poor Law Commissioners' inquiry, 1839; British Medical Association proposals; proposed Bill; Medical Order, 1841; amendments suggested by British Medical Association deputations; additional fees for surgery and consultation; Medical Officers' agitation against inadequacy of Order regarding salaries; criticism of Order by Guardians; Poor Law Commissioners' justification; Select Committee, 1844; demand for higher salaries continued—fixed on pauper list and 'per case' system; General Consolidated Order, 1847; districts—divergency in size; Select Committee, 1838; Farr, Assistant Commissioners, doctors; Poor Law Commissioners inquiry, 1839—British Medical Association, Provincial Medical and Surgical Association; Medical Order, 1842, regarding districts; Rumsey, 1844, other evidence to Select Committee, 1844; 1847 Order. Contracts of Medical Officers —length of tenure of office; Select Committee, 1838; Poor Law Commissioners inquiry; Medical Order, 1842; Select Committee, 1844; Medical Officers oppose annual election; duties under contract—medical order required first; 1842 Order; provision of drugs by Medical Officer; drug dispensaries; quality of medicines; keeping of records by Medical Officers; Select Committees, 1838 and 1844; 1847 Order regarding Medical Officers' Reports; vaccination; duties of workhouse Medical Officers; assessment of efficiency of Poor Law Medical Officers; criticism and complaints against Medical Officers; satisfaction on part of poor—Select Committee, 1844; other peoples' testimony and that of Guardians and Assistant Commissioners; druggists; quacks; midwives; use of assistants by Medical Officers—apprentices, newly qualified, British Medical Association; Status of Poor Law Medical Officers; Poor Law Commissioners accused of prejudice against profession; Provincial Medical and Surgical Association; a Medical Authority demanded—several schemes proposed regarding duties and influence—Select Committees, 1838 and 1844.

No special institutional provision outlined 1834; need for additional accommodation for the sick; advantages of indoor relief; sick poor disinclined to enter workhouse; detailed rules for improvement issued by Poor Law Commissioners; duties of officers; local variation in facilities provided—London, rural areas, large towns; conditions in 'forties not as salutary as officials tried to make out; complaints and criticism of provision by Medical Officers; cross-infection within workhouse; spread of disease into and from neighbourhood; Poor Law

public dispensaries; Rumsey; difficulties overcome after 1840s; growth of dispensaries; specialized institutions.

PART II, 1847-71

leader late 'sixties; Association of Metropolitan Workhouse Medical Officers
formed 1866; Workhouse Infirmary Association; Rogers' influence on Poor
Law Board; Metropolitan Poor Act; Rogers' dismissal from Strand; meetings;
Lancet and private doctors' support for Metropolitan Workhouse Medical
Officers' Association; Rogers advocate of reform of Poor Law Board; Rogers
forms Poor Law Medical Officers' Association. Ireland—dispensaries, super-
annuation; Association assured of future success and permanency, Parliamen-
tary support, demands and future programme; Rogers and Local Government
Act; assessment of his work; value of aid of medical press; importance of Poor
Law Medical Officers for future developments of country's medical system.

Survey 1834–71; change in policy as to who should be given institutional relief,
and in attitude to treatment of sick who now entered workhouses; complacency
of Guardians shaken by doctors; demand for reforms by various unions; some
Guardians made improvements of own accord; intervention of Poor Law
Board—St. Pancras inquiry, 1856; inactivity because of deficient inspection;
Visiting Committees; Medical Officers' Reports; Regional Inspectorate;
Ernest Hart's long analysis of latter and change necessary; need for accurate
returns; Parliamentary returns in 'sixties; workhouses had become large
hospitals; statistics in London; high mortality rate in workhouses; public out-
burst; Wakley; *Lancet* Inquiry, 1865; proposed scheme of reform by *Lancet* and
Association for improving Workhouse Infirmaries; women's movement and
Workhouse Visiting Society; Louisa Twining; Workhouse Infirmary Association; *Lancet*'s second inquiry—improvement noticed; work of Joseph Rogers
in Strand; official inquiries, 1866, through nurses; Poor Law Board deputed
Farnall and Smith to investigate into Metropolitan infirmaries; Smith's long
report and suggested reforms; Cubic Space Committee and further reports by
two Inspectors; Metropolitan Poor Act, 1867; press comments; J. S. Mill;
efficiency of Act; great improvements and activity in construction; activity of
Sick Asylums Districts; Poor Law Board alarmed at expenditure; unification
of Metropolitan Unions and dissolution of four Sick Asylums Districts; activity
of amalgamated Unions, 1869, and of two remaining Sick Asylums Districts;
Poor Law Board induced independent Unions also to undertake improvements
for accommodation of sick, 1869–71; additional buildings erected everywhere;
Poor Law Board attentively watched progress; regulations; Metropolitan
Asylums Board; lunatic asylums, ambulances, isolation hospitals; epidemics,
1869–71; results of Metropolitan Poor Act; resuscitation of Workhouse
Infirmary Association, 1871; Rogers; *Provinces*: Workhouse infirmaries;
Lancet inquiries and Poor Law Board's investigations. Reports of Inspectors on
provincial institutions: Smith's long report on forty-eight infirmaries, 1867;
Poor Law Board and report; Ernest Hart's plan for reform, 1867 (similar to
Metropolitan scheme); Poor Law Amendment Act, 1867; Poor Law Board and
reform; regulations, progress; fever and smallpox epidemics in provinces; conference of Guardians of northern industrial towns regarding grants in aid
demanded; deputation to Poor Law Board. Widespread activity in Unions,
1870; abuses continued, agitation for further reform; superiority of gaols

pointed out; repugnance of poor to enter workhouse remained; deterrence still implied by some officials. Besides development in structural arrangements— also improvements regarding classification—chronics, aged, provision for these people; provisions for maternity; infants; children in workhouses and schools; sickness; nursing in workhouses—great developments.

profession, fear; consequences of 1848 Act on relation between Poor Law and Public Health; provisions of Act; Board of Health; opposition. Subsequent amending legislation; criticisms of Board of Health; appraisal of Chadwick; overthrow of Board of Health; Simon and Medical Department of Privy Council; Poor Law and Public Health, 1854–71; work of Poor Law Board and Guardians in Public Health fields; cholera epidemic, 1849; activity of Poor Law authorities; importance of epidemic to Public Health reform; medical science and epidemic diseases; cholera epidemic, 1853–54; activity of Poor Law authorities; Nuisances Removal Act, 1855; Registrar-General's Statistics; Greenhow's and Simon's Report, 1857, into zymotic diseases; Farr's statistics; smallpox epidemic, 1863–64; cotton famine; Farnall and Rawlinson Reports; cholera epidemic; fever and smallpox, 1869–71; local administrative chaos, overlapping of functions of Poor Law Board and Public Health authorities; agitation for fusion of Poor Law medical service and Public Health, Poor Law Medical Officers, Medical Officers of Health; Rumsey, 1844, Provincial Medical and Surgical Association; Select Committees, 1844 and 1854, evidence on Poor Law—Public Health; Convention of Poor Law Medical Officers; Rumsey, 1854; Chadwick and Rumsey; Simon. Nuisances Removal Act, 1860; Poor Law Medical Officers virtually Medical Officers of Health; *Lancet* objection; Griffin; registration of disease demanded; legislation, 1866, 1867; Royal Commission, 1868–71; Act, 1871; Opinions of leaders of movements; need for consolidated department for Poor Law medical services and Public Health.

Need for 1834 Act; Poor Law Commissioners; Poor Law Board; Inspectorate; Boards of Guardians; Legal system; Government attitude; legislation; doctors; interplay of reformers; societies and other services; Select Committees; Public Opinion; Workhouse Infirmaries; outdoor medical relief; Poor Law and Public Health; value of treatment; narrow scope of medical relief, hence the desirability of divorce from Poor Law, voluntary and self-help auxiliaries; efficiency—but inadequacy of service; first Public Service—functions under Poor Law too many; granting of medical relief to *all* the poor, i.e., increased scope; parent of Welfare State and National Health Service.

Preface

Medical and sanitary care, like education and religious instruction, are matters which
are beyond the means of the largest proportion of the population, and even if some of
the poor temporarily provide for themselves in these respects, they are incompetent
to provide adequately, properly, or continuously.

H. W. Rumsey, Evidence to Select Committee, 1844.

T HE medical provisions of the nineteenth-century Poor Law formed a nucleus for the development of the modern Welfare State. The story is one of optimism and sustained progress, pointing to gradual achievement, despite the act of 1834, its omissions and mistakes.
A growing awareness that the many evils could no longer be ignored made imperative
either reforms or inventions in many fields, ranging from pure medical science to public
and domestic architecture, from civil service to civil engineering. The total upheaval and
those who participated in it emerge in a greater dimension than has hitherto been accorded
them.

Whilst a general knowledge of nineteenth-century economic, political, and medical
history is assumed, the study has been made in the context of labour market conditions and
shows the relationship between social environments, poverty and ill-health, and the influence of philosophical and traditional beliefs among the poor, the ruling classes and local
society.

To underline the inadequacy of the Poor Law medical services a description has been
given of the charitable institutions such as voluntary hospitals and public dispensaries, and
of self-help measures taken by the poor themselves. A survey has been included of medical
relief to paupers in places outside the new Poor Law as well as of the reformers' agitation
regarding the necessity for supplying free medical care to *all* the poor.

Economic, demographic, and historical factors have made it impossible to present a
unified 'English system'. The marked difference between north and south, between agricultural and urban areas in the variety of their problems and solutions provides a separate
interest and makes a contribution to the whole ultimate development. In addition, the subject grew in other ways, and specialization in the care of lunatics, sick children, the aged,
maternity cases, and patients suffering from infectious diseases has been covered.

Progress was made during the period in the workhouse infirmary, in the provision of
competent nurses and especially in the appointment of well-qualified doctors. The Poor
Law Medical Officers, who gradually became an organized body, stand out particularly as
good public servants, fighting not only for recognition and improvement on their own

behalf, but also for positive health measures. They are a new important force, the new experts who struck a path apart from politician, ratepayer, philanthropist, or apathetic rich and poor. Women, too, played their part, and their work, as well as that of many reforming societies has been examined.

The pioneers of the public medical service struggled forcefully against an unsympathetic background and with little legislative aid or guidance. It is not only because their long campaign was eventually successful in its outcome that the variety of their efforts has been described but also to reveal something of the work and interaction of nineteenth-century public opinion, officialdom, local administration, State activity, philanthropists, and social and medical reformers.

This book is therefore long. I hope I have increased its value by giving details rather than generalizations. I have tried to make the study equally interesting to the medical historian, the sociologist, and the student of social and economic history. For those undertaking regional or local research, and for biographers in the health or the political field the wealth of material I have examined may offer a challenge to probe further. This material was frequently difficult to obtain, and often tedious to sift and analyse owing to its quantity and the many discrepancies in the facts presented. I trust that the paths I have traced through it may save others a little time.

Some anomalies and inconsistencies will be found in the statistical comparisons quoted. The figures are printed as they appear in the original reports and papers, but clearly more than one method was used to arrive at annual totals. It must be remembered that the period during which these figures were compiled and used was one when the precise modern techniques of statistical computation had not yet been developed. Readers who may wish to use this statistical information are assured that the figures have been checked with the sources at several stages and that the arguments and comparisons based on them by the advocates of reform are correctly quoted.

My research was begun at a time when there was very little interest in England in the Social History of Medicine. It appears now, after my long absence from the country, when the investigation of this new field is being rapidly expanded. I believe that there is a close and necessary interdependence between the People, Health, and the State, and that only by exploring what has gone before can we understand and effectively solve contemporary problems. I hope that this book makes some contribution to demonstrating the truth of these views.

I owe much gratitude to those with whom I had stimulating discussions in the early days of my research, particularly to the late Dr. H. Sigerist, the late Professor R. H. Tawney, and especially to Mr. H. L. Beales, formerly of the London School of Economics. His inspiring teaching laid the foundations on which many of his students have built. The work was in its original form approved for the Ph.D. degree by the University of London and was aided in its initial stages by a grant from the Central Research Fund of that University and the Metcalfe Studentship for Women. May I take this opportunity of thanking the Record Keepers or Librarians in the following institutions for permission to use documents or books, and also for their kind assistance: The Public Records Office, the County Hall, London, the British Museum, the Wellcome Historical Medical Library, the British Library of Political and Economic Science. the Royal Society of Medicine, the British Medical Association, and the many provincial Town Halls and Libraries mentioned in the text.

No formal acknowledgment could express my indebtedness to Dr. F. N. L. Poynter, Director of the Wellcome Historical Medical Museum and Library. It is due to his interest and encouragement and the most generous gift of his time and knowledge that this book is finally being published.

London

October 1966

Ruth G. Hodgkinson

The Origins of the
National Health Service

PART I—1834-1847

CHAPTER 1

The New Poor Law and the
Medical Services 1834–47

THE new Poor Law was thrust on England in an age of economic and social dislocation. The grave consequences of this upheaval were the mass of actual pauperism engendered and the migratory army of poor who were turned adrift to find livelihood and shelter in the new urban slums. Action for this chaotic flotsam and jetsam was inevitable, but fear was its conditioning agent; and national unrest made immediate legislation in the early 'thirties imperative.

The Act of 1834, however, was no emergency measure rushed through Parliament, for the famous Royal Commission had a long time in which to consider the causes of the old disease and the new remedies which were needed. It was therefore to the shortcomings of the prevailing economic and political philosophy, and the composition of the legislature, that the failings of the Act must be attributed. Landed gentlemen, with their ears attuned only to agricultural riots, lacked understanding and prescience of the economic future of the country. Therefore the Act was based on a faulty diagnosis. Saint Simon had not been read.

The faulty diagnosis resulted in the two cardinal principles of the Act being deterrence and rigid centralization. For poverty, it was maintained, originated in some inherent moral vice of the poor, and this had remained uncurbed through the over indulgence and laxity of the administration. An article in the *Edinburgh Review* clearly illustrated this belief. It declared that it was the weakness of the central authorities that had led to an increase in pauperism, and it was this failing which the new Act tried to combat. Rigid control would remove the dominant cause of pauperism. 'The new principles came out in opposition— almost antithesis—to previously received doctrines.' The writer continued that the source of misplaced sympathy to pauper classes arose from the impression produced by the weekly bankruptcy list, and the belief had been created that numerous respectable families had been reduced to pauperism by the vicissitudes of trade. Whilst the Poor Law inquiry had been proceeding there had been an enormous outcry against the distress which was said to be pervading the trading classes, particularly in the Metropolis—distress arising from the decay of trade and from pressure of taxes. It was roundly asserted that in a populous street (Regent Street) every third shopkeeper was insolvent through economic circumstances. This was assumed to be the indirect but potent element of pauperism, but the anonymous writer in the *Edinburgh Review* asserted that if the cases were examined, the instances of blameless distress in trade were as rare as the cases of unavoidable and blameless poverty. He therefore concluded that pauperism was rooted in the vices of the individual and that the problem was magnified by misapplied charity.[1]

Because the new measure was based on faulty analysis, no provision was made to destroy the real old roots and equally important new roots of pauperism. Relief remained a palliative, and the question was left unsolved in the nineteenth century. Although it continued to be the dominant Poor Act for eighty years, its shortcomings were registered, not only in the great number of amending Acts which changing circumstances made necessary, but also in the divergence from national uniformity which was tolerated to make allowances for varying local characteristics.

The new Poor Law was based on the prevailing *laissez-faire* principles in so far as the administration aimed at a gradual restriction in the amount of assistance afforded, and the fostering of self-help through sick clubs, benefit societies, and savings banks.[2] Benjamin Franklin's analysis was to be applied: 'I observed in the different countries, that the more public provisions were made for the poor, the less they provided for themselves and of course became poorer.'[3] But the Act diverged from *laissez-faire* in the rigid centralization which was to be enforced. This was to combat the incompetence and corruption of the local authorities, which had been exposed by the Royal Commission. It was Chadwick's idea to replace their inadequate administration by that of a central staff of salaried public servants, with specialized knowledge, who would formulate a uniform policy for the local executive to obey. The local servants were, however, also changed; for the Poor Law dethroned the country gentlemen, 'it left them either excluded from influence in the management of their own parishes, or forced them to accept a seat on the Board of Guardians to debate among shopkeepers and farmers'.[4] Hence the great opposition by the magistrates to the new Poor Law.

Acting on the principle of utilizing the self-interest of the ratepayers, the Poor Law Commissioners' promised economy would only be realized by the abolition of parochial management and the formation of large Unions, and the segregation of pauper classes would only be possible with an aggregation of the atomic bodies in comprehensive authorities. It was decided that no discretion was to be granted to these bodies in the administration of relief, because a repetition of the old evils might occur. They were to become comparatively cheap instruments, whose self-interest as ratepayers would provide a check on any rashness to which the Central Board might be tempted. But as the Poor

[1] 'Extracts from the information received by His Majesty's Commissioners as to the administration and operation of the Poor Laws. . . ', *Edinburgh Review*, 1836, **63**, 493–4.

[2] Very frequent references were made to encouragement of these in Commissioners' Annual Reports.

[3] In *London and Westminster Review*, 1837, **26**, 362.

[4] A. de Tocqueville, letter, 18 February 1851—*Correspondence and Conversations of Alexis de Tocqueville with Nassau Senior 1834–59*, edited by M. C. M. Simpson, 1872.

Law Commission was a curious hybrid, a legal body without Parliamentary voice, it became a supervising and regulating authority, expressly restrained from interfering in individual management. Therefore in time the administration of the Poor Law became a partnership between central and local government. The Union authorities, reorganized and placed on a representative basis, assumed a position in many ways unassailable by the Central Board. And this was what the legislature had intended; for in dread of patronage and jobbing it delegated the appointment of paid officers to local Guardians, while confiding to the Commissioners the power of prescribing the qualifications and salaries of the officials, and of determining their continuation in office.

The Boards of Guardians, because they became a deeply-rooted institution in the life of the country, increasingly influenced the development of provisions for relief. Hard work and heavy responsibility fell on them, and as they were not confirmed converts to the new principles of 1834, they sometimes applied the brake to an occasional acceleration towards improvement in central policy. In 1839 the Poor Law Commissioners were forced to declare that they 'always abstained from doing anything which might extinguish the spirit of local independence and self-sufficiency', and before relinquishing office they complained that much criticism which had been levelled against them was unjust, 'for such local abuses as may occur, the Guardians are primarily responsible. They have the chief part of local responsibility.'

In no sphere of Poor Law administration was the deference to pure central control deviated from so much as in the supply of medical relief. This was because neither the Royal Commission nor the subsequent Act made any recommendations for the institution of a medical service. Nassau Senior himself, however, had written to Lord Howick (letter, 1831) that there should be compulsory provision for medical treatment of disease and insanity, although he opposed it for the aged and orphans. But the idea was never openly canvassed, and the Poor Law Commissioners had to build up a system with responsible functionaries where comparatively few foundations existed. As no Poor Law medical acts were passed subsequently, their Orders and Regulations, dictated by some exigency, provided the only compulsory direction to the Guardians. A social service therefore grew gradually, but its efficiency and salutariness suffered because it depended on constantly changing quantities and on the vagaries of sceptical local authorities.

The denial of outdoor relief to the able-bodied pauper was the dominant principle of the Act, but the sick and mentally defective were expressly excepted from the prohibitory order. The proposed Poor Law Bill of 1840 contained suggestions approved by Nassau Senior and the three Commissioners for extending the statutory right to outdoor relief to cases of urgent necessity, illness in the family, widows, and wives and families of soldiers,[1] but the Bill was abortive and the 1834 Act remained unaltered, subsequent prohibitory Orders reaffirming its principles. *The Times* declared of the Act of 1834 that 'a more

[1] Chadwick found this in Nassau Senior's papers. 'Statutory Sanction of Outdoor Relief to Able-bodied in Contravention of Principles of Poor Law Amendment Act.' Letter of Chadwick's to Normanby, Home Secretary, 1840; requoted by T. Mackay, 1900, in *A Recurrent Error.*

dangerous, more mischievous, or a more unconstitutional measure was never penned'.[1] The objection was to its strict centralization, but the criticism would have been more justifiable had it referred to the arbitrary differentiation between the 'deserving poor' and the 'rogues' being made between sick and able-bodied. This harshness of the new Poor Law had its roots in enactments of previous centuries, and even in 1832 Archbishop Whately had suggested tattooing or cutting-off of women's hair as a means of branding the able-bodied.[2] Dr. Kay (Shuttleworth) pointed to the advantages of the new system in refusing indiscriminate relief.

> In the absence of scale allowances, marriages among cripples, the victims of scrofula, and other hereditary taints, have been more rare, and the transmission of such deformities and maladies less frequent. Moreover, when apathy and physical inertness are encouraged, a more general neglect of cleanliness and a less careful provision for the household prevail. The independent and pauperized poor may thus be compared. The wife of a pauper is more generally a slattern, the cottage less cleanly, the children fed on more meagre food, and the habits of the father more profligate, than those of the industrious labourer. The tendencies of such defects in the domestic and social condition of the class are the spread of physical degeneracy, and I am prepared to find that statistical documents will prove that a pauper population contains more idiots, more victims of scrofula, more defective and helpless beings; and that children die younger than in a population 'cet par' not maintained on scale allowances.[3]

Some Unions, however, were slow in carrying out the chief stipulation of the Act immediately. A letter of Chadwick's revealed, for example, that: 'No order had yet been issued to the Wallingham Union forbidding outdoor relief to any class of pauper male or female.'[4] Assistant Commissioner Power reported to the Central Board in 1836 that his investigations had led him to believe that the distinction was not at once desirable.

> The unequal rate of wages existing in different localities, and the unequal resources of the different strata of the labouring population, inequalities mainly induced and sustained by the system of the Poor Law hitherto prevailing, might render the sudden introduction of one unvarying line of distinction the occasion of harshness, in its immediate application to particular districts. . . . The regulations are not expected to lay down any absolute and imperative rule with respect to the allowance of medical relief to the able-bodied class . . . but the new principles should be introduced without delay, and to such a degree as the circumstances of each particular Union might admit. I feel assured that your regulations on this head of medical relief, did not enforce any line of proceeding directly tending to the exclusion of any portion of the class of able-bodied from the pale of medical pauperism.[5]

[1] Leading article, 1 July 1834.
[2] E. J. Whately, *Life and Correspondence of Archbishop Whately*, London, 1866, Vol. 1, p. 163.
[3] J. P. Kay, M.D., 'Report on Suffolk and Norfolk', p. 147. Second Annual Report, 1836.
[4] Minutes of the Poor Law Commissioners, 27 August 1836.
[5] A. Power, Assistant Commissioner, Essex, Cambridgeshire, and part of Hertfordshire.

Therefore, as doubts remained as to who was entitled to assistance, and probably impelled by Chadwick's desire for an immediate and rapid introduction of the new principles, the Commissioners attempted to make the situation quite clear in a circular sent out in 1836, stating: 'Medical relief in cases of sickness or accident . . . is the condition on which all applications for outdoor relief are to be decided.' Again in the following year the Commissioners wrote in an Instructional Letter to Guardians:

In all cases which may hereafter arise, it will be necessary to adhere strictly to the provisions of the 43rd of Elizabeth in administering to 'the *necessary* relief of the lame, impotent, old, and blind', and such other among them being poor, and not able to work, as well as relieving the children and the able-bodied. By the words of the act you are only entitled to relieve those capable of working 'who have no means to maintain them'. None therefore are legally entitled to relief who have any property or any means, or who are not in a state of absolute destitution, and in danger of perishing from want if relief is withheld. . . .

From the pauper lists of some Unions it appeared that several Boards of Guardians carried out this principle to the letter. St. Margaret's and St. John's, Westminster, only granted outdoor relief, and in 1842 one of the lists showed the only people who were eligible:

> 56 widows old and ill
> 5 men old or ill
> 15 married couples old and ill
> 4 single women

This also reveals that the aged, impotent, and infirm were to be granted outdoor relief—and they were generally treated leniently. Assistant Commissioner Weale in 1836 reported that in the counties of Gloucester, Worcester, and Somerset, the 'aged, impotent, and helpless have . . . in the majority of cases . . . been placed on a higher scale of allowances than they were by their respective parishes previous to the formation of the Unions'. In the fifteen rural counties which had come under the new Poor Law by the end of 1835 over 6,000 aged, insane, and orphans were receiving indoor relief, and over 42,000 outdoor relief per quarter, out of a total population of $1\frac{1}{2}$ million.

By the end of 1837 there were nearly 9,000 indoor and 55,000 outdoor paupers relieved in this class in three months. In the first quarter of 1839 over 236,000 aged alone received outdoor relief, and by the following year this had risen to nearly a quarter of a million. From 1842 statistics became more elaborate and annual tables were produced giving a comparative statement of the number of aged and infirm outdoor paupers relieved in England and Wales during the first quarters of the years, Table 1.1.

Not only were the principles of 1834 gradually reversed for the aged and infirm, but it was found increasingly impossible to give institutional relief to the able-bodied and temporary sick. In the early years, however, a determined but unsuccessful attempt had been

TABLE I.I

Comparative statement of the Number of Aged and Infirm Outdoor Paupers, partially or wholly disabled, relieved during the Quarters ending Lady Day, 1842 and 1843, in 584 Unions in England and Wales.—Tenth Annual Report of the Poor Law Commissioners, 1844. (The following figures are taken from the Annual Reports for the years 1845, 1846, and 1847.)

	Wholly unable to work		Partially able to work		Total
	Male	Female	Male	Female	
584 Unions					
1842	59,747	111,584	31,118	69,320	271,769
1843	63,878	116,973	34,387	73,510	288,748
585 Unions					
1844	67,262	119,655	34,407	73,258	294,582
1845	68,311	123,350	35,918	75,115	302,694
1846	66,049	123,115	33,816	72,386	295,379

made to relieve all sickness in the workhouse and to abolish outdoor assistance altogether. As Kay (Shuttleworth) declared: 'The gradual disallowance of outdoor medical relief may require the exercise of greater prudence than the removal of other forms of outdoor relief, but this form of dependence is unnecessary and injurious'; and in their Second Annual Report the Commissioners affirmed that 'the main object of the Poor Law Amendment Act, as it was the first recommendation of the Commissioners of Inquiry, was expressly declared to be the ending of *all* outdoor relief to the able-bodied'; but they continued that the rule was with very few exceptions applied only to the able-bodied male paupers. Charles Mott reported from Middlesex and Surrey that: 'The Poor Law Amendment Act may indeed be called an Act of renovation, for it causes the lame to walk, the blind to see, and the dumb to speak.' He intended to imply that the workhouse acted as a deterrent to imposters, but the attempted refusal to give outdoor relief or even medical relief only, to the sick pauper, was a direct contravention and misinterpretation of the Act of 1834, and the Unions which followed this practice caused great hardship and suffering to the poor.

Guardians of the Ampthill Union in Bedford continued this policy rigidly throughout the century and even refused assistance to cripples, unless they entered the workhouse, which meant their losing both cottage and furniture. The Select Committee of 1838 heard evidence of several cases of relief having been refused here where wives but not the husbands were sick, or where the men would enter the workhouse to avoid breaking up their homes. In this Union no one could claim gratuitous medical attention unless he was already a pauper before the illness.[1] Atchen Union in Shropshire, which for generations

[1] James Turner, evidence to Select Committee on the Further Amendment of the Poor Law Act, 1838, B.P.P., 1840, xvii.

6

refused outdoor relief to the able-bodied, discontinued a man's relief because he refused to send his children to the workhouse. His wife desired medical attention at her confinement, but on applying for this, the order was given for the admission of the children into the workhouse. The Guardians wrote to the Medical Officer: 'It is the opinion of this Board that an able-bodied man with only two children, where no peculiar circumstances affecting such a man's situation exist, should procure medical attention for his wife in her confinement, and you are not therefore required to attend the wife in your capacity as Medical Officer of this Union.' Hove and Rye Unions also refused to give any outdoor medical relief, but in Norfolk and Suffolk sick mothers and children were offered medical attention in their homes, and as the years went by a far greater proportion was given outside the workhouse, where provisions were quite inadequate for the large numbers of destitute. Although in the first three years following the Act the proportion of institutional medical relief increased over outdoor assistance, an overwhelming majority of paupers were attended in their own homes. This can be seen from figures published in the first quarters of 1835, 1836, and 1837, Table 1.2.

TABLE 1.2

Paupers relieved because of temporary sickness

First quarter	Indoor	Outdoor
1835	240	4,584
1836*	646	11,089
1837	337	4,481

* Five additional counties included in this year.

The Commissioners realized the inevitability of this trend and were well aware that disease speedily reduced the independent poor labourer to destitution. They therefore believed that in these circumstances it was less repugnant for the poor to apply for medical relief, and more difficult for the parish to scrutinize the necessity for granting it, so that where outdoor relief in money or kind was denied medical aid could still be obtained. As an inducement therefore to the labourer to maintain his independence and to prevent his falling on Union resources even in cases of illness or accident, Guardians were to foster the formation of independent sick clubs.[1]

By the Act the Commissioners were only empowered to make regulations for the treatment of the sick if they were relieved in the workhouse. No attempt was made to interfere with the existing practice under which sick paupers received outdoor relief. The sole legislative guidance the central authorities received was that they should make rules for directing and controlling local officers, and that any magistrate could sanction an order

[1] Instructional letter respecting formation of Medical Clubs, 3 May 1836.

for medical attendance without restriction in cases of sudden or dangerous illness. It was from these two meagre clauses that the provision of a regular medical service had to evolve. As Richard Earle wrote: 'There is no part of the arrangement connected with the relief of the poor of more real importance and none to which less has been commonly attached, than the means of supplying medical aid to the poor.'[1]

The necessity of granting efficient treatment to the sick poor had been ably stated as early as 1819. Henry Lilley Smith[2] realized that illness arose chiefly from 'the unwholesome nature of employment, or the disorders and accidents that are common to all', and that in all such cases 'it is absolutely necessary that relief should be administered as speedily as possible'. Parsimony, he affirmed, increased parochial burdens which reasonable aid would have prevented. 'Instant relief to the poor when in sickness is in great measure to save money to the parish . . . yet by hesitation and delay . . . the evil is allowed to become inveterate. . . . How mistaken is our treatment of the sick pauper!'

The medical services provided before 1834 varied throughout the country, and great diversity of opinion was entertained concerning medical relief. The independent northern poor were offered little relief—'Black beer' and gin, or Morrison's pills, were commonly their only treatment. In the agricultural south the poor regarded the receipt of parochial medical aid as a right, but even here, and in Worcestershire, relief was given on a very small scale, most parishes spending little more than £15 to £20 a year on a doctor. In the north where the prevalence of unqualified quacks made relief both inefficient and insufficient, and in the south where the Medical Officers were often overworked, there is no doubt that the amended Poor Law was hailed by the medical profession as an opportunity for reforming the abuses in their department.

Unfortunately, in the years that followed, all proposals for the improvement of the medical system were received with distrust and suspicion, and were generally rejected by the central authorities who, neglecting to appoint a medical adviser, remained ignorant of the necessities of the sick and the nature of their duties in this field. Two ideas motivated the action of the Commissioners: one, that the recommendations of doctors sprang from self-interest; and the other, that there was danger in making Poor Law medical relief superior to that afforded to the remainder of the working class. This was the excuse given in 1841, when they pointed to the difficulties attending the provision of a complete system of medical relief. For in medical relief, as in general relief, strict differentiation was to be made between poor and pauper.

Before 1834 it was the common practice in many rural areas for the Medical Officer to enter into a general contract for attending the sick poor. His remuneration was pitifully low and his liability indefinite. Parochial authorities granted orders for assistance without scruple, and without reference to the circumstances of the applicant, for each case was attended without incurring additional expense to the parish. Medical men acquiesced in

[1] Assistant Commissioner, Northamptonshire and Warwickshire, 1836 Report.
[2] *Observations on the Prevailing Practice of Supplying Medical Assistance to the Poor, Commonly Called Farming of Parishes*, 1819.

this unfair advantage taken of them from fear of losing their appointment, which would be detrimental to their private practice. Therefore, in poor districts, the whole mass of the labouring population might be constituted medical paupers. Because the parish doctor could not afford to supply so large a class of patients with the best drugs and treatment, the 'indigent true poor', the 'legitimate objects of parish relief', had been made to suffer in the medical, as in other departments of relief, 'from the rash and indiscriminate attempt to extend the implications of the word "poor" to parties never contemplated by the original spirit of the poor law'.[1] It was for this reason that all the Assistant Commissioners recommended in their first reports that the primary object of any change in the system of providing medical relief should be to diminish the liabilities of the medical contractor, by excluding those who had previously been improperly admitted to parish benefits.

The first rule of the central authorities, therefore, directed Guardians to contract for attendance on paupers only, words which involved far greater changes in the administration of medical relief than was anticipated. In the Instructional Letter to various Boards of Guardians on their formation,[2] the Commissioners pointed out that poor rates were by law confined to the relief of absolute destitution, and that medical relief should not, as frequently assumed, be provided for the whole of the labouring classes. Although, they continued, it might appear at first sight that the application for medical relief should be treated with indulgence, yet a 'closer view of the causes and effects of pauperism would show that they would thereby produce evils of considerable magnitude'. Medical relief, they believed, operated as an easy introduction to further applications. They pointed to the districts which had 'correctly administered' medical relief, so that sick clubs and self-supporting dispensaries had rapidly increased, affording to the poor 'more efficient relief than could be hoped for by any form of parochial relief'.

When the Act had been in operation for only two years the Commissioners could confirm that the efficacy of such an arrangement had been proved. Their Second Annual Report stated that as relief was confined to the really destitute, the new system had already converted many paupers into independent labourers, and that they were providing against the contingency of medical pauperism through their clubs. The Assistant Commissioners, however, questioned whether the success of the policy was as rapid as had been hoped in reducing medical relief itself. Assistant Commissioner W. H. F. Hawley stated that there had been a general decrease in pauperism in Sussex, extensive beyond all expectations, but that he regretted he was unable to report 'medical relief as exhibiting a corresponding ratio of diminution'. He had tried to follow the instructions of the Poor Law Commissioners in attempting to abolish this species of relief to the able-bodied, but had found it difficult to overcome the deeply rooted and generally received opinion, entertained concurrently by the Guardians, Medical Officers, and the poor, that the parish doctor was a sort of permanently established dispensary, to whom all the labouring classes had a right

[1] Power's Report. Second Annual Report, 1836.
[2] 31 January 1837.

to apply for assistance. In Cambridgeshire and Essex, Power's endeavours had also been frustrated in many Unions; so, to overcome the indiscriminate provision of medical relief, and the vague and indefinite contract between the Medical Officer and the Guardians, he proposed the adoption of a pauper schedule of aged and sick, which would exclude the improvident poor. But such was the inveterate state of medical pauperism, that it was quite impossible for Guardians to pursue a line of strict exclusion of improper subjects for relief without incurring a risk of harshness and severity. Power therefore stated that an auxiliary service in the form of medical clubs was imperative.

Where the practice of limiting the amount of medical assistance was enforced, however, it was regarded as successful by Poor Law officials. For when the Commissioners asked for a report from all Unions in 1836 as to the efficiency of the policy, only one Union (Uppingham) stated that medical assistance was not as salutary as previously because no person could obtain aid without being actually destitute. Arrangements were stated to be fully as efficient by 112 Unions, and more so by 61. Again, of the 296 Unions sending reports, 177 declared that the medical arrangements were found to be fully as adequate for the relief of paupers, five said they were superior, and only Tamworth complained that the arrangements were not altogether sufficient. Nearly all the explanatory letters from the Clerks of the Unions to Chadwick read to the effect that great improvements had been accomplished through the new regulations, and that there was greater efficiency. Fewer paupers were seeking medical relief as they were apprehensive of applying for orders, and therefore medical costs had been reduced.

To increase the spirit of independence in the poor was just a spurious argument of the Poor Law authorities for scrutinizing rigidly all applications for relief; the whole pivot of the principle was the reduction in costs. This was the test of efficiency, and there was no other for adequacy. Shaw-Lefevre, one of the three Poor Law Commissioners, wrote in 1837 to Lord John Russell, the Home Secretary, suggesting various alterations in the Poor Law,[1] but he emphasized that ' . . . the most obvious and most immediate benefit which has resulted from the Poor Law Amendment Act, is *the very great reduction of the rates*', and concluded that the destitute had benefited and had not suffered through the fall in expenditure of over £1½ million, in two years. In the same year it was found that decreases from 20 to 65 per cent had been achieved, and Unions like Thame (Lincoln) received special comment because it had reduced its medical expenditure from £66 to £44. Of Swaffham Union (Norfolk) it was said that reduction had led to a healthier and higher tone of feeling among the working class.[2]

Evidence was given to the Select Committee of 1838 that in pauperized districts only half the number were receiving medical relief who formerly had it: 'all the poor were once medically pauperized; the Guardians now exercise a discretion—but humanely'![3] Sir Eardley Smith, writing to Chadwick that no resident Medical Officer could be found

[1] Poor Law Commissioners' Records, 23 February 1837.
[2] Poor Law Commissioners' Records, January 1837.
[3] Evidence, Assistant Commissioner Gulson, Select Committee, 1838.

in his area to undertake Poor Law duties because of the meagreness of the remuneration, stressed the fact that Guardians would render the existing salaries adequate if they diminished the numbers for which the Medical Officers were contracting to attend. It amounted to condemning the poor to suffer in order to save the ratepayers' pocket. Smith did not make his argument sound as callous as the inference, because he endeavoured to show that paupers who would receive medical attention would benefit from greater individual care.

This was true. It was not so much the actual treatment they received, but the principle of the administration affecting eligibility for it, that the poor objected to most vehemently. The Medical Officer of the Peterborough Union complained to his Guardians that they were not sending many cases to him, because they adhered to the rule of never allowing medical relief to any labourer who had any means whatsoever. At a large meeting held in 1836 in Worcestershire for the purpose of censuring the medical service of the Poor Law, the Medical Officer of the Pershore Union stated that from his weekly returns of thirty-eight parishes it could be seen that only nine cases of midwifery and four cases of fracture were sent to him. The doctors at the meeting realized it was impossible and impracticable for every maternity case to be attended by a surgeon, but they complained that they were never sent for until a case had become serious or even fatal.

The Medical Officers were the most blameless party in the provision of medical relief. In answer to the Inquiry about the doctors which the Commissioners sent to the Guardians in 1836, 199 Unions stated that they had received no complaint from the poor as to their treatment, and the thirty-eight who had received complaints declared the majority of these had proved groundless on investigation. The Assistant Commissioners furnished similar reports on the doctors. In Essex and Cambridge, for example, there was not a single complaint against them; even Unions in which an unusual degree of illness existed said every attention was paid to the patient. A letter to Chadwick from the Chairman of a Worcestershire Union[1] spoke of the improvement which the new medical system had brought about. Formerly eleven parishes in the Union were doctored by people who had 'no other pretension than having been a shop boy to a druggist or grocer'. Therefore the poor had been exposed to the worst treatment, but had now been rescued from their hands and were being attended by doctors of skill, experience, and good moral character, under the strictest observation of the Guardians. The Commissioners depended on reports such as these to facilitate the introduction of the Poor Law and make it popular.

The first test case for the Poor Law medical services came at the beginning of 1837. In February, Commissioner Shaw-Lefevre communicated with the Home Secretary on the severe outbreak of influenza which prevailed. Speaking of the epidemic, he wrote: 'I believe I can confidently state that we have not received a single complaint of the inadequacy of medical attendance.' The Assistant Commissioners were asked to investigate conditions in the various areas under their supervision. Every Union in Hampshire and

---

[1] Major-General M. Marriott, Chairman, Pershore Union, Worcester, 1836.

Wiltshire, for example, was visited, and not a single instance of neglect or insufficiency of attendance on the poor by the Medical Officer was heard.

> Although worn down with fatigue . . . [the doctors] performed their duties in a most praiseworthy and exemplary manner. The Relieving Officers have been active, and have invariably been instructed to administer to the sick whatever articles the medical gentlemen deem necessary. General as the sickness has been—the mortality has not been so great as might have been expected.[1]

In Sussex

> little or no complaint was made either by the poor, as having been neglected, or on the part of the Medical Officers being unable to fulfil their duties from the overwhelming accession of new cases accruing from the disease. . . . Other cases on the medical lists have been doubled or trebled . . . through the prevalence of the epidemic, but not an instance has come to my knowledge of any expression of discontent or avowal of inability to pay proper attention to patients by Medical Officers. . . . The amount of expenditure for outdoor relief during the quarter has been considerably increased by the number of cases which have been relieved on the plea of emergency in consequence of sickness.[2]

In Kent also, medical relief was reported to have been much more efficient than it was previously, and in twelve Unions only seven deaths resulted in 2,200 cases. Here one Medical Officer, who had for the past ten years given gratuitous attention one day a week to the poor, amounting to 1,500 to 2,000 cases a year, said that before the introduction of the new system the poor had complained to him incessantly of the insufficiency of medical relief, but since the new law had come into operation he had not heard one expression of dissatisfaction. The doctor attributed this to the impossibility, under the new arrangements, for the Medical Officer to neglect his work without being detected. This was explained in the Third Annual Report: 'Medical Officers are now under the superintendence of the leading persons of the district'—the local Board of Guardians—'to these the Medical Officer is responsible in his character as a practitioner. He is dismissed also on any well authenticated complaint to this Board [Commissioners]. He is required to report to the Guardians his visits to his patients in the workhouse. He is as a further security required to register the particulars of each case, the character of the disease and of its treatment. These records serve as a guide to the Guardians in the administration of relief, and we are assured that they will become available as a valuable body of medical statistics.'

The latter expressed admirable hopes, which were not, however, realized, and the Guardians had very few other guides to resort to. In the first two years only two orders were issued by the central board on the subject of medical relief. In 1839 it stated that

[1] Colonel A'Court.
[2] Hawkins.

'medical attendance . . . did not seem to call for any immediate general change.'[1] The Commissioners could not understand the opposition and complaints which were registered to the Home Office, nor the perseverance with which it was maintained that the system of medical relief was inadequate and injurious to the medical profession. They questioned why this should be so, as it had been their wish and intention to provide adequately for this important branch of relief by interfering as little as possible in local arrangements. The central authorities failed to realize that the cause of the complaints lay in their own inaction and because they gave so few directions to the local executive.

During the whole period from 1834 to 1847 there was nothing in the Commissioners' Orders showing a change in policy, and only the General Medical Order of 1842 and the General Consolidated Order of 1847 provided any guidance for the establishment of a comprehensive medical system. The Select Committees of 1838 and 1844, and the agitation of the Provincial Medical and Surgical Association and the short-lived first British Medical Association, paved the way for these two Orders. Most witnesses to the first Select Committee stated that although many of the evils of the old system had been corrected, many new ones had arisen. Medical districts were too large, and the number of doctors too few, to conduce to efficiency. The Committee felt 'it to be most important that the poor should be perfectly satisfied with their attendants' and that as the Poor Law Medical Officer treated the poor with such 'great liberality and humanity' it hoped some of the objections that had been pointed out by them would be removed.

In the following year the British Medical Association interested itself in the problem and wrote to the Commissioners that its investigations revealed that the provision of medical relief always depended on the feelings and conduct of the Board of Guardians. Because of this it had in some Unions been administered with unnecessary harshness, producing great discontent, while in others it had been mildly administered and had given great satisfaction. It directed attention to the lack of uniformity and pointed out that some of the gravest evils arose from the varying methods of selecting and paying Medical Officers, from the large size of medical districts, and from the attempt to deter paupers from seeking medical assistance—all of which sprang from the motive of rigid economy which Guardians had been induced to adopt. From inquiries that the Association had made throughout the country in 1838 it had found that, on the whole, the sick had not been discouraged to any appreciable extent from applying for relief, but that the practice varied. Where the 'per case' system of paying the Medical Officer obtained, so that each order constituted an additional expense to the parish, orders were withheld; but where salaries were fixed and the trouble and expense fell on the medical practitioner, orders were often indiscriminately given. Midwifery cases were also numerous when included in the general salary, but less frequent when paid for separately. Lack of uniformity was also evident in the method by which the aged and infirm could apply for relief. Some Unions drew up a 'pauper list', members of which required no orders, but more frequently orders had to be

[1] Report on Further Amendment of the Poor Law, 1839.

3

obtained, the surgeon being enjoined not to attend without them except in cases of emergency. This the Association's deputation found oppressive to the poor when the Relieving and Medical Officers lived long distances away. On the strength of the investigations, the Council considered a general change in the system absolutely necessary, and drew up a 'Plan for the Reform of the Medical Services'. This recommended a reduction in the area of medical districts to include only 10,000 inhabitants, and that the Medical Officer should be required to live as centrally as possible. Also the 'pauper list' should be abolished to facilitate the prompt administration of medical relief and to lessen the trouble to the poor and the parish, and the time lost in obtaining orders.[1]

Many of the ideas expressed in this plan were adopted three years later. For by the only General Medical Order ever issued, the maximum area for medical districts was to be 15,000 acres containing a population not exceeding 15,000 people. Where it was impracticable for Guardians to redivide areas exceeding these stipulations, special permission had to be obtained from the Poor Law Commissioners to retain the existing arrangements. In addition, the method by which paupers were to be granted relief orders was re-examined. It was realized that varying practices had been resorted to in the Unions through the absence of a comprehensive rule from the central authorities. In future Boards of Guardians were to prepare a list every six months of all aged and infirm, sick and disabled persons who were in constant receipt of relief and who were settled in the district. Such a schedule was to be supplied to the Medical Officer, who would then be required to visit all applicants from the 'permanent list' whenever they sent for him. These people were to receive special tickets which would entitle them to attendance and medicine without any order from the Relieving Officer or Guardians. Should a pauper on the list be found using his ticket on frivolous grounds, he was to be warned on the first offence, and on subsequent occasions to be deprived of his privilege for the following six months.

There was widespread opposition to the Medical Order, and Boards of Guardians from all over the country demanded its suspension for their own Unions on one or several grounds. For many Unions had seen statistical evidence that the twenty largest Unions saved six times as much as the twenty smallest, and therefore, as long as distances were convenient for their officers, and the Guardians could exercise efficient supervision, they objected to limiting areas. The northern towns such as Derby, Sheffield, Leeds, Manchester, and Liverpool, declared that sufficient charitable provisions were made for the poor by the voluntary hospitals and dispensaries, and that the medical districts were so compact that the rules limiting areas were inapplicable. It was also asserted that the larger number of patients allocated to each Medical Officer caused no hardship because he resided so close to the poor. Elsewhere, Guardians objected to the additional fees to be paid to Medical Officers for surgical and midwifery cases, because the increased cost would make them less disposed to grant many orders for such patients. In addition, it was

[1] Communication from the Council of the British Medical Association, April 1839, to the Poor Law Commissioners.

held that these 'extras' would discourage the independent labourer from making his own provision for sickness if he knew the doctor was to receive higher remuneration for special cases. In the following year between twenty and thirty Unions were successful in receiving exemption from the Order. The increase in the number of Medical Officers by a few hundred every year produced the desired effect of diminishing the size of medical districts. But there were still many parts of the country where it was impossible, because of the lack of resident doctors, to make the size of the districts as small as desirable in order that a physician would be within convenient reach of every poor person.

Despite the Order, the adequacy and the method of providing medical relief were still not clear, and in 1844 the Select Committee on Poor Law Medical Relief was appointed to investigate the general position. Lord Ashley (later Lord Shaftesbury) was an admirable choice for chairman, especially as Cornewall Lewis frequently called the medical services 'Ashleyite Policy'. The inquiry was extremely lengthy and thorough, and a comprehensive picture of the varying and the uniform circumstances in the country were obtained. Unfortunately no legislation followed, and the General Consolidation Order of 1847 only reiterated the 1842 Order. There was, however, one very important and significant outcome: for the last Order, giving a comprehensive survey of all poor law provisions, embraced also medical relief. *The medical services had become a recognized part of the Poor Law system.*

Evidence was given to the Select Committee of 1844 showing that the Commissioners had not deviated from their early policy in classifying as destitute everyone who applied for medical assistance. 'Medical relief', said Cornewall Lewis, 'is parochial relief; ... the giving of an order for it constitutes the person receiving it a pauper, ... irrespective of whether he is in receipt of general relief at the time or not. ...' Therefore the people who were just able in normal circumstances to keep on the right side of the slender line of demarcation, but who were unable to meet the emergency of sickness, lost their independence and received the stigma of pauperism as soon as they applied for a medical order. Many witnesses saw the injustice of this policy, and the Duke of Rutland suggested that the law might be altered so as to allow medical relief to be given to independent labourers without pauperizing them. Ten years later the Medical Officer of Marylebone wrote a letter to a witness of the 1854 Select Committee, pointing to the defects in the principles under which medical relief had been administered in the years 1834–47.

There is [the letter runs] a large class of persons, not paupers in the legal sense, but what Dickens would call the quiet poor, who are much more worthy of assistance than regular paupers. I have visited them without an order and on telling them that they must procure one, have often been met with the answer: 'It is no use sir, as long as that remains'—pointing to some solitary remnant of better days in the shape of furniture— 'for the inspector told me, the last time mother was ill, that it was no use his coming here again as long as we had that. I have been to the broker and he will only give me a few shillings for it, and how long will that last?' I believe that the labouring classes cannot afford to pay for medical attendance, ... it is true they do attempt it, run into debt, lose their independence and self-respect, and become dependent parish paupers if nothing worse.[1]

But as long as anachronistic opinions as to the causes of poverty were maintained, deterrence was the established principle for its remedy. Proud of their victory in receiving legislative sanction for enforcing national uniformity, the central authorities in the 'thirties thought they would have equal success in rigidly pursuing the policy in the country. It has been seen that in the early years they had attempted not only to enforce the strictest prohibition of outdoor relief to the able-bodied, but also endeavoured to deter them from applying for medical relief. In the 'forties, however, scepticism as to the efficacy or possibility of enforcing such principles crept into the Commissioners' communications. The British Medical Association had pointed out to them in 1839 that it found no uniform or well-regulated plan regarding the practice of granting medical relief to the able-bodied had been adopted, and that the various Boards of Guardians were deciding for themselves whether medical relief should be given to members of large families where the men were employed at ordinary wages. Some Unions gave relief, others withheld it, the particular practice depending on the mode of paying the Medical Officer, and the vagaries of the Guardians. To the Select Committee of 1838 it was reported that medical attention for two women had been made dependent on their husbands entering the workhouse. On these cases the Committee offered the opinion, that

> when application is made on account of the illness of the wife, to make the offer of relief conditional on the husband's going into the workhouse is a most harsh and improper practice, and not founded on any instructions or rules which have been brought to their notice ... if parties are really in a condition to provide their families with medical assistance it would have been much better to assign the reason, and refuse relief altogether.

The Committee trusted 'that this expression of their opinion may prevent the chance of their occurrence'.

Perhaps because of this admonition, or perhaps through the strength of the Chartist campaigns, but more probably because it was found necessary by the force of circumstances, local authorities were compelled to relax the reluctance with which medical relief was given. But leniency crept only slowly into the administration. For the Commissioners were still anxious to curtail medical relief to the able-bodied pauper, as was seen in 1841, when Medical Officers were ordered to enter a special minute in their reports and furnish a medical certificate in cases of relief given to able-bodied sick paupers. This system had been introduced, stated the explanatory circular,

> in consequence of a tendency which has displayed itself in various parts of the country to make exceptions to the prohibitory order on too slight grounds, and the Com-

[1] Dr. Boyd, evidence to Select Committee, 1854.

missioners think that this provision will have the useful effect of calling the special attention of the Guardians to every such case.[1]

To the Select Committee of 1844, Dr. H. W. Rumsey[2] pointed out 'the impossibility of predetermining the class of poor who ought to be entitled to the gratuitous supply of medical relief'. And evidence was given on Whitechapel that the Guardians there were still not drawing any distinction between those who were and those who were not entitled to medical relief among the labouring classes. But no doubt the practically general adoption of 'permanent lists', after the 1842 Order, assisted the Guardians, although qualifications for inclusion must have varied in the absence of any statutory definition of what constituted 'destitution', for the purpose of sick relief. In the later 'forties the severity of the rule requiring a complete absence of possessions was relaxed by most Unions. Where people were forced to receive their medical relief in the workhouse, their furniture was sometimes stored for them. Nevertheless the practice increased of giving medical attention and general relief to families in their homes rather than separating them.

Cornewall Lewis was also able to give evidence in 1844 that the rule had become general for the labourer who fell ill to look to the Union for medical aid, indoor and outdoor. The policy obtained less in the North and in the Welsh mining areas, where voluntary provision for the workers was made by the owners of mines and where benefit clubs were most widespread, but throughout the remainder of England the labourer depended on the Unions. It also resulted in his receiving superior medical attention, because the inducement for a doctor to attend the independent poor was very small and uncertain, and the fear of bad debts led to very imperfect private medical care.

An expedient which had been resorted to since 1834 and one closely linked to the idea of reducing medical expenditure and applications for relief, was to grant it on loan. In 1837 the Commissioners, reiterating that great care should be taken to prevent the mis-application of medical relief, recommended that a salutary check should be imposed on people who might have the means of repayment, by giving medical assistance by way of a loan, to be repaid by 'carefully enforced' instalments. Assistant Commissioners had in 1836 adopted this system of encouraging people to enter sick clubs, and Richard Earle, reporting on Northamptonshire and Warwickshire, callously suggested: 'The only present expedient for at once securing the safety of the poor and promoting their independence, is to withhold all medical relief except on loan, to those who can, but will not, subscribe to a dispensary or club.'[3] The Loan Medical Ticket he introduced was to be sent by the surgeon to the Relieving Officer immediately after the patient was dismissed, in order that it could be laid before two magistrates, 'who are authorized to order the amount to be paid by the patient to the parish; but in cases where such a return shall not be ordered, the patient's name will be published in the quarterly list of paupers'. Earle stated that the

[1] Official Circular No. 12, October 1841.
[2] One of the foremost people connected with the Poor Law Medical Service and a great campaigner for its reform and development.
[3] See Chapters 8 and 9 on dispensaries and sick clubs.

tickets were in considerable use, because they 'served to remind the overseers, to whom an instructional letter is sent, that a distinction was to be made between the pauper and the independent labourer, and also served as means of conveying information respecting the intention of the Guardians to the party who receives them'.[1]

The loan system was also used in Devon, Cornwall, Essex, and Cambridgeshire, as was stated in the Assistant Commissioners' Reports on the Further Amendment of the Poor Law in 1839. In 1841 the Commissioners, hinting that the principle of less eligibility should be applied as a deterrent regarding medical relief as well as in general relief, suggested also that the loan system should be adopted to prevent the able-bodied from applying for assistance and to encourage them to enter sick clubs and friendly societies.

It is interesting to examine the policy of a few Unions individually. For example, very frequent reference was made in the Bradfield (Yorkshire) Board of Guardians' Minutes to the giving of medical loans to the poor whose earnings were just sufficient for their maintenance. The Guardians directed attention to the efficacy of the system in preventing pauperization. In 1836 they stated that 'such loans have been general, and often with due acknowledgements for benefits conferred, have been repaid by weekly or other instalments'.[2] When the Commissioners recommended payment of Medical Officers by the 'pauper list', and 'per case' system for casual paupers in 1839, their explanatory circular stated that there would be no inducement to refuse relief where really necessary, 'in as much as the system of payment per case admits of medical relief being granted by way of loan, an arrangement which inevitably operates to encourage the labourer to provide himself with medical aid on easier terms by subscribing beforehand to a sick club or friendly society'.[3] In 1844 the Select Committee found that loans were granted generally in Unions where 'per case' payment to Medical Officers was made, for this enabled the actual cost of relief to be ascertained. Yet it was found, perhaps because of the number of unpaid debts, that more medical relief was provided in Unions which paid fixed salaries to their doctors. The loan system, therefore, was acting as a deterrent. After the 'forties the practical failure to recover appreciable sums for relief on loan discouraged the system. The West Ham Guardians, as the Chairman stated, gave medical relief on loan, but they never attempted to recover them. Theoretically the Board would not grant relief to people earning over 16s. or 18s. a week, unless they had a very large family, but this Union was extremely liberal in giving medical relief. As the Chairman said, 'we give medical relief

---

[1] *Loan Medical Ticket for 1 Case Only*:
...... being in want of medical aid for self, or for ...... his wife, or for ...... his child, having represented that ...... is not able at the present time to pay for it, is to receive the same of surgeon for district No. ....
(signed)
1836, second Annual Report, Appendix, Richard Earle's Report on Northamptonshire and Warwickshire.
[2] In 1876 Bradfield abolished gratuitous medical relief and resorted solely to the loan system—see Charity Organisation Society 'Reporter', 1876.
[3] Minute of Poor Law Commissioners, June 1839, followed by Official Circular No. 3, April 1840.

more freely than other relief ... this is important and should not be discouraged in the Board of Guardians'.[1]

The problem of the 'non-settled' poor always caused difficulties in Poor Law administration. The policy which existed before 1834, and which continued after the Act, was for a person belonging to another district to obtain medical relief from the parish in which he was residing if he were suddenly taken ill. The Union affording assistance would recover the cost from his place of settlement. This had often resulted in gross abuses under the old system, for the doctor, aware that another parish was compelled to pay his fee, charged large sums—one case of fracture was said to have cost a parish £40. Under the new Act, however, where the Medical Officer was paid by fixed salary, Unions only repaid each other the cost of maintenance: 'Until the whole kingdom is under the same order, no parish is secure from great and unavoidable expense.' Sick paupers were also not to be removed. As Assistant Commissioner Weale stated in 1836: 'We never think of removing a pauper afflicted with sickness until the Medical Officer has pronounced it safe to do so.' Richard Earle also stated that although much offence had been taken against this ruling, 'The Order ... which directs contracts shall include all paupers found within the Union gives great satisfaction to parishes, and will in my opinion prevent many injudicious removals.' But even in the 'forties this rule was not adhered to by every Union, and severe suffering was often caused. Evidence proving this was given to two Select Committees formed to inquire into cases of gross maltreatment in 1844. The Act of Settlement was repealed in 1846, but several towns sent petitions to the House of Commons for its suspension. The Manchester Guardians in November 1846 resolved not to give any more outdoor relief to non-settled paupers.[2] Leicester followed suit, and suggested that all manufacturing towns should co-operate in this direction. The action was probably taken for economic reasons, and because of the large migratory population the industrial North admitted. But in agricultural areas also, cases of suffering caused by the peculiar anomaly, which the Poor Law Commissioners did not rectify, were reported after 1846. In Thingoe Union (Suffolk), for example, a man found insensible by the roadside died without medical attention. The Relieving Officer refused an order because the man did not belong to the Union, and the Medical Officer explained that he was not bound to attend a case without an order. The jury returned a verdict of natural death and reproved his daughter for neglect, although the doctor affirmed at the post mortem that the man would not have died if he had received medical attention.

To aid the Guardians in exercising a necessary discretion, and to reduce the demands for gratuitous medical relief, the post of Relieving Officer had been created. Bye-laws already existed in Norfolk and Suffolk before the Act, requiring the poor to obtain orders from overseers, but the extreme laxity with which such measures were enforced rendered them valueless. Under the new enactment all applications for medical relief had to be made to the Relieving Officer. After exercising his judicious discretion he provided the

[1] Evidence Select Committee, 1844. W. Champion Streatfield.
[2] Minutes, Manchester Board of Guardians, 1846.

poor with an order and notified the Medical Officer of the case. In an emergency he had to furnish any relief the case called for. This was the second method by which the invidious principle of the Poor Law, the encouragement of the poor to support themselves by the gradual pressure of necessity, was to be achieved. The Relieving Officer was to be the functionary ensuring that a correct method of administration would constantly diminish the numbers desiring gratuitous medical relief. Persons who were to receive medical aid under Union contracts could not be predetermined sufficiently to arrange them into a definite class, so this form of intimidation was used on the whole category of able-bodied. Therefore the amount of general relief and the amount of medical relief, and the proportion of one to the other, depended on the Relieving Officer. He became the pivot on which the whole organization of Poor Law medical relief turned. In fact he was the executive authority and although he possessed no medical qualifications, it was his unaided judgement which alone sent the Medical Officer into action. Though his activity was to be checked by the scrutiny of his reports by the Board of Guardians the latter rarely investigated whether he was being efficient and fair, or whether he was refusing justifiable applications, or overworking the doctors. As he was in constant attendance at the Board of Guardians' weekly meetings he could virtually overrule the Medical Officer's recommendations. This is apparent from an analysis of the complaints made by the poor, which were nearly always directed against the Relieving Officer and not the Medical Officer. His refusal of orders often caused scandalous suffering, and in the Bridgwater Union a public inquiry had to be held. Here, as no doctors could be found to undertake Poor Law duties, local practitioners were being paid 'per case' to attend the poor during the interim period. This naturally led to the exercise of the greatest parsimony by the Relieving Officer, and he continually refused orders. One child died without medical attention, the mother having pawned his bed and clothing for 1s. 6d. in order to pay for medicine. Other heart-rending cases were reported, such as bedclothes being stripped off the dying to be pawned to obtain relief.

In rural areas hardship was caused because the Relieving Officer was not always accessible, for he often lived many miles away, and the poor had no easy or cheap means of conveyance. In urban districts it was the custom for him to receive applications at his home or at the workhouse at fixed hours only. Unlike the Medical Officer he was not required to be resident in the Union, and much suffering must have been caused through the poor having to tramp many miles, as well as through the delay in obtaining the Medical Officer, who quite often lived as far in the opposite direction. Unnecessary hardship was entailed if a man had to spend a long time away from his work to attend the Relieving Officer, as it meant losing his day's wages. But the Poor Law Commissioners hoped that the new system would benefit the poor, because formerly if a pauper needed a doctor many parishes required an application to be made to an overseer, who frequently allowed several days to elapse before giving an order. Whether the Medical Officer gave adequate treatment or not depended more on his own humanity than on any control by the overseer, whose duty it was merely to pay the salary agreed upon at the end of the year, if there were sufficient parish funds. This was frequently not the case, as seen by the arrears still due several years after the introduction of the new Poor Law. Under the new scheme occasional Unions made it part of the Relieving Officer's duty to deliver medicines, or they authorized the employment of a pauper or a cripple to go errands for him to those whom he should have attended.

No doubt the intention of the Poor Law authorities in instituting an intermediary between application and assistance, was to bring some order into the system and also to combat the indiscriminate giving of relief, by providing a restraint for the Medical Officer's humanitarianism. In Northamptonshire and Warwickshire, Earle, as well as instituting 'Loan Medical Tickets', had also provided the Relieving Officer with 'Pauper Medical Tickets'.[1]

In many Unions the check of the Relieving Officer was important in preventing unnecessary work for the medical practitioners. The Medical Officer of Peterborough complained of the inconvenience and unnecessary trouble to which many doctors were subjected by irresponsible paupers. He quoted one of his own cases, where a woman had sent for him in haste to see her child. On seeing the patient he had remarked that it was hardly necessary for him to have travelled five miles, as a small dose of salts was all that was required. To this the mother replied that she was aware of this, but added: 'Why am I to save the parish the salts?' In the same Union men refused to join medical clubs because they were sure they would be given medical aid without question, on account of the expense their families would entail on the parish during their own illness.

The Preston Medical Officers complained of the large number of patients which the Relieving Officers sent them. The Minutes of the Board of Guardians' meetings record the misunderstanding which arose in the Union as to whether the doctors should attend all cases sent by the Relieving Officer whether they were paupers or not. One of the Medical Officers stated that he considered it his duty to attend only such as were actual paupers. He called attention to the fact that the Relieving Officer of the district had in several instances, when applied to by poor persons for a medical order, given them money for the purpose of pauperizing them, and had then granted them a certificate for medical attendance. A Medical Officer of another district in Preston declared that he had been requested by influential people to attend the poor who were not destitute, and had done so rather than incur their displeasure. The doctors pleaded that the waste of public money and their time should be discontinued.[2]

The system pursued in various Unions was far from uniform. Divergence in principle was increased, because the Commissioners advocated the giving of medical relief without

---

[1] *Poor Law Medical Ticket*

From..........to..........

..........being sick and not able to pay for medical aid, is to receive the same of surgeons for district No.......

(signed)

[2] Board of Guardians' Minutes, 1839.

an order from the Relieving Officer in cases of sudden illness. Difficulties arose because there was no ruling on what constituted an 'emergency', and individual Unions were at liberty to interpret the word in their own way. In the Instructional Letter sent to Guardians on the formation of their Unions, the Commissioners pointed out that although all claims on account of sickness should be investigated and decided on by the Board of Guardians with the assistance of the Relieving Officer, this was not possible in cases of sudden or dangerous illness or accident. For such contingencies overseers could give the order to a Medical Officer, and the Commissioners also alluded to the 1834 Act[1] which authorized a single magistrate to order medical relief in an emergency. The poor were never really made aware of this fact, and sometimes when complaints of negligence or delay were reported, the Coroner or investigating party stated that suffering had been unnecessary because a magistrate could have been applied to. The poor also remained ignorant of the provision that any magistrate could overrule the Relieving Officer's decision. Only once was this ever mentioned in Poor Law records: A man, earning 8s. a week, had a wife and four children who had all been ailing for some time, the family therefore being in very straitened circumstances. The wife was taken ill with typhus[2] fever and the husband applied for a doctor. He received an order, but the doctor refused to attend because the man was not a member of his sick club. The Relieving Officer withdrew the order and refused to go into the house to see the condition of the family. The woman therefore remained without medical attention and the family without extra general relief. At the inquiry the man was told he should have applied to a magistrate, who had the power to order relief even when it had been refused by Poor Law officers.[3]

The Commissioners, however, had directed that in 'all cases of sudden or dangerous illness or serious accident it is imperative on the Relieving Officer to grant an order for medical relief'. Much again depended on the Relieving Officer's interpretation. In Westoning Union (Bedford) a poacher's wife required obstetrical aid, but the Relieving Officer refused to heed the note written by the overseer urging immediate medical attention for her. In 1839 an Assistant Commissioner had to hold an inquiry into a case of alleged refusal of medical relief because the Relieving Officer did not believe the case to be urgent and the man could have afforded to subscribe to a club.[4]

Generally Unions allowed attendance on emergency cases without orders, but where the Medical Officer was not conscientious he could always refuse to give treatment. If he was accused of negligence he excused his conduct by pointing out that no order had been given. This was frequently stated in evidence at Coroners' inquiries. In the Thetford Union (Suffolk) a woman made several applications to the Medical Officer for assistance, but without previously obtaining an order, and she died without medical attention. But

[1] Section 54.
[2] The nineteenth century diagnosis as given in the original texts is quoted throughout the work.
[3] Evidence Select Committee 1838, James Turner, Ampthill Union (Bedford). (In no other Poor Law documents examined was this provision mentioned.)
[4] Minutes of the Poor Law Commissioners, 1 March 1839.

here the Medical Officer was exonerated because the district was too large and he had too many patients.[1] To the Select Committee of 1844 Sir John Walsham commented that in his district there was never any refusal on the part of the doctors to attend cases of emergency without orders, or any difficulty offered by the Guardians in sanctioning attendance subsequently. He said this system worked very well with the institution of the 'permanent list', whereby the old, infirm, and habitually sick might apply directly to the Medical Officer. In Bethnal Green medical men were also required to attend on emergency cases without the applicant's making previous reference to the Relieving Officer. Such cases in Stepney also applied directly to the doctor and received an order from the Relieving Officer afterwards. Ordinary cases applied to him previously at the workhouse between 9 and 12 a.m., but by 1844 the practice was growing of granting medical relief by direct application to the Medical Officer without the intervention of the Relieving Officer. Here medical relief was also offered to the poor irrespective of their being paupers. In Whitechapel practitioners often attended the poor without orders, to ensure prompt attention for the sick, although it entailed more work for them. In this Union there had been an increase from 1,330 to 2,743 in the number of outdoor sick attended in the years 1840–43. West Ham Union required all first applications to be made to the Relieving Officer, but on subsequent occasions the poor could go directly to the surgeon. It was maintained that this procedure afforded great advantages to the sick. In contrast, St. George the Martyr, Southwark, showed great scepticism in allowing relief to paupers in emergencies, and tried to deter the Medical Officer from visiting them without orders. Even when orders had been obtained, the Guardians complained that they had been improperly granted, and that many people had been given medical relief who were not entitled to it.

To save time and to prevent disease from becoming serious, the Wycombe Guardians allowed their paupers at all times to visit the Medical Officer without an order, and they could apply to the Relieving Officer later. In Newmarket, however, the poor were afraid to apply for medical orders, and the doctors unanimously sent a memorial to the Select Committee of 1844 pointing out the evils existing there, the poor being required to apply to the Relieving Officer whose policy it was to refuse very many applications. It was also a six-mile walk to his residence, and the nine Medical Officers alluded to the danger to the sick if early medical intervention were delayed.

An abundant number of objections were given to the Select Committee of 1844 to the interference of the Relieving Officer. Nearly every doctor giving evidence desired that the first application for treatment should be made directly to them. It was pointed out that the Relieving Officer was not qualified to judge the necessity of medical attention. In midwifery cases particularly, the Relieving Officer had been found to withhold orders, since extra fees had been granted for this by the Medical Order of 1842. The medical witnesses maintained that time, expense, and trouble would also be saved if the poor were

[1] After this inquiry the area was reduced in size.

allowed to obtain a Relieving Officer's order after initial treatment. As one doctor significantly stated: *Early and good attention to the poor is the end of the very best economy.*

Even before the Select Committee was formed, the evils of the system had been pointed out. In 1836 the Poor Law Committee of the Provincial Medical and Surgical Association raised the question: 'Who are to decide on the particular ailments of paupers which require relief? . . . the medical profession alone are competent to judge the necessity for medical treatment in any particular case, and ought to be freely entrusted with discretionary power, which they alone are able to exercise.' At a meeting held in Manchester in the same year, the Association stated that in order to avoid the evils arising from delay in securing medical relief, and to prevent imposition on parochial funds, the patient should apply first to the Medical Officer. As he made a weekly return of all cases under treatment, the Guardians might then determine who on the list were paupers and who were not. The reform they suggested was that every sick applicant, at the time of receiving medical relief, should be furnished by the doctor with a certificate stating that the case required treatment, which should be left with the Relieving Officer within a specified time. He would then be able to make inquiries into the circumstances of each patient before the subsequent meeting of the Board, and if the Guardians did not consider the case to be entitled to gratuitous aid, it could be given by way of loan. This would obviate the necessity for any application in the first instance to the Relieving Officer, and the form of an order might be dispensed with. 'Prompt attention would be ensured to the sick, and the condition and capabilities of persons for whom medical assistance is required would undergo a far stricter investigation than is at present practicable.'[1]

Similar proposals for reform were made to the Select Committee of 1844 by men not in the medical profession. The Chairman of the East London Union suggested that the poor should go directly to the Medical Officer if they were known by him, but that they might be required to obtain a ticket before visiting him a second time or when the emergency was over. He stressed the importance of this in midwifery cases, where speedy help was essential, and said it was a monstrous abuse of power for the Relieving Officer to take on himself the decision whether the assistance of a surgeon was required in childbirth. But as on so many other questions concerning the medical services of the Poor Law, it was Rumsey who most clearly outlined the case for reform. He was opposed to any and every check between a sick man and his medical attendant, and asserted that it was essential that communication between them should be direct and immediate. He pointed to the suffering caused by the Relieving Officer having the power to grant or refuse orders for medical relief, the needless delay which the system occasioned, and the frequent hesitancy and disinclination of the poor to go to him. Many objected to being stigmatized as paupers thereby, or were afraid of being removed under the settlement laws. Some poor were uncertain where to apply for orders and many preferred to struggle through their illness without help. The poor therefore became fatalists and placed less reliance on medical aid

---

[1] Report of Provincial Medical and Surgical Association, Manchester, July 1836.

than the upper classes, resigning themselves to disease, and allowing it to take its course. Rumsey also quoted cases where the sick, on applying for orders, had been dismissed with a shilling and advised to go to the druggist.

The Poor Law authorities, however, did not listen to these arguments, and Cornewall Lewis in his evidence affirmed that the Boards of Guardians were the most suitable parties to determine who were fit recipients of medical relief, and that no inconvenience resulted to the poor through having to call on the Relieving Officer first. Alfred Austin, voicing the opinion of the Assistant Commissioners, also favoured the retention of the Relieving Officer. Therefore the Select Committee gave no recommendation on the subject in its Report, and it received no further mention from the central authorities before the Commissioners went out of office. Charles Buller, who was in 1848 to succeed them on the Poor Law Board did, however, state in a speech in the House of Commons in 1844, that in his opinion

> it would be the best administration of the Poor Law, if Medical Officers were entrusted with the discretion on their own responsibility of attending such sick poor as applied to them for relief, subject to the approval or non-approval of the Board of Guardians at their next meeting . . . and the Board of Guardians and not the Relieving Officer should decide the question whether the applicant was a pauper or not.

It was unfortunate that Buller, through his untimely death, was Chairman of the Central Board for only one year. Nothing was altered in the power or the duties of the Relieving Officer by the General Consolidated Order of 1847. Therefore, whether a sick person was entitled to medical attendance or not continued to depend 'not on his character, or the severity of his illness, or its probable effect on his family and neighbours, but on the decision of a non-medical officer, as to non-medical circumstance—destitution'.

The Poor Law Medical Officer had also become a firmly established and necessary institution and had now an important position in the community.

> The peculiar habits of the poor, their privations and attempts to impose on the Relieving Officers, require all the experience and talent of the Medical Officer to counteract. In fact, medical men, after they have for some time been engaged in attending the poor, are as necessary in their situation, as surgeons in the navy or army are in theirs; besides which their knowledge should be rendered available in all cases in which it is required.[1]

The Guardians knew how much depended on the Medical Officer. The Commissioners had repeatedly stressed that it was their object 'to secure an efficient attendance on the sick poor', and it was the local authorities who were responsible for ensuring this, while called on at the same time to reduce the poor rates by deterring the poor from applying for medical relief, and by keeping salaries low. The amount of work imposed on the Medical Officer depended on the policy of the Board of Guardians and the character of the Relieving Officer, and it was this that was generally complained of by the poor, and not

---

[1] One of the Medical Officers of Whitechapel, Select Committee, 1844.

the medical treatment. Where the public doctor was accused of negligence it was due in most cases to the size of the area and the population of his district, which rendered it impossible for him to treat everyone efficiently.

William Farr,[1] in his examination before the Select Committee of 1838, stated that his communications with the British Medical Association, the Provincial Medical and Surgical Association, as well as with individuals, revealed that many poor were neglected because the Medical Officers were too few, or because the poor had to travel from five to ten miles to procure a doctor and medicines. Neglect similarly occurred in towns because the practitioner had too many patients assigned to his care. He compared the large number of cases the Poor Law Medical Officer had to attend with the average of 8,810 cases per year which the seventy-six surgeons in English gaols cared for. In addition Farr pointed out that 13s. 7d. was spent per case of sickness in the prisons compared with 2s. 1½d. on paupers.

The deputation of the British Medical Association to the Commissioners in 1839 alluded to the 'lamentable instances of deficient skill which have occurred in the Bridgwater and Kingston Unions, as shown by the verdict of the juries'. But this was unusual, and complaints of neglect were generally followed by exoneration of the doctor. A private practitioner in Anglesey gave evidence to the Select Committee of 1844 that the poor were not receiving adequate medical attention because parochial staff was too limited. The Chairman of the Thirsk Board of Guardians wrote to the Committee that efficiency could only be achieved in rural areas if districts embraced towns, for only in this way could frequent visits of a doctor be ensured. He stated that the labouring poor were very jealous of the neglect of medical men and

> if their visits are not so frequent as they imagine they require, or the quantity of medicine sent be not equal to what they suppose to be needful, they become dissatisfied and find fault. With the better educated classes, and those who are able to pay for attendance, the apothecary has no difficulty in persuading them that frequent visits and medicine are not necessary. . . . But the poor, feeling their dependent position, or inability to pay the doctor, are very incredulous on this point, and do not give him credit for disinterestedness, but conclude that because of their poverty they are neglected.

The Chairman concluded that the Union doctors were frequently unfairly dealt with, because the public too readily accepted the complaints of the poor as a proved fact of negligence.

A clergyman of Devon reported that the sick poor were very much neglected and instanced several cases to prove his assertion. The surgeon denied this, but the minister gave evidence that the former lived at such a distance from his medical district that it was impossible for him to attend the poor properly. The Guardians were not disposed to take

[1] Compiler of statistics for the Registrar-General, who was to provide valuable aid to Poor Law and Public Health reformers.

action because the doctor had agreed to attend the area at a reduced salary. Generally, however, the evidence given to the Select Committee of 1844 showed that the poor were not dissatisfied with their medical attention and that it was decidedly better under the new than under the old law. In their last Annual Report in 1847, the Commissioners realized that many evils still needed rectifying, such as the bad conditions in the workhouses, but they declared that they never received any complaint against the lack of attention paid to the poor by the doctors—although there had been a great increase in the amount of work they were being required to perform.

The Stepney Union originally employed eight Medical Officers, but later reduced the number to five, despite the fact that for the three years ending December 1842 the doctors attended an annual average of 8,000 people. Nearly 6,000 were outdoor patients and over 2,000 indoor, and included 540 special midwifery and surgical cases. By 1844 the number of outdoor patients had risen to nearly 8,000, including 132 midwifery cases, and over 3,300 were treated in the workhouse. For visiting 15,000 homes the five Medical Officers salaries totalled £460. Despite the great amount of poorly remunerated work, the poor expressed no dissatisfaction with their treatment by the doctors. Stepney refused to adopt the 'permanent list' system because, as the Guardians stated, there were such numerous claims constantly being made for urgent and pressing cases. They refused also to adopt the 'ticket' system because they believed it might lead to a revival of the old regime and remind the poor of former laxness, thereby giving them additional inducement to apply for even more medical relief.

West Ham Union, with a total population of 12,500, gave outdoor medical treatment to 1,500 people on an average for the years 1836–43, the number having risen to over 2,000 by the last year. But only two Medical Officers were employed over the whole period with a combined salary of £210 per annum. The Chairman of the Board of Guardians stated that the poor would receive more efficient attention if the doctors were paid better, but that in any case the Board was extremely satisfied with the medical treatment the poor were receiving.[1] To the Select Committee of 1844 the Chairman stated that 'medical relief as now administered is more efficient than before the Union . . . the Medical Officers give a better class of medicine and attendance is more full now'. He thought the poor decidedly had the right to the best treatment which could be procured, and that more money should be spent on medical relief. In 1836 the Commissioners had written to the Guardians, expressly stating that only the destitute should receive gratuitous medical attention. The Chairman, however, remained unconvinced, and eight years later maintained that the poor would benefit by increased expenditure: There was nothing 'in which we ought to be so liberal as in medical attention to the poor'.[2] Although the ratepayers complained, the Guardians sanctioned any diet the Medical Officers directed, and even provided a nurse and bedding for very urgent cases. They refused other relief in the form

[1] Minutes of the Board of Guardians for several years.
[2] Evidence by William Champion Streatfield, Chairman of the West Ham Union, to Select Committee, 1844.

of 'extras', however, if they thought the family could afford it and only agreed to pay for medical treatment in such cases. In 1844 the Chairman suggested that a medical station should be established, which might also be used for administering outdoor relief, where paupers should call weekly with their tickets. The doctor was to attend at this medical station three days a week at fixed hours and supply medicines. The names of the Relieving Officer and overseers should be affixed to the outside, so that paupers would be able to discover quickly where to apply for an order, and the station would also save the poor from going long journeys.

This was regarded as one of the best run Unions in the country. A great contrast was provided by the Union of St. George the Martyr, Southwark. The supply of medical relief need not be examined closely, for the expenditure speaks for itself. Here the annual average expenditure on medical services amounted to no more than £60, although the total poor relief cost between £11,000 and £15,000. Comparing the Metropolitan arrangements with some of those existing in rural Unions, it is seen that a similar extent of medical relief existed. Ely with a population of 20,000 employed five Medical Officers and gave medical aid to an average of 12,000 paupers a year, excluding severe cases, which cost about £320 or 3⅘d. per head of the population, plus £43 for midwifery. St. Albans spent an average of £140 a year on sickness and gave medical relief to the value of £6 on loan, out of a total expenditure of over £4,000. Ross Union had spent £176 a year on medical relief prior to the formation of the Union in 1836, and by 1842 this amount had risen to £313. Doctors were paid 7s. for attending an individual case or 10s. for attending a family.

There was a rise in medical expenditure in every Union, but it never equalled or caught up with the amount of work which doctors were asked to perform. An increasing number of people required to be visited in their homes and the doctors' duties grew out of all proportion to their numbers—a trend which became even more marked when the Poor Law Medical Officer also became the Public Vaccinator after the 1840–41 Acts.

For vaccination was another health service which came under the administration of Poor Law Officers. In the 'thirties and 'forties this was not the anomaly it later became, for they were the only uniform central and local authorities existing on a national scale. Also it was amongst the poor that the smallpox epidemics raged most fiercely. The Report of Dr. Neil Arnott and Dr. Kay (Shuttleworth) to the Commissioners in 1838 illustrated the necessity for the introduction of universal and controlled vaccination on a national basis. The Medical Officer of the Brentford Union pointed out to them that he had no recollection of any epidemic save influenza troubling the labouring classes in his area, but 'the evil which appears most serious . . . is the general prevalence . . . of the worst species of smallpox . . . which is generally propagated and increased by indiscriminate inoculation by improper persons. It is also rendered more general by the neglect of the poor to have their children vaccinated.' He expressed the fear that the prevailing epidemic would grow worse as attacks were daily multiplying and widening in range, throwing more and more people on parochial resources. It was amongst the overcrowded poorer classes, he stated, that the epidemic was most serious and where most improvement could be made.[1]

In 1840 the Poor Law Commissioners reported 10,434 deaths from smallpox. The Vaccination Act of that year extended the privilege of free vaccination to all who applied for it without reference to their circumstances, and the Amendment of 1841 removed the pauperizing tendency and inference of gratuitous relief. Dr. Thomas Wakley, M.P., succeeded in having a clause inserted whereby it became a punishable offence to inoculate with smallpox or expose persons to the infection. In future only qualified doctors might vaccinate and the service generally fell on the Poor Law Medical Officer. Ignorant on the subject of their new duty, the Poor Law Commissioners desired the assistance of the National Vaccine Establishment, members of which were appointed by the government and paid by an annual vote of money. They regularly reported to the Home Secretary, and Chadwick corresponded with the Board to obtain information.

The Acts brought about an improvement almost immediately, as the statistics proved. In London the deaths from smallpox were 1,235 in 1840, 1,053 in 1841, and only 360 in 1842. For the whole country 10,434 deaths were reported in 1840, whilst in 1841 the figure had fallen to 6,368—mortality from this cause had therefore diminished by over 4,000 in one year. In 1842 the number of deaths had been reduced to 2,715. Whenever there was a decline in the amount paid for vaccination in the Unions, the Commissioners directed inquiries to be made. Unfortunately in 1843 mortality rates began to increase again. In London in that year they rose to 438, and in the following twelve months had reached nearly 2,000. The increase in the incidence of smallpox was ascribed to a falling off in the diligence of the vaccinators, after the first two years of the act, in seeking out children who had not been vaccinated. Parents also recovered their aversion to the vaccination being performed, and others remained indifferent as long as the fever was absent from their district. In 1842 the number of children vaccinated was 378,331; in the following year the number had halved to 183,074. The proportion varied from place to place—in Crickhowel Union, for example, all children were vaccinated; in Lambeth very few save the Irish.

The Commissioners therefore urged Guardians to use every means in their power to extend the provisions of the Act, both by individual expostulation with parents, and by addressing circular letters to magistrates and clergymen, requesting them to use their influence on the labouring population in permitting their children to be vaccinated. This was generally done, with good effect in many instances.[2] The large amount of time spent by some of the Boards of Guardians on vaccination arrangements can be seen in the Minutes of the Kensington Board of Guardians in the 1840s. In 1844 smallpox was very prevalent in the Metropolis, and once again the Commissioners asked for a Return to be made by

---

[1] Thomas Litchfield, Surgeon, Brentford Union, quoted in *Report on the prevalence of certain physical causes of fever in the Metropolis which might be removed by proper sanitary measures* by Neil Arnott, M.D., and James Phillips Kay, M.D., to the Poor Law Commissioners, May 1838.

[2] Tenth Annual Report of the Poor Law Commissioners.

Unions and parishes of the numbers vaccinated. Annual Returns became a permanent feature in their Reports from 1845 onwards. Of the Unions, 93 did not reply to the Commissioners' questionnaire in 1844, but the remaining 542 stated that 2,614 vaccinators had vaccinated 290,453 people. The number of births registered during the year was nearly half-a-million. The vaccinators attended nearly 4,000 cases of smallpox, a third of which had previously been vaccinated.[1]

In the following years, whenever births greatly exceeded the numbers vaccinated, the Commissioners regularly drew the attention of the Guardians to the fact, and in serious instances suggested that vaccinators should be directed to visit each house of the poorer classes. Many of the ignorant poor refused to be vaccinated because they lived under the 'erroneous apprehension that other eruptive and cutaneous diseases would be communicated to them'. But this prejudice declined as increased facilities for education helped to broaden their minds. In some Welsh Unions, and in Hayfield and Todmorden in the North,[2] no provision was made for gratuitous vaccination, but the doctors vaccinated all the poor who applied to them, free of charge. The superiority of Unions over the parishes which remained under Local Acts, was shown here; for in very few of the parishes had contracts been made for vaccination. Schemes varied in different localities. Some Unions, like Leighton Buzzard, only employed Union doctors; others, such as West Ham, allowed every practitioner to vaccinate. In St. George the Martyr, Southwark, all vaccination was done in the workhouse, but the Commissioners disagreed with this policy, as vaccination was to include the whole population and not only paupers. They pointed out that independent people would be reluctant to take their children to the workhouse and, in fact, in the following years there was almost a complete cessation of vaccination in the district.

In 1845 the smallpox scare abated. Only 909 deaths were reported in London, half the number of the previous year, and the progress of vaccination was declared to be highly satisfactory.[3] This year, 362,087 people were vaccinated, of which 96 per cent were said to have 'taken' successfully. The numbers vaccinated under one year old formed 43 per cent of the total, and 32 per cent of the number of births. Registrars of the 115 districts, who collected statistics for the quarterly tables of mortality published by the Registrar-General, were requested, when deaths were above the average, to state to the Poor Law Commissioners whether any epidemic disease prevailed in their areas, or if any other known circumstance could account for the increase. This enabled the Commissioners to keep a check on smallpox and other epidemics and to circularize the Guardians with information as to prevention and future action.

From the mid 1840s Boards of Guardians and vaccinators were fully sensible of the importance of giving complete effect to the provisions of the Vaccination Act, and 'manifest great zeal in the extension of the practice of vaccination'. The Commissioners'

[1] Eleventh Annual Report of the Poor Law Commissioners, 1845.
[2] Refused to come under the Poor Law Act of 1834.
[3] Twelfth Annual Report of the Poor Law Commissioners.

Thirteenth Annual Report in 1847 illustrated this fact with the statistics shown in Table 1.3.

TABLE 1.3

Vaccinations.—Thirteenth Annual Report of the Poor Law Commissioners, 1847.

England and Wales	Number of Unions	Number of persons vaccinated	Successfully	Number of registered births	Ratio vaccinated to number of births	Ratio of persons successfully vaccinated to number of births
1845	580	362,087	347,765	486,632	100/134	100/140
1846	539	271,219	258,165	483,480	100/178	100/187
1847	621	267,895	247,762	523,682	—	—

The amount paid in fees to vaccinators in 1845 was £26,000, an increase of 35 per cent on the previous year, and in 1846 the sum increased again by £2,000.

The failing of the provisions for vaccination was that they were not compulsory, but it cannot be denied that they were a great step forward towards combating one of the severest of epidemic diseases. *Vaccination was the first of the free health services provided by the legislature on a national scale. A beginning in positive health measures had been made, and it was administered through the channels of the Poor Law!*

Although the Poor Law medical service progressed favourably in the 'forties, the giving of assistance for midwifery cases fell into a separate category. This arose partly because incompetent midwives continued to be employed, for Guardians were reluctant to pay the extra fees of 10s. to 20s. as was ordered in 1842. Through this parsimony many women were disabled for life through childbirth. Some Unions had given additional remuneration to Medical Officers before the 1842 Order, but the majority, particularly in densely populated areas, refused payment per case because it increased the burden on the ratepayer. In the Stepney Union, which had about 500 midwifery cases a year, the Guardians frequently refused to sanction applications for a medical order after 1842. An inquiry into the death of a woman found that it was through delay in giving her the necessary assistance, and also brought to light that many women were compelled to send for incompetent midwives on their own account. Guardians failed to realize that their parsimony led to an increase in ill-health in women, and ultimately to additional expenditure on relief. In this Union also, only the husband could apply for an order for maternity cases, and not the woman herself, which meant that either he lost part of a day's wages, or his wife would not receive assistance. Only in 1844 had the Guardians begun giving instructions for Medical Officers to attend every case of emergency.[1] A Union doctor,

[1] Stepney Board of Guardians, Minutes.

giving evidence in the same year, gave three instances of midwifery cases ending fatally and after much suffering, through the incompetence of midwives and because the doctor was not sent for until it was too late. He concluded: 'I have no hesitation in saying if midwifery orders could be as readily procured now as before the Union, such cases would scarcely be heard of.' In the West Ham Union, however, the Medical Officer was entirely responsible for the midwifery. The Guardians did not pay the midwives any fees, but a doctor could employ them, paying them himself. He was given 10s. a case out of which he could allow the midwife 5s. if he thought the case was normal and did not warrant his personal attendance. He was, however, entirely responsible for the woman's welfare. The Medical Officer maintained that women employed as midwives should always be under the direction of a Union surgeon and paid only on his recommendation of good conduct.

But arrangements varied from Union to Union. In Bethnal Green no payment was given to the District Medical Officer for attending midwifery cases, but according to the Chairman no mischief was reported from the course the Guardians had adopted. The doctor, however, described how lives had been lost through maltreatment by midwives and how often serious accidents maimed a woman for life. The East London Union had adopted the Order of 1842, but had not previously paid any extras for midwifery. In St. George the Martyr, Southwark, the sanction of the Board of Guardians was required before midwifery orders were executed, and great difficulty was experienced by the poor in obtaining such orders. The extreme restrictions exercised for maternity cases caused many scandals about the unnecessary delay before women received treatment. The Medical Officer complained of the conservatism in calling him because he was paid extra fees. In the Lambeth Union the doctor received payment for deliveries, but not for subsequent treatment, and in Croydon midwifery orders were only granted in very difficult cases.

Such circumstances were general in the country. The Langport Union, for example, refused midwifery orders, and only a midwife attended at childbirth. In Newent (Gloucester) the Guardians also generally withheld relief for a confinement. *The Times* in 1837 published an article entitled 'Facts connected with the medical relief of the poor in the Bridgwater Union' which revealed the scandals the midwifery arrangements of that Union fostered. The Poor Law Commissioners were compelled to institute an inquiry. Assistant Commissioner Weale was informed that the Medical Officer suddenly discontinued attending a woman in her confinement, and the Union gave her 1s. 6d. a week and a loaf instead. The Guardians declared that the doctor never reported she would require his attention during childbirth, and so they had sent a midwife. They insisted that they had 'done all they could for the comfort of the patient'—but she subsequently died of puerperal fever. The midwife was not trained and had taken over from her mother. Her remedy for puerperal fever was: senna tea and castor oil, with flannels and hot water for fomenting the bowels![1] The Relieving Officer denied having refused to continue relief

[1] Poor Law Commissioners' Records, 14 December 1837.

because it was expensive, and stated that on this occasion, as on others when death from similar causes had resulted, the Medical Officer stopped treatment of his own accord, before he himself discontinued orders. Weale reported that the neglect had been grossly overstated and that the article in *The Times* was libellous. Although he concluded 'the Medical Officer overstated the case and attempted to vilify and traduce the Guardians', he had refused to grant him an interview. Seven years later Dr. Toogood, one of the five physicians and surgeons of Bridgwater Union, could still give evidence of the ignorance of the midwives, and restated his disapproval of the sick being obliged to apply to the Relieving Officer before receiving treatment.

In contrast to the Bridgwater arrangements, the generosity of the Kensington Board of Guardians afforded welcome relief. In 1844 a woman was taken suddenly in labour and carried into the nearest house. She was a pauper through the desertion of her husband. The occupiers of the house charged the Guardians 7s. for washing, 8s. for board and lodging, 2s. for two tumblers broken by the Medical Officer during the delivery, and 6s. for damage done to the carpet and sofa. The Guardians paid the sum immediately and without question.[1] As there was an average of 3,000 deaths a year in childbirth, the arrangements regarding midwifery in the country were amply surveyed in evidence given to the Select Committee of 1844. It was found that a general disinclination existed among the Guardians to pay for midwifery (and surgical) cases, because of their endeavour to reduce the salaries of Medical Officers. There were one or two complaints of doctors receiving fees and then employing midwives, but the Poor Law Commissioners had not intended by the Medical Order that the doctor should be called to attend every midwifery case. There was a consensus among medical witnesses that all midwifery should be under the direction of the district surgeon, and they stressed the importance of early attendance by the doctor. Some demanded that Boards of Guardians should always grant orders for surgeons to attend all midwifery cases and that subsequent treatment should be provided for. One Medical Officer stressed the importance of post-natal care, and repeated visits by the doctor, because of the prevalence of contagious disorders, particularly puerperal fever consequent on childbirth. This suggestion no doubt arose because of the great deal of investigation being carried out into puerperal fever in England and America early in the 'forties. It was of particular importance to the Poor Law medical service because it always occurred where other fevers were most prevalent. One Medical Officer, quoted in the Registrar-General's Report for 1837–38, stated that typhus and puerperal fever were epidemic together, and a doctor had the alternative of leaving one patient to perish of typhus and rushing to a childbed fever, or vice versa.

In the Fifth Annual Report of the Registrar-General (1843), Farr emphasized the great number of deaths caused by the contagion of puerperal fever being communicated by nurses and doctors. He also spoke of the large proportion of the half-million women who were confined every year who never had any medical attention at all, save that of inferior

[1] Minutes, Board of Guardians, 1844.

midwives. In France, he said, the latter were required to attend courses on theory and practice. The Prussian government also had schools of midwifery in its eight provinces and over 11,000 midwives were examined and passed by the Medical Boards every year. Farr therefore advocated establishment of schools for the education of nurses and midwives in the Metropolis and in large towns, under medical supervision. He said it would open a highly useful profession to women, and a body of respectable and educated nurses would be of great utility to the community. He suggested that nursing schools should be connected with hospitals and lying-in institutions, and that poor women should receive gratuitous attendance in return for young nurses being afforded practical experience under trained supervision. But he was only in favour of teaching them the minimum about drugs, as, for instance, 'a few drops of laudanum after delivery, castor oil, and tincture of rhubarb', and how to administer medicines prescribed by the doctors. For he realized the hazard of attempting to give any advanced instruction which would lead to the establishing of a new class of half-educated practitioners like the druggists.

In the same article Farr recommended the appointment of trained parish nurses to serve under the Poor Law Medical Officer, for not only would they be able to give patients better treatment, but they would also be less costly than 'the spirit-drinking nurses now met with who demoralize the mother and poison the children'. Several practitioners in extensive private practice expressed the need for good, educated, and trustworthy nurses, for their absence was felt in the homes of the higher ranks of society as well as in the hovels of the poor. But the incalculable advantage of efficient nurses for the outdoor sick poor was expressed most emphatically by Rumsey to the Select Committee of 1844. The diseases of the poor were aggravated by the lack of proper nursing, he declared.

> Every medical man who has practised among the poor must have seen not unfrequently the fatal results of neglect or the imperfect performance of his directions. The application of external remedies and dressings are never properly attended to, and in those cases where baths or enemas ought to be substituted for violent internal medicines, the poor are unable to adopt a milder or better remedy, or they are left to the clumsy mismanagement of an ignorant nurse or neighbour. There are no Sisters of Charity here, no well-trained nurses are to be found at the bedside of the poor.'

If there were, he concluded, and if they were under the direction of the Medical Officer, it would mean a shortening of the length of the illness, and render the application of powerful medicines less necessary, as well as lessening the duties of the doctor.

Another problem which had been under discussion for many years was the supply of medicines to the sick poor. Statements were frequently made by the Poor Law authorities that the best drugs and medicines should be administered. Medical witnesses to the Select Committee fully concurred in the desirability of the provision. This was particularly emphasized by Sir Benjamin Brodie, who had for many years been surgeon to the St. George's Hospital, London, and who had there become well-acquainted with the diseases of the poor. He suggested that 'furnishing medicines should be made a distinct thing from medical attendance'. Rumsey also maintained that the poor could not be properly treated until the supply of drugs was removed from practitioners and provided separately at the expense of the ratepayer. The Medical Officer of St. Pancras condemned the 'vicious system' which required Poor Law doctors to supply medicines at their own expense, and recommended that a depot for drugs should be established in workhouses.[1] Stepney Union, however, had a special drug committee to deal with supplies, under the Chairman of the local hospital. Farr had undertaken an analysis of the question. He discovered that the poor in some areas, where they were attended by wealthy and conscientious Medical Officers, were supplied with the same medicines as private patients, at a great loss to the doctor. But looking at a pharmacopoeia he had found it easy to trace how the remainder of the Medical Officers could reduce the expense of drugs supplied, by never giving the poor the ten to twenty of the most expensive medicines which eminent physicians and surgeons of hospitals prescribed under the conviction that those remedies were most conducive to a patient's recovery.[2]

But, as was so often stated by Union doctors, it was not medicines but nourishment the people needed. That deaths from starvation still occurred, was seen from the inquiries the Poor Law Commission had to undertake in 1840 into a great number of such scandals.[3] The commonest instance was where death occurred through a disease of the lungs coupled with starvation, although regarding these cases the Guardians argued they had given adequate outdoor relief during the time of illness. The verdicts on all such deaths were always the same—natural death accelerated by want of food and destitution, or disease of... accelerated by lack of food. Giving evidence on typhus and consumptive cases, the Medical Officers frequently declared that the disease had been contracted because relief in food had previously been denied them. Doctors generally attended those sick, or sent those into the workhouse, whose homes were too filthy or poverty-stricken for them to live there. But people starved to death in some Unions, because they were afraid to apply for medical and general relief, knowing that it meant entering the workhouse. For example, a potter of Burslem, aged 26, suffered from malignant ulceration of the mouth and violent diarrhoea caused by want of food. He had applied for relief, but refused it because he was offered the workhouse, and he did not wish to be parted from his family. After fourteen days of illness the Medical Officer was sent and the Relieving Officer allowed food and medicines, but it was too late. There was another case of a child of 16 who died from want and scarlet fever. The parents had been refused relief and were too poor to procure medical attendance or extra food. From testimonies given at the inquiries there is no doubt that many of the sufferers were depraved characters who sold the food given to them by the Guardians for drink—but what had brought them to this impasse?

[1] H. Cooper, Medical Officer, St. Pancras, Select Committee, 1844.

[2] Explanatory remarks on statistics compiled at St. George's Hospital, 1844. (Medically qualified readers will no doubt ponder over the efficacy of the drugs and the medical treatment offered at this time.)

[3] Poor Law Commissioners Minutes, 1840: 'Abstract of circumstances of alleged deaths from want and results of enquiries'.

The Poor Law Commissioners, commenting on the inquiries, pointed out that 'notes for necessaries such as sugar, groats, bread, and candles' could have been given by Union surgeons. And they concluded that these cases indicated the danger of giving outdoor relief, because parents starved their children even if they obtained 'extras'.[1]

Farr pointed out the relationship between malnutrition and disease; that people not actually ill suffered from debility and lack of stamina, so that they had less resistance to infection when exposed to it. It was, however, important to give to the poor not only food but also fuel, because the appalling ventilation in the houses with its evil consequences was due to their keeping doors and windows constantly closed in order to exclude the cold. Evidence given in 1844 by an agent of the London City Mission showed that typhus seized those that were destitute and undernourished. A Medical Officer of Bethnal Green stated that one of his patients had for a fortnight lived on a diet of potatoes and fresh water poured on the same tea-leaves night and morning. Both the Presidents of the Royal Colleges of Physicians and Surgeons declared that medical aid was not enough to offer the poor, but that they seriously required better nourishment. The necessity of giving the poor food before they became actual paupers through sickness was not recognized by the Poor Law authorities, although it was not expressly forbidden by the Act of 1834. For section 52 stated: 'In cases of emergency Guardians may depart from the rules and report to the Commissioners. If the Commissioners approve, or if relief so given is given in food, temporary lodging or medicine and has been reported, such relief will not be unlawful or subject to be disallowed.' Evidence was given to the Select Committee of 1838 that outdoor assistance in the form of food was given in Leeds in extreme cases, such as sickness in a large family which was not normally destitute.[2]

An order was also issued following the Prohibitory Outdoor Relief Act of 1844, allowing relief to be given at least half in food and clothing and articles of necessity, in return for which the recipients were to be set to work by the Guardians. In times of economic crisis, as in 1847, food was often given to the unemployed poor, but probably not through any comprehension that incipient starvation would lead to an increase in sickness. Flexibility was, however, introduced by these regulations to that the system could expand in times of emergency.

However severe and short-sighted the Poor Law authorities were in giving outdoor relief in kind to the able-bodied, the necessity of supplying additional food to the sick was understood and allowed under the provision of the Act. In the Instructional Letter to Guardians on the formation of Unions, the Commissioners referred to the already existing practice of granting food or clothing to the outdoor sick without criticism. It was an old arrangement which came under the category of those the central authorities wished to leave undisturbed. From many accounts, however, the parochial authorities seemed to have been more liberal than their successors: 'In the parish of Chipping Ongar (Essex) are provided for the use of the poor in time of sickness, not only bed linen, and a wrapping

---

[1] Minutes of the Poor Law Commissioners, 1840.
[2] Matthew Johnson, Leeds woollen merchant, Select Committee, 1838.

flannel gown, but also a large easy wicker chair, with a head to it, a bed chair, and a stand for a candlestick, with a convenient apparatus for a pannikin at the top, in which any kind of liquid may be heated, merely by a rush light. These articles, with blankets which are distributed amongst the [sick] poor in winter, and are required to be returned in warm weather, are kept at the workhouse, and may be obtained on application'! If this was an isolated case of benevolence under the old Poor Law, it at least had no similar unique parallel under the new.[1]

The Commissioners never really stated what was meant by a medical 'extra'. Therefore some Unions did not recognize the word and substituted 'nourishment', meaning that they would supply only 'those necessary articles of food, or medical and surgical appliances, which will be conducive to the recovery or improvement of the health of the patient'. In some Unions like Derby and Steyning (Sussex) medical extras were held to be covered by monetary relief, the Clerk of the latter Union writing that 'medical extras are not favoured, we give liberal relief in cases of sickness, and insist that all extras be purchased by the pauper'. Clerkenwell Union also gave outdoor relief to the sick poor in money. In the first quarter of 1841 this was nearly £302, in 1842 it was £319 for three months, in 1843 £201, and in 1844 this had fallen to £135. Wines and spirits were, however, supplied by the Guardians, but there are no means of ascertaining the expenditure save for sick indoor paupers, who for this item cost an average of £18 a quarter. When reviewing the whole system of the Poor Law administration in their Report on the Further Amendment of the Poor Law in 1839, the Commissioners accepted the giving of additional sick relief in money, for they did not even allude to what was becoming a widespread practice.

Many Unions required that, as recommendations of the Medical Officer for food and stimulants were equivalent to orders for additional relief, they should be accompanied by a report from him on a prescribed form, giving particulars of each case, ascertained by personal inquiry. Some Unions, like Holborn and Lewisham, ruled that 'medical extras' should only be supplied in case of emergency, or that they should not be given unless the Medical Officer certified that the patient could be efficiently treated at home. A few Unions only supplied extras on loan, except where applicants were really destitute. This system obtained in Merthyr Tydfil, Eastbourne, and Trowbridge. The Bradfield (Yorkshire) Board of Guardians Minutes frequently refer to extras being given on loan and to their repayment in instalments. A singular system existed in Eccleshall (Yorkshire) where money and bread were automatically given to the sick on a graded scale. Relief to sick persons was given as shown in Table 1.4.

A similar practice was adopted in Bradfield, but there was no fixed scale, nor was additional relief automatic. Here a large amount of sick relief was given in money and kind. One case occurred where a man and wife and their three children were ill; they were allowed 2s. and 3 gallons of bread a week. Another time a widow was given 3s. a week which was later changed to 1½ gallons of bread. One sick widow in the workhouse

[1] Extract from *Account of Provision for the Poor at Ongar during sickness* by the Rev. Wm. Hetherington, 1805.

TABLE 1.4
Relief to Sick Persons.—Minutes of the Eccleshall Board of Guardians, 1841
and 1842 (Webb MSS.)

	1841 per week				1842 altered to: per week		
	s.	d.	s.	d.	s.	d.	loaves
Single man	2	6	to 3	8½	1	6	plus 2
Man and wife—							
when man only sick	3	6	4	8½	2	6	3
with 1 child	3	6	5	3¾	3	0	4
2 children	4	0	5	9¾	3	6	5
3 children	4	6	6	11	4	0	6
4 children	5	0	8	0¼	4	6	7
5 children	6	0	9	0¼	5	0	8
6 children	7	0	—		5	6	9

desired to return home, and the Guardians allowed her 2s. 6d. a week to pay for a nurse there. In 1842 a man was given 2s. a week for a nurse, and a bedridden woman was given 1s. for the same purpose. On another occasion, however, the Relieving Officer reported that he had allowed a man who was very ill 2s. a week, and the Guardians reproved him for giving relief in money and disallowed the practice on future occasions. One deaf and dumb person without any resources was given a pair of shoes; and an old woman was allowed 3 glasses of wine a day and 3 lb. of mutton a week on loan. There were many similar cases of relief in food for the sick and aged in varying amounts, generally half a gallon of bread and 2–3 lb. of mutton a week. In 1843 nurses were frequently supplied to families where the mother was ill or in confinement, especially where there were many children already. It seemed, however, that no logical system existed in Bradfield, save that in the 'forties extra relief in money was gradually withdrawn and in 1845 the Guardians disallowed all cases of outdoor medical relief.[1]

In Holborn, nutritious diet was never given to the poor, and the Medical Officer had no authority to order it, but the poor were sometimes given money to procure it. The system varied so much throughout the country because the Commissioners made no regulation on the subject. The most general practice was for the Medical Officer to order specific articles based on the requirements of the individual. In 1841 the Commissioners stated that the doctor could not give an authoritative direction to the Relieving Officer to provide extra food for the outdoor sick pauper (as he could in the workhouse); he could only give a recommendation. The responsibility of following this recommendation, they

[1] Minutes, Bradfield Board of Guardians (Webb MSS.).

said, rested with the Relieving Officer until the Board of Guardians considered it at a subsequent meeting.

> We conceive that it would not be prudent, as regards outdoor paupers, to deprive the Guardians of the power of deciding on their own responsibility, upon these recommendations of the Medical Officer, except in emergent cases. . . . We think that without this check the Medical Officers would often themselves be importuned or deceived in recommending extra food to their patients, and that a large amount of relief of an expensive character would be afforded, which frequently would not be applied to the wants of the sick person, but be consumed by other members of the family.

In cases of emergency, however, which might arise between Guardians' meetings, recommendations of the doctors were to be considered as an order to the Relieving Officer, until the latter could bring the case before a Board meeting.[1]

This ruling showed a strange contradiction. When a medical order was granted, the Poor Law doctor assumed he was dealing with a case of destitution and was legally bound to attend it without question. Yet as soon as a patient required additional nourishment, he had to give particulars ascertained by personal inquiry into the circumstances of the case. Also, disputes were bound to arise between the Relieving Officer and the doctor over what constituted an emergency, and the poor would be greatly affected by the outcome.

The administration as regards medical extras illustrated the clash of the two principles—the Poor Law deterrence principle, and the medical principle that the best should be done for the patient. The decision as to what was necessary to restore the patient rested with the Medical Officer, yet the onus of the decision legally was in the hands of the Relieving Officer and Guardians. The layman was again allowed to supervene over the specialist, and the principles of economy over welfare. The doctor must have seen numberless cases where more nourishment was essential to recovery, besides better housing and clothing. Yet he had no more power than that of recommendation. The doctors of St. Margaret's and St. John's, Westminster, for example, complained that they could only obtain a supply of extra food for the poor after the Relieving Officer had given his order. The Provincial Medical and Surgical Association voiced its objection in its 1841 Report, in which it recalled that before 1834 medical men possessed and exercised the power of recommending relief in kind to the sick to a far greater extent than after the Act. Formerly 'the Medical Officer was considered the sole judge of the amount of extra diet, and his directions were respectfully treated and always complied with'.

Fortunately, in the majority of Unions medical recommendations were seldom disregarded, although they were sometimes refused and often greatly discouraged. No doubt the system was at times abused, when doctors recommended necessaries to be given either for the sake of becoming popular, or, more particularly, because their meagre salaries did not allow them to supply all medicines—so they ordered a little extra food

[1] Seventh Annual Report of the Poor Law Commissioners.

hoping it would benefit the patient equally. Rumsey confessed that the existing system subjected the Medical Officer to the 'suspicion of ordering unnecessary amounts of stimulating and supporting diet'. The Guardians of Atchen Union (Shropshire) communicated with their Medical Officer in 1842 that he was overstating the poverty of a family, and that he was only to order medicines, and such articles of nourishment that might be classed as such, like wine, but not flour, bread, and potatoes.[1] Two years later he was informed that in cases where no great urgency existed, he should send directions for the supply of wine to the Relieving Officer and not to the overseers, and that as a general rule the Board would not afford relief to persons earning 10s. a week. His prescription of wine for as long as eighteen months for one patient was also questioned.[2]

Evidence was given to the Select Committee of 1844 on the reluctance of Boards of Guardians to grant the supply of 'extras'. The Medical Officer of one Union complained that the sick poor were suffering from insufficient food, and that many diseases arose from malnutrition. But he always felt restrained in ordering proper nourishment, because he had been warned not to apply for it frequently.[3] Doctors in Merionethshire and other Unions, also declared that the sick poor had insufficient nourishment during illness and convalescence. A surgeon in private practice in Aberystwyth asserted that a great many people died annually in the town through lack of relief.[4] In Plympton St. Mary, Devon, nourishment was not given freely to outdoor sick, therefore tickets signed by the surgeon were sent round to apply to charitable people in the neighbourhood. In Poplar where there was much whooping-cough, measles, and smallpox, the Medical Officer stated that nourishment was more important than medicine to the poor. He therefore resorted to the practice of ordering tonics, bitters and medicine to the sick, so that they would recover their general tone of health, and to stimulate their appetite, and then when the patient became convalescent, recommended meat, bread, wine and porter.

In a letter to Lord Ashley in 1844, the Chairman of St. George the Martyr, Southwark, stated that ninety out of every 100 cases brought under the care of the Medical Officers were suffering from exhaustion. The year previously the Board of Guardians realized that people were applying for medical orders to enable them to come before the Relieving Officer for general relief—therefore the Board had resolved 'where the doctor saw such to be the fact, he might order stores and not physic and subdue typhus'. It was not very long, however, the letter continued, before the Guardians realized that placing the Medical Officer in the role of Relieving Officer was leading to the 'certainty of ruining half the ratepayers of the parish'. The increase in the cost of extras given was shown to have risen from £10 in 1841, and £20 in 1842, to £44 in 1843, and £69 in 1844. The Medical Officer of the Union gave evidence to the Select Committee of 1844 that the poor were constantly ailing; low inflammation of the lungs, low fever and indigestion were

[1] Minutes, Board of Guardians, 1842.
[2] Minutes, Board of Guardians, 1844.
[3] John Price, M.D., Medical Officer, Corwen Union.
[4] Richard Williams, M.D.

very common diseases. The children were subject to convulsions, skin troubles and bowel complaints. Nearly every patient required support and nourishment. Whatever the disease, a large proportion of the illnesses he had to treat would never have arisen had the poor enjoyed a better diet. He also said he experienced great difficulty in obtaining wine and bread for the sick, and that the Board of Guardians ignored his complaints, because they refused to believe he had no ulterior motive in ordering useful things. The poor were also threatened when they called for food the doctors had ordered. Very often, he said, he had to resort to strong language in writing to the Relieving Officer for food for paupers, using such expressions as: 'Not ill, but starving', 'Wants relief, not physic', or 'If they have not meat or something similar, they will sink'! In consequence of the lack of necessaries in the early stages of an illness, the case became protracted and even danger-ous; this was uniformly his experience with fever. Mortality rates, the Medical Officer said, were rising on this account, and eventually parish rates would suffer. His experience had proved Dr. Southwood Smith's contention that fever fell principally on the heads of families. Those between the ages of 20 and 40 suffered the worst, and from them fever proceeded to attack the rest of the family. He particularly blamed the Relieving Officer, but realized that the fault lay in the policy of the central authorities and the Poor Law Act in deprecating outdoor relief.[1]

The Relieving Officer of Bethnal Green gave the unusual evidence to the Select Committee that he had not had one application for an order for additional food in three months. This, he said, was due to the Medical Officers generally recommending the sick for admission into the infirmary or hospital, because in the past, medical dietaries had frequently been misapplied. Therefore the number of medical orders issued and the quantity of meat, wine and porter given was very scanty. But he affirmed that patients requiring wine and porter who received domiciliary treatment, were supplied with them.[2] One of the doctors said no restraint was imposed on him from giving nutritious food by any fear of the Guardians, or apprehension that he would not be re-elected in the following year. Very different was the evidence of another surgeon of Bethnal Green Union. He had assumed the duty, whenever he saw great distress, to write to the Relieving Officer. Some-times people would be starving because the head of the family was suffering from fever or other disease. But he was always reprimanded for writing such letters and forbidden to do so. He accused the Guardians of not treating his orders for extras fairly: 'When I attend a case of fever I am often prevented from giving the quantity of relief the patient ought to have. They cannot get wine or porter *ad lib.*, or animal food to the extent they ought to have. The Guardians do not refuse certificates, but they give insufficient quantities.' People, he said, died from diseases because their stamina was so low, when otherwise they might have had a chance of recovery. He had on several occasions been cautioned by parish officers, who, he said, had no right to interfere in the ordering of medical relief or

[1] Evans, Medical Officer, St. George the Martyr, Southwark, Select Committee, 1844.
[2] Wine was regarded as a medicine by the medical profession in the mid-nineteenth century.

sustenance; but in extraordinary cases he had broken through their opposition and the rules.

An agent of the London City Mission gave an even less rosy picture, for he had spoken to the poor themselves. They had informed him that certificates given to them by medical officers for extras were not attended to by Guardians and that doctors themselves were generally discouraged from recommending nourishment for them. If they were not settled in the parish, necessaries were refused the sick, as was also the case with whole families who were pauperized when one of its members had gone into hospital. Cornewall Lewis however declared that the Commissioners recommended relief in kind should be given when a member of a family entered the workhouse hospital. They had suggested a family of eight should be allowed five to six shillings a week and a family of five two to four shillings in food. In general sick people complained not of medical treatment but of lack of extra nourishment. Sometimes Boards of Guardians refused to give food but supplied bedding, which, it was stated, was often sold by the poor.

Even a Relieving Officer of one Union attributed the prevalence of smallpox and typhus to malnutrition and inadequate clothing for inclement weather. Stepney Union, which was said to have 'exercised a liberal spirit in the distribution of medical relief', spent a total of £20,000 in poor relief in a year or 4s. 6d. per head of the population. Here the Board of Guardians always supplied food and necessaries ordered by the Medical Officer. In one month in 1843 the Board had supplied 1,574 lb. of meat; 736 lb. of oatmeal; 1,030 qt. of milk; 7½ lb. of sugar; 431 glasses of wine; as well as sago, arrowroot, and other comforts. An average of £12 per week was spent on these necessities for the sick poor. Yet before 1834 the giving of relief in nourishment to the outdoor poor was almost unknown here, and when it was given, it was supplied only in small quantities.[1]

In the East London Union similar liberality obtained, and the Medical Officer stated that he had never experienced any difficulty in obtaining necessaries for his patients. He had given unlimited orders, and they had always been attended to. On one occasion the Guardians half-furnished a room for a poor woman who was in a state of extreme misery. She had not a single object in her room and was confined on the floor with only a chamber pot for the doctor to wash his hands in. He gave an order for a bed, blankets, and chairs, and everything was provided. He gave another example of generosity. A family in one month had a wine bill of £3 and a butcher's bill of nearly £2. He signed a certificate to show that this was correct and the Guardians paid for it immediately.[2] In the Lambeth Union also, no objections were ever made by the Board of Guardians to the Medical Officer ordering nutritious diet for the destitute poor, although bedding and clothing were withheld. The Select Committee of 1844 heard evidence from one rural Union, Leighton Buzzard, where no restraint was put on the doctor in his recommendations for food in cases of sickness and convalescence, and from another, Ampthill, where the Relieving

[1] Frederick Young, Chairman, Stepney Union, Select Committee, 1844.
[2] Evidence, Mr. Lobb, Medical Officer, Aldersgate, Select Committee, 1844.

Officer gave orders on a shop to provide the articles recommended by the doctor, and the bill was laid before the Guardians afterwards.

As the Commissioners made no regulation on the provision of 'extras', it was little wonder that such divergencies in their provision existed throughout the country. Cornewall Lewis stated in 1844 that abuses arose occasionally, but analysing the evidence on the subject, the Commissioners had little cause to fear that any evil would result from the Medical Officers having the power to recommend orders for extras according to their own judgement. Many people desired to see the abolition of the control by Relieving Officers and Guardians over their provision, but this hope was never realized, nor did the local and central authorities ever learn that adequate food would mean less medicine. The magnitude of the problem was proved by the relatively few people who received medical treatment only. An illustration of this is afforded by the statistics of medical relief given by the West Ham Union, Table 1.5.

TABLE 1.5

West Ham Union Expenditure on Medical Relief.—Evidence by W. Champion Streatfield, Chairman of the West Ham Union, to the Select Committee of 1844

Year	Total expenditure on poor	Medical amount	Cases		Medical orders only	Population
			In Workhouse	Domiciliary		
	£ s. d.	£ s. d.				
1836–37	10,758 5 11	432 0 0	673	1,742	—	1831—24,770
1837–38	9,470 3 7¾	285 0 0	531	1,386	500	1841—26,405
1838–39	9,990 7 11	443 7 0	638	1,210	—	
1839–40	10,546 10 4	472 2 0	669	1,395	—	
1840–41	12,559 7 7	643 16 10	753	1,329	396	
1841–42	13,027 16 11	445 0 0	396	1,501	295	
1842–43	11,672 7 0	445 0 0	813	2,026	316	
Average	11,146 8 5½		639	1,512		

These statistics also reveal that sickness grew more rapidly than the population. For, taking West Ham as an example, the numbers requiring medical assistance increased by one sixth while the population rose by only one twelfth. Not only was this trend a warning of what was going to be required of the Poor Law medical services, but it also made apparent the close relationship between poverty and disease. Throughout the country there were few sick who did not require general relief, and on average 50 per cent (Wales 40 per cent) of those obtaining general relief required medical assistance. In the Blything Union

(Suffolk) where the proportion of pauperism to the population was 10 per cent, and pauper medical relief only 25 per cent, the significant observation was made: 'The proportion of medical pauperism prevailing is verified by the number of persons receiving outrelief in proportion to the population . . . since where medical pauperism prevails, every other species of pauperism will be found to prevail also in equal or greater degree'.[1]

Probably aware of the increasing significance of the relationship between sickness and pauperism, and also because of the development of the idea of the necessity for more accurate and informative statistics, the Poor Law Commissioner in 1842 ordered detailed figures to be prepared every quarter by all Unions of the classes of paupers obtaining relief. These statistics were published in their annual reports in every year following, Table 1.6.

The tabular statements have an additional importance because they reveal the over-whelming preponderance of outdoor over indoor sick relief. By the 1840s it had become increasingly impossible to attempt to give institutional medical assistance. Already in 1835, 1836, and 1837 the proportion was only 1 in 20 receiving medical relief, and from the above table it can be seen that the percentage of people receiving outdoor relief to those obtaining it in the workhouse grew increasingly after 1842. Only in the Metropolitan area was this trend less marked. Middlesex in 1843 still relieved over 20,000 sick paupers institutionally, compared with 44,500 out of doors, and Surrey had nearly 11,000 indoor against 27,500 outdoor patients.

The statistics of expenditure reveal in the first instance the disproportionately low amount spent on medical relief compared with total expenditure, a fact made more obvious when the proportion of sick to the total number of paupers is considered. In 1836 Somerset spent 3·2 per cent of the total Poor Law expenditure on medical relief, Worcestershire 4 per cent, and Wiltshire and Dorset 3 per cent. To the Select Committee of 1838 it was stated that Essex was the county with the highest Poor Law expenditure, and even here only about 3 per cent of it was used for medical relief, and the same proportion existed in the industrial towns. But however low the figure of medical expenditure, statistics also show a far more rapid proportionate increase on this account, indeed it rose steadily although total expenditure was sometimes stationary and often fell. The large amount of general assistance the sick must have received can also be inferred from the disproportion between the medical and total expenditure, as well as the extent to which whole families required general relief through the sickness of one of its members. In the early years figures were published of the number of families relieved because of sickness in them. In the last quarter of 1835, in the fifteen rural counties already under the new Poor Law, 74 families received institutional relief and 2,361 were assisted in their own homes. By 1837 the number had risen to 150 families indoor, and 2,573 outdoor.[2]

[1] Report on 'The Rules, Objects and the Working of the Blything Union "Pauper Health Assurance Association" (founded in 1839)', Appendix, Select Committee on Medical Relief, 1844.

[2] The fifteen counties were Northamptonshire, Oxfordshire, Buckinghamshire, Bedfordshire, Hampshire, Suffolk, Kent, Berkshire, Dorset, Cambridgeshire, Hertfordshire, Sussex, Essex, Wiltshire, and Gloucestershire. See also table for 1836, Poor Law Commissioners' Abstracts.

TABLE 1.6

The Number of Indoor and Outdoor Adult Able-bodied Paupers relieved in England and Wales during the Quarters ending Lady Day, 1842 to 1847. Compiled from Annual Reports of the Poor Law Commissioners.

Year	INDOOR					OUTDOOR					Total Indoor and Outdoor	Total indoor and outdoor relieved because of accident or temporary sickness	Proportional percentage total number of indoor and outdoor poor
	Through temporary sickness or accident	Proportional percentage to total	Other causes, including vagrants	Proportional percentage to total	Total Indoor	Through temporary sickness or accident	Proportional percentage to total	Other causes, including vagrants	Proportional percentage to total	Total Outdoor			
1842	10,992	13	74,249	87	85,171	134,641	41	192,078	54	326,719	411,890	145,563	35
1843	10,880	11	88,239	89	99,119	146,369	40	219,384	60	365,753	464,872	157,249	34
1844	11,458	13	86,329	87	97,785	158,280	52	175,419	48	333,699	431,484	169,738	39
1845	11,406	14	76,199	86	87,605	167,280	55	165,044	45	332,278	419,883	178,686	43
1846	11,229	14	71,991	86	83,220	143,479	50	148,864	50	292,343	375,563	154,708	42
1847	13,485	11	109,739	89	123,224	202,403	50	236,728	50	439,131	562,355	215,888	39

5

THE ORIGINS OF THE NATIONAL HEALTH SERVICE

A summary of the annual figures published by the Commissioners, Table 1.7, is most useful for comparative purposes, but three factors must be borne in mind. First, the increase in medical expenditure was not as salutary in extent as the table reveals, because the amount was offset by the increase in population. Second, the price of provisions considerably influenced the amount and the cost of relief, and third, the 'Hungry Forties' saw much abnormal distress in manufacturing and agricultural areas, so that expenditure was not more liberal than it would have been in normal circumstances.

TABLE 1.7

Poor Law Expenditure.—Summary of the annual figures published by the Poor Law Commissioners

Year	Total relief	Medical relief	Vaccination	Average price of wheat per quarter
	£	£	£	s. d.
1834	6,317,254			59 11
1835	5,526,416	Not given	—	44 2
1836	4,717,629		—	39 5
1837	4,044,741		—	52 6
1838	4,123,604	136,775	—	55 3
1839	4,406,907	148,652	—	69 4
1840	4,576,965	151,781	—	68 6
1841	4,760,929	154,054	11,564	65 3
1842	4,911,498	153,481	33,744	64 0
1843	5,208,027	160,726	16,425	54 4
1844	4,976,093	166,257	16,980	51 5
1845	5,039,703	174,330*	25,905	49 2
1846	4,962,026	175,269*	27,486	53 3
1847	5,298,787	179,526	18,115	59 0

* Medical expenditure in these years was almost stationary, but note total expenditure on relief fell in these years.

These comprehensive figures however, give no account of the differences in the country.[1] This was seen in the years when the Poor Law was in operation only in agricultural areas. In the fifteen counties, with a total population of 1½ million, the number of able-bodied relieved amounted to 38,500 and the number of paupers receiving relief because of sickness to nearly 5,000, a much lower percentage than when other areas were

[1] See Table 1.8—comparison of amount of medical relief spent in each county; 1842 given as an example (from summary of Poor Rate Returns 1842).

added later. But even this situation did not last as the more able-bodied migrated and poverty in rural England increased.

TABLE 1.8

Amount spent on Medical Relief by each County, 1842.—Ninth Annual Report of the Poor Law Commissioners, 1843: Appendix

County	Population, 1841	Medical Relief	County	Population, 1841	Medical Relief
	000's	£		000's	£
Bedford	108	1,601	N'thumberland	250	1,306
Berks	160	3,354	Notts	250	2,101
Bucks	156	2,705	Oxford	162	2,717
Cambridge	165	2,198	Rutland	21	306
Cheshire	395	2,498	Salop	239	2,784
Cornwall	341	2,097	Somerset	436	5,819
Cumberland	178	978	Southampton	354	5,477
Derby	272	1,259	Stafford	510	2,951
Devon	534	5,522	Suffolk	315	5,251
Dorset	175	2,997	Surrey	583	5,928
Durham	324	1,386	Sussex	300	5,512
Essex	344	8,130	Warwick	402	3,297
Gloucester	431	3,801	Westmorland	56	587
Hereford	114	1,948	Wilts	260	4,558
Hertford	157	3,110	Worcester	233	3,042
Huntingdon	59	1,082	York-E. Riding	232	1,516
Kent	548	6,572	N. Riding	205	1,506
Lancaster	1,667	6,131	W. Riding	1,155	4,865
Leicester	216	2,399			
Lincoln	363	3,244	Total: England	14,996,000	146,700
Middlesex	1,577	13,688			
Monmouth	134	946	Wales	911,321	6,781
Norfolk	413	6,671			
Northants	199	2,740	Aggregate	15,912,000	153,481

Robert Ceely the well known doctor and an influential voice in the Provincial Medical and Surgical Association described the agricultural labourer as a sickly race of people, suffering from insufficient food, especially since the introduction of the new Poor Law. Thomas Wakley was by far the most able of the members of the Select Committee of 1838 and drew important information from the witnesses. Through the questions he asked, a picture typical of the life in agricultural communities was obtained. He questioned Ceely, who himself had an extensive practice in Aylesbury, Bucks. Here the physical conditions for the labourer were bad owing to the damp, clay soil. Agricultural wages were between seven and nine shillings a week, not enough to purchase adequate food. To the combination of depressing environmental conditions, and the diet of bread and potatoes with little animal food, he attributed the great prevalence of scrofula (bovine tuberculosis) and fevers of all types. If anything the position had worsened since 1834 because unemployment was greater, yet the Union was saving 50 per cent on the poor rates! Ceely expressed surprise at the contrast between these people and those amongst whom he had previously practised in London. Wakley included in his questions that it was 'extremely distressing and harassing to medical men to observe the state of destitution in which labourers are found, when they are suffering under disease'. Ceely agreed, and added that so much was this the truth, that for this reason he would never again take an extensive parish practice. He insisted that the poor required more attention than the wealthier classes, as their diseases were more severe and prolonged, and because they were unable to procure nourishing food, so essential to recovery. 'It is', he said, 'sometimes consistent with policy and economy, as well as in unison with all my own feelings, to furnish that assistance out of my own pocket.' Therefore on one occasion when an epidemic prevailed in his district, it cost him £10 to furnish wine and beef tea for his patients, because he was anxious to get them well as soon as he could. The cases, he said, were so distressing that he could not withhold the assistance the Guardians refused to provide.

The Poor Law Commissioners when they instituted their lengthy enquiries into diets in 1835, found the average quantity of food consumed by agricultural labourers did not exceed 20 oz. a day or $15\frac{1}{2}$ oz. of nutritive substance, in contrast to felons who were receiving 49 oz. daily or nearly 38 oz. of nutritive matter. It was stated that 18–24 oz. or 16 oz. of nutritive food per day was requisite to 'support life in a sound and healthy state', and 24–30 oz. for those doing hard labour.[1]

The importance of the influence of economic factors on the poor in agricultural areas was realized by the central Poor Law authorities, and in 1842 Assistant Commissioner E. C. Tufnell was asked to investigate the effect of railways on pauperism in Kent and Sussex. He was to enquire into the validity of the assertion that the construction of the South-Eastern and Brighton Railways materially and favourably affected the labour market in these areas, and also that large scale emigration had taken place from these counties. To ascertain whether there had been any diminution in able-bodied pauperism and in the poor rates, he procured accounts from the engineers as to the numbers of labourers employed. From these he discovered that only one in sixty-six workers were recruited locally, nine-tenths being navvies who travelled from railway to railway solely for this purpose and belonged to no county. Therefore the new construction had a trivial effect on the local labour market. Tufnell actually asserted that not only did the building

[1] Report by Assistant Commissioner Charles Mott, Second Annual Report of the Poor Law Commissioners, 1836.

of the railways bring no advantage to the districts through which they ran, but it caused serious evils, such as an increase in crime and a considerable addition to Poor Law expenditure. This was because of the great number of dangerous accidents which occurred, through which men and families were thrown on the rates for a considerable period. That the men were mostly strangers made no difference in their chargeability when thus disabled, because they were casual paupers, and therefore incapable of removal. Almost every Board of Guardians of the Unions through which the two railways ran, complained to Tufnell of the heavy expenses entailed—in some cases poor rates were doubled. The great intemperance also disposed men to sickness, and the increase in bastardy meant midwifery charges fell on the Union as well as the maintenance of the women.

A small parish (Coulsden) had in eighteen months to pay £273 16s. od. in relief because of accidents to railway workmen not belonging to the district. 'Rough characters' from every Union, Tufnell said, sought employment in new railway enterprises but 'well-conditioned and steady workmen' left them after a short period of employment, because of the truck system. The Chairman of Cuckfield Union stated that the effect of railway construction and the temporary high rates of payment was a great increase in drunkenness, bastardy, and prostitution. About every third woman that entered the workhouse, he said, 'either itched, or had contracted venereal disease from the railroad'. In the last two years, of the twenty-eight bastards born in the workhouse twenty-four were attributable to the railway. The Vice-Chairman of the same Union stated he was unable to find a trustworthy man to employ, because the villagers were so demoralized through their contact with the railway workers. Tufnell only attacked the building of railways, however, not their utility subsequently. He ascribed the decrease in pauperism in Kent and Sussex, not to any influence of the railways, because the greatest decline in numbers and expenditure (£400,000 in one year) had taken place 'before a spadeful of earth had been removed', whilst since the works were in operation, the poor cost about £50,000 more than previously.

In the same report, Tufnell gave an account of the effects of migration. People had attributed the decrease in pauperism in these areas to the poor seeking work in manufacturing counties. Yet not fifty families had left Kent and Sussex, and several had returned. The Poor Law authorities found that aided migration was not an answer to their problem and the policy was short-lived. Tufnell's Malthusian principles had been proved by the little effect migration or emigration had on pauperism in these areas.[1]

Richard Muggeridge, the Poor Law migration agent, had in 1836 given an account to the Commissioners of the effect of migration in reception areas.[2] He believed the most important consideration was the effect migration had in the industrial centres on the health of people newly introduced into those districts, particularly those engaged in factories.

[1] Report by E. C. Tufnell, Assistant Commissioner for Kent and Sussex, 1 March 1842. Eighth Annual Report of the Poor Law Commissioners 1842. [This is an extremely interesting and informative description for the social and economic historian.]

[2] Report by R. Muggeridge to Poor Law Commissioners, reprinted in Second Annual Report, 1836.

Because if 'it appeared that the experiment had, or was likely to trench on vital economy . . . neither public or private interest . . . should be permitted by the Board to urge its continuance under their sanction'. Returns made to him showed that 2,673 people had migrated to Lancashire, and of these fourteen had died there (nine children under 9 years of age and unemployed and two engaged in factories). The causes of death had been smallpox, whooping-cough, inflammation, typhus, ague, and fever, and Muggeridge concluded that with the exception of smallpox, by which several families had been attacked, no disorder or sickness had particularly affected migrants. He said that many inquiries had been conducted by several independent deputations into the important point of the general health of the people who had migrated, yet their reports presented no evidence that any ill-health or undue mortality had occurred. The returns which the Poor Law migration agency received from employers confirmed the absence of any serious illness and generally stated that the labourers were doing well and were in good health.

The Poor Law Commissioners further interested themselves in the influence of economic factors on pauperism, by conducting an inquiry in 1839 into the effect of high prices.[1] Reports from Hertfordshire, Huntingdonshire, Cambridgeshire, and Essex stated that employers there were on the whole convinced it was more in their own interest to pay labourers wages sufficient to support their families, than to support them all in the workhouse. In Norfolk and Suffolk also, a rise in wages had accompanied the rise in prices for the same reason, and hardships, it was found, were relieved more and more by individual charity than by an increase in the poor rates. In Devon and Cornwall the amount of relief afforded to the aged and infirm increased, and from the North, Sir John Walsham reported much less distress than was anticipated. Employment was constant at high wages in Northumberland, Durham and Cumberland, but the poorer classes suffered by the rise in the price of flour and oatmeal. They had not however fallen on the poor rates in an increased proportion. In the areas of South Wales where wages were lowest, and where they had not risen with the increase in the cost of living, no pressure on the workhouse was reported, and Assistant Commissioner Edward Senior congratulated the new workhouse test in reducing expenditure from 7s. 2d. per head in 1834 to 6s. in 1837. (In England it had fallen from 9s. 3d. to 5s. 10d.) Although wages in mining districts were three times those in agricultural areas around them, labourers had shown little inclination to migrate. In cotton manufacturing districts the number relieved and the amount of relief was declining, although total expenditure figures did not show this through the rise in prices. In the whole country there was only a 5 per cent increase in the number of paupers relieved indoor and outdoor in 1837–38, whilst prices rose $18\frac{1}{2}$ per cent.

The Poor Law Commissioners attempted to judge the condition of labourers not by money wages but by the amount of employment and the contribution to savings—and

---

[1] Fifth Annual Report of the Poor Law Commissioners, 1839. The long reports of the Assistant Commissioners again provide an excellent account of the economic distress at this time.

Tidd Pratt had shown that there were 50,000 more small depositors in 1838 over 1837 and an increase of £1,800,000 in deposits.[1]

In 1839, four-fifths of the money expended on poor relief was given in outdoor relief. No doubt many able-bodied were receiving assistance out of the workhouse, because the supply of institutional relief never caught up with the demand, until the idea had to be abandoned. But as it was the confirmed policy of the Poor Law authorities to give out-door relief particularly to the sick and aged, this high percentage shows the great amount of sickness that must have prevailed in this year of high prices, and that the salutariness of the reduction in the numbers of able-bodied requiring assistance, as the above reports attempted to convey, was an arbitrary inference.

An unusual amount of pressure on the poor in Kent and Sussex was reported by Tufnell in 1842.[2] The winter had been the worst for fifty years, and had caused the total failure of the hop crop. Yet pauperism, he said, was on the whole not as onerous as in several preceding years because 'the poor had learnt to be more independent since the Poor Law'! The labour account had increased as the poor rate diminished as was seen from a table of expenditure of one farm in the Eastry Union, Table 1.9.

TABLE 1.9
Table of Expenditure of one farm in the Eastry Union

	Paid for labour	Paid for Poor Rates
Christmas 1834 to Christmas 1835	£793	£165
1835 1836	£815	£108
1836 1837	£894	£69

And at Bickham Escott a farmer examined before the Agricultural Committee of the House of Commons stated he had saved £200 a year in rates and spent over £500 a year more in labour on the farm. In the same year great distress was reported from the handloom weavers particularly in Bradford, the West Riding, and Lancashire, but here the Poor Law had an adverse effect because the giving of relief prevented weavers from abandoning that type of employment for the factory, and also most of those engaged in this outmoded industry were too old to be capable of moving. Severe hardship was also experienced in 1842 among the cotton operatives in Lancashire and Cheshire and the Commissioners instituted an inquiry into the circumstances of a typical town. Stockport was selected, because it appeared from previous information that it had suffered more remarkable

[1] Fifth Annual Report of the Poor Law Commissioners, 1839, section on cotton and other manu-facturing districts. Tidd Pratt was a barrister and statistician, appointed by the Poor Law Commissioners, to certify the Rules of Savings Banks and Benefit Societies. First Report 1835 published in First Annual Report of the Poor Law Commissioners, 1835.
[2] Eighth Annual Report of the Poor Law Commissioners, 1842, Appendix B8.

reverses of prosperity than any other part of the cotton manufacturing district. The two Assistant Commissioners, Power and Twisleton, laid the results of their extensive and detailed inquiry before the House of Commons. The report proved incontestably that 'the operative classes of Stockport have been, and still are, enduring severe privation . . . and all the extreme consequences of suffering such as starvation and infectious fever caused by destitution have been averted by the active and judicious measures of the Board of Guardians.'[1] Great distress was reported also from other manufacturing towns, and from the cloth manufacturing district of West Wiltshire, where the able-bodied inmates of the workhouse rioted.[2] It must also be remembered that this was the year when Chartism reached its zenith.

In 1842, 63,000 able-bodied required outdoor relief through unemployment and 50,000 through insufficient earnings, and a further 250,000 aged and infirm were given outdoor relief. These people did not come under the Poor Law medical services but it is a matter for conjecture how many of them suffered from debility, minor ailments, and malnutrition, and in whom the seeds of future sickness were already sown.

In 1843 the Poor Law Commissioners again reported distress in the textile, iron, and manufacturing districts, a fall in prices in agricultural districts, and the difficulty of paupers in finding employment. In the following year, they stated that the demand for labour everywhere was increasing steadily, and that the mild winter had been favourable to the poor. In 1845 Poor Law expenditure was practically stationary, but conditions were not uniform throughout the country. On the whole pauperism increased in agricultural areas and decreased in manufacturing areas. For example, in the West Riding it decreased by 11 per cent while in the Eastern parts of the county which were purely rural, it increased by 1 per cent. This was chiefly because the demand for labour in manufacturing districts was extensive and constant in 1845, whilst the summer drought and severe winter of 1844–45 had interrupted employment in agriculture. The number of able-bodied paupers who had received outdoor relief because of temporary sickness or accident increased by 5 per cent. But the number of the same class who received outdoor relief from all other causes decreased by 6 per cent.[3] The failure of the potato crop induced the Commissioners

---

[1] Eighth Annual Report of the Poor Law Commissioners, 1842.
[2] Ibid.
[3] Extent of pauperism shown by the proportion of general poor relieved to the population:

England	Percentage of population		Percentage of population
Highest—Wilts	16	Stafford	8
Essex, Sussex	14	Chester, Lincoln, Cornwall, Monmouth, Warwick	7
Bucks, Dorset, Oxford, Suffolk, Westmorland	13	Lowest—Derby, Cumberland ..	6
Bedford, Leicester, Somerset ..	12	Average—10 per cent	
Wales			
Highest—Montgomery	14	Lowest—Glamorgan, Pembroke ..	7
		Average—9 per cent	

—Ninth Annual Report of the Poor Law Commissioners, 1843.

to issue two circular letters (November 1845) to all Boards of Guardians suggesting precautionary measures. One indicated the possibility of extracting farina from diseased potatoes as a mode of employment in the workhouse, and the other pointed to the expediency of substituting some article for potatoes in workhouse dietaries. Only from a few Unions, however, in Devon and Somerset, did the Commissioners receive applications to permit outdoor relief for the able-bodied because of the potato shortage, and it was stated that the diet in the workhouses was superior to that of independent labourers![1]

At the beginning of 1846 the working classes in general were being steadily employed on wages on the whole above the average rates, in both manufacturing and agricultural areas. In the winter of 1845–46 scarcely a workhouse in rural Unions was full enough to necessitate the granting of outdoor relief to the able-bodied. There was a general diminution in expenditure for poor relief throughout England, though as always at varying rates. In the summer and autumn, employment was constant and the rates of wages not below the average. But the general failure of the crops in 1846 influenced the condition of the poor, for the price of nearly all foodstuffs rose. It also hit the labourer because his own garden produce failed, especially in Wiltshire, Somerset and Devon, where people depended on it. The prohibitory outdoor-relief order had to be relaxed in the South, and in the North, in Manchester, Nottingham, and Derby, for the high price of cotton had caused severe unemployment and an increase in expenditure on relief. The severity of the distress in Ireland produced a great influx of destitute Irish to the West coast of England, especially to Liverpool. From January to April 1847, 133,000 arrived in Liverpool alone. Precautions were taken by the Vestry on a large and expensive scale, against the spread of fever and disease from the overcrowded dwellings of the Irish but not as it was feared, beyond the necessity of the emergency.

It can be seen therefore that varying economic conditions greatly influenced pauperism, and the amount of destitution which existed was an indication of the extent to which sickness prevailed. Economic conditions also affected Poor Law expenditure because trade fluctuations influenced ratepayers. In times of crisis they demanded retrenchment, which automatically affected the salaries the Guardians were willing to offer the Medical Officers, and the medical relief as well as 'extras' they were disposed to give.

Although the Poor Law Commissioners were interested in the influence of environmental and economic factors on pauperism and pauper sickness, they instituted no investigation into occupational diseases. This deficiency was to some extent rectified by Farr. In the late 'thirties he inquired into the incidence of sickness in the Portsmouth and Woolwich Dockyards. In the East India Docks he had discovered that 2 per cent of the workers were constantly kept at home by diseases of one kind or another—diseases independent of external mechanical injury constituting two-thirds of the entire sickness. As much as 7.8 per cent of a dockyard labourer's lifetime was spent in illness. Mortality under 40 years of age was not high among labourers because only healthy men between

[1] Report from Tufnell on potato disease, 1846. Appendix to Twelfth Annual Report of the Poor Law Commissioners, 1846.

the ages of 20 and 35 were selected for engagement. Between 40 and 50 years of age the mortality rate was 67 per cent and between 50 and 60, 82 per cent—higher than the mortality at the same ages in the rest of England. Such facts, Farr concluded 'annihilate the supposition that increased mortality in cities is due to want of food and greater misery'. The dockers' food, he said, was good, and they had sufficient muscular exercise. Tables of the East India Company and the labourers' friendly societies threw light on the state of health prevailing in the Metropolis. They showed that men labouring in warehouses in the heart of the city were well provided for, and occupied as regards health a mid-point between the worst classes and the inhabitants of cleaner and less crowded districts. The surgeon who attended the East India Company's labourers was responsible for their selection, and examined all recruits for hernia and varicose veins, so that the Company was sure of only engaging strong and healthy men. The surgeon had to report all severe illnesses and had to attend such cases every day. The company paid 1s. 6d. a day including Sundays to all sick men, and the labourers themselves subscribed to a sick and pension fund. When influenza and cholera prevailed, from forty to fifty men attended the doctor's surgery daily for coughs and bowel complaints. Those slightly ill remained at work and were not entered on the sick list. Cases of venereal disease and accidents which arose through intemperance were not attended by the Company doctor. Consumption and pulmonary complaints were very prevalent as well as fever. The longshoremen, often Irish, were very liable to phthisis and all consumptive patients were put on a permanent sick list.[1]

Farr also quoted the research of a doctor into the health of Cornish miners; he had personally examined 120 of them in actual employment and had found only 63 in good health. Another Medical Officer examined factory children, and out of 115 children below 18 years of age he reported that only 84 were healthy. Therefore only 53 per cent of the miners and 73 per cent of the children in factories were free from some complaint.[2] In conclusion Farr declared: 'How much sickness exists among actual labourers of this country, independent of those definitely incapacitated by disease, and who are either discharged on this account or set aside as inefficient, there are no satisfactory statistics for determining.'

In 1846 a doctor read a paper to the Manchester Statistical Society on 'Some of the evils affecting labourers engaged in Railway Construction'.[3] He described the intemperance of the men due to the truck system and the generally depraved, degraded and reckless characters of both men and women. The paper took the form of a letter addressed to Chadwick (a significant gesture as he was Secretary to the Poor Law Commissioners), who immediately sent a memorandum suggesting measures for the prevention of the evils.[4] Both papers revealed the great risk to men engaged in railway construction—the

---

[1] Farr's chapter on Vital Statistics in J. R. McCulloch's *Statistics of the British Empire*, Vol. II, 1837.

[2] J. Forbes, M.D., *Medical Topography of Penrith, Cornwall*, and (2) Dr. Bisset Hawkins (quoted by Farr).

[3] John Robertson, Surgeon to Manchester Lying-in Hospital.

[4] *Memoranda of Facts and Suggestions in Respect of measures for the prevention of evils attendant on Want of Regulation as to mode of employing and paying labourers on Railways*, 1846. (Quoted T. S. Ashton, *Economic and Social Investigation*. Manchester Statistical Society, 1837-1933.)

losses in killed and wounded being nearly proportionate to the losses of an army in war.

> Men are crowded together to an undue and injurious extent; their moral condition is most deplorable, especially as regards sexual morality and drunkenness, there is much vagabondage among the class; and a great reason to fear that when these works are discontinued, the dispersion of such a class among the general community will be attended with similar mischief as the disbanding of a small army.

In the building of the Summit Tunnel on the Manchester to Sheffield railway, three men were killed and 14 per cent injured—'The maintenance of families and widows of men killed or maimed is thrown on the ratepayers of parishes where they have settlements'. Chadwick suggested that the system which Prussia had adopted in her mines should be instituted, whereby contractors should be made responsible for losses caused by accidents, and men should contribute to a sick and accident fund. Chadwick also stated that the navvies began with the finest physical stamina—'but they do not last beyond their fortieth year . . . with fair treatment they would last with health and vigour their term of three score'. (These two inquiries led to the Select Committee on Railway Labourers in 1846.)

In 1837 a report was made to the Manchester Statistical Society by two well-known cotton manufacturers—the Greg brothers.[1] Although they were enlightened and humanitarian masters, they maintained that the

> health and morals of the people employed in cotton mills at least equals that of those engaged in other occupations in the towns in which they are situated; long hours of labour do *not* over-fatigue the children, or injure their health and constitution . . . the poor rates are lower in Lancashire than any other county . . . and the wages of labour are such as in agricultural districts would be regarded as positive opulence.

The Assistant Poor Law Commissioner for Shropshire in 1836[2] showed the high accident rate which existed in the mines there. Between the ages of 20 and 50, twelve accidents caused deaths in the high death rate of 51, and 25 per cent of all accidents were very severe or fatal. The best years of a man's life were between 18 and 20, and he began to fail at 40. Pulmonary affections and stomach troubles were very widespread, and most became asthmatic and suffered from rheumatism. The mortality rates of Shropshire were compared with those in the agricultural county of Sussex, Table 1.10, and it is seen that the proportion of widows was much higher. If the mining areas could have been extracted from the total county rate it would have been greater still.

It was important and necessary that both the Registrar-General George Graham, and Farr, as the Compiler of Abstracts, were deeply interested in the condition of the poor. And it is in their Annual Reports that so much light is shed on the general incidence of sickness in the country and the diseases most prevalent. In a circular letter to Coroners

---

[1] Quoted T. S. Ashton, *ibid*.
[2] Second Annual Report of the Poor Law Commissioners, 1836.

TABLE 1.10

Expectation of Life table, Shropshire and Sussex (Women were not employed in mining in Shropshire)

Years of age	Sussex Deaths, per cent		Shropshire Deaths, per cent	
	Male	Female	Male	Female
40–49	14	16	15	14
50–59	19	19	20	16
60–69	31	31	33	29
70–79	61	59	60	52

(10 August 1845) Graham asked them to help 'to discover the dangers attendant on occupations, pursuits and various circumstances in which the population are placed'—hoping that if the cause of death were ascertained, 'additional security might be thrown round human life, and thus the great objective of Coroners' inquests might be promoted by the Registration Act'. Another circular was sent to the Presidents of the Royal Colleges and the Society of Apothecaries, and these asked medical practitioners to help make the registration system more efficient. Between 10,000 and 11,000 doctors complied with the request to assist the Registrar General.[1]

In his first explanatory letter on Vital Statistics,[2] Farr stated that in 1838 epidemics of smallpox and typhus had followed the influenza epidemic of the previous winter. Pulmonary diseases were also much more fatal and so were convulsions in young children, than they had seen in previous years. This was ascribed to the rigorous weather and if the incidence rate had been shown, Farr could probably have proved that the poor suffered most because of their lower vitality which rendered them less resistant to disease and more liable to infection. It was consumption—the disease of malnutrition, and overcrowding—and the epidemics, that took an overwhelming toll of lives. 60,000 people died of pulmonary tuberculosis—18 per cent of the total, and 78,000 (24 per cent), from epidemic diseases such as smallpox, measles, dysentery, cholera and influenza. Diseases of the respiratory organs accounted for 28 per cent of the total deaths. On the fact that 161 people were registered as having died of intemperance, Farr commented:

> The consumption of intoxicating liquor increased faster than the population in the last 20 years, and the sale of spirits [to which the poor were addicted] at a much more rapid rate than that of ale or wine. Spirit drinking almost always ends in impairing health; it takes away the appetite, wastes the limited means of the artisan, deprives his family of food, firing, clothing and clean ventilated lodgings; leads to dissoluteness of every

[1] Seventh Annual Report, Registrar-General, 1845.
[2] Second Annual Report, Registrar-General, Appendix.

kind, and must therefore be considered one of the indirect but certain causes of epidemics of fever and other diseases

—and, what he failed to add, pauperism.

In 1837 Farr pointed out, there were 63, and in 1838, 167 deaths from starvation.
Coroners' inquests were held on 77 of them and the verdicts returned that deaths were due
to 'complication of cold and want of food'. The majority of those who starved to death
appeared to be in their best working years, and some died in the workhouse. He also drew
attention to the higher rate of sickness and mortality in overcrowded urban districts, and
the variation in the expectation of life that existed within towns. For example, in the
Eastern districts of London the mean duration was 25–30 years and in the North and West
40–50.

A growing interest was taken in these years by individual doctors in the incidence, the
economic and social causes, and the effects of diseases. In the mid 'thirties, Doctors Young
and Woolacombe calculated that a quarter of the deaths in England and Ireland were from
consumption. Another well-known doctor Sir James Clark, demonstrated that after deducting the deaths in early infancy, one-third of the mortality in the country arose from tubercular diseases. But he believed consumption and scrofula to be stationary among the labouring
classes, whilst they were increasing in the middle and upper ranks of society.[1] Farr, commenting on this research, believed mortality from the disease to be rising among those between the ages of 20 and 30, and declared that if Clark's proposals of hygienic precautions
were not enforced, the country would observe a great increase in 'weakly bodies and
consumption'. He also observed in 1837 that venereal disease was diminishing in intensity,
if not in frequency of onset. The commonest skin complaint among children was scald
head and itch.

In his explanatory letter on Vital Statistics in 1843,[2] Farr pointed out, that of the decrease in mortality of over a thousand for the past year, 900 were in the zymotic class of
diseases (i.e. epidemic, endemic, contagious—or dirt diseases). Scarlatina raged in increasing
severity until 1840, but then started a lasting decline. Smallpox also began diminishing
after the introduction of the Vaccination Acts. Measles destroyed 11,000 lives in the
epidemic of 1839, and 7,000 in 1841. Influenza and ague were growing more fatal every
year, but typhus was also declining in normal circumstances. Phthisis claimed nearly
60,000 lives a year from 1838 to 1841 and deaths from syphilis averaged 200 a year. These
years were also notorious for their high infant mortality, for an average of 23,000 babies
died in the first month of their lives.

The importance of paediatrics was first realized in this period, chiefly because of the
high mortality rate among the children of the poor. Destitution and dirt diseases took a
heavy toll of infant lives and this was recognized first by the Poor Law authorities. For the
problem of the care of children was precipitated acutely by the reforms introduced by the

[1] J. Clark, M.D., F.R.S., *Treatise on Pulmonary Consumption*; Farr, *Vital Statistics*, 1837.
[2] Fifth Annual Report, Registrar-General, 1843.

new Poor Law, whereby the Commissioners tried to provide for children as a separate class in the workhouse and in the Poor Law schools. Crowding them together only perpetuated and sometimes increased the spread of infection and disease, and it was at this time that the prevalence of ophthalmia of various types was recognized. 'Gonorrheal opthalmia with all its dire consequences, was to rack the workhouses and Poor Law schools for the whole of the nineteenth century.'[1] Virulent outbreaks took place in many years, but less severe forms of the disease were endemic wherever children were herded together. That it was contagious, and that isolation was essential, had been pointed out as far back as 1804, but the report of 1841 by Dr. Kay (Shuttleworth) showed that the warning had been in vain. He visited one school and ordered the affected children to be segregated, and they were moved into a separate room as the sick ward was much too small. But no sooner had he left the establishment than the children were returned to the schoolroom and allowed to mix with all the other children. In the Mile End workhouse also, he discovered ninety affected children living with the healthy. In his report on Norwood in 1838, he had stressed that sanitary precautions were necessary wherever children were collected together, and had pointed out 'the liability of children to contagious maladies' and the 'frequency with which pauper children were affected with other infectious diseases'. The Select Committee of 1844 also heard evidence of severe cases of ophthalmia which existed in the workhouses, particularly in Holborn.

The Poor Law Medical Officers were in the supreme position for providing information on diseases to which the poor were most subject. From their reports on the workhouse sick we learn that the inmates suffered particularly from fevers, bronchitis, diseased joints, rheumatism, pneumonia, consumption, scald, itch (scabies probably), syphilis, and eye diseases. An analysis of the reports on the outdoor sick gives very similar complaints—fevers, consumption, asthma and other pulmonary affections, rheumatism, erysipelas, and itch. They showed puerperal fever to be very common in midwifery and doctors often reported general debility. Prostitutes were either paupers or attempted to appear so, in order to gain admittance to the workhouse, because this was the only place where they could obtain treatment for venereal disease. Medical Officers often reported they were having to give prolonged treatment because cases were of the most aggravated description.

The Poor Law doctor, all too well aware of the diseases from which the poor suffered, and of their causes, was however not empowered to take any prophylactic action. Typical of the principles of the Poor Law, he was to relieve suffering where in so many instances he could have acted to prevent it. It was no part of his duty to search out disease. As the Medical Officer of St. George the Martyr, Southwark, pointed out to the Select Committee of 1844, if he had had more power he could have produced very beneficial effects among the poor. He could have insisted in the 'improvement of the dwellings by having the power to interfere for cleanliness and ventilation', and this he said, would have been for the good of the community, for the wealthy were not immune from infection spreading

[1] Arnold Sorsby, M.D., F.R.C.S., *Origin and Development of White Oak Hospital*, 1935.

to them from the poor. Servants and washerwomen could quite easily carry disease to their employers, and the doctor had heard the latter say they would not employ a parish physician from the fear that he would communicate the diseases from the poor to them. The Poor Law Medical Officer, he continued, was the only person who ever saw the poor as they really lived. He pointed to the state of their dwellings as a cause of disease, and said that he had come across people who slept week after week without undressing and scarcely ever washing themselves. He also knew of families who let their beds and slept together on the filthy floor, and whole neighbourhoods where, for the sake of warmth, no fresh air was ever let into the houses. He complained of the inadequate sanitation and the insufficient water supply. To alleviate these conditions he and other doctors and individuals had formed themselves into a committee, and succeeded in getting an Act of Parliament passed for building a new street. But for two years nothing had been done because it would have entailed demolishing a whole row of dilapidated houses in the neighbourhood—houses where vagrants from all over the country lived, and which were described as 'nests of thieves and vice of every description'. And it was here where the first cases of cholera appeared.

Generally, doctors were not even given the opportunity, like those of St. George's, to point out the evils to their Guardians. A surgeon of Bethnal Green Union was threatened with non-election at the end of a year, because he complained to the constable about the terrible conditions in one court which belonged to a Guardian. The Poor Law Medical Officer was therefore frustrated in his attempts to remedy one of the dominant causes of public ill-health. Even the dictates of his professional conscience were limited by the word destitution, when the sickness of the poor had to become the sickness of the pauper before he was allowed to intervene. *The strict demarcation between poor law frontiers and medical frontiers was one of the most short-sighted policies nineteenth century social legislation produced. But the provision of medical services for the destitute was in itself a problem of such magnitude that it would have required statesmen of great prescience, with very different political theories, to have realized the important necessity of establishing a comprehensive medical service for the entire working class.*

With their limited outlook and with only meagre powers at their disposal, the Poor Law Commissioners were however responsible for initiating a service whose dimensions grew as the nineteenth century progressed. From the beginning they had realized that

sickness destroys a man's capacity for labour, and if he has failed to make timely provision [or if wages were too low to do so!] he is at once prostrated, when sickness overtakes him, and has therefore of necessity to look for help to others. Whilst therefore adhering in their entirety to the principles of the Poor Law Amendment Act, *we may yet admit that medical relief is in its nature, not only the least objectionable of all modes of relief, but it is within reasonable limits admissible and in the existing state of society, even necessary.*[1]

[1] Sir George Nicholls, *History of the English Poor Law*, 1854. (He was one of the original three Poor Law Commissioners.)

At the outset, the Commissioners had stated that the provision of medical relief for the sick poor was a source of great difficulty. This was because they had to correlate three objects, which were: 'to secure efficient attendance on the sick poor, to prevent all just cause of complaint by the medical profession, and that the Guardians should not be put to any undue charge for medical relief' . . .[1] They set themselves the task of allying humanitarianism and deterrence. In their Annual Reports they constantly reiterated that they hoped one of the results of the Act would be the prompt and adequate relief of the sick, aged and infirm.

Yet the principle of less eligibility was to be applied also, as was carefully stated in 1841:

Although we entertain no doubt of our being able ultimately, and at no distant period, to establish a complete and effective system of medical relief for all paupers, yet its very completeness and effectiveness, however beneficial to those who are its objects, may have an influence which ought not to be disregarded, on other classes of society. If the pauper is always promptly attended by a skilful and well qualified medical practitioner; if such a practitioner is not only under the usual responsibilities of his profession, but is liable to reprimand or dismissal from office in case of neglect or error; if the patient be furnished with all the cordials and stimulants which may promote his recovery; it cannot be denied that his condition, in these respects, is better than that of the needy but industrious ratepayer who has neither the money nor the influence to secure equally prompt and careful attendance, nor any means to provide himself or his family with the more expensive kind of nutriment which his medical superintendent may recommend. This superiority of the condition of the pauper over that of the independent labourer as regards medical aid will, on the one hand, encourage a resort to the poor rates for medical relief, so far as it is given out of the workhouse, and will thus tempt the industrious labourer into pauperism; and on the other hand, it will discourage sick clubs and friendly societies and other similar institutions, which are not only valuable in reference to contingencies against which they provide, but as creating and fostering a spirit of frugality and forethought amongst the labouring classes.[2]

It was because the general Poor Law principles of less eligibility and deterrence were applied to the giving of medical relief also, that demands for reform of the shortcomings of the service were so frequent and insistent. As early as 1836 the Poor Law Committee of the Provincial Medical and Surgical Association sent a petition to both Houses of Parliament complaining of the Poor Law medical service, and a copy was also forwarded to the Royal Colleges and the Society of Apothecaries to solicit their co-operation in procuring reform. The Association deprecated the principles of the Poor Law being applied to the sick and infirm, and pressed the urgency of providing them with the best medical attention. A new committee was formed to inquire into the means of extending medical relief to the

[1] *Ibid.*
[2] Seventh Annual Report of the Poor Law Commissioners, 1841.

sick poor who were not paupers, and in 1840 the Association reported in favour of free administration of medical aid to the labouring classes unfettered by the machinery of Relieving Officers, 'pauper lists' and 'orders'. Its proposals clearly set aside the question of medical pauperism, and assumed that the receipt of medical relief should be provided like education, at public charge, and ought not to constitute the person a pauper. The Association quoted that high authorities favoured this principle, but concluded: '*The public mind is not yet prepared for the national provision of medical relief, or for its necessary consequence—the "establishment" of a profession in connexion with the State*'.[1] *It took over a century to realize the ideals which were advocated by individuals as a result of the inadequate provision made by the Poor Law.*[2] In 1838 Farr also stated to the Select Committee that 'medical relief should be found for all that class of population which have not the surplus over necessary subsistence to provide for medical assistance for themselves'.

Rumsey had been a member of the special committee established by the Provincial Medical and Surgical Association in 1836, and with the backing of the Association he gave a comprehensive outline of reforms to the Select Committee of 1844. He not only re-iterated that medical attendance on the poor should never be separated from that on other classes of the community, but also suggested measures which appeared more practicable at the time. The notion, he said, that the receipt of medical relief led to pauperism, and was necessarily connected with it, had been a source of all the errors committed in the past. The independence of the labouring classes depended greatly on their moral and intellectual condition, and if their minds were degraded and uninstructed they would care little about who maintained them. 'The present connexion between medical aid and poor law relief subjects the recipients of the former to all the disabilities and degradation of pauperism'. Therefore he recommended that medical poor relief should be separated from the adminis-tration of the Poor Law, and that the receipt of such relief should not constitute the person a pauper. The necessity of this was seen in the administration of the Vaccination Act, which had to be amended to make it quite clear that no one vaccinated would in any way be connected with pauperism. The experience of the ten years since the passing of the new Poor Law, Rumsey said, had shown that while general relief might be restricted and subjected to certain rules, medical assistance had to be extended, and the official check removed which intervened between the sick and the prompt relief they needed. Many amendments had been made in the direction of bringing a greater proportion of the population under the influence of the Poor Law medical service, so that to leave it to the management of the destitution authorities must continually place them in the dilemma

[1] Report of Provincial and Surgical Association, 1840, on the Parliamentary Select Committee of 1838.
[2] In April 1832 (p. 137) the Cambrian Quarterly Magazine included a remarkable article: 'A Letter to the Lord Chancellor on the expediency of establishing a General State Insurance, to defray the expense of an efficient Rural Police and to operate towards the gradual Reduction of the Poor Rates', signed E.W. and dated Radnorshire, 1 February, 1832. Provision for the sick was one of its objects and the finance was to be based on *compulsory insurance of all houses and buildings* with the government. The State was to be the sole and universal assurer, and the article goes into an elaborate scheme of the various provisions the govern-ment could make to deal with pauperism, unemployment, police, sickness, etc.

of creating pauperism with the one hand, while endeavouring to diminish it with the other.

The harm caused by connecting the medical services with the Poor Law was pointed out by Rumsey in another direction.

> The Poor Law principles, viz., that those who are dependent on the public for support must be content with inferior provision to that obtained by those who support themselves, may be a safe principle as applied to general relief, but if applied to medical care, it must lead to the most deplorable results both to the poor and to the whole community.

The hardship endured by the poor who did not apply for medical aid because of the stigma of pauperism attached to it was seen in the suffering caused to them when they did without a doctor or resorted to inferior treatment by a quack or druggist. But Rumsey intended his statement to apply to the niggardliness with which Guardians often granted orders, and to the inferior practitioners, many of them employed for the sake of economy, as well as to the inadequate treatment several good doctors gave because they received insufficient remuneration. To ensure better medical treatment to the poor, he suggested Medical Inspectors should be appointed, not only for the benefit of the medical profession, but also to examine the general conduct of the doctors. He proposed there should be twenty-four such Inspectors for England and Wales, one for every 650,000 people. 'Many of the social burdens', he concluded, 'arising from widowhood, orphanage, and funeral expenses, which have been attributed to defective sanitary regulations, depend also in great measure on the want of *early care and attention* at the hands of *duly qualified* medical practitioners'.

The importance not only of establishing an adequate Poor Law medical system, but also of employing competent doctors, was proved by yet another extract from Farr's invaluable statistics.[1] The Poor Law Medical Officer attended nearly $1\frac{1}{2}$ million people in a year, and in 1837 the mortality of paupers returned was 4-2/5ths in 1,000 of the entire population, whilst the general mortality in the Kingdom was 22-1/5th in 1,000 a year. The number of deaths registered were 346,652. According to these proportions 65,000 (1/5)[2] people died under the care of the doctors of the poor and these figures were confirmed by later reports—although the proportion of paupers in the population was only 1/14. The deaths in London workhouses in 1840 amounted to 4,282 compared with a total mortality rate in the metropolis of 45,500, and Farr believed that it was not improbable that the number of deaths among the poor under the care of the Medical Officers outside the workhouse was as great as the mortality in them. This would make a total death rate of 8,000 paupers in London under the care of Poor Law doctors. He also, therefore, emphasized the importance of securing for the poor adequate attention and the best medicines, and suggested Returns should be made of the number sick and dying under the

[1] William Farr to Select Committee on Medical Relief, 1844, Third Report, quoting extracts from Annual Reports of the Registrar-General.
[2] Farr quoted this figure also in his evidence to the Select Committee of 1838.

care of the Poor Law Medical Officers. But the destitution authorities deemed the sick poor well cared for, and were not interested in the medical profession as such.

Many years previously Farr had written an article, which was never published, on the importance of training good doctors: 'Improve the health of mankind, by improving medical institutions and by improving the status of practitioners.'[1] Speaking of the Poor Law Medical Officer he pointed to the necessity of giving him full responsibility and of making the retention of office dependent on his continued exertion. But, he concluded, 'no statesman has ever applied his mind to the subject, and [to] the present medical institutions, how they are planned, their nature and results. . . . Medical Reform affects the whole population . . . the advance of science . . . and the promotion of public health . . .'.[2] The central Poor Law authorities, although they reprimanded and dismissed doctors, were however no more interested in their training than they were in the fundamentals of preventing destitution. In both cases their work began half-way, with certain established facts, and the background was taken for granted.

None of the revolutionary reforms suggested in the 'forties were ever carried out by the Poor Law Commissioners or their successors in the nineteenth century. Some of the witnesses to the Select Committee of 1844 questioned whether any considerable improvement in the system of medical relief could be introduced consistent with the existing law, by the interference of the Commissioners and by the alteration in the practice of the Boards of Guardians, and whether, if this were impossible, it would not be expedient to alter the Act. The doctors giving critical evidence, all of whom affirmed the desirability of offering the best medical attendance to the poor, no doubt appeared to try the regulations of the Commissioners by an ideal standard, and not by the standard of the existing law or the prevailing social and political thought. The principle which was adhered to was succinctly put in a speech by Charles Buller, later to become a President of the Poor Law Board. Speaking on Poor Law Medical Relief in the House of Commons in 1844 he said: 'the object of the House should be to improve the details of the present system of administering medical relief through the agency of the Poor Law rather than to change the general system itself'.[3]

In surveying the work of the Poor Law Commissioners it cannot be questioned that they did achieve improvements in the details of the system. Had it not been for the authority of the Commissioners, the amount of medical relief throughout the country would have been greatly diminished. They examined medical contracts from the point of view of doctors' salaries and duties and studied the Guardians' provision for outdoor and indoor medical arrangements, frequently refusing to sanction applications for reducing expenditure and relief.[4] In their fourteen years of office they instituted several inquiries and received many reports from the Assistant Commissioners containing detailed accounts

[1] Writing on 'The Medical Profession' in the 'thirties. MSS.
[2] Farr MSS., Vol. II.
[3] Parliamentary Debates, House of Commons, 3rd series, vol. 97, col. 641, 16 March 1844.
[4] Much evidence of this may be found in the Poor Law Commissioners Minutes and Correspondence.

of the state of the arrangements for medical relief, and they gradually introduced measures for removing some of the defects pointed out. In 1836 they stated they did not seek 'to disturb existing arrangements, wherever they were found sufficient for the purpose'. But the inadequate and haphazard method of providing medical relief under the old regime made intervention imperative, and the extent of the Commissioners' activity can be proved by a comparison of early provisions with the recognizable system which had evolved by the time they went out of office. The importance and the magnitude the Poor Law medical service assumed can be deduced from a statement of Cornewall Lewis to the Select Committee of 1844. The Commissioners, he said, were in perpetual communication with the Unions on the subject of medical relief and they had obtained comprehensive material. Half the business of the past eighteen months had related to medical arrangements. But their work was on the whole connected with routine and the establishment of a uniform system. Their orders were never revolutionary, and were always based on some salutary practice instituted previously by one or several Unions. The last Annual Report stated that on the subject of medical relief they had nothing material to add to the explanations given in 1842. The Medical Order of that year had been a landmark, and the General Consolidated Order of 1847 only reiterated its regulations and drew together into a comprehensive account the developments which had taken place during their term of office.

Of 1834, one of the Commissioners could say: 'No part of the proceedings for bringing the new law into operation called for more persevering clamour and mis-representation than the arrangements regarding medical relief'.[1] Yet ten years later, another[2] had no hesitation in saying 'very decidedly, that taking the country as a whole . . . there has been great amelioration, and a great extension of the amount of medical relief to the poor, since the passing of the Act'. And in 1839[3] the central authorities referred to the provisions they had made for the sick as a defence of their whole activity! Although the Commissioners indulged in overstatement on the benefits of the medical system, there is no question that infinitely better attention was bestowed on the pauper than before the new Poor Law. The qualifications demanded of the Medical Officers were raised, the responsibilities of the Guardians grew, and expenditure on this account increased steadily. Although Rumsey advocated that medical provisions should vary with local circumstances, the principle of establishing national uniformity answered the demand more efficiently in the absence of any adequate existing arrangements. The Poor Law medical service was sufficiently flexible to allow for expansion in times of emergency, for the Commissioners knew only too well how quickly illness brought a man to destitution.

In an appraisal of the work of the Poor Law Commissioners, and of the medical relief system they instituted, it must always be remembered that the Act made no specific provision for sickness. By the Act the central authority was left in a weak position, and was

[1] Sir George Nicholls, *History of the English Poor Law*, 1898, Vol. 2, p. 319.
[2] Cornewall Lewis, Select Committee 1844, Third Report.
[3] Report on Further Amendment of the Poor Law.

subjected to misleading doctrinaire theories. They knew their efficiency would be judged by the decrease in expenditure, and in the early stages of the administration 'reaction against high rates and wholesale relief' led to the grossest excesses and cruelties. Almost the only thought from officials high and low was 'reduce expenditure and save the rates'. Year after year the Annual Reports congratulated the country that the cost of relief was diminishing when compared with the wealth and population of the nation.[1] The opposition the Commissioners had to contend with was aroused chiefly by hatred of the 'principles of 1834', rather than by any 'inefficiency in the methods used, or by the faults in the construction of the administrative machine'.[2] Working in a limited framework their record in the field of the provision of a medical service was one of steady achievement, especially as they often had to struggle with ignorant Guardians who systematically opposed improvements. The Commissioners had to make it clear to the working classes that 'the provision of the existing law confines medical relief to paupers, and the law does not contemplate a general provision of medical relief for the working-classes at large'.[3] It was however more liberally given than any other species of relief because it was recognized that men had less power to guard against sickness. And in 1844 Cornewall Lewis stated that he did not suppose any general or strong desire existed on the part of the poor to obtain increased facilities for medical relief beyond that provided under the existing law!

[1] J. F. Oakeshott, *Humanising of the Poor Law*, Fabian Tracts, 54, 1894.
[2] T. Simey, *Principles of Social Administration*, 1937.
[3] Select Committee, 1844.

CHAPTER 2

The Poor Law Medical Officer, 1834–47

THE development of a comprehensive medical service for the poor and destitute was difficult enough without any legislative guidance in 1834, but the disorganized condition of the medical profession itself was a hindrance. In the early nineteenth century medical practice was handicapped by the absence of any law compelling qualified medical practitioners to register. By the Act of 1815 (55 Geo. III c. 194) the Society of Apothecaries could prosecute all apothecaries—who were by now the general practitioners—who had not qualified by its examinations. Until the Medical Act of 1858, this was the sole exception to the domination of medical organization by *laissez-faire* doctrines.

Unpredicted, a new branch of the medical profession grew out of the Poor Law. Medical relief, practically ignored by legislators, was, of all the provisions which developed in the nineteenth century for pauper relief, to grow into the most important and most necessary. To foresee that economic progress would bring into being a new social service, which was destined to reach such great dimensions, would have seemed incongruous to the ruling agricultural classes and the lords of industry. In the advance of medical science, and in the evolution of the medical profession, the Poor Law Medical Officer was to play an increasingly important part. A classification which was ragged and unsystematized in 1834, was during the next half century to become a compact and comprehensive body, having its own associations, and demanding reforms with increasing volume and forcefulness.

In framing their Orders in 1834, the Poor Law Commissioners authorized the Boards of Guardians in the newly-formed Unions to appoint Medical Officers for the districts within the administrative areas, and also a medical attendant for the workhouse. This power was given to the Commissioners under the Forty-sixth Section of the Act, by which they could generally direct the appointment of paid officers. Only in the interpretation clause was the qualification of the doctors touched on. This briefly stipulated that the medical man must be duly licensed to practise. In the first two years only two of the Rules and Regulations issued for the direction of the Guardians referred to the actual appointment of Medical Officers:

> The Guardians shall, for such period as they may think proper, contract with some competent person, or persons, duly licensed to practise as medical man, or men, to be Medical Officer or Medical Officers of the Union, and to attend duly and punctually

upon all paupers falling sick within the limits of the Union, either in the workhouse or otherwise, and to supply such sick paupers with the necessary medicines and appliances whatsoever, but such a contract may, if the Guardians think proper, contain a clause, by which the said Medical Officer shall engage to attend, at a fair and reasonable charge per head, to be named in such a contract, on all persons not belonging to any parish or place, comprised in the said Union, whom by law any such parish or place may be bound to relieve under suspended order of removal.

The other Order of 1836 decreed that: 'The Medical Officer shall give all necessary directions as to diet, classification, and treatment of sick and lunatic paupers, and shall provide the requisite medicines'. But in the country the position was not clear. Letters poured in asking for information, particularly about qualifications. A Guardian of Hastings, for example, wished to know whether he could be the Medical Officer of the town as well as holding administrative office. The Commissioners confessed they were loth to enlarge upon the subject, but in their Second Annual Report stated it was their duty

to notice the differences of opinion, as to who may be held, in the words of the Act, to be 'duly licensed to practise as a medical man'. The Apothecaries have continued strongly to contend that we should exclude all persons who are not duly authorized by law to practise as apothecaries. To this we have answered . . . we do not exclude any persons whom the Guardians may prefer, although he may only be authorized to practise as a physician or a surgeon. How far a member of either of these branches of the profession would render himself liable to penalties by acting as a Medical Officer in a Union, is a question of law, which we hold it to be no part of our duty to determine.

A letter typical of the controversy came from Robert B. Upton, Clerk to the Society of Apothecaries. Behind the hint of desired monopoly, there was no doubt real truth in the assertion of 'great mischief arising from ignorant and unqualified practitioners' and of the Society's desire 'to secure to the public, and especially to the lower classes the benefit of a regularly educated medical attendant'. The effect of the 1815 Act had been, he continued,

to disperse throughout the Kingdom a large body of educated and efficient medical practitioners, but there is still cause for regret, that unqualified persons are to be found practising as apothecaries, in many parts of the country. It unfortunately happens too frequently that parish officers confide to individuals of this latter class the medical care of their poor, who are thus deprived of the advantage of a provision calculated peculiarly for their benefit. An unqualified person elected to the office of parish apothecary, subjects himself to penalties by discharging its duties, but it is not found on the one hand, that dread of prosecution deters the party from accepting the office, or on the other, that knowledge of his being unable to practise legally as an apothecary prevents overseers from electing him to it.

He demanded that the Commissioners should regulate the appointment of Medical Officers more strictly—on the lines that the legislature expressly provided Acts regulating the treatment of insane people. Typical in this age of *laissez-faire* came the Commissioners' reply—they relied on the vigilance of the medical profession to protect the public as well as themselves against the competition of unqualified practitioners, and this would be far more effective than any regulation of the Board.[1]

On any proof of incompetency the Guardians could suspend the doctor without any hesitation, and the Commissioners, practically without exception, dismissed him on the Guardians' recommendation. When an apothecary had been appointed Medical Officer, and the case required a surgeon—the latter, wrote the Commissioners, would be specially called in, or the patient sent to hospital.[2] This theoretical assertion worked out differently in practice, for in the early years, the administrators dismissed as impossible the attempt by the medical profession to have only Medical Officers appointed who were registered both as surgeons and apothecaries. For a time they had the final word: 'We see no reason whatever to apprehend that under the operation of the existing law, medical relief for the poor will not be fully and adequately provided for.' (See Table 2.1 for numbers employed and qualifications of Medical Officers.)

From Table 2.1 it is evident that out of the 1,830 Union doctors, twenty-seven were practising illegally, i.e. without any diploma or licence, five gave no answer as to their qualifications, 327 were apothecaries or physicians only, 294 were surgeons only, and 201 were legalized (though not qualified by examination) by Apothecaries Acts. Only 930 had been examined in both medicine and surgery and had been over three years in practice.

The medical profession did not agree with the finality of the Commissioners' statement. Evidence of incompetent quacks accumulated. In 1837 alone, forty-two petitions on the medical treatment of the poor reached Somerset House, from the Royal College of Surgeons, the Society of Apothecaries, the Medical Society of London, the British Medical Association, the Bridgwater members of the College of Surgeons, and from the Medical Officers of thirty-nine other Unions. In 1838 the British Medical Association, the Provincial Medical and Surgical Association, the Cheltenham Medical Association, the Medical Officers of Kent and those of Edmonton sent petitions. The Provincial Medical and Surgical Association,[3] which had established a special Poor Law Medical Committee to safeguard the interests of the District Medical Officers, was foremost in its investigations and suggestions for reform. A committee set up in 1838 reported two years later that it was in full agreement with Sir Astley Cooper (the most eminent surgeon of his day) in advocating the double qualification of a doctor and that he should have been in practice at least two years before his appointment. Important also was the requirement that every District Medical Officer should have a thorough knowledge of the locality and the inhabitants.

[1] Letter from Robert B. Upton, Clerk to the Society of Apothecaries, to the Poor Law Commissioners. Reprinted in the Appendix to the Second Annual Report, 1836.

[2] Letter from the Poor Law Commissioners to Lord John Russell, Home Secretray, 28 August 1835.

[3] This was the parent of the present British Medical Association. The British Medical Association which existed at the time was a short-lived association.

TABLE 2.1

A statement of the Number of Medical Officers employed under the Regulations of the Poor Law Commissioners specifying the qualifications under which they act and the number of years which they have severally been in practice. Prepared from a Return called for by the House of Commons, 1836.—Third Annual Report of the Poor Law Commissioners, 1847, p. 215.

Description of practitioner	Total number in class	Number of years in practice according to date of several diplomas and licences																				Date of diplomas not specified
		1	2	3	4	5	6	7	8	9	10	11	12	13	14	15	16	17	18	19	20 and over	
Physicians only	9	—	—	—	—	—	—	1	—	1	1	1	1	1	—	—	—	1	—	—	2	—
Surgeons only	294	5	2	3	4	5	7	6	7	4	3	2	6	2	3	7	9	6	4	4	200	5
Licentiates of Apothecaries Company only	316	11	9	16	12	23	21	20	11	19	27	26	13	15	11	11	13	14	11	13	19	1
Legalized under Act of 1815	201	—	—	—	—	—	—	—	—	—	—	—	—	—	—	—	—	—	—	—	201	—
Physicians, Surgeons, and Apothecaries	14	—	2	2	1	1	1	—	1	1	—	1	—	1	1	—	—	1	1	—	—	—
Physicians and Surgeons	19	2	—	—	—	2	1	—	1	1	2	—	1	1	1	—	—	1	—	—	6	—
Physicians and Apothecaries	2	—	—	—	—	—	—	—	—	—	—	—	—	1	—	—	—	1	—	—	—	—
Surgeons and Apothecaries	914	34	48	57	46	61	44	61	56	54	80	58	36	33	38	31	22	27	30	24	53	21
Surgeons in Army	6	—	—	—	—	—	—	—	—	—	—	—	—	—	—	—	—	—	—	—	5	1
Surgeons in Navy	23	—	—	—	—	—	—	—	—	—	1	—	—	—	—	—	1	—	—	—	21	—
Practising without Licence or Diploma and not specified as acting prior to 1815	27	2	3	2	1	1	1	2	1	—	1	—	—	2	1	1	1	—	2	2	4	—
Practitioners who sent no reply	5	—	—	—	—	—	—	—	—	—	—	—	—	—	—	—	—	—	—	—	—	5
TOTAL	1,830	54	64	80	64	93	75	90	77	80	115	88	57	56	55	50	46	51	48	43	511	33

Of the above numbers the proportion of Medical Officers under 5 years' standing was 1/7th or 262; over 5 years and under 10 years was 1/4th or 415; over 10 years was 2/3rds or 1,120.

In April 1839 a deputation of the British Medical Association presented the Commissioners with a long report on Poor Law medical relief questions. It not only expressed dissatisfaction with single qualifications of Medical Officers, but made the drastic assertion that no single examination or diploma from any one college or medical corporation could be considered sufficient evidence of the proficiency of physicians or surgeons.

At the Medical Conference held in February 1841, both the British Medical Association and the Provincial Medical and Surgical Association included in their programme the discussion of Medical Officers' qualifications, and the Medical Order of the following year adopting almost all of the recommendations, including a clause on qualifications.[1] It was the first victory of the profession. By the Order a Medical Officer had to possess one of the following four qualifications: (i) He had to have *either* a diploma of the Royal College of Surgeons, London, *plus* a degree in medicine from an English University; *or* a diploma or licence from the Royal College of Physicians, London. (ii) He could have a diploma from the Royal College of Surgeons, London, *plus* a certificate to practise as an apothecary from the Society of Apothecaries, London. (iii) He would be considered adequately qualified should he possess a diploma from the Royal College of Surgeons, London, if he had been an apothecary in actual practice on 1 August 1815. (iv) A warrant certifying that the candidate for office had held a commission as surgeon or assistant surgeon in the Navy, Army, or the East India Company before 1 August 1826, would be regarded as an adequate qualification. A loophole was left for the Guardians in the stipulation that any Medical Officer already appointed who did not have one of the requisite qualifications could be retained if the Commissioners' consent was requested. They did, however, emphasize the desirability of introducing the double qualification. Scottish and Irish degrees could count in the double qualifications, but they could not stand alone, so that an English qualification had to be obtained as well. Naturally the Irish and Scottish colleges were vehement in demanding redress of the order and the British Medical Association joined in the demand for equality in the qualifications offered by the medical schools of the three countries.

The laxity which had prevailed in the earlier years in some of the Scottish colleges in giving degrees without examination, had ceased in the late 'twenties. Rigid examinations had been instituted in all three branches of medicine, and in reality those of the two Royal Colleges of London were the most inefficient in the British Empire.[2] This accusation in-

---

[1] General Medical Order, 12 March 1842, addressed to 575 Unions. (This requirement of a double qualification was a new departure in medical practice. As no name existed for the doubly qualified doctor, years of controversy followed. Out of it, and due to the Poor Law, the term 'General Practitioner', first coined thirty years earlier, was adopted. See *Lancet* and Provincial Medical and Surgical Association journal for arguments regarding name.)

[2] Deputation of the British Medical Association to the Poor Law Commissioners, 29 April 1842, and communications from President, Royal College of Physicians and Surgeons, Edinburgh; Principals Glasgow University, Edinburgh University; President of Faculty of Physicians and Surgeons, Glasgow; Lord Provost of Edinburgh—all complaining against the injustice of the Order. (This was part of a centuries' old struggle between the medical corporations.)

duced the Commissioners to ask the Association to furnish them with a list of those colleges and universities whose curricula and examinations were sufficiently extensive to place them on a footing with the London Corporations, and to qualify them for acting as examiners to prospective Union doctors.[1] The argument began to centre round the anomaly that whereas English Colleges licensed their qualifying doctors to practise, the Scottish and Irish Universities only licensed their graduates to practise in their own countries—and the Poor Law Commissioners required their Medical Officers to possess a licence to practise in England. They did not try to conceal the quandary in which the state of the law on this subject had left them. They experienced the practical inconveniences of the unsatisfactory law and admitted the injustices which it produced. But the remedy, they said, did not lie in the limited functions of the Commissioners, it could only be applied by the power of Parliament. 'Parliament should establish a uniform medical qualification, extending over the whole of the United Kingdom . . . it would be the wish, not less than the duty of all Commissioners to give immediate and complete effect to so wholesome a regulation.'[2] They then sent an urgent communication to the Home Office asking 'whether medical degrees, diplomas, or licences, conferred by other Universities or medical authorities in Scotland and Ireland are competent to be appointed and act as Medical Officers of the Poor Law'. The answer came in the affirmative, and the Commissioners sent a letter to all Boards of Guardians modifying the General Medical Order. It was one step forward towards a comprehensive medical service.

Legally an advance had been achieved, but despite the order unqualified medical men were still being employed as Poor Law Medical Officers late into the 'forties. Yet on the other hand the Commissioners enforced their ruling with great strictness, even to the extent of overlooking the new Home Office ruling. The Manchester Board of Guardians, for example, in July 1847, appointed a doctor who was M.R.C.S., Edinburgh, and had a degree in medicine from Edinburgh. The Commissioners refused to ratify the appointment. They said they would accept the M.R.C.S., Edinburgh, as equivalent to the M.R.C.S., London, but they refused to recognize the second qualification. Therefore as the candidate possessed only a single qualification the appointment would have constituted an infringement of the Order, and the Guardians had to advertise for another Medical Officer. As the Guardians in the North experienced such difficulty in finding doctors qualified in England, the Commissioners were eventually compelled to agree to the

---

[1] British Medical Association Medical Deputation, 29 April 1842.

Bodies granting medical degrees and surgical diplomas equivalent to examination of English Universities and Corporations:

University of Edinburgh;
University of Aberdeen and King's College and Marischal College;
University of St. Andrews;
University of Glasgow;
Royal College of Surgeons, Ireland;

Royal College of Surgeons, Edinburgh;
Faculty of Physicians and Surgeons, Glasgow;
Queen's College of Physicians, Dublin.

[2] Ninth Annual Report of the Poor Law Commissioners, 1843.

appointment on a temporary basis of medical practitioners possessing other qualifications, blaming the general quandary on the state of the law.[1] In 1845 they reported that the questions which presented the 'chief embarrassment in connexion with medical relief, and which admit of the least satisfactory solution, are those which arise from the inconvenient, intricate, and obscure state of the law respecting medical qualifications'.

Whilst the administrators kept to the narrow legal and practical aspect of a medical officer's qualifications, the two Medical Associations entreated that idealism should not be overlooked. The Provincial Medical and Surgical Association claimed that the Poor Law doctor should combine the highest qualifications of the medical body as 'no professional responsibility, public or private, equals it in variety and extent'. His daily work embraced a variety of problems which required as profound a knowledge and diligent care as any public institution afforded in any single branch of medicine. He therefore should unite 'an acute perception of the incipient stages of disease, with well directed efforts for its prevention, accompanied by most diligent and scientific treatment'.[2]

The British Medical Association[3] also asserted that it was not sufficiently understood that the Poor Law doctor was called on to act in the 'united capacity of physician, surgeon, accoucheur, apothecary, friend, and adviser'. From him the poor had no appeal, and therefore if possible, he ought to be more highly qualified than the attendant of the rich man, 'who may summon the additional aid of the most eminent and most experienced in the profession'. The Association stressed the importance of the parochial doctor being of some standing in the profession and that he should have resided in the district, so as to be acquainted with the locality and the habits of the poor.[4] As the British Medical Association desired to see the doctor freely entrusted with power to decide who were objects for gratuitous attendance, they emphasized the importance of the Guardians' appointing some-one with 'integrity and honour', but as was pointed out to the Select Committee of 1838, benevolence and kindness of disposition or written testimonials of character were not a quality the Guardians required of their doctors.[5] In general however, not only the selection of the Medical Officer but also the remuneration and the detailed conditions of his appointment were left entirely to the discretion of the Guardians. At the creation of the Unions there was no standard to which the Commissioners or Guardians could refer. The old means of pauper medical care could scarcely be called a system, and it had failed lamentably in its objects. It was the source of the more numerous and flagrant abuses which prevailed after the Act.

The Poor Law Committee of the Provincial Medical and Surgical Association in its first report of 1836 enumerated the four main evils which prevailed before 1834. These

---

[1] Ninth Annual Report of the Poor Law Commissioners, 1843.

[2] Report of the Poor Law Committee of the Provincial Medical and Surgical Association, 1836.

[3] Deputation of the Council of the British Medical Association to the Poor Law Commissioners, April 1839.

[4] Also stated by Dr. Toogood, Medical Officer of the Bridgwater Union for forty years, to Select Committee, 1838.

[5] Assistant Commissioner Gulson suggested such testimonials be required! Select Committee, 1838.

were, the adoption of the 'tender' system; the monopolization of numerous parishes by one Medical Officer—which resulted in the sick poor being grossly neglected; the employment of ignorant and unqualified Medical Officers; and the extension of medical parochial relief to improper objects, which led to an increase of public burdens. This was the legacy on which the foundations of a new system had to be built. That the evils had long been realized, was most clearly shown in a Report of a Committee formed in Warwick in 1827, to inquire into the state of the sick poor. The Committee condemned the appointment of unqualified doctors and especially the system of appointment by tender, which made medical men accept ridiculously low payments. Insufficient remuneration in its turn forced the Medical Officer to accept many parishes at once, and often it was the most distant practitioner who was the lowest bidder. This entailed long journeys, and both factors meant that the poor would be neglected. There was a total disregard of fairness towards the doctors, and an entire sacrifice of the well-being of the destitute sick. Parishes with 500–600 paupers would be taken for £5, or twenty to thirty parishes would be farmed by one practitioner. The contract was generally not limited to paupers, and the whole labouring population was at liberty to avail itself of free medical aid, if the overseer gave an order without inquiry. Medical aid had often to answer the purpose of relief in money—for the authorities were aware that as a contract existed the parish would not be put to any immediate expense by throwing the burden on the doctor. There was no allusion to this fertile cause of pauperism in the Poor Law Inquiry of 1832–33. No supervision for medical efficiency existed, and the Medical Officer was reappointed indefinitely as long as he would work for the same salary. Protégés of influential ratepayers procured election, while better qualified men were excluded. All these evils clearly depicted by the Warwick Committee in 1827 were overlooked by the legislators. As the subject was not regarded as sufficiently important for reference in legislation, the Commissioners, Guardians, and Medical Officers had to build an efficient system on the ruins of ramshackle makeshifts. The edifice took too long to build, because the architects and masons were split into two camps and because the old structure took so long to crumble. When it did, it gave way unevenly over the country.

To refer back to the former system was the only guidance the Commissioners could look to. The old method of appointment, and determination regarding salaries, was found necessary by men who lacked imagination and sympathetic understanding of the new problems. Cornewall Lewis defended appointments by tender, when he pointed out that many medical districts were not coterminous with former parishes, and therefore no one could ascertain what the fair salary should be, if no previous standard existed. It was as injurious to the poor and as repugnant to medical men as under the old system. Grossly underpaid, some medical men were obliged to make collateral charges to ensure themselves against losses. The most general method of selecting Medical Officers at the beginning was to appoint former medical attendants at greatly reduced salaries 'fixed by Guardians without sufficient data, or proper reference to the nature and extent of the duties and responsibilities of the office'. The differences of opinion between Guardians and doctors led to the 'tender' system being widespread, with the approbation of the Poor Law Commissioners. 'Frequently the lowest tender was taken in opposition to character, personal qualifications and residence, as in Aylesbury, Wallingford, Eastry, Ongar, Hambledon, Penshurst, Wheatehurst, Leighton Buzzard, Bridgwater, and other Unions . . .', and lately it had been adopted in Halifax, Cirencester, Westbury, and the Severn Union. In the Windsor Union, where a stranger was introduced, and at Greenwich, the lowest tender was taken as late as 1839.[1]

Opposition to appointment by tender started immediately, and continued fiercely until it was abolished. The Commissioners approved of the system and did not suppose it was derogatory to the character of the profession:

> We are ready to admit the principle of competition, though strictly and to the fullest extent, applicable to the supply of drugs and many other articles used by the medical practitioners, is yet capable of only a modified application when brought to bear on the acquired skill and knowledge, and other personal qualifications, the possession of which must and ought so materially to influence the Guardians, in the selection they shall make from amongst medical candidates, and in all our opinions this limitation of principle of competition has been recognized and acted on; the Guardians having never been required to accept the lowest tender, and having in fact, in very many instances, been induced to set it aside solely with reference to considerations of character and personal qualifications to which we have alluded.
>
> [In the new Unions] the elements upon which the calculation must be founded are in themselves obscure, and are utterly unknown to persons who are selected for the office of Guardian. Medical practitioners themselves cannot fail to be possessed individually of the knowledge necessary for making calculations, and in asking them to bring it forward in the way of tender, nothing more was meant than that they themselves should, in first instance, suggest the amount of the reward, which in their view their services might entitle them to; thus in truth, constituting the practitioner and not the Board of Guardians, the judges of a fitting amount of remuneration for their attendance, a proceeding that surely ought not to operate painfully on the feelings of the medical profession, as it has been represented to do.[2]

Whatever the opinion of the Commissioners, opposition continued loudly. Typical of this consensus in the medical profession was the memorial of the Medical Association of Dorsetshire.[3] Considering, it said, the liberal and scientific education of medical practitioners required by the law, and the highly important duties that devolved on them, the Dorsetshire Medical Officers denounced the application of any principle that assimilated them to the grade of tradesmen or artisans. They protested against the principle of tender

---

[1] From replies received by the British Medical Association to a questionnaire. This was similar to an inquiry which the Poor Law Commissioners asked the Assistant Commissioners to undertake, February 1839.

[2] Second Annual Report, 1836.

[3] 15 June 1836 to the Poor Law Commissioners.

for attendance on the sick on the grounds that it was degrading to the profession; that it was injurious because it depreciated the value of knowledge by indiscriminately placing the experienced and inexperienced on the same level; and that, because of the inadequate remuneration, the duties of the practitioners would be imperfectly fulfilled. They considered it unjust that of all the professions, the medical profession alone had to subject itself to the system of tender, and they demanded that salaries for such important services should be fixed on just and equitable principles. The Commissioners refuted these arguments and instituted an inquiry.[1] But, as always, the Boards of Guardians were alone detailed to supply the information as to the effects of the medical arrangements in their Unions. The result of the inquiry showed that the medical duties were not being imperfectly fulfilled. On the contrary, the Guardians assured the Commissioners that, compared with the system which prevailed before the Act, medical relief to actual paupers was much more efficient. Regarding the statement that Medical Officers were being degraded to a class of tradesmen, the Guardians argued that the tender was no more than the expression on the part of the person offering it of his being willing to undertake the duty, and the value which he deemed his services were worth. When individual Medical Officers complained of the inadequacy of their remuneration, they always received a similar reply: as they were employed by tender, they fixed their salary themselves!

The Clerk to the Brentford Guardians graphically outlined the charges and supplied the answers:

Medical periodicals complain that medical skill should be sold . . . like butter and bacon, by tender. The reason for this objection is obvious, for if medical gentlemen make out a bill for medicine, they charge it as any other tradesman does his articles, but if it always went by canvas and election, would not the greatest influence, rather than the man of greatest ability be the most likely to be elected? Would not the Guardians be liable to a charge of jobbing and bartering offices to serve their own private interests, or be degraded by medical men petitioning them for their votes? It is infinitely less derogatory for them to state to the Board the amount they will attend the poor for in a given district, and depend for success on the moderation of their charges and the weight of their professional characters. In this Union the Medical Officers are engaged by tender, and there is never any complaint from the gentlemen themselves of the mode of making the engagement![2]

But a pamphlet from Thomas Hodgkin in 1836 enumerated the evils of the tender system clearly. It pointed out that a man with a large private practice could afford to accept a low salary to keep away rivals, and he could hand over the care of the paupers to his assistants, who would pay him a good apprenticeship fee. He would also, if he did not delegate the work, rush through his visits to the poor and supply them with cheap medi-

[1] Poor Law Commissioners' Report to Lord John Russell, 1 July 1836.

[2] W. Hammond, a Guardian of the Brentford Union, pamphlet: *A letter to Sir Robert Peel, M.P. on the practical operations of the Poor Law Amendment Act by a Guardian*, January 1838.

cines. Above all, the system, Hodgkin affirmed, created jealousy among the practitioners and afforded a low standard of attention to the Union patients.[1]

As was generally the case, reform only came when the collective pressure of the Provincial Medical and Surgical Association and the British Medical Association was brought to bear on the Commissioners and the legislature. In July 1838 the Provincial Medical and Surgical Association sent a petition to the House of Commons, and its demands included the abolition of contracting by tender. The British Medical Association recommended that if a return were not made to specific charges, the next best mode of remuneration was by a salary calculated with reference to the number of cases attended, the number of attendances, the size of the district and the number and extent of the journeys, and to the other circumstances exhibiting the real amount of professional labour actually performed.[2]

In the following year the Poor Law Commissioners instituted an inquiry into the whole field of medical relief. One of the subjects the Assistant Commissioners had to investigate was the method of selecting doctors, whether tender had been adopted or whether salaries were fixed by the 'per case' system and pauper list, and to note any dissatisfaction shown by the Medical Officers with their method of remuneration. The British Medical Association circulated the same questionnaire to all the District Medical Officers individually, primarily to offset the bias the official reports would have, but also because the Commissioners solicited any plans for improving the medical attendance on the poor from the Association.

The general tenor of the replies was to express great dissatisfaction as to the amount of remuneration. Although it had been very inadequate under the old system, it was now lower. Duties had increased as the districts were much larger, and the number of doctors were fewer, whereas patients were more numerous. Where the salaries were fixed by Guardians, it was generally done without consulting the medical men 'and without consulting the intrinsic value or usual remuneration for medical skill and attendance'. If objections were made or reasons advanced against these arbitrary proceedings, the reply was: 'If you do not choose to accept our terms we can easily procure a candidate who will', and therefore 'many have been frightened into accepting inadequate sums lest their private practice be interfered with by strangers'. The British Medical Association Committee Report quoted instances of the Assistant Commissioners refusing their consent to appointments, when the Guardians were willing to meet the fair demands of the profession, such as in Thame, Eastry, Penshurst, Dorchester, Tonbridge, and other Unions.[3]

The Commissioners laid their own complete report before Parliament in 1840.[4] They

[1] Thomas Hodgkin, M.D., pamphlet: *On mode of selecting and remunerating medical men for professional attendance on the poor of a Parish or District*, read before the Hunterian Society, 1836. (He was one of the leading pathologists of his time, and gave his name to Hodgkin's Disease.)
[2] Report of the Council of the British Medical Association on the Poor Law question, containing suggestions for an amended system of parochial medical relief, April 1838.
[3] Replies to British Medical Association circular in Report, April 1839.
[4] Report on the Further Amendment of the Poor Laws, Poor Law Commissioners, 1840.

gave the arguments in favour of the tender system as being the great difficulty in ascertaining proper remuneration, and that it promoted the private practice of the Medical Officer through which the public derived some benefit. On the other side, they admitted that the system lowered the remuneration beyond what was reasonable, and beyond what would admit the doctor to supply the proper medicines. Those who offered their services at a low price for the sake of the collateral advantage, were apt to give more attention to that object than to their duties to the poor. The Commissioners also confessed that Guardians neglected the qualifications of candidates and appointed incompetent practitioners on the grounds of the lowness of their tender. Medical men complained that the system promoted the intrusion of doctors from other neighbourhoods and therefore disturbed the existing distribution of private practices among resident men. The Commissioners concluded that they were disposed to think the latter arguments prevailed, and that as experience over the past years had afforded facilities for ascertaining what was a fair and reasonable remuneration for medical attendance, the system of tender ought to be abandoned! They also suggested that salaries should be fixed by the number of cases on the pauper list, proposing 6s. or 6s. 6d. per case and 10s. for casual paupers. (This was to remain one of the most controversial of all questions.) The conclusion of the Commissioners was typical of their vacillating mood. Unless Parliament objected, they would carry out the proposal; but they had decided to proceed very gradually as the Assistant Commissioners had demonstrated there was little dissatisfaction prevailing with regard to the existing medical arrangements—and 'none which called for an immediate general change'!

For some time, however, Guardians in certain parts of the country had found it expedient to abandon the tender system of appointment. In 1836 an Assistant Commissioner admitted that in his experience no advantage was to be gained by the practice of requiring tenders. 'After having induced several of the Boards of Guardians to ask for tenders for medical services, and after finding that the practice produced coalition rather than competition, I tried the method of fixing the amount of the salary, and I am bound to say that some of the profession have showed themselves very willing to accept moderate terms. To this practice I have since adhered', and at the end of this year, 'we shall have in the diaries of the Medical Officers the means of adjusting the scale of remuneration'.[1]

Mr. Serjeant Talfourd, who with Thomas Wakley generally represented the House of Commons in dealings with the medical associations, prepared a series of clauses on the subject of medical relief, and legislation was proposed in the session of 1840. They were printed in Votes for the House, and a reprint was circulated by the Provincial Medical and Surgical Association for discussion amongst the profession. The Poor Law Bill, however, did not come up for discussion, and the clauses merely stood on votes.

In these years the Poor Law Commissioners had come to realize the growing importance of the medical side of the Poor Law. They spent much time in obtaining information both on the actual position of the service in the country, and on the suggested reforms.

[1] Report of Richard Earle on Northamptonshire and Warwickshire. Second Annual Report, 1836.

They garnered many new ideas for improvement, but with their policy based on re-trenchment, it was not to be expected that these would be put into practice. So often their labours struck a pathetic note. When they themselves agreed to a suggested change, their orders were treated by many Unions merely as permissive, and not as compulsory regula-tions. The medical profession had not only the obstruction of the Guardians to overcome and the general opposition of the Commissioners, but also the latters' weakness.

In 1841 they confessed: 'Our recommendations (regarding the abolition of tenders and moderating the size of districts) appeared to have caused little or no alteration in the medical arrangements made by the Guardians.' But as the subject of medical relief was expected to come before Parliament in 1841–42, they 'deemed it right to do no more than issue a letter to a large number of Boards of Guardians'.[1] In this letter[2] they can again only 'hope that the system of advertising for tenders of pecuniary terms of service is generally aban-doned'. A circular was issued with the letter, and from the replies it was obvious that Guardians were averse to adopting a 'per case' system of remuneration. The Com-missioners proposed a gross amount of salary for the pauper list and the 'per case' system of payment for those able-bodied male paupers and their families who would not be on the permanent list. This would have made possible the giving of medical relief by way of a recoverable loan, which could not be done previously, it was maintained, when the Medical Officer was paid a gross amount, as the price of relief given to a single applicant could not be ascertained.

The Commissioners were prepared to accept legislation on fixed salaries, 'provided they are adequate, provided surgical operations and difficult midwifery cases are separately paid for'. Fine sentiment was expressed, but the difficulty remained over the interpretation of 'adequate'. In 1841 the Commissioners were ready to issue the regulation that in all future elections of Medical Officers the terms of remuneration should not only be fixed, but should also be stated in advertisements for candidates. It was obvious however, that their exertions to obtain a voluntary modification of the existing practice were ineffectual, so in March 1842 the subject was included in the important General Medical Order.

By the first part of the order the Commissioners made the practice of advertising for tenders by medical men illegal, and declared that 'all payments made towards such a salary or in fulfilment of such a contract were not allowed'. All salaries had to be fixed and stated in the advertisement. The system of inviting tenders was hereby abolished, but evasion was widespread, for low salaries had been one of the most important factors in keeping Poor Relief expenditure down. From some parts of the country complaints came that Guardians were privately communicating with medical men, to ascertain from them what sum they would be willing to accept for certain medical districts, and then they advertised the post at the price of the lowest bidder. Doctors might complain to the Commissioners, but it was impossible to prevent such private communications. Cornewall Lewis, questioned by the Select Committee on Medical Relief in 1844 about this practice,

---

[1] Seventh Annual Report, 1841, p. 8.   [2] 6 March 1841.

neatly evaded the issue, but exposed the Commissioners to the accusation that they condoned low salaries, for he affirmed that the Guardians had no power to advertise for medical attendants save at a salary approved by the central authorities. Some argument had been put forward in the country for fixing the salaries of Medical Officers from the top, but this the Commissioners declined, on the grounds that areas and populations were so diverse, although it might have been feasible under a per case system.

In 1844 the injurious effects of the tender system still remained. George James Guthrie, President of the Royal College of Surgeons, and a man who had interested himself in the treatment of the sick poor for over ten years, stated then that it was as much in force as ever.[1] Half the Unions for all practical purposes, he said, adhered to the tender system, with the inevitable result that it brought forward the evil of all kinds of incompetent persons applying for office. Robert Ceely, one of the most active members of the Provincial Medical and Surgical Association had pointed out to the Select Committee in 1838 that advertising for tenders had the mischievous effect of getting only the lower class of medical practitioners to attend the poor, and Guthrie six years later confirmed the assertion that incompetent doctors would take office at any price for the purpose of getting a livelihood. He also exposed the new trick of the Guardians, whereby they advertised for a Medical Officer at one salary and then reduced it year by year, so that by the third or fourth year they had ascertained an average of the lowest price any person would take—it was only a question of degree or time. No one, he asserted, attended to the Order of the Commissioners, forbidding a lower offer being made in the years following the appointment, and salaries remained as inadequate as when Medical Officers were originally appointed by tender.

The predominant feature in an examination of the salaries paid in these transitional years is their extreme lowness. The expense of medical relief did not form such a substantial item in the annual amount of Union expenditure, but 'unfortunately it was taken for granted that many and great abuses existed in the pecuniary part of this department, and that medical attendants had been greatly overpaid; and that therefore the system ought to undergo some process of retrenchment.'[2] Payment to Medical Officers throughout England before the Act was extremely low, only averaging about threepence per head. In the North it was particularly inadequate, a doctor receiving about £50 a year—Chorlton-on-Medlock, near Manchester, paid its Medical Officer £100, but here the population was 60,000 strong, and this was an exception. The South on an average paid its medical men three times as much as the North. The Commissioners commented that one of the reasons why the system of tender had been resorted to, besides the absence of data for estimating salaries, was the impossibility of introducing any uniform scale of payment for a country where such wide diversity of rates existed previously.

Little evidence on the actual remuneration of doctors emerged from the Select Com-

[1] Evidence before Select Committee on Medical Relief, 1844.
[2] Communication from deputation from the Council of the British Medical Association to the Poor Law Commissioners, April 1839.

mittee's inquiry in 1838. The Newmarket Medical Officers complained, but an Assistant Commissioner clamped down on their arguments by affirming the poor had never been so well attended. The Provincial Medical and Surgical Association, believing the oral evidence given to be defective, made further inquiries, and obtained much valuable information, necessary before reform could be demanded.

The Lincoln Union containing 89 parishes with a population of 30,230 employed sixteen medical men before the Act, and paid them an aggregate salary of £350 a year. On the formation of the Union in 1836 the area was reformed into four districts and tenders for the offices of Poor Law Medical Attendants were invited from the resident practitioners. The total amount of the highest tenders was £430 and of the lowest £380[1]—the Assistant Commissioners stated in their evidence in 1838 that it had been £700 to £450. The Guardians rejected all the tenders as too high and fixed the total medical salaries at £270, about twopence per head of the population. A resident Medical Officer said he would accept the whole Union (20 miles in diameter) for £300, with extras for midwifery, but another outsider offered less and was immediately accepted.[2] The Assistant Commissioners condoned this action because the other doctors were so 'unreasonable'! The result was that 'the majority of paupers, suspicious of the transactions which consigned them to the care of a stranger employed by the Guardians at a depressed rate of remuneration, refused the proffered aid, and applied to the established practitioners in great numbers for gratuitous aid'. Save for the sick in the workhouse the Union Medical Officer had no pauper patients on his list for six to seven weeks, and only fourteen in his first year. His private practice was negligible and although the Guardians did everything to retain him, he was obliged to leave the Union after two years. The comparison of deaths in the Lincoln Workhouse in those two years compared with the following years, when some of the former medical attendants were restored, was marked:

	Patients	Deaths		Patients	Deaths	
1837	253	34	1839	259	22	i.e. 8·5 per cent
1838	218	31				
	471	65	i.e. 13·8 per cent			

In 1838 five Medical Officers were appointed with a total salary of £270, and later nine for a reduced salary of £240! The statement made by Gulson, the Assistant Commissioner reporting on the Lincoln Union to the 1838 Select Committee, affords the cynic a fitting conclusion: 'I think that, in this instance, *no Board of Guardians could be shewn to be more anxious to do the best that could be done for the poor.*'

Perhaps most notorious of all was the case of the Bridgwater Union (Somerset). Before 1836 the population of 28,000 was attended by sixteen or seventeen practitioners for a total sum of £579. The Guardians immediately reduced this amount to £363. Remon-

[1] Minutes of Lincoln Union Board of Guardians, January 1837 (Webb MSS.).
[2] *Ibid.*, February 1837.

strances were met by an assurance that the first year was only one of probation, and that if the remuneration proved inadequate it would be raised. In 1837 the number of districts was increased—but the total salary rose only to £370 with £30 for the Medical Officer appointed to the new workhouse. Again the medical men complained and proposed threepence or fourpence a head of the population and £50 for the workhouse officer who saw an average of 300 people weekly. The total amount would still have been £50 less than before 1834. Rejecting this, the Board appointed two medical practitioners of very inferior qualifications and advertised the remaining districts in the London and provincial press. An unknown candidate was appointed, unacquainted with the locality and not a member of the College of Surgeons. Three of the former Medical Officers were re-appointed. For the three weeks that negotiations were being undertaken the Guardians arranged for the former surgeons to attend the poor on the same terms as they did their private patients. Simultaneously the Relieving Officers were instructed to give as few orders as possible for medical relief, with the result that the sick suffered severely. The Provincial Medical and Surgical Association quoted the pamphlet 'Facts connected with Medical Relief of the Poor in the Bridgwater Union' to illustrate the frightful results of the inhuman system.[1] Payment was also subsequently refused the surgeons for this interim period, and the lawsuit alone cost the Guardians £500; the Medical Officers however were able to recover only two-thirds of their fees. One surgeon committed suicide because, it was rumoured, the action of the Guardians had left him in such straitened circumstances. The Board saved £17 a year through the appointment of the unqualified doctor. He was soon tried at the Assizes for neglect and maltreatment, but he was reinstated for a second year until more moderate views prevailed among the Guardians. By 1842 eight Medical Officers were employed with a combined salary of £260.

Very many similar cases could be quoted of reduction in salaries and the consequent effect on the treatment of the sick poor. The Assistant Commissioners themselves tried to reduce payments in some areas. The demands of the established practitioners were always fair and reasonable, and in scarcely a single Union were they higher than the expenses incurred before the Act. In their First Annual Report the Commissioners laid down the rule that the 'aggregate charges for medical relief shall not exceed the aggregate of former expenditure for medical relief in the separate parishes'. Before the Act, in the great majority of instances the medical man contracted with the parish to attend settled paupers for a small fixed sum, with the implied or expressed condition that he was allowed to charge what he pleased for his attendance on non-parishioners under suspended orders of removal, or on an order for medical relief from the overseer. When the patient recovered he was sent home to his parish with a bill for medical attendance, including charges for medicines, at the highest rate. Against these charges the distant parishes possessed no adequate protec-

[1] There had been an article in *The Times* 'Facts connected with the Medical Relief of the Poor in the Bridgwater Union', and the Association's pamphlet of the same title. Therefore the Poor Law Commissioners instructed Assistant Commissioner Weale to hold an inquiry. This was published as a Poor Law Commissioners Report, 14 December 1837.

tion. The Commissioners asserted that in large populous parishes the Medical Officer made a profit of £300 or more a year for attending paupers. Therefore as a check to this system and to the general expense of medical relief, the Commissioners in 1835 ruled that the doctor should attend at the same charge all the patients on the order of the overseer whether they were parishioners or not.[1] A letter to this effect was sent to all the Assistant Commissioners and it gave an example of the proceedings of the Colne Union Guardians: 'Mr. King was elected, having first agreed to provide all medicines, and surgery cases and attendances on poor of the district whether belonging to any parish of the Union or not . . . The Commissioners request that you will in all cases direct the attention of the Guardians to the propriety of adopting a similar arrangement.'[2]

In 1837 the Commissioners again complained of heavy charges being made for attendance on paupers under orders of removal, and they again directed that the Medical Officer 'shall attend on all sick paupers in the Union, whether settled or not settled, without any other remuneration than his salary'.[3] This was only one instance of the methods used for retrenching salaries. The most important was to use the weapon of competition, by which the doctors were induced to fight against their own interests.

The readiness with which some resident practitioners fell in with the proposition of the Guardians arose solely from a desire to maintain their private interests in those localities. In the Abingdon Union, the service was rendered gratuitously rather than allow of competition.[4] The hope of obtaining a private practice was the main motive for strangers accepting parochial appointments. Even a threat by the Guardians to introduce outsiders was enough to bring acquiescence, as was seen in the Banbury, Chipping Norton, Cookham, Eastry, and Reading Unions.[5] The Provincial Medical and Surgical Association reported in 1842, that Sir Francis (Edmund?) Head, Assistant Commissioner for Herefordshire, Monmouthshire, and Gloucestershire, openly boasted that the immense reductions which he had made in medical salaries was principally effected by the free use of such threats. Procedure could have been much improved had the Guardians invited the medical men practising within their respective Unions, to meet and assist them in the medical arrangements, and the determination of salaries. But co-operation between the two sections was rarely achieved amicably and without ulterior motives, and the most controversial question was that of remuneration.

In Gloucester, Worcester and Somerset the original contracts were by tender, but so much dissatisfaction prevailed amongst the Guardians and Medical Officers, that the Assistant Commissioner[6] recommended salaries should be fixed at threepence per head on the gross population in agricultural Unions, according to the census of 1831, and fourpence or fourpence-halfpenny per head in very scattered Unions. Midwifery cases entitled the doctor to an extra payment of ten shillings. The scheme, vouched the Commissioner,

---

[1] First Annual Report, 1835.
[2] 2 April 1835, Poor Law Commissioners' Minute Books.   [3] Third Annual Report, 1837.
[4] Select Committee, 1838.   [5] First Annual Poor Law Report.
[6] Report, Robert Weale. Second Annual Report, 1836.

worked satisfactorily to all parties, and did not cause an increase in expenditure. In the towns, the Boards of Guardians fixed salaries in proportion to the duties expected to be performed. A committee appointed in the Stroud Union, suggested that the Medical Officer should attend the sick at a rate per annum of 3s. for every adult, 4s. for man and wife, 2s. for each member of the family over sixteen years of age, 6d. for those under sixteen, and 10s. for midwifery cases. Even so the doctor received on an average only 3 per cent of the total expenditure of poor relief in the South-Western counties.

Sir John Walsham reported that in Dorset the medical contracts in the past averaged £3,700 a year and in 1836 only £2,700. Again this was only 3 per cent of the total expenditure on poor relief. But Walsham maintained that the Medical Officers had increasingly less work to do, through the introduction of Medical Clubs, for which practitioners received additional payments.

There is abundant evidence from all over the country as to the amounts of salary received, but generalization on the sums or methods of calculation is practically impossible. To get an overall picture it is necessary to select examples of the various types. A committee at Bradfield suggested 2s. per head on one-third of the population, with a guinea for each case of midwifery.[1] Brixworth Union offered a total salary of £346 15s. with extra payments for midwifery and surgery, for six districts of 13,600 people. By 1844, this was £25 lower. Some Unions paid salaries varying with the district. Preston offered £100 for one area and £60 for the other four districts.[2] A special committee appointed in Bakewell recommended salaries for the various districts of £40, £25, £20, £15, £10, and £5. Eccleshall (Yorks.)[3] divided the Union into three districts carrying salaries of £60, £30, and £25, with 10s. 6d. for each case of midwifery. Paddington appointed two Medical Officers in 1845 at £50 each.[4] Totnes readvertised annually for medical men, with cheapness as the chief consideration. The Chorlton Union (near Manchester) in 1837 appointed a doctor to their workhouse at £30, which was to include everything save the provision of leeches and trusses, but by 1842 he was receiving £100 a year. The District Medical Officer in 1837 demanded £70 for attending outdoor paupers or 8s. per case, and offered to sign certificates for 1s. each, but five years later he was still receiving only £35 a year.[5]

A magistrate in Suffolk wrote to Walsham pointing out the inadequacy of the salaries in his parish.[6] In his area of 4,124 people, the total remuneration the Medical Officer received was £81 13s. which included surgery and midwifery cases and the supply of medicines. He criticised the appointment of the surgeon who would accept the lowest terms. 'In a matter of so much importance to the poor man as the care of his health, such recklessly

[1] Minutes, Bradfield Board of Guardians, 1835 (Webb MSS.).
[2] Minutes, Preston Board of Guardians, 1835 (Webb MSS.).
[3] Minutes, Eccleshall Board of Guardians, 1837 (Webb MSS.).
[4] Minutes, Paddington Board of Guardians.
[5] Minutes, Chorlton Board of Guardians, 1837 and 1842.
[6] Thomas Wilkinson, letter to Sir John Walsham, reprinted, Select Committee, 1844: Appendix.

parsimonious methods of proceeding can scarcely fail to have an evil influence on his feelings and morals'. He suggested the size of the population should be the basis for remuneration, as in general, cases requiring medical relief were nearly relative in proportion to the population. A Medical Officer had suggested to him that sevenpence or eightpence on the *gross* number of people would be most satisfactory, because if charges were allowed per case, the Relieving Officer might not report pauper cases until the symptoms had become serious, and the chance of cure more doubtful. In addition, early attention would save expense in the long run.

John Ayrton Paris, President of the Royal College of Physicians, quoted cases of the poor being grossly neglected through inadequate salaries being paid to doctors. In Shropshire, for example, only unqualified surgeons could be obtained because the remuneration was only £50. In the Langport Union, the Medical Officer begged the Guardians to appoint an additional physician, because he could not possibly carry on alone. Some of the magistrates had given him extra money as his work was so arduous. He had received £55 a year for 683 cases in 1843 and he had made 5,707 journeys. In his evidence before the Select Committee of 1844 he reported that the Guardians avoided paying 'extras' whenever they could, and he experienced great difficulty in obtaining payment for attending the poor in an emergency, when no order had first been granted. He added that the average duration of each case of sickness was eight to fourteen days, and his outlay on drugs, turnpikes, and keeping a horse amounted to more than his salary. 'My labours are rendered wholly gratuitous to the sick poor' yet, the following year he applied again for the post, and was successful, because he undertook to do the vaccination as well! It was very rare for a Medical Officer, however inadequate his remuneration, to resign, because he always had to take his private practice into consideration. Witnesses to the Select Committee of 1844 from Carmarthen, Cranbrook, Hambledon, and Wycombe for example, brought out the jealousy felt towards interlopers. The case of the Blything Medical Officer who resigned because his salary was inadequate and less than before the formation of the Union, was unique in the evidence collected in 1844.

Unique also was the system adopted in the Leighton Buzzard Union, where one doctor was entirely the servant of the Guardians and had no private practice.[1] He received, in 1840, £200 and lived in the workhouse. It was believed that by this arrangement the Medical Officer could devote all his time and attention to his official duties, and the Guardians thought they could protect the practices of the resident practitioners. After the doctor had held office for two years however, he resigned to obtain a private practice, and soon afterwards left the district 'suffering from a combination of disappointment and ill health'. The evidence on the Union in 1844 showed that the Guardians maintained their unique system. The Medical Officer was still resident in the workhouse, but his salary had risen to £269. The Union was 14 miles long and 4 miles wide, with a population of 14,000, and out of his salary the Medical Officer had to find all medicines and appliances,

---

[1] 1840 Report of the Provincial Medical and Surgical Association.

keep a horse and a boy to look after it. It was little wonder that the Guardians reported the system to be most economical to work and very satisfactory to them.

The Provincial Medical and Surgical Association disagreed with the separation of public and private practice. It was said that practitioners only accepted office under the Poor Law so that they could build a reputation through attending a great number of patients. The poor lost the benefit of the doctor's experience among the wealthy, and the Medical Officer himself, if he attended only the upper classes, had no opportunity to learn of the epidemic diseases that prevailed among the poor. The Provincial Medical and Surgical Association advocated the combined system on the grounds that it was 'valuable to the poor, useful to the Medical Officer and advantageous to the community'.

Turning to the London area, we see that remuneration there was no higher. Six doctors were employed by the West Ham Union for a population of 26,400 at salaries ranging from £20 to £65, one only received £5 a year, from which he had to provide medicines. The Chairman of the Union remarked: 'the more Medical Officers we can employ the better, if it is not carried so far as to compel us to pay a larger total sum, for the larger the number of Medical Officers, the nearer they would probably be to the residence of the poor'. The workhouse doctor received £75 a year with extra payment for midwifery. His average number of patients was 639 and previously he had attended 813 patients at 2s. per case. It is interesting to compare the Medical Officer's salaries with that of the clerk to the Union. He earned £200 a year, had an assistant at £50 a year, and did not work more than two days a week. The Relieving Officer in the West Ham Union also received £100 a year.[1] The Poor Law Commissioners had suggested to the Guardians of this Union that they should pay 6s. per person on the permanent pauper list, 10s. 6d. for cases of midwifery, and 10s. for attending a case of actual illness by a medical order. This would have meant a total salary of £636. Alternatively they suggested that all people on the pauper schedule and their children should be paid for at the rate of 6s. each, with 10s. extra for midwifery—the total sum payable by this method would then have amounted to £900. This the Chairman said was utterly beyond the Guardians' consideration, although he himself was more enlightened than his contemporary Guardians. He realized that it

> was the worst economy possible to get medical men to do their duties at a less rate than [they were] giving, because the more superior the attainments of the medical gentle-man, the sooner will he cure his case, and therefore the sooner will he relieve the poor rate of the chargeability of that family. . . . Our sick cases are the most expensive; we have some to which we give 6s., 8s., 10s., or even 20s. a week, and therefore the time saved in illness is beneficial to the parish.

The Chairman of the East London Union had also more prescience than his fellow Guardians.[2] He contended that medical men ought to have been independent, to enable

[1] Evidence, William Champion Streatfield, Chairman of the West Ham Union, to Select Committee 1844.
[2] Evidence, Rev. J. Russell, Chairman of the East London Union, to Select Committee, 1844.

them to do their duty justly to the poor, but his proposals were always defeated by the Board. The salary of the Medical Officer who attended the female workhouse was £140 and he made 16,000 visits a year. For extras, principally midwifery, he received another £58 10s. in 1843. The other Medical Officer who attended the male workhouse and the Aldersgate district received only £80 a year with only 10s. for extras, for seeing 2,223 workhouse patients and 900 outdoor paupers. The discrepancy, the Chairman explained, was due to there being a large dispensary at Aldersgate, and St. Bartholomew's Hospital was close by. The dispensary, he said, was well managed, and long established, so that the poor made little application for medical relief to the Union. In the other two districts, Cripplegate and Aldgate, the Medical Officers received £95 with £37 for extras, and £85, with £42 for extras. Although one of the Medical Officers complained of the poor salaries, this was liberal payment compared with the general position, but as the Chairman had pointed out, it was more economical to secure the best attention for the poor. To safeguard the latter the first two doctors held permanent appointments and the last two were reconsidered every Lady Day. A plan had been proposed to pay the Medical Officer 4–6 per cent on the net poor rate—4 per cent in populous places and 6 per cent in scattered districts—but this the Guardians of the East London Union refused to consider, as it would have greatly increased the cost of medical relief.

In Stepney there were five Union doctors for a total population of 91,078 which included nearly 2,000 in the workhouse. From 1840 to 1842 they visited on an average 5,727 outdoor sick and 2,271 indoor. For this annual average of 8,000 sick poor the Medical Officers received a combined salary of £460 which included midwifery and extras. In answer to the question whether he thought adequate medical attendance could be provided by the doctors for only £460 the Chairman replied:

Looking at it as an abstract the question of payment made to the Medical Officers is utterly inadequate to remunerate them for the services they render; but from the readiness I have always seen on the part of the medical gentlemen to take upon them those situations, I am led to the conclusion that there are other inducements with them, which I can very readily imagine. Their practice among the poor tends to acquire them a reputation in their general practice, and thus lead to that which is always an object of greatest importance with medical men. There is always great anxiety to get appointments in the London Hospital as surgeons or physicians ... the duties of all those officers are very onerous and they act entirely gratuitously.... If therefore the Medical Officers of high reputation are ready to take on themselves gratuitously, duties in the London Hospital and compete actively with each other for appointments to such situations, it does not appear an unfair inference that the parochial surgeon may find his remuneration from similar inducements.[1]

A Guardian of the Stepney Union, and a former Medical Officer told another story.

[1] Evidence, Frederick Young, Chairman of the Stepney Union, to Select Committee, 1844.

The duties of the medical men, he stated, were far more arduous and extensive than before the Union, and far more unpleasant. Much more medical relief was given to the poor, and yet the doctors received only half the sum that they did previously. As the remuneration was so very inadequate, and certainly could not cover the provision of good medicines and appliances, the poor inevitably had to suffer.[1]

A poverty-stricken and disease-ridden population of 74,000 lived in Bethnal Green. Two doctors with salaries of £70 attended an average of 666 patients a year each, and six, receiving £90 nearly 1,000 patients. Payment therefore amounted to about 2s. per case irrespective of the duration of the illness or the number of visits required. One of the doctors confessed he was losing heavily by retaining his office, and only remained because he anticipated an inquiry which would have led to an improvement in salaries. The Chairman of the Union himself testified that under the old law Medical Officers received more than under the amended system, and that salaries were not sufficient to remunerate doctors for attendance, let alone for the expenses incurred in providing medicines. A more adequate salary, he predicted, would lead to a far higher talent becoming available for the pauper medical service.[2]

In a letter to Lord Ashley (Chairman of the 1844 Inquiry) the position in St. George the Martyr, Southwark—another fever infested area of London—was compared before and after the formation of the Union. Up to 1836, a highly respectable practitioner attended the 1,300-1,400 outdoor paupers for £100. Under the new Poor Law, two Medical Officers were appointed with a total salary of £110 each to take all duties of outdoor and indoor patients alternately. Complaints revealed that the sick poor were often attended by assistants, a common occurrence where the populations and the areas were too large for the number of doctors employed, and the salaries too low. The ratepayers decided that these two doctors were gaining an unfair advantage over the numerous other practitioners, as they were simultaneously increasing their private practices. Therefore four Medical Officers were appointed with salaries of £55 each. When one was compelled to resign because of a complaint, the remaining three succeeded in obtaining permission to divide the duties of the fourth between them and received an advance of £50 on their joint salaries. The medical profession was not always innocent of chicanery—and the Guardians saved £5! When the Poor Law Commissioners ordered the adoption of the 'per case' system in 1843, the final amount of remuneration came to practically the same as the previous fixed salaries, for the average of the former payments was taken to compute the 'per case' fee. In 1843, 500-600 indoor paupers were attended and 1,000 outdoor and the Chairman of the Union concluded that if the value of money then was compared with the value in 1836, the ratepayers were paying more than double for attendance on a thousand persons, than was paid for attending 1,700 in 1836.[3]

[1] Evidence, T. W. Barnett, Guardian of the Stepney Union, to Select Committee, 1844. See Table 2.2 regarding salaries and duties in the Stepney Union.
[2] Evidence, Chairman, Bethnal Green Union, Select Committee on Medical Relief, 1844.
[3] Report of the Select Committee of 1844: Appendix 5.

TABLE 2.2

Stepney Union: Cases seen by Medical Officers, and Salaries.[1]—Appendix to the Report of the Select Committee of 1844.

Names of Medical Officers	Union districts	Population 1841	OUTDOOR			INDOOR				Total Numbers			Number of houses in each District	Salary to each Medical Officer £
			Number of patients attended during 12 months ending March 1843	Midwifery cases 12 months ending March 1843	Patients constantly on the sick list	Number of patients in workhouses	Number of patients attended during 12 months ending March 1843	Midwifery cases 12 months ending March 1843	Patients constantly on the sick list	Number of patients attended during 12 months ending March 1843	Midwifery cases 12 months ending March 1843	Patients constantly on the sick list		
Mr. Falconer	Upper District of Mile End	25,570	1,100	15	76	—	—	—	—	1,100	15	76	4,263	80
Mr. Story	Lower District of Mile End	19,735	2,477	23	107	230	511	—	57	2,988	23	164	3,610	80
Mr. Heelis	Limehouse	19,338	1,597	32	98	430	543	—	84	2,140	32	182	2,966	100
Dr. Barnett	Radcliff	11,870	1,358	40	110	240	125	—	75	1,483	32	185	1,952	100
Mr. Ross	Shadwell and Wapping	14,565	719	22	41	320	595	40	45	1,314	62	86	2,141	100
Total		91,078	7,251	132	432	1,220	1,774	40	261	9,025	172	693	14,932	460

[1] Amount paid before Union in workhouse was £282. 9s. (twopence per head on population of same district, with £30 per 100 innates for workhouse, and 10s. for midwifery cases—producing £294; or 1s. on each house in district with £30 per 100 for workhouses and 10s. for midwifery cases—producing £284).

Besides the accounts given by Guardians to the Select Committee of 1844, the Medical Officers also gave evidence, and there was not a single one who did not maintain that he was grossly underpaid. The most explicit description of the position was given by James Thomas Vallance, surgeon to the West Ham Union workhouse and also to one of the districts. His evidence appeared the more interesting because this Union was considered one of the best managed and most liberally conducted in the county. He provided a table of his duties in the workhouse, Table 2.3.

TABLE 2.3

Duties in the Workhouse.—Evidence, J. T. Vallance, Surgeon of the West Ham Union workhouse, to the Select Committee, 1844.

Number of inmates	Number of cases yearly	Number of patients weekly	Number of visits yearly	Number of miles yearly	Salary	Time,* hours
540	722 Sum per case— 2s. 1d.	45	521 Sum per visit— 2s. 8d.	1,042 Sum per mile— 1s. 6d.	£75 Sum per day— 4s. 1½d.	4½

* Time occupied daily in visiting, dispensing, examining poor and going to and from workhouse.

In his calculation Vallance pointed out he was paid 1s. 6d. per mile for the distance to and from the workhouse, but this had to include payment for: 'the four and half hours daily consumed, the visiting, and attending the sick, book-keeping, examining the incoming poor, directing the necessary diet, supplying all necessary medicines and appliances, half the expense of an assistant, and the very serious responsibility of the situation'. Besides the indoor paupers, he saw on an average 53 parish patients daily and 17–20 private patients.

He drew up another schedule of his duties as District Medical Officer from his 'Weekly Returns', Table 2.4.

TABLE 2.4

Stratford District: Schedule of Duties of District Medical Officer

Population	Number of outdoor cases per annum	Average number of patients per day	Number of visits per annum	Salary per annum	Extras
7,469 Sum per head— 3¼d.	640 Sum per case— 3s. 1½d.	53	10,509 Sum per visit— 2¼d.	£100 Salary weekly— £1 18s. 5¼d.	Midwifery: £7 Fractures: £2 2s. £9 2s.

Neither of the tables contained every case attended, he said, 'Indeed many poor persons when sick, and who have not obtained an order, are nevertheless attended to, and supplied with medicine'. For practically the same duties for which he had been receiving £100 since the Union was formed, he had obtained £209 previously. His total salary amounted to £236 7s., £2 7s. 9d. more than before, but this, he pointed out, was not equivalent to the difference in the time and trouble in superintending relief, in keeping books and the other Poor Law duties, which had increased as the number of paupers attended had risen.

A beneficial result of the formation of the Union was the termination of the degrading gratuity system. In the past, when an epidemic, particularly cholera, had broken out, it had been customary to give the parish surgeon a lump sum of £40 or so, for the responsibility of attending all cases. This Vallance described as an objectionable and degrading means of payment. He had also calculated that he was entitled to a far higher salary, £185 for the workhouse, for example, and £192 for the outdoor poor—a total of £377 independent of his private practice. These calculations he had based on tables submitted by William Farr to the Committee of Inquiry of 1838.

It was vitally significant that Farr had been educated as a doctor. To his keen interest in social questions, particularly Public Health and the Poor Law medical services, and to his statistical information, he could therefore add his knowledge of, and his sympathy for, the medical profession. Through this comprehensive outlook his opinions and suggestions were of the highest value.

Before the Select Committee in 1844, he repeated what he had already stated in the inquiry six years before. He took the nine metropolitan Unions, where in 1837 the cost in medical salaries for 36,231 cases had been £2,636 or 1s. 8½d. per case cured and 1s. 5½d. for each patient treated. Comparing this with the provinces, he gave a total of nearly 90,000 patients treated in seven counties in 1837, for an aggregate salary of £13,511 or 3s. 3½d. per case on the average.[1] The disparity in the payments 'per case' in the different Unions was equally singular. In 1838[2] Farr had shown that in Devon it ranged from 1s. 6d. to 8s. or 10s., without reference to area or distance. In Buckingham it was 2s., whilst in Kent it was as high as 10s. per case per quarter in some areas. He concluded:

Neither the Guardians nor the Commissioners appear to have proceeded on any fixed principle in determining payment per case, but to guard against too liberal an estimate, they almost uniformly limited the number of cases to be paid for . . . and secured themselves by a maximum cost, whilst leaving the medical officer with certain prospect of loss either by their effecting a reduction in the number of his cases below the proposed

[1] Wiltshire 1s. 11½d.; Devonshire 3s. 5d.; Dorset 3s. 6d.; Lincolnshire 5s. 4d.; Cheshire and Lancashire 6s. 1½d.
[2] Select Committee 1838. He compared this with returns he had of twenty-two dispensaries, thirty county infirmaries, St. George's Hospital, London, and Canterbury and Bristol infirmaries. Over ten years the average expense (at cost price) for each case of sickness, for medicines, leeches, surgical instruments, was 2s. 1¼d. for out-patients and 6s. 5½d. for in-patients, an average of nearly 4s. 3½d.

maximum, or by granting orders to a greater number of sick than they meant to pay for.

The districts in the provinces, according to Farr, averaged an area of 22 square miles; the average duration of illness he computed at twenty-three days, and a Medical Officer visited his patient every three days. He calculated the prime cost of medicine alone at 2s. 6d. per case. Therefore in the Metropolitan area the fee paid was 1s. per case less than was sufficient to supply only the drugs, whilst in the country only 9d. was allowed on an average for the time, labour, and cost of the journeys. In some counties the remuneration was absolutely below cost. The average prime cost of drugs alone for each case of illness in dispensaries and hospitals was about 4s. 3½d.

Farr also estimated that in 1838 an average of £1,627 was expended in each medical district on poor relief, of which £59 was paid in salaries to every Medical Officer, that is 3·6 per cent of the amount of relief. In 1842 this had fallen to 3·1 per cent.[1] Therefore the amount of remuneration for medical attendance had gone on diminishing progressively ever since the Report of the House of Commons of 1838, and in direct contravention of one of its recommendations.[2] Farr handed in several tables to prove his assertions.

Previous to the Parliamentary Inquiry, reforms for more liberal remuneration had been suggested, not only by the Medical Officers and medical associations, but also by several Guardians and even Assistant Commissioners. Ideas were many. First in the field had been the Poor Law Committee of the Provincial Medical and Surgical Association, which sent a report to Parliament drawn up at a meeting in Manchester in July 1836. It asked for the intervention of a third party in determining remuneration which should eventually be fixed by legislation. Allowances for travelling and the supply of drugs were to be separately charged and dispensaries should be established everywhere for providing medicines.

Another suggestion was that the population and area of the district should form the basis for calculation—but this would have been no improvement, as it would not guarantee that the salary would bear a constant proportion to the amount of medical duty performed. Others agreed with the proposal of Mr. Ben Lupton of Cheadle, near Manchester, that salaries should be calculated as a percentage on the amount expended on poor relief. This again would have avoided details of travelling expenses, the number of visits and special charges, although it would have meant that the salary would vary with the number of paupers—as the change in the poor rates would affect the percentage set aside for doctors. Epidemics and unemployment would raise the salary, and prosperity and improved health would reduce the poor rates and diminish medical remuneration. Several witnesses to the Select Committee of 1838, and the Poor Law Committee of the Provincial Medical and Surgical Association, approved of this idea. The minimum rate

[1] 1838—£136,775; 1839—£148,652; 1840—£151,781; 1841—£153,401: salaries increased but greater rise in numbers.—Evidence, Select Committee, 1844.

[2] 1838: Select Committee Report recommendations: limited areas and proper remuneration to ensure, poor get proper attention and best medicines, stated Poor Law Commissioners should attend to this.

proposed for rural districts and small towns was 4 per cent, and that for scattered populations 7 per cent. A smaller ratio than 4 per cent was considered adequate for large and densely populated towns, as the medical areas would be compact.

Farr considered the average throughout the country should not be less than 7 per cent. Mr. Power, Assistant Commissioner for Lancashire and the West Riding of Yorkshire, objected to the scheme on the grounds that if definite rates were fixed for the country, the salary might not bear the same relation to the amount of duty performed, for there would still be no safeguard against the authorities giving an indefinite number of orders for medical attendance without an increase in payment.

A plan devised by Dr. Kay (Shuttleworth) received general approval from the medical profession. In 1838 he suggested that the recipients of medical relief should be divided into two classes—permanent and casual paupers. All paupers receiving outdoor relief, widows and men with large families, would constitute the former class, which could obtain medical assistance at any time without an order. Therefore those on the 'permanent list'—the aged, infirm and helpless—as well as those whom it was known could never provide medical aid for their families, would be provided for; and the Medical Officer, because no preliminary order was required and because he could be called in the early stages of the disease, would have the opportunity of curtailing the duration of treatment and therefore his own duties. These 'permanent lists' of those expected to be recipients of outdoor relief would be made out at half-yearly intervals, and new salaries would be estimated at a percentage of that pauper population.

Another scheme proposed by Mr. Davies of Hertford suggested that 2s. 6d. should be paid for each person registered, plus 1s. per mile for visits and journeys. Although approving of the proposition, the Parliamentary Committee of 1838 felt that the handicap lay in compiling the lists. The 'regulars' would not be a difficulty. There would, however, be the case of those who were just able to live without assistance, but who would be quite unable to meet the expenses of sudden illness in the family. This class really fell into a second group of patients—the casual receivers of poor relief. Payment for medical attendance on these, Dr. Kay and others suggested, should be made on a 'per case' basis.

But even if the Medical Officer had received an increase in salary, by either of these proposals, the adequate and efficient provision of treatment for the sick poor would have depended on the discretion of the Guardians, and especially of the Relieving Officer, in deciding which cases were fit subjects to receive gratuitous attention. The abolition of the requirement of preliminary medical orders by the paupers would have been the next step in reform.

The Provincial Medical and Surgical Association summed up the findings of the Select Committee of 1838.

The principle assented to by all was that the remuneration should be strictly proportioned to the duty actually performed, and the expense incurred by the medical officer; both of which could be determined by a reference only to 'the number constantly sick, the distance and extent of the district' and the density of population. . . . Such a principle of remuneration involved the necessity either of predetermining the class of poor, or portion of the population which should receive medical relief; or else of exercising a discretion on the case of each applicant. *Indiscriminate relief for the whole labouring population* would of course be incompatible with a salary based on the above specific data.[1]

Not satisfied with the conclusions of the Parliamentary Inquiry, the Poor Law Commissioners, as we have seen, in February 1839 instituted an investigation of their own through the Assistant Commissioners and Guardians. They had on several occasions confessed that the first arrangements were only experimental and they had travelled some way since their first Annual Report in which they stated that: 'aggregate charges for medical relief shall not exceed the aggregate of former expenditure', and in which they also agreed that competition among doctors in relation to tenders must be encouraged, and that highly pauperized districts were the result of 'high' medical salaries. Pauperism, they had contended, could be reduced by reducing the salaries of medical attendants: 'sickness and destitution will decrease where relief is withheld'. In the Third Annual Report (1837) the Commissioners had written that they did not consider it expedient for them to fix either the number or the remuneration of the Medical Officers: 'They conceive that the Guardians, from their knowledge of the localities of the Union, of the means of communication between the parishes, and of the distribution of the population, will, with the aid of an Assistant Commissioner, be able to form the most correct judgement as to the number of the districts into which it might be desirable to divide it for the purposes of medical relief' . . . and the amount of salaries.

It was therefore not surprising that the Provincial Medical and Surgical Association read cynical motives into the proposed new Inquiry. In a circular of 21 February 1839, the Commissioners had stated that they did not 'deem it advisable to originate any immediate general change in medical arrangements' and the profession, anxiously awaiting some ruling on the recommendations of the 1838 Committee, regarded the Commissioners' inquiry as part of their delaying tactics.

The impartiality of such an investigation was questionable, seeing that the very people who were supervising the administration regionally and locally were to conduct an inquiry into their own proceedings. It was obvious that, knowing the subject 'must in the course of a short time come under the consideration of the legislature' (Circular, February 1839) they wished to create as favourable an impression as possible. Although the inquiry was not scientifically carried out, and the replies were prejudiced, the tenor of opinions threw further light on the position in the country. It was to be expected that little proof would appear of the inadequacy of remuneration, but 'dissatisfaction' was an expression of the Medical Officers occurring too frequently to be disregarded.

Colonel Wade, Assistant Commissioner for Cambridge and Essex, was the only one

[1] Poor Law Committee Report of Provincial Medical and Surgical Association, 1842.

to give actual rates of payment, and these revealed the lack of uniformity in the system. In four Unions the rate per case was 5s., in two it was as low as 3s. In those Unions where the Pauper Lists had already been adopted (since 1838), the rate per head was under 3s. and in one only 1s. 6d., with the children charged at only 9d. or 1s. each a year. He offered candid observations on the system of pauper lists and payment per case, for the benefit of the advocates of the system. Lists, he suggested, should not be drawn up in anticipation, but at the end of every quarter, as the condition of the labourers was constantly changing. Another innovation he recommended was that there should be a uniform rate of payment for all, irrespective of age and sex. His proposed estimates for payment per head on the pauper list were terribly low—2s. to 3s., and the average payment on the 'per case' system for casuals he suggested should be 6s. to 7s. inclusive of travelling expenses. He did, however, believe in an extra allowance of £3 to £5 for fractures and capital operations. Although he pointed out the advantages of the payment per case system for casual paupers, he preferred a return to the old fixed salary scheme, for he could think of no expedient 'to relieve the parish officers from the responsibility of finally deciding on the several cases'. Cambridgeshire Unions, after a short trial of the 'per case' method of payment, did return to the fixed salary method of remunerating their Medical Officers.

Several of the Assistant Commissioners defended the existing scale of salaries in the inquiry. Colonel A'Court, speaking for Southampton, Dorset, and Wiltshire, proved that the remuneration was adequate by quoting the number of candidates desiring appointments. Sir Edmund Head of Hereford, Monmouth, and Gloucester rejected the idea of a general increase in salaries, because this would not guarantee an improvement in the quality of attendance. He also argued that the District Medical Officer viewed the salary paid by the Guardians in isolation without taking into account the indirect reward which accrued from an increase in private practice. Head in his turn omitted to state that without the income from private practice a practitioner could not undertake the duties of a Poor Law Medical Officer at all as no financial support was drawn from the public office.

Sir John Walsham reported on the peculiarities of medical relief in the North (Northumberland, Durham, Cumberland). The small proportion of paupers and their aversion to public assistance, meant that medical salaries averaged about twopence per head of the population, a quarter less than the general average, and half that of the Southern counties, but payment per case was 10s., three times the amount of Farr's average. The 10s. constituted payment for serious cases only, which were few in number, for the poor only applied for medical relief in extreme urgency. Because of this the pauper list system was introduced, but as the salary of the Medical Officer averaged only 1s. or 1s. 6d. a head, Walsham suggested payment per case as a more feasible system for his area.

The British Medical Association, as we have already seen, circulated the questionnaire, which the Poor Law Commissioners sent to their Assistants, to all the individual Medical Officers. In the ensuing report they pointed out that the subject of medical relief was little understood by the Commissioners and Guardians and nothing but a well-digested plan, produced by those with sufficient knowledge of the subject, could effect a system at once beneficial to the poor and satisfactory to the profession. A deputation from the British Medical Association to the Poor Law Commissioners in April 1839, pointed out that the worst of the old evils still prevailed. 'Fixing the proper amount of medical remuneration has been not the greatest difficulty, as the elements for calculating the value of medical services are sufficiently simple, but they are the greatest bar to cordial work.' It mattered little which of the various methods in use—payment per case, per head, by pauper list, or the arbitrary fixing of salaries was adopted

provided the amount was sufficient to do justice to both parties; that is to ensure the best medicines and efficient skill and attendance for the poor, and adequate remuneration to the Medical Officer for supplying them. Anything short of this will not effect the purpose intended. Misunderstandings which have so repeatedly arisen between the Boards of Guardians and the medical men have been occasioned not so much by the mode, as the *amount* of remuneration. Were this point thoroughly understood and settled, all the other points of the system might readily be arranged.

Theory was not as important as the adoption of a plan which was likely to work most efficiently in practice. The British Medical Association suggested that the best solution was a fixed salary—adjusted to the principles submitted in the medical evidence just collected, and having reference to the average number of cases, the average number constantly on the sick list, the distance and extent of the district, the density of population, the absolute cost of medicine and medical appliances, and the value of time and skill. Second they advocated separate charges for midwifery, capital operations in surgery, fractures, and vaccinations. A schedule of charges used in the Dunmow Union was suggested:

	£	s.	d.		£	s.	d.
Midwifery within one mile		15	0	might be		10	6
Midwifery beyond one mile	1	1	0		1	1	0
Simple fractures or dislocations	1	11	6		2	2	0
Compound fractures	3	3	0		5	5	0
Operation for strangulated hernia	5	5	0		5	5	0
Amputation of a limb	5	5	0		5	5	0
Vaccination per case		1	6			2	6

and all other operations in proportion.

Further the British Medical Association proposed an average charge for each pauper, constantly on the sick list, of about £5 5s. a year and a payment of 7s. 6d. per case for casuals. The workhouse doctor was to be remunerated proportionately to the number of cases sick or to the number of paupers in the house. These charges, it was calculated, would amount to about sixpence a head on the whole population.

The Association greatly favoured the appointment of neutral assessors to supervise the amounts paid to Medical Officers, and suggested that reassessments should take place every three years, taking the practitioner's expenditure and the value of his labour in the previous period into account. Should the Central Board or Parliament refuse to appoint a medical director or assessors, it was suggested that a list should be compiled of all legally qualified practitioners in the Union willing to attend paupers, and who had been in practice a given time and were resident in the area. A yearly or half-yearly ticket should then be issued to all the poor on the pauper list, and to all others whom the Guardians might consider proper objects for medical relief. These tickets would bear a certain value, according to the locality, and the poor would deposit them with the medical practitioner they selected for their attendant. Acceptance of a ticket would guarantee the doctor's attendance for the period, and he would be paid the amount of the value of his tickets quarterly. As an alternative it was suggested that if the total salary were fixed for the area, it might be divided according to the number of tickets each doctor held. An emergency ticket given to a sick pauper not settled in the parish, would entitle the Medical Officer to a higher remuneration.

As the British Medical Association felt so strongly about the institution of central and regional medical directors, they wished to see their first plan implemented, and they also felt the second would divide the medical profession in the Unions, weaken their responsibility and lessen the value of parochial appointments.

At a Medical Conference held in February 1841, a deputation of the British Medical Association and Provincial Medical and Surgical Association met Mr. Serjeant Talfourd, M.P., to discuss the whole subject of medical relief and the improvement of the laws regarding the subject. Similar schemes to those proposed two years previously were agreed upon and Talfourd arranged to draw up clauses to be inserted in the Poor Law Bill of 1841, on less stringent lines. Both Wakley and Talfourd repeatedly told the medical associations that it was useless to attempt to embody the entire proposals in the Bill, for they would only prejudice the cause, and their obvious defects would greatly embarrass all future proceedings. Talfourd cautioned the more radical elements that considerable discretion as to salaries would have to be left to the Guardians, on the grounds of existing local differences and the nature of the habits of the population. It was a reiteration of one of the predominating themes of nineteenth-century political philosophy—control by local authorities must not be destroyed!

The two members of Parliament drew up the new clauses—they were in fact very similar to the recommendations of the medical bodies—and they also asked Lord John Russell, the Home Secretary, to meet their entire deputation in order to solicit the support of the Government. They were 'emboldened to ask for this, because all that the profession desired, had been recommended to be granted by the Committee of the House of Commons of 1838, on which (Russell) himself had been so influential a member'. But neither the Poor Law Amendment Act of 1842 nor the Acts of 1845 and 1847 touched on any problem connected with medical relief. Talfourd's and Wakley's efforts were abortive.

In 1842 a considerable number of the British Medical Association's proposals were acted upon and the Council 'began to express satisfaction that the Commissioners have at length so far listened to the voice of the profession, that they have adopted, and intend to carry out several of the points, which have so long been contended for'. There was how-ever no proposal for determining the salaries of the Medical Officers in the Medical Order of March 1842. As heretofore, the amounts fixed were to be left to the discretion of the Guardians—the problem was to remain local.

The Commissioners explained that although they had previously recommended the adoption of the per case system with a pauper list, after a

most careful consideration of the subject, and of the various circumstances which modify the fair scale of payment to medical men, it appears to us impossible to put forward any one method of payment, or any one rate of remuneration, as equally applicable to all cases and all circumstances. Payment per case is well adapted for most Unions but does not equally suit populous towns.

In rural Unions, they contended, distance was the determining element in the rate of pay-ment, and in the towns, where cases were near at hand, skill and medicine were the chief considerations. Therefore, as even medical men differed in their views on the subject, they thought it expedient to leave the question alone.

But rates of payment were fixed for surgical and midwifery cases.[1] All trusses furnished by the doctor were to be charged to the Guardians at cost price. An extra fee of £5 was to be allowed for major surgical operations and £1 to £3 for fractures. The fee a Medical Officer could claim for attending difficult obstetrical cases was 10s. to 20s., the amount depending on the distance travelled. In very special cases, where a long subsequent attend-ance was necessary, the doctor was to receive £2, but if any dispute arose between him and the Guardians the fee was not to be paid until the Commissioners had signified their approval.

Almost immediately the British Medical Association suggested amendments, and asked for additions to the extra payments list. Operations for aneurism of large vessels were to entitle the Medical Officer to an extra fee of £5, excision of large tumours £3, operations for cataract £2, and abdominal and thorax operations £2. Obstetrical operations of embryotomy and cæsarian sections were also to be remunerated by £5.[2] The British Medical Association also disagreed with fees for capital operations being made contingent on their success, or on the patient's surviving for 36 hours:[3] 'This no-cure, no-pay plan is derogatory and unjust to the character of the profession . . . and would lead to improper inferences.' A deputation therefore suggested half the proposed fee be paid for the opera-tion and the other half for subsequent attendance. The question of consultation was also extremely important, especially in the early days, when many incompetent or unqualified Medical Officers were appointed. In very serious cases Union surgeons and physicians did

---

[1] Commissioners were assisted in this question by Mr. George J. Guthrie, President of the Royal College of Surgeons in 1833, 1841 and 1854, and a friend of the Poor Law Medical Officers' 'cause'.

[2] *Suggestions and remarks by the Council of the British Medical Association on the Medical Order lately issued by the Poor Law Commissioners and on the further amendment of Relief*, May 1842.

[3] 29 April 1842.

consult with a fellow practitioner, but there was no regulation on the subject, and no sum was set apart to aid the doctors in such emergencies. Dr. Kay in his evidence in 1838 suggested the desirability of consultation whenever a capital operation was to be performed in the workhouse, and that there should be some means of remunerating the consultant. But he confined his proposal strictly to the workhouse or to Unions which had appointed a doctor qualified only in medicine or only in surgery and who needed advice in the other field. The attitude of the administrators to the subject was illustrated by a case which occurred in Essex. A non-resident surgeon was called to advise the Union practitioner on an operation for hernia. The Guardians refused to pay him his charge of two guineas, and the Commissioners upheld the decision, writing that they could not 'justify so expensive a practice as that of having recourse to a consultation in every case of difficulty that might occur'!

The importance of obtaining experienced advice was only gradually realized by the authorities and then through their cynical belief that the doctor might be induced to perform unnecessary operations to obtain the fees allowed by the Medical Order. The Order itself stipulated that no payment for operations could be made unless the surgeon had previously obtained at his own cost the advice of some member of the Royal College of Surgeons or Physicians, and could produce a certificate to show the operation was 'right and proper'.

Because the Medical Officer had to pay for these consultations, many disobeyed the regulations, and often much harm was done to the patient. A well-known Bristol surgeon, for example, was called to a case where the Poor Law Medical Officer had suggested to the Guardians that he should amputate the leg of a labourer because he broke it once a year owing to one of the bones being diseased. The Board of Guardians consented, and the doctor performed the operation without consulting anyone and without assistance. A messenger called for the Bristol surgeon at 4 a.m. and took him 10 miles to the case as the doctor was in great difficulty and obviously quite ignorant of the procedure.[1] Therefore the British Medical Association also claimed that fees for consultation prior to the operation (as prescribed by the Commissioners) ought not to be at the expense of, nor at the instance of Union officers. To avoid partiality, such consultations should be arranged and paid for by the Guardians, or if a medical director were appointed and medical assessors employed by each Union, the emergency in question would be provided for at once. The Commissioners refused to consider the additional fees suggested or the payment for consultations. They pointed out that they had already experienced some difficulty with the Guardians as to medical expenses, and expected more as to the amount of separate fees now ordered. Closing the discussion, they explained feebly that the Poor Law Act provided no machinery for the appointment of a medical director or assessors as consulting medical officers.

Determined to combat the negative attitude of the Commissioners, the doctors drew

[1] Evidence of Dr. Wallis, Medical Officer of Clifton Union, Bristol, Select Committee, 1854, re his early experiences.

attention to the 'grand omissions' in the Medical Order.[1] They felt strongly that little had been accomplished for the profession, as even the abolition of the tender system had neglected the method of calculating or fixing salaries. Organized physicians queried how efficient attendance and the best drugs could be supplied to the poor when salaries were only half of what they should be. A rational method of computing remuneration should have replaced the guesswork and caprice of the existing method. The Commissioners themselves had in 1839 stated that they preferred the payment per case system and had suggested a fee of 6s., but no order was ever issued and the Guardians simply disregarded the recommendation.

This obvious weakness in the Medical Order was explained away by the excuse that as the limitation in the size of the medical districts was recently enforced, an increase in salaries would automatically follow. The fees paid for vaccination—about £10,000 a year —the Commissioners admitted to be small, but they confessed that they could not introduce reforms in all sectors at once, especially as the Guardians demurred at the increase in medical salaries. Their vacillation and fear of centralized control was apparent. Despite the supposition that the Poor Law Amendment Act was a piece of pure Benthamism, the deference to *laissez-faire* doctrines was patent, not only in the omissions in the Act itself, but in the tentative activity and writings of the Commissioners.

In appraising their work, the significance of their phrase: 'We are not omnipotent, and cannot overcome the long existing prejudices and strong feelings' supplies the key. For them it provided a fundamental and eternal excuse; for the social historian, it formed the basis for future condemnation. The Commissioners had accomplished much good in some fields. They had introduced a medical service into many extensive Unions, particularly in Wales and in the North, where none had existed before. Gradually they were obtaining an increase in remuneration for Medical Officers for they were 'anxious to ensure the best medicines and attendance for the poor'; but to their excuse for proceeding slowly with reforms, the British Medical Association had the obvious retort—if the Commissioners could abolish tender and introduce other alterations, it presumed they had the power legally to fix the amount and method of calculating medical salaries. (The problem of finance must be borne in mind, and it is doubtful whether the local authorities could have afforded a more costly service.)

But criticism of the Order came from many other sources.[2] Not only did twenty-nine Boards of Guardians send petitions complaining of the table of 'extras' and praying they might be allowed to fix remunerations themselves, but Cornewall Lewis himself agreed that the amounts Guardians were called to pay for extras was higher than the class of smaller ratepayers and farmers were generally able to afford for individual medical

---

[1] Deputation of the Council of the British Medical Association to the Poor Law Commissioners, April 1842.

[2] Most of the *actual criticism* of the Order came from the Guardians; the profession generally pointed to the omissions.

treatment.[1] But this condition he said was inseparable from a uniform scale of payment for all Unions, for no schedule could be fixed which would suit both thickly peopled and remote parts of the country. The Commissioners had therefore adopted an average amount which appeared best suited to the majority of Unions, and believed the fees would not be found excessively high if the Medical Officer performed his duty efficiently.[2]

The Commissioners disagreed with the allegation that extra fees would discourage medical clubs and pauperize labour. And they presciently asserted that the fees prescribed would afford no inducement to Guardians to give an order; on the contrary, they would probably be inclined to greater circumspection, and therefore if the fees decreased the number of medical orders given there would be no tendency for the new rules to encourage pauperism. The Commissioners did everything they could to placate the Guardians. They pointed to the infrequent occurrence of fractures and dislocations, and maintained that the midwifery fees did not generally differ from what had previously been paid; midwives were to be employed as formerly and the Medical Officer would therefore only need to be called for the occasional emergency.[3]

Because the Guardians condemned the fees as exorbitant, there was a strong disposition to reduce the fixed salaries. The Commissioners tried to resist this procedure, and Cornewall Lewis admitted that were it not 'for the authority and influence of the Commissioners, the salaries of the medical officers, and the amount of medical relief throughout the country would be very much diminished'. A new practice was condoned, however, whereby Guardians took the average of preceding years, without making allowances for the increasing demand for medical attendance, and to that extent reducing salaries, without actually disobeying orders. Frequently, complaints were forwarded by Medical Officers from whole Unions jointly. This led to them being accused of forming corporations. They insisted that their salaries were no higher than before 1842, as Guardians evened out the increase for extras with a lower fixed salary, and yet there was much more work to be done.

In the wilder parts of the country, the opinion prevailed that medical attendance was unnecessary and that the provision of food, clothes, and lodgings was all that was required. The small farmers, particularly in Wales, were averse to paying doctors' salaries which to them appeared very high. They also maintained that if the prices of agricultural products

---

[1] Evidence, Select Committee, 1844.   [2] Ninth Annual Report, 1843.
[3] Examples of extra fees—from Ninth Annual Report of the Poor Law Commissioners, 1843.

GODSTONE UNION (Surrey). *Accidents and midwifery in one district of Union since its formation in* 1836
Total amount of extra charges 1836–42   £105 15s.
Average amount of extra charges per annum   £15
Average number of accidents per annum liable to be charged for= 1 and a fraction only.

AMPTHILL UNION. *Cases of fracture and midwifery* 1841–43
Fractures—1841–42, 5; 1842–43, 7.   Midwifery—1841–42, 10; 1842–43, 3 or 4

TOTALS OF SOME AREAS IN LANCASHIRE: Chorley, Leyland, Brindle, Croston, and Rivington.
Total midwifery—1842, 129. Total fractures—1842, 3. Total attendances—1842, 334.

depreciated and the cost of living was thereby reduced then salaries should fall correspondingly.[1]

The Commissioners' scheme for extra fees met with such resistance that they had to resort to the Court of Queen's Bench to compel obedience in the case of the Wycombe (Bucks) Board of Guardians. But this was a rare occurrence and evasions were generally overlooked. The feelings of the Commissioners were succinctly expressed in their Eighth Annual Report:—

> The people of this country are so much accustomed to local management, and to the opinion that expenditure of local funds is to be controlled by themselves, that even the extent of superintendence and interference which we exercise is extremely repugnant to habits and opinions. But fixing a uniform rate of payment for the whole of England which should be independent of the habits of the people and to the opinions of the ratepayers would be a measure going far beyond anything that we could venture to attempt or that we could hope to enforce.

The procedure followed was that the Guardians suggested a salary and the Commissioners had to ratify it. Although they occasionally refused to sanction a reduction in a salary, they generally obeyed the law that the Guardians were the elected representatives of the ratepayers and had the best local information with respect to the duties of the officer and his claims on a salary.

The clamour on the part of the Medical Officers for higher remuneration continued. Witnesses to the Select Committee of 1844 gave evidence of salaries not only remaining stationary but being actually reduced through the operation of the Order of 1842. The doctors of Brecon complained they were worse off than before. The seven Medical Officers of the Wiste Union had been paid a total of £21 for surgery and £1,610 for midwifery in 1843 for a total number of 2,000 cases, and the Guardians wished to reduce the individual salaries from £75 to £50 in the following year.

An interesting letter from the Medical Officer of the Cerne Abbas Union (Dorset) revealed not only that he was inadequately paid £110 for attending eleven parishes, 9 miles in length with a total population of nearly 4,000 and an average of eighty-seven paupers in the workhouse, and that his salary had diminished by an amount equivalent to the allowance made by the Medical Order for extras, but also that the Guardians improperly refused medical orders for midwifery cases, so that they might avoid paying the extra fees. A poor family had been attended by the parish Medical Officer and the wife also in a previous confinement when no extra charge had been allowed. She applied for an order from the Board for her second confinement; this was refused, so the doctor attended her without payment. The following day the mother and her infant again required further attention, and as this no longer constituted a case of midwifery, the order was immediately granted!

[1] The Medical Order was suspended for Blything, Derby, Calne, Nottingham, Sheffield, and Merthyr Tydfil. It was suspended regarding extra fees in Whitechapel, Stepney, City of London, and Manchester.

The Royal Colleges added their voice to the demand for higher salaries. Guthrie, President of the Royal College of Surgeons, calculated that they had fallen one-fifth in six years. Payments as low as £17, £18, and £27 were still heard of, as in the Southam Union, and even in wealthier industrial areas such as Bolton appointments were advertised at £37 and £40. Robert Keate, an ex-President of the College of Surgeons, favoured a national minimum rate of payment. No practitioner, he maintained, ought to be appointed to a Union, who would condescend to take less than a certain sum, and no respectable man would do so. He contended that the poor should be attended by the same practitioners as the rich, for there was a 'vast number of medical men who were unemployed, and glad to take office for a less sum than they could possibly do duty for'.—This was the reason for the survival of the tender system despite the Order of 1842.[1]

The President of the Royal College of Physicians believed that if a minimum salary were fixed for the Medical Officer it would in practice become the maximum, because it would be considered a sort of standard from which the Boards of Guardians would not deviate. He did not think 5s. for attending a patient and supplying the medicines was too much as the basis for computing a salary, when the case on an average was three weeks in duration.[2]

Rumsey, always a bold campaigner, demanded that the annual total gross salary of £160,000 for 2,000–3,000 Poor Law doctors should be raised to £335,000. This sum was to include the supply of drugs by the Guardians and another £40,000, he suggested, should be spent on sanitary care to alleviate the increasing burden of sick pauperism.

Praise for the system came from the Thirsk Union (North Riding). The Guardians' opinion in favour of a pauper list and 'per case' plan had been confirmed by their experience, and 'although it may occasion to the Guardians a little more trouble—yet it has decided advantages . . . over every other mode of medical relief adapted for rural districts. The pauper list and tickets, being now required by the Medical Order, means the trouble to the Clerk and the Relieving Officer, occasioned by the introduction of the pauper list and "per case" plan are increased in a very small degree.' Examples of payment to Medical Officers under the other different schemes showed the 'inequality of paying by salary, and the advantages of a self-adjusting mode of remuneration, which proportions payment to the work performed, and varies with the altering circumstances of the districts whether such alterations have reference to pauperism or sickness. In this Union at the present time, there is an epidemic cold or influenza prevailing, in one or two villages, which has occasioned a great increase of sickness, and several families have therefore become chargeable.' If payment by salary had existed the doctor would have been much underpaid, but by the plan in operation he was fairly remunerated. The table produced illustrated the injustice of paying by salary instead of paying according to the amount of pauperism or sickness. The Guardians, the Chairman stated, had discovered that their method of remuneration ensured

---

[1] Evidence, Select Committee, 1844.
[2] *Ibid.*

the greatest efficiency in medical arrangements, and they had given full scope to the varia-tion in local circumstances.—'In fixing the payment in this Union reference was had to the sum paid by members of sick clubs. . . . It was found that 2s. 6d. each was paid yearly by every individual in the largest club in Thirsk, for which the medical officer was expected to attend all members resident within five miles of the town.' The pauper list was therefore arranged on this principle—but the clubs generally consisted of the middle-aged and the generally healthy, whilst the pauper list was principally made up of aged and infirm, or children, all more liable to illness. Therefore a little was added to the payment for each case resident out of Thirsk and Sowerby, a contiguous village where a large population of paupers were concentrated near the residence of the doctor. Payment per head on the pauper list was therefore 2s. 6d. in the town and 3s. 6d. in other parts of the Union. The remuneration equalled the Commissioners' demands and practitioners seldom complained, save the workhouse Medical Officer, who received only £15 a year without any fees for surgery or midwifery.[1] Workhouse doctors only received additional fees if patients were admitted in consequence of an accident, that is, if they had not been in the institution 48 hours.

Despite the long report which the Select Committee of 1844 on Medical Relief presented to Parliament, the Poor Law legislation of that year made not the slightest reference to the service or to the position of Medical Officers. It seemed that this important subject was still considered irrelevant and it continued to remain neglected. The Com-missioners and the medical profession were left to struggle alone on the burning question of salaries. It was fortunate that the practitioners occasionally had the support of the central administration against the Guardians. The disposition in the 'forties to reduce salaries was particularly prevalent in Cornwall, Devon, Somerset, and some of the Western counties. The Commissioners in most cases refused to sanction these reductions, proposed on the grounds of falling prices of agricultural products. In their Ninth Annual Report the Commissioners stated that salaries ought not to be regulated by temporary fluctuations in the price of provisions and pertinently observed that they had not heard of Boards of Guardians proposing to augment salaries on account of temporary advances in prices! Their conversion was tardy but it was progressing: 'We think that in many parts of the country, instead of salaries of Medical Officers demanding reduction, the rates are too low to enable the Medical Officer consistently with fair remuneration for his labour and expenditure, to bestow on pauper patients the amount of care and medicines which the Guardians profess to ensure them by a medical order.'[2]

The Consolidated General Order of 1847[3] however, introduced no reform for the benefit of Medical Officers; the Commissioners only reiterated that appointment by tender was forbidden, as was the supply of medicines by tender. They also restated the requisite

[1] Letter, Chairman of the Thirsk Board of Guardians to Select Committee, 1844.
[2] Ninth Annual Report, Poor Law Commissioners.
[3] 24 July 1847, Consolidated General Order issued to all Unions and published the day after the Poor Law Administration Act became Law.

qualifications for a Poor Law doctor, and ordered that a certificate from a member of the Royal College of Surgeons must be obtained to prove the necessity for a major surgical operation. This clause, so derogatory to the profession, was by now unnecessary, as Cornewall Lewis himself stated—he had not heard of a single case in which an operation had been improperly performed because of the extra fee. Instead of no fee, as laid down in 1842, half the payment was to be made if the operation proved unsuccessful. This last General Order of the Commissioners showed little sympathy for the medical profession's point of view. In one of their final assertions they stated: 'On the subject of Medical Relief we felt especially anxious to introduce every possible amendment.' Before relinquishing office they did however feel it their duty to issue individual orders to Unions *raising* the salary of one or more of the Medical Officers. Such Unions were: Bangor and Beaumaris, Boston, Brampton, Calne, Cockermouth, Haltwistle, Hinckley, Honiton, Horncastle, Leek, Lutterworth, Thorne, and Whitechapel, towns representative of every part of the country. Wycombe Union provided one of the most outrageous examples of a reduction in salary which was passed over without comment. The poor of one parish were attended gratuitously for one year, and the other seven Doctors had had their salaries cut from £444 to £310 10s., a reduction of £133 10s., despite the introduction of extra fees for surgery and midwifery. The Guardians were so loth to pay these 'extras' that they had cut down the medical orders for cases requiring surgical or obstetrical treatment by one twelfth. The Totnes Union on the other hand had increased the doctors' salaries by £100 over a period of five years. Bradford Union had raised its salaries from £100 to £527 in the years 1844–48, but the number of cases in one district alone had increased from 49 in 1844 to 1,274 in 1848.[1] In the Hambledon Union remuneration remained stationary during the 'forties and the five Medical Officers received salaries ranging from £17 to £53 a year.

These examples illustrate that the Poor Law Commissioners, when they went out of office in 1847, had not succeeded in settling one of the most urgent problems necessary to the efficient provision of medical relief for the poor. Lack of uniformity in the payment of medical salaries, occasioned by variations in local characteristics and the obscurantist differences of opinion among the Guardians, was still pronounced. The Commissioners from time to time had stated that the wide diversities which already existed in the rates of payment for Medical Officers made it impossible for them to introduce any uniform scale of salary or payment per case for the entire country. Not only did the existing rates of payment differ greatly, but the voluntary arrangements made for medical attendance on the poor in some districts were such as to relieve the Union doctor of a large part of his ordinary duties. The mining districts of Cornwall and South Wales possessed well supported medical clubs for working people, and the manufacturing towns of Lancashire and the West Riding of Yorkshire commonly had large dispensaries maintained by voluntary subscriptions. The comparative lowness in the rates of payment for the Northern Counties

---

[1] *Bradford Observer*, 14 December 1848.

was mainly due to there being little gratuitous medical relief before 1834, for the practice of employing permanent parish doctors paid by salary—almost universal in the south—had scarcely come into existence (see Table 2.5).

TABLE 2.5

Return showing number of Medical Officers employed in 591 Unions in England and Wales with the amount paid to them in Fixed Salaries for the year 1844–45.—Compiled from Appendices B6 and C of the Annual Report of the Poor Law Commissioners, 1846.

Counties	Medical Officers		Nurses		Medical Relief	Population 1841
	Number	Salary	Number	Salary		
		£		£	£	
Bedford	19	1,348	4	50	1,719	107,936
Berkshire	46	3,297	3	50	3,752	161,147
Bucks	42	1,945	1	20	2,932	155,983
Cambridge	34	1,782	6	74	2,959	164,459
Chester	45	2,228	3	51	2,776	395,660
Cornwall	67	2,168	4	51	2,416	341,279
Cumberland	35	790	—	—	1,333	178,038
Derby	39	1,145	2	24	1,486	272,217
Devon	146	4,627	9	95	6,379	533,460
Dorset	51	2,912	5	53	3,328	175,043
Durham	52	1,370	—	—	1,779	324,284
Essex	80	4,532	7	119	8,067	344,979
Gloucester	57	3,358	12	127	4,541	431,383
Hertford	42	2,130	2	27	3,878	157,207
Hereford	25	1,575	1	6	2,242	113,878
Huntingdon	10	624	2	20	1,155	58,549
Kent	98	5,883	11	175	7,572	548,337
Lancashire	120	5,214	4	84	7,339	1,667,054
Leicester	47	2,375	1	5	2,542	215,867
Lincoln	99	3,375	12	82	4,089	362,602
Middlesex	92	6,921	14	205	14,951	1,576,636
Monmouth	24	898	3	30	1,259	134,335
Norfolk	108	4,870	4	36	6,165	412,664
Northants	52	2,710	2	22	3,183	199,228
Northumberland	53	1,249	—	—	1,694	250,278
Notts	52	1,943	—	—	2,424	249,910
Oxford	42	2,548	3	43	2,856	161,643
Rutland	8	308	—	—	338	21,302

Counties	Medical Officers		Nurses		Medical Relief	Population, 1841
	Number	Salary	Number	Salary		
		£		£	£	
Salop	58	2,245	2	23	3,130	239,048
Somerset	111	5,661	14	186	6,428	435,982
Southampton	76	4,483	2	20	6,837	355,004
Stafford	73	2,793	4	47	3,570	510,504
Suffolk	87	4,852	12	134	5,595	315,073
Surrey	80	5,022	6	95	7,403	582,678
Sussex	85	3,973	4	67	6,446	299,753
Warwick	42	4,661	1	3	3,731	401,715
Westmorland	11	400	—	—	643	56,454
Wilts	69	4,131	—	—	4,825	258,733
Worcester	59	2,974	5	79	3,498	233,336
York ⎰ E. Riding	53	1,374	1	10	1,748	233,257
N. Riding	54	1,314	—	—	1,706	204,122
W. Riding	107	3,022	1	18	5,831	1,154,101
TOTAL, England	2,550	118,030	167	2,131	166,375	14,995,138
Wales						
Anglesey	5	240	—	—	285	50,891
Brecon	10	570	—	—	717	55,603
Cardigan	9	390	—	—	404	68,766
Carmarthen	16	797	—	—	819	106,326
Carnarvon	13	650	—	—	781	81,093
Denbigh	11	555	—	—	620	88,866
Flint	8	462	1	10	538	66,919
Glamorgan	21	854	—	—	1,015	171,188
Merioneth	11	457	—	—	491	39,332
Montgomery	10	669	1	5	1,295	69,219
Pembroke	12	639	2	15	753	88,044
Radnor	4	219	—	—	242	25,356
TOTAL, Wales	130	6,502	4	30	7,955	911,603
Total 591 Unions England and Wales	2,680	124,532	171	2,161	174,330	15,906,741

Causing almost as much controversy as remuneration was the problem of the size of the districts and population for which the Medical Officer was responsible. And similar diversity existed in the arrangements throughout the country. As soon as Unions were formed it became apparent that a new and more combined distribution of districts had to be resorted to. The effecting of this disturbed medical practitioners as it extended the practices of some, whilst curtailing those of others. The districts were 'deliberately formed by the respective Boards of Guardians, who, from their local knowledge must be considered the most competent judges on the subject, and we have reason to believe that in almost every instance the best arrangement was adopted.'[1]

But complaints that medical units were too large and inconvenient were universal. Guardians originally divided the Unions into as many medical districts as they pleased, and made them large or small according to their judgement. It was left entirely to their discretion whether there should be two or three, twelve or twenty, with as many Medical Officers. The principle of delegating to local authorities as much power as was practicable was justified in this case, because Guardians were obviously better acquainted with local characteristics; and as they pointed out, if any inconvenience was felt on this score, it would be the fault of the Boards and not of the law or the Commissioners, and so could easily be remedied.[2]

The Commissioners frequently praised the speed with which Guardians embarked on reorganizing the separate parishes, but nowhere did they mention any inconvenience occasioned to the poor or the medical attendant. No evidence was published to show that the poor had had to travel unnecessary distances for relief in the past, although this must have been the case in many places, and reasons were given (even by the Commissioners) supporting the old system, which from a personal and pecuniary point of view placed the poor under a village practitioner whose residence was most convenient.[3] Illustrations were produced to show how separate parochial arrangements might be advantageously adopted in the new Unions. The large Unions of Wycombe and Newport Pagnell fixed the salaries for each parish, and then allowed the Medical Officers to undertake the care of the parishes most suitable for their private practice. Under the new system there was much unnecessary overlapping of doctors and practices. The Provincial Medical and Surgical Association inferred that such rearrangement of districts was undertaken to excite competition among the Medical Officers, with the ultimate object of reducing salaries.[4]

Some Unions, such as Aylesbury, Lincoln and Shipston, abandoned their early redistribution projects. Banbury, containing fifty-one parishes formerly attended by fourteen or fifteen practitioners, in 1836 entrusted the whole Union to three doctors, one of whom held a district comprising thirty-three parishes, 15 miles in width. The prompt attendance on patients was impossible, and many died unvisited. The weekly reprimands of the Guardians proved the impossibility of maintaining such a situation, and in 1838 it was

[1] Second Annual Report of the Poor Law Commissioners, 1836.
[2] W. Hammond, a Guardian of the Brentford Union, pamphlet: *A letter to Sir Robert Peel, M.P., on the practical operations of the Poor Law Amendment Act, by a Guardian*, January 1838.
[3] General only in the South.
[4] Provincial Medical and Surgical Association Report, 1840.

found imperative to rearrange the Union into eight districts with the same number of Medical Officers.

Penshurst Union employed only one medical attendant, a stranger to the district, introduced by the Assistant Commissioner. He was often found in a neighbouring beer-shop and did not possess a proper supply of drugs. When he was dismissed in 1837, the Guardians still only replaced him by a single physician. Easthampstead with a population of 7,000 and 14 miles in diameter, also employed only one doctor. The destitute sick suffered and often called for gratuitous aid from their former parochial doctors. Eastry Union consisting of thirty parishes with a population of 23,000 replaced the former eleven Medical Officers by five. Similar cases of long distances travelled and of an insufficient number of officers were widespread. In Pettistree, for example, the surgeon lived 4 miles from his parish whilst three private practitioners lived within one mile of it. Doctors some-times resided as far as ten miles from their districts. It was little wonder, therefore, that many deaths due to delay in attendance were recorded. In North Aylesford all nine Union Medical Officers appointed to the fifteen parishes, lived from 4 to 10 miles away. The resident practitioners refused to undertake the duties because of the inadequate salaries offered. In 1838 the Aylesford Guardians were forced to increase the remuneration to obtain the services of three additional doctors, one of whom again lived 10 miles distant from his nine parishes. Sometimes, as in the case of the Bradfield Union, the Guardians amalgamated districts after a few years and appointed a smaller number of doctors.

That the Guardians were incompetent to form medical districts was perhaps best illustrated by the procedure in the Thame (Oxfordshire) Union. This extensive Union was divided into three districts of 28, 22, and 31 square miles, all of very inconvenient shape, one being 17 miles in length. Because of the nature of the country, and the difficulty of communication, the three surgeons found it impossible to attend their districts efficiently. Consequently they were compelled to employ deputies from among the local practitioners. 'Re-letting' parishes had formerly been widely practised, and the Guardians, thinking their duty done when they had employed three Medical Officers, did not object to the continuation of the system.

Medical witnesses to the Select Committee of 1838 pointed to the absurdity of such procedure, for the sub-contractors had no responsibility to the Guardians. They insisted that if Medical Officers could not perform their duties adequately, their number should be increased; and each practitioner should be individually responsible to the authorities. It seemed incongruous that so eminent a doctor and social reformer as Dr. Kay (Shuttle-worth) should have defended the system of contracting. His arguments virtually nulli-fied the district arrangement, for by sub-contracting, parishes were merely apportioned to resident practitioners according to their convenience. It seemed as if those responsible for the creation of Poor Law Unions were condoning the modification of their planned districts. The Provincial Medical and Surgical Association suggested that the whole professional body in each Union should have assisted the Board of Guardians in determin-ing the number of districts, *before* the Medical Officers were appointed, so that the 'strange anomaly of rearranging districts immediately afterwards might have been avoided'.

As always, it was Farr's evidence that provided invaluable statistical information.[1] (See Table 2.6.)

TABLE 2.6

Medical Districts in 1837: Table showing in Several Counties the average area of Medical Districts, the average estimated population (1837), the number of cases treated, the number of constantly sick, the number of deaths, and Medical Officers' salaries.—Farr MSS., Vol. III, 1838, p. 389.

	Area, square miles	Population 1837	Cases	Constantly sick	Deaths	Medical Officers salaries
						£
Lincoln	35	5,550	204	18	15	55
Devon	20	3,198	191	15	10	41
Dorset	20	3,514	353	21	16	62
Cheshire and Lancashire	25	5,523	142	14	17	43
Suffolk	22	4,786	525	32	23	72
Norfolk	22	4,530	275	16	15	65
Wilts	25	4,050	764	34	24	75
Average of eight Counties	22	4,341	358	22	17	59
Metropolitan Districts	1·36	15,207	1,449	53	77	105

From parliamentary returns he deduced the following facts:—

The Newbury Union is 72 square miles in area, the Leighton Buzzard Union 55 square miles. The surgeon appears to reside nearly in the centre of the district, but it is 8 miles from his residence in one direction. District 2 of the Oakhampton Union is 54 square miles and the boundary 8 miles from the surgeon's residence. In Northleach Union the area of the two medical districts is 109 square miles and the boundary 8 miles from the surgeon's residence. In Northumberland the Haltwistle Union has two districts, comprising 108 square miles. In Westmorland the Shapwest ward comprises 98 square miles; the distance from the surgeon's residence in one direction is 9 miles. In York, the Driffield Union comprises 115 square miles, its population being 14,718.

The Medical Officer of the latter Union informed the Board of Guardians that he was

[1] Select Committee, 1838, and requoted in Provincial Medical and Surgical Association Report, 1840.

unable to continue his arduous duties at the inadequate salary. He stated that he had to attend the sick poor of forty-six parishes extending 16 miles from his house. For this he received £120 a year, and in supplying the medicines alone he lost by the contract, without taking into account the salary of his assistant and the extra expenses of keeping a horse. He resigned because the Guardians refused to increase his salary or reduce his area.

Not only were the areas so extensive, but the population in many districts for which one Medical Officer was responsible, were immense. Farr quoted that Dover had 20,500 people, Sevenoaks and Shoreham 13,735. One district of Leicester comprised 24,000 inhabitants and the three districts of Bethnal Green 62,000. He observed that 'it has been said that making the district large increases the interest of the medical officer in the appointment, but the remuneration can never be sufficient to cover the increase of expense; and no salary that the Poor Law Guardians could give would be equivalent to the labour, if properly performed, in those large districts.' The result of the surgeon having to attend so many patients was that 'he cannot examine the cases with sufficient care, though he may have the best intentions . . .; errors innumerable must be committed and those errors must lead to fatal results in many cases'. Farr deduced from the returns that the number *constantly* sick under the care of the Medical Officer in the Leighton Buzzard Union, for example, amounted to 100, scattered over an area of 55 square miles; in Newbury Union to 93. "If those persons were seen every other day, the surgeon would have daily to visit forty-six patients, scattered over an area of 72 square miles.'

Wakley with cynical acumen suggested that the Guardians had framed extensive districts, so that fewer applications for relief would be made from distant parishes. The Provincial Medical and Surgical Association agreed that 'a simpler method of depriving the poor of medical aid *without the trouble of refusing it* could not have been devised'.[1] Under the new arrangements the sick poor of some parishes were placed a great distance from the medical advice they had been used to, and yet the Commissioners had stated that they had 'never sought to disturb the medical practitioners in their respective districts'.

Assistant Commissioner Gulson recommended to the Select Committee of 1838 that medical districts should extend about five miles round the Medical Officer—embracing an area of 60 square miles. Small districts, he believed, would not give doctors sufficient motive to attend their patients conscientiously, nor could their private practices be so extensive. A large contract, he suggested, would be a great inducement to a prospective Medical Officer and it is interesting to note that he mentioned the fact that Boards of Guardians calculated the income derivable from a private practice in drawing up the salary schedules for their officers.

All the Assistant Commissioners giving evidence in 1838 reported dissatisfaction as to the size of districts, but on the part of the Medical Officers 'only'. Some of them had tried to modify the areas. Power, in Lancashire and the West Riding, had tried to secure the services of all eligible doctors, so that the poor should not be confined to a few attendants,

[1] To the Select Committee, 1838.

and the Medical Officers, if they so wished, he suggested should portion out the duties. Dr. Kay (Shuttleworth) succeeded in modifying the areas in Norfolk and Suffolk below the general average. In Suffolk the mean was $16\frac{1}{2}$ square miles and in Norfolk $20\frac{1}{4}$ square miles, but the areas were still too large to secure efficiency. In Norfolk, however, there were, he pointed out, 'wide, waste tracts of barren land, that very much interfere with the apportionment of proper districts'. The few inhabitants of marsh, fen, and barren country were unavoidably situated far from medical attendance, but this was no excuse for combining the areas into unwieldy sizes impossible for a single Medical Officer to reach. Kay condoned this arrangement by affirming that small and convenient districts would have led to favouritism and undue consideration of the interests of individuals. In fact, this was exactly what happened in the excessively large areas, as reports from Shipston, Tonbridge, and Eastry revealed.

One of the results of the attempted rationalization of districts was that fewer practitioners were employed. In fact by the end of the 'thirties statistics showed a 71 per cent reduction in the numbers employed for attending the poor. A well-known doctor gave the profession reasons for advocating reduced areas to the Select Committee. The poor, he said, required more attendance than the rich, for they were more liable to contagious diseases. Fevers and serious illnesses required at least a twenty-minute inspection, and they could not be satisfactorily treated when the patient lived at a great distance from the doctor. Time and sagacity, he stated, were necessary for a careful and successful diagnosis, but the majority of Medical Officers had only time for hurried examinations. He asserted that practitioners who undertook the care of dense populations had sufficient duty to perform with a population of 10,000–12,000.[1]

Robert Ceely, another doctor and a prominent member of the Provincial Medical and Surgical Association, suggested that small districts would enable medical men to stimulate private charity more effectually than was possible in large areas. He desired to see the appointment of a medical mediator, as did Marshall Hall and Rumsey, not only for settling salary disputes, but also for determining the extent of districts. But on the question of areas and population the Select Committee only passed the resolution that there was still further room for improvement: '. . . medical districts, in some instances, seem inconveniently large; they should be of such size as to admit an easy access of the medical man to his patients'.

As we have seen, the Commissioners followed the inquiry of 1838 with an investigation of their own. One of the arrangements on which they desired the Assistant Commissioners to obtain information was whether the size of districts needed any special or general alteration. D. G. Adley, responsible for Somerset, Gloucester, Wiltshire, and Dorset reported that out of the thirty-nine Unions, ten groups of practitioners were dissatisfied with the size of their districts. In Devon and Cornwall unsuccessful candidates complained that the areas were too large, whilst those appointed said they were too small. Investiga-

---

[1] Evidence, Marshall Hall, M.D., a London practitioner, to Select Committee of 1838.

tions in Kent, Sussex, Bedford, Buckingham, Hertford, Northampton, and Warwick showed that the poor as well as the Medical Officers were dissatisfied. In Wales also the poor complained that the doctor lived at an inaccessible distance, but here, as in Northumberland and Durham, the Guardians refused to appoint more medical men to smaller districts. Interesting and important was Colonel Wade's evidence on Cambridge and Essex. He had steadily pursued a course opposite to that of the other administrators. Objecting to the reformation of districts because they created greater distances between the Medical Officer and his pauper patients, he had advocated that every eligible practitioner should be included in the Guardians' arrangements. Consequently he had reduced the districts in Cambridgeshire, Essex, and Hertfordshire, which were as a result smaller than any save those of Suffolk. The average population was 3,000 within an average area of 16 square miles.

The Commissioners however, in drawing up their report, tried to weaken not only the force of several important recommendations, but also the advice of the Parliamentary Committee of 1838. They declared that no rule or scale of limitation could be generally enforced, and that the division of the Union must be left to the uncontrolled discretion of the Guardians. The main principle of the Commissioners' recommendations for regulating the extent of the districts was that 'they should be sufficiently large to engage an important portion of the time and attention of the medical officer, and to create those responsibilities, those personal and pecuniary interests in the continuance to hold the office, which should stimulate the officer to the efficient performance of his duty'. To have implemented this suggestion would have meant the doctor devoting very little time to his private practice, yet there was no proposal of any compensating increase in salary.

It will be remembered that the British Medical Association, dissatisfied with the impartiality of the inquiry instituted by the Commissioners, sent out a circular asking for similar information from all individual Medical Officers. There was practical unanimity among the profession in its dissatisfaction with the size of areas. Medical men considered districts were about twice the size they ought to have been for ensuring adequate attention to the poor, and many examples were quoted. The report of the British Medical Association was far more concrete in its recommendations than that of the Commissioners.

In 1838 the Association had already suggested that the number of parochial patients allotted to each practitioner should be fixed, and that districts were to be no greater than the Medical Officer could reasonably cover himself; otherwise, areas should be re-divided.[1] In 1840 they suggested that in densely populated districts, such as in the Metropolis and in large towns, the number of inhabitants for each Medical Officer was not to exceed 10,000, with a reduction in number according to the state of destitution.

The average size of the country districts, they proposed, should be about 10 to 12 square miles, instead of the existing mean of $21\frac{1}{2}$ square miles. This would have entailed halving the areas, with a resulting population of 2,500. It was also recommended that the residence

[1] Report of the Council of the British Medical Association on the Poor Law question, containing suggestions for an amended system of parochial medical relief, April 1838.

of the Medical Officer should be as central as possible, so that the poor might have easy access to his surgery. This would have obviated the recurrence of situations where, for the sake of a few pounds, a medical practitioner had been appointed residing 8–10 miles distant, when another, equally well qualified, lived in the midst of the pauper patients.

The Provincial Medical and Surgical Association desired actual legislation on the matter. Their proposals were based on valuable statistical data furnished by Farr and Kay (Shuttleworth) to the Parliamentary Committee. They condemned the abandonment of the distribution of parochial duties to the caprice of the Guardians, and distrusted the biased judgement of the Commissioners. They therefore submitted Serjeant Talfourd's recommendations of 1840 for insertion in the proposed Poor Law Bill. One of the clauses he had designed was that the medical commissioner (the office the Provincial Medical and Surgical Association wished to see created),

> with the aid and under the authority of the Poor Law Commissioners, shall . . . proceed with all convenient dispatch to take into consideration the size and population of every district, for the administration of medical relief throughout England and Wales, to be committed to the charge of the medical officer, in order to settle the extent and boundaries therof. . . . No district shall include a larger population than 10,000 . . . and districts of greater area than 8,000 acres (12 square miles) shall not include a population of more than 4,000 people.

Districts greater than $1\frac{1}{2}$ square miles were not to include a population of over 6,000 people and small areas were not to contain more than 10,000 people. It was also suggested in the clause that the medical commissioner, within three years after the passing of the Act, should complete the regulation of all districts in England and Wales, and submit a scheme specifying the extent, the boundaries, and the population of all areas to one of the principle Secretaries of State and to Parliament. A clause which was added later to the recommendations stipulated that if the Medical Officer resided outside his parish, his remuneration was to be augmented by a quarter for every mile between his home and the nearest point of the parish, and further, if the parish exceeded 2,000 acres his salary was also to be increased by a quarter.

But an Act of 1841 made no reference to medical questions and the Commissioners restated that it would be impossible for them to establish by direct enactment the maximum limits to the extent and population of medical districts.[1]

The specious argument for their inaction was that in thinly populated areas any positive limitation to the size or population of districts would deprive Guardians of the power of arranging for medical relief altogether, or oblige them to appoint the sole practitioner on his own terms, however high and whatever his conduct. A makeshift had occurred to them nevertheless. If medical districts were to be reduced in size, legislation could be enacted, whereby, if any area or population exceeded a certain limit, a special Minute should be

[1] Seventh Annual Report, 1841.

written about it by the Commissioners, stating the reasons for the excess, and this should then be laid before Parliament.

But such a proposed check could not withdraw all the attention that was being focused on the problem. An increasing amount of the business of the Poor Law Commissioners was connected with the subject, and they eventually attempted rationalization in the Medical Order of 1842. The Order made it illegal for districts to exceed 15,000 acres or contain a population exceeding 10,000. Medical Officers who were attending much greater populations were to continue performing their duties until their term of office expired, or not longer than twelve months. By March 1843, all districts were to be reduced to the specified limit, unless it was impracticable for the Guardians to undertake such a rearrangement. If areas were not reformed, then the reasons were to be recorded in a special minute to be forwarded to the Commissioners for their consideration. This part of the order did not apply to Wales, but no Medical Officer was to reside further than 7 miles from any part of his parish.[1]

The Order effected considerable improvement in diminishing the extent of medical areas, but as so many Unions were granted exemptions from the regulations the evil of employing insufficient doctors, and its consequence—unattended sick paupers—continued. The British Medical Association complained that districts and populations were still too large.[2] The Commissioners retorted that although they desired to reduce extensive regions, the difficulties of obtaining suitably qualified practitioners, particularly in Wales and the Northern Counties, still made it impracticable. In these areas medical districts continued to exceed 20,000, 30,000, and even 40,000 acres.[3]

Rumsey, a staunch supporter of every reform suggested by the profession, had on this question, as on every other problem of pauper medical relief, collected much valuable material. To the Select Committee of 1844 he pointed out how little the Commissioners' Order for a maximum population was being obeyed. In Liverpool the average population attended by each Medical Officer was 37,000; in Manchester it was 27,000, and in Sheffield and Stockport 17,000. He advocated a great increase in the numbers of Union practitioners; and, contrary to the Commissioners' evidence, stated that there was an abundance of medical advice available in the towns, and more could easily be obtained. In rural areas too, he desired to see Unions divided further, to avoid the extreme distances physicians were compelled to travel. It would be better, he warned, 'for the community at large, and for the poor in particular', that more medical men should be employed, 'at public cost for medical and sanitary purposes, than that they should be tempted to disgrace themselves and the profession by attending low clubs, or by vainly endeavouring to obtain a small payment for medicines, from parties who have barely sufficient to supply their wants when in health'.

There were many objections to the proposed arrangements of medical men living in

[1] Articles 6, 7, 8, and 9, General Medical Order, 12 March 1842.
[2] Deputation from the Council of the British Medical Association, 29 April 1842.
[3] Ninth Annual Report of the Poor Law Commissioners, 1843.

workhouses and not being allowed to engage in private practice. Arguments on the other side indicated the desirability of having a corps of Medical Officers who, because they were not tied to a practice, could change from Union to Union; or a single man residing in the workhouse could give his undivided attention to the poor throughout the Union.[1] Dr. Kay (Shuttleworth) proposed that workhouse appointments should be held in rotation by several Medical Officers during the year.[2] Rumsey suggested that, where the workhouse was more than a mile distant from the practitioner's surgery, it should have a resident doctor and a dispenser. The importance of the Union medical men residing within their own districts and being well acquainted with the inhabitants was a point over which there was no controversy.

Of particular Unions, cases of evil were quoted which showed the state of affairs more graphically than generalization. In Bangor scandalous cases arose not from want of ability on the Medical Officer's part, but from his inattention, because he lived so far away. In Newmarket, too, deaths had ensued from the delay caused by the distance the relatives of the sick had to travel, not only for the doctor, but also for the Relieving Officer's ticket granting relief. In the Totnes Union the Guardians had not only stimulated much unfair competition by engaging men who lived a long way from their parishes, but they had also introduced unqualified men. A magistrate for Suffolk, living in an area where there was a large agricultural population, said that the Medical Officer lived so far from the labourers that he could not visit the sick as often as their illnesses demanded, nor when he was needed most urgently. Medicines also could not be procured because of the long journeys required, and many poor preferred to forgo medical aid. The witness believed however, that even in such an unsatisfactory situation, a Medical Officer would, with better remuneration, visit urgent cases and assist patients more frequently. He therefore suggested that the Union doctor should reside in the centre of his area, each district being confined to a diameter of eight miles. Any pauper living at a greater distance from his medical attendant than this, should be allowed to apply to the Relieving Officer for an order to see the nearest practitioner of the Union to which he belonged.[3] Further evidence on agricultural Unions revealed that Guardians in such areas were disposed to forming large districts in order to decrease expenditure. The desirability of fixing the distance beyond which poor labourers should not be compelled to travel for attendance and medicines was generally agreed upon and a plan for establishing medical stations was proposed.

The weight of the Royal College of Surgeons was added to the demand for reform by the evidence of its president, G. J. Guthrie. He admitted that the Commissioners had reduced the size of districts, but not sufficiently, and he advocated that no practitioner in a town should be in charge of more than 10,000 people. In crowded places he advised the most efficient system would be to employ a medical man without a practice to take charge of all the poor and become a full-time employee of the Guardians.

[1] Evidence, J. T. Vallance Select Committee, 1844.
[2] Evidence, Dr. Kay (Shuttleworth), Select Committee, 1838.
[3] Thomas Wilkinson, J.P., Suffolk. Letter to Sir John Walsham, Assistant Commissioner.

Gratification was expressed by the British Medical Association that the Commissioners acknowledged the necessity of limiting the size of medical districts. In their Tenth Annual Report, however, the Commissioners showed that they were still experiencing difficulties with the Guardians over the maximum size of areas and population of the medical districts. The greatest reluctance to the adoption of the Medical Order had come from the Metropolitan Unions. This was because London provided a special case. Active competition among the numerous medical practitioners here made it possible to obtain the services of well qualified doctors at moderate cost. Also a large number of metropolitan parishes were governed by local acts, whose exemption from the Medical Orders of the Commissioners naturally influenced the neighbouring Boards of Guardians.[1] Lastly, extensive provision for the treatment of the sick poor was made by the hospitals, dispensaries, and other institutions depending on voluntary subscriptions.

Throughout the country, opposition to the Commissioners' regulations gave rise to much correspondence between them and the Guardians. Although great reluctance was shown to the break-up of existing arrangements, to the altering of boundaries and to the diminution of the Medical Officer's areas, the Commissioners believed, when their term of office was drawing to a close, that 'the districts were reduced within the prescribed limits *whenever the circumstances of the Union rendered the observance practicable*'. By the General Consolidated Order of 1847 (Art. 158) the Guardians were authorized to divide the Unions from time to time for general and medical relief, with the consent of the Commissioners. On any change in the division of Unions into districts, or in the assignment of additional Relieving Officers or Medical Officers to such a new area, the Clerk was to report such an alteration to the Commissioners for their approbation. Otherwise the regulations of the 1842 Medical Order were restated and no reforms were indicated.

But the Commissioners' decrees and the Guardians' activities were never too closely related, and when the central administration was changed there was as little uniformity in the existing arrangement regarding areas and population as there was in the determination of medical salaries—and just as little contentment and satisfaction were expressed.

There was great diversity also in the length of the Medical Officer's appointment. Contracts were drawn to suit the Guardians as there were no simplifying instructions or orders issued by the Commissioners on this question. Their policy was vacillating and inconsistent.

In 1836, Chadwick wrote to a prospective Medical Officer that the appointments of paid officers were *not* annual, but during good behaviour. In 1837 he informed another doctor that the appointment of Medical Officers *was* annual.[2] Therefore it appeared that the mere caprice of the Commissioners was substituted for a precise regulation. Witnesses to the medical inquiry of the Select Committee of 1838, mentioned several times that the tenure of office by annual contract tended to diminish the value of the appointment in the

---

[1] Tenth Annual Report, 1844.
[2] *Medical Gazette*, 1837, *20*, 367–80.

opinion of the medical practitioner. It was also irreconcilable with the normal procedure of appointing public officers permanently, subject to good conduct. It was generally agreed that the poor should not be deprived at the end of a year of the doctor who had gained their confidence by fulfilling his duties efficiently. Rumsey indicated the danger to the independence of a Medical Officer subject to annual re-election and suggested that the practitioner should be chosen by ratepayers by ballot, as the Guardians exhibited as much partiality in their medical appointments as was formerly shown by parish overseers.

The just principle of permanent appointments was, the Provincial Medical and Surgical Association decided, confined in practice to the protégés of the Commissioners. They discovered that permanency bore no relation to duty executed satisfactorily to the poor. One medical witness to the Committee illustrated the cause of the favouritism: 'I imagine that a kindly feeling and a sense of mutual obligation has risen up between the Guardians and the stranger by whose means they have been enabled to obtain their economical object . . . and those feelings influence the Guardians to retain the stranger in his Union appointment, though the plea on which he was introduced is relinquished. I have heard a Guardian say, "We do not like to abandon a gentleman who has helped us out of our difficulties".' Such circumstances tended to diminish the value and utility of medical appointments under the Poor Law.[1]

The Commissioners considered the question of contracts in the Inquiry which they instituted following the Select Committee's report.[2] They realized that a contract which was subject to annual renewal and revision did not lead to permanency and therefore would not attract such a good class of doctor. As Farr had said:—'If medical men attached to parochial offices feel themselves oppressed or degraded, this will drive away all but men of desperate fortunes, without any other resources.' The Commissioners continued that if officers were appointed for an indefinite period; they could only be removed from office by an order of dismissal, a power which they would exercise only if there was a breach of regulation or unfitness on the Medical Officer's part. The practitioner would also be more directly subject to the regulations of the central authority, and the statutory power of dismissal and its consequences would afford greater security against misconduct than would be created by any clause in an annual contract. On these grounds therefore, and because it was known to be the wish of the doctors to be placed on the same footing as chaplains, clerks, and other Union officers, the Commissioners proposed to modify their regulations regarding the permanency of appointment.

A regulation on this subject was inserted in the Medical Order of 1842: every doctor whose term of office was not expressly stated in his contract was to continue in office until he resigned, or died, or became legally disqualified to hold such office, or was removed by the Commissioners. That the Guardians found loopholes for evasion in this clause was evinced in 1844, when it was stated that of the 2,825 Medical Officers employed, only 1,270

[1] Report of the Poor Law Committee of the Provincial Medical and Surgical Association on the Select Committee, 1838.
[2] Report on the Further Amendment of the Poor Laws, Poor Law Commissioners, 31 December 1839.

were permanent. How loosely 'permanency' was interpreted was obvious from the great care practitioners took not to displease their employers in any way. The precarious nature of their tenure of office was proved by the several cases of doctors accepting Guardians' recommendations or warnings against their own better judgement.

Complaints against the continuance of annual appointments were widespread. A Guardian of the Stepney Union, once a Medical Officer himself, testified to the importance of permanent appointments. 'A great number of Guardians are owners of small houses and if the Medical Officer made a report of the nuisances situated on such property, he would not be re-elected', and he could not suggest sanitary reforms. The Guardian had obtained his information from conversation with the other members of the Board, and one of the Medical Officers confirmed the statement, showing how the uncertainty of re-election prevented him expressing his independent views.[1] The Chairman of the East London Union also pointed to the uncomfortable position the Union doctor put himself into if he acted in an independent spirit, or made too liberal recommendations on the paupers' behalf. The Guardians did not desire an independent Medical Officer and they were extremely cautious in appointing a man if they knew he was to be a permanent officer.[2] The doctors of Bethnal Green and Whitechapel expressed their fervent wish for the permanency of appointments, as they were continually at loggerheads with the Guardians.

The East London Union had the anomaly of two permanent Medical Officers and two with annual appointments. One of the two irremovable practitioners stated that medical men were constantly being changed, and that he owed his comparative independence to the permanency of his position. He had given unlimited orders which had always been attended to. But many doctors were needy men who had a hard struggle to make a livelihood, and if they did their duty properly they were afraid of the consequences. They hesitated to give recommendations for meat, wine, and beer, even when necessary, because they knew that at the next election they would have to contend with a body of men anxious to reduce the rates. Yet if they did not perform their duties efficiently they were still dischargeable.[3]

On the other hand, proof was given to the Select Committee that several Medical Officers who had been elected annually for years, had maintained their independence and performed their duties beneficially. It was argued that medical men needed a check which the system of employing permanent officers did not provide—a specious argument, considering that any 'permanent' Medical Officer could be removed for inefficiency or unsuitable conduct. The prevailing system, G. F. Young, Chairman of the Stepney Union said, was

the system of perfect check; it appears that decisions as to the manner in which medical officers discharge their duties in detail, most properly rests with the Guardians, who

[1] Evidence, T. W. Barnett, Select Committee, 1844.
[2] Evidence, Rev. J. Russell, Chairman, East London Union.
[3] Evidence, Mr. Lobb, Medical Officer, Aldersgate, to Select Committee, 1844.

must be most cognisant of the facts; but inasmuch as the Guardians might possibly for some motives or others, exercise their authority indiscreetly—there is a supervising appellate jurisdiction in the Poor Law Commissioners, who will determine in the last resort any such case if it should arise.

But as the Poor Law Commissioners had no power of initiating the election if the medical candidate was not approved by the Guardians, the latter had the equivalent power of removing the doctor without the Commissioners' consent at the annual election. Young stated that the Medical Officers had been in office since before the Act and had been re-elected annually. They had never made representation to the Board for an increase in salary, although they had done so to the Commissioners.

When asked the pertinent question, why a Clerk to the Union should be a more permanent officer than the doctor, Young replied that the duties of the former involved the necessity of intimate acquaintance with so many problems, both of law and the practical administration of the Poor Law, that if the Board of Guardians changed, it was a great advantage to have an officer who could lead the Board on points which required a good deal of information. He omitted to mention that it was essential for the Poor Law Medical Officer to be well acquainted with his district, both on economic and social matters, besides having a thorough understanding of the poor and paupers, who might become his patients. The Clerk's salary, it was indicated, was £350, because so much responsibility was attached to his office, because he had to pay for his assistant, and because he could earn two or three times as much as a solicitor. The Stepney Union Chairman again neglected to compare the Medical Officer's position. He, too, had to pay for his assistant, and could earn far more, if he devoted himself to building up his private practice. And the implication made as to whose was the greater responsibility unfortunately revealed the prevalent opinion regarding the importance attached to the provision of medical relief for the poor.

It was for the sake of safeguarding the independent action of the medical profession that the President of the Royal College of Physicians added his condemnation of the practice of annual elections, and in the General Consolidated Order of 1847 the Poor Law Commissioners recognized the overwhelming demand for the abolition of the noxious system. They restated the principle embodied in the Order of 1842, which had been so grossly disobeyed, that all doctors were to continue in office until they died or resigned, or were removed by the Commissioners for malpractice.

Robert Ceely, the prominent member of the Provincial Medical and Surgical Association and a surgeon for twenty-three years in Aylesbury, deprecated the practice, sanctioned by the Medical Order of 1842, of written contracts being drawn up for medical services. He pointed out that this was an indignity to which no other official was subjected.

The first rule of the contract was obviously that the doctor undertook to attend all sick paupers.—'These words have been held to involve a far greater change in the administration of medical relief than could have been anticipated.'[1] For it meant a rigorous distinction

[1] Second Annual Report of the Poor Law Commissioners.

between poor and paupers—one of the primary aims of the Poor Law Amendment Act. To ensure that only the destitute obtained Union relief the Relieving Officer was appointed as an intermediary, and through him alone could an order be obtained permitting gratuitous medical attention. Only in cases of emergency (and this principle was often evaded) could the order be dispensed with, but it had to be obtained immediately after the first visit of the doctor. Medical Officers frequently complained of the great difficulty in recovering their fees, and very often orders were held back until it was too late to arrest the disease in its early stages.

The Provincial Medical and Surgical Association suggested that a more efficacious, and equally safe means of affording medical relief to the casual poor was by the abolition of orders altogether. Doctors also recommended that they should be allowed to provide relief conditionally.[1] They would give patients a certificate proving the necessity of medical treatment, which they would then present to the Receiving Officer or Guardians, who should inquire into the circumstances of the patient *after* treatment. The Provincial Medical and Surgical Association concluded: 'The prospect of such an investigation by a superior tribunal would be more likely to deter improper applicants, than the difficulty of obtaining orders from the inferior and half-informed persons, who generally occupy the post of Relieving Officer or overseer.' The objection to such a proposal was that the Medical Officer would very often have great difficulty in recovering his fees and that the poor would be too timid to go to him straight away without some authorization. The Medical Order of 1842 amended the existing practice to some extent, for it stipulated that all those placed on the permanent 'pauper list' were to receive tickets entitling the bearers to free medical advice without any further order from the Relieving Officer.

Another rule inserted in a Medical Officer's contract was that he had to provide the drugs for his patients out of his salary. As was often asserted, it was not always treatment and medicines the sick poor needed, but nourishment. The Guardians supplied all the 'extras' recommended by the doctor, sometimes liberally and in other Unions sparsely, and very often the question led to heated controversy. The supply of medicines was a constant financial embarrassment to doctors, and the struggle to have the policy amended began early and lasted long. Medical practitioners who wrote on the subject, particularly Rumsey, strongly urged that the sick poor could not be properly treated until medicines were provided at a separate cost to the ratepayers. The separation had been found advisable in all other public departments—e.g. by the Army in 1793, and by the prison commission and the East India Company. All Medical Officers favoured the change, and they had the strong backing of the Provincial Medical and Surgical Association. Farr had produced statistics to show that the average cost per patient for drugs was 2s. 6d. Therefore the Provincial Medical and Surgical Association reported that at the existing low salaries, doctors were of necessity induced to withhold necessary expensive medicines, 'for example, quinine, sarsaparilla, castor oil, tinctures, and aromatics'. Cheap substitutes had to be

[1] Evidence, Select Committee, 1838.

resorted to, so that there was one set of medicines for the rich and another for the poor.

Dr. Yelloly, not a Medical Officer, but still the ablest exponent of separate provision of drugs under medical supervision, mentioned to the Select Committee of 1838 that a large parish in West Ham previously supplied drugs at an expense of £70; later they contracted with a doctor who was to receive £50 a year for attendance and the supply of medicines. An Assistant Commissioner himself confessed that one of the evils of low salaries was that it led to 'a worse description of drugs than could be safely applied to private patients'.[1] Dr. Thompson, who studied the problem of adulteration in food and drugs, affirmed that adulteration in drugs was extensively practised, and it was the lives of the poor that were endangered, as the Medical Officer had to buy in the cheapest market for them.[2]

Ceely said that the great diversity in the quality of drugs used and their prices was general knowledge. He had been offered drugs for paupers at cheaper rates than similar articles for his private practice, and he knew them to be adulterated, although the offers were made by respectable houses. He suggested that medical chests should be established; one containing ordinary remedies for 500 people could be provided for a sum of £3 to £5.[3] In his Union, the Guardians had set up small dispensaries in remote villages. But above all, he insisted on the principle of separating the supply of medicines from the doctor's commitments, or alternatively giving him an additional allowance for drugs.

Norwich and Sheffield were pioneers in this reform, for here Guardians provided medicines and contracted with Medical Officers only for attendance. A separate apothecary was employed who dispensed the drugs in a regularly established dispensary. It meant that the doctor could order whatever he regarded necessary and best for the patient, without having to consider the cost to himself. Other Unions did not follow suit despite the fact that the medical expenditure in these two places was no higher than in other towns. The supposition that such a scheme would lead to reckless prescription was refuted by the argument that while catering for the welfare of the patient, the extravagant consumption of medicines by the sick poor would be prevented by the necessity of the doctor maintaining amicable relations with the Guardians. Also the early administration of good medicines would enable the patient to recover more quickly, and therefore diminish the demand for them.

Rumsey advocated the use of existing dispensaries until new ones could be built for storing medicines, but he deprecated the idea of dispensing medicines from the work-houses. For, contrary to the view held by the administrators, he believed it was important to prevent the appearance of any intrinsic connection between the Poor Law medical relief and pauperism. He maintained that as dispensaries already existed, if the change were introduced in a conciliatory and cautious manner, no objections could be raised by influential parties to any legal interference with established voluntary charities.

Cornewall Lewis stated that the provision of a medical chest by the Unions to ensure a

[1] A. Power, evidence, Select Committee, 1838.
[2] Evidence, Select Committee, 1838.
[3] Dr. Kay (Shuttleworth), and the eminent surgeon Sir Astley Cooper concurred in this proposal.

supply of good quality drugs had often been considered by the Commissioners for areas where salaries were too low for Medical Officers to afford the supply of drugs. But the difficulty presented itself that a depository of drugs would need a keeper, and the expense of a capable dispenser made the project impracticable.[1] The Chairman of the Stepney Union agreed that inadequate salaries were an inducement to withhold expensive drugs, but concluded:

> While I am ready to bear the most unqualified testimony to the propriety and liberality with which our medical officers have always discharged their functions—I think it is always objectionable that any man's interest and his duty should be placed in collision; I think therefore that in the administration of drugs, some of which are expensive, a medical man ought not to have any possible inducement to withhold that which the case might require, lest he should be put to an additional expense, which it is quite clear his salary would not enable him to pay.

The drugs supplied in his Union, he said, should be of the same quality as those supplied to the London Hospitals, but salaries were far from making this possible.[2] Another Guardian of the same Union realized the great expense that would be incurred, but he was quite sure the provision of a public dispensary was the only way of ensuring proper medicines to the poor. Sir Benjamin Brodie, the famous physician, added his authority to the cause of reform, stating that it was both desirable and practicable to make the provision of medicines for the sick poor distinct from medical attendance. Dr. Kay thought certain instruments, such as forceps, which were used in severe midwifery cases should be supplied by Guardians, and leeches also.

These illustrations tend to create the illusion that the Poor Law Medical Officers did not supply good quality medicines to their patients. But complaints to this effect from the poor were rare. They lacked medical knowledge and the means of articulation anyway. The doctors generally used the drugs they thought necessary and complained of their loss afterwards.[3] Calomel and antimony were widely used and were cheap, although 'two calomel pills at night and a black dose in the morning cost threepence-halfpenny'. Quinine cost 10s. 6d. to 12s. an ounce, and the smallest dose three times a day cost a doctor threepence a day. The provision of sarsaparilla also cost them sixpence a day (a pint) per patient, and opium used for chronic asthma and other pulmonary affections were similarly expensive. There is continual reference to the use of quinine for agues and fevers of all types. In the demand for higher salaries the doctors referred to the importance and expense of quinine very often and demanded increased remuneration to meet the high cost of their liberal use of the drug.[4]

---

[1] Evidence, Select Committee, 1844.
[2] Evidence, G. F. Young.
[3] This Chapter ignores the medical value of drugs available at the time.
[4] William Champion Streatfield, Chairman of the West Ham Union, was convinced that quinine was rarely used, but a much cheaper substitute instead.

An unexpected and unusual reform was proposed by the Provincial Medical and Surgical Association. A clause they had wished to see inserted in the abortive Poor Law Bill of 1840 was that doctors' salaries should be halved where Guardians supplied the medicines! Farr, in favour of amending the prevalent practice, made the interesting suggestion that an experiment into the extent to which it would be practicable to separate the supply of medicines from a Medical Officer's duties, should be carried out in Gloucestershire. This county, he asserted, contained every variety of population, and any deductions made from it would be applicable generally to the population of England.[1]

By the 'order for keeping, examining and auditing of accounts' of August 1836, the Poor Law Commissioners required that doctors should keep accurate records of their work. Two forms were provided for the purpose by the Union, one, a register of sickness and mortality which was to give data regarding the patient, and the other, a weekly return book which was to record the number of attendances made by the Medical Officer at the workhouse or at the private homes of paupers.[2] The weekly reports of the Medical Officers were occasionally mentioned in the communications of the Assistant Commissioners, but they, as well as the Guardians, considerably moderated their tone of satisfaction on the utility of these records after the Parliamentary Inquiry of 1838 published its findings. There was little confidence in the value of the weekly reports, or their object to secure adequate and regular attendance on the sick. The Guardians themselves discovered that they were utterly incompetent to form an opinion on the facts laid before them. It was suggested to the Select Committee of 1838 that doctors should prepare periodical reports for the Boards of Guardians as to the state of health prevalent in the medical districts. The Committee agreed with the recommendations that great care should be exercised in requiring accounts of diseases, and that the treatment of individuals attended should be accurately recorded.

Among the clauses outlined by Serjeant Talfourd for the 1840 Bill, there was one suggesting that Medical Officers should be required on 25 March every year, to furnish an appointed medical commissioner with a distinct report of the number of sick patients, the expenses incurred, the manner in which the expenses had been defrayed, the distances travelled, and other information which the Poor Law Commissioners should from time to time have found they needed as the provision of medical relief expanded.

Witnesses to the Select Committee of 1844 declared that the utility of providing a check on the Medical Officer by his records required regular inspection of them by the Guardians. This was often inadequately and apathetically done, and it was proposed that a simplification in the compiling of the records might make them more comprehensible to the Guardians.

---

[1] Evidence, Select Committee, 1844.
[2] See Forms 27 and 28, Second Annual Report.

Form 27: The register of sickness and mortality was to show the name, age, residence, disease, cause of disease, dates and method of treatment of each patient.

Form 28: The weekly return book had to state name, age, disease of patient, whether treated at home or in workhouse, the days the Medical Officer gave treatment, extras ordered, and observations.

Rumsey, on this subject, as on every other aspect of Poor Law medical relief, had his criticism and his reforms to offer. He condemned the careless manner in which medical reports were frequently made, rendering them useless to anyone. From his own experience he quoted the difficulty he had found in ascertaining the exact number of patients attended by doctors. Trifling cases were not recorded, nor those which were seen at unusual hours, as they were not worth the extra trouble. In Unions where fixed salaries were paid, which were the majority, the doctors saw no point in entering up all the cases attended. Most doctors showed a strong objection to the additional work entailed by keeping books, particularly as they were not compensated for the time spent on them. From some Unions no returns were received at all by Somerset House. The reason why there was so much adverse criticism of the Medical Officers' reports was stated in a letter from a Guardian to Rumsey: '. . . The present system of medical relief holds no inducement to the medical officer to keep registers of sickness with accuracy, neither has the attention of the Boards of Guardians been quickened on the subject by any sensible or tangible interest on their part'.[1] The returns as then required could not have secured the adequate execution of medical duties to the Guardians, but if the practitioners had compiled their statistics on a regular and systematic plan they would have been of assistance to themselves. Termination of cases could rarely be ascertained, nor could the duration of each case and its severity, and such information could have been a valuable aid to a medical man's knowledge.

The reports could also have provided important material from a general statistical and scientific point of view. The defect of the Medical Officers' inaccurate and irregular method of compiling their records was equalled by the neglect of the administrators in seeking relevant information. 'A great mass of facts, most important to the welfare of the sick and the progress of medical knowledge, was lost to the country from the want of a well-regulated system of reports under medical inspection.'[2]

Practitioners never felt the responsibility of their position as long as they were under the control of non-professional parties, and laymen could never check the efficiency of medical treatment. The obvious reform, and the one suggested by Rumsey (and the Provincial Medical and Surgical Association in 1840), was the institution of a competent medical authority to which annual reports of the causes and methods of relief given to the poor should be forwarded. Dr. Walker, who had studied the subject attentively, proposed that such an authority should institute inquiries, and draw up comprehensive reports from the local material furnished. Local health accounts and reports of professional interest would have led to scientific progress in public health on a national scale, and a central repository for data would have been invaluable.

There was however no reference to medical reports or the compilation of statistics in the Order of 1842. It was not until 1847 that a comprehensive regulation stipulated the requirements for medical reports. By the General Consolidated Order, the Medical Officer

[1] Mr. Clissold, Guardian in Blything (Suffolk) Union, 1844.
[2] Rumsey, evidence, Select Committee, 1844.

was to furnish Guardians with reasonable information on the pauper cases under his care. He was to make a written report relative to any sickness prevalent among paupers, as the Guardians or central authority might require, and he was to attend the meetings of the Board for supplying information when he was requested to do so. A medical certificate had to be supplied respecting any child whom it was proposed to apprentice, and a certificate was also to be given to the Guardians or the Relieving Officer on every pauper the doctor was attending, stating the nature of the sickness, or any other cause for his attendance. Further, in keeping his books, the Order prescribed that the Medical Officer should employ, so far as practicable, the terms used or recommended in the regulations and the statistical nosology issued by the Registrar General.—Was the close connection between Poor Relief and Public Health becoming recognized?

The Union doctor was also expected to show when and how many visits he made to each case, and state when the patient was attended by someone else, an assistant or deputy. All extras provided by the Guardians on the recommendation of the doctor had also to be recorded on a prescribed form, no longer in the book; and the forms were to be separately bound at the end of each year.

Vaccination was another additional duty which generally fell on the Poor Law Medical Officer after 1840. Attention had been drawn to the prevalence of smallpox through the neglect of vaccination by witnesses to the Select Committee of 1838. Rumsey deprecated the insufficient encouragement of the operation and the careless manner in which it was performed, and the Provincial Medical and Surgical Association had agitated for an extension of the practice for years. The Vaccination Extension Act of 1840[1] made it imperative for Guardians to contract with doctors for the vaccination of all persons. Paupers as a class were more generally vaccinated than the wealthy, because the Medical Officer knew nearly all the poor in the parish and attended so many women in childbirth that it was relatively simple for him to keep a check on infants not vaccinated. The doctor signed a printed form of the Commissioners after the operation had been declared successful and the mother received a certificate on the day of the vaccination, which was signed by the Medical Officer after subsequent examination showed the operation had taken. If the vaccination was not successful the doctor was not paid for it. Arrangements adopted for vaccination were that the Union was divided into districts with stations in each—generally the doctor's residence. They were therefore so numerous and near to each other that few persons were required to walk more than two miles to one. The vaccinator for the district

---

[1] *The Vaccination Extension Act, July 1840.* Local Authorities (i) Boards of Guardians, (ii) Overseer, where no Guardians.

Duties (1) To contract with Medical Officers of their respective Unions or any legally qualified medical practitioner for vaccination of all persons residing in the Union . . . Copies of contracts to be sent to the Commissioners.

(2) To receive reports from such Medical Officers of the number of persons successfully vaccinated, and such further reports as the Poor Law Commissioners require Medical Officers to make.

Act of 1841. Expenses of executing Act of 1840 to be defrayed out of Poor Rates. Vaccination was declared not to constitute Poor Law relief, although it was to be given gratuitously.

attended each station periodically at a fixed day and hour, and again a week later to inspect the cases. In well populated areas, the stations were open every week, but in remote places, a series of weekly sessions were organized during parts of the year only. It was however arranged that the Medical Officer was to vaccinate any person at any reasonable time that he might apply at the surgery.

Though incompetent to deal with the new problems for which they were becoming responsible, the Commissioners did endeavour to the utmost of their limited ability to fulfil the new medical requirements. They took pains to enlighten the Guardians on the theory and practice of vaccination, and in 1841 they issued a circular letter to all Unions and incorporated parishes calling in a Return of the number of cases vaccinated and other particulars of useful observations. A report of the experiences of vaccination was also invited, and the Commissioners hoped thereby to be able to correct any defects in the arrangements.[1] They had gone into the question efficiently by consulting the Royal Vaccine Board in London and medical authorities in Dublin and Edinburgh. They also tried to glean information from individuals of the profession who had had particular opportunities of experience in this field.

The only serious difficulty they encountered was the rate of remuneration to be paid for vaccination. Under the previous haphazard system, some cases had been paid for by local authorities, others had not, and some parishes had included the operation in the duties of the Poor Law Medical Officer without additional remuneration. The Commissioners recommended that 1s. 6d. for each successful case should be paid in England and Wales, subject to modification to meet the peculiar circumstances of districts, the difficulty of access, or the scantiness of population.

> Having regard to the small amount of time necessary for the performance of vaccination and the subsequent inspection and registration, we believe that 1s. 6d. per [successful] case will be found sufficient remuneration for single cases where parties come to the residence of the medical officer, and for groups of cases who are in attendance at a fixed hour at the Vaccination Station. . . . Although the recommendations which we have made respecting remuneration for Vaccination have been suggestive and not peremptory, yet in the vast majority of vaccination contracts, the Guardians and medical practitioners have acquiesced in the terms proposed of 1s. 6d. per case, a fact which induces us to believe that the terms are not inadequate.[2]

The difficulty of determining the fee for vaccination had been increased at the beginning through the impossibility of estimating the probable number of persons to be vaccinated. In the first years, the figures of the annual number of births which in future years made such an estimate possible, could not be relied upon, nor was there any means of computing the proportion of them which would be vaccinated under the provisions of the Act as in 1840 there was such a vast number of unvaccinated adults and children. In 1841, of the 583

[1] Circular, 23 November 1840.
[2] Seventh Annual Report of the Poor Law Commission.

Boards of Guardians, 533 had entered into vaccination contracts. The remainder had delayed, or refused to comply with the Act, because they had doubted whether it authorized payment out of the poor rates, and if it did so, whether the provision of free vaccination out of parochial funds would not constitute people paupers as they were in fact recipients of poor relief. (See previous footnote, re Act of 1841, p. 125.)

The progress made by the Unions in providing a medical service for the poor was illustrated by the comparison of vaccination figures for these Unions with those of the parishes still operating under the Gilbert Act, where they were very low indeed.—'It shows', said the Commissioners, 'the relative superiority of the manner in which parochial business is conducted by paid officers of the Unions, as compared with the unpaid parochial officers.'

The medical section of the community did not regard the vaccination arrangements as favourably as did the administrators. No sooner had the Act of 1840 come into operation than the Provincial Medical and Surgical Association began a vigorous campaign for its reform. Previously they had deprecated the proposal to commit the superintendence of public vaccination to the Poor Law authorities, and had recommended that a comprehensive view of the subject indicated the necessity for a national Board of Health, or failing this that the National Vaccine Establishment, with an improved organization and extended powers, should be adapted for directing national vaccination.

The Marquis of Lansdowne presented a petition on behalf of the Provincial Medical and Surgical Association:—

It appears the duty of the State to remedy this great evil by appointing regularly educated vaccinators, with suitable salaries, in districts sufficiently numerous to embrace the whole of the poor population of the country, and who shall offer gratuitous vaccination at stated periods to all within their bounds, keeping accurate registers of their proceedings and communicating regularly with the National Vaccine establishment.

But the House of Commons, dedicated to a policy of *laissez-faire*, and afraid of creating more centralized controls, subjected vaccination, like all sanitary regulations, to the direction of the Poor Law authorities. The unsuitability of the Commissioners for fulfilling their new important duties was shown by their omission of any provision for ensuring a constant supply of fresh vaccine lymph and, as the Provincial Medical and Surgical Association termed it, 'their absurd stipulation regarding the services of the medical contractor "whenever he is personally applied to at his own residence" '.[1]

The medical colleges and the Royal Vaccine Board remained supine, so the remonstrances of the majority of the profession went unheeded. The clause most objectionable to the doctors was that empowering Guardians to *contract* for the general vaccination of the community. They did not always adhere to the Commissioners' recommendations of

[1] Provincial Medical and Surgical Association, 1841 Report.

1s. 6d., and in many Unions advertised for tenders offering vaccinators 1s. or even 6d. a case. In Stockport 6d. a case was offered, and as only one person accepted, he was appointed to the whole Union, and later had his fee raised to 1s. The Bradford Guardians offered 9d. a case and Bethnal Green 1s., which were accepted; and tenders at Whitechapel were proffered for 6d. and at Bridport for 1s. Not only the profession, but also the better informed and more humane portion of society condemned 'so vicious a principle', and the Council of the Provincial Medical and Surgical Association urged further legislation directing the payment of a specific sum of 2s. 6d. for each vaccination. This, and Wakley's proposal that every applicant for the operation should be allowed to select his own doctor, was rejected. Wakley's other suggestion—that any doctor should be allowed to vaccinate— was embodied in the Act, but in practice only the Poor Law Medical Officers were engaged by the Guardians for this purpose.

The Provincial Medical and Surgical Association thought the Poor Law Commissioners' recommendation of 1s. 6d. per successful case too low. Before the Act, it had been even smaller—generally 1s.—for attending paupers at their homes. In very few Unions had it been as high as at West Ham where 2s. 6d. was paid, and generally it had been included in the medical salary. Previously, local authorities had contracted for paupers and the poorer working class only, whereas gratuitous vaccination had now been extended to all. This meant that the people who had formerly been vaccinated at a cost of anything between 2s. 6d. and 10s. 6d., after the Act applied to the public vaccinator, whose income was therefore much reduced, as he lost all his private patients. The reduction in remuneration was felt not only by the bulk of the profession, but also by the Union Medical Officers— the district vaccinators. For their work was greatly increased for little extra payment, and also they lost much time compiling weekly schedules, quarterly registrations of cases, signing certificates and furnishing the authorities with copies of registers. The Provincial Medical and Surgical Association, attentive to every detail, demanded in consequence that a much simpler method of registration should be devised.

But the Poor Law administrators were often helped in avoiding the reform of abuses by medical men who were eager for public office or jealous of an interloper. 'In almost every locality, the working of the Act had led to dissension and altercation, either between the Guardians and the resident practitioners, or among the latter themselves.' The Provincial Medical and Surgical Association concluded its condemnation:

As respects the profession therefore, the measure has proved one of injury, oppression and degradation; while with reference to its professed object it must be considered a failure. . . . Efforts of medical practitioners to extend vaccination among the working classes have been checked by removing the ordinary inducements and facilities for its performance; and the distrust and apathy of the poor has been increased, by connecting this invaluable protection with the administration of the Poor Law.[1]

[1] Provincial Medical and Surgical Association, 1841 report.

This latter point was of great significance and might have been applied to the whole field of Poor Law Medical Services.[1]

That the receipt of free medical attention constituted a man a pauper, deterred many sick poor from applying for relief. In several Unions the rule obtained that no one could receive medical relief without entering the workhouse, and here the deterrence enforced was more efficacious than elsewhere. The relief offered in the workhouse, so far as the Medical Officer was concerned, was as good as that given outside, and there were many regulations to secure efficient medical attention. The duties of the Medical Officer were defined in Article 78 of the workhouse regulations and were recapitulated in the 2nd Annual Report of the Commissioners in 1836. The workhouse doctor was to attend patients at the times stated by the Guardians and any time the master sent for him in cases of sudden illness, accident or emergency. He was to visit patients as often as their illness required, and also to examine all lunatics and new entrants to the house. He had to give all necessary directions as to the diet, classification and treatment of the sick and lunatic paupers, and to provide the requisite medicines. Certificates of a patient's illness and its probable duration were to be furnished to the Guardians, and it was the doctor's responsibility to report any death to them immediately, stating its cause and circumstance. He was also required to keep a register of sickness and mortality, and make returns as to the nature of the duty he had performed, including reference to the number of visits made, treatment ordered and any extra nourishment the patient required.

The Order of 1847 added a few responsibilities. The Medical Officer was to report any pauper of unsound mind in the workhouse, whom he deemed dangerous or who should be sent to a lunatic asylum. He was also required to vaccinate every child entering the house. The Order illustrated the progress made by the Commissioners in taking an interest in the welfare of the paupers. For the doctor was asked to report any defect in diet, drainage, ventilation, warmth, or other arrangement of the workhouse, or any excess in the numbers of any class of inmates, which he might deem detrimental to the health of all the others. He also had to furnish the Guardians with a report of any defect which he might observe in the arrangements of the infirmary, and in the nurses' performance of their duties. The workhouse Medical Officers generally attended the outdoor poor as well, but very occasionally they resided in the institution, and were not allowed a private practice.

The Provincial Medical and Surgical Association agitated for higher salaries for workhouse doctors as for all others. In the Bill they proposed in 1840, they asked that a fixed remuneration should be calculated according to the weekly average number of inmates, and suggested from 4s. 6d. to 6s.—a higher rate per head than that proposed for outdoor

---

[1] Just previous to the passing of the Vaccination Extension Act the Government sanctioned a far superior system for the West Indian Colonies. The Barbadoes Board of Health in 1839 offered free vaccination to all who wished (not compulsory). Vaccinators General were established, who were to visit all houses of all classes on the island and vaccinate everyone living there. Full statistical reports were required, which were to be forwarded to the Governor-General. A sum of 5s. per case was to be paid and an account was to be kept of all those refusing to be vaccinated.

paupers. This they justified by pointing to the much greater proportion of illness incident in the workhouse and the number of cases attended each year, far exceeding the average weekly number of inmates. Besides which, the doctor had constant and laborious duties unconnected with the mere treatment of disease. He was at this time paid nothing for visiting and certifying lunatics. The Whitechapel Medical Officer for example visited Hanwell twice a year and frequently attended at the other asylums. Further evidence from this Union showed how medical salaries remained stationary whilst the work greatly increased.[1]

In 1839 the total number of cases was 1,660, of which 700 were indoor paupers and 960 outdoor; the figures for the following years, given as published, were:

1840	total cases	2,160 [i.e. 2,200]	indoor	830	outdoor	1,370
1841		2,283		731		1,552
1842		2,647		649		1,998
1843		3,319 [i.e. 3,320]		577		2,743

Although their work grew steadily, the Medical Officers desired to impose even more on themselves. They demanded additional powers to enforce sanitary precautions in the workhouses, in particular they desired the means of removing nuisances producing febrile symptoms. The necessity for obtaining such powers was illustrated by a description of the Spitalfields workhouse. This was separated only by a narrow street from a yard where horses were slaughtered and night soil received. Another yard nearby was used for desiccating and evaporating night soil, so that it could be sent in small cases to the West Indies as manure. The doctor warned that the intolerable stench and the contaminated air produced dyspepsia and stomach complaints, and a tendency to fever. When there was any epidemic disease in the workhouse among the children, a more malignant character was given to it. A far larger percentage of fatal cases of scarlatina, measles, and typhoid existed than there would normally have done, he said, and erysipelas always became a contagious disease in the institution, which was not the case in private houses, where the air was salubrious. The firm had been prosecuted for the nuisance before, and fined £30 a day by the magistrates for every day the yards were used subsequently, but no alterations were made. The Medical Officer anxiously desired the means to have such nuisances removed himself, but the Guardians never envisaged the necessity or the practicability of providing him with additional Public Health powers.

Doctors were not always equally conscientious. Duties were often not efficiently executed. A case was investigated by a Select Committee in 1844[2] in which a pauper had been removed from Kensington to Chelsea workhouse in a dying condition. No medical certificate had been granted as to his fitness and safety for removal, and he died the following morning of inflammation of the lungs. The Chairman of the Chelsea Guardians

[1] Evidence, Select Committee, 1844. Whitechapel Medical Officer.
[2] Second Report of Select Committee, 1844. Evidence: Chairman of the Chelsea Board of Guardians—John Bromfield Ryder on Henry Osman case.

charged the Poor Law Commissioners with refusing an inquiry into the maltreatment of the sick pauper, for he claimed that much public good would have resulted from such an investigation, in preventing further similar incidents of gross cruelty. It was a case appertaining to only one individual, but it was for the common good of the sick poor of the country. As the Commissioners refused the inquiry he successfully petitioned for a House of Commons investigation. The evidence revealed that the pauper arrived at Chelsea workhouse in a filthy and grossly neglected condition—this negligence would have come to light in an inquiry. The Medical Officer of Kensington claimed the patient would have died in any case, even if he had not been moved, and revealed that sick patients who were critically ill, were often transported to another workhouse if they belonged to another parish. This cruelty was still anomalously practised, although it was legal under the Settlement Act for one Union to pay another for the maintenance of its paupers if they were too ill to be removed.

It was seen that the Medical Officer was not even present when sick paupers were taken away, as he should have been. Dr. Thomas Wakley, Coroner for West Middlesex from 1839, interested himself in the case because no inquest had been ordered on the patient's death. The Select Committee heard very conflicting reports; but the inefficiency of the doctor was unquestionable. He kept no record of his patients, nor of the medicines he administered. Only a rough book of prescriptions and diets could be produced. He kept no books for making returns to the Guardians, only the workhouse general sick book was sent to the Board's meetings. The statistics of deaths revealed that there were practically twice the number of deaths in the Kensington workhouse as in the rest of the parish, and Wakley discovered a large percentage of deaths on which no inquests were held. Troublesome paupers were often certified insane and literally carted away to lunatic asylums when the Medical Officer and the workhouse authorities were tired of looking after them.

The Committee reported that the action of the Kensington doctor had been irregular in having the pauper removed without a medical certificate and without having seen him within twenty-four hours of his removal, but that the Poor Law Commissioners had not committed an indiscretion in not having made further inquiries. The latter was of some consequence, but was to be expected. The importance of the second report of the special Select Committee of 1844 was that it revealed a scandal which, because it was left unpunished could well occur again. Above all, the evidence to the Select Committee disclosed the arrangements in which such scandals could flourish, and therefore threw new light on the character of the Poor Law medical system.

Other scandals arose where the rule was adhered to that paupers should only receive treatment in the workhouse, and had to be moved to them, whatever their condition. As a result, it was suggested that an instruction should be issued by the Commissioners to all Medical Officers, that their responsibility did not cease on their certifying that a pauper might be moved to a workhouse with safety whilst suffering from ill health. Doctors were to be present, it was proposed, whenever long distances—sometimes 15 miles or so—had to be travelled, especially in inclement weather. If he were unable to attend, then he was to arrange for a deputy, who had to be a competent judge regarding the fitness of the pauper to travel. In either case compensation for loss of time and the cost of the conveyance was to be defrayed by the Guardians.[1] But the Commissioners took no further interest in the subject. Complaints were frequently made and were sometimes investigated, but rarely was an order issued to reform the abuse which made a scandal possible.

To assess the efficiency of medical attendance on the poor is difficult, in so far as the lack of uniformity in supplying relief and the varying local circumstances and characteristics were conducive to very different results. Generalization would be misleading because the reports from the administrators were on the whole favourable, whilst complaints from the poor were rarely recorded. It is questionable whether an unbiased account was ever written.

The Commissioners asked for statements from their Assistants from time to time, but they pointed to uniform efficiency. Rumsey investigated some Guardians' reports and found that they were far from the truth, and he affirmed the difficulty of procuring evidence from medical men owing to their fear of giving offence to the Guardians or other members of the profession.[2]

Once the question of providing medical relief to the poor had resolved itself into becoming a system, it was obvious that the doctor had more work than previously, with little or no increase in remuneration. One surgeon put the figure as three or four times as much. The Commissioners compiled statistics of the number of cases a Medical Officer was required to attend. Forty-four Unions were selected impartially from all parts of the country, some containing large populations and others small, some were urban Unions and others agricultural. They deduced that a fair average could be obtained in this way and found that a District Medical Officer attended ninety-seven patients a quarter. This, Cornewall Lewis said, meant a yearly average of not less than 300 cases or 717,200 for the whole country. On an average each case received four attendances, and therefore he showed that three million visits was an extremely moderate estimate of the doctors' work. From so large a number of attendances Cornewall Lewis inferred it was only reasonable to expect that some instances of neglect should occur.[3]

It was unquestionably the opinion of the central administration and of the doctors, that the poor should receive the best medical attention. This was patent in the many statements of the Commissioners, and in their attempt, however inadequate and dilatory, to improve the system. That the object was not achieved was partly attributable to the Guardians, who, as representatives of the ratepayers, were pledged to a policy of niggardly retrench-

[1] Letter from Thomas Wilkinson, J.P., of Suffolk, to Sir J. Walsham, 1844.
[2] Guardians' reports—North Aylesford, Wallingford, Eton, Faversham, Hambledon, Tendring, Penshurst, and Woodbridge Unions. Quoted evidence, Select Committee, 1838.
[3] Evidence, G. Cornewall Lewis, Select Committee, 1844. The ninth Annual Report gives returns of the numbers of cases attended by Medical Officers in several Unions. For example in Whitechapel 5,300 sick received treatment in 1838, and 6,600 in 1843. In Poplar three Medical Officers attended nearly 5,000 patients in 1843.

ment; and also to the lack of prescience in the *laissez-faire* dominated middle and upper classes, who little realized the economic and social advantages which would accrue, even to themselves, from a healthy labouring class. Medical science, too, had still to make great progress, and there was also no doubt that several doctors were negligent.

The predominant factor, however, which emerges from all available evidence, is the large amount of good work the Poor Law Medical Officers accomplished. Their credit is increased, when the paucity of remuneration, the difficult journeys and the continuous battle against the apathy and obstinacy of ignorant Guardians is considered. It was repeatedly pointed out that with better conditions, superior treatment and medicines could have been given to the poor. This was illustrated by the Chairman of the East London Union who, in advocating that the medical men that attended the poor should be of the same character and capacity as those that attended the rich, showed how the 'liberal' system of his Union produced the most beneficial results. He had not heard of a single complaint from any person against the Medical Officers since the Union was established.[1]

Complaints of neglect were more frequent in districts where medical men were the best paid. This was not because lower salaries made the doctors work harder—a spurious argument of the Guardians—but because large salaries were only paid for very extensive or difficult areas containing a great number of potential patients. Also in the counties where salaries were lowest, chiefly in the North, the working classes were not so much in the habit of looking to the Poor Law doctor for aid. Farr offered some interesting statistics: in Unions where salaries were fixed sixty-eight people in 1,000 were attended, and in Unions where payment per case obtained (chiefly in the North) only 50 people in 1,000 received free medical attention. He pointed to the importance of efficient medical treatment for the poor, as nearly a fifth of the deaths in the country came from patients under the District Medical Officer's care. He drew an analogy with the prison system. Gaol surgeons received superior remuneration and were appointed by magistrates, who were not as difficult to deal with as the Guardians. Duty and not salary was the first criterion. The neglect of prisoners, made evident by an outbreak of gaol fever or other disease, quickly and often attracted the attention of the Government. The number of deaths occurring in prisons were recorded and known by everybody, said Farr, but the mortality in Poor Law Unions, over scattered districts and isolated parts of the country was too frequently forgotten and made no general impression.[2]

Sir John Walsham had only one complaint in the six years that he was Assistant Commissioner in the North. But he was referring to official complaints into which he had to carry out an investigation, and it was therefore no index to the amount of grievance which existed among the poor. Clergymen very often received accounts of abuses from their congregation, but these were neither investigated nor recorded. In the South, criticism was more general, probably because the new system had got under way so much more quickly there. They were nearly always about delay in attendance, and instances of

[1] Evidence, Rev. J. Russell, Chairman of the East London Union, Select Committee, 1844.
[2] Select Committee, 1838.

the dismissal of doctors for this reason occurred, after an Assistant Commissioner had held an inquiry. For gross negligence a doctor was publicly dismissed, and at least one Medical Officer a year suffered this highest censure.

Possible procrastination by the doctor was the argument offered for the retention of the Relieving Officer. If the poor sent for a physician, he could always deny having received the message, but a Relieving Officer's order provided a check to prevent neglect of duty. However there was evidence that when a practitioner failed to attend the sick after an order had been given, the Relieving Officer often took no steps to see that his orders were obeyed, nor did he evoke punishment on the recalcitrant.

Ceely spoke for the Provincial Medical and Surgical Association, and individual doctors were supported by the Presidents of the Royal Colleges, in demanding the abolition of the Relieving Officer.[1] It was asserted that great evil might arise if the poor could not go directly to the Medical Officer. One surgeon alone quoted three cases where deaths had occurred within a short space of time owing to the regulation of obtaining an order before medical aid could be obtained. In the first case, he had been called by friends to attend a man in another Union suffering from an illness which terminated fatally. The jury at the inquest returned a verdict of natural death and stated no proper application had been made for medical relief. Yet the people living with the man had twice been to the Union surgeon, who had promised to attend but had not been to see the patient for four days. If he had done so the man would not have died, but the doctor was not even reprimanded. The surgeon recalling the incident attached the blame to the state of the law, requiring an order, although the case was an emergency. The Relieving Officer lived 7 miles away, the Medical Officer 6 miles, in opposite directions, and it was stated that doctors frequently attended the poor in urgent cases gratuitously out of humanity, for Guardians had the legal right to refuse payment for aid given without an order. In this case also the surgeon giving evidence was refused remuneration by the Guardians, and their decision was upheld by the Commissioners, although he had made a long journey in the middle of the night.[2]

The Guardians on their part, however, had an immediate answer for neglect of duty, or the too liberal ordering of extra comforts for the poor, in that they had full powers for suspending the Medical Officer—and it was rare for the Commissioners not to dismiss him, with or without a fair inquiry. In general, the Guardians did not have a Union doctor dismissed for neglect, but for recalcitrance against their policy, or for demanding the removal of nuisances detrimental to public health. This was also their reason for favouring the annual election of doctors. Guthrie, the President of the Royal College of Surgeons, pointed out how many cases of complaints by the poor were neglected by the Guardians and were never inquired into. A typical case was one which occurred in St. George's, Southwark, where the Union practitioner was merely reprimanded for neglecting a

[1] Select Committee, 1844.

[2] Evidence, H. R. Cooper, surgeon to the Stowe Union, Select Committee, 1854, Medical Relief of Poor Law, on his experience twelve years before.

patient, and even when death occurred, he was reinstated after a short period of suspension, because his docility and his acceptance of a low salary suited the Guardians. (The records of these Guardians have no reference at any time to medical relief!)

An interesting inquiry was held in 1844. A Select Committee was appointed to investigate allegations contained in a petition by David Philipps, the Medical Officer of Totnes Union (Devon). The Guardians, he affirmed, had reprimanded him in a manner likely to affect his character injuriously. They accused him of frequenting pot-houses for two years, and inciting the people against the Poor Law. From the evidence it appeared that the accusation was true, yet the Guardians had never suspended him. He informed men in the ale-houses that the Guardians made the law suit themselves, and that it was not the Poor Law which was being administered, but that made by 'a parcel of fools'. Some of the men in this agricultural and wool manufacturing area, were unemployed for six to eight months in the year, and lived for a great part of that time on club money. If they struck against the system, they were disqualified from obtaining a workhouse order. Philipps incited the men to go to the workhouse in an organized body and demand relief, which would not then be refused. He had great influence over the men, and it appeared that he calmed their riotous moods. The vicar, who kept a medicine chest for the poor, defended Philipps. The result of the inquiry was more interesting even than the evidence—Philipps was not dismissed—his salary amounted to a total of £15 a year for a population of 3,500 in one parish, and he was responsible for two other parishes.

The Medical Officers generally had great influence over the poor, probably a proof that they obtained their confidence by attending them efficiently. A doctor of Whitechapel maintained: 'Generally speaking, no person has more influence over them [the poor] than the medical officer. I always receive great marks of deference from them.'

Satisfaction was expressed by witnesses on behalf of the poor to the Select Committee on Medical Relief of 1844. In Derby the Medical Officer had been appointed in 1837, and in all the succeeding years, not a single complaint had been made of want of attendance by or on behalf of the poor. 'His engagements were regularly and punctually fulfilled', despite the fact that the whole of Derby constituted a single medical district. Five doctors were responsible for the medical treatment of a total population of 91,500 in Stepney, of which over 1,000 were inmates of the workhouse. Yet, the Chairman stated, he had never had a complaint of neglect, although 8,000 sick paupers were relieved annually. The 1842 Order had been modified for this Union, and the combined salaries of the five practitioners amounted to only £460 including midwifery and surgery fees. A churchwarden of thirty years' standing wrote that only one doctor attended the whole of the Newbury Union, but he had 'never known the poor better attended, or better satisfied with any medical man . . . and I gladly bear my testimony to his skill and attention'. About the single Medical Officer for Shipton-on-Stour, another agricultural area, the Commissioners heard

the strongest terms of kindness . . . smallpox in one parish is raging, and his attendance is unremitted . . . medical relief is now more efficient than it ever used to be, and there are no complaints from any parish. I do not think the extent of his district has at all interfered with his attending properly to the poor; larger contracts appear to insure to the poor the first attention of the medical man; in small districts private patients take the lead.

A magistrate of Hampshire affirmed:—

I have rarely detected any dereliction of duty on the part of the profession. Indeed since the peace of 1814, every town and village has had so many practitioners settled in it, all properly jealous of their reputation, anxious for employment and observant of each other's conduct, that in my opinion, the sick and infirm are better attended to at the present moment than at any period within my recollection. In many instances the medical gentlemen have been confessedly underpaid; nevertheless they appear to me to have performed their ill requited services with exemplary cheerfulness and alacrity.[1]

In 1836 an epidemic of influenza prevailed in the Southern counties, but the Assistant Commissioners for the regions reported that no complaints were received against the over-worked doctors. Some of the Medical Officers themselves were attacked and many Unions praised the amount of unremunerated attention given by their practitioners.

Although the positions of the people making these favourable reports have to be taken into account, there were however no general or widespread complaints from the poor. Cornewall Lewis summed up the situation when he stated in 1844, that the dissatisfaction which prevailed against medical relief, was in great measure confined to the medical profession.—'It could scarcely be considered as extending to the poor ... there is no prevalent wish on the part of the poor, in a large part of the country, to obtain a better or more skilful medical assistance, than is now afforded to them. . . . They would derive great benefits from a superior class of medical assistance, and from a more extensive supply of it.' But no facts had come to his knowledge which led him to suppose that there was a 'strong desire on the part of the poorest class to obtain greater facilities for medical attention than are provided'. He therefore concluded with the fallacious argument that 'increased advantages might be put within their reach—but it does not follow that the poor will avail themselves of them'.

Poor quality in medical attention did not generally emanate from the services of legally qualified Medical Officers. Scandals of inefficiency were in most cases reported from Unions where unqualified doctors or assistants had been appointed, on the basis of cheapness, and contrary to the Order of 1842. But above all it was the malpractice of the druggists and untrained midwives, which the Poor Law Commissioners had no power to control, that caused the greatest harm to the sick poor.

Druggists flourished particularly in Wales and Northern England. In the wilder regions of Wales, the supply of medical relief was extremely deficient. Regular medical contracts except in the largest towns were entirely unknown, and almost 'the only relief in sickness

---

[1] Quoted in Second Annual Report, Poor Law Commissioners, 1836.

which was given was a small sum of money, which is expended at the druggists, in the purchase of some favourite specific, or more commonly taken to the popular quack of the neighbourhood, who is not infrequently a woman'.[1]

Bone-setters also were widely patronized in Wales and in the North. In the Dolgelly Union bone-setters only were known—they were men from the neighbourhood, without any skill save the use of physical force. A doctor in Bangor gave up his practical surgery, because he had all the responsibility for treating sick paupers, whilst he always lost control of his cases by patients going to a bone-setter as soon as the operation had been performed. Evidence was also given in 1844 of the 'tribe of bone-setters' who were very numerous in the North of England and to whom the people were very partial.

Serious evils also arose from the employment of ignorant midwives. Gruesome tales were told of accidents which happened during childbirth. The poor often resorted to those not sanctioned by the Guardians, and paid them about 2s. 6d. or 5s., but even the women employed by the Guardians were no more competent. Witnesses to the Select Committee of 1844, from Bangor, Brecon, Swansea, and Bridgwater for example, complained of the excessive ignorance of their midwives, and that they were employed by the Guardians without any previous examination or certificate of qualification. The wide differences in system which prevailed in the country illustrated how little attention the administrators had paid to the subject. In Bethnal Green, midwives were not subject to the control of the Medical Officers, but were appointed specially by the Guardians. In Dolgelly they were supervised by the doctors, and in Greenwich they were never employed by order of the Guardians. Generally, however, female midwives were engaged and the Medical Officer was called in case of difficulty. Guardians could fix any fee for the practitioner from 10s. to £1 for ordinary cases of midwifery, but £2 was paid for emergency operations. Occasionally a surgeon charged 10s. to the Board and then used a midwife himself at 5s. The Commissioners never objected to midwives being employed, but they condemned a doctor delegating his duty and making a profit from it. Several complaints were made regarding this procedure.

There was a general consensus among the medical profession that midwives should be exclusively under the control of the Union surgeon and should be paid on his certificate of a successful delivery. If the midwife could claim her fee independently, it was believed she would not send for the surgeon for fear of losing her remuneration. A Medical Officer of East London called them selfish creatures who should only be appointed as long as the surgeon testified to their good behaviour. He claimed some rule was imperative to ensure that a surgeon would be called for early in cases of difficulty. This he deemed of vital importance, for maltreated childbirth might render a woman unfit for work during the remainder of her life, or might even prove fatal. It was fairer to the doctor to be in charge of all difficult labour, as any consequent sickness would be his responsibility and it would also be cheaper for the Guardians in the long run.

[1] Third Annual Report of the Poor Law Commissioners, 1837.

Doctors on the whole complained of the character of midwives attending the poor and the fatal results from their ignorance. They suggested that they should be educated by the surgeon and undergo an examination by him. Some Medical Officers objected to employing women altogether, but this was not a universal opinion—so long as they were educated, skilled and competent.[1] Union midwives were not uniformly bad, and some were employed by people in respectable positions, who could afford to pay the customary 10s. 6d., and yet engaged the Union one at 5s. Previous to the appointment in 1844 of an incompetent midwife, the Clerkenwell Union had engaged one woman for thirty-four years. That the Guardians were anxious to secure an able successor was illustrated by notices affixed to the workhouse, inviting tenders and testimonials of an experienced midwife resident in the parish. One applicant forwarded a tender for 4s. a case and the other one of 5s., and the latter was appointed, although she was more expensive! Her testimonial showed she had been a midwife of the Royal Maternity Hospital for twenty years and one of the physicians certified that she had performed her duty creditably and satisfactorily. It seemed in this instance that the Guardians were to be exonerated from engaging a person later proved incompetent, and the case also revealed that famous hospitals did not always employ efficient staff. Obviously the necessity for the institution of some kind of training scheme was revealed by the shortcomings of the midwifery service under the Poor Law.

Once again the Poor Law medical system indicated that reforms—benefiting the whole population—were required. The most enlightened Medical Officers suggested that England should follow the Continent in establishing a regularly educated class of midwives, who should receive a certificate of attendance at a course of obstetrical lectures and of experience in a lying-in hospital. This would authorize her to practise midwifery and she would then come under some central supervising body. Cornewall Lewis, without passing comment on the first recommendations, far from agreeing to legislation, observed that he was 'at a loss to know what superintendence could be exercised on the ignorant class of women, who now practise midwifery'. For many decades to come therefore, the Poor Law authorities and the legislature allowed a patent abuse to continue.

Another evil which caused suffering to the poor was the use by Union doctors of deputies or assistants. One of the very first instructional letters from the Poor Law Commissioners to Boards of Guardians, stated that the Medical Officer was 'responsible for the proper performance of his contract, by himself or his agent. The Board cannot require the personal attendance of the medical officer.' This was probably sanctioned because districts were too extensive, or communication in widespread areas, difficult. As Rumsey pointed out, no control could be exercised over the assistant by the Guardians, jobbing became prevalent, and the remedy for one evil only led to a different abuse. An example was provided by the Epping Union. The doctor developed cataract, and while he was away in London for treatment, a poor man had an accident and applied to the druggist who was the doctor's deputy. The quack supplied the patient with an ointment. After two days torture

---

[1] Select Committee, 1844.

the man went to an old established physician, relying on his charity to see him, and his shoulder was found to be badly dislocated.[1]

Assistants of Medical Officers were not acknowledged by the West Ham Union Guardians, but on the whole no objection was raised to the practice, as surgeons were responsible for their assistants' actions and also paid their salaries. Apprentices, too, were taken for training by the doctors, as parochial officers were regarded as good teachers. Despite the 1842 Order regarding the qualifications of those attending the sick poor, these apprentices often attended pauper cases, without the Guardians' objection. An apprentice of three years' standing was considered sufficiently qualified—though not legally—to order treatment and attend midwifery cases.

A similar evil, and one about which the British Medical Association felt strongly, was the great influx into the Unions of 'young men, just let loose from hospital, and about to commence practice, but ignorant of the responsibilities and expenses of parochial attendance'.[2] They were glad to locate themselves in any neighbourhood, while an experienced and resident practitioner would refuse to undertake an office in which he knew he could not do justice either to himself or to the poor. Older doctors had to contend with the situation that their wealthier patients might object to being attended by a Poor Law Medical Officer from a fear of infection. But, as it was often stated, the profession was crowded, so that newly qualified men were glad to get any situation on any conditions. These made exploitation by the Guardians possible. The British Medical Association also asserted that men of indifferent character or ability would take employment on the Guardians' terms. But, the Association asked:— 'Should the lives of the poor be entrusted to the care of the inexperienced and half educated, or to persons whose character or abilities would preclude him [sic] from being called to the families of any member of the Board of Guardians? . . . On the other hand should an established practitioner be forced to undertake duties at a loss to himself.'[3]

---

[1] Evidence, G. R. Rowe, Epping Union, Select Committee, 1838.

[2] Deputation from the Council of the British Medical Association, April 1839.

[3] British Medical Association, 1839, deputation. Thomas Hodgkin, M.D., had a plan to improve the standard of medical officers attending the poor. He proposed that not only should the character and ability of the candidate be carefully inquired into, but that public examinations, oral, written, and practical, should be instituted. This would lead to doctors keeping abreast of medical science and standards, and would also get rid of quacks. Graduation from a medical school, he contended, did not differentiate between those who had scraped through the examination and those who were really first class, and the proposed additional local examinations would help to grade applicants for public office.

He illustrated his argument by outlining the French system. There, 'nearly all public medical posts from the lowest class of dresserships in hospital up to the highest medical professorships, were filled by those who had proved their superiority . . . by more or less rigorous competition'. Candidates were always numerous for the frequent competitions which did not merely lead to 'the empty distinction of possessing a medal, but to the attainment of a position'. The advantages of this system were proved by the great numbers of distinguished doctors produced and the important contribution made to medical science by France over the past thirty years. Hodgkin also maintained that this plan would remove the oppressive influence of a system of pecuniary competition.—Thomas Hodgkin, 'On mode of selecting and remunerating medical men for professional attendance of the poor of a Parish or District'. Paper read before the Hunterian Society, 1836.

Closely allied to the circumstances which induced young practitioners rather than the experienced to undertake Poor Law duties, was the stigma attached to being a doctor of the destitute. Of this situation Farr afforded the penetrating summary:—'If medical men attached to parochial offices feel themselves oppressed or degraded, this will drive away all but men of desperate fortunes, without any other resources. I think cheap services may be obtained by making the service honourable, agreeable or indirectly profitable.' To secure reforms not only to benefit the poor but also to further their own interest and social status was the doctors' aim in combining. It was for this reason chiefly that the early short-lived British Medical Association had been established. It was, as the President stated '*in consequence of the injuries inflicted on the medical profession in connection with the Poor Law Amendment Act, and those medical clubs introduced under the authority of the Guardians.*'[1] The Poor Law Committee was formed in the Association for conducting inquiries into the operation of the medical department of the Act. As we have seen, the desire to alter the method of giving sick relief to the poor engaged much of its time and attention. In 1838 the Council of the British Medical Association reported that it was too much the custom to underrate the value of the services of the Medical Officer. The principal results in the Public Health field, which should have been required from an efficient doctor, had been overlooked, and therefore the best means of obtaining these results had been neglected.

> It is for a medical man's anxious and constant watchfulness in detecting and removing the causes of diseases, for his care and caution in preventing their occurrence and extension, that his services are chiefly valuable, but, so small have hitherto been the inducements offered to medical men to exert themselves in the performance of duties of such incalculable importance to the community . . . that it is a matter of astonishment, and highly creditable to the philanthropy of the medical profession, that its members have fulfilled their various and arduous duties so well as they have done.[2]

Besides the existence of the Provincial Medical and Surgical Association and the British Medical Association, the two large organized bodies, Medical Officers in several Unions formed associations for resisting the Guardians or demanding reforms. In 1835 the Berkshire Association sent a petition to Parliament and the Hertfordshire practitioners presented a memorial to the Commissioners. Three Associations were formed in Kent for protecting the 'interests and respectability' of the profession, and one forwarded a memorial to the Commissioners. In 1836 the practitioners of Surrey petitioned Parliament for a Committee of Inquiry. The Buckinghamshire Association presented a protest against the first Report of the Commissioners to the Secretary of State, who remarked he had received no complaints from any other quarter.

[1] George Webster, M.D., M.R.C.S.(Edin.), President of the British Medical Association, on Poor Law Amendment Act, Medical Inquiry, to Select Committee, 1838.

[2] Report of the Council of the British Medical Association on the Poor Law question, containing suggestions for an amended system of parochial medical relief, April 1838. See also Chapter 13 on Medical Officers' organizations.

The Warwickshire and Worcestershire Medical Officers petitioned Parliament for a Committee of Inquiry, and Worcester also memorialized the Home Secretary, as did the Dorsetshire Association. Petitions were also sent to Parliament from Essex, Colchester, Chipping Ongar, Gloucester, and Stroud. The Epping Union doctors held meetings on the question of remuneration and agreed on terms that were not accepted by the Guardians. They continued to defy the Guardians and all save one refused the salaries offered.

Collective action by medical practitioners raised an outcry from the central and local authorities, for combination of any kind was anathema in the eyes of mid-Victorians. To accuse the medical profession of such activity was rather absurd. The Guardians and Commissioners, in resisting the demands of the doctors, might just as well have been charged with the same leanings.

The Commissioners in 1835 even accused the profession of having 'a compact in the great majority of cases' with the parochial authorities, by which the former supplied medical attendance at a small fixed sum on 'condition' the Guardians allowed them to charge distant Unions exorbitantly and dishonestly for relief afforded to extra-parishioners. The accusation obviously dated back to the system prevailing before the Act, and the Commissioners overlooked the numerous cases in which medical men were defrauded of fees by the refusal of the Guardians to pay for treatment given without a written order. The Medical Association of Dorsetshire wrote to the central authorities deprecating the attack on the medical practitioners of England and Wales, and expressed strong indignation that 'the reprehensible conduct of a few', should have been made 'the occasion of so sweeping and undeserved a charge against a profession, distinguished for its humane exertions and for its gratuitous services'.

The First Report of the Commissioners further maligned the character of the medical profession, by stating that: 'inferior officers have been fee'd by medical officers to search out and give them information of cases of illness occurring in non-parishioners, in order that they might have opportunities for making these disgraceful charges'. The Provincial Medical and Surgical Association in its Report of 1836, admitted that cases of this nature occurred, but they were far from being general. The Poor Law Committee of the Association therefore came 'to the unwelcome conclusion that the Commissioners, by impugning the character of the professional body, hoped to reconcile the public to the unjust treatment which they have so arbitrarily inflicted on it'.

The Provincial Medical and Surgical Association firmly believed that the administrators conceived some prejudice against the medical profession as soon as the new law came into operation. For, although they were 'necessarily and totally unacquainted with the various bearings of this important subject, not less than with the best mode of affecting an alteration, yet in general, they distrusted, and sternly resisted suggestions of those who alone were able to assist them—the medical practitioners'. The statement concluded that if the conciliatory spirit which was evinced by some Unions and some Assistant Commissioners had been allowed full expression, more satisfactory and efficient arrangements could have been achieved.

When the Poor Law Commissioners went out of office in 1847 progress had however been made. The Medical Order of 1842 particularly, was an important step towards the development of an efficient service for medical relief. Improvements in salaries, in the size of districts and population to be attended, and in the supply of medicines had been achieved, although these questions remained a permanent source of agitation for reform. In 1846 the House of Commons voted a grant of £61,000 for payment of a moiety of doctors' salaries, exclusive of extra fees payable under the Commissioners' Order, and for the payment of the whole of the salaries of workhouse schoolteachers and district auditors. Rumsey's proposal of a system of national medical endowment was the first of its kind and was never considered, and this 'grant-in-aid' was the nearest approach ever achieved. In a letter to the Assistant Commissioners,[1] the Commissioners stated that it was the intention of the Government in proposing these votes to contribute to an improvement in the character of workhouse schools and in the supply of medical relief to the poor. The Assistant Commissioners were instructed to report on their districts where schools were least effective and medical attention least satisfactory, so that the Commissioners might take further steps for improving both these branches of Union management.

There was one question which received no consideration from the Commissioners, and on which the medical profession urgently demanded reform. This was the institution of some responsible medical authority. In 1836 the Provincial Medical and Surgical Association suggested that something should be done to check 'the wretched spirit of rivalry, speculation, underbidding, and jobbing, which unfortunately are but too frequently found among medical men'. A disciplinary force was needed. Even lecturers at the London Schools encouraged rivalry by advising all students to apply for Poor Law appointments and they supplied the Assistant Commissioners with lists of names from which to select officers.—'Traitors in our own camps'—according to the Provincial Medical and Surgical Association. The Association therefore recommended the intervention of a third party in fixing remuneration, or alternatively, as disagreement was bound to exist between the Guardians and Medical Officers, the latter were to be elected by the ratepayers as a whole for each parish, the legislature having previously fixed the salaries. It would have meant a return to the old parochial system of one doctor for each parish. The British Medical Association in 1839 agreed that there were important reasons for the latter suggestion, especially where a small Board of Guardians was conducive to favouritism. But as they protested against proxies and plural voting, they considered the appointment of officers had better be left in the Guardians' hands. Ceely and Rumsey, suggested that the Medical Officers should be responsible to a more comprehensive local authority than the Guardians. This would ensure to them greater individual responsibility, especially as the Boards were considered incompetent as an employing or supervisory body.

But wider issues overshadowed these suggestions. The increasing dimensions and growing importance of medical relief were revealed by the demand for a more drastic reform.

---

[1] 7 November 1846.

The Provincial Medical and Surgical Association, the British Medical Association and individual doctors for many years proposed the setting up of a medical board or director-ship, with regional superintendents or assessors. From the point of view of public welfare the institution of a medical authority, to which the Poor Law doctors would have been responsible, would have secured greater efficiency. One of the principal evils of the old system of parochial relief was the absence of efficient supervision and control over the practitioners employed to attend the poor. The Commissioners tried to remedy this defect by requiring weekly returns and periodical reports. But, as it has been seen, this check was both ineffective and offensive. Ineffective because Medical Officers either neglected to furnish adequate reports or the Guardians were not competent to understand them, and offensive to the medical profession because they were being judged by laymen.

As early as 1836 the Provincial Medical and Surgical Association suggested that medical relief should be under the supervision of competent authorities. They proposed that medical superintendents should act either in conjunction with the Commissioners, or they might be appointed to counties, travelling from place to place to investigate alleged abuses in the administration of medical relief and to examine Medical Officers' reports. The Association suggested that the manner in which the Board of Guardians frequently exer-cised their power of electing practitioners was not such as to warrant the opinion that they were the most suitable parties to possess this privilege, and that justice could not be done to the medical men or the pauper patients.[1] In 1838 the British Medical Association proposed a board of superintendence to determine the qualifications, the moral character, and the length of residence required of a Medical Officer. It should also be responsible for intro-ducing as much simplicity and uniformity as possible into future arrangements for paro-chial medical assistance.[2]

Much evidence was furnished to the Select Committee of 1838 in favour of appointing a medical commissioner. It was argued that in the absence of such an officer, disputes between practitioners and Guardians could not easily be resolved. He should be appointed by the government and bear the same relation to the Poor Law Commissioners as the Army and Navy medical departments had to the Horse Guards and Admiralty. Other doctors wanted a medical referee, with powers to arbitrate between Medical Officers and Guardians on the question of districts, and the scale of payments, adapted to the peculiari-ties of each Union. The opinion running through all the arguments was that the Poor Law medical services could not be well conducted without medical knowledge and medical con-trol. Famous doctors like Dr. Marshall Hall of London pointed out that control of District Medical Officers by a medical commissioner would be beneficial, and that no satisfaction would ever result, regarding remuneration, without reference to a professional authority. Sir Astley Cooper, the most eminent surgeon of his day, suggested that a medical Guardian should be referred to in cases connected with the medical treatment of the poor. Farr,

[1] Report of the Provincial Medical and Surgical Association read at a meeting in Manchester, July 1836.
[2] Report of the Council of the British Medical Association on the Poor Law question, containing sugges-tions for an amended system of parochial medical relief, April 1838.

however, desired only that resident practitioners in each district should elect one of their members to confer with the Guardians, and Kay (Shuttleworth) disagreed with the necessity of any medical supervision if the recommendations of the Select Committee regarding districts and remuneration were acted upon.

The recommendations of the Committee ignored the matter completely; so the agitation by the medical profession continued unabated. Ideas were gradually crystallized, and a comprehensive plan agreed upon in later years. The scheme advocated by the British Medical Association proposed that a central medical director or commissioner should be appointed to superintend all the medical arrangements throughout England and Wales, under the authority of the Commissioners.[1] He should be a highly qualified man, a member of the medical colleges, and should have practised not less than five years. All the medical returns of the Unions were to be sent to him, and he was to present an annual report on the nation's health, which the Poor Law Commissioners should append to their Annual Reports. All disputes on duties and remuneration were to be referred to him. *The idea was born, therefore, of gradually withdrawing the health side of pauper relief from Poor Law administration.* The British Medical Association further suggested that a medical Guardian or assessor should be elected from each Union by the resident practitioners willing to attend the poor, to act on their behalf, while Guardians should nominate a similar assessor to act in the interests of the ratepayers. These assessors should fix the amount of remuneration to be paid to the doctors, and, together with the Assistant Commissioners, they would determine the size of the medical districts. If any group of practitioners declined, or were unable to elect an assessor, the medical director was to appoint one.

It was also proposed that the medical assessor might act as consulting practitioner for the Union in cases which were dangerous or difficult and he should, if called upon, give advice to the Guardians on matters requiring medical knowledge. His quarterly, half-yearly, and annual reports on the health of the Union, would be a medium of communication between the doctors, the director, and the Commissioners. The medical assessor was also to inquire into the qualifications of candidates where vacancies occurred. Particulars of prospective Medical Officers would be sent to him and he would prepare a list from which Guardians could select their officers. In cases of real or alleged malpractice, or where the poor expressed dissatisfaction, the Guardians could always consult the medical assessor, who would conduct an investigation and decide the issue, or refer the case to the medical director. The British Medical Association insisted that if the central authority possessed the power of dismissing doctors, that authority should be both competent and responsible.

The Provincial Medical and Surgical Association included similar proposals in the Bill which they submitted to Serjeant Talfourd for consideration by the House of Commons. They added that medical assessors' salaries should be calculated at 10s. for every £100 of the total expenditure for poor relief, and deducted from the salaries of Medical Officers in

---

[1] Deputation from the Council of the British Medical Association to the Poor Law Commissioners, April 1839.

proportion to their respective amounts. In fact, of all the recommendations which the Provincial Medical and Surgical Association included in their Bill, the

> first and perhaps the most important object we propose to contend for, is the *appointment of an additional commissioner of the medical profession.* . . . We neither propose to invest him with a share in the general powers of the Commissioners nor with exclusive power in medical cases; we are contented to leave to the discretion of the board, the degree of influence which he shall exert within his peculiar province; chiefly desiring that the feelings and knowledge of the medical profession should have an appropriate organ to express them, and be satisfied with the result which may thus be produced.

The Commissioners refused to consider the schemes, making their excuse that no machinery or powers existed under the Act of 1834 for carrying out such a reform, and that the Guardians already objected to the expense of medical relief. The medical profession refused to accept this as a legitimate answer, and renewed their appeal to the Select Committee of 1844.

Ceely commented that the tardy and imperfect manner in which the recommendations of the previous Select Committee has been implemented, and the difficulty experienced by the Commissioners in so many instances in enforcing the Medical Order of 1842, proved that the authorities charged with the administration of medical relief were incompetent or averse to the task. Friction between the Guardians, the Commissioners and the Medical Officers would be greatly diminished if the medical side of Poor Law relief was transferred to other hands. He proposed the institution of a Central Health Authority with local Boards of Health. The Central Board should consist of three eminent medical men, a distinguished civil engineer (appointed by the government), and one of the Poor Law Commissioners, as well as Chadwick. This Board might later, Ceely advocated, form a section of a National Medical Board for other purposes connected with the government.

Other witnesses to the Select Committee continued with their demand for a medical commissioner and assessors. Guthrie, President of the Royal College of Surgeons, and Farr showed the propriety of having a medical commissioner to decide on disputed cases. Various arguments were given by other doctors,—one stressed the importance to a Medical Officer of being able to confer with a superior of his own profession;[1] another that the medical authority alone could arrange districts and duties;[2] and a third that the poor would benefit greatly.[3] All objected to control by laymen, but Rumsey disapproved of a system which might lead to the Poor Law Commissioners relinquishing the administration of medical relief entirely. Some witnesses suggested that medical inspectors should be appointed by the government to examine into the conduct of the doctors,[4] and that their districts should coincide with those of the Assistant Commissioners. Rumsey thought it

[1] Evidence, Select Committee, 1844; Dr. King.
[2] Evidence, Select Committee, 1844; Dr. Batt.
[3] Evidence, Select Committee, 1844; Dr. Wakeman.
[4] Evidence, Select Committee, 1844; Medical Officer of Greenwich and Dr. H. W. Rumsey.

advisable that these itinerant inspectors should examine the workhouses periodically. But Cornewall Lewis expressed the opinion of the administrators. Again he affirmed that there was no necessity for a medical commissioner to superintend the medical arrangements, and disagreed with all the schemes proposed. He confessed that he could not understand how any plans of medical superintendence, particularly those proposed by the associations, could be put into practice. He did not speak of the advantages that might accrue to the medical profession, but in reviewing the effects the scheme might have on the poor, he concluded: 'Whatever the mode of relief adopted, it will be inevitable, considering the extent of relief afforded, that a certain number of cases of neglect and misconduct on the part of the various officers concerned would appear.'

This was the final word of the Commissioners on the subject before they relinquished office. So the measure which would have had such great importance in beginning the removal of the medical services from the jurisdiction of the Poor Law authorities was never contemplated by the central authorities. The demands for this reform grew in intensity as the volume and complexity of the medical services increased. But it was only one item over which the profession struggled against the obscurantism and apathy of the administrators in an attempt to progress towards a comprehensive medical system.[1]

[1] See also 'Poor Law Medical Officers of England 1834–1871', Ruth G. Hodgkinson, *Journal of the History of Medicine and Allied Sciences*, 1956, Vol. XI, No. 3, pp. 299–338.

CHAPTER 3

Institutional Provision for the Sick—the Workhouse 1834–47

IT has been seen that despite the revolutionary proposals of the Poor Law Report of 1833, no change was recommended regarding the sick. As a deterrent the able-bodied were offered poor relief in the workhouse, whilst the current practice of giving outdoor relief to the sick was to be continued. They were to be given a small pittance, sometimes food or clothing, and the attendance of the Poor Law Medical Officer. The new principle of classification was to be adopted for the aged, infirm, and children, and it was hoped new institutions would be erected for them. But in general little attempt was made to implement this idea, and all were indiscriminately mixed together in the common workhouse. There was strange significance in the absence of any allusion to the institutional provision for the sick, when the Commissioners approved of the extension of hospital treatment for lunatics and the blind.

It was force of circumstance, and the ever-increasing pressure of pauperism, that reversed the process of segregating those who were to be assisted outside from those who were to receive institutional relief. For it was very quickly seen that workhouse accommodation was inadequate to house the army of healthy paupers, and that hospital treatment was better for the sick. Already in 1837 the Commissioners reported that accommodation could only be provided for 1 or 2 per cent of the destitute, and even in the worst pauperized districts, not more than 4–5 per cent of the able-bodied could be accepted in the workhouse. In 1843, 85 per cent of poor relief was domiciliary, and in 1847 the 603 Unions, despite the fact that they had 689 workhouses, could only give indoor assistance to 184,320 paupers, of whom 10 per cent were sick.

When the Poor Law administrators drew up the proposals for workhouse management in 1834, they failed to include anything in the nature of a hospital; only gradually did the exigency of the increased amount of pauper sickness force Guardians to provide separate accommodation for their patients. Charles Mott, who was to become an Assistant Commissioner and was previous to the Act 'contractor for the maintenance of the poor' at Lambeth, had given evidence to Chadwick in 1833 that although good provision for the sick poor might exist in large towns, it was wretched in the country. Therefore he had suggested the appropriation of a house for the sick of the district, all the parishes contributing together towards the expenditure. By this means he believed a hospital for the poor could be established without any additional expense, the sick would be better treated, and the advantages of a medical school would be derived from it. But the Commissioners only stipulated that the sick were to have separate rooms, and added, that although care was to be taken to improve their health, their condition was to be rendered in all respects less desirable than that of those receiving domiciliary aid.[1] These sick wards were for inmates who fell ill, as the order was not intended for those admitted from their homes in a sick condition—there was no mention of a provision for this category.[2]

Gradually as it was found imperative to admit the destitute sick who had no one to attend them, or who lived in such filthy and insanitary houses that the Medical Officer found it impossible to give treatment, rooms in the workhouse were converted into sick wards, or annexes were built haphazardly and without design. Then, when no device could squeeze the necessary room into the workhouse, Guardians acquired neighbouring houses for their infirmary. It was not until the 'sixties, when the makeshift devices of the preceding generation were found intolerable and utterly inadequate, that attention was paid to the special requirements of the sick.

The Poor Law doctors did much to encourage institutional treatment, and in some Unions they fought a constant campaign to have patients removed to the workhouse. The economic argument used was that the poor rates could be reduced by curing the sick more quickly, and this could be achieved by the superior treatment obtainable in the institution. The doctor, more than anyone else, was witness to the evil consequences of the bad social conditions of his locality, and he realized the necessity of removing a patient from its disease-breeding influences, and from the ill-nourished family which would share any extras ordered. A surgeon of Poplar described the miserable homes—often without furniture—and the squalor amidst which the Irish lived, and also pointed out that the poor had no nurses to attend them.[3] At an inquest held on a death from consumption at the Stroud workhouse, the Medical Officer gave evidence that the woman had been culpably neglected by her father. She had been given the minimum of food, and the home was horribly filthy, so that the doctor had had to remove her to the workhouse, although she was beyond medical aid before she was admitted.[4]

In 1840 the central authorities, commenting on the death of a boy whose father had been in receipt of outdoor-relief, said that 'illness was likely to be more quickly cured with the advantages of superior cleanliness, and the better regulated warmth and ventilation, of appropriate rooms or sick ward' of the workhouse, together with 'superior nursing,

[1] This was reiterated in 1840. 'The modern workhouse furnishes the mode . . . consistent with humanity of making the condition of the pauper less desirable than that of the independent labourer.' Official Circular, June 1840.
[2] Memorandum of essentials to be observed in the arrangement and discipline of workhouses, No. 1. Minutes of the Poor Law Commissioners, 1834: sixteen clauses but none mentioned medical attention.
[3] The Medical Officer, giving evidence to the Select Committee in 1844, reiterated the need for trained nurses in Poplar.
[4] Poor Law Commissioners' Correspondence, February 1837.

148

dietary and doctoring there possible', and that where there was a likelihood of outdoor relief or other family income being unwisely applied, it was 'better to relieve by admission to the workhouse'. This was the first proposal of the Commissioners for alternate sick relief, but it was not embodied in an order, for they did not contemplate that the sick should be received in the workhouse as part of their definite policy. In 1840 they supported an abortive government bill for the establishment of district infirmaries, but these were for the infirm and not for the sick,[1] and two years later they reminded the Guardians that they had the power to send the sick, deaf, dumb, and blind to hospitals outside the Unions.[2] Apart from this, no further mention was ever made of the last two categories of infirm.

But the sick themselves were loth to enter the workhouse, for they were aware of the conditions which existed in the old institutions. The squalor, filth, neglect, and cruelty had become proverbial, and had been given poetic expression in Crabbe's 'Village' of 1783. These still existed in the early years of the new Poor Law, and Dr. Kay described the workhouse in his area (Norfolk and Suffolk) in a report to the Poor Law Commissioners in 1836:

> The parochial mismanagement appeared in concentrated impurity in that receptacle of age, vice, disease and infirmity, the parish poorhouse. These houses I generally found to be almost ruinous structures of lath and plaster, built without design and totally destitute of convenience. . . . In the interim, the aged and infirm, and infants promiscuously mingled with the sturdy able-bodied paupers, idiots and sick, in groups which presented to the eye only a picture of common misery or depravity. In such houses the aged and infirm were tormented by their co-mates in want; the sick were left to waste the remnant of their lives with little care or sympathy, the able-bodied pauper lounged in listless apathy with the idiot over the fire. The sexes could scarcely be said to be separated at night in the miserable, and ill arranged apartments. Children had no school, but marauded the neighbouring fields. The rest of the mass, festered in idleness and vacancy.

That the Commissioners desired to remedy such affairs is obvious from the detailed rules they made for the regulation of the workhouses. The sick entering the institutions came to be dealt with as a class by themselves, and in 1842 the Commissioners reported,

> we have in several cases when the arrangements for the accommodation of the sick appeared defective, strongly urged the necessity of erecting wards for that special purpose, and we are happy to say that our representations have in some instances been acted on, and an increase in the means of separating paupers as may be suffering from disease has been provided by the Guardians.[3]

The Assistant Commissioners were detailed to watch the state of the workhouses, but by

[1] Official Circular, June 1840.
[2] Eighth Annual Report.
[3] Eighth Annual Report.

1847 each had an average of seventy-one Unions and parishes and seventy-eight work-houses under his superintendence, so that it was scarcely possible for them to attend the Board of Guardians weekly meeting or inspect the workhouses of every Union more than once every six months.

It was also hoped that inspection by Visiting Committees, which the Guardians were asked to appoint, would ensure tolerable conditions. These Committees had to keep records and report to the Guardians weekly on whether the workhouses were clean and well ventilated, and whether the established dietary was observed. They were supposed to examine the bedding and to point out any defects in the sanitary and building arrangements, as well as to find out whether the medical officer attended regularly, and whether the inmates were healthy and not overcrowded. If any sickness prevailed they were to give particulars, especially if any dangerous or highly infectious case of illness existed in the house. They were required to determine whether the children were vaccinated, properly nursed, and whether the nurses were efficient, also if any dangerous lunatics or idiots lived in the institution.

Another workhouse regulation stated that as soon as any pauper was admitted, he was to be placed in a probationary ward until he could be examined by the doctor, who was responsible for sending him to a particular ward. It was the master's duty to send for the Medical Officer immediately, should any pauper become suddenly ill, or whose illness became serious. A sick patient was to receive treatment and be maintained in the workhouse on the orders of the Medical officer, who was also responsible for individual diets. Therefore the master had really no jurisdiction over the sick; control was left entirely to the doctor. The doctor was expected to attend the workhouse one or more hours a day and to keep separate records of his patients, periodically furnishing reports to the Guardians.[1] He was not entitled to extra remuneration for operations performed in the workhouse, and his continued attendance there after a severe surgical case usually formed the most burdensome part of his extra services. Either from motives of economy, or because they realized it was necessary to the health of the patient, the Guardians generally sent all surgical cases to the workhouse, or sometimes to the local hospital if one existed. Only a doctor, and not a Relieving Officer could decide whether a sick person was well enough to be removed into the workhouse. The question was tentatively asked whether a doctor might not have a pecuniary interest after the Order of 1842, in not transferring the sick to the workhouse, and often 'extra' fees collected by surgeons for operations performed in the homes of the poor were quite high in the 'forties.

Under the workhouse rules the ordinary welfare of sick paupers was the responsibility of the matron, and she had to ensure that the pauper nurses carried out the instructions of the doctor. Any pauper, including young girls and aged and infirm women, could be employed as nurses in any of the sick wards. Their duties consisted in attending sick and

---

[1] The report books of the workhouse Medical Officer were similar to those of the District Medical Officer. Registers were to be kept stating name, age, disease of patient, the treatment and 'extras' given, and the days attended, with any 'observation'.

lying-in women and administering medicines; they were to take care that a light was kept burning all night in the wards; and they were to inform the Medical Officer of any defects which they might observe in the arrangements. But as the Commissioners omitted to lay down any rules either for the training of nurses or as to the nature of their character and education, it is difficult to imagine how they hoped to create an efficient service. The nurses were to receive no payment, and the case of one of the London parishes paying a total of £2 9s. 3d. a week for forty nurses was unique at the time.[1] St. Leonard's, Shoreditch, had spent £135 a year for nurses and servants in the workhouse in 1832 and 1834—but after these years their account books give no further mention of this item until 1854.[2]

The sick were generally the only inmates of the workhouse who were allowed visitors, and that they were to be granted this privilege was reiterated in a lengthy circular from the Commissioners to the Guardians in 1844.[3] Other paupers had to receive permission first, and also to converse with their friends in a separate room in the presence of the master or matron, 'to prevent visits for improper purposes'. It was through the statements of these visitors that gross scandals were often revealed, although in this early period no organized workhouse visiting society existed, and the allegations made by the illiterate poor relatives and friends of the paupers were discountenanced or never investigated. Detailed rules were also laid down by the Poor Law Commissioners for the diets to be given to workhouse inmates. In 1834 elaborate inquiries had been made, and in the absence of any knowledge of calorific values, it is remarkable how scientific the method of computing food values and their proportions was. The lengthy investigation of the Commissioners must have been one of the earliest of its kind. Eventually a choice of six schedules was offered the Guardians, slight relaxation being made in the principle of national uniformity so that diets could vary somewhat according to the habits and requirements of the locality. An average quantity of 161 oz. of food was to be allowed weekly (theoretically)—a larger amount than that enjoyed by the independent agricultural labourer (122 oz.) or the industrial worker. The sick, however, were always to be dieted according to the directions of the Medical Officers, but the food the able-bodied received in the workhouse was necessarily connected with the medical side of poor relief. For the diet affected the health of inmates, many of whom must have developed deficiency diseases, as no fresh vegetables and little fat were given to them. Soup and broth was given *ad nauseam*, but it was only after a few years had elapsed that regulations were instituted to determine their content. Adulteration, such as adding soda to the tea, was also resorted to.

The inferior food, coupled with the hard work exacted from the able-bodied (they were *work*-houses) must have left the health of many impaired, so that they were more liable to contract any disease introduced into the workhouse. In times of epidemic, the Poor Law Commissioners issued orders for more solid diets to be given, and they tried to prevent

---

[1] Charles Mott, Report on Middlesex and Surrey, Second Annual Report.
[2] Abstract of Accounts relative to Poor Rates, Board of Guardians Records, St. Leonard's, Shoreditch (1830–63).
[3] Circular Letter, re Article 25 of Workhouse Rules, October 1844.

scandals, such as that connected with the Bridgwater Union, where all the inmates were ill with diarrhoea because milk was replaced by oatmeal gruel.[1]

Punishments meted out in the workhouse often took the form of withholding tea and sugar for a week or two from the recalcitrants. Therefore in 1847 the General Consolidated Order stated that no pauper under medical care, or person over 60, or pregnant or nursing women, were to be punished by an alteration in diet, or by confinement, unless the Medical Officer had previously certified in writing that no injury to health would ensue. The doctor could also suggest any modification regarding the diminution of punishment, if he thought the health of the able-bodied would suffer. The Commissioners tried to safeguard the health of the inmates of the workhouses in another way, for by an Order issued in 1846, bone-crushing and stone-breaking were prohibited. In the past a certificate had been required from the Medical Officer to state no injury to the health of the pauper would follow from being thus employed, and by the General Rule of 1 January 1847 it was totally prohibited.

If the instructions of the Commissioners to the Boards of Guardians and workhouse officials had been carried out, and the duties listed obeyed, the condition of the sick pauper in the institutions would not have been much worse than that of the poorest independent labourer. Over a period of years minute details were recommended—from the daily cooking and distribution of food, to the general inspection of wards and their cleanliness—so that by the time these were collected into the General Consolidated Order of 1847, the theory governing institutional medical relief was relatively humane, if allowances are made for the ideas prevalent at the time. This Order remained the basis of the rules regulating the work of Poor Law officers until the end of the century.

But practice differed throughout the country. As in every branch of poor relief, the local incidence of pauperism, the prevalence of disease, and the attitude of the Guardians as to how retrenchment could best be achieved, all varied, and caused divergent policies and administrations. There was national uniformity in so far as the workhouse was the only publicly provided medical institution for the pauper, but actual experience varied with each Union.

There were forty-four workhouses in London and within a 5-mile radius. The four in the Stepney Union had no infirmaries attached at this time, but there were convalescent wards. Together the workhouses held 1,220 inmates, and in one year an average of 1,774 sick, as well as forty midwifery cases, were treated there, including 261 patients constantly on the sick list. This compared with over 7,000 ill paupers who received outdoor medical relief. There was an establishment at Mile End which consisted of a number of old buildings, a detached portion of which was set aside for the fever cases of the Union. An attempt had been made in the workhouses to segregate the sick, but great inconvenience was experienced in classifying them. The Chairman of the Guardians realized the great disadvantage of the absence of separate infirmaries, and constantly agitated for them. The

[1] John Bowen, *The new poor law—the Bridgwater case*, 1839.

Medical Officers urged the Board to make representations to the Poor Law Commissioners, for it was felt that such provision would not only be a humane consideration for the sick but also be a measure of true economy.[1]

In Whitechapel both workhouses were old. The infirmaries were, according to the doctors very imperfect, and as there were no detached wards, every room in the house more or less formed a sick ward. There was no classification of patients, and no suitable place to accommodate infectious diseases. The Spitalfields workhouse was regarded as healthy because it had few inmates, but the other, Christchurch, was overcrowded, and there was a much greater prevalence of disease. Here some of the wards were underground and the ceilings were so low that the rooms were only $6\frac{1}{2}$ feet in height. It contained a ward for casual fever patients, but it was also occupied by imbeciles, idiots, and lunatics, many of whom therefore caught fevers. In 1839, 700 patients were treated in the workhouse; in 1840—830; in 1841—731; in 1842—649; and in 1843—577. A doctor was employed full-time to attend the institution, for which he was paid £150 a year with no 'extras'. Dr. Southwood Smith in his famous Report of 1838[2] observed the extreme deficiency in the space, ventilation, and drainage of the workhouses. In the larger workhouse, he had discovered that of the 154 girls residing in the institution, 89 had recently been attacked with fever. On examining the dormitary 'my wonder ceased. In a room 88 feet long, $16\frac{1}{2}$ feet wide and 7 feet high . . . all these children, together with four women who had charge of them slept.' The beds were close together, and never less than four children occupied a bed. The ventilation in the room was bad, and therefore, Smith said, the outbreak of fever was inevitable. In another establishment nearby, the Jews' Hospital, very similar conditions, with the same results appertained, until adequate ventilation was installed, since when fever had never once been epidemic. Smith was also struck by the pale and unhealthy appearance of the children in the infant nursery, where twenty-three slept in one small room, seldom leaving it for air and exercise. He criticized two wards where two fever patients occupied one bed, which in themselves were far too close together. The ventilation in the room was so bad that it was dangerous for anyone to enter it, and most injurious to the sick. Smith found not a single bath in the workhouse, the privies were in a filthy state, and the whole place imperfectly drained. And yet before he went over the workhouse the condition there had always been represented to him as being excellent in all respects.

The West Ham Union workhouse held nearly 600 paupers, and an infirmary was provided to house forty people, as well as two small detached rooms to hold ten. As there were no convalescent wards, the Medical Officer kept his patients as long as he could in the infirmary, before they were moved into the other parts of the house. He complained to the Guardians that although this was supposed to be one of the model institutions, when it

---

[1] Select Committee, 1844.

[2] Report on Some of the Physical Causes of Sickness and Mortality to which Poor are particularly exposed and which are capable of removal by Sanitary Regulations exemplified in the present condition of Bethnal Green or Whitechapel, as ascertained on a personal inspection by Southwood Smith, M.D., physician to London Fever Hospital, May 1838.

was full, people with pulmonary complaints had to go into rooms where the able-bodied were picking oakum. There was a separate ward for the infirm and chronics, fitted to hold forty-eight paupers, and in this Union, the Guardians, and not the Medical Officer held the authority to define who was to be put in this ward. This practice had been adopted because patients might be ill from year to year, and never come under the doctor's care, for according to workhouse rules, it was the Medical Officer's duty to visit the sick regularly, but not the aged or infirm. From 1836 to 1843 an average of 639 patients were treated in the workhouse, the numbers having risen to over 800 by 1843, some costing the Union as much as 6s., 8s., 10s., or even 20s. a week, and the average was 2s.–3s. The sick in the West Ham Union Infirmary enjoyed an elaborate diet scale, Table 3.1

TABLE 3.1
West Ham Union Infirmary—Diet Scale

	Full Diet	*Half Diet*	*Low Diet*	*Fever Diet*
Breakfast	1 pt. milk porridge, bread and butter.	1 pt. milk porridge or $\frac{1}{2}$ oz. coffee, $\frac{1}{2}$ oz. sugar; bread and butter.	$\frac{3}{4}$ pt. milk porridge or $\frac{1}{2}$ oz. coffee, $\frac{1}{2}$ oz. sugar.	1 pt. milk porridge or $\frac{1}{2}$ oz. coffee, $\frac{1}{2}$ oz. sugar.
Dinner	$\frac{1}{2}$ lb. meat, $\frac{1}{2}$ lb. potatoes and bread and beer.	$\frac{1}{4}$ lb. meat, $\frac{1}{2}$ lb. potatoes and bread and beer.	1 pt. milk arrow-root, rice or sago, and bread.	1 pt. broth, 6 oz. potatoes and bread.
Supper	bread, butter, beer.	bread, butter, beer.	bread, butter, gruel.	bread, butter, gruel.
Daily allowance per patient.	1 pt. milk porridge, 14 oz. bread, $\frac{1}{2}$ lb. meat, $\frac{1}{2}$ lb. potatoes, $1\frac{1}{2}$ pt. beer, $\frac{3}{4}$ oz. butter.	Above + 12 oz. bread, $\frac{3}{4}$ oz. butter, 1 pt. beer	Above + 10 oz. bread, $\frac{3}{4}$ oz. butter.	Above + 10 oz. bread, $\frac{3}{4}$ oz. butter.

Children under ten—half allowances.

Every article of diet or additional comfort ordered by the Medical Officer was always liberally attended to. The Chairman of the Union maintained that the poor had a decided right to the best medical treatment, for the sick were the most expensive, and 'the time saved in illness was beneficial to the parish'. He preferred the sick poor to enter the workhouse because they could obtain greater attention there, and remain under the constant supervision of the doctor. Arsenic and other dangerous and expensive medicines could not safely be prescribed for patients receiving domiciliary treatment, and in the workhouse they could also benefit from a special diet, which if it were ordered out of the house, might be eaten by the rest of a hungry family.[1]

[1] Evidence, Select Committee, 1844. W. C. Streatfield, Chairman, and J. T. Vallance, Medical Officer of the West Ham Union.

Poplar Union had a large house out of town where all severe cases of smallpox and typhus fever were removed, and a convalescent ward was also to be found there. Here too, the surgeon laid great stress on the sick in the workhouse receiving an adequate diet; for, he said, food was in many cases more important than medicines. In Bethnal Green, the children in the workhouse had their own space in the grounds for air and exercise, and conditions were very different from those in the old institution. The children here suffered from only two diseases—but two of the most serious—scrofula and spinal affections. The Jews of Bethnal Green looked after their own poor in the great Jewish Hospital there.

Another poverty-stricken area, with a population of 40,000, was East London Union. Here a workhouse was provided for 200 men, and another for 350 women and children— it is significant that the larger was for women. The average number of sick in the various sick wards amounted to forty or fifty, besides the many old and infirm. In normal times fifteen to twenty casual sick paupers were also admitted, but this was always greatly augmented by fever epidemics, when whole families would come in together. In 1844 a great influx into the female fever ward was reported, but only two deaths occurred because 'of the care and attention of the medical officer'. He attended the sick four times a week, and the infirm twice a week, but returned day or night on the slightest occasion. In these two workhouses there were no convalescent wards, but the doctor was at liberty to transfer the sick from one ward to another, the Guardians allowing him any accommodation he wished, giving him full responsibility to make any other arrangements necessary for the health of the patients.

Against such provisions, those offered by the Guardians of St. George the Martyr, Southwark, afforded a startling contrast. In 1836 Dr. Arnott reported on the conditions existing there[1]:

> Plastered walls and ceilings in need of repair, without conveniences for aged or infirm . . . without a distributed water supply . . . badly ventilated. . . . All the wards crowded by people who pass their whole time in them, eating, working, sleeping there . . . the sick wards are crowded by a mixture of persons—the merely infirm, and the others with various kinds and degrees of disease, without a probationary ward in which newcomers may be placed to be examined and cleansed, and to receive house-dress; without any separate room for a surgery in which operations, dressings, etc., may be properly performed . . . not well lighted . . . only wire grating instead of glass windows, and no fire. . . .

It was little wonder that Arnott recommended that the cheapest way of altering these conditions was to build an entirely new workhouse on a good plan. Alternatively, he recited a long list of suggestions for improvements, such as the reducing of the numbers in each ward, the provision of privies and suitable washing places, fires and furniture, and increased ventilation, and the erection of several additional wards. He concluded that to call

---

[1] Minutes, Poor Law Commissioners, 19 December 1836. H.O. Papers.

new workhouses 'Bastilles', whilst regarding the old ones which were being retained as 'the good old English poor house' was a curious perversion of language. No improvements had been made by 1844, for in that year the Medical Officer complained that the workhouse was in the most unhealthy part of the district, and that he had frequently made representations to the Guardians about it. The house, he said, was sometimes so overcrowded that beds had to be improvised on the floor, between other beds in the infirmary wards, and there was still no fever ward, so that infectious cases were mixed with the rest of the sick in general wards. In examining the Minutes of the Guardians there is never any evidence of alterations made in the workhouse either for the healthy or for invalids, and the apathy of the authorities was registered in the singularly few references to medical relief throughout their weekly reports.[1]

In 1846 the Paddington Board of Guardians submitted to the Commissioners a plan for a workhouse in which the sick wards were to form a separate building. But already by 1847, the Medical Officer declared that additional wards were necessary—two for sick cases, two for fever, and two for the insane.[2] Kensington was also constantly forced to squeeze additional accommodation for the sick into its workhouse. Here the Guardians seemed to be solicitous for the welfare of the patients; in 1845 for example, they authorized the fixing of two gauze-wire blinds as a protection against draughts, at the front and rear of an invalid carriage which they provided for conveying sick paupers to the workhouse.[3] St. George in the East, Middlesex, also purchased a light covered cart in 1847 for transporting patients to the Fever Hospital.[4]

Several of the London Unions and parishes in the 'forties jointly maintained institutions. The best known schemes were those relating to the Poor Law Schools such as Norwood and Tooting, but Unions such as Poplar, Bethnal Green, and Holborn came to an arrangement whereby their tubercular children were sent to Margate, where they were maintained in a private institution unconnected with the Margate Poor Infirmary. These arrangements were undertaken under the auspices of the central authorities, but there were also private combinations for various schemes regarding the sick, which unfortunately received only brief mention in the Guardians' records. The Stepney Union, St. George in the East, and Kensington formed a North-Eastern Metropolitan Asylums District, but as there are no statutory records the Guardians must have made private arrangements. In their Minutes they mentioned the contributions paid to the joint scheme, and also that there was a separate Board of Management. In 1847–48 an Exchequer Loan was alluded to for the building of a Sick Asylum at Mile End. For some unstated reason Gravesend also belonged to the North-Eastern Metropolitan Asylums District. After the early 'fifties records of it cease and it may have been dissolved. It was however an interesting precursor

[1] Noticed in the study of the Board of Guardians' Minutes (in the 1830s and 1840s) of this Union.
[2] Paddington Board of Guardians, Minutes, 1847.
[3] Kensington Board of Guardians, Minutes.
[4] St. George in the East. (This Union supplied the London Hospital with cadavers from the workhouse for the purpose of anatomy.)

of the arrangements sanctioned and encouraged by the central authorities after the Act of 1867.

The 'forties saw general improvement in the provision for the sick in the workhouses, and this in most instances took the shape of additional accommodation and a better classification of patients according to the nature of their illness. Rural Unions began their reforms later, but some, such as Missenden in Buckingham, immediately built a new workhouse in which separate sick wards for men and women were provided, with special beds and fireplaces, and where patients could be guarded from interruption and noise. It was stated that these wards were preserved in the highest state of order and cleanliness, and the aged, especially the sick, were given every care and attention. The Curate described the diet as being far from luxurious, but sufficient to keep all the inmates in the best of health. The children looked better than any cottagers in the parish, and special attention was paid to the wants of the aged and the sick.[1] From Middlesex reports were received of good dietaries in the workhouses and that everything the Medical Officer ordered was supplied.[2] In some of the rural Unions in Suffolk, Kay (Shuttleworth) said, the diet of the sick was 'greatly excessive', and complained that charity beer was supplied to the female sick rooms twice a week and to the men's sick and aged rooms every night. Atchen Union in Shropshire, provided a separate ward for fifteen sick men and another for ten women, as well as a lying-in room for five. On the recommendation of the Workhouse Visiting Committee, a wash building and a new infirmary of two extra wards to be used for contagious cases, were erected in 1842.[3] In Eccleshall, Yorkshire, the Guardians appointed a woman in 1843 'to see that the women properly attended their sickly children, and those under two years'.[4]

Two eminent doctors were sent by the Commissioners to inquire into the state of the Sevenoaks Workhouse in the early 'forties. They found that the institution contained one general male sick ward and one general female sick ward, both sufficiently lighted, but poorly ventilated. They stated that the lying-in ward, only 12 ft. × 10 ft. in size, was ill-adapted for the purpose in area and accommodation. It was deficient in the supply of water and the ordinary necessary furniture, but one of the patients informed the investigators that the sheets were changed three times a fortnight, their clothing as frequently, and that the infants were supplied with two dozen napkins which were washed as often as necessary. A fire was also kept up all day and night. A minute adjoining room was occupied by the laundress (who acted as the midwife) and the woman next awaiting her confinement. The doctors only recommended that the lying-in ward should be furnished with a washstand and basin, more chairs, a pan to wash the child in, and be better supplied with water. And these demands were immediately complied with.[5]

[1] Pamphlet: 'Practical Results of Workhouse system in the parish of Great Missenden, Bucks' 1834, by the Curate.
[2] Poor Law Commissioners' Records, January 1838.
[3] Board of Guardians' Minutes, 1842, Atchen Union.
[4] Board of Guardians' Minutes, 1843, Eccleshall Union.
[5] Report Drs. Rigby and Henry Hancock, 'State of Sevenoaks Workhouse, 1842'.

But it was in the large provincial industrial cities that improvements came, and were forced to come, more quickly. Liverpool, the vast insensate conurbation, with its filth and congestion, provided the greatest amount of accommodation for the sick poor. This was probably because the city, with a population of nearly a quarter of a million, formed the largest single destitution authority in the country,[1] and here also voluntary hospitals offered medical relief on a very large scale. The main building of the workhouse contained seven wards, and some attempt was made to classify the patients. There were separate male and female surgical wards, containing sixteen beds in each, male and female medical wards of nineteen beds in each, and three wards for cases of venereal disease with four beds in each. Another part of the workhouse provided a lying-in ward and a sick nursery for infants, the former with nine single and the latter with ten double beds. An ophthalmic ward containing ten double beds and an additional lock ward for women with twelve beds were also provided. In the building appropriated to the children there was a ward for sick boys under the age of 14, containing fourteen double beds, under the immediate supervision of a paid schoolmistress. Altogether the institution contained 248 beds, sixty-five of which were double, and provision was also made for forty old and infirm patients in another part of the building. No paid nurses were employed, but in 1843 it was recommended that each medical department of the workhouse should have a paid superintending nurse, and that a midwife should be engaged. The salaries suggested were £15–20 a year, plus board and lodging.

The Liverpool destitution authorities also provided a fever hospital, and this, with the sick wards in the workhouse, was under the management of an Honorary Medical Board, consisting of two physicians and one surgeon. This Board gave the general directions, whilst stipendiary officers were responsible for all details connected with the treatment that the doctors might suggest. The Poor Law Commissioners however informed the Liverpool Vestry that the honorary medical staff could not be held to account for the medical relief given, the sole responsibility lay with the paid medical officers. But as the supervisory body, the Medical Board in 1844 proposed several reforms, all of which were adopted by the Poor Law authorities without alteration. They recommended that a resident house surgeon should be appointed at a salary of £150, to be responsible for the efficient management of the medical department of the workhouse, and he was to have an assistant, also resident. In addition a full-time apothecary was to be engaged at a salary of £105. He was to be subordinate to the house surgeon, and act as dispenser, cupper and dresser, and his post was to be permanent, subject to good conduct. The Medical Board also advocated that a nurse should be made responsible for supervising the whole medical department. She was to receive £30 a year, board and lodging, and was to be intelligent, active, and experienced.

Manchester, the second largest of the chaotic urban complexes, with a population of 170,000 in 1841, maintained 1,261 paupers in its vastly overcrowded workhouse. The sick wards consisted of two male surgical and two female surgical wards, with separate kitchens,

[1] Still under the local Poor Act.

accommodating together forty-eight patients; two male medical wards for thirty patients with a separate kitchen, and three female medical wards for forty patients, also with a kitchen, nurses' room, servants' room, and bathroom; an old men's hospital, consisting of three dry, comfortable cellars and a kitchen, adapted for fifty-four; and an old women's hospital—six dry, comfortable cellars, but where there was no day room, holding forty-eight. There was also a male 'itch ward' for twelve patients, and a boys' for twelve, and two female 'itch wards' for thirty. A boys' and girls' 'sore head ward' and a day room for eighty were also provided. The lying-in ward consisted of two rooms for eight people and there was also a children's sick ward for eighteen. In the medical department there was also a large surgery, conveniently situated so that out-patients could attend it. The Union engaged a resident surgeon for the institution, and three honorary consulting physicians and three honorary surgeons also attended. 1,600 patients were seen annually at the work-house hospital, generally all acute and chronic cases.

In 1841 the Guardians of Stockport proposed the erection of a new and larger work-house costing £8,000 in which there was to be a 'commodious infirmary, detached from the house, adequate to the great variety of diseases continually occurring in such an establishment'. To build a new, separate medical institution was indeed an innovation in the 'forties, and this was the forerunner of the Poor Law hospitals, which it was found necessary to build all over the country a generation later.[1]

In 1843 Bradford converted a sick ward out of the 'idle ward', and two years later provided a fever ward.[2] The Bradford *Observer* reported a Guardians' meeting held in 1843, at which it was stated that there were so many sick inmates in the institution 'that it was more like a hospital than a workhouse', and five years later the same paper remarked that the workhouse was 'at present more like a lying-in hospital than a poor house, in consequence of many young women coming to live in, three months before childbirth'.

The Workhouse Committee in Preston recommended in 1841, that certain rooms in the workhouse be set aside 'for women labouring under a certain disease'. As a result of this, women from outlying workhouses, suffering from venereal disease were sent to Preston, to be maintained with those 'similarly situated, [and kept] as much apart as practicable by day and night from other inmates'. Pregnant women were also removed from other district workhouses to Preston, and all lying-in women were in future to be confined in the town's House of Recovery. In 1846 a nurse was employed there, to assist the matron.[3] But conditions in Preston were not as salubrious as these alterations suggested, for the disgraceful state of the workhouse called for the interference of the Commissioners. The Assistant Poor Law Commissioner for Lancashire reported that he had on several occasions reminded the Board of Guardians of the 'discreditable and neglected state of the workhouses ... a far greater number of paupers are crowded into the separate workhouses than the medical officers have certified them of being capable of accommodating with reference to the health

[1] Report of Board of Guardians of Stockport Union, 4 March 1841.
[2] Minutes, Board of Guardians, Bradford (Webb MSS.).
[3] Minutes, Board of Guardians, Preston (Webb MSS.).

of the inmates'. But the order of the Commissioners requesting the Guardians to limit admissions was ignored, and the Board also postponed the consideration of a further order, directing a continuance of the scheme whereby the several workhouses in the neighbourhood were to be appropriated to different classes of inmates and sick.[1]

The improvements made in the 'forties only throw light on the deplorable conditions which existed in the workhouses in these years. There were far more scandals to report than reforms, and an overwhelmingly greater number of disreputable institutions than good ones. The eulogies of the Commissioners can be of no account in the light of reported experience. In the first year of the operation of the Act the Master of St. Pancras Workhouse told Chadwick that if the independent poor went into the institution and saw how well the paupers lived, it would be difficult to get rid of them. Therefore he advocated a separate institution for the sick. Also the comforts patients received during their illness induced them to remain in the workhouse a long time. Praise for the poor-houses came also in the Commissioners' Third Annual Report. They stated how amply the destitute were provided with food and clothing, that cleanliness was a matter of great consideration, and that they received the utmost attention when necessary from the Medical Officer.

> Their general comforts most indubitably exceed by far what could possibly be enjoyed elsewhere . . . it is admitted that there are, nay must be, individual cases of hardship . . . and what great measure was or can be adopted or enacted without falling heavily on some? Still, though doubtless such there be, it cannot amount to cruelty or destitution, since there is a workhouse open to all needing relief.

Neither can the reports of the Boards of Guardians be trusted to give an accurate description of conditions. For example, year after year the Bradfield (Yorks) workhouse committee stated: 'House is well aired', 'inmates all healthy and clean', and that 'no separation of classes is required'. Yet in the 1840s questions were asked why there were no fever wards; so these were added in the following year, and in 1842 general improvements were planned for the workhouse. The sick were to be removed from the existing crowded and unhealthy wards, women in labour and suffering from diseases were to be treated in 'an airy and well constructed infirmary', with a separate lying-in ward, and a nurse was to be appointed. The children also were to have spacious and airy rooms and yards, which the Guardians hoped would prevent a recurrence of epidemics. The aged and infirm were to be transferred to another workhouse, where they would be wholly separated from the able-bodied and enjoy greater comfort.

In Croydon, the Medical Officer suggested the removal of the whole infirmary. He complained that whereas the workhouse was situated on a hill, and was very clean, dry, and healthy, the infirmary had been built on the lowest part of the grounds. Here, 'from the exclusion of air and numerous cesspools and drains under and about it', it was in a 'very

[1] Preston workhouse, eighteen boys slept in three beds, wetted them so each night that it went through the bedding and the wooden bases of the beds on to the floor underneath. Assistant Commissioner Power said the large pans were not emptied for weeks. Also a room on the first floor was used for a mortuary, and this had no ventilation!

improper situation, and predisposes its inmates to typhus[1] fever, which at all times is of long duration, and in some instances fatal'. The doctor asserted without the slightest hesitation, that if the infirmary were in a healthy situation, the annual expenditure would be greatly diminished. He had been reporting this to the Board of Guardians since 1841 without ever having received a reply. Several times he had also complained to them of the smallness of the lying-in ward, which was so overcrowded that the women had to be moved to an adjoining ward after two or three days instead of lying-in for fourteen days. The infants also were far too weak to live in the 'able-bodied' room. The Medical Officer warned that if an infectious fever, [puerperal] to which lying-in women were subject, were to break out, the result would be very serious. He also directed attention to the bad drainage, and the prevalence of fever in the infirmary. Every case 'that goes there—fracture, ulceration, or any other disease, is almost certain of being in there much longer than it should be, because of the low character of the fever proceeding from the causes before stated'. The old building had been in a healthy situation, but no improvement had been made to the new one since its erection in 1838.[2] None of the remonstrances of the doctor were heeded, and the case throws light on the grave anomaly in the Poor Law. For, whilst the Commissioners exhibited great anxiety to remove the causes of fever and epidemic diseases, they could not confer any power on the Medical Officer to order their removal. They could only 'desire' the doctor to draw the attention of the Board to the want of drainage and ventilation, which remonstrance the Guardians were at liberty to ignore, should they not realize the economy which would result from prompt action.

It is a moot point whether diseases were not unnecessarily spread within the workhouses through the unhygienic conditions and overcrowding in them. In Liverpool the Honorary Medical Board complained that the surgery was situated too close to the receiving ward and 'itch ward' for safety. In 1834 there was a serious outbreak of cholera in the Leeds workhouse. Forty cases of malignant cholera were reported, of which eighteen died, and fifty ordinary cases, which recovered. The Governor himself succumbed, and some of the members of the workhouse board—yet there were few cases in the town. The Medical Officer reported:

> Of the origin of this fatal epidemic within the walls of the establishment we do not presume to offer an opinion; there is no evidence of its having been introduced by contagion; but whatever may have been its origin, its very rapid diffusion in its most aggravated form during the first few days . . . is sufficiently explained by the fact of the extremely crowded state of the workhouse at the time the disease broke out.[3]

He pointed out that 253 people lived in an area of 271 square yards, surrounded by very high walls which allowed little air to reach the building.

The Times and the *Standard* both published reports in 1839 that in the workhouse of

---

[1] What we should now call typhoid fever; the distinction between these two different diseases was only becoming clear to doctors at this time.

[2] Select Committee, 1844. G. Bottomley, Medical Officer in Croydon for thirty-three years.

[3] Evidence, Dr. Kay (Shuttleworth), Select Committee, 1838.

Wimborne and Cranborne (Dorset) mothers with their children slept three in a bed, despite the spread of smallpox in the institution. In one very small room there were five beds for thirteen people, five of whom had smallpox. No nurse was appointed to attend them, and no precautions were taken to prevent its further progress. It was ironical that the Commissioners congratulated the Guardians on their great humanity and remarkable promptitude in putting thirteen in five beds in one room, because by this means they separated the sick from the less moral class of female inmates of the workhouse! The article continued that smallpox had been brought into the institution by a child, and had spread from there to the village, for the schoolroom had been fitted up as a hospital, into which thirteen smallpox patients were moved. The Assistant Poor Law Commissioner inquiring into the allegations of the newspapers regarded this temporary institution as admirable, 'it was airy and comfortable, and the patients wanted for nothing, and not a life was lost there'. All the paupers were vaccinated as soon as possible, and two nurses were appointed to the temporary hospital making eight in all for the Union institutions.[1] (Here the Medical Officer was condemned to attend 195 paupers for £10 a year—the barber receiving the same sum!)

What the Commissioners failed to realize was the danger of diseases from the workhouse spreading into the neighbourhood, and this must have been common at the time—no less than from the gaols at an earlier period. For with the unsuitable conglomeration of establishments, the absence of cleanliness within the workhouse, and the large number of casuals who undoubtedly carried infection in and out, much disease must have been spread into surrounding areas, where the insanitary conditions themselves formed fertile breeding grounds. On the one hand, cross-infection within the workhouse must have been rife when the first principles of hygiene were not understood, and on the other, epidemic diseases must certainly have been communicated between the workhouse and the neighbourhood. But the Poor Law medical services existed to cure and not to prevent sickness.

It was not until 1847 that a change of attitude can be detected in the writings of the Commissioners. Lamenting the great increase in the number of fever cases in many Unions, particularly in the north, they pointed out the necessity for providing temporary accommodation for the reception of the Irish poor, and others suffering from fever, and later congratulated the Guardians who 'for the most part have met the evil readily and cheerfully'. The Commissioners were able to conclude their term of office with the report that

> our special attention has been directed to the defective conditions of the infirmaries and the sick wards in many workhouses, and have great satisfaction in stating that, under the advice of the Assistant Commissioners, we believe great improvements in the accommodation and separation of these classes will be found to have been effected in the course of the summer.[2]

[1] Letter, Poor Law Commissioners to Lord John Russell—from Poor Law Commissioners Correspondence, 1839. These conditions existed in the Union which was on Lord Shaftesbury's doorstep!
[2] Fourteenth Annual Report.

Such was the force of circumstance, and the salutary result of an outbreak of epidemic cholera!

Although the Guardians before 1847 took little interest in Public Health reform, it had been suggested to them ten years previously, that they should at least make some provision to alleviate the evil consequences of this neglect, in the establishment of hospitals for epidemic diseases. In 1838 Southwood Smith, in his Report, recommended that the insanitary state of London and the other large cities rendered the erection of one or two hospitals on however large a scale for the reception of fever cases exclusively, insufficient to meet the demand. Therefore, to prevent the spread of the epidemic, he advocated that Unions should combine and provide hospitals specially for the paupers, which would then make one large fever hospital sufficient for the requirements of the rest of the community —an illustration of the uneven distribution of fever cases among classes. The Report of Arnott and Kay in the same year emphasized the importance of isolation and institutional treatment for contagious diseases. In commenting on the reluctance of the poor to enter the workhouse when suffering from typhus, the Medical Officers of Bermondsey stated that they had several times urged the Guardians to consider the possibility of insisting on the compulsory removal of every inmate from an infected house until it had been properly cleansed and fumigated. They had experienced great difficulty in persuading the sick to be conveyed to the workhouse or hospital before the last stage of typhus had set in, and then it was often too late for treatment. They related how they had to attend every member of a family of fourteen one after the other. As each contracted the disease he was sent to the workhouse, and as soon as he was cured and allowed to return home, so another member took his place. If the Guardians had insisted on earlier removal 'the parish would in all probability have been saved the expense of maintaining them'.

No doubt the poor refused institutional treatment not only because of the stigma attached to their becoming paupers thereby, but also because of the conditions they knew to exist in the workhouse. For Guardians had taken no pains to conceal that they were following a policy of deterrence in offering relief in the workhouse. And although the sick were to be dealt with more humanely as a separate class, the treatment they received and the conditions under which they lived in it, were often detrimental to speedy recovery.

From many Unions instances of gross cruelty were reported. In one case the evidence taken before a Coroner was published in a newspaper and later reprinted in pamphlet form. This was the story of 'Mary Wilden, a victim to the new Poor Law, or the Malthusian and Marcusian system exposed'. The *Sheffield Idris* reported that the woman's body had been found in Worksop Union workhouse in an emaciated condition, and was disfigured by several very deep ulcers, and a number of bruises on her arms, legs, chest, and back. She had suffered from epilepsy and dropsy. The sister of the deceased said that Mary Wilden had been the victim of great cruelty, she had been beaten and kept in a filthy state by an Irish woman—herself a pauper—who had to take care of her. 'Irish Molly' had even beaten her because she could not eat her breakfast quickly enough. The sister took her out of the workhouse a week before she died, and stated she had not been seen by a doctor for a week. She had wounds on both sides of her thighs with her chemise sticking to them, as well as open wounds on her shoulder. She was said to have been covered with thousands of lice of three kinds. At the inquiry all cruelty was denied, and it was declared that the wounds were either bedsores or obtained by falls during her fits. The Medical Officer stated that he attended her continuously and often saw her fall down in the yard. Evidence for the deceased maintained that the surgeon saw her only twice during her fifteen weeks' illness and never gave her any medicine and never dressed any of her numerous wounds—of which a horrible description was offered. The woman was only forty but she was said to have looked over seventy. The verdict returned was death from natural causes, and not because the woman was hurt through any violence or injury.[1]

In Middlesex, a minister who was also a magistrate appeared before the Commissioners to report complaints he and other magistrates had received regarding the workhouse of Harrow. He had inspected it, and found it in a filthy and ill-regulated condition, with three people on an average sleeping in a bed. He had also discovered a sick girl of fifteen who was subject to fits, almost naked, and showing evidence of great neglect.[2] In the Basford Union workhouse an inspector found the sheets had not been changed for thirteen weeks, shirts for four, and stockings from two to ten months.

Engels made some investigations into workhouse conditions, and wrote in 1844[3] that in the Bactum workhouse (Suffolk) the nurse was a feeble-minded woman, and took care of the sick accordingly. If her patients were restless at night or tried to get up, she tied them down to save her the trouble of sitting up all night. One patient was found dead, bound in this way. Engels also wrote a tirade against the terrible food given to the inmates, maintaining that it was much worse than that of criminals in prison. But his most gruesome story was the description of cruelty exercised in one workhouse, where a little boy passed through all the grades of punishment there meted out. He was first locked up in a damp, vaulted, narrow, lumber-room, then in the 'dog-hole' for three days and nights, then in the tramp room, a 'stinking, disgusting, filthy hole, with wooden sleeping stalls, where an official in the course of his inspection found two other tattered boys shrivelled with cold', who had spent three days there. In the 'dog-hole' there were often seven, and in the tramp room, twenty men huddled together. Women were also placed in the dog-hole because they refused to go to church, one was even locked in four days while she was ill and receiving medical treatment.

In 1844 a Select Committee was held to investigate a case of neglect brought to the notice of the House of Commons by a petition of a schoolmaster.[4] He himself had been an

---

[1] Pamphlet sent to Poor Law Commissioners regarding charges made and Poor Law Commissioners' correspondence, 5 June 1839.

[2] Poor Law Commissioners' Records, 12 February 1835.

[3] F. Engels, *Conditions of the Working Class in England*, 1844.

[4] Thomas King gave a lengthy description to Sir John Walsham, the Assistant Poor Law Commissioner who was sent to conduct an inquiry. Although some of his statements were exaggerated many inmates corroborated King's statements. The report of this inquiry was reprinted in the First Report of the Select Committee on Medical Poor Relief, 22 May 1844.

inmate of the Woodbridge Union Workhouse in Suffolk, and had witnessed there 'the most heart-rending acts of cruelty, oppression, and neglect of the sick and other inmates of the establishment'. He stated that the poor were left to die in the night without care and attention, and under the most painful circumstances, yet Coroners' inquests were never held. Whilst he was in the workhouse, two men died a few hours after admittance, and in each case no Medical Officer had been sent for, nor was any notice of the sudden deaths communicated to the Coroner, although this was the law. Another patient was starved to death, because the nurse refused to give him the sago the doctor ordered as he was unable to swallow bread. The treatment of the sick children appeared to have been worse than that of the adults, for besides being neglected, they were also beaten when they complained. In 1840 a nurse beat a four-year-old orphan so violently that the child died eight hours later. She also caused another boy to lose the use of his limbs and later his life. The linen in the sick ward was changed only once a month, whatever the nature of the illness, and one candle was provided for a ward to last six days. All the patients had to wash themselves because the nurse was too lazy, and she also refused to do night duty.

It was the Andover Scandal of 1845, where the master of the workhouse starved his paupers to such an extent that they fought over the gristle and marrow in the half-putrid bones they had to crush, that led to the investigations into the work of the Poor Law Commissioners and the ultimate replacement of the fragile structure of the Board.

These instances are all from rural Union workhouses, and it was in them that the disgraceful conditions existed the longest. The buildings were never intended for the reception of the sick, and were only slowly, if ever, adapted to meet the requirements of an infirmary. Overcrowding was general, the water supply and sanitary accommodation often defective, and the separation of inmates or classification of patients was never undertaken to the extent that became imperative in the towns. Although rural workhouse medical aid was so unsatisfactory at this period, urban institutions were only beginning to become somewhat superior. Because the town institutions were situated in insalubrious neighbourhoods and were responsible for a large unhealthy population, the provision for the sick was bound automatically to be defective, especially when this was coupled with the Guardians' policy of reducing the poor rates. To ensure the latter they not only tried to restrict offering medical relief, but also showed unwillingness to undertake large expenditure for rebuilding or altering existing institutions.

Probably the best and worst conditions were to be found in the Metropolitan institutions. The Medical Officer of Bayswater complained that the workhouse was ill adapted for the sick, and that child inmates suffered extremely from the improper nursing arrangements. In St. Margaret's and St. John's, Westminster, frequent complaints were registered in the Minutes of the Governors and Directors as to the inadequate accommodation in the workhouse, the spreading of infectious diseases in it, and the tardiness with which medical relief was given. Also no separate room was set aside for lunatics. The Commissioners wrote incessantly to the Board asking for explanations, but the curt replies indicated that they were opposed to this interference. Therefore in 1846 an Assistant Commissioner was sent to inspect conditions in the institution, and he reported it to be considerably over-crowded. He recommended that 600 paupers should be the maximum admitted, and to this the Board of Governors retorted that they were 'competent to decide as to the number the House is capable of accommodating with suitable convenience, at all seasons and under any circumstance . . . and in this respect the Governors will, so long as the Board exists, exercise a just and reasonable discretion without reference to the control attempted to be exercised by the Commissioners'. Less resentment was expressed at the various letters received from the Commissioners regarding smallpox and cholera, and fairly active measures were taken for the prevention of diseases, and accommodation was provided for contagious cases.

A churchwarden of St. Martin-in-the-Fields also desired no interference from the Commissioners, because friction between those who favoured, and those who disagreed with, the parish coming under the new Poor Law caused the doctors' orders to be disobeyed. Through this, one of the paupers suffering from a severe attack of typhus had died in the workhouse, for the matron had not administered any of the medicines prescribed by the Medical Officer for him, and had also collected all the other medicines which had been prepared for various patients, so that they could not be used.[1]

In Marylebone, the Poor Man's Guardian Society held a meeting in January 1846 for the purpose of promoting sanitary improvements in the parish. The Committee wrote to the Commissioners recommending the necessity for holding an inquiry into the internal arrangements of the workhouse. One of the members of the society who had been an inmate for three years had made investigations, and reported on the bad conditions. There were over 2,000 inmates in the workhouse, including the infirmary wards, with no adequate washing facilities. In the women's convalescent wards for example, twenty-seven inmates washed their faces and hands in their chamber-pots, and many inmates had not had an overall wash for two to five years. The Medical Officer of St. Pancras also gave evidence to the Select Committee of 1844 on the barbarous conditions in the workhouse.

Engels also turned his critical gaze on conditions in the Metropolitan workhouses, where he discovered cruelties equal to those suffered in the rural workhouses. In St. Pancras an epileptic had died of suffocation during an attack in bed, because no one came to his relief. And in this workhouse, six to eight children were found sleeping in one bed. In Shoreditch a man was placed together with a fever patient who was violently ill, in a bed teeming with vermin; and in Bethnal Green workhouse, a woman six months' pregnant, was retained in the reception room with a two-year-old child for three weeks without being admitted to a ward, and 'without a trace of a bed, or means of satisfying the most natural wants'. The husband begged to have his wife released from this imprisonment, and for this 'insolence' he got 24 hours' imprisonment with bread and water.

Engels had similar stories from the provincial towns. In Stockport a man was brought before the magistrate for refusing to break stones because of his age and his stiff knees.

[1] Letter to the Poor Law Commissioners, 8 April 1835.

Although he offered to do the work for which he was physically capable, he was sentenced to two weeks on the treadmill. In Coventry workhouse a man with a severe wound in his shoulder was given no treatment and was set to work on the water pump using his sound arm. Because of his wound and his general debility he could not digest the workhouse food and no alternative nourishment was given him. As he grew weaker he complained and was brutally treated. When his wife tried to bring him her allowance of beer she was reprimanded and compelled to drink it herself in the presence of the female warder. Finally he was discharged and two days later died in Leicester workhouse, the surgeon at the inquest testifying to his death having been caused by neglect and starvation.

Because of the economic crisis in 1839 the numbers in the Nottingham workhouse increased so much that the Commissioners allowed outdoor relief to be given. But in the workhouse many deaths occurred necessitating inquests, and the verdict the Coroner gave on the deaths of the sick patients, was that the wards were not adapted to the number of persons required to live in them, and that it had been impossible to give treatment to all the sick. Because of these reports the Commissioners in 1841 invited Henry Hancock, an eminent surgeon of Charing Cross Hospital to investigate conditions in the Nottingham workhouse.[1] He found the institution far too overcrowded to be healthy for the inmates, who were sleeping three and four in a bed. There were two male sick wards, one containing only four beds, which previously was used as a tailor's shop and had very little ventilation, and the other which could only hold nine patients, had been formed out of the roof, with equally little ventilation. The women were provided with a ward appropriated to six syphilitic cases, which was described as being foul and close, and with two larger wards, badly ventilated and dirty, containing together nineteen beds. The 'foul' wards consisted of two very small rooms, one of which housed twelve children suffering from porrigo, and the other into which four men suffering from itch had been collected. Hancock wrote of these: 'it appears, cleanliness is not considered necessary in the treatment of these disorders'. The lying-in ward was too small and low, with insufficient light or ventilation. The beds were inconveniently small and very narrow, and although the bedding was clean and ample, the room was quite deficient in the necessary supply of warm water and furniture. There was no bath for infants and no convenience for washing patients. In fact, no accommodation was provided for washing in the whole of the workhouse, there was only a trough in each female and male ward, and the privies were situated in the middle of the wards, so that they were 'offensive and contaminated the air'.

In the sick wards patients suffering from rheumatism, pulmonary complaints, venereal disease, diseased limbs, epilepsy, and many other illnesses as well as lunatics, all lived together. And in the general wards men and women were found with bronchitis, consumption, paralysis, cataract, fever, haemorrhoids, and various infectious diseases, quite free to communicate them to the able-bodied. The general condition of the children Hancock reported to be by no means healthy:

[1] Report on the Nottingham Workhouse by Henry Hancock. Eighth Annual Report of the Poor Law Commissioners, 1842, Appendix 3.

The flesh, especially that of the girls, was flabby, their abdomens large, and their tongues bear evident signs of gastric irritations. A very large proportion of both girls and boys are of strumous[1] habit, which although not at present assuming an active form, still exists, predisposing them to disease, and rendering them unable to resist its attacks, or to bear the remedies necessary for their cure. These children require much more airy and better ventilated apartments than is at present allotted to them, and I would observe that during my experience as surgeon to one of the largest infirmaries for children in London, I never met with an instance in which so many children were collected in such offensive, close and badly ventilated apartments, as those which they now inhabit in the Nottingham workhouse.

The Medical Officer of the Union had frequently reported and complained about these conditions to the Guardians but to no avail. Hancock concluded his report:

I should ill perform my duty were I not in conclusion respectfully to urge the necessity of immediately adopting measures for ameliorating the condition of the inmates of the Nottingham Workhouse . . . and again to express my conviction that the present condition of that house is prejudicial to health, especially that of the children.

Similar reports were made on Chorley and York, and it was not surprising, therefore, that both doctors Rumsey, two years later, suggested to the Select Committee of 1844 that it would be advisable for the workhouses to be inspected from time to time. Impartial investigations would have greatly assisted the workhouse doctor, for if he was conscientious, he undertook great responsibility single-handed. He had neither the time nor did he receive sufficient remuneration, to inquire into case-histories thoroughly, or examine the condition of the beds, linen, wards, and workhouses in general, which should really have been part of his routine duty, to ensure not only the recovery of his patients, but to prevent the spread and development of disease in the institution. The workhouse Medical Officer was generally in charge of a district as well, and was grossly overworked. In 1839 the Commissioners commended Leighton Buzzard Union where the Guardians engaged a full-time doctor to reside in the workhouse in order to attend both indoor and outdoor poor there.[2] Many Metropolitan Unions, like St. Marylebone, engaged non-resident workhouse Medical Officers, but this arrangement, as that in large Unions where several doctors were employed, meant that a case which had been diagnosed outside, passed into the hands of an entirely different doctor as soon as it entered the workhouse infirmary. There was no arrangement by which diagnosis or notes of treatment could be transmitted, and there was no consultation between the two doctors. When the patient was discharged from the institution, he passed out of the care of the doctor who had been treating him, and the District Medical Officer watched him through convalescence. No history of patients was kept for medical purposes; the records, if written at all, were for statistical reports on the amount of

[1] Scrofulous, i.e. infected with bovine tuberculosis generally affecting the glands of the neck.
[2] Special Report Poor Law Commissioners on Further Amendment of Poor Law, 1839.

relief the Union was granting. A cardinal point of Poor Law policy was to keep the classification of indoor and outdoor medical relief entirely separate, and to this end, preventive and curative medicine were subordinate.

Another defect in the workhouse infirmary system, was that the medical men had to provide their own drugs. From their meagre salary they could prescribe only the simplest remedies, and it was because of the dangers to which such arrangements were subject, that Dr. Kay in 1838 recommended to the Select Committee that the efficiency of medical treatment in the workhouses would be increased if Guardians supplied the drugs to be used there. There was no authority which could prevent an unscrupulous Medical Officer from having recourse to the use of inferior drugs and stinting his patients of medicines. But the medical profession denied that its members might have resort to such practice, and very few complaints were heard on this score from patients. An examination of statistics however reveals that Medical Officers prescribed a large amount of alcohol and spirits—for which the Guardians willingly paid—as an accepted part of medical treatment.

It was not the doctors, but the nurses, who brought such great abuse to the medical treatment offered by the workhouse infirmary. These nurses were always paupers, and generally aged or infirm, and stories of their inhumanity and harshness abound in mid-nineteenth-century literature. Shiftless and idle, without any training, and quite illiterate, they were a great encumbrance to the doctor. Medicines were misappropriated to be resold; and the nurses were bribed by the sick to obtain a few extras, which they had stolen in turn from other patients. As they were remunerated by additional allowances of beer, their intemperance, often leading to violence, had a serious effect on the morals of the institutions; and because they did not understand the necessity for cleanliness they themselves must have been responsible for much cross-infection in the wards. It is surprising that the necessity for employing trained, efficient and honest nurses was not realized and demanded earlier, for it was not until the 'sixties that reforms in the workhouse nursing system were introduced, and then reformers encountered great opposition from the parsimonious Guardians, so that improvement was depressingly and pathetically slow.[1]

Reformers of the insanitary and corruptly administered workhouses had already begun a serious agitation in the early 'forties, and of these none was more active than Wakley, whose son was to instigate the famous and successful inquiries in the 'sixties. Thomas Wakley led the attack in the House of Commons and in the editorials of the *Lancet* by publishing revealing and condemnatory statistics. In 1841 he wrote:

> We know of no fact in statistical science, so firmly established as that of the excessive mortality in the present workhouse. . . . According to the returns of the Officers it appears that out of 12,313 poor people in the workhouses, 2,552 perished in one year. . . . [The poor law authorities] are bound to prove that the workhouses do not increase the mortality and sufferings of the destitute. But this they have never attempted. The

[1] It must be remembered that no competent nursing service existed in the country anyway and a change in the workhouse nursing system could only follow the reforms introduced in the general hospitals in the 1860s.

Commissioners have, on the contrary, circumspectly withheld the most decisive information and kept the Government, the House of Commons, and the public in the dark. They have never even stated in their reports the number of deaths in the workhouses under their administration. . . . Do 2,552 in 12,313 paupers perish annually out of doors? . . . In the absence of the direct observations which should have been furnished to the Secretary of State and to Parliament we submit the following facts to public attention: In 1837 2,552 paupers died out of 12,313 in the workhouses; 382 persons died out of 12,313 persons in the district of St. Giles, London. How is this enormous difference to be accounted for? The age of the inmates will account for a part of the difference. The proportion of old persons is greater in the workhouses than in the unhealthy district of the Metropolis. But the mortality of persons in England above the age of sixty is $7\frac{1}{2}$ per cent . . . and if none of the 12,313 inmates of the workhouses had been under sixty years of age the deaths should not have exceeded 933. . . . Are the paupers sick at the time of their admission into the destructive workhouses? A certain number are admitted in a state of sickness, but the proportion is not much greater than in the general population. About eight in a 100 are constantly sick in St. Giles' district . . . and only six in a 100 are relieved on account of sickness or accident into the workhouses. The diseases which prove so fatal, therefore, assail the poor after their entrance into *these ante-chambers of the grave.*

[1838–9] . . . The number constantly sick in the 110 workhouses was 1,407 in 12,713 or nearly 11 per cent, the number stated to be infirm was 36 per cent but this evidently included the infirm from age as well as the infirm from lameness, blindness, and chronic diseases of various kinds. The mortality among the infirm pensioners on the list of the East India Company's labourers in London was 16 per cent annually. It is at least as high among infirm outdoor paupers in the Metropolis. But the mortality of young able-bodied adults and the aged and infirm taken together was 29 per cent in the ten Metropolitan workhouses![1]

Farr also interested himself in the mortality rates of workhouses and in 1837 made an analysis of death rates in ten Metropolitan and 100 provincial workhouses, Table 3, and it is probably from these that Wakley obtained some of his information.

Although the barrack-like general mixed workhouse was shunned by the sick poor whenever possible, because they realized relief there was detrimental both to their social standing and to their health, the Poor Law authorities did attempt in these years to improve institutional relief for the aged and the children. Classification principles, too, were relaxed for the sick from the beginning. In 1835 complaints were made to the Commissioners that man and wife, if both were sick or infirm, were kept in separate wards and therefore never saw each other. Wakley raised the matter in the House of Commons, and inquiries were often made by Dr. Kay. Leniency was therefore introduced. Sometimes, as in the case of the blind, man and wife were given an outhouse in which to live together, or arrangements

[1] *Lancet,* 10 April 1841, pp. 97–101.

were made whereby one could visit the ward of the other. Chadwick also wrote to the Guardians that young children should not be separated from their mothers even in cases of illness.

TABLE 3

Mortality in Public Institutions. W. Farr's chapter on 'Vital Statistics' in McCulloch's *Statistics of the British Empire*, 1837.

Year 1837	Average number resident constantly		Average number constantly			Admitted ill
	Male	Female	Sick	Infirm	Healthy	
10 Metropolitan workhouses	1,252	1,926	462	1,591	1,125	1,318
100 workhouses in various counties taken indiscriminately	4,650	4,485	945	2,864	5,334	2,717

	Total admitted		Total discharged (including deaths)		Total deaths	
	Male	Female	Male	Female	Male	Female
10 Metropolitan	2,316	2,942	2,174	2,749	402	504
100 workhouses in various counties taken indiscriminately	10,764	9,172	8,935	7,341	970	676

	Average number of paupers in each workhouse	Proportion in 100 paupers			Annual deaths to 100 constantly resident		
		Sick	Infirm	Healthy	Male	Female	Mean
10 Metropolitan workhouses	317·8	14·5	50·1	35·4	32·1	26·2	29·1
100 workhouses in various counties taken indiscriminately	91·35	10·3	31·3	58·3	20·9	15·1	18

The aged and infirm benefited wherever classification principles were put into effect. A clergyman wrote to the Commissioners, that he had never realized the advantage this class of pauper would enjoy by being removed from several workhouses to one special one, where they could be segregated from 'noisy children, disorderly and disreputable women and idleness', and where they had the opportunity of having 'the best interests of their declining years attended to more effectually'.[1] The Guardians of Bradfield (Yorks) also recorded, as early as 1836, that they had not received a single complaint of their having 'infringed on the just privilege or comforts of the aged, and blind' . . . but on the contrary, '. . . the cleanliness of the linen and habits, the regularity of wholesome and sufficient meals, and the medical attendance', had resulted in '. . . their condition being ameliorated and enhanced'. In 1837 this Union established a poorhouse devoted solely to the care of the aged and infirm, 'where they would not be annoyed by children', and where they would enjoy a special dietary.[2]

In their Third Annual Report, the Commissioners referred to what they regarded as the general position in the country. 'The warmth and cleanliness, the wholesomeness of the workhouse, as well as the regularity of the diet, could scarcely fail to be manifested in the general health of the infirm and the aged inmates.' They maintained that the proportion of deaths in the workhouse was less than the number of people of like age and class outside, and stated that on all occasions they had given special consideration to cases of age and infirmity. Regarding this class the master and matron had received special instructions, as to the 'hours for rising and going to bed, the occupation in which they were to be employed . . . and the meals which were to be provided'. People over sixty years old were to be allowed 1 oz. of tea, 5 oz. of butter and 7 oz. of sugar a week, in place of the normal gruel for breakfast. The Poplar Workhouse Visiting Committee complained of the indiscriminate allowance of tea, sugar, butter, and beer to all classes, and desired a distinction should be made between the able-bodied, and the aged and infirm, and that beer should only be allowed to nurses and the sick.[3]

The Poor Law authorities similarly attempted to introduce improvements in the provision for pauper children, and frequently expressed anxiety as to their welfare. For example in the spring of 1841, when considerable pressure had been brought on the workhouses through the severity of the winter, the Assistant Commissioners kept greater watch than usual to see what effects overcrowding was having on the health of inmates. E. C. Tufnell, Inspector for Kent, reported an outbreak of glandular trouble among the children in the Sevenoaks workhouse. Therefore the Commissioners sent two doctors from London, who had been recommended by the Royal College of Surgeons as being specially qualified in paediatrics, to investigate the cause and nature of the disease, and a special medical report was furnished on the state of the Sevenoaks workhouse. Each child was carefully examined, and many were found to be suffering from thyroid complaints, scrofula, chilblains, scald head and ophthalmia. When the doctors complained that the workhouse was overcrowded, the Commissioners immediately asked the Guardians to enlarge it, because of the dangerous

[1] Letter to Assistant Commissioner Hawley from Rev. J. C. F. Tufnell, Minister of Hurstpierpoint, Sussex.
[2] Minutes, Board of Guardians, Bradfield. (Webb MSS.).
[3] Minutes, Board of Guardians, November 1837.

position of the children. However, a new district school was in course of erection near the locality, and the Guardians proposed to withdraw the children from the institution so that they would receive special care in the school.

It was by the establishment of such schools, to house the children from several Unions where the workhouses were overcrowded, and where no classification of inmates had been attempted, that the Commissioners hoped to provide better conditions for pauper children. London had the first, and the two largest, at Norwood and Tooting. Other well-populated towns followed gradually, but the rural Unions were rarely ever in the position to make such provision. No doubt the theory of segregation underlying the foundation of the schools was of good intention. Sometimes fit children only were sent, in order to segregate them from the sick who were retained in the workhouse infirmaries; other Unions followed the policy of maintaining ailing children there, so that they might live in the country. For example, Charles Mott reporting on Norwood in 1836, discovered that 'nearly all the children sent from St. James' were suffering from some disease . . . such as scald and ringworm heads, scrofula, dysentery, and other internal complaints'. Parish officers stated to him that this was because the strongest children were placed at an institution provided by the Children's Friendly Society, with a view to their becoming emigrants in later years.

In the same year Dr. Neil Arnott was appointed by the Commissioners to examine the 'establishments for the reception of pauper children near the Metropolis . . . and report on any requirements which may be advantageously adopted for the preservation of the health of the inmates, and their general medical treatment'.[1] In a small school he visited at Brixton Hill, which housed only 150 children, he found the inmates remarkably healthy, with only three ailing, and with no one seriously ill. Only three had died there in the previous three years. This Arnott attributed possibly to the selection of the children admitted, but he emphasized the important influence which the arrangements regarding space and ventilation must have exercised. The mortality rate of one per cent was five per cent less than the rate for the children of the whole of London.

At Norwood, Arnott found great contrast. The 650 children maintained here in overcrowded conditions were superior in appearance to the mass of poor children in London, but they looked pale and weakly, with no sign of having benefited from living in the country. The master of the school, the well-known figure Aubin, explained that the Guardians chiefly sent him invalid children, and Arnott also realized that they were 'the offspring of the most dissolute, diseased and wretched of the human race, and naturally inherit the consequences of their parents' debauchery'. The mortality rate was one in twenty (five per cent) and he felt people ought to have been surprised that the rate was not greater. Even in Norwood it was one per cent lower than in London generally, which Arnott thought, proved that the schools counteracted the morbid influence of home life. The food at Norwood he found to be superior in quantity and quality to what the in-

[1] Report on Metropolitan Houses for the Reception of Pauper Children, by Neil Arnott, M.D., included in the Second Annual Report of the Poor Law Commissioners, 1836.

dustrious labouring poor usually gave, or could afford to give to their children, and he maintained that the rumours which were spread that sickness was caused at Norwood through the bad and insufficient food were without foundation.[1] The air round Norwood he also stated to be good, and the institution took care that kitchen and sanitary odours did not enter the schoolroom or bedrooms. But this forethought was rendered nugatory by the lack of ventilation and overcrowding, and it was to these factors that he attributed the high death rate. When Arnott entered the great schoolroom which contained three to four hundred children he found the atmosphere unbearable, and the infirmary was worst of all. He also criticized the provision of warmth for the school, and pointed out that only two hundred beds existed for the 650 children. In the infirmary he found many in an advanced stage of severe diseases, chiefly scrofula. The sick were treated by an able doctor, but Arnott wondered whether he was alive to the question of the comparative prevalence of sickness in the school, and whether he was not merely paying attention to the treatment of diseases as they arose.

Arnott's investigations, and those made by Mott on Tooting and other institutions for the reception of pauper children from London, were followed by suggestions for reform, of which Dr. Kay's Report in 1838 on the 'Training of Pauper Children' was the most penetrating.[2] As to medical improvements, 'certain sanitary precautions are necessary in all establishments in which many children are assembled. The liability of all children to contagious maladies, and the frequency with which pauper children are affected with certain other infectious diseases, render great care necessary in the cleansing of children on their admission.' He advised also that all new entrants should be minutely examined by the Medical Officer in the receiving wards, before they mingled with the rest of the inmates. Each establishment, he suggested, should be provided with a common sick ward, and with separate wards, one for isolating children with scabies and itch, another for those with tinea capitis or scald head, and a third for receiving those with infectious diseases like ophthalmia, or contagious illnesses like measles, scarlatina, and smallpox. These wards should be large enough to admit the complete isolation of a considerable number of children in an emergency. A yard for the exercise of convalescents should be adjacent to the wards, and the infirmary and probationary wards were to be supplied with baths, the former also having a separate wash-house attached to it, as infectious diseases would spread if the children's clothes were washed in the same building. In the new institutions, the size and height of the schoolrooms and wards, the means of ventilation and warmth, and the sanitary arrangements of the premises, should all be subject to careful and precise regulations. Lastly, Arnott recommended that not more than two children over the age of seven should be permitted to sleep in one bed, and boys over twelve should sleep alone.

---

[1] It is open to question whether masters of workhouses, or of such schools, did not temporarily improve conditions, e.g. food., when they expected an inspection by an official. Warning was generally given beforehand and this, as well as an official's bias, may have led to descriptions of arrangements being more salutary than they really were.

[2] Fourth Annual Report of the Poor Law Commissioners, 1838.

All the Guardians appointed a committee, or one of their Medical Officers to visit the establishments to which they sent their pauper children, and from these reports, the high incidence of disease in the schools can be shown. For example, in 1838 the surgeon of St. George in the East, Stepney, inspected the Tooting school, and found great prevalence of the very contagious purulent ophthalmia. Precautions had been taken in the recourse to isolation, cleanliness, and frequent bathing, but the disease spread through the whole institution. In 1841, the surgeon said, thirty-six children from St. George's alone had died there in one year, and several subsequent reports contained complaints of the ill-health of the children. In 1847 an epidemic of measles and skin eruptions broke out, and in that year the children leaving Tooting were required to be given a medical certificate as to their health, and similarly, those entering the establishment had to bring one with them.

This innovation was an indication that the importance of preventive measures was being realized. Although the schools never really provided salutary conditions they formed an important addition to the provisions made by the Poor Law authorities for relieving pauper children. But despite the fact that the Commissioners often stressed that the sick, the aged, and children should have preferential treatment, co-operation on a national scale was never achieved. The general mixed workhouse in these years—and in many areas always—remained the only provision the vast majority of Unions made for the indoor relief of all classes of paupers.

Measures for the actual prevention of disease or the promotion of good health, as a principle of humanity or economy, was beyond the comprehension of most Guardians, until in the 'fifties and later, they questioned whether so large an expenditure on relief, with so complete an ignoring of preventive medicine was justified. In these early years however, curative treatment alone was their responsibility, and for this they provided at first mainly domiciliary treatment and later the workhouse infirmary. But because they were associated with the destitution authority, the medical institutional provisions of the Poor Law, on however expanding a scale, retained their deterrent and therefore their inadequate and often cruel aspects.

CHAPTER 4

Provision for Lunatics, 1834–47

As a large proportion of lunatics were, or became through their infirmity, paupers, a brief account must be given of their treatment under the Poor Law medical service.[1]

Attention given to this subject was reluctant and spasmodic. In the eighteenth century scandals were left to flourish almost unchecked, and the Bills introduced from 1814 to 1819 were rejected. It was not until 1827 that a prominent committee of inquiry revealed the disgusting and cruel state of affairs. As a result of the subsequent agitation, two Acts were passed in 1828, 'one to regulate the care and treatment of the insane in England', and the other, 'dealing with the erection of County Asylums and the care of pauper and criminal lunatics'.[2] By these two measures, magistrates were empowered to take the initiative in building County Asylums, in engaging managers, and levying a rate. Fifteen Commissioners in Lunacy were appointed, but the County Asylums and public hospitals were exempted from their inspection. Solitary lunatics were also left unprotected. 'An immense burden of unpaid and disagreeable work was thrown on the shoulders of the Metropolitan Commissioners.'[3] They plodded slowly and doggedly to accumulate facts with which to rouse public opinion and overcome opposition. From 1834, when he became Chairman, until his death in 1885, it was Lord Shaftesbury who devoted himself, untiringly and unsparingly, to the cause of reform.

Progress was tardy, and public awareness of existing evils awakened very gradually. Once again, it was to a high degree through the Poor Law officers' and administrators' investigations and reports, that the urgency for reforms was made patent. The Commissioners in Lunacy, and the Visitors and Inspectors for their part, from time to time revealed the horrors existing in pauper institutions, and in turn the destitution authorities showed by the explanations furnished, how much, and on what lines, redress was necessary. In instituting a body of Assistant Commissioners, the Poor Law authority possessed an inspectorate which reported on conditions in its establishments, and they therefore also covered the treatment of lunatics.

Already in the First Annual Report, the type of existence a lunatic led before 1834, was

[1] See also: Ruth G. Hodgkinson, 'Provision for Pauper Lunatics, 1834–1871', *Medical History*, Vol. X, 1966, pp. 138–154. For a more general aspect of Lunacy in a broader context see Kathleen Jones, *Lunacy, Laws and Conscience 1744–1845*, 1935.

[2] J. L. and Barbara Hammond, *Lord Shaftesbury*, Pelican edition, 1939.

[3] *Ibid.*

portrayed and an illustration was afforded by Charles Mott.[1] In Bristol he discovered the

> workhouse was filthy in the extreme, the appearance of the inmates dirty and wretched.
> . . . There was no classification whatever, men, women and children were promiscu-
> ously huddled together. . . . In one corner of the building I discovered the most filthy,
> dismal-looking room, which altogether presented such a sombre, wretched appearance,
> that curiosity prompted me to explore it. I entered it, and the scene which I witnessed,
> it is almost impossible to forget. Judging from the appearance of the room, I should
> think water must have been excluded from it for years. In short it reminded me of a
> coal cellar, or any place rather than the residence of a human being. The sole tenant of
> this abode was a poor distressed lunatic. His appearance was pitiable in the extreme; his
> clothing was extremely ragged; his flesh literally as dirty as the floor; his head and face
> were much bruised, apparently from repeated falls. Shoes he had been furnished with
> at some time or other, but they had done their duty, and his feet protruded through
> them. He sat listless and alone, without any human being to attend upon or take care of
> him, staring vacantly around, insensible even to the calls of nature, and apparently un-
> mindful of anything which was passing in the room. He was endeavouring to avail
> himself of the only comfort allowed him from the few embers which were yet burning
> in the grate, for he had thrust his arms through an iron grating, which was placed before
> the fire, intended doubtless to prevent the poor creature from burning himself; but as it
> was, his hands just reached the embers. I endeavoured to arouse this poor, pitiable
> fellow-creature, but attempt was useless, all sensibility had forsaken him. To the very
> great shame of the parish officers, I found he had been in this disgusting state for years.

Mott therefore complained of the case to the magistrates who ordered a strict investigation, but he found similarly wretched treatment had been meted out to other lunatics in the same workhouse.

In 1836 it was shown that no people suffered so much under the imperfect accommodation and in the relief given by single parishes, as pauper lunatics, who were generally
treated as harmless.[2] In one parish in the Gloucester Union, the Medical Officer discovered
a destitute woman who had for the past five years been boarded out for 5s. a week on an
aged woman of seventy. For security the officers had provided a wooden cage, in which
she was confined for weeks at a time, although it was so small she could neither sit nor lie
down in it. As soon as the Medical Officer reported this to the Guardians, she was promptly
removed to an asylum. The Assistant Commissioner also reported that the appearance of
many of the inmates in the old workhouses indicated a state of insanity, but governors
uniformly maintained they were harmless. Even when they were seriously dangerous to
other inmates, the governors refused to send them to an asylum because of the expense.

[1] Report, Assistant Commissioner Charles Mott, First Annual Report of the Poor Law Commissioners, 1835.

[2] Report by Robert Weale, Assistant Commissioner for Worcester and Somerset, Second Annual Report of the Poor Law Commissioners, 1836.

The complaint of the cost of maintaining a lunatic (10s. to 12s. a week in some areas) was universal, and therefore the Assistant Commissioners advocated that several Unions should subscribe towards a joint house for hopeless and dangerous cases. Many Boards of Guardians passed resolutions earnestly recommending that facilities should be given them to put this proposal into practice.

W. J. Gilbert's report on Devon echoed the same desire. The County magistrates intended to buy Exeter barracks for £15,000 for the erection of a pauper lunatic asylum, under the provision of the Act of 1828. The Guardians deemed the establishment a necessity, but the ratepayers objected to the expense, especially as they believed they would have no voice in the administration. Gilbert therefore suggested that inmates should be maintained in the asylum by their own parishes and Unions, who should share the cost of erection and maintenance. The establishment, he further recommended, was not to be controlled by the magistrates but by a joint committee of ratepayers elected by the Guardians. This scheme was approved, for not only was it difficult for parishes to dispose of their lunatics, but the expense to the small individual bodies was great. Gilbert, like the other Assistant Commissioners, revealed the scandals of the inco-ordinate system which existed where the new Poor Law was not in operation, and the improvements achieved through the formation of Unions. At Tiverton, a woman had been confined in a workhouse for twenty-eight years, in a small room devoid of furniture and fireplace. She slept on straw and had no clothing winter or summer. On the formation of the Union she was immediately removed to an asylum. In another village a male lunatic had lived naked and in total darkness in a miserable outhouse for eight years. He had been fastened to the wall by a chain not a foot long round his leg. Gilbert immediately insisted on his instant removal to an asylum. At Bideford, he found a male and female lunatic confined in dens like wild beasts, and equally offensive. The woman he had sent to an asylum, where she was expected to recover, and the man was released and was employed in the workhouse. Medical Officers told many stories of cruelty and 'there were few or no poor houses where [there were] not some objects for whose welfare a lunatic asylum [was] wanted'. Gilbert therefore supported the Guardians in their desire for the government to advance the sum necessary for the erection of asylums, in the same manner as loans were given for the building of workhouses. Each Union acting under the joint scheme, would pay a proportion for the number of pauper lunatics relieved in the new asylums. 'At the moment we do not know what to do with the pauper lunatic . . .; the expense of sending them to the asylum is so great that they have been kept in the workhouse until they become troublesome and . . . until the disease has become inveterate and recovery hopeless.'

Evidence was also given before the Select Committee of 1838[1] on the scandalous conditions tolerated for destitute lunatics, and recommending that the Poor Law Commissioners or the Home Secretary should have the power to unite several Unions for the purpose of maintaining a common lunatic asylum distinct from the County Asylums.

[1] See particularly, evidence of Assistant Commissioner Gulson, Select Committee on the Further Amendment of the Poor Law Act, 1838.

Witnesses drew attention to the forty-seventh Clause of the Poor Law Amendment Act, whereby lunatics and idiots were not to be detained in workhouses for longer than fourteen days. But this humane provision of the law, it was pointed out, was not adhered to, indeed it was difficult to obey, in the face of the Commissioners' recommendation that asylums for pauper lunatics would be most properly combined with a large workhouse. The Commissioners maintained that this latter expedient was preferable to 'sending these unfortunate persons to private institutions, in which it is in the interest of the proprietors that they should remain. . . . It would also be better as a point of mere economy, the price paid to private asylums being 10s. to 12s. weekly, whilst in the poor house they could be kept for less than half that amount.' A resolution of the Committee of Inquiry mentioned the retention of the insane destitute in workhouses: 'better provision should be made for the due custody of pauper lunatics and idiots, either in separate wards in the workhouse, or in district or county asylums.'

There is no doubt that the tendency became prevalent to remove paupers to special institutions, partly because workhouses were becoming increasingly overcrowded, and partly because of the growing humaneness, which indicated the anomaly and injury of maintaining lunatics with ordinary paupers. Where separate district asylums had been established results were salutary, socially and economically, and the mentally infirm received superior medical attention which afforded them a greater chance of recovery.[1]

London was well provided for, because of the activity of the Lunacy Commissioners. Between 3,000 and 4,000 persons were confined as lunatics in public institutions in the Metropolis. That it was foremost in sending paupers away is evident from a study of the Minutes of the Boards of Guardians and Select Vestries, in which there is constant reference to the lunacy problem. A report of 1835 on the local government of the Metropolis[2] cited the extravagant expenditure on Hanwell Lunatic Asylum. Farr also wrote in 1839 that Bethlem charged 15s. a week for criminal lunatics, whereas the cost of such patients in workhouses would only amount to 2s. 6d. to 3s. 6d.[3] From the Account Books of St. Leonard's, Shoreditch, it is seen that in 1837 lunatics cost the Union £814 and in 1843 £945. Unions also periodically sent their Medical Officers to report on the condition of their patients in the County Asylums, and the fees shown in the account books varied from £4 to £6 a year. In 1829 St. Leonard's was already spending £1,213 a year on outdoor relief to lunatics, which rose to £1,500 by 1844 and increased progressively every year following. In 1838 the County Lunatic Asylum wrote to the Kensington, and presumably other Boards of Guardians, requiring information on the number of lunatics who were being maintained in places other than in the Asylum, as new wards were about to be opened. Nevertheless, the workhouses retained a great number of idiots and chronic lunatics. In 1840 Sir Edmund Head, the Assistant Commissioner, reported to one of the Boards of

[1] No attempt is made to criticize nineteenth-century treatment in the light of modern medical knowledge (see footnote p. 580).
[2] By a committee of St. George's, Hanover Square.
[3] Farr MSS., Vol. II.

Guardians that on an examination of the workhouse he had seen iron handcuffs and manacles used in the lunatic ward, and recommended their immediate removal. Not only was this done, but the Medical Officer was instructed to report to the Guardians anyone whom he considered should be removed to an asylum.

In 1839 a clause was inserted in the Poor Law Bill, which was however later withdrawn, in which the Poor Law Commissioners proposed that County Lunatic Asylums should be controlled in part by themselves and the Board of Guardians, or alternatively that power should be vested in the Commissioners to combine a number of Unions for the purpose of forming asylums solely for paupers. The Provincial Medical and Surgical Association vigorously opposed the interference of the Poor Law authorities in the direction of these institutions and protested against 'depriving the most unfortunate class of mental sufferers of the generous and humane protection which they now enjoy under a superior order of managers'. Actually, the managers were not always as superior as the Association tried to make out, for conditions in many County Asylums left much to be desired, although they were the best institutions at the time. Many of the provincial magistrates were negligent in their inspection and in using the powers conferred on them in 1828 for establishing new asylums. Therefore an Act was passed in 1842 (through the work of Lord Ashley and Wakley) whereby two itinerant Lunacy Commissioners were appointed to inspect provincial institutions.

The effect of the Act[1] respecting the lunatic poor was to ensure that the Poor Law Commissioners received statistics from the Unions of the number of paupers of unsound mind. This enabled them to inquire into cases which were improperly retained in workhouses. Also the quality of the information obtained from the Guardians, and their disposition to deal efficiently with patients, became more satisfactory when they and their paid officers were invested with these powers instead of overseers of single parishes. 'We are deeply convinced that the paupers of unsound mind should, where there is a chance of cure, be sent to an asylum as soon as possible after the commencement of the malady.'[2] Therefore on receipt of the list of lunatics in the autumn of 1843, the Commissioners circularized the Clerks of all Boards of Guardians, calling their attention 'to the extreme importance of suffering no motive of economy to deter the Guardians from sending pauper patients to an asylum where they might receive proper treatment as early as possible.' Medical Officers were also to inform Guardians of any lunatic paupers who might present a reasonable prospect of cure if they were submitted to the treatment of an asylum—and such cases were to be sent away—'to receive the full benefit of medical care and professional superintendence . . .; humanity and sound policy equally demand that persons so situated should receive the best professional aid at an early stage of the malady.'

The Commissioners, when they doubted whether patients were being effectively dealt with, addressed inquiries to the particular Boards of Guardians. In 1842 the number of individual cases brought under the special notice of the Guardians was 115, in 1843 it was

[1] 5 & 6 Vict. c. 57, s. 6.
[2] Tenth Annual Report of the Poor Law Commissioners, 1844.

137. As a result of correspondence with the Commissioners 35 people were in the two years sent to asylums. In these years, as in former reports, the Commissioners again expressed their opinion that the number of County Asylums in England was too small in proportion to requirements. (There were sixteen of these in 1842.) But besides expressing regret at the deficiency, the central authority effected few tangible remedies. The provision of institutions was left to lag behind the increasing demand.

In March 1836, in the 173 Unions established in England there were

922 lunatics or insane (176 indoor; 372 outdoor; 374 in asylums or elsewhere)
1,723 idiots (554 indoor; 1,169 outdoor).

Figures given in 1837 were:

			Cost per week
			s. d.
The numbers confined in			
(a) County asylums	Lunatics	2,610	6 6
	Idiots	170	7 3
(b) In private asylums	Lunatics	1,403	9 3
	Idiots	88	8 0
(c) In workhouses or as outdoor paupers	Lunatics	2,389	3 6 (av.)
	Idiots	7,007	2 9 (av.)
	Total	13,667	
		or 0·1 per cent of population	

Of these nearly 4,000 were believed incurable, and nearly 3,000 idiots from birth.[1] Returns made to Parliament in 1839 gave 7,265 lunatic and 6,402 idiot paupers in England and Wales. In 1841 there were nearly this number in England alone costing £119,600. This was the first year that the total cost was stated, and already by the following year it had risen by £2,000. In 1842 in England 42 per cent (5,553) of lunatics were receiving medical treatment in County Asylums or licensed houses, but 3,700 were living with friends or elsewhere, and the same number in workhouses. The two latter classes contained the largest proportion of incurable cases and idiots. In Wales there were over 1,000 lunatics chargeable to the poor rates, of whom only 41 were in County Asylums, and 56 in licensed houses— 8·4 per cent of the whole. Ninety-three were in workhouses, and nearly 1,000 were supported elsewhere, without permanent medical superintendence.

In 1843 the total number of lunatics chargeable in England was 13,615 and of these

3,489 were maintained in county asylums costing 7s. 6¼d. each a week
2,257 in licensed houses costing 8s. 11½d. each a week
3,896 by friends or farmed out, costing 2s. 7½d. each a week
3,973 in workhouses

[1] Appendix C, No. 8, Third Annual Report of the Poor Law Commissioners, 1837.

In Wales 1,177 were chargeable of which only 36 were in county asylums at a cost of 9s. 7d. a week per patient, 41 in licensed houses costing 8s. 11¾d., and 90 in Union workhouses. Over 1,000 were still supported elsewhere.

In 1844 the total number of lunatic and idiot paupers in England was 14,158 of whom:

3,579	were maintained in a county asylum at a cost of 7s. 3½d. (average)	
2,559	licensed houses	8s. 8¾d.
4,080	workhouses	
3,940	elsewhere	2s. 7d.

In Wales the total number was 1,199, of whom:

37	were maintained in county asylums at a cost of 7s. 9½d. (average)	
55	licensed houses	8s. 4¾d.
91	workhouses	
1,016	elsewhere	2s. 3¼d.

Farr gave a romantic picture of the situation in Wales, when he described the village idiot lodging in a cottage, supported by the parish, the qualified butt and the favourite of the neighbourhood. He told the story of Jack of Pool in Montgomeryshire, who died aged 109, clothed and maintained by the neighbouring lord, to secure his vote at every election.[1] Treatment of the village idiot was however seldom as kind, and the Poor Law Commissioners had as hard a struggle to introduce some form of asylum in Wales as they had to get the whole of the new Poor Law adopted there. They recommended one asylum for North Wales and another for South Wales, but the practical difficulties in bringing about a voluntary junction between the counties were very great. They threatened, however, that if the erection of one or more asylums was not speedily resolved on, they would press for legislative interference. Some lunatics were sent out of Wales, to Bristol for example, but the numbers were few, as the expense was prohibitive. It cost Monmouth 13s. 9d. per week to maintain a patient in an asylum, while in Nottingham and Lincoln it cost only 9s. 3d., in Norfolk 5s. and in Devon 12s. 6d.

An important fact to be deduced from the statistics, is that in both England and Wales the proportion of lunatics to the entire pauper population was 1:10 and the ratio was constant throughout the years until the 'sixties. Every year saw an increase in the number of mentally infirm, and the Commissioners realized that this was yet another problem of growing magnitude, which would warrant specialized attention. Farr had shown that seven in ten lunatics in London institutions were paupers, and had pointed out that insanity in the head of the family reduced labourers to destitution.[2] Many middle-class families were also ruined because the affliction usually attacked the middle-aged. This was borne out by an Abstract of Returns of 1845,[3] which gave the incidence of insanity for various age groups:

[1] Chapter on Vital Statistics in J. R. McCulloch's *Statistics of the British Empire*, 1837.
[2] Farr MSS.
[3] February 1845, B.P.P. No. 38.

0–5	6	20–30	2,828	50–60	2,272
5–10	40[1]	30–40	3,117[2]	60–70	1,430
10–20	818	40–50	3,046	70 +	596

Farr also maintained that if congenital idiots were excluded, and only the proportions of the insane calculated, it was probable that the tendency to insanity would be found greater in the towns than in the country, and greater in England than in Wales and Scotland. Further, if lunatics received more efficient treatment, as was becoming the case, their lives would be prolonged, so that their numbers would increase relatively to the population. The question was therefore becoming an important social and economic problem. And before they relinquished office the Commissioners affirmed:

> It will be our endeavour to impress, as we have hitherto done, on the minds of Guardians, the expediency of affording medical treatment to lunatics, and at as early a stage as possible of their disease, and to discourage the improper retention of any patients of unsound mind in the workhouse.

In 1844 the Commissioners in Lunacy published a report which revealed that 9,000, or three-quarters of the total number of lunatics, were still in workhouses, farmed out, or in private asylums where their condition was often pitiable. Ashley gave illustrations of the foul and disgusting state of the many institutions.[3] Up to this date twenty-one counties had made no provision for an asylum, on the plea of economy, for the erection of a workhouse cost on an average £40 per head, whereas a County Asylum varied from £100 to £350.

'Ashley's Act' was passed in 1845.[4] By it the Lunacy Commission was reformed on a permanent basis, and a definite order and certificate were required for the confinement of a lunatic. Case books and records were to be rigidly kept in asylums, and all pauper lunatics were to be removed from the workhouse. The Poor Law Commissioners circularized the Medical Officers with the clauses relevant to their office, and Guardians were advised to keep these new duties of the doctors in mind in making future arrangements and contracts. The Act also stipulated, that when the asylum was full and paupers had to be maintained in the workhouse or be farmed out, they were to receive medical attention every three months. The Medical Officers were required to compile a list of such cases, copies of which were to be sent to the Visitors of Asylums and the Commissioners in Lunacy. A doctor was liable to a fine of £10 to £50 for any mis-statement regarding the fitness of a person of unsound mind to be at large. The Guardians also received letters of information and instruction from the Poor Law Commissioners. Every year a physician or surgeon and one barrister were to visit every Union workhouse in which any lunatics were maintained. These Lunacy Commissioners and Visitors would supervise diet, accom-

---

[1] For the whole of England.
[2] N.B.—This age group had the greatest family responsibilities.
[3] In a speech to the House of Commons, 6 June 1845.
[4] 8 & 9 Vict. c. 126.

modation and treatment in the work-houses, and then report to the Poor Law Commissioners. Every pauper detained had to be certified by a magistrate or clergyman as well as by the Relieving Officer of the Union. A medical certificate had also to be supplied by a Union doctor and an outside practitioner. No pauper could in future be admitted to an asylum, licensed house or workhouse insane ward, without these formalities. Guardians similarly could not discharge a patient without a medical certificate, and any two visiting magistrates could direct the Relieving Officer of a Union to remove a pauper from an asylum if a Medical Officer certified to his sanity. The Act also provided for the compulsory erection of pauper lunatic asylums in counties and boroughs, and for the appointment of committees of visitors to regulate and superintend them, and to scrutinize all records. As soon as the new asylums were built, all lunatic paupers were to be removed to them, so that in time there would be no more in workhouses or hospitals.[1] The Act was amended in 1853, but in substance its provisions remained until 1889. It was not such a dead letter as many of the regulations dealing with paupers and lunatics were, but there was an exasperating delay in putting its stipulations into practice, so that a uniform system never existed in the country. There is no doubt however that reforms were begun after this date, although many of the conditions of the 'forties still existed in the 'eighties.

More important than the legislation was the improvement in the treatment of the insane who remained in the workhouses, although wide variations continued. In Middlesex where John Conolly of Hanwell had introduced 'non-restraint' methods, no coercion was used from September 1839, whilst in other areas, cruelties and scandals were still reported in the 'fifties and 'sixties. However, in the latter decades the upward trend was obvious, if slow. This was, as we have seen, in no small way due to the activities connected with Poor Law administration. The Act of 1834 established the rule for the formation of Unions, which made large-scale and joint activity possible. It instituted Assistant Commissioners, who were responsible for the inspection of workhouses and investigation into Union malpractices. For the first time responsible Medical Officers were appointed, whose work and voice generally led to improvement in the treatment of paupers. Lastly the reports and interests of the Poor Law Commissioners themselves were useful, even if their constructive policy was vacillating and timid. All these factors helped to influence the social conscience and the legislative on behalf of humane treatment of lunatics which developed in the latter half of the century. The Commissioners in Lunacy could justifiably point to the tardiness with which the cruelties and anomalies regarding insane paupers were redressed, but indirectly they also had able and useful allies.

[1] The Minutes of the Manchester Board of Guardians for October 1846 had an entry which showed foresight in withdrawing defectives from the sane, but also revealed the need for specialized institutions, because they had only the workhouse to send the children to: 'All boys of weak intellect at schools in Swinton, being certified, to be removed forthwith to workhouse, and in future no such boys are to be sent to the schools.'

CHAPTER 5

Medical Relief given to Paupers in places not under the new Poor Law

IT has been seen that, contrary to expectations, the 'principles of 1834' were not uniformly applied by the local authorities who came under the new provisions. The self-exclusion of many districts right into the 1840s and 1850s, and often to the end of the century, meant that relief for the destitute was given under an inco-ordinate system, by which the poor were the chief sufferers. Either because of the opposition of the inhabitants to the new ideas, or because they believed their existing regulations were superior, many towns and some villages continued to administer poor relief under local eighteenth-century Acts. Some of these towns were in fact more liberal in their provision, but in the majority of cases, expenditure, particularly on officers' salaries, was below that of the average of the newly-created Unions. In their supply of medical relief, several districts operating under local Acts followed the regulations of the Poor Law Commissioners closely, save that they refused to recognize their orders as binding. Others employed quite different systems. They were all, however, liable to the inspection of the Assistant Commissioners.

The old City of Norwich for example, which had a population of 62,000, an eighth of whom were paupers, had instituted a system whereby a medical committee, elected by ratepayers, was responsible for all pauper medical relief. All medical attention was given in the dispensary and workhouse infirmary, which worked jointly. New rules for the dispensary were set out in 1838. Its committee was to consist of eight honorary Medical Officers (who were, however, in the 'forties paid £25 a year), and a resident Apothecary at a salary of £100 and board. Qualifications from English, Scottish, Irish, or foreign universities were accepted, although the surgeons had to be Members of the Royal College of Surgeons and Licentiates of the Society of Apothecaries, unless they had been in practice before 1815, or if they already held office. The committee divided the town into eight districts and each Medical Officer was responsible for one of them. They were given strict instructions to give treatment to the destitute only. Four of the doctors were on duty in the dispensary half the week and the remainder the other half. All sick applicants had to attend at the institution unless they were too ill, in which instances the doctors visited their homes. Children of the poor, after the Act of 1840, were vaccinated here every Friday. Medicines were prescribed on forms which patients took to the Apothecary. Besides dispensing drugs the latter was also expected to attend all emergencies at night, and he was assisted by a dispensary servant who received £13 a year. Books were kept carefully and forwarded every month to the Dispensary Committee. The Relieving Officer and Removal Officer examined the register of patients kept by the Apothecary every week. One of the eight Medical Officers was in charge of the workhouse and its infirmary for six months, and this duty was taken in rotation, an additional sum of £25 being paid for the service. The sick wing of Norwich workhouse contained a day room, five bedrooms, a smallpox room, a lying-in room, a sleeping room, a bathroom, surgeons' rooms, and a wash-house and yard. When Assistant Commissioner Walsham inspected this he could find no fault with it. It was clean and the inmates appeared remarkably healthy.[1] The medical committee also employed a male midwife, who was called if midwives selected by women inmates of the workhouse considered the case beyond their skill. The ordinary midwives received 3s. 9d. a case, and the special male attendant a guinea. He generally earned on an average about ten guineas a year.

The Norwich Poor Infirmary was situated in an open space on the outskirts of the city, and the Bethel was a well arranged and well managed lunatic asylum for sixty inmates. The Guardians set great value on their infirmary. It was a charitable hospital to which, as vacancies occurred, old paupers of six months standing, of over sixty-five years of age and good character, were transferred from the out-relief lists or from the workhouse. Admission to this infirmary was greatly coveted by the poor. The building had originally been a 'pest-house and hospital for the sick'. In 1844 there were 139 inmates, and it was questioned whether the scheme was not injurious, because the hope of sharing the advantages the place afforded was detrimental to the 'fostering of the habits of independence and forethought among the middle-aged poor'. Nevertheless it was a 'pleasing feature in the administration of poor relief'.[2]

The Norwich corporation also provided all the drugs required by the medical staff, at a cost of over £200 a year. The total expenditure of the Vestry for medical relief, including £23 for midwifery, £21 for trusses, instruments and vaccination, and £25 for subscriptions to the Norfolk and Norwich Hospital, averaged £600 a year, or $2\frac{1}{4}$d. per head of the population. Compared with Newcastle and Sunderland who had similar populations, but which were both under the new Poor Law, Norwich had a total expenditure on salaries to Poor Law officials of £1,768 a year. Newcastle spent £1,766 and Sunderland £1,365, but as the rates in Norwich were collected voluntarily, whereas in Newcastle £600 and in Sunderland £377 was spent on this service, much more was really spent on actual relief in the first town. Also, medical salaries in Newcastle and Sunderland covered drugs whilst in Norwich the corporation paid for them.

Sir John Walsham, commenting on the medical relief given by Norwich, drew attention to the absence of restrictions on Medical Officers in the important item of the

[1] Tenth Annual Report, 1844.
[2] Tenth Annual Report. Sir J. Walsham, Assistant Commissioner.

supply of medicines, which was everywhere a source of distrust and complaint. The combination of the doctor who prescribed with a resident apothecary who superintended the preparation of medicines, supplied at a charge to the corporation, worked satisfactorily to all parties. But he also pointed out that the aggregate salaries of the eight doctors (with which they seemed perfectly satisfied), added to the average annual cost of the best drugs, furnished liberally at the orders of those who did not pay for them, amounted only to £400 a year or 1½d. per head of the population. Medicines alone came to ¾d. per head in a city in which one-eighth of the people were paupers. In drawing these conclusions, Walsham was attempting to give evidence in favour of the provisions of the new Poor Law and the adequacy of the salaries paid by the Unions. He tried to prove, from the Norwich experience, that salaries and medicines needed only to form 1¾d. per head of a town's total expenditure on poor relief, which in this town was £22,700.

In Coventry a policy of retrenchment was begun in the 'forties and total expenditure on poor relief fell from £12,000 to £8,000 in the first four years. Here the Directors of the Poor, the clerk, the inspector and the governor of the workhouse gave medical orders and the responsibility rarely fell on churchwardens or overseers. Four Medical Officers were employed for district relief and they also attended the workhouse in rotation for three months each. Leeches, trusses, and appliances were supplied by the parish, but the doctors had to pay for medicines out of their salaries. These were reduced from £79 to £47 a year and they only received 10s. 6d. for midwifery cases. The four doctors attended an average of 3,500 cases in one year, although this figure rose steeply in 1842 because of the increase in fever patients. No regular records were kept in the workhouse, nor were there any books registering outdoor medical cases. Printed weekly forms were completed by doctors and forwarded to the Guardians, stating briefly the name, age, residence, and disease of the patient, but these had little scientific value. They only revealed in the 'remarks' column, how many 'extras' the doctors felt it necessary to order for the paupers. Fortunately the Medical Officer frequently gave tickets recommending additional relief, and they were always attended to. Sometimes money was given for the purchase of food, and occasionally even blankets and bedding were supplied from the workhouse store. It was stated that not a third of the patients received relief from the parish in any other way.

Oldham did not give any remuneration to its doctors, but they were provided with medicines. Their bills for this item in 1844 amounted to between £400 and £500. Three surgeons were appointed to attend the paupers, but they performed their duty in rotation, each serving for three months. Shrewsbury had a similar system but the authorities paid the Medical Officers a meagre pittance. The salaries averaged £175 a year, less than 1s. a case, including the supply of medicines. Hull, with a population similar to that of Oldham (40,000) engaged only one doctor for the entire district, including the workhouse. He was paid £100 a year, which included the supply of medicines. The Board provided trusses and appliances and supplied midwives for confinements, paying them 5s. a case. Here no returns were made of the number of visits made by the Medical Officer or on the condition of patients, for instead of keeping books, the doctor attended the meetings of the Board and reported on cases in person. This was most unsatisfactory, because when he was unable to be present, the authorities were completely in the dark. The number of public charities in Hull precluded the necessity of the town affording medical relief to anyone save the absolutely destitute.

Opposed to Hull, there was no fixed principle in Plymouth as to who was eligible for sick relief, and cases varied. Also, if the relief ordered was regarded as insufficient, it could be reported to the inspector, who took the claim to the Court of Guardians, and they decided what extra provision should be supplied. Therefore instances occurred in which paupers were given commodities like wine and spirits beyond the ordinary relief ordered by the Medical Officer. But conditions for the poor were not altogether salutary here, for the workhouse was an ill-arranged mass of buildings in the town centre. All rooms were overcrowded, the ventilation was defective, and a 'disagreeable stench' was reported to exist in every quarter of it. Seventeen lunatics and idiots were retained in the workhouse, and when an Assistant Poor Law Commissioner inspected it[1] he found one of the women in a state of absolute nakedness lying on straw in a cell. Others freely associated with the sane inmates, and there was no segregation between the diseased and the healthy. The nursing was done by fifteen paupers who received 6d. a week. In Plymouth, as in Hull, only one parish doctor was appointed and he received a salary of £60 a year.

Stoke Damerell, also in Devon, like Plymouth afforded a large number of people who were not paupers with medical relief, or additional relief in the form of money. Further, in giving orders for treatment, no distinction was made as to whether the applicant was settled or not. The town was divided into two districts, North and South, and the two Medical Officers had to stand for re-election in alternate years. As to qualification, the doctors were required to produce certificates proving they had attended courses of 'anatomy, dissection in surgery, the practise of medicine and midwifery at a hospital,' as well as having served a regular apprenticeship. Their individual salaries of £60 included the provision of medicines and maternity work, but the Commissioners of Guardians found trusses, bandages and linseed. Twice a week a list of patients and their diseases had to be entered in a report book. The workhouse was an ill-constructed institution, but a special 'medical diet' was offered to patients, Table 5.1, and every extra beyond this which was ordered by the Medical Officer was provided.

Regulations were also made respecting workhouse visiting. One day a week was specified and the hours fixed from 12 noon to 4 p.m. All interviews had to take place at the gateway as no visitor was allowed in the wards without permission from the governor or the matron. No patient in the infirmary could be seen without leave from the surgeon.

A licensed lunatic asylum was also connected with the workhouse, but it was kept entirely apart from it and was under the care of a separate master and matron. No inmate of the workhouse or other person could be sent to the asylum save by an order of a magistrate under the provisions of the Act of 1828. In the institution the sexes were not only

---

[1] R. Weale, Assistant Commissioner, Tenth Annual Report.

separated by day as well as by night but they were also classified according to the degree of insanity from which they suffered, and were given appropriate amusing occupations. Strict rules were laid down for the care of these sufferers, and no patient could be visited without the doctor's permission.

TABLE 5.1

Medical Sick Diet. (This was said to have been superior to that given to the able-bodied)

Per day	Potatoes, oz.	Bread, oz.	Beef, Mutton before cooking, oz.	Barley, oz.	Broth, pt.	Salt, drachmas	Sago or Groats, oz.	Tea, oz.	Sugar, oz.	Milk, pt.
Half diet	8	12	8	16	1	6	0	$1\frac{1}{2}$	16	$\frac{1}{4}$
Low diet	0	8	4	10	1	6	1	$1\frac{1}{2}$	1	$\frac{1}{2}$
Fever diet	$\frac{1}{2}$ lb. bread or $\frac{1}{4}$ lb. sago, rice or fish as Medical Officer may prescribe.									$\frac{1}{2}$

The rice pudding was to contain 2 oz. of the best rice, 16 drachmas of sugar, $\frac{1}{2}$ pt. of milk, 1 egg and 1 blade of cinnamon. Gruel was made from 1 oz. sago or 1 oz. groats or 2 oz. oatmeal + $\frac{1}{2}$ oz. sugar.

Another small town of nearly 10,000 people was Salisbury. Here every person who applied for medical relief was said to have received it as a matter of course. Only one Medical Officer attended the indoor and outdoor sick poor and he received a salary of £80 a year. He was however allowed to make distinct charges for attendance and medicine supplied to the destitute placed under orders of removal.

The administration of pauper relief in the city of Exeter was regulated by five local acts, those of 1697, 1757, 1774, 1785, and 1788. The sick poor applied directly to the Medical Officer of their district, who was obliged to attend them without any order from the Clerk of the poor. The doctors were not very strict regarding settlement or the actual destitution of the applicant. They were appointed by Guardians for the first year but were re-elected annually as a matter of course. One Medical Officer was engaged for the workhouse and three for the three districts of the town. An individual salary of £40 was paid, as well as £15 for drugs, and 7 guineas for vaccination. For midwifery cases £1 was allowed, but these averaged only about ten in a year because there was a lying-in charity. Leeches and trusses were supplied by the corporation, but no additional remuneration was offered for accidents or operations.[1] In 1831-36 the total expenditure on poor relief

[1] Compare the salaries of Medical Officers with those of other parochial officers:

Chaplain	£100 a year	Head beadle	£110 a year
Clerk and treasurer	210	Second beadle	90
Housekeeper	80	Assistant beadle	26
Matron	20	Schoolmaster and mistress	40

amounted to £53,276, but between 1837 and 1842 this had fallen by £5,000. During the first period sick relief amounted to £1,542, but this had halved to £760 by 1837–42.[1]

But Exeter compared very favourably with Leeds, one of the largest northern industrial towns. Whereas in Exeter the average number of people to each Medical Officer was 10,400, in Leeds it was 75,000.[2] Here two surgeons were appointed by a workhouse board to attend all the paupers of the town. They received a salary of £80 a year each, exclusive of midwifery. Drugs were provided by the town, and a dispenser was employed to compound the prescriptions of the doctors. The latter were at liberty to order any kind of medicine necessary including wines. Indeed, this was the only arrangement in which Leeds was superior to Exeter, and yet in its industrial squalor it harboured far more pauperism and more disease.

Birmingham, the third largest single parish in the country, having a population of 138,000, in many respects had introduced into its system of medical relief schemes which were unknown elsewhere and more progressive than those of the Poor Law Unions. Not only was a resident house surgeon employed at the workhouse infirmary with two assistant dispensers, but paid outside nurses and paid pauper nurses were also engaged. Of the staff of non-pauper nurses, there was one for both the men's and women's infirmary at a salary of £10 a year. There was also one to superintend the women's bedridden ward who received £8, one for the women's venereal diseases ward at £8, one for the women's insane ward at £10, and another for the aged and infirm women at £8. An assistant keeper in the men's insane ward was employed at £8 a year. These nurses supervised the work of the pauper nurses, and not only was their engagement unusual, but so also was the remuneration to the pauper staff. A total of £206 was paid in gratuities to the latter for work connected with the workhouse and the asylum, e.g.:

Attendants in men's venereal diseases wards and sick wards, 1s. 9d. a week
fever wards, 1s. 9d. a week
Nurses in women's fever ward, £1 10s. a qtr.
lying-in ward, £1 5s. a qtr.
Keeper in men's insane ward, 4s. 6d. a week
Nurse in women's insane attic, £1 7s. 6d. a qtr.
children's ward, 1/- a week
women's day room, 1/- a week
Several other nurses and keepers, 1/- a week
Leech bleeder, 1/- a week

The house surgeon was paid £70 a year and board and his assistants £1 10s. a week. The

[1] Report by E. C. Tufnell, Assistant Poor Law Commissioner, Ninth Annual Report of the Poor Law Commissioners, 1843.
[2] H. W. Rumsey, Evidence to Select Committee, 1844.

parish was divided into six districts each with a Medical Officer earning £30 a year.[1] But the doctors did not have much travelling, as they attended all patients who were not bedridden at the workhouse infirmary. Medical relief was confined to paupers and the Relieving Officer was the sole judge as to the necessity of treatment, which was therefore given under many restrictions. The poor who were not actually already in receipt of out-door relief were required to obtain recommendations of ratepayers before going to the Relieving Officer.

In conclusion, the provisions for pauper medical relief which existed in Bristol must be given, for here a singular system obtained by which a voluntary hospital was provided solely for the care of sick paupers. A workhouse infirmary existed also, and the two institutions ran in close conjunction with each other and were really joint establishments. Very elaborate rules and bye-laws had accumulated over generations for the administering of medical relief, and the scheme which had evolved by the 'forties was very comprehensive. Three honorary physicians and three honorary surgeons, elected by open competition, attended the sick inmates of the St. Peter's Hospital and the workhouse, settling amongst themselves a weekly rotation of duty. Those admitted during an individual's term of duty became his patient. Every physician was required to see his cases once a week, and the surgeons' theirs three times. All emergencies had to be seen by the two doctors on duty for the week, and all were liable to be called in for consultation at any time. The honoraries prescribed the treatment and the medicines which were dispensed by the resident apothecary. Pupils and assistants of the doctors could be forbidden attendance on a patient. Rules were even made that no post-mortem could be held unless all doctors were present, and this had to be carried out after the patient had been dead twenty-four hours and before forty-eight hours had elapsed. Fees of one guinea were paid for giving evidence at a Coroner's Inquest.

The Apothecary was the only paid medical man of the Bristol Poor Law authorities. He was engaged full-time for which he received £120 a year, and he had to be unmarried and reside in the institution. He was never absent when the physicians or surgeons were attending patients, or when the Committee was sitting, nor was he allowed to be out after 11 p.m. without the consent of the governor of the workhouse. Whenever he left the establishment he had to leave an account of where he could be contacted. He was responsible for the accurate dispensing of medicines and was in charge of treatment. He had to keep a patient's case-card up to date, and this was affixed over every bed. A separate diary recorded all extraordinary cases. Before ten o'clock every day he had to make a list in the orderly book of patients needing the attention of a particular surgeon or physician. He also kept an out-patients' book, containing the name, address, disease, dates admitted, and discharged of every patient, and a similar one for in-patients. In addition he was in charge of

---

[1] Salaries of other parochial officers: Vestry clerk £200 a year, Treasurer £200, Governor and Matron £150 + board, Chaplain £150. Report by Assistant Commissioners Weale and Power in Ninth Annual Report, 1843.

the Consultants' register and a book for drugs and medicines. The latter ensured that these commodities were procured only by a written order signed by himself, and a separate record was kept of doctors' prescriptions. The Apothecary was also responsible for drawing attention to any outbreak of infectious disease in the wards. These duties applied both to the workhouse infirmary and to the hospital.

Rules for nurses were made in 1836, and they were strictly enforced. Wards had to be kept clean and in order, absentees were to be reported, and if any patients returned after regular hours drunk or quarrelsome, the governor had to be informed. The nurses were responsible for everything in the wards and kept reports on them; they had to be strictly impartial in the distribution of food, and see that the linen was changed regularly. Patients were to be kept clean and no one was allowed to smoke in wards. Children were to be bathed every Saturday and were to be washed and combed daily. The nurses were also required to attend their patients carefully and report immediately if their condition worsened. If any inmate wished to see the governor or make a complaint, the nurses had to report this to the steward and put the name on a list provided. There were many other rules, and for any disobedience or failure to carry out the instructions, the wages of the nurses were stopped.

The poor obtained medical relief by making an application to the Apothecary, who was always in attendance on committee days. He wrote a note on each case and sent this to the Committee. If applicants were recommended for admittance into medical or surgical wards, a ticket was given to them addressed to the house steward. The family of an in-patient was given outdoor relief and was therefore not forced to enter the workhouse. If the applicant was not admitted, but was unable to work, he was given an out-patient's note and asked to return every week with it, signed by the Medical Officer, and present it to the Committee. As long as this was signed, he and his family were afforded relief. Paupers too ill to attend at the hospital were visited by one of the doctors at their home, and he either continued treatment there, or recommended their removal to hospital. Permanent cases such as the aged, widows and their families, and persons reported by a Medical Officer as permanently unable to work, were placed on the Permanent List. These were relieved every Wednesday and Friday by the Visitor and Inspector of Outdoor Poor at the hospital—in the section which was situated in a grave-yard! This generally took three or four hours. Allowances to the aged and permanently sick equalled 1s. to 2s. a person with or without loaves, according to the number of dependants.

Save under very peculiar circumstances, medical relief was confined to paupers already in receipt of such relief. Lunatics, male and female, were given treatment in the hospital. There were very few aged or infirm in it, and on the whole its main work consisted of attending to accidents, midwifery, and the treatment of ordinary sickness. As at Birmingham, Leeds, and Oldham, medicines were provided by the parochial authorities, and the average cost of drugs at Bristol was £235 a year. In 1837, 1,200 cases were attended and this rose to 2,663 by 1844. Yet for this service the corporation remunerated only one doctor, although there were 64,000 inhabitants. In May 1837 the Guardians had written to the

TABLE 5.2

Amount expended for Medical Relief during the year ending Lady Day 1843 in the following places, not in Unions under the Poor Law Amendment Act. Population 1841 and Rate per Head of Medical Relief on Population.—Evidence by G. C. Lewis to the Select Committee on Poor Law Medical Relief, 1844.

County	Name of Parishes	Population 1841	Amount expended on Medical Relief 1843	Rate per head of population
			£	d.
DEVON:	Exeter	31,312	165	1¼
	Plymouth	36,527	167	1
	Stoke Damerell	33,820	120	¾
GLOUCESTER:	Bristol	64,266	561	2
KENT:	Canterbury	15,435	103	1½
LANCASTER:	Oldham	72,394	60	¼
	Ashton u. Lyne[1]	101,570	151	¼
	Rochdale[1]	60,577	83	¼
MIDDLESEX:	St. Luke	49,829	411	2
	St. Mary	55,690	267	1¼
	St. James, Clerkenwell	56,756	200	¾
	St. Sepulchre	4,801	69	3½
	St. Giles and St. George, Bloomsbury	54,292	804	3½
	St. Marylebone	138,164	1,236	2¼
	St. Pancras	129,763	840	1½
	St. Leonards, Shoreditch	83,432	422	1¼
	St. George, Hanover Sq.	66,453	658	2½
	St. James, Westminster	37,398	350	2¼
	St. Margaret and St. John	46,481	319	1¾
NORFOLK:	Norwich	61,846	537	2
OXFORD:	Oxford	22,205	53	½
SALOP:	Shrewsbury	18,285	349	4½
SOUTHAMPTON:	Gosport	13,510	201	3½
	Southampton	27,744	143	1¼
SURREY:	Farnham	6,615	131	4¾
	St. Mary, Newington	54,606	291	1¼
SUSSEX:	Chichester	8,512	85	2½
	Brighton	46,661	380	2
WARWICK:	Coventry	30,743	241	2
	Birmingham	138,215	1,114	2
WILTSHIRE:	Salisbury	10,086	87	2
YORKS, E. RIDING:	Kingston upon Hull	41,629	100	½
W. RIDING:	Saddleworth	16,829	77	1
	Knaresborough	4,678	53	2¾
	Pontefract	4,669	44	2¼
	Leeds (borough incl. all parishes)	152,054	788	1¼
	Totals	1,797,847	11,660	1½d. (Av.)

The difference between the rates of payment in parishes under Local Acts and in Unions under the Poor Law Amendment Act throw light on the rate of payment which existed before the introduction of the 1834 Act, because in those parishes relief was left to the discretion of the local authorities.

[1] Unions formed for registration purposes only.

Poor Law Commissioners that many beneficial results to the poor had accrued since he was paid adequately![1]

On the whole, the chief criticism against places which did not adopt the new Poor Law was their dependence on charity, and their inability to recognize the importance of remunerating their medical staff adequately. It has been seen, that some areas enjoyed improvements not tolerated by the Act of 1834, particularly in offering relief to all the poor and not only to the pauper. The Poor Law Medical Officers agitated constantly in these years for the supply of drugs to be charged to the Guardians and envied the old corporations where this was done. But here magnanimity in one field was tempered by a niggardly attitude towards salaries, so that on the whole, expenditure on medical relief was less in towns not under the new Poor Law than in the Unions. (See Tables 5.2 and 5.3 for a comparison of expenditure on Medical Relief between Unions and places not under the Act.)

TABLE 5.3

Rate per head of Expenditure for Medical Relief in the year ending Lady Day 1843 on Population of 1841 in 587 Unions in England and Wales. Counties placed according to highest Rate per Head of Expenditure.— Evidence by G. C. Lewis to the Select Committee on Poor Law Medical Relief, 1844.

Counties	Rate per head of expenditure for Medical Relief	Counties	Rate per head of expenditure for Medical Relief	Counties	Rate per head of expenditure for Medical Relief
	d.		d.		d.
1. Essex	6	20. Kent	3	38. Yorks, North Riding	2
2. Sussex	$5\frac{1}{4}$	21. Rutland	3		2
3. Huntingdon	$4\frac{3}{4}$	22. Salop	3	39. Denbigh	2
4. Oxford	$4\frac{3}{4}$	23. Radnor	$2\frac{3}{4}$	40. Chester	$1\frac{3}{4}$
5. Southampton	$4\frac{3}{4}$	24. Gloucester	$2\frac{3}{4}$	41. Monmouth	$1\frac{3}{4}$
6. Wiltshire	$4\frac{3}{4}$	25. Surrey	$2\frac{3}{4}$	42. Stafford	$1\frac{3}{4}$
7. Berkshire	$4\frac{1}{2}$	26. Leicester	$2\frac{1}{2}$	43. Anglesea	$1\frac{3}{4}$
8. Buckingham	$4\frac{1}{2}$	27. Brecon	$2\frac{1}{4}$	44. Carmarthen	$1\frac{3}{4}$
9. Hertford	$4\frac{1}{2}$	28. Lincoln	$2\frac{1}{4}$	45. Flint	$1\frac{3}{4}$
10. Dorset	$4\frac{1}{4}$	29. Warwick	$2\frac{1}{4}$	46. Cornwall	$1\frac{1}{2}$
11. Hereford	$4\frac{1}{4}$	30. Westmorland	$2\frac{1}{4}$	47. Cumberland	$1\frac{1}{4}$
12. Norfolk	$4\frac{1}{4}$	31. Worcester	$2\frac{1}{4}$	48. Derby	$1\frac{1}{4}$
13. Suffolk	$4\frac{1}{4}$	32. Merioneth	$2\frac{1}{4}$	49. Durham	$1\frac{1}{4}$
14. Bedford	4	33. Pembroke	$2\frac{1}{4}$	50. Lancaster	$1\frac{1}{4}$
15. Northampton	$3\frac{3}{4}$	34. Middlesex	2	51. Northumberland	$1\frac{1}{4}$
16. Cambridge	$3\frac{1}{2}$	35. Nottingham	2	52. Cardigan	$1\frac{1}{4}$
17. Somerset	$3\frac{1}{4}$	36. Carnarvon	2	53. Glamorgan	$1\frac{1}{4}$
18. Montgomery	$3\frac{1}{4}$	37. Yorks, East Riding	2	54. Yorks, West Riding	1
19. Devon	3				

Average $2\frac{1}{2}$d.

[1] Report by Assistant Commissioner Weale, Ninth Annual Report of the Poor Law Commissioners, 1843: see also Appendix A of the Report.

CHAPTER 6

Auxiliaries to the
Poor Law Medical Service

(1) THE VOLUNTARY HOSPITAL

The great number of hospitals, almshouses, and other charitable institutions maintained by voluntary contributions, for the sick, the aged, and the impotent, denote the proportion of the more especial objects of the statute, who, as the law was administered, failed in obtaining the relief which was intended for them by the Legislature.[1]

THE voluntary hospital found its origin in medieval piety, and grew in later centuries through the philanthropy of laymen and doctors. The eighteenth century particularly saw the establishment of hospitals to give medical relief to the sick poor, but unlike the development on the Continent, they depended on charity and not on public provision. It was not until economic and social developments of the Victorian age made these institutions in their turn inadequate, that the public hospital was established, and this last phase in the development of the hospital movement, began with the provision of Poor Law workhouse infirmaries, which again expanded into the separate Poor Law hospital and later the municipal hospital.

The endowed or voluntary hospitals in the nineteenth century were an important and necessary auxiliary to the Poor Law medical services. They generally provided for the poor, and relatively few actual paupers were given treatment. The numbers were never differentiated statistically, but this fact can be deduced from the small subscriptions the Guardians paid to cover the parish patients they wished to have admitted. In nearly all the rural Unions, which were the majority of the whole, the workhouse was in any case the only hospital available to the destitute. In many places their functions impinged on each other, and instead of being supplementary, their development was impeded by the overlapping.

As in the case of the public dispensary, the poor could often attend the out-patients' department without formality, but generally a ticket had to be obtained from a subscriber or a Medical Officer. Access to free medical treatment did much to mitigate the hardships of the restrictions surrounding Poor Law medical relief, and explained in great degree why in large towns, self-supporting clubs and dispensaries made little headway. Assistant Poor

---

[1] *Edinburgh Review*, 1836, **63**, p. 488.

Law Commissioner Gulson however denied that parochial contributions to hospitals provided an obstacle to the formation of medical clubs, because the former were only for severe cases and accident.[1] Boards of Guardians made use of the treatment offered by these hospitals for their surgical and accident cases, and contributed towards the cost of maintenance of a particular number of patients, or paid an annual subscription proportionate to the number of patients they wished to send to them. Strictly, charges for parochial subscriptions to hospitals were not allowed under the Poor Law Amendment Act, because they constituted legal charges on the poor rates if payment was made with the proper formalities. In 1838, the Poor Law Commissioners decided that all subscriptions to charities were illegal, and desired Guardians to discontinue contributing to hospitals, even if they had patients in them:—

> It appears to the Commissioners that attendance on cases of acute or chronic disease, and on injuries arising from accident may be rendered quite as skilful and useful in every respect in Union workhouses, as it could possibly be in a County Hospital. Information is so widely diffused among practitioners of medicine in rural districts of these counties, that few or no Unions are without officers competent to perform whatever operations may be requisite, or to the treatment of whatever diseases may present themselves.[2]

Yet in practice the Commissioners seemed to offer no objection to Unions subscribing to a hospital, and gave their assent to Guardians who applied for permission to do so. A letter circularized to the Board of Guardians in 1842 stated that in cases of accidents, and where operations were required, paupers should be sent to a hospital: 'where they might enjoy the practised skill and combined judgement usually connected with such establishments'—and that the Commissioners would sanction any reasonable subscription to a hospital or similar establishment by the Guardians for a Union. This principle was reiterated by Cornewall Lewis himself in his evidence to the Select Committee of 1844. He maintained that if a patient was fit enough to be removed into a workhouse he might in general be removed with safety to an infirmary or hospital, and that the 'Commissioners think it desirable where distance or other circumstance do not present serious obstacles, paupers should enjoy the practised skill and combined judgement of medical men in such establishments', and he concluded that the Commissioners wished to discourage the performance of operations in workhouses as much as possible.

That the central authorities realized the anomalous nature of the law was seen in a communication to the Newcastle Board of Guardians in 1843. The Union asked for permission to pay the local Fever Hospital for diet, necessaries and medicine for nine pauper patients who were sent there from the workhouse. Considering the Guardians' application, the Commissioners replied: 'We are fully aware of the difficulty caused by the present

---

[1] Gulson, Select Committee, 1838.

[2] 21 January 1838, from the Report of the Commissioners to Lord John Russell on the appearance of cholera in Shepton Mallett Union.

state of the law, and we hope that some change in the system of medical charities may tend to diminish it.' Generally Guardians subscribed from about £5 to £10 to a hospital. Kensington Union, for example, paid £5 a year to the Lock Hospital, and £7 14s. to the smallpox hospital, for which they were permitted to send seven paupers there.[1] St. Leonard's, Shoreditch, subscribed £4 4s. a year to the Fever Hospital, until in 1844–45 it erected its own at a cost of £818, and also paid £25 after the middle 'forties to the Infirmary.[2] Bedford Union contributed the unusually high sum of £150 to the County Hospital, but in Bristol the Infirmaries refused to accept subscriptions from the Guardians, so that great difficulty was experienced in gaining admission for the paupers, and the hospitals were also generally full.[3]

The disadvantage of the voluntary hospital service was that institutions were not distributed geographically, and were mainly concentrated in London, the ancient provincial towns, and the new, large industrial cities. The reason for this was that here was the finance, a large population, and the congregation of physicians and surgeons with their students. The Poor Law authorities in London were aided by several hospitals. Whitechapel, for example, sent away all its surgical cases, and was also served by two lying-in charities and the London Hospital for general cases. The number of people belonging to St. Margaret's and St. John's, Westminster who applied for relief to the Royal Ophthalmic Hospital, Charing Cross, in 1843 were ten in-patients and 462 out-patients. In that year the hospital admitted a total of 6,864 cases, which illustrates the magnitude of relief offered by the voluntary institutions in the metropolis. St. Mark's Hospital, founded in 1835 almost single-handed by Frederick Salmon especially for treating anal fistula had 3,500 successful surgical cases in twenty years.[4] This was one of the forerunners of specialist institutions which were to become so important generations later. Stepney, besides sending patients to two dispensaries, sent all its accident cases to the Dreadnought Hospital Ship. The London Hospital was also in the immediate vicinity, and had been founded for the express purpose of affording adequate relief in the various contingencies arising from the hazardous occupations carried on in the district containing shipping, docks, shipyards and warehouses. The reason given by the Stepney Guardians in applying for exemption from the General Medical Order of 1842, was that to maintain such an institution by voluntary contributions required the greatest local exertions; and

> it need scarcely be urged, that it would be highly impolitic to adopt any measure which might have the tendency in many cases to deprive the poorer classes of the advantages, resulting from the combined talent and medical skill, which such an establishment presents, and to throw additional burdens on the locality by whose contributions the charity is to a great extent supported.

[1] Minutes, Board of Guardians.
[2] Abstract of Accounts, Records of Board of Guardians, 1830–63, St. Leonard's, Shoreditch.
[3] G. Carter, Relieving Officer, Clifton, Select Committee, 1854. See above, pp. 191–2.
[4] *Collected papers of St. Mark's Hospital, London.* Centenary Volume 1835–1935. London, J. Lewis, 1935.

The average number of patients relieved at the London Hospital in the years 1841 to 1843 were:

	1841	1842	1843
In-patients	3,308	3,309	3,530
Out-patients	11,142	11,769	12,605
Casualties	3,089	3,117	3,410
Totals	17,539	18,195	19,545

The average daily relief afforded was:

310	In the wards
15	Accidents
300	Out-patients
10	Casualties
635	Total patients

The annual expenditure for drugs, wines, and leeches amounted to £2,574 in 1841, £2,163 in 1842, and £1,873 in 1843; and a salary of £350 a year was paid plus board, to two dispensers and an apothecary.[1]

Other hospitals in London also relieved the Poor Law authorities of a vast number of patients, and the large amount of information given on St. George's Hospital makes it possible to use this institution as an example. In the ten years 1833–42, 70,000 cases were treated, of which nearly 19,000 were in-patients for a long period, and 44,000 were out-patients only. In 1833 the cost of drugs amounted to nearly £2,000 and the number of patients to 8,589. An average of 4s. 3¼d. was spent per case in these years, though the amount had fallen to 3s. 1d. per case by 1847. This was because in the early period, patients remained in the hospital an average of seven weeks, with a mortality rate of 12 per cent whilst in the later years they were discharged after five weeks and the mortality rate had fallen to 9 per cent. But the average number of patients constantly in hospital in 1833–5 was 270, which rose to 311 by 1840–2. In both periods the mortality of permanent patients was 83 per cent. The difference in the mortality of cases, as well as the difference of the cost of drugs per case was accounted for by the increase in the demand for admission to the hospital, for this meant that a policy had to be adopted of retaining incurables and hopeless cases for as short a time as possible. As in other hospitals, medicines were the highest single item of expenditure in St. George's. A Drug Committee saved expense by procuring them in bulk from thirty-two of the principal houses. From the apothecary's book it appeared that sarsaparilla, a very expensive drug (in those days), was used in far greater quantities

[1] Statistical Appendix to Select Committee, 1844.

than in ordinary practices but, on the other hand, this expense was offset by the high proportion of out-patient cases, whose slight injuries required no medicine.[1]

In 1838 a statistical return was made of twenty-one provincial hospitals. The total number of out-patients treated was nearly 50,000, and there were nearly 17,000 in-patients, making an average sick population of over 3,000 treated by each hospital. The cost of drugs, medical appliances, and wines for in-patients amounted to over £15,000 and over £5,000 for out-patients.[2] In the same year Farr analysed the expenditure of nine older established county hospitals, at Salop, Chester, Bedford, York, Colchester, Winchester, Salisbury, Aylesbury, and Lincoln. Here the total number of out-patients treated was over 25,000 yearly, as well as 13,000 in-patients and 1,450 chronics. The cost of drugs and appliances was nearly £7,000, or 2s. 1½d. for each out-patient and 6s. 5¼d. for each in-patient.

Outside London, Liverpool was the town best supplied with charitable institutions. The Infirmary had been established in 1749, and a school for the blind in 1791, which was dedicated solely to the poor. After 1809 this school undertook curative and occupational functions and had its own medical committee. It was completely rebuilt in 1850, with modern improvements. A lunatic asylum was established in 1792 and a second in 1830, and a hospital for consumption and diseases of the chest was built in 1802. An institution for eye diseases was in operation before 1834 and this became the Ophthalmic Infirmary in 1839. A Lock Hospital was established in 1834 and an Ear Institution in 1839, which developed into the Eye and Ear Infirmary in 1841. This infirmary employed a full-time assistant surgeon at a salary of £52 per annum. Conditions in it were described as good, for every room was light and airy, and each ward contained only three patients, and all were clean and comfortable. Before 1846, out-patients had to wait their turn outside, but a waiting room with a fire was added in that year. Liverpool also boasted of two general hospitals, the Northern, which was established in 1834 and rebuilt in 1845, and the Southern which was opened in 1842. Both were subscribed to by the Poor Law authorities because of the considerable increase in the amount of medical relief they were undertaking for them. The Liverpool Fever Hospital (1806–95) was managed by the parish, and admission involved all the disabilities associated with the relief of destitution. Therefore, those not actually paupers were unwilling to make application for admission to the institution. But the accommodation it offered for the great proportion of fever cases which Liverpool had to

---

[1] Detail of expenditure (useful for comparison of remedies used), 1835—13,258 patients:

Cost of drugs	£2,046
herbs and leeches	601
bottles and utensils	121
vinegar and chlorides of lime	136
brandy and spirits of wine	301
Total of medical and surgical appliances	£3,509

—Explanatory remarks on Table by Farr, Select Committee, 1844: Appendix 21.

[2] Rev. C. Oxenden, *Statistical Return of County Infirmaries*, 1838.

deal with, was grossly inadequate, for according to the Report of 1844 of the Committee of Honorary Medical Officers of the hospital, there were only eighty-four beds, twenty-eight of which were generally set aside for ophthalmic and smallpox uses.

Only at the end of the eighteenth century were great strides made in obstetrics and the principle accepted that assistance should be given in childbirth. A Ladies' Charity was begun in Liverpool in 1796, for the misery and poverty associated with the Napoleonic Wars stimulated interest, and the charity collected food, clothing, soap, and money and also gave poor women loans of temporary requisites. Midwives, and if necessary doctors, were also provided. In its first year £340 was spent, and nearly five hundred women received attention, one-third of the total average births in the town coming under the Charity's supervision. Maternal mortality was low in the early years of migration from the country to Liverpool,[1] and all children born had to be vaccinated, on pain of no further relief being given on future occasions. In the 1840s the strictest economy was enforced and surgeons' applications to hire a cab to attend cases were refused. To safeguard funds, and the interest of midwives and doctors, requests for assistance were scrutinized rigidly. When in 1869 the Charity amalgamated with the Lying-in Hospital it had afforded singular service to the poor, and its experiences and work had led to improvements in the management of childbirth. Public opinion long remained prejudiced against the provision of a lying-in hospital for the poorer classes. It was not until 1841 that a lying-in hospital and a dispensary for diseases of women and children was built in Liverpool. It then employed nine nurses and midwives, with trainee assistants. In the first four years 2,500 out-patients received gynaecological treatment, over 1,000 of whom were cured.

Manchester was also well supplied with medical charities, so that the Union Medical Officers were relieved of many duties. The great bulk of applicants for Poor Law sick relief were those already receiving treatment from one of the voluntary medical institutions and who continued so, after having seen the Medical Officer with the object of obtaining a certificate of ill-health from him. There was a General Infirmary with an outdoor patients' dispensary attached, an Eye Institution, the Ancoats Dispensary, a Lying-in Hospital, and Infants, Fever, and Lock Hospitals. All save the Fever Hospital had an outdoor patients' department attached, on the same principle as the Infirmary, and the sick were also, if necessary, visited by the doctors in their homes. To be received as a patient, only a recommendation from a subscriber was required, and this was easily obtained. Lists of patients treated by various Manchester charities, when compared with the numbers receiving Union medical relief, show the insignificance of the latter service to the former. Therefore the Poor Law Commissioners suspended the 1842 Order whereby Guardians should have employed more doctors in proportion to the population. By a singular act of ingratitude the Guardians withdrew the subscriptions they had formerly paid to the various charities, on the even more extraordinary plea that they now had their own surgeons to perform their work. Although the charities lost some of their pecuniary support, the

---

[1] Henry Park's *Book of Genesis* 1769–1830 recorded nearly 4,000 midwifery cases, very few abnormal.

amount of medical relief they afforded to recipients of general outdoor Poor Law assistance remained much the same as before. The Lying-in Hospital for example had formerly received £20 but there was no diminution in the number of destitute sick attended. District surgeons were hardly ever called to a pauper midwifery case, and as the number of patients were very numerous, the great expense they would have entailed to the Union was borne by the Charity. Such a system could not continue, for as a report of these arrangements stated: 'The truth is, the whole medical arrangements are planned by individuals profoundly ignorant of medical affairs of the town, and who have adopted precisely the same arrangements as are usual in country districts, where circumstances are entirely different.' The hospital doctors gave gratuitous aid to the hospitals because they hoped to derive other advantages. They obtained valuable experience from the large and varied number of cases they saw, and also gained a high reputation from their employment in a voluntary hospital. The ratio of Poor Law cases to the population of Manchester was little over 3 per cent, that of the medical charities nearly 20 per cent. Therefore nearly a quarter of the population of Manchester was attended gratuitously by the medical profession.[1]

But this was not appreciated by the destitution authorities, and in 1836 Dr. Kay (Shuttleworth) deprecated the amount of charitable medical relief given, because he said: '...all undiscriminating gratuitous aid, undermines the independence of the poor, and increases the number of those who cease to rely on their own resources and resort to the proffered assistance of parish or public.' Speaking of Manchester (where he himself had been a practitioner in previous years), he said:

> The wealth of Manchester is daily on the increase, and the wages of the population are at this period such, as with frugality and forethought, would enable them to avoid reliance on charity, yet the records of the Lying-in Charity ... prove, that dependence on charitable aid for medical attendance at the period of childbirth, has increased in much more rapid ratio than the population, and has spread to a most mischievous extent.

The ratio he gave was 7:5, and continued that the trend was similar in the number of patients relieved by all charities. In 1821 one-twelfth of the population had received treatment from the medical charities; ten years later it had doubled to one-sixth. 'If public opinion interposed no check to the increase of this form of reliance, it would probably continue to increase in future years in the ratio similar to that observed in the past.' The annual expenditure of about £18,000 would under such circumstances soon be doubled, he maintained, and a similar tendency to an increase in the number of persons relieved by medical charities at a more rapid rate than the expansion of the population was also exhibited in other towns such as Liverpool, Leeds, and Birmingham.[2]

[1] Report by Mr. Dorrington on Manchester to Rumsey, 1844. Quoted by Rumsey in evidence to Select Committee, 1844.
[2] Assistant Commissioner Kay's Report on Norfolk and Suffolk, 1836.

Kay's wish that the charitable institutions should become more discriminating in their provision of medical relief for the poor was granted. Therefore the Guardians were compelled to give more relief to those who became sick paupers, when the hospitals were forced to turn away many applicants for admission. As with the case of voluntarily maintained public dispensaries, donations in this decade did not keep pace with an increase in the number of patients. In the metropolis the situation was not as serious because so many of the hospitals received contributions from the poor rates, but in the country straitened financial circumstances were reported throughout the 'hungry forties'. In 1843, for example, Bristol, Cumberland, Leeds, Salop, Sheffield, Worcester, and the Liverpool Eye and Ear Hospitals all showed deficits, a tendency which continued throughout the country in the next few years.[1]

The hospital returns were extremely inaccurate, and therefore a fair assessment of the value of their work is difficult. Dr. Kay complained of the way hospital records were kept in 1838, and six years later Rumsey deprecated the loss for scientific purposes through the defective statistics. The reports rarely conveyed any notion of the social conditions peculiar to different localities, which can therefore only be deduced from the incidence of particular diseases. Mr. Baker, in a valuable report on the sanitary conditions of Leeds, directed attention to the immense advantage which would be derived from making medical charities responsible to the Home Office for returns of cases and expenditure. Statistical discipline, he argued, should have been thought of long ago, and would have proved useful 'beyond measure, to the legislature, philanthropist, and above all to medical science'. In Leeds no correct report was kept of any case, and in many instances there were not even records of the residences or localities where fever was most prevalent. Dr. Baron Howard of Manchester, found great difficulty in compiling his Sanitary Report, because of the imperfect records in the public medical institutions. Of Huddersfield, Dr. Walker wrote:

> I know so much of the manner of making up lists of diseases from thirty years' experience in our medical charity, where we have 5,000–6,000 patients per annum, that I have little confidence in the accuracy of any such lists.

He pointed out the vast field of potential information, but that no good could arise from the returns as they were being compiled at the time. In the comparative inutility of the hospital reports, Rumsey found a cogent reason for advocating public or compulsory support for these institutions. For this would bring them under public inspection, 'which they greatly need, both as to their general management, and in order to secure all the advantages which they might confer on the community'.[2]

But also from the point of view of medical treatment the voluntary hospitals suffered from grave defects. In 1838, Marshall Hall, a famous London practitioner and a former physician to the Nottingham Hospital, declared medical attendance in the English hospitals

[1] *Reports from Medical Charities*, 1844.
[2] Evidence, Select Committee, 1844.

to be shamefully deficient. There were far too many patients for the number of doctors attending them. Examination always took place in a hurry, and he did not believe a physician of great reputation could examine his patient in the usual time of two minutes. Neither did he think a medical officer could perform his work efficiently if he had a private practice besides his hospital duties, and this was generally the case as hospital posts were honorary. Patients also suffered from being crowded together in a common waiting-room. Here young and old, with every type of illness, sometimes infectious diseases, frequently waited for hours in dirty and insanitary surroundings. It is a matter for conjecture, whether the hospital spread more disease than it cured. As an overworked doctor could not inquire into the details of a patient's history or environment, preventive or really curative treatment was impossible. The sick who were too ill to visit the hospital, and who yet were not ill enough to be admitted as in-patients, were neglected, and in this category must be included the thousands of cases of debility and exhaustion so common among the under-fed and overworked labouring population, and who provided the greatest breeding centres of chronic or epidemic diseases. The liberty of the hospitals to select cases which they were willing to admit for treatment was criticized. But this procedure was not as arbitrary as it appeared, for, from the Minutes of the various Boards of Guardians, it seems that the general hospital refused fever or infectious cases not only because they were filled with other illnesses, but because of the fear of the spread of infection. They were similarly accused of transferring patients as soon as it was apparent that they were chronic or incurable, to the workhouse infirmary when the acute stage had passed. This was not generally because they preferred to deal with 'interesting cases' only, but because of the great demand for beds and medical treatment. Criticism of the unhygienic conditions, the lack of cleanliness and ventilation, the large amount of preventable cross-infection and the appalling nursing service came after this period, when the progress of medical science and public health reform aroused public attention to the scandals which were tolerated in most of the hospitals.

Several specialized voluntary hospitals already existed in the first half of the century, but they were quite inadequate to deal with the infectious diseases or epidemics so prevalent at this time. It was to meet these contingencies, and that of chronic disablement, that the Poor Law had to develop its 'hospitals branch'. Increase in the demand for medical relief filled the general hospital and workhouse infirmary, and a high percentage of the new institutions built after the mid-'forties were specialist ones. The increase in medical knowledge and the growing awareness of the elementary principles of public health taught people the importance of isolation, as well as the fact that superior treatment could be obtained from specialist doctors. Unions too discovered that it was more economical to erect a joint infirmary for particular diseases, but this scheme was not developed until the 'sixties. In the previous decades, Guardians usually boarded out patients in the workhouse infirmaries of other Unions, if these provided accommodation for special cases.

As with the public dispensaries, the great blessing conferred on the poor man by the voluntary hospital, was that it provided medical attention without pauperizing him, although where sickness involved unemployment, he had to fall on the parish for general relief. The fact that he could obtain treatment quickly and without the formality of the Relieving Officer inquiring into his circumstances before issuing an order, was also an advantage. The accommodation and the diet he was offered in the hospital were generally superior to that of the workhouse, and above all he received the attention of the best doctors in the locality,[1] and obtained a quantity and quality of medicine which the Poor Law Medical Officer could not afford to give him.

[1] Sir Astley Cooper, the most eminent surgeon of his day, who had great experience among the poor, himself established an infirmary.

CHAPTER 7

Auxiliaries to the Poor Law Medical Service

(2) THE PUBLIC DISPENSARY

THE public dispensary originated towards the end of the eighteenth century on a small scale, in order to afford relief to the poor who had no access to a doctor. Established by charitable people, and run by voluntary subscriptions of the middle and upper classes, many of these institutions had grown to important dimensions by the time the amended Poor Law came into operation, and many new ones were built throughout the nineteenth century. They were closely connected with the voluntary hospitals and often worked in conjunction with them, becoming a type of out-patients' department.

As the amount of medical relief given by the Unions began to assume greater proportions, the Guardians also began to establish dispensaries as means of keeping abreast of this ever-growing demand for relief, and from the 'fifties dispensaries began to be built from Union Rates, or the Poor Law authorities (when the Commissioners' approval had been received) contributed to the already existing voluntary dispensary, to enable the poor to receive treatment there. Sometimes the public dispensary grew out of the Union 'dispensary', which was really only a chemist's store—a room where drugs were dispensed if they were supplied by the Guardians. As the Union medical department grew, a consulting room for the Poor Law Medical Officer was added so that the surgery would be central, and save the large amount of travelling a busy practice entailed. In time these early stores had to be enlarged, and so became a complete dispensary like the others.

Dispensaries were particularly numerous in the manufacturing towns of Lancashire and the West Riding of Yorkshire, and in other large towns throughout the country. Those maintained by voluntary subscription generally refused assistance to persons entitled to Poor Law medical relief and catered for the poor just above the destitution line. They offered gratuitous medical treatment to those who attended at stated times without any formality, but sometimes required the presentation of subscribers' letters.

The parent institution, and the model from which the others sprang, was the General Dispensary at Aldersgate Street, in the city of London, close to St. Bartholomew's Hospital. Established in 1770 by voluntary contributions, it confined its activity to no district, and patients visited it from every parish in or around the City of London, and occasionally from remoter parts of the country. Its constitution and functions afford an illustration of the other dispensaries which grew up in the nineteenth century. As Officers it had a president, vice-president, treasurer, trustees; a secretary, a collector, a medical committee, auditors, physicians and surgeons, and an apothecary; all except the apothecary and the collector performed their duties gratuitously. The medical staff consisted of three physicians and an assistant, and three surgeons, one physician and one surgeon attending the dispensary each day from one to four hours, while the others visited the poor residing in any part of the City, whenever the severity of the disease precluded the patient's personal attendance at the institution. The licensed apothecary resided at the dispensary and was not allowed to engage in private practice, although he could take apprentices to learn the trade and assist him. He was required to dispense all medicines, and attend emergencies during the day or night until a doctor arrived. His duties were so arduous that he was later provided with an assistant receiving £30 and a porter receiving £38 per annum. The complete separation of duties, between the prescribers of medicine and the dispenser, was of utmost importance to the poor, because the temptation to supply remedies which were at hand and easiest to prepare was removed, and the best drugs could be ordered without regard for the trouble that might be required in their preparation.

The Dispensary was open each day from 11 a.m. to 4 p.m. and from 6 p.m. to 7 p.m., except Sundays, when it opened for an hour between 1 p.m. and 2 p.m. for the collection of medicines only. The building was large, with separate consulting and dispensing rooms, and often two hundred people congregated at a time in the waiting-room. No restriction was placed on the liberal use of expensive medicines, the quality and quantity depending entirely on the doctor. But the utmost economy was practised in the purchase of drugs and chemicals, as these were obtained wholesale directly from the manufacturers. As the drug merchant was excluded, and medicines were inspected by the medical committee and the apothecary, quality was assured, and it was maintained that they were as good as any administered to the wealthy. Liberal in its distribution of drugs, this dispensary was of necessity conducted on the most economical principles.

Patients were required to produce letters of recommendation from a governor, in order to maintain the reputation of the institution, as well as to prevent a greater number of applicants for relief than the funds of the charity would allow. (Other dispensaries in well-populated parts of the country later also adopted this method, so the scramble to obtain the limited number of tickets issued yearly to the governors and officials for distribution, was generally acute.) Often no more tickets were available within a short time of their being handed out to the subscribers, and the waiting lists were long. To obviate any injury which might arise from delay in attending a poor person seriously ill, the doctors or the apothecary could supply letters to urgent cases, and give them immediate attention. Another advantage of admitting patients by tickets or letters was that those distributing an authorization for relief, could ascertain the efficiency with which patients were treated. This particular dispensary obtained the services of some of the most distinguished doctors in the profession, and therefore the medical attention supplied to the poor was of the highest order, see Table 7.1.

TABLE 7.1
Expenditure of the General Dispensary, Aldersgate.—From Select Committee, 1844: Appendix.

	£	s.	d.
DRUGS: wine, chemicals, etc.	360	13	8
SALARIES: Apothecary £120; Assistant £30; Poundage to Collector £18 6s. 6d.; Porter £62 8s.	230	14	6
INCIDENTALS: furniture, advertising stationery, fuel, rent, etc.	189	16	8
	781	4	10
EXPENSES of conducting Dispensary	814	2	6

AMOUNT OF RELIEF GIVEN

ATTENDANCES at Dispensary—Physicians	17,976
Surgeons	6,325
	24,301
VISITATIONS—at houses of poor	4,660
at houses of doctors	8,295
REPETITIONS of medicine without being seen by doctor	6,000
	43,256

Average number receiving medicine per day	138	
Number of times each person seen by doctor	4·5	
receives medicine	5·22	

Therefore, average cost of

materials supplied to individual		$10\frac{1}{4}$d.
labour in preparing and dispensing them		$6\frac{1}{4}$d.
rent, firing, to each individual		7d.
	1s.	$11\frac{1}{2}$d.

Most public dispensaries engaged honorary physicians and surgeons of good reputation, and many doctors offered their services free in order to gain the esteem which employment in one of these institutions afforded. But as the work of the dispensaries increased, the withholding of remuneration became regarded as an abuse. James Black reporting on Bolton to the Provincial Medical and Surgical Association in 1837 stated that there were only a few thousand in the whole population of the town available as a field of remunerative practice, and that except for the house surgeon of the dispensary, no medical man received any salary or gratuity for attending the poor and paupers.[1] A distinguished Liverpool doctor, John Rutter, who had served the dispensaries there for thirteen years, addressed the local Medical Institution on the new discontent which was arising[2]:—

> In this place you (doctors) may be able sooner or later, to originate measures which may terminate in procuring for all who are engaged in the service of our public institutions, a fair and just remuneration for their labours. . . . Some time must elapse before you can prevail on the inhabitants of Liverpool to think that it is neither just nor reasonable that so many of you should be expected to employ the best and most active period of your lives in labouring for the public without reward. Unrewarded duties and services such as yours, so extensive, and so unremitting, have not yet been expected from any other portion of the community, and ought not to be expected from you.

The number of patients attended by Poor Law doctors in Liverpool was trifling when compared with those receiving relief from the dispensaries. The anomalous position obtained whereby the senior officers of the dispensary were also the unpaid honoraries of the workhouse and Union fever hospital. Therefore half the Poor Law Medical Officers were paid and the other half not, and as one doctor said: 'It cannot be . . . compatible with the Poor Law Act that any medical men should attend the inmates of the workhouse without remuneration.' Parochial officers on an average attended $2\frac{3}{8}$ per cent of the population of Liverpool, while the medical charities relieved 23 per cent. In 1843 60,000 patients were admitted into the hospitals or dispensaries, of whom nearly 13,000 were visited in their own homes.

In the rest of the country Guardians began to subscribe £5, £10, or £20 to voluntary dispensary funds, but in Liverpool they took the opposite course. Formerly the parish had contributed the high sum of £500 to the public dispensaries, which had provided relief to all the sick poor of the town on the certificate of their officers. But as soon as Poor Law doctors were appointed, the subscriptions were withdrawn and attendance on the poor was put on an unsatisfactory footing. All former pauper dispensary patients were moved to the District Medical Officers' lists, and many chose to forgo medical relief rather than be transferred to them. In 1844 a report on the Liverpool dispensaries showed that the parish authorities still withheld assistance: 'notwithstanding that the dispensaries relieve them of an expenditure of several thousands a year, which but for these institutions would fall on the town at large in the shape of additional poor rates.'[3]

It was to reduce the amount of Union medical relief and to save the poor rate, that the Guardians subscribed to the voluntarily provided dispensaries, until the problem assumed

---

[1] James Black, *Bolton and Neighbourhood*, Report 1837 to Provincial Medical and Surgical Association (printed as separate volume).
[2] Quoted by T. H. Bickerton, *A Medical History of Liverpool*, London, 1936.
[3] Rumsey, Select Committee, 1844.

such dimensions that Poor Law dispensaries had to be erected in addition. Evidence was given to the Select Committee of 1844 as to the desirability of each Union having a dispensary, for only by this means could the poor be assured of adequate treatment and proper medicines.[1] The great expense this would incur was however also added, and this provided a deterrent to the Guardians. The Derby Union in asking for exemption from applying the Medical Order of 1842, stated that such facilities were given to the poor by the infirmary and dispensary that Poor Law orders were not applicable. Indeed, if there was an increase in Union medical attendance, it would restrict the spirit of independence in the poor, and they would decline to visit the dispensary. The comparison between the numbers attended by the Poor Law Medical Officer and the two voluntary organizations is a further illustration of how much work charitable organizations took off the shoulders of the destitution authorities, and to what an extent ratepayers preferred to contribute large sums voluntarily, rather than pay a small sum compulsorily in the form of poor rates. It is an example of Victorian logic and philosophy.

Number of in-patients attended weekly at the Derby Infirmary	73
Number of out-patients attended weekly at the Derby Infirmary	200
Number of patients (out-patients) attended weekly at the Derby Dispensary	175
Number of patients attended weekly by the Union Medical Officer	40
Number of patients attended weekly at the workhouse	10[2]

The Sheffield Union likewise demanded the suspension of the 1842 Medical Order because of the work of the medical charities of the town. As the public dispensary and the general infirmary were attended by so great a proportion of pauper cases the number of patients who required to be visited by the District Medical Officer was extremely small. Therefore the Guardians did not think it expedient to increase the Poor Law medical staff as required by the Order. Indeed, had it not been for the dispensaries, it would have been impossible for the small number of Poor Law Medical Officers to attend all the sick poor of their districts, nor would it have been fair, in view of what they were paid.

Districts round large towns took advantage of the institutional treatment offered by them and subscribed to their charities. For example, Eccleshall (Yorkshire) Guardians contributed £10 to the Sheffield General Infirmary and £5 to the Public Dispensary.[3] The number of patients the districts were allowed to send for treatment depended on the amount of the subscription. In some outlying areas, individual doctors tried to set up dispensaries in their surgeries, but this was deprecated, as their facilities were inadequate, and the authorities did not trust their honesty in the provision of suitable medicines.

It was in London that the greatest progress was made in establishing dispensaries. Liverpool had six by 1870, but already in 1830 London had 35 and in 1844 Whitechapel alone was served by three—the London Dispensary, the Eastern Dispensary, and the

[1] Evidence T. W. Barnett, Select Committee, 1844.
[2] Letter from Clerk of the Guardians to Poor Law Commissioners, 30 March 1842.
[3] Minutes, Eccleshall Board of Guardians, 1837 (Webb MSS).

Dispensary for Diseases of the Lungs. The Surrey Dispensary at Southwark, gave medical relief to 6,438 patients in 1842, over 1,000 of whom were attended at their homes by the physicians and surgeons. In the same year, 514 midwifery cases were dealt with, and it was calculated that the average daily attendance at the dispensary was 300. The total expenditure of the Charity for 1842–43 was £1,337 or 3s. 9½d. per head. The return, Table 7.2, affords an example of how the income of a dispensary was disbursed.

TABLE 7.2

Disbursement of the Income of a Dispensary.—Return made by the Secretary of the Surrey Dispensary, South- wark, by direction of the Monthly Committee thereof, by order of the Select Committee on Medical Poor Relief, 1844.

	£	s.	d.
Gratuities to physicians and surgeons	252	0	0
Salaries to apothecary	180	0	0
Apothecary's disbursements	50	0	0
Secretary's salary	36	15	0
Medicines	477	13	8
Midwives	94	8	0
Rent, taxes, and insurance	44	8	11
Printing, stationery, and advertisement	107	3	5
Collector's poundage	65	0	6
Incidentals	15	13	11
Repairs to building	11	8	3
Household and shop furniture	2	5	7
	£1,336	17	3

The Tower Hamlets Dispensary admitted 1,500 patients, including 246 midwifery cases, in 1843, at a total cost of nearly £400 or 3s. 11¼d. a case. The London Dispensary at Spital- fields spent nearly £400 in 1843 on 3,312 patients. In 1838 Farr calculated the average cost of medicines for patients of dispensaries throughout the country at 2s. 1½d., although they were probably supplied more cheaply than could be bought by persons in private practice. Dr. Bigsby in a pamphlet gave figures which corresponded with Farr's. The cost of medicines in a sample of twenty-two dispensaries was £2,866, and the number of patients for which they provided was 26,479, making the cost per case 2s. 1½d. Dr. Kay thought this calculation too high, and said that it must have included the cost of trusses, but there is no doubt that the expenditure on drugs was an expensive item for the dispensaries, and no evidence was ever given that a doctor deliberately used inferior medicines for the sake of economy. A doctor of the Blenheim Street Free Dispensary, London, even supplied many of the drugs himself.[1]

The Provincial Medical and Surgical Association instituted its own investigation into the cost of drugs to dispensaries in 1842–43, and found great diversity existing, the reason for this, in their opinion, being that managerial arrangements differed widely. Their conclusions also diverged from Farr's statistics but this was because maintenance and dispensary expenses were not included. In the metropolitan dispensaries the investigators found that Tower Hamlets paid 1s. 3½d. per case for drugs, the Royal South London Dispensary 1s. 2¾d., the Surrey 1s. 5¾d., and the Aldersgate 1s. 1d. (medical officers' gratuities included in each instance), and the Spitalfields 4¼d. In the country, in the Walcot Bath Dispensary drugs cost 8¼d. per case, in the Western Dispensary Bath 1s. 9d., in Burton on Trent 1s. 10¼d., in Atherstone 1s., in Chesham 1s. 1½d., and others ranged to 1s. 9d., which was generally the maximum recorded. In Bristol the cost of medicine for patients suffering from cholera alone amounted to 2¾d. per head of all cases attended by the dispensaries.[2]

Although the expenditure and the number of those seeking treatment in the dispensaries constantly increased, there was a general falling off in the amount of voluntary subscriptions to them. The Report on Medical Charities in 1843 revealed that the Leeds, Liverpool, Portsmouth, and Cheltenham dispensaries were in debt, and quoted the case of Huddersfield, where such a decline in the annual subscriptions had taken place that the Board of Management

> considered it their duty to give admission within the house to none but cases of the most urgent description. The Governors are aware, that the duty of administering medical assistance to such of the sick poor as are recipients of parochial relief, more immediately belongs to the surgeons of the Unions, and not to the medical officers of the infirmaries, whose resources should more *appropriately be directed* to the *prevention of pauperism*.

Also in Liverpool, there was

> serious contemplation to close one of the establishments, but on considering the immense amount of misery and poverty which would be occasioned amongst the dense population of the poorer districts of the towns, we have hesitated to take so painful a step, in the hope that so wealthy and large a community as Liverpool would not withhold the means requisite for continuing the operations without diminution.

Rumsey suggested that the Government should introduce some change in the constitution of the voluntary dispensaries to help them overcome their temporary unsatisfactory financial position, and that all sorts of expedients for augmenting funds, such as bazaars, balls, and sermons, should be resorted to.

---

[1] Dr. R. D. Thomson to Select Committee, 1838. (By his research, this doctor became an expert on the adulteration of drugs.)

[2] Evidence on Bristol by Dr. Wallis, Select Committee, 1854.

Despite all the advantages offered by the dispensary system in providing an auxiliary to the Poor Law medical service it was attacked in the 'forties. It was Rumsey who offered evidence on the charitable institutions to the Select Committee of 1844 and drew together the defects into a comprehensive analysis. He criticized the irregular and uncertain attendance on dispensary patients at their own homes. In a few towns they were visited regularly by honorary physicians and surgeons, but it was not to be expected that any regular or extensive system of domiciliary visiting would be maintained by unpaid officers. In the majority of cases the paid resident apothecary was the sole visitor, and the honoraries only attended serious cases in the homes when specially requested to do so by the apothecary. Rumsey did not believe that dispensary patients were as conscientiously treated as patients of the Union Medical Officer. The large number of cases requiring attendance every day only allowed a hurried and imperfect examination. Often patients were detained in the waiting-room for an inconvenient and 'injurious' length of time, and the regulations for attendance at the dispensary 'precluded the possibility of prompt relief in many urgent cases, and often deprived them of the advantage of necessary changes in the treatment of their case'. It was also stated that an unnecessary and excessive consumption of drugs, even if they were of the best quality, was substituted for regular and frequent attendance.

Rumsey advocated the division of medical labour in large towns, whereby honorary officers should assist chronic cases and those able to attend at the dispensary, 'whilst paid officers should be responsible for the treatment of acute cases at their own homes and all the medical duties of the districts'. In this way he believed all the medical skill and energy of the town could be used for the relief of the sick poor. He described the constant clash of opinions between the Poor Law Medical Officers and the dispensaries. The latter were called on to relieve patients who ought to have been attended by the Union officers, although this was not their original function, but the sick poor could not be turned away from a charitable institution. The Gloucester Dispensary felt this problem so strongly that it asked the Poor Law Commissioners to make a rule whereby medicines should be provided by the Guardians at the cost of the Union.

But little further criticism was heard of the Dispensary Service. The difficulties experienced in the distressed 'forties were overcome, and the institutions grew in increasing numbers until 100,000 sick poor benefited from their help. The nineteenth century also saw the development of specialized dispensaries. London had one for pulmonary affections; Liverpool, besides its four general dispensaries, established one for the diseases of the eye in 1838 and a homeopathic dispensary in 1841. Robert Hibbert Taylor was its founder, and he bore all the expenses including free medicines except for a few subscriptions from his friends, and the payment of a penny by each patient on his first visit and every time he called for extra medicines. In eight years 10,000 cases had been treated. It was rebuilt in 1847, and in 1853 joined the Ear and Eye Hospital.

The Dispensary System has been accused of shifting the burden from the whole of the community and imposing it on the charitable few. As Lord Clarendon wrote to Rumsey:

It is the duty of the whole of the parish adequately to provide for the life and recovery of the poor in the case of sickness. . . . If the dispensaries are so constituted as to shift this burden from the whole parish and imposing it on those only who are charitably disposed . . . they are in so much objectionable.

But although the public authorities could regard them from the economic angle of saving rates, they also secured many poor from becoming paupers through illness. With the increasing requirements of the medical service the voluntary movement was followed by dispensaries established by the Guardians, and these in fact became Poor Law hospitals for out-patients. See Table 7.3 for the returns from twenty-four dispensaries.

TABLE 7.3

Returns of the Number of Patients and the Cost of Drugs, etc. for one year in Twenty-four Dispensaries.—Evidence by Thomas Cooper to Select Committee, 1844.

Town	Population	Annual number of patients (Average three years)	Annual cost of leeches, drugs, etc.	Average cost of drugs for each patient
			£ s. d.	s. d.
Kendal	10,225	2,455	94 0 0	9
Whitehaven	11,854	1,556	69 19 2	10¾
Morpeth	4,237	574	29 15 0	1 0½
Kingston on Thames	9,760	110	6 10 0	1 2
Lichfield	6,761	860	50 0 0	1 2
Windsor	7,528	2,089	130 0 0	1 3
Wolverhampton	70,370	3,460	217 0 0	1 3
Gainsborough	7,860	663	45 0 0	1 4½
Cockermouth	4,940	350	25 0 0	1 5
Reading	18,937	800	60 0 0	1 6
Dover	13,872	400	36 6 5	1 9¾
Wigan	51,988	2,531	250 0 0	1 11½
Louth	8,935	360	36 9 0	2 1
Newark	10,195	600	69 0 9	2 3½
Bradford	105,257	2,104	258 17 9	2 4½
Hertford	51,450	983	118 0 0	2 4¾
Loughborough	10,170	974	135 0 0	2 9¼
Ipswich	24,940	200	30 0 0	3 0
Cheltenham	31,411	4,080	680 0 0	3 4
Doncaster	11,245	1,561	272 15 1	3 6
Tewkesbury	5,802	413	73 10 2	3 6½
Rotherham	5,505	614	151 8 7	3 8¼
Horncastle	4,521	548	104 11 4	3 9¾
Darlington	11,877	290	60 0 0	4 2

In *first twelve*: cost of drugs for the 15,848 patients = £1,013 10s. 7d.—average of 1s. 3½d. per patient.

In *whole twenty-four*: cost of drugs for the 28,621 patients = £3,003 3s. 3d.—average of 2s. 0½d. per patient.

In *fifteen other dispensaries* the cost of drugs for 26,708 patients = £1,571—average of nearly 1s. 3d. per patient.

In *twenty-nine hospitals* during one year,

the cost of drugs and leeches	£11,044
the cost of spirits, wines, and instruments	6,925
	£17,969

There were 90,426 patients (23,180 in-patients; 67,246 out-patients).
Therefore, average for drugs 2s. 5¼d. per patient
average of whole cost 3s. 11¾d. per patient.

CHAPTER 8

Self-help of the Labouring Classes

(1) MEDICAL CLUBS

IT has been seen that the Poor Law administrators tried to prevent the working classes from falling on the poor rates, and that they also attempted to apply the new principle of deterrence to medical relief. In the 'thirties and early 'forties Commissioners and Guardians did their utmost to promote the idea of medical self-help, and in no other field did this typical Victorian principle fail so quickly.

The origin of the medical club was closely linked to the early struggle of the administrators to divide poor and pauper. It has already been seen that there had existed little differentiation between the two classes before the Act, and that in pauperized districts, the whole mass of the labouring population might have been deemed medical paupers, in so far as no effort was made to restrain the reliance on gratuitous aid. With the introduction of rigid control over eligibility for poor relief, and with the institution of strict classification, Poor Law officers came to realize how quickly the slender demarcation between poor and pauper could be crossed through sickness. It was to prevent those on the borderline from falling on the rates in such an emergency, that the Poor Law Commissioners laid so great an emphasis on the importance of Guardians forming sick clubs in their Unions. The idea was made palatable and attractive to the labourer by pointing out that in this provision lay the means of averting for himself and his family the degradation of pauperism. It was an attempt to ally materialism and idealism, to save the ratepayers' pocket and to maintain the independence of the poor.

The Commissioners obtained as much information as possible on the formation of medical clubs and issued a circular in 1835 calling on the Guardians to exert themselves to their utmost to introduce them in their districts. They also sent letters to the Medical Officers to influence them to establish medical clubs 'so that the habits of self-reliance and forethought might be gradually substituted among labourers for complete dependence on the parish, which is not prevalent at present'.[1] The Commissioners pointed out that clubs had already been established by benevolent individuals aided by the co-operation of doctors. The terms had proved satisfactory to the profession, and yet had been within the reach of every labourer earning the ordinary rate of wages. They believed that the only

[1] Letter of the Poor Law Commissioners, 5 May 1836.

reason for the clubs not having become general was because little was known of the rules by which they should be formed and governed. Therefore the Commissioners appended the rules for these 'independent clubs' to their circular, recommending adaptation to be made to suit varying local circumstances. The leading principle, which was never to be lost sight of, was that the clubs should be self-supporting and independent of parochial aid. In towns and densely populated parishes it would be feasible for wealthy individuals to establish a benevolent voluntary institution as an auxiliary to the medical club, for the purpose of providing food and clothing for the sick. But the Commissioners stressed the importance of the funds of such associations being kept entirely distinct from the club.

They could give no positive order regarding these new institutions, but their rules were lengthy. They desired more than one doctor to attend a club, each to be paid for the number of members he actually treated. The members of the club were to consist of labourers, craftsmen, servants, male and female, and anyone else strictly belonging to the working class. Anyone with wages over £1 a week was to be denied membership, as was a servant earning over £6 a year. Members were to pay a year's subscription in advance; every individual was expected to contribute from 3s. 4d. to 4s. 6d. if he or she had no dependants, or were a widow with only one child. The rates for families were scaled according to size and were to vary according to the nature of the district:

Every man and wife were required to contribute .. from 4s. to 6s.

with 1 child   .. .. 5s. 6d., 6s. 6d., or 7s.
with 3 children .. .. 7s., 8s. 3d., or 9s.
with 4 children .. .. 7s. 9d., 9s., or 10s.
with 5 children .. .. 8s. 6d., 10s., or 11s.

Members' children over 16 years of age were to pay for themselves as independent members. A woman who desired to obtain gratuitous medical attention from the club doctor during her confinement was to be required to pay 5s., 7s. 6d., or 10s. according to the district, one month before she expected to be confined.[1] No person should enter a club during the time of his illness, and members were to supply their own bottles, bandages, and trusses as required. Drunkards and profligates were also to be excluded. On entry a member was to choose his doctor from the panel, and detailed records were to be strictly kept. Ministers or Guardians were to be the stewards of the clubs, receiving the subscriptions, paying the Medical Officers and acting as arbitrators in disputes. There were many other minor regulations, and the urgent appeal of the Commissioners was not in vain, for the results were registered in the correspondence they received.

Already in 1835, Gulson, the Assistant Commissioner for Oxfordshire wrote that medical clubs were springing up in all directions, and that the proceedings of Guardians were producing the best results. Highly respectable medical men, he said, were undertaking to attend all cases for an annual subscription of 2s. for single persons and 4s. 4d. for visiting a

---

[1] Circular letter, 6 May 1836. 'Instructional Letter respecting function of independent Medical Clubs.'

whole family. From Buckinghamshire, the Assistant Commissioner reported similar striking effects resulting directly from the change in the medical relief system.

Clergymen supported the campaign, and a typical address to the parish was a pamphlet published by a rector in 1836.

> Sickness [he wrote] is the chief cause which brings people on the parish; and everyone who would wish to be independent of relief—I strongly recommend to belong to one of the clubs established by the medical men of this Union. For little more than two-pence a week, the largest family can be provided with advice and medicines during sickness, and smaller ones for less. A subscription of honorary members has been entered into, to furnish actual members of such clubs with leeches, wine, etc. . . . which medical men are not bound by [their] agreement to supply, and thus the poor might avoid the necessity of applying for relief or of having to pay a large bill for medicines should relief be refused them.[1]

All Assistant Commissioners' Reports of 1836 insisted on the importance of establishing medical clubs. Weale, writing on Gloucester, Worcester, and Somerset stated that benefit clubs had long been general and that sick clubs were in the process of formation, 'the germs of greater providence and economy are appearing'. Dr. Kay reported the speedy substitution of independent medical clubs for the old parochial contracts in Norfolk and Suffolk. In the Cosford Union in Suffolk, all twenty-five parishes had established a club in 1835, embracing the whole labouring population. He compared the old and the new systems. Formerly, the total number of orders which would have been issued for medical relief in the spring quarter among the population of 17,000 would have been not less than 1,000. During the three months of the medical clubs' existence, only sixty-five medical orders had been issued by the Guardians, and in the week previous to the writing of the report only twelve. A great saving on the rates had been achieved, for the Medical Officers' salaries in this Union were lower than in any other in Suffolk. A Relieving Officer of Suffolk wrote that the poor were providing medical assistance for themselves:

> I am sure the surgeons are well satisfied, and the poor decidedly much better attended as a member of an independent medical club, than they were under the old parochial contracts. The poor are pleased with the change; they now go to their surgeon as a matter of right whenever they are ill.

A minister who was the treasurer and manager of a club wrote to the Commissioners asking them to relieve the Union of appointing and paying a Poor Law Medical Officer, as the subscriptions of the club would not only enable him to double the former salary of the surgeon, but also to raise a fund for necessaries for the sick. In Norfolk and Suffolk excluding the city of Norwich, Kay calculated that £10,000 a year could be raised. All over the two counties, doctors desired to assist the Guardians and were zealously forming

---

[1] *Few words to the Poor and Overseers on the New Poor Law*, 1836. Pamphlet by the Rector of Solihull, Archer Clive.

clubs. Indeed, in the first two years, many Medical Officers from various parts of the country wrote to the Commissioners that the system worked well for the profession and beneficially for the poor. Both were more contented; first, because they were independent of each other; second, the doctor was in general better paid at this stage than previously; and third, the poor were entitled to choose their own doctor without necessarily having to accept the Poor Law Medical Officer.

Alfred Power, the Assistant Commissioner for Essex and Cambridge, another agricultural area, sent a circular to all Unions in his district asking for information on medical relief. Several Unions replied that they had not established any medical clubs, nor were they intending to do so. One reason given was that the poor had discovered that those who had refused to enter into membership were as well attended as those paying subscriptions to the club. Other reasons were that no doctors could be found to serve them, or that old contracts were still running. Several Unions offered practitioners far less than the remuneration which they could obtain as District Medical Officers, and other Unions were too thinly populated to make clubs practicable. In these two counties people seemed particularly biased against clubs, a sentiment which was echoed by the doctors. The payment Medical Officers generally received for attending husband and wife was 4s. 6d. a year, with 3s. for single individuals and 1s. for children. These fees seem extremely low, but remuneration on the 'per case' and pauper list system which existed in many Unions in these counties was even less, generally 1s. 6d. per head a year. The Newmarket Guardians claimed:

> where medical officers are ill paid, it is either because no pains have been taken by the Guardians and parish authorities to form independent sick clubs, or the poor themselves have formed them and appointed doctors to whom they have hitherto been accustomed, instead of the medical officers of districts who are not as popular.

The Epping Guardians believed that the difference between the rates of contribution for children and adults to the clubs was too great, as children were more liable to diseases than the latter, and therefore they suggested subscriptions should be on the same terms. In practice the Epping Board only demanded that sixpence a year should be contributed for each child, but if one child in a family was introduced into a club, all the children of that family had to become members also. The parents fell into a separate category, paying 4s. a year for joint membership.

Assistant Commissioner Power considered that medical clubs were a necessary auxiliary to the pauper list system, and that the two should work side by side. Classification would then be complete, and the amount of payment for the medical treatment of both sections of the labouring class could be more easily determined. In Chesterton (Cambridge) many paupers entered on the Pauper List voluntarily subscribed to the medical club, and in some cases the Guardians entered them on the club's register and paid their contributions for them. Indeed, many Boards of Guardians in Southern England were such ardent enthusiasts of the medical club scheme that they advanced subscriptions to the poor on loan. Power concluded that the new system was extremely favourable to the medical profession, and asserted that salaries were considerably increased where medical clubs had been established. He did not fail to point out the advantages to the parishes in so far as they had to contract for only a fraction of the labouring population with a Medical Officer, as the remainder contributed to a club. Power believed that the hostility evinced by the doctors in his two counties would be overcome if the medical profession were allowed to take some financial responsibility into its own hands and fix the terms of subscriptions by reference to the resources of the able-bodied labourers. He suggested that 8s. a year for a family would not be too much for some workers, as Tendring, for example, already levied a rate of 14s. on its members.

This was no original idea, for in some parts of the country it was the Union Medical Officers who formed the medical clubs, as in Gloucester, Worcester, and Somerset, although they were not as frequent here as the Poor Law authorities would have wished. The Bradfield (Yorkshire) Board of Guardians wrote to the Commissioners in 1838, that so great and frequent had been the complaints of surgeons that their private practices had been injured by the indiscriminate manner in which medical orders had been given to labourers who were not paupers, that the Board had inserted a clause in the medical contract, by which Medical Officers of the Union were in future compelled to form medical clubs in each parish on such terms as not to preclude the agricultural classes from entry. They were in fact to be entirely for this class, and twenty-nine parishes very quickly possessed such clubs. The Guardians explained why they frequently paid the subscriptions for the labourers or offered them on loan:

> The Board commenced to act on a principle which they thought would do justice to all parties, particularly in keeping the agricultural labourer who did not apply for relief, save medical, an independent member of society . . .; on that principle alone was medical relief given on loan to people, who should not be made paupers for the sake of 1s. 3d. per quarter, for which sum he himself, his wife and family can be attended during illness and supplied with all necessary medicines.[1]

Sir John Walsham, Assistant Commissioner for Dorset, also considered the appointment of Union Medical Officers under the Poor Law only as an auxiliary to the introduction of a system of independent medical clubs. He anticipated that Guardians would in time begin to investigate all the applications for medical relief, so that (without causing suffering!) the poor should learn:

> by occasional experience of well grounded refusals, to comprehend the honest pride derivable from a thorough reliance on their own resources, and may be led, without harshness, to look forward eagerly to the possibility of obtaining that complete emancipation from the thraldom of pauperism, which can be placed within their reach by a combination of medical clubs with the medical arrangements of each Union.[2]

[1] Letter from Clerk, Bradfield Board of Guardians, 1838.
[2] Report, reprinted in Second Annual Report, 1836: Appendix.

Richard Earle, reporting on Northamptonshire and Warwickshire, echoed similar sentiments when he cynically pointed out that the withholding of parish relief altogether would be advantageous to doctor and poor, for they would realize the benefit of medical clubs and would also co-operate together, instead of looking independently to the parish. Brackley Union put this into effect and the Club of ninety-four subscribers in a population of 500 afforded medical relief to the whole family for three-halfpence a week subscription.

Subscriptions to medical clubs varied greatly from one part of the country to the other and were often above or below the range suggested by the central authority. In Bedford, Buckingham, and Huntingdon 5s. was paid for a whole family, and in Hertfordshire it ranged from 5s. to 10s. Honorary members generally subscribed from 10s. 6d. to a guinea and constituted the management committee. Sir Culling Eardley Smith wrote a letter to Chadwick stating how the whole medical profession in his area opposed the introduction of medical clubs and that 'outsiders' had had to be introduced. He also spoke of the large class of the population which 'vibrated between pauperism and independence' and which was 'imperceptibly sucked into the vortex of pauperism' by unforeseen contingencies, so that it had been attempted to introduce medical clubs, not only as a matter of economy, but also as a utility for the labouring class. He excused the high yearly subscription of 10s. by arguing that people who could pay £3–£5 for rent, could surely afford to contribute 10s. to ensure their independence. But here as elsewhere, distrust and misapprehension of the new scheme was reported, which was never overcome.

In 1836 the Poor Law Commissioners received the following answers from 307 Unions to which a circular had been sent asking for information: 167 Unions had taken no steps at all for the formation of sick clubs, ninety had established clubs in some of their parishes, and fifty offered no reply. Lancashire and the North had no clubs, as the new Poor Law was only coming into operation when the scheme was dying out elsewhere.

By 1838 the British Medical Association recorded its unqualified disapprobation of what it called the 'fallacious system of "medical clubs" . . . established on a basis so strongly recommended, and in some cases enforced, by the Poor Law Commissioners and the Board of Guardians, as being alike injurious to the poor, delusive to the public, and unjust and degrading to the medical profession.'[1] The Select Committee of that year heard evidence on the subject. Power, speaking on behalf of the Poor Law administration, recommended the adoption of clubs, and proposed that no Medical Officer should be appointed unless he consented to attend club members. He suggested that subscriptions should not be fixed by Guardians but should be arranged between the doctor and the club. He reported to the Commission that although he himself had formed all the clubs in Cambridgeshire up to 1837 he had not received a single complaint from the poor and only one Medical Officer had resigned because of his low stipend. He concluded that on the whole doctors received lower salaries from the parish where clubs existed, but that the difference was made up by club subscriptions, so that finally they received more than formerly, whilst the Union

[1] Report of the Council of the British Medical Association on the Poor Law question, April 1838.

saved at the same time. Rumsey and Ceely, representing the Provincial Medical and Surgical Association and the medical profession at the inquiry, condemned the interference of the Guardians in what should have been independent clubs. For the intervention of a destitution authority was a deterrent to any doctor or labourer of independent feelings from having connections with a club. Both parties should be left to work out the constitution and functions of the club together.

As early as 1836 the Provincial Medical and Surgical Association had voiced its opposition to the scheme, objecting to the association of paupers in the same club with independent labourers, who should have been entirely exempt from the control of the Board of Guardians, and from any contact with pauperism. The Association drew attention to the striking injustice inflicted on the Medical Officer by a club system which was allied with the 'Pauper List' scheme, where Guardians had the privilege of adding any sick pauper to the 'schedule' on the same terms as was paid by other contractors.[1] In 1840 the Poor Law Committee of the Association published the report on its inquiry into the medical club system, and showed how Union doctors were often intimidated to form clubs (as by Assistant Commissioner Colonel Wade) or their appointment was made conditional on such activity (as in Camberwell). It was not only a cynical device of Guardians to reduce Medical Officers' fixed salaries, but also did not really diminish the dependence of paupers on the Union. For although the poor were not required to obtain a medical order, they did as a rule become paupers in so far as they were driven to apply for general relief, when sickness caused unemployment. The condition of the labouring classes in these years made it impossible for the majority to preserve their independence under adverse circumstances. Indeed, when the income of the labourer was hardly sufficient to maintain health, there seemed little wisdom or humanity in asking them to subscribe to a club to restore it. It seemed ludicrous to extol the virtues of independence to a labourer who had not the means to obtain it, and when the latter was generally withheld from him, by those who were asking him to safeguard the former. Those who supplied the theory were the same as those who could have made the practice possible.

The Provincial Medical and Surgical Association reported that the Medical Officer hated stooping to collect the paltry subscriptions, and they were often very hard to obtain. It was also stated that the club system evoked unnecessary competition in the profession as in some districts doctors canvassed for members and cut subscription rates against each other.[2] The infirm and helpless often contributed on lower terms, which meant that the greater the liability to sickness, the smaller the contribution, with the result that a healthy family paid indirectly for the relief of a sick one. The Association itself confessed that Medical Officers constantly contrived means of attending club patients with the least possible sacrifice of time, exertion, and expense to themselves. It showed that the remuneration of 2s. to 4s. a case per year in densely populated areas was inadequate, and even more

[1] Report of the Poor Law Committee of the Provincial Medical and Surgical Association at Anniversary Meeting, Manchester, 21 July 1836.
[2] H. W. Rumsey, *Medical Relief of Labouring Classes, 1837*, London, 1842.

so in rural areas, for in dispensaries the average cost per case for medicines, appliances, and attendances was 4s. Farr had in 1838 directed attention to the low terms on which medical men attended Friendly Societies and Medical Clubs, terms which did not allow them to supply members with efficient drugs. Arsenic for example, he said, had to be substituted for quinine, otherwise the cost of medicine in these societies would have risen as high as 9s. to 9s. 6d. a case. The amount of duty performed and the cost of medicines furnished was never published. According to Farr, Medical Officers were generally irresponsible and their treatment of diseases was never questioned. On this score the sick pauper enjoyed greater protection, for Guardians could, if they exerted themselves, check the activities of their medical employees.

By the end of the 'thirties, Dr. Kay as Assistant Commissioner, was himself questioning the efficacy of the medical club. He opposed the Guardians' interference in their formation, even refusing to institute inquiries regarding them, their numbers, membership and amount of subscription, for he realized this would provide data for the reduction of salaries.

In the 'forties the early form of medical club was abandoned. The reasons given were that too great an effort was needed to get the clubs started; that the labouring classes were unable to afford to subscribe to them; and that they were often deterred from joining one because they disliked the doctors, under whose direction the club was to be run, or who formed the panel. The Select Committee of 1844 heard the last evidence of these clubs, and a clergyman of Tendring Union forwarded a letter summarizing the general objection. In this Union, membership of the club was obligatory to the poor, and the minister pointed out that the scheme was unremunerative, for it did not relieve the parochial poor solely from parochial resources. The independent poor contributed to the relief of the destitute, because Union Medical Officers were compelled to attend the clubs, which provided them with additional incomes outside their salaries. Tendring was typical of the Unions, where, to ensure the entrance of the independent poor into the clubs, the Board of Guardians held out the threat of removal to the workhouse to all the sick who were not members. Therefore, as no outdoor medical relief was supplied, the workhouse was often subjected to being converted into a hospital. The clergyman continued his evidence by pointing to the degrading competition amongst doctors and the constant antagonism through their activities in seeking new members for their particular clubs. He also believed that club members were not as well attended as others and that they were supplied with less medicine. He concluded that unconscientious medical practitioners could always attract members by the facility with which in sickness they could recommend extras, such as food and wine. In fact in such instances people were receiving parochial relief and were therefore paupers in all but name.[1] The margin between poor and pauper could not be widened by this system.

Side by side with these 'independent' medical clubs sponsored by the Poor Law authorities, the working class had in some areas established their own sick clubs and other forms of association which afforded relief in case of illness. In Essex and Cambridge a few medical

[1] Letter, Rector G. Burmaster to Select Committee, 1844: Appendix II.

clubs, such as in Rochford and Newmarket, had been started independently of the Union, and Power described them as being very beneficial and satisfactory. In Wales and Cornwall also, well supported medical clubs were run by and for the working people. In 1839 the Assistant Commissioner for Devon and Cornwall reported the great number of self-supporting clubs and that non-members received medical relief on loan.[1] Dolgelley in Wales had a club exclusive to men, but this was extremely rare.

It is interesting to examine the different and typical provision made in the iron-mining districts for medical relief. The system was unique, because it was unusual at this time for societies to distinguish between accident and sickness, or occupational disease. The schemes were old, and had developed as the industry created the necessity for them, and were not therefore dependent for their origin on the new Poor Law. In Shropshire for example the accident rate in the mines was high.[2] Four mining firms gave accident rates as follows:

(a) 25 per cent permanently disabled
30 per cent fatal
(b) 75 per cent slight accidents
15 per cent wholly disabled
10 per cent fatal
(c) 50 per cent fatal
1 in 70 permanently disabled
1 in 30 temporarily disabled
(d) 16 out of 31 deaths were caused by accidents of those under 20 years old.
12 accidents caused deaths out of death rate of 51 of those between the ages of 20 and 50.

Few, or none, escaped injury, and a large proportion of workers were disabled for a long time. The Field Club gave an average of 25 per cent of fatal and severe accidents. Occupational disease too, was of high incidence, and the expectation of life was short. The best years of an iron-miner's life were between 18 and 20, and at 40 it was almost over. All forms of pulmonary complaints and dyspepsia were common. One ironmaster in 1836 himself stated: 'In coal and ironstone pits, men labour very hard during the hours they work, and compress themselves into such postures . . . and imbibe so much impure air . . . that they very soon become asthmatic.' The colliers in the area were also subject to rheumatism and asthma and they too were regarded as aged at 50. The men averaged about 3s. 6d. wages a day, women 1s. and children tenpence. Even if these rates were regarded as sufficient to enable a labourer to insure against the disability of age, the important question still remained, how far was his power to obtain these wages interfered with by the casualties to which his occupation was liable. From such contingencies no miner could save himself,

[1] Report, Gilbert: Appendix to Report of Commissioners on Further Amendment of Poor Law, based on Assistant Commissioners' Investigations, 1839.
[2] William Day, Report on Shropshire, 1836. Included in Second Annual Report.

and he had long realized the absolute necessity of joining a society for a small sum, which by its strength of numbers could alone provide insurance against sickness. It was therefore against accidents of a temporary nature that miners, assisted by their masters, insured themselves in 'Field Clubs'.

How these clubs worked can be illustrated by inquiring into a particular and typical one, the Madeley Woods Company Field Club, which had been established in the first decade of the nineteenth century.[1] The funds for the clubs were raised by the payment of twopence a week by men and a penny by women and children. For this they were entitled to medical attention in case of accident, as well as the payment of 5s. a week to men and 2s. 6d. a week to women and children, whilst they remained on the books or for a period of six months. They were entitled to half this amount for the second six months if necessary, after which, payment ceased. This particular club had found for the last fifteen years that contributions had not only been sufficient, but that capital had been accumulated to the extent of nearly 10 per cent of deposits, from which reserve fund further help had been given in cases of severe accidents. The Club received nearly £200 a year, the constant weekly contributions of 455 people. The average weekly allowance for the same period was £142, the surgeon's salary, medicines, and capital accumulation being defrayed out of the residue. The number of those disabled equalled one in forty-one, or eleven men totally disabled for a year, but the number of sufferers through those actually incapacitated was very much higher. The surgeon of the Field Club affirmed that at least as much of the premature decay of the miner was induced by his drinking orgies on pay day as by the deleterious nature of his work. This directly resulted in the malnutrition of the family, for little remained for food, so that the constitutions of the women and children were also undermined. It was an evil consequence of the butty and truck system.

In Wolverhampton the miners also received medical attention through their Field Clubs, but again only for accidents. Masters deducted a small sum from their wages, so that membership was compulsory. Similarly, in the iron mines of South Wales a rate of a penny in the pound was levied, or twopence for a whole family. The majority of ironmasters adopted the latter scheme so that the whole labouring population was provided with medical attendance. Well qualified surgeons were appointed, some of whom derived large incomes in this way and obtained a great deal of very important and valuable surgical experience. (See appendix at end of chapter.)

But these Field Clubs neglected the provision for permanent disablement or premature old age. For this purpose benefit societies appeared the only remedy, and they had in the past been widespread in mining districts. In the 'thirties they were almost extinct. The cause of their decay was that because of the premature enfeeblement of workers in these areas, young people had refused to join the established societies and continually formed new

---

[1] Report on an inquiry on Shropshire by William Day, Assistant Poor Law Commissioner, reprinted in Second Annual Report of the Poor Law Commissioners, 1836.

clubs, with fatal results to both. New societies were in their turn deserted or were prematurely dissolved through insolvency. No club had attempted to fulfil a dual purpose and divide its functions and resources. The Assistant Commissioner for Shropshire suggested that the Government should give a guarantee to foster the permanency of such an institution, to which no one would then object to subscribing. This plan, he thought, would extinguish the necessity for the Poor Law altogether, save on the strictest scale.

The benefit clubs and friendly societies of various kinds which had either been long established, or which arose when the Guardian-sponsored medical clubs failed, were assuming greater importance in the lives of the working-class. Since the discriminating principle of the Poor Law Act had been put into operation, people were more willing to co-operate in associations. As one of the poor stated: 'We must now look to ourselves, and provide for the day of sickness and old age, now that there is no parish to look to.'[1] In Dorset two very large general clubs or friendly societies had been established—but no sick clubs—with four hundred members, each giving medical and other relief in cases of illness. Walsham reported that friendly societies and benefit clubs were rapidly becoming general throughout the country, and a new stimulus had been given where they already existed. Already in 1835, Gulson had found a great increase in provident institutions arising from the general influence of the change in the poor relief system. In the following year a clergyman wrote to him of the impulse given to the formation of friendly societies in Leicestershire, principally with a view to medical assistance. The Board of Guardians of St. Albans stated in 1840 that great progress had been made by the Benefit Society which had been established in 1836 for provision in sickness and old age. It consisted chiefly of the young of both sexes and in 1840 had 203 members and £300 stock, and the Guardians reported that they were trying to abolish the giving of outdoor relief altogether in the Union. The Poor Law officials of this Union (together with those of Hitchin, which also had a long established Benefit Society embracing a sick club's functions) were foremost in the general objection made by Guardians to the extra fees for surgical operations and midwifery cases prescribed by the 1842 Medical Order, on the grounds that the measure discouraged sick clubs and societies. In West Ham, where the Guardians failed to establish sick clubs after trying for two years, a large benefit society was formed with a medical club attached to it. Every member of the society was also called on to join the club. Club payments, if members insured on account of sickness, were not higher than 6s. weekly, for which benefit a monthly contribution of threepence was required. A sum of threepence-halfpenny a month secured a weekly payment of 8s.; fourpence—12s.; fivepence-halfpenny —15s. and sevenpence—18s. For every 3s. additional weekly benefit an extra subscription of twopence a month was demanded. Apparently Medical Officers were very willing to assist the scheme, but the members of the society and medical club were not those who would apply for parish relief. Therefore it did not materially affect the number of applicants for medical relief, pauperism, or the rates.[2]

[1] Evidence W. C. Streatfield, Chairman, West Ham Union, Select Committee, 1844.
[2] Weale's Report on Gloucester, Worcester, and Somerset, 1836.

Savings banks deposits were also increasing, and were being made by labourers, many of whom had previously been in the pauper class. Tidd Pratt, the barrister, who was appointed Registrar to certify the rules of savings banks and benefit societies in 1836, wrote to the Poor Law Commissioners that from August 1833 to August 1834, 360 Friendly Societies had been certified and, from 1834 to 1835, 750. In the first year, depositors had increased by 33,000, nearly as many as in the three previous years together, with an increase of nearly £1 million in money deposited. The increase in depositors was among the lowest class and in the agricultural areas, Pratt showing that the rise was most marked in Bedfordshire, Berkshire, Buckinghamshire, Cambridgeshire, Essex, Hertfordshire, Kent, Norfolk, Suffolk, and Sussex. Economic reasons apart, it is probable that this factor was in some degree coincident with the progress made in these counties in the enforcement of the new Poor Law. Tidd Pratt's evidence to the Select Committee of 1838 seems to bear out this inference. He stated that he had received communications from groups wishing to form benefit societies who had previously had no inducement to belong to one, for if a man belonged to such a society, the allowance he received from it was deducted from his poor relief, so that he received less by being provident. Under the new law no outdoor relief could be obtained in any case, so Pratt assumed that the poor were providing for unexpected contingencies by insuring themselves in a society. *It is important to note that up to the 1870s, sickness benefit was by far the largest item in the expenditure of Friendly Societies.* But although they provided such large amounts for sickness or accident, they strictly examined the health certificate of a prospective member. In towns men engaged in unhealthy trades were even excluded from membership. For example, the Cannon Street Male Adult Provident Institution in Birmingham, which was established in 1841, included in its rules that no person could be admitted without a certificate of health from the society's Medical Officer nor could anyone under 16 or over 40, nor anyone 'whose occupation is deemed dangerous or unhealthy, such as watergilders, grinders, painters, colour-makers, varnish-makers, pearl-workers, nor such railway servants as engine-drivers, stokers, guards, plate-layers, or porters, or any other pernicious or dangerous calling; nor police officers, nor bailiffs' followers.'[1]

Besides the medical clubs formed under the auspices of the Guardians and the medical relief given by benefit societies, another type of club was established in the villages and county rural areas. Their distinctive feature was that they were generally established and managed by the clergy or landed gentry.[2] Without the initiative and patronage of the gentry they would probably have failed. Their financial aid was essential because the clubs were often not accessible to labourers earning over 12s. a week. One of these clubs had been established in Wiltshire in 1828 and it was still in existence in 1882. A small sick club was started in 1834 by a clergyman of Leamington Hastings (the Rev. Mr. Sitwell), and

[1] J. M. Baernreither, *English Associations of Working Men*, London, 1893, p. 180.
[2] They were most common in Berkshire, Dorset, Essex, Hampshire, Hereford, Nottinghamshire, Rutland, Salop, Wiltshire, Devonshire, Gloucestershire, Oxford, Somerset, Suffolk, and Surrey.

this was to provide the model for many societies established in the following years. The object of the club was to give a sum less than the labourer's wages had been, for the first six months of sickness. Each farthing a week subscribed entitled the member to 1s. in sickness benefit. The allowance for the first three months was paid from the free members' fund, that of the second three months from a fund subscribed to by honorary members, and a reserve fund was raised to provide for a deficiency in resources, should an unusual amount of sickness prevail. Funds remaining at the end of the year were divided out amongst the members. The club succeeded beyond all expectations, every head of a family in the parish of 460 joined. The charges of the district for sick poor relief were greatly curtailed, falling from £45 before the club was established to £1 17s. in its third year. The minister also described the great moral change which had come over his parish in this period; men began to feel too ashamed to ask the parish for relief.

A similar club which was to have a long life was the Medical Provident Society established in 1834 by the Rev. C. Oxenden at Barham Downs (Kent). It was a wholly rural area comprising twenty-seven parishes and in twenty years the club covered 32 per cent of the population. The society was practically self-supporting with some honorary subscriptions, and admitted only farm servants, journeymen, apprentices, labourers, single women, widows and their families. No family whose total income exceeded 28s. a week could join. Contributions varied from 1s. to 6s. according to the member's employment and the number of children in the family. If medical assistance was not called for during the year, a member would receive back a quarter of his year's subscription, but if he got in arrears with his contributions, no medical relief could be obtained for that year. Doctors were paid 7s. 6d. a case, with which they seemed entirely satisfied, and they divided nearly the whole income of the society in proportion to the number of attendances given. Every doctor in the neighbourhood could be put on the panel for an entrance fee of a guinea, and members could select the practitioner they preferred from it, provided he resided within a radius of 4 miles.

The advantage of the club, the minister pointed out, was that the poor had a free choice of doctors, who also paid greater attention to members than they did to sick paupers. He advocated the institution of sick clubs everywhere as he believed it secured for the poor superior medical attention, whilst he maintained that ordinary friendly societies and sick clubs in manufacturing districts offered inferior treatment, because the doctor's remuneration was so small. He further drew attention to the fact that better medicines were administered to society members, because the Medical Officers took a genuine interest in the club and because of the rivalry among them for patients. The activities of the club did not greatly affect Union medical relief, although the club spent £100 for every £60 the parish spent. The advantage it offered was not that it decreased the cost of medical relief to the Union, but that it provided additional comfort to the sick poor of the district.[1]

[1] Evidence, Rev. C. Oxenden, Select Committee, 1854, speaking of earlier period. Rumsey stated that in this club Medical Officers were overworked because the poor called for attention far more than other classes of people and the doctors did nothing to check the demand for medicines.

The principle of these two clubs was followed in 1839 by the formation of the Provident Institution and Self-Aiding Medical Club in Newmarket. This society also enabled the labourer to secure a weekly allowance for himself or his family in sickness or old age. Within three months the club enrolled 134 subscribers. The most encouraging result was that the medical branch in the first year admitted 7,258 members who contributed over £560. The total payment given for medical assistance was £939, the balance between the two being made up by contributions of honorary members and by payment from the auxiliary fund. Considerable aid was given by voluntary subscriptions and donations. This caused the only fear for the permanent prosperity of the society, for any relaxation in the benevolence of the ratepayers endangered the solvency of the institution. The most influential of the promoters, the Duke of Rutland, therefore attempted to establish a more permanent fund by trying to obtain aid from a compulsory rate. He suggested legal provision might be made for levying a rate-in-aid if other similar clubs were to be established throughout the country. It was maintained that such a tax would not materially affect ratepayers, if the proportion of medical aid afforded to labourers was considered, for the poor rate would be diminished proportionately. But such a scheme was rejected, because it was alleged that it was quite inconsistent to provide aid from a compulsory fund for an institution whose independent and voluntary character was its chief recommendation.[1]

Reporting on this club in 1844, Rumsey directed attention to the arrears of £100 or so in the subscriptions from the very first year, and he cynically remarked that if this state of affairs was supposed to encourage a feeling of honest independence in the minds of the labourers, he did not see why a man should be called a pauper who received relief from the Union. He also pointed out the lack of logic in the argument offered in favour of the club, that the expenses of the Union had been reduced by £150 through the scheme, whilst over £300 had been contributed by the ratepayers to save this £150. The economy of the scheme was not apparent to him.

A similar self-aiding medical club was formed at Grantham, also by the Duke of Rutland. In its first year, 1839, it admitted 2,368 members, but the thirteen doctors and the incidental expenses cost the society £470, nearly twice as much as the total subscriptions. A few years later, the Duke, giving evidence to the Select Committee of 1844, insisted on the importance of these clubs for encouraging the independence of the labourer and stressed the necessity for extending them over the whole country. Again he put forward his proposal for the giving of a grant-in-aid from the poor rate. Guthrie, President of the Royal College of Surgeons, opposed the Duke of Rutland. He agreed that medical clubs when actively supported by the nobility and gentry, were valuable, but contended that instead of the poor rates supporting them the subscriptions should be augmented by the employers of the labourers.

Besides Grantham and Newmarket, Stratford-on-Avon contained the other flourishing

---

[1] Eighth Annual Report, 1842, contains much of this.

club run by the gentry. Here the Medical Provident Institution covered 39 parishes and employed fifteen surgeons for its 2,660 members, 60 per cent of whom received medical relief on an average every year. Although this was regarded as a prosperous club, doctors only received £240 or about 3s. a case, a very meagre sum, considering it was an extensive rural district necessitating long journeys. The honorary members contributed £105 a year, of which £70 to £80 was paid to the Medical Officer in extra fees for fractures, consultations, operations, and midwifery. Here again therefore members were not really independent, and fees for the most serious illnesses were provided by charity—a situation very different therefore from ordinary Poor Law arrangements, where Guardians paid from ratepayers' money.

A medical club supported by the wealthy, yet run on progressive lines, was the South Buckingham Association, which Ceely told the Select Committee of 1838 was the only medical club he could tolerate. The reasons he gave were that it was founded on the principle of mutual assurance and because the doctors were paid according to an estimate of the value of their services. In other medical clubs, remuneration was not proportionate to duty done, and bore no ratio to the amount of liability. The surgeons' remuneration varied from 2s. to 9s. 6d. per case according to the length of illness and the number of visits made. Fractures and other surgical operations were paid for at the rate of 10s. 6d. to £2 2s., and sixpence a mile was added for journeys, which was doubled for night calls. Members' subscriptions were framed on the basis of capability to pay and also varied according to age. Children under 15 contributed threepence a month, after which age payments rose progressively by $\frac{1}{4}$d. for every five years of life, so that at 20 a member paid fourpence. Those between the ages of 32 to 36 contributed fivepence and those between 42 and 45, $5\frac{3}{4}$d. Members constantly liable to sickness paid double the amount of monthly contribution and long journeys had also to be paid for. Some families were admitted to the club without any charge for the children, and others at a graduated scale. For example if the average amount of income was less than 12s. a week nothing was paid for children, and the average wage for a labourer in Buckinghamshire was only from 8s. to 10s.

> If the average income was 12s.–15s. — 2d. was paid for the first child and the rest free
> 15s.–20s. — 2d. two children
> 18s.–21s. — 2d. three children
> 21s.–25s. — 3d. three children

No members were entitled to relief unless all arrears, and fines for arrears, were paid. Members had the choice of any surgeon belonging to the society and could transfer their assurance to another medical society if they removed, so that they would not lose previous payments. A member applying for medical relief was required to produce a certificate within twenty-four hours from the Secretary, entitling him to medical aid, and this had to be returned with the medical reports to the secretary on his recovery. 'Sick Visitors' were appointed by the society, who visited patients once a week and entered their reports on a 'Sick List'. The club also had the power to send notices to any other member living near the patient, to visit him and report if anything was amiss. There was also a dispensary where members who were sufficiently fit had to attend at special times and days, bringing their own 'sick list' (probably like a case card) to every attendance and returning it to the secretary when they were discharged, for which they were given a penny. The doctor entered a report on the card each time and his remuneration was calculated from it. Vaccination was free, but no member could obtain medical attention for diseases contracted by profligacy or immorality.

Rumsey, who also came from Buckingham, had many connections with this society and approved of the unique principles introduced. He stated that the society consisted chiefly of healthy persons because a certificate of health was demanded on admission, placing it therefore completely on the footing of mutual assurance. He elaborated Ceely's account, pointing out that the controlling body was elected from honorary members, who were also originators of the scheme. To this Rumsey did not object because he said the safety of the society depended on good management, and the poor were not sufficiently educated to govern without them, otherwise he would have favoured control being vested in the poor. Wakley, who was a member of the Select Committee of 1838, postulated one of his interesting questions—which always drew revealing answers—and made it known that the amount subscribed by the wealthy was far less than the total subscribed by the poor, so that those who contributed least were in control!

Dr. Kay expressed apprehension to the Select Committee of the value of sick clubs managed and supported in the main by the wealthy. His experience in agricultural districts had taught him that labourers should have a large share in the management of clubs, because they were institutions for mutual assurance and there was no automatic means of preventing fraud. The feeling of self-preservation provided the only inducement for members to watch proceedings vigilantly and prevent undue reliance on funds. Kay himself prepared rules for the general organization of benefit societies and medical clubs. He suggested that the appointment of officers and the formulation of the general principles and regulations of societies should be left to honorary members, but the distribution of relief was to be the responsibility of the ordinary members. In the past, mutual assurance societies organized by labourers themselves had had a precarious existence. Kay was aware of this, and of how quickly funds had been exhausted, or how officers had absconded with the entire capital of a society. Clubs which had been established by publicans had had to contend not only with the dangers of mismanagement, but had also had to fight against the waste of resources by labourers on drink. Frequent failure of associations before 1834 spread distrust among the poor, and it was not until the working-class obtained sufficient information on how to run such a society that permanent existence could be promised. It was therefore fortunate that in the year the Poor Law was passed to make self-help imperative to a high degree, the Treasury began to issue rules and tables for societies and these were distributed gratuitously.

Kay insisted that clubs should depend on the energies of the labourers and on their contributions alone, for only by these means would individuals interest themselves in the prosperity of their societies. They had an unquestionable right in the management of funds so hard earned and would guard expenditure jealously. Further, Kay believed that the Guardians could assist by circularizing information, and that subscriptions from the gentry and clergy might be used to defray general expenses. A joint council might also be elected from all honorary subscribers to societies in the Union, which could prepare rules for each of the district associations, and have the right of veto on the appointment of all superior officers. Therefore individual societies would be linked, whilst each retained separate funds, assurance, and management. In addition every club was to have a board of Wardens, which would visit the sick, collect funds and regulate allowances. Lastly Kay suggested funds should be invested in property mortgages or government securities ($4\frac{1}{2}$ per cent) and that small sums should be placed in local savings banks.[1]

Blything Union offered the poor an unusual system of medical relief, for here it could only be obtained through the Medical Assurance Association. For this reason the Union was exempt from the Medical Order of 1842 and other orders of the Poor Law authorities. Before the formation of the association in 1839 the Board had lost all control over the giving of medical relief, and the poor were quite unscrupulous in applying directly to the Union Medical Officer for gratuitous treatment, who in turn attended them without an order at his own discretion. The doctor certified his patient's illness to the Relieving Officer, and this enabled the sick to obtain ordinary relief in the form of food and 'extras' as well. It was discovered that the doctor registered many poor as his patients in order that they might obtain these extras, whilst in several instances they attended for treatment, and paid another private practitioner of their own choice. Left unchecked, this system induced every independent labourer to become a 'pauper', and offered him every facility to fraud, and to simulate sickness for the sake of obtaining general relief. The Board of Guardians had been so lax that gradually they had neglected to keep or examine the books required by the Commissioners. It was stated that the Guardians, having failed to discharge their duties for so long, in the end became quite ignorant of them. The whole of the labouring population had begun to consider and demand medical relief as an established right, the granting of which brought no burden on their own parish as the Union Medical Officer was paid a fixed sum. It amounted to the worst evils of the old parochial system being perpetuated, and the medical pauperism thus generated thwarted early attempts to establish independent sick clubs in the Union. Therefore several influential people determined to establish a Pauper Health Assurance Association, and reform the system of medical relief.

It was an interesting Association because it differed from other clubs in so far as the promoters and the members belonged to the medical profession. In February 1839 all the practitioners of the area held a general meeting to determine the rules of the proposed association. The objects which the doctors hoped to achieve were:

to make the skill and experience of every qualified practitioner available for the relief of paupers; to substitute and encourage open competition of professional character and

[1] Draft circular respecting Medical Associations for Husbandmen and Mechanics by J. P. Kay, M.D., 1838.

ability [for financial rivalry]; to give every pauper when ill the privilege enjoyed by every other class of the community of selecting a practitioner; ... to establish more efficient superintendence over the issue of all orders; ... to charge medical and surgical relief to the separate parishes to which the paupers belonged; ... to institute a closer examination into every case; ... to classify all cases, and to obtain correct data for vital statistics.

Therefore the Association was to be the means of reforming the whole system of medical relief in the Union, and was not to provide only an auxiliary to the method of relief laid down by the Poor Law Commissioners. It was unique in that members were to consist of all resident qualified practitioners. Paupers could choose any doctor, but they had to produce an order from the Guardians or the Relieving Officer before treatment. Registers and records were to be kept similar to those specified by the Poor Law authorities. Patients were to be classified into seven categories according to the severity of the illness and their distance from the doctor, and fees were to be on a scale based on these classifications. Payment of doctors was complicated, for the total assurance premium was divided into it, thus forming a fee per patient. Therefore the rate of remuneration per class varied each quarter because the number of patients in each category varied. This was to ensure that payment to practitioners fluctuated according to the amount of work and its nature. The premium of assurance was fixed by the Guardians and was about £325 a year, and this was divided among the members of the Association quarterly.

The scheme was sanctioned by the Poor Law Commissioners and evidence given to the Select Committee of 1844 on the Blything system pointed to its advantages. Praise was given because Medical Officers were paid according to the number of their patients, the distance travelled and their responsibility, and because the sick pauper enjoyed the privilege of obtaining the attendance of the doctor in whom he had confidence. As this established fair competition among the doctors in so far as salaries depended indirectly on ability, the poor were also given some guarantee of being well attended.[1]

The Blything Association therefore avoided the mistake which other forms of clubs fell into, and when Rumsey deprecated the practice of medical clubs and benefit societies as well as the Poor Law's medical contract system, whereby the Medical Officer's salary bore no reference to the benefit supplied, 'but merely depended on the fears and necessities of the two contracting parties', the Blything system was regarded as a step forward. George Webster, M.D., M.R.C.S., President of the British Medical Association, giving evidence in 1844, voiced his disapprobation of the existing club system, calling it unjust and unsatisfactory. He favoured a plan of allowing the poor to select their own attendants, either on assurance per head or on a per case system, or by dividing the salary fixed for the district

[1] Appendices. Select Committee on Medical Relief, 1844.
(1) The Practice of Medical Relief before the forming of the Medical Assurance Association (25 March 1839).
(2) Blything Union Pauper Health Association—Objects and Rules.
(3) Results of the new form of Medical Relief in the Blything Union.

among the practitioners according to the services they had rendered. He too was a convert to the scheme inaugurated in Blything.

There was no inquiry into the functions and constitutions of the various types of medical club and benefit society which had grown up or sprung into new life since 1834 until the Select Committee of 1844. It was Rumsey who was then asked to supply a detailed paper on the subject. He reported that he had found it impossible without 'protracted and troublesome investigation to gain precise information regarding the number of persons provided with medical assistance from sick clubs'. For inquiries were disliked both by the labourers and the doctors of the associations. In Dr. Brown of Sunderland Rumsey found an able assistant for his investigations. With a population of 53,000, Sunderland had nearly sixty clubs embracing 4,500 members who were entitled to medical attendance for 2s. or 3s. a year. The practitioners were, however, trying to end the system and thirty-five had signed a document declaring their disapproval of it. There was general conviction that the system would be abandoned as hundreds of people were obtaining medical relief who were in comfortable circumstances and able to remunerate their doctors. The latter were therefore losing heavily, and Brown stated that he had had to prescribe so much quinine, which was very expensive, for one patient that it consumed the whole of his annual salary for the club of seventy people.

Rumsey gave a comparative statement of the payment to Medical Officers of clubs in the country. For example, in Bradford it was 2s. 6d., in Oldham 2s., in Rotherham 2s., in Gloucester 2s. 6d. to 4s., in Shrewsbury 2s. 6d. to 4s., in Worcester 4s. and in Yarmouth 2s. 6d. Where the sum was over 2s. 6d. Rumsey believed members were not of the working class, but were small tradesmen, shopkeepers, office workers, and craftsmen, who could afford to give the usual fee to their doctors. The numerous societies of 'Odd Fellows' consisted chiefly of this class, their numbers and influence enabling them to bargain with the more needy members of the medical profession. The 'Odd Fellows' of Leeds, for example, consisting of 5,000 members, had to advertise in London for a doctor, because no local man was willing to accept the trend of salaries made general through the operation of the Poor Law authorities, and take 2s. 6d. per head for attendance and medicines. As there were so many indigent doctors at the time (it seems that the medical profession was overstocked or unevenly distributed) young practitioners accepted club terms, not for the sake of the salary, but in the hope of the experience leading them to a better position. Generally if they attended patients conscientiously they subjected themselves to financial losses.

The members of the sick clubs themselves, Rumsey discovered, were also generally discontented. They disapproved of a doctor being provided for them and would have preferred to select their own. Complaints of poor treatment and an insufficient supply of medicine were frequent, but no doubt the dissatisfaction was often unjust and due to the awareness that doctors were underpaid, which made members suspicious about their ability to fulfil their contracts conscientiously. Rumsey regarded the whole custom of contracting for clubs and benefit societies 'injurious and degrading to the profession'. 'It encourages the lower order of practitioners, the half-educated, ill-conditioned men, who are of no benefit to the community.' He did not infer that this was the general character of club doctors, but that the system introduced such men into the profession and lowered its standard.

The proportion of club members to the population of a town varied according to the occupation of the working class. In Sunderland one-twelfth of the inhabitants belonged to benefit societies and clubs; in Liverpool, Dr. Duncan estimated the total number of members at 20,000, although another Liverpool doctor put it at a much higher figure, stating that medical officers disliked the schemes and therefore resented inquiries. In Wolverhampton there were about thirty clubs with about 3,000 members, and in Glouces-ter there was a similar proportion. In Bath, Cheltenham, Shrewsbury, and Worcester the proportion was only one in thirty of the population and one in twenty belonged to clubs in Stroud and Lincoln. It was over one in eleven in Rotherham, Wakefield, Chester, Hull, and Southampton. Exeter, Reading, and Wrexham contained very few benefit societies which contracted for medical attendance. And it was the general opinion that if the State increased its provision of medical relief, the great majority of assurance societies would cease to contract with doctors.

None of the ordinary benefit societies provided medical attendance for the families of members. There were very few women's clubs, but save in medical clubs and self-support-ing dispensaries, wives and children were attended by the parish doctor or left to charity. Occasionally, arrangements were made with practitioners whereby families of labourers were attended for a small sum contributed fortnightly, and Dr. Brown stated that this plan 'is adopted by surgeons in collieries (in the North) who are paid so much annually for attendance on accidents in mines, as a mode of compensation for visiting families of pitmen'. It has been seen that a similar practice obtained in Shropshire, Wolverhampton and South Wales. [See appendix.]

Rumsey's chief objection to the provision of medical aid by benefit societies and medical clubs, was that patients were not afforded any security that they would receive efficient attention. It was just a contract system without real responsibility, and in this respect, the independent poor were worse off than the paupers who were to some degree protected by the Poor Law authorities. He pointed out that the clubs' permanency depen-ded on compelling the independent labourer to subscribe, and if such were the case he ceased to be independent. The Duke of Rutland said that at Grantham it was an invariable rule to ask a labourer who came for assistance whether he belonged to the medical club. If he replied in the negative he was told: 'We will give you relief now, but never come back here again unless you subscribe to a medical club. Let us never see your face again.' It was such a position which made Rumsey claim he had never heard of a club which could fairly or honestly be called an independent club! 'When you look at the means which are adopted to establish it, or at the parties who subscribe to it, or at those who are employed by it, everything like independence is wanting.'

The system was more honest in the ironworks of South Wales, where proprietors openly deducted the medical penny or twopence for every £1 of wages, and provided the labourers with assistance. It amounted to the truck system being applied to medical relief, but no one pretended to call it an independent provision of the miners, and here the medical attendance provided was superior to any supplied by 'independent' clubs.

Inquiring into the success of the clubs, Rumsey found that they were dwindling, and generally failed altogether after three or four years. Even in places where they had appeared successful at first, such as at Grantham, Newmarket, and Stratford-on-Avon, because they had been assisted by the patronage of the nobility and large honorary subscriptions from the wealthy, fears were already entertained that they would decline as honorary subscriptions fell off. In Stratford 50 per cent of the subscriptions had come from honorary members; in Newmarket it had been over 50 per cent and in Grantham more than 75 per cent. Rumsey objected strongly to the suggestion made by the Poor Law Commissioners in their Eighth Annual Report, that some legal provision should be made for levying a rate in aid of the funds of these institutions to counteract the decline and the uncertainty of honorary subscriptions. To give legal protection to these institutions would have perpetuated a system whose serious defects were already making it crumble. Rumsey, however, welcomed legal protection and encouragement if the clubs and societies were entirely remodelled. The reforms which he recommended were that the circumstances and amount of income of a prospective member should determine his right to admission. This meant the exclusion of all who could afford to employ a doctor at the usual fee. Second, Medical Officers were to be assured adequate remuneration, and medicines were to be provided by the institutions, or paid for separately per case to the doctor. By these means the supply of medicines should be separated from attendance. Finally the contributions of the poor were to be calculated according to their liabilities to need the benefit for which they were insuring. This would mean that the principle which regulated other types of mutual assurance would be employed.[1]

A few of the medical clubs, which were also friendly societies and which had been founded under the patronage of landlords, clergy, and gentry, survived as friendly societies, dropping their actual medical relief, but providing sickness benefits. Finances were consolidated, and gradually the reins of management fell into the hands of the subscribers, as they became educated to their task—often with the help of the gentry.

Generally, however, little more was heard of the strictly medical club after the 'forties. Members rarely subscribed for any length of time; first, wages were too low, and second, the poor, finding they could obtain relief from the Union, saw no further necessity for a medical club. As the medical attendance provided by the Poor Law improved, the number of members diminished, and clubs eventually ceased altogether. Where the working class wished to insure themselves against sickness, they did so through the general benefit association or savings bank, which began to develop into important institutions of in-

---

[1] H. W. Rumsey, lengthy evidence on Sick Clubs to Select Committee, 1844.

creasing dimensions as the self-reliance and mutual confidence of the Victorian worker grew. It is an interesting speculation that the beginning of the increase in the prosperity of provident societies or the establishment of new institutions were coincident with the change in the Poor Law. Never, however, were the weaker and more helpless elements of the working class successful in effecting a system of lasting consolidated societies. For generally, weak physical constitutions resulting from low wages, malnutrition, bad housing and squalid and filthy environments entailed an increase in disease, and therefore multiplied the claims for sickness benefits on a society which would obviously be impecunious. The submerged class was forced, therefore, to depend on better paid and stronger grades of workers. This meant they had to await the growth of class solidarity before they could provide relief for themselves.

APPENDIX

THE following extracts from a lengthy and detailed paper delivered to the Select Committee of 1844 by Mr. Guthrie, President of the Royal College of Surgeons, show the system of medical relief which obtained in the Northern counties:

'Extracts from Correspondence between certain (Poor Law) Medical Officers of Northern Unions in England and Mr. Guthrie, stating facts in each Union which relate to *payment made by Owners of Mines, Collieries, Factories* for *workmen in illness*, and when they suffer from Accidents; Relief given by Hospitals and Dispensaries, with relation to the Duties of Union Surgeons and whether any circumstances exist which ought to deprive them of any Advantages which have been, or are, at any time to be granted to the Southern Unions of England'—Guthrie, 8 July 1844.

NORTHUMBERLAND. Some proprietors as at Alnwick and Tweedmouth engaged a doctor at about £20 per annum for attending accident cases in collieries; other owners made no provision for their employees. The work of the Union Medical Officers was not reduced as serious accidents, protracted illness or premature old age always meant that the poor fell on the parish. In a few places as at Bellingham, colliery owners paid a doctor 12s. per case but no fixed contracts were entered into. Mutual Assurance Companies existed in some districts, where every family paid about 1s. a month to a doctor, who then attended any member of a family in sickness. Accidents were paid for by mine owners. There were also a few dispensaries. In Haltwistle there was a colliery club of seventy members who paid the doctor a small weekly sum while in work, but when unemployed a man became a pauper dependent on the destitution authorities. In Newcastle and Gateshead colliery owners employed doctors for accidents only, but families of pitmen were attended by the parish Medical Officer. Two or three factory owners also engaged a doctor for accident cases. Clubs had seriously declined here. In the agricultural areas of Northumberland the poor received no relief from any charitable medical institution and there were no medical clubs. Throughout the entire county Union Medical Officers complained of the terribly low salaries they were paid, and in the border towns such as Berwick they were grossly overworked because the districts were inundated with casual poor from Scotland. Parts of the county were very wild, which made the obtaining of medical relief by the poor difficult, and also entailed arduous and long journeys for the doctors.

DURHAM. Here also many colliery owners provided treatment for accidents but not for illness. In some mines, as at Bishop Auckland, workmen subscribed threepence a week if married and three-halfpence if single, to a colliery doctor. They also belonged to a benefit society, paying 2s. 6d. a year for medical attendance. In Houghton-le-Spring, for example, colliery owners only contracted for accidents with a Medical Officer for boys and bound men, and not for free men and families. Even if workers received gratuitous attention if injured—their families generally became chargeable to the poor rates through unemployment. All parish Medical Officers here also complained of their low salaries—generally about £25 per annum—especially as they were responsible for the casual poor without additional remuneration. As in Northumberland, all maintained the provisions made by colliery owners did not diminish the numbers falling to their care, nor was the amount of general relief afforded reduced. In South Shields colliers were paid 5s. a week smart money if they were ill through accident—a sum to which they had contributed by a small amount being deducted weekly from their wages. This was completely inadequate to maintain a family, and it was also not given for ordinary illness. Because of the high death rate in mines, a considerable number of widows and orphans were left destitute and only the Poor Law authorities took care of them. Factory owners in these areas did not make any provision for accident cases, but a few benefit societies had been established by the workers in the south of the region and these had their own doctors. In Weardale and Teasdale the London Lead Mining Company employed its own surgeon, but the destitution authorities reduced the salary of their Medical Officers in consequence. Durham had several benefit societies and medical clubs, but the work of the Union doctor was not reduced because of the high accident rate among casual labourers working on the Great Northern Railway. Darlington similarly had hundreds of vagrants constantly on the sick list and no provision for medical relief was made by railway contractors or factory owners. Tremendous poverty existed in the new railway town of Middlesbrough and here also only the destitution authorities supplied medical relief to workers and paupers. In Stanhope the Union Medical Officer pointed out the low expectation of life of the miners and the high accident rate, and although a mine surgeon was engaged for accidents, lingering illness and chronic debility was not covered. These cases and the large number of orphans greatly increased the responsibility of the Guardians and Medical Officer. In the largest collieries in the world, at Hetton, Murton, and Castle Eden, sixpence was subtracted from the fortnightly wage payment if a man wished to contribute to the mine surgeon. For this a collier and his family were entitled to medical attendance and medicine until the next pay day. If contributions ceased at any time, medical aid was refused and past subscriptions were not taken into consideration even if they had been made for a long period. A sick man then became a pauper and had to fall on the parish Medical Officer. No accidents were paid for if they happened outside the colliery, but 5s. a week was given by employers as smart money besides the medical treatment, if they occurred while at work. The sixpence contribution did not cover the doctor's expenses but the doctors submitted to it in order to keep out the quacks who infested the North. It was said that the medical profession was in a lamentable state here. Resort to bone-setters, apprentices of all grades and itinerant charlatans with packs on their backs was a most common procedure. In the agricultural and wilder areas of Durham, Union Medical Officers stated that few were able to stand the fatigue and harassing duties of a general practitioner for a long period.—Mortality among doctors was high and few settled here permanently, especially as salaries were so absurdly low that poverty often confronted them and decent subsistence was impossible.

CUMBERLAND. In rural and wilder areas parish doctors were generally paid about £16 per annum. In towns such as Carlisle, factory owners did not provide medical attendance or make an allowance during sickness. The disabled were therefore the responsibility of the destitution authorities. Infirmaries and dispensaries afforded some relief but complaints of inadequate remuneration and overwork of the doctors was unanimous. In the Earl of Lonsdale's mines in Whitehaven a scheme had long existed of stopping so much per month from colliers' wages for providing medical attendance for men and families, and fourpence a month was retained if aid was required for a confinement. Over and above the subscriptions to the sick fund, the colliery surgeon was given a small fixed salary. If any of the miners either from sickness or accident became paupers, the colliery doctor continued his attendance, and the Union Medical Officer only visited the patients for the purpose of supplying the Board of Guardians with a certificate of incapacity to work.

WESTMORLAND. In Kendal there had been a flourishing dispensary which began to fail in the 'forties through the want of financial support. Mill and factory owners contributed a small sum to the institution. Paupers also received attention here, and Medical Officers stated that if this had not been so, their few pounds of salary would not have permitted them to provide adequate treatment or drugs.

YORKSHIRE. Here factory and mine owners made no medical provisions, save in isolated instances, and then only for accidents. In manufacturing and colliery towns occupational disease greatly increased the work of the Union Medical Officers. Medical clubs failed in this county. Poor Law doctors complained of their inadequate remuneration, and most in the bleakest areas could not afford to keep a horse. The sickness rate was high both in North and West Riding towns and Guardians ignored the recommendations of the Poor Law Commissioners regarding salaries and medical attendance.

LANCASHIRE. In Bolton, Blackburn, Burnley, Bury, Leigh, Warrington, and Wigan only isolated colliery and factory owners appointed their own surgeons. Union Medical Officers pointed out that in no way was the number of their cases reduced thereby, but an excuse was afforded to Guardians to keep salaries low. Again employers only provided a doctor for accidents and no account was taken of occupational disease. Few medical clubs existed. In Chorlton (near Manchester) there were many charitable institutions and owners of factories nearby subscribed to these instead of making their own arrangements. Many dispensaries were however closing in the mid 'forties, through the lack of funds. Under the old Poor Law, owners had apparently made large donations to infirmaries and dispensaries but these had practically ceased after 1834. Some workers belonged to the Odd Fellows, Foresters, and Ancient Druids friendly societies, and obtained medical relief through them. In Preston, Manchester, and Liverpool, factory owners did not provide medical assistance, but in these towns there were, as we have seen, many charitable institutions, and medical assistance for poor and pauper was on a comprehensive footing.

CHESHIRE AND DERBYSHIRE. Factory or mine owners rarely made medical provisions for their employees. Although infirmaries and dispensaries were responsible for the care of a great proportion of the sick, here as elsewhere subscriptions had fallen off, and Guardians also, as at Macclesfield and Stockport, ceased making contributions, so that charitable organizations were in a precarious position. In Stockport some factory owners provided a doctor and in Chapel-le-Frith the Peak Forest Canal Company compelled quarrymen to pay a small monthly sum to its Medical Officer. Union practitioners, save in large industrial towns, received from £15 to £25 per annum —for extensive and often well-populated districts.

STAFFORDSHIRE. Here there were very few dispensaries or public charities, and scarcely any provision was made for medical relief by employers. Therefore the Union Medical Officers demanded that the Poor Law Commissioners should survey the whole problem and bring their position more in line with that existing in Southern England.

CHAPTER 9

Self-help of the Labouring Classes

(2) SELF-SUPPORTING DISPENSARIES

BESIDES obtaining medical relief from the Union, a charity, the medical club, or benefit society, the poor had the opportunity if they lived in a town or well-populated rural area, of receiving medical attention from a self-supporting dispensary. These were like the self-supporting medical clubs, and often closely linked to them. But as they only received one reference from the Poor Law Commissioners, and as comparatively little material seems available on them in these years, it appears that they were not very common. They were however a salutary example of working-class self-help, and many were in existence before the new Poor Law was enacted.

Their early history was closely connected with Friendly Societies and Clubs, and rules of over a hundred of these organizations, which existed at the end of the eighteenth century, are still available in the British Museum. An Association for the Encouragement of Dispensaries existed in 1833, and the specialization of the provident dispensary from the Friendly Society can be traced in many references scattered throughout the voluminous appendices to the first report of the Poor Law Commissioners' Inquiry in 1834. Dr. J. M. Calvert produced a long memorandum on 'Dispensary Associations' between 1820 and 1833,[1] describing in detail the machinery and operation of many provident dispensaries such as those at Birmingham, Coventry, Rugby, Burton, Lymington, Walsall, Sheffield, Hatfield, Manchester, Hulme, Chorlton, Worcester, Frome, and Derby. The *Lancet* also had an article on them in April 1831, and it appears that the idea attracted more comment and attention before the middle 'thirties and after the 'sixties than it did in the intervening years. This was probably due to this being a period of transition between one form of dispensary movement and another.

The honour of promulgating the idea which was put into practice in the nineteenth century has been given to the schemes promoted by Henry Lilley Smith of Southam, a Warwickshire doctor.[2] In 1818 he wrote a pamphlet entitled: *Observations on the Prevailing Practise of Supplying Medical Assistance to the Poor commonly called the Farming of Parishes,*

---

[1] Third volume, Appendix C.
[2] Eye and Ear Infirmary established by wealthy and nobility for poor in Southam, 1818. Smith was a surgeon there.

with suggestions for the establishment of Parochial Medicine chests or Infirmaries in agricultural districts. Subscribers to his self-supporting dispensaries were to consist of donors and honorary subscribers, benefiting subscribers, and subscribing parishes. He formulated twenty-nine rules, the most important of which were:

(1) The association should be supported by voluntary contributions from parishes of £3 for every 100 inhabitants.

(2) Mechanics and labourers were to subscribe 5s. a year.

(3) Women were to contribute 5s. a year and children 2s. 6d.

(4) Subscribers of one guinea were to be allowed to recommend two patients and form the Committee.

(5) Surgeons were to be appointed from the district, and the annual subscriptions, after expenses had been paid and £50 set aside for a standing fund, were to be divided out among the Medical Officers in proportion to the number of miles travelled and visits made.

(6) The hours of attendance at the dispensary were to be fixed but if patients were seriously ill, they would be visited at their homes.

(7) Doctors were to provide their own instruments, but not trusses, and were to purchase the medicines under the direction of the committee.

(8) No important operation was to be performed at the dispensary unless two Medical Officers were present.

(9) Doctors were to call in consultants, whose fees were to be paid from the funds.

(10) A midwife was to attend confinements, but a guinea was to be paid to a doctor if he was called in.

(11) The names of surgeons, and the days and hours of attendance were to be fixed in the common room.

(12) Patients were to be allowed to demand special consultations with particular doctors if the consent of the governors was given.

(13) The poor were to find their own bottles and bandages.

(14) Any complaint of neglect or inattention of the nurse, secretary, or surgeon was to be reported to the committee.

Smith claimed the advantages of his dispensary scheme as being: that the poor would have easy access to medical attention; that it would unite the aid of all the medical talent in a vicinity; that doctors, because of the publicity which would be centred on the dispensary, and because of the liberality of the committee would give their best attention and supply superior drugs; and lastly extra comforts and necessaries would be offered to convalescent patients. Accidents, besides sickness, were to be covered and paupers were to receive gratuitous attention.

After trying for nearly twenty years to establish self-supporting dispensaries, Smith in 1837 produced a plan for forming very small organizations, subscriptions to which were to be so low as to leave no one with an excuse not to join them. In a pamphlet addressed to

the working class,[1] in which he accused labourers of improvidence, he stressed the importance of establishing self-supporting dispensaries, to save people from falling on Poor Law
relief or having recourse to quack medicines. He recommended that a district should be
divided into several very small societies, containing not more than forty members so as to
allow arrangements to be made by people of similar habits and circumstances. 'The
advantages of a minute subdivision of society, is that persons of the same habits and pursuits,
and receiving the same wages, would be associated together, and all knowing each other,
and will really and truly feel a mutual delight in each others' welfare.' Small clubs would
also not require a committee to run them. In a single area he suggested there should be the
following associations:

(1) An Agricultural Labourers' Alfred Society, members of which were to contribute
    threepence a week and to receive 6s. a week in sickness benefit, besides medical
    attention. (Yet wages in the area were under 10s.!)
(2) A Matrons' Society, consisting of wives of the above, to contribute twopence and
    receive 4s.
(3) A Manufacturers', Mechanics' and Tradesmen's Alfred Society, members of
    which were to receive 12s. a week for sixpence contributions.
(4) A Matrons' Society for wives of manufacturers.
(5) A Single Man's Alfred Society.
(6) A Single Woman's Alfred Society.
(7) A Widows' Alfred Society.

Smith thought doctors would be the most influential people to get the societies started,
because they had access to every class of people, and saw more of the labourers in times of
sickness and misfortune than even the clergy. The rules for these self-supporting dispensaries were liberal. Subscriptions which exceeded expenditure at the end of a year, were to
be put into a standing fund, until it equalled £1 per member. The surplus over this was to
be shared out amongst members. Six months' sick pay was to be given and the sick were to
be visited once a week and paid weekly. Smith had formed the Harbury Day Labourers'
Alfred Society on these lines and it was such a flourishing institution, that he believed Poor
Law Guardians would become superfluous if similar societies were established throughout
the country. In his Club, a subscription of threepence a week secured 6s. sickness benefit,
but no one could receive over £3 12s. a year unless the standing fund contained the
equivalent of £1 a member, in which case, sick pay was extended to £7 4s. a year. At the
death of a member, a shilling was subscribed by everyone towards the funeral expenses,
and if a wife died, sixpence was collected from each person for the survivor. At the end of
1837 the Harbury Club had a surplus of £7 11s. 6d. from its twenty members and had had
eighteen weeks' payment at 6s. a week.

---

[1] Henry Lilley Smith, M.R.C.S., *Alfred Societies or a Plan for very small Sick Clubs*, 1837. (Alfred, after
King Alfred, whom Smith greatly admired.)

The self-supporting or provident dispensary system therefore differed from other medical clubs in that the poor received not only treatment and drugs but also were ensured an income during sickness. They were similar to the clubs, and different from public dispensaries, in that the doctors received a salary.

In 1836 the Guardians of the Brackley Union (Northants) also stated the difference between the medical club and the self-supporting dispensary. To reduce applications for parish relief to a minimum the Union sponsored the provision by the village of both dispensary and club. The former, the Guardians claimed, provided relief as a form of bargain between the medical profession and the labourer directly, and the latter between honorary members and doctors. 'The dispensary fills faster than the club', it was said, which was accounted for by the 'medical man having absolute power over the poor man, whom he may not choose to attend unless he enters the dispensary', but in this Union such a fear was groundless because doctors acted very liberally in the dispensary.

After 1834 several self-supporting dispensaries were established, but it was a difficult achievement in agricultural areas. The best account of the operation of these institutions was given in a paper delivered in 1836 by Dr. Thomas Hodgkin.[1] They may, he said,

> be justly regarded as the best, and at the same time the most economical means of supplying prompt and efficient medical assistance to the working classes. Their important advantages are not however confined to the administration of prompt and able succour to physical suffering. They have a strong tendency to maintain and elevate moral character, since they are calculated to avert those calamities, which, commencing in sickness, end in absolute degradation of families.

As an encouragement to independence, the dispensary had for the Guardians the double virtue of diminishing the amount of medical relief they were asked to provide.

The self-supporting dispensary was chiefly maintained by contributions of the working class, generally about 4s. a person for a year. The great advantage it possessed over Union medical relief, was that treatment and medicine could be obtained without delay, for the scheme avoided the necessity of patients applying to the Relieving Officer for an order, or of obtaining a ticket for admission to a public dispensary or hospital. Generally several Medical Officers were attached to a self-supporting dispensary, and patients selected whoever they desired from the panel. Prescriptions were made up there by a qualified dispenser. Separate registration and subscription were required of women claiming obstetric assistance. Sick people who were not subscribers, could use the dispensary service if they paid half a year's subscription in advance, and if they got two new members to enrol who also paid their contributions in advance. Benefit societies availed themselves of these institutions, and paid a comprehensive subscription proportionate to their members. Lower terms were asked for from them, because there was little difficulty in collecting the money,

---

[1] 'On mode of selecting and remunerating medical men for Professional Attendance on the Poor of a Parish or District.'

and because membership of one of these societies implied that the individual enjoyed comparatively good health. Paupers were occasionally given treatment by the dispensaries, if the parishes purchased tickets of admission for them. To have given gratuitous relief would have meant destroying the purpose of the dispensaries.

The advantages to the working class were that they were guaranteed against the de-moralizing pressure of heavy doctors' bills incurred by sudden or protracted illness, and also against the evils of Union medical relief inefficiently administered. The doctor was safeguarded against bad debts, he could treat a large number of patients with less expense to himself, and also had a good opportunity of establishing his reputation by attending a large and known institution. As the self-supporting dispensaries were an economic pro-position to the Guardians, they received complete approval from the destitution authori-ties, central and local. But promoters constantly reiterated their desire that there should be no direct interference, as the important object of raising the poor above the rank of paupers would be defeated if the institutions were established by those employed in the adminis-tration of the Poor Law. Anything hinting, however faintly, at the Poor Law could act as a deterrent to many of the respectable working class. The stigma of retrenchment which attached itself to anything touched by Guardians would be sufficient to arouse in the minds of the poor the idea that the dispensary had been established to reduce the rates, and this would be strong enough to overshadow the attraction of the main aim of the movement: 'to supply the working class with the most effective assistance in sickness and to increase and maintain their prosperity in health'.

Hodgkin advised in his paper, that promoters should state emphatically that the self-supporting dispensary was as necessary and useful to the mechanic and labourer as assurance against fire was to wealthy property owners, and that the payment of a small sum was the means of protection against heavy and ruinous loss. He even suggested that when the advantages of the self-supporting dispensary had been experienced, Guardians might seek to obtain medical assistance from it for outdoor sick paupers, so that the Poor Law Medical Officer could confine his duties to the workhouse.

A reform recommended by Hodgkin was that the doctors attached to a dispensary should be appointed for only five years, and that re-appointment for a second term of office should be discouraged. He advocated this on the grounds that five years was long enough for a man to execute his duties competently, for not only should the poor receive conscientious care, but statistical inquiries and records should be made of great value to the public and the profession. Private practice was unfavourable to the prosecution of such researches, and it was desirable that the opportunities offered should be shared by doctors in rotation. After five years, Hodgkin concluded, a practitioner would be weary of his office and become lax, and also by then, he would have reaped all the benefits which the circumstances of his connections with the dispensary could afford him.

As in every other field of medical relief for the poor, Rumsey also interested himself in the self-supporting dispensary movement. In 1837 he read a memoir to the Buckingham

Philanthropic Association, which had assembled to discuss the supply of adequate medical attention for the poor.[1] He introduced his paper by reiterating that the poor, able to support themselves in health, were unable to meet heavy expenditure for medical treatment precisely at a time when their ordinary resources failed. Similarly they were powerless to attempt, by uncombined and unaided exertion, to guard against this misfortune. He therefore stressed that people under these circumstances should raise a general fund by united contribution, and that no better theory or more practical scheme could be devised than mutual assurance. But he did not speak for the poor alone, for he wished to include the petty tradesmen, small farmers and persons living on scanty annuities, who were more numerous than was supposed. He suggested also that the wealthy should be members of such mutual assurance societies, because, 'in the present condition of the labouring classes, it is more than doubtful whether they are prepared, either in circumstances or in disposition to contribute premiums, which would meet the total expenditure and liabilities of an insurance office for medical relief'. It would be a long time also before such a society could support itself without honorary assistance.

He fully concurred in the principle that it was indispensable to a properly constituted medical relief society to be entirely exempt from interference by the destitution authorities. He therefore objected to the Guardian sponsored medical clubs, because they possessed all the evils of the parish contract without the check of rigid superintendence. The amount of duty performed and the cost of medicines furnished was never known, nor did the Commissioners or Guardians ever investigate the subject. They were satisfied with the diminution of applications for parochial relief and the pecuniary saving to the Union. Another evil of the clubs was the way in which the Poor Law authorities *enforced* their adoption and dictated to the Medical Officer, often making it part of the written contract. But Rumsey also opposed the institution of many of the independent medical clubs, because their influence was circumscribed, particularly in rural districts, where their extent was often limited to the practice of one doctor who opened his own separate club. These institutions, which professed to be designed for the benefit of the poor, were frequently employed by medical men as instruments for injuring and annoying each other. Rumsey had received a letter from a Medical Officer in Buckingham reporting that his club had promised to supersede his parish practice, but that he was outwitted by some neighbours, who offered similar relief on more advantageous terms, 'a penny a week for the whole family', and had canvassed for village members.

Therefore to the club system Rumsey opposed the self-supporting dispensary. Flourishing self-supporting dispensaries, consisting of honorary members and the working class, needed only a very small proportion of honorary subscriptions, whereas purely charitable dispensaries required a large expenditure, and much less medical relief was afforded. As an illustration he described the operation of the Coventry Dispensary, which in the four years 1834–37, had treated 7,234 patients. The honorary subscriptions had totalled £360, less

---

[1] *The Medical Relief for the Labouring Classes on the Principle of Mutual Assurance*, London, 1837.

than 2s. per patient, yet in Dr. Digsby's statistics on twenty-six public dispensaries wholly supported by charity, the average expenditure for each patient was 5s. Ordinary or bene-fiting members were strictly limited to the labouring class, and many dispensaries fixed a maximum wage limit for membership. The Medical Officers of the Coventry self-support-ing dispensary had had their attention directed to the peculiar advantages the institution afforded for statistical research, especially in the study of epidemics and diseases of artisans. Dispensaries run on the mutual assurance principle were able to afford more correct evidence as to the general proportion of sickness, because they included at least a quarter of the whole community. And because they necessarily involved the services of several doctors, they possessed the most suitable agents for collecting the required materials.

Evidence was given on the operation of self-supporting dispensaries to the Select Committee of 1838 by Assistant Commissioner Gulson. He also took Coventry as an example because he had been Director of the Poor there. During the execution of his duties, he said, he had come to realize that Union medical relief was a means by which a vast number of people made themselves eligible for ordinary relief. This had been practised to such a degree that he and others had succeeded in getting a self-supporting dispensary established. For several years the institution had had nearly 3,000 members. Only two doctors were employed, and these were not local men, for all resident practitioners opposed the scheme and refused to assist it. The new men received £300 for their services and had gained such credit by treating the poor well that they had gained excellent practices. A public meeting was held every year, and the number and nature of cases treated, as well as the expenditure, were printed for the public.

The dispensaries at Coventry and Burton-on-Trent (with 2,500 members) were two of the most flourishing in the country, and in these, patients in one year totalled on an average 70 per cent of the members. In Lymington the ratio was 90 per cent, in Derby 127 per cent, and at Chesham (where Rumsey was a surgeon) 112 per cent. Because they used the service more freely, illness among the members seemed much greater than that of the community at large, and occupational diseases in the mining districts and other areas where dangerous trades were practised must also have affected the work and estab-lishment of dispensaries. Rumsey suggested that as artisans and mechanics were more liable to sickness than agricultural labourers, their contributions should be proportionately higher, and they could also afford to pay more, because they received higher wages. He had himself compiled some vital statistics after an elaborate study, which he offered as a guide to self-supporting dispensaries. In the country, he had found that 4 per cent of the people were constantly ill; that in middle-age sickness increased 34 per cent for every decennial period; that sixty cases of illness or accident occurred annually in every hundred persons; and that the average duration of each case was twenty-four days.

He emphasized the importance of obtaining the active co-operation of all general practitioners, because many self-supporting dispensaries and medical clubs had failed entirely or been stifled through the lack of support from influential medical men in the locality. The greatest success had been achieved where all doctors participated. Further, he suggested that the government might promote the objects of the institutions if it appointed medical inspectors to examine the reports and compile tables of returns furnished by the societies. But the best self-supporting dispensaries published their own reports annually. They were, he maintained, generally full and explicit, and gave valuable information obtained through scientific observation.[1]

Where they existed and flourished therefore, they were admirable institutions for providing an additional source of medical relief for the poor. Generally, they were well conducted by highly respectable committees and gave efficient service. The honorary fund seemed to cover the establishment costs, and medical remuneration was provided from members' funds. On the whole, salaries were regarded as satisfactory, considering doctors were saved much expense and trouble by the limited and compact districts in which the patients resided and by the convenient regulations which were adopted for attendance at the dispensary.

Many abuses gradually crept into the self-supporting dispensary system. Already in 1839 Dr. William Fergusson could write:

Dispensaries were established for the relief of the destitute and helpless, and those alone of the working classes who could not afford to pay for medicine, but now, at those great towns especially, the gaily dressed flaunt there in troops, and male applicants may be seen better attired than their prescribers. So much is privilege abused that it may be called a robbery of every practitioner in the place, and of none more than the prescribers themselves.[2]

He therefore suggested abandoning the schemes and using the buildings for casualty hospitals for the destitute, servants and labourers, and to get this class alone to subscribe one penny or twopence every sixth week. This should constitute a fund for supplying medical attendance without sick pay, and would, he hoped, prevent the entry of wealthier classes.

But the most serious obstacle to the growth of the self-supporting dispensary was the disinclination of the poor to subscribe. The temptation of a cheaper supply of medical treatment from an inferior source, was always present in these years. During the parliamentary inquiry of 1838, Wakley, with his usual penetrating cross-examination, drew from Gulson the admission that it was the class just above the poor who subscribed to the dispensary. The indigence of the poor proved in some instances an unsurmountable barrier.[3]

As Rumsey recognized: 'When his [the labourer's] income is barely sufficient to

[1] H. W. Rumsey, *Medical Relief for the Labouring Classes on the Principle of Mutual Assurance*, London, 1837.

[2] *Thoughts and observations on Pauperism, Poor Laws, Emigration, Medical Relief, and Prevention of Crime*, by William Fergusson, M.D., F.R.S.E., Inspector General of Army Hospitals, 1839.

[3] Northampton formed the Royal Victoria Dispensary in 1845—and only charged twopence a week per family; it flourished and had a large membership. (Special Commissioner of *Lancet*, Inquiry into the 'Battle of the Clubs', 1895.)

TABLE 9.1

Analysis of Expenditure of Three Important Dispensaries.—Dr. Kay (Shuttleworth) Select Committee of Inquiry into the Operation of the Poor Laws, 1838.

Period	Number of cases attended	Surgeons' salaries	Medicines	Surgical instruments	Dispenser's salary	Total	Average cost*	Total other expenses†	Aggregate total	Average cost per case
		£ s. d.	£ s. d.	£ s. d.	£ s. d.	£ s. d.	s. d.	£ s. d.	£ s. d.	s. d.
COVENTRY Self-supporting Dispensary, July 1831–March 1837										
From 18 July 1831 to 25 March 1832	1,505	80 17 8	45 10 3	30 0 0	10 0 0	166 7 11	2 2½	62 1 8	228 9 7	3 0¼
1833	2,437	263 1 5	103 2 4	5 14 0	38 6 8	410 4 5	3 4½	94 7 1	504 11 6	4 1½
1834	1,668	268 2 0	112 12 0	13 10 0	40 0 0	421 5 10	5 0½	93 2 2	514 8 0	6 2
1835	1,629	287 2 0	88 11 1	not given	60 0 0	435 13 1	5 4	91 1 3½	526 14 4½	6 5½
1836	1,500	262 3 0	95 6 3	3 18 3½	60 0 0	421 7 6½	5 7¼	64 12 8	486 0 2½	6 5¾
1837	1,530	261 15 0	90 7 1	6 0 11	60 0 0	418 3 0	5 5½	61 11 10	479 14 10	6 3¼
Total	10,269					2,273 1 9½	4 5		2,739 18 6	5 4
BURTON-ON-TRENT, Years ending October 1836 and 1837										
Year ending 31 October 1836	1,460	160 5 4	106 12 4	57 1 9	*a*	324 4 5	4 5¼	26 6 0	350 10 5	4 9½
1837	1,310	127 6 9	104 14 11	62 10 0	*a*	294 11 8	4 5¾	28 13 4	323 5 0	4 11
Total	2,770					618 16 1	4 5½		673 15 5	4 10¼
DERBY, November 1830–November 1836										
30 November 1830–30 November 1831	792	41 6 6	108 3 7	55 0 0	*a*	204 10 1	5 2	*b*	482 10 6	12 2
1832	1,434	78 13 0½	51 15 7	70 0 0	*a*	200 8 7½	2 9½	*b*	298 10 8	4 2
1833	1,279	77 7 0	41 14 11½	70 0 0	*a*	189 1 11½	2 11½	*b*	259 7 1	4 0½
1834	1,071	75 19 5	42 18 4	70 0 0	*a*	188 17 9	3 6¼	*b*	257 14 3	4 9¾
1835	1,229	91 7 7½	42 1 3	70 0 0	*a*	203 8 10½	3 3½	*b*	274 6 7½	4 5½
1836	1,490	110 9 1½	62 8 3½	70 0 0	*a*	242 17 5	3 3	*b*	317 2 10½	4 2½
Total	7,295					1,229 4 10½	3 4½		1,889 12 0½	4 9

* Average cost per case for medicines, instruments, and salaries.
† Total other expenses including Secretary's salary, postage, advertising, repair, fuel, rent, poor and church rates.
a Dispenser's salary includes coal, candles, and care of linen. *b* Not given separately but included in aggregate total.

maintain health, there is neither wisdom, humanity, nor justice, in calling on him to sub-scribe to a fund for its *repair*'; and he quoted Dr. Yelloly: 'In supplying to the poor the motives of independence you must also furnish them with the *means*, or you do nothing.'[1] [See Table 9.1 for analysis of expenditure of three important dispensaries.]

[1] H. W. Rumsey, *Medical Relief for the Labouring Classes on the Principle of Mutual Assurance*, London, 1837.

CHAPTER 10

The Necessity for supplying Gratuitous Medical Relief to all the Poor

BECAUSE of the great variation which existed throughout the country in the amount and method of supplying medical relief to the poor, many enlightened men, particularly among the doctors, advocated that gratuitous medical assistance should be given not only to the paupers, but to the entire poor population.

Long before the formation of Poor Law Unions, the arrangements regarding medical relief in the north differed widely from those of southern England. The system of contracting by fixed salary for attendance on the destitute was rare, and where it was in operation, doctors' salaries were very low. The more general practice was for a town to incur separate bills for attendance on paupers who had been granted an order by the overseers or vestry. This meant that much less medical relief was provided than under the new system and insufficient responsibility was attached to the medical man. His pauper patient was in a similar situation to any other patient, whereas under the new law the conduct of the doctor was liable to investigation and the medical standard was raised.

There was also a great difference in the habits of individuals in the two parts of the country. The northerners were more independent, and rather than seek parochial medical relief they were commonly disposed to allow sickness to take its course without calling in medical assistance, so that their health inevitably suffered in consequence. Also there was a greater number of unqualified practitioners in the north. In the south, there was no reluctance on the part of the poor to apply for medical relief before 1834, and every agricultural labourer believed he had a right to claim relief from the parish doctor. After the introduction of the new Poor Law, agricultural wages were so low that sickness, especially if it overtook the head of the family, compelled the labourer to apply for relief. But in the early years, when rigid enforcement of the new principles was practised, medical aid was granted only to young men with small families in cases of emergency or dire necessity. The comforts and general habits of the poor were much inferior in the south compared with the north of England. From the Ampthill Union in Bedfordshire, it was reported that a labourer was not capable of doing an adequate day's work because insufficient food left him too weak, and this was most serious as labour was engaged by the task work system.

A close spirit of economy had also existed on the part of overseers and vestries in the north, which distinguished the management of parochial affairs between the two parts of the country. Further, the high degree of independence and hardihood of the northerners had led to the establishment of numerous clubs and societies which provided against the contingency of sickness. There too the doctors had been used to making, or being offered, very moderate charges for attending pauper patients. Two of the more remarkable examples of this were the Chorlton (near Manchester) and West Derby Unions, each with populations of 60,000, neither of which spent £100 a year on medical relief.

But on the introduction of the new system, many Unions realized the propriety of appointing Medical Officers at fixed salaries and agreed to a more liberal dispensation of medical relief than existed previously. Many of the northern Unions however adopted the payment per case system, and on the whole a much smaller amount of medical relief continued to be given in proportion to the population and to general expenditure on the destitute. Some Unions, afraid of incurring medical bills, gave relief in money, and left the applicant to find his own medical aid, which inevitably resulted in the poor seeking inferior attendance and in the increase of disease. Although much blame for the inadequacy of relief rested on the conservative policies of the Guardians in the north, the people also made fewer applications for parochial medical aid, because of their great opposition to the 'cruel charity of the new Poor Law'. (The northerners constituted the fiery element in the Chartist movement because they wished to coerce the administration to mitigate the law's harshness.) The most important result of the difficulty of obtaining medical relief, allied to the indisposition of the poor to apply for it, was that it induced multitudes to flock to druggists, with its inevitable result to the community of a fearful loss of life and destruction of health.

In Northumberland, Durham, Cumberland, and Westmorland, medical relief under the old system, had constituted so insignificant a feature among parochial disbursements, that in the early years of the operation of the new Act, neither Guardians nor Assistant Commissioners could find any comprehensive data of past experience on which to calculate the future remuneration of Medical Officers. To the Select Committee of 1838, Assistant Commissioner Power stated that no definite arrangements had been made by them in various northern Unions, and he confessed that he himself had not been able to take any steps regarding new contracts or new arrangements. In 1844, Sir John Walsham found that the rate per head of medical expenses on the population of the Unions in Northumberland and Durham and Lancashire was a penny or penny-farthing as compared with Sussex where it was fivepence, Berkshire and Hereford where it was fourpence-halfpenny, and Norfolk and Suffolk where it was fourpence-farthing. He produced a table, Table 10.1, showing the proportion of medical relief to total relief in several Unions of Northumberland and Durham compared with Norfolk and Suffolk for the year ending Lady Day 1843.

Another table, Table 10.2, showed the number of medical cases in two Suffolk and two Norfolk Unions as compared with two in Durham and two in Northumberland, of similar populations:

THE ORIGINS OF THE NATIONAL HEALTH SERVICE

TABLE 10.1

Proportion of Medical Relief to Total Relief. Comparison between northern Unions and southern Unions for the Year ending Lady Day 1843.

	Durham	Norfolk	Northumberland	Suffolk
The total amount paid for medical relief	£1,548	£5,632	£1,372	£4,940
The total amount paid for relief to poor	80,512	162,497	74,446	140,337
Proportion of medical relief to total expenditure	1·9	3·5	1·8	3·5

TABLE 10.2

Number of Medical Cases in southern Unions compared with northern Unions of similar populations.

Unions		Pop:	Number of medical cases Indoor & Outdoor, 1843
Erpingham	Norfolk	20,513	872
Downham		19,200	530
Hartismere	Suffolk	18,529	647
Hoxne		15,797	451
		74,039	2,500
Darlington	Durham	21,488	186
Teesdale		19,574	147
Alnwick	Northumberland	18,768	174
Castle Ward		14,537	36
		74,367	543

Therefore there was nearly four times as much medical relief afforded by the two southern counties as by the two northern ones. A third table, Table 10.3 (page 253), showing the comparative cost of medical relief in the northern Unions before and several years after the introduction of the new Poor Law, showed that much improvement had been achieved in six years:

Wales had been in a similar position to these counties and here also great improvements were made in the medical service by the introduction of the new system. Disturbances, generally connected with Chartism, which occurred in South Wales in 1843, directed

TABLE 10.3

Table showing Comparative Cost of Medical Relief in the undermentioned Unions of Northern England before and since formation.—Paper by Sir J. Walsham, Assistant Poor Law Commissioner, to the Select Committee on Poor Law Medical Relief, 1844: Appendix 2.

Name of Union	Annual Cost of Medical Relief (as far as ascertainable) previous to formation of Union in 1836–37	Annual Cost of Medical Relief as paid during Year ending Christmas, 1843
	£	£
Alnwick	38	149
Auckland	80	90
Carlisle	173	309
Cockermouth	95	195
Darlington	123	203
East Ward	128	108
Gateshead	105	194
Hexham	41	121
Newcastle-on-Tyne	235	354
South Shields	120	170
Sunderland	155	354
Tynemouth	15	248
	£1,143*	£2,495

*This is the total given. In fact it is £1,308.

attention to the administration of the Poor Law in that region, and in 1844 a Commission was appointed to inquire into the state of the district. Before 1834 no system of organized medical relief existed, and one of the causes of the disturbances was that salaries paid to Medical Officers and Relieving Officers were regarded as being too high. The small farmers objected to the increased burden on their rates (although the charges were grossly exaggerated) and they universally drew a contrast between the paid services and the gratuitous, such as the collection of the poor rate, which they considered the more onerous. The Commissioners replied that such expenditure had to be regarded as a portion of substantial relief to be afforded to the poor, and that the Guardians were to contemplate the improvement of existing arrangements, rather than hold out hopes of diminishing their cost and consequently their efficiency. They tried to impress on local authorities the expediency of voluntarily adopting an adequate scale of remunerating Medical Officers and pointed out that it was an injustice to disregard the reforms which had taken place respecting medical relief. It would have been false economy, they maintained, to revert to the old system. The doctors employed were not remarkable for their greater skill, for Guardians frequently had occasion to call on them for an explanation of negligence, but they were responsible to higher authorities who were empowered to call on them for explanations of their treatment. Prejudice unfortunately continued to exist among the poor themselves, who remained blind to the benefits accruing to them from having recourse to treatment by a qualified physician, and ignorance induced them to cling to uneducated village practitioners.

Much of the well-being of the poor depended on the disputes of local authorities on what constituted pauperism, and some Medical Officers themselves objected to attending anybody unless they were receiving parochial relief. But no just distinction could be made, and as a practitioner of Bangor pointed out, three-fifths of the people who came to the parish strove hard, and very often in sickness sold half their possessions, to avoid making an application to the parish for medical relief. Generally it was sheer necessity that compelled the poor to apply at all. Therefore the doctor maintained it would be good economy to provide medical relief for all the poor:—'£1 laid out in medical relief would often be better than £10 laid out in other relief, after a man has been driven to pauperism.'[1]

Medical Clubs existed in Wales for the better situated members of the working-class, but they were not popular among the people. Many preferred to go to a doctor and pay fees, and buy medicines from a druggist, when they might have had the advice and medicine from their club without payment. In some of the large towns dispensaries and infirmaries had been established, but as statistics were difficult to obtain from Wales, it is impossible to ascertain the proportion of the population which received gratuitous medical treatment from the charities. It was certainly not great, and in 1844 figures were published of Poor Law expenditure which showed what a small amount of medical relief was obtained from Unions also. In South Wales £180,500 was spent on poor relief, of which only £3,415 was on medical assistance. In North Wales the total figure was £156,108 and that for medical relief £1,193. Altogether expenditure on Poor Law medical relief was less than 2 per cent of total expenditure.

The greatest difference in the supply of parochial medical relief occurred in towns not under the new Poor Law. In Exeter the proportion of the cases attended by the Medical Officers was 19 per cent of the population, the highest ratio of any town from which returns were received. No Poor Law Union offered medical aid to so great a proportion of its people. Sixteen per cent of the population came annually under the care of the parochial doctors,[2] and the dispensary and infirmary relieved another 8·75 per cent, excluding the people who received treatment at specialist institutions, such as those devoted to diseases of the eye and skin, and obstetrics. Leeds formed a remarkable contrast. A careful investigation was made, based on the number of workhouses under a certain rental, and it was found that the working class constituted 63,000 out of the total population of 87,000, i.e. 70 per

[1] Evidence by O. O. Roberts, Consulting Surgeon (not a Poor Law Medical Officer) in Bangor, to Select Committee, 1844.

[2] 19% refers to cases, 16% to individuals, some of whom were 'cases' more than once a year.

cent. Yet only 10 per cent of the people received parochial medical relief. Medical charities did not make up the difference, as only 5 per cent of the inhabitants received treatment from this source. Therefore of these two large towns Leeds, which was more unhealthy and had a higher mortality rate, supplied medical aid for only 6·7 per cent of its population while Exeter provided it for 25 per cent.[1]

In Shrewsbury, where free medical relief was granted to all the poor, cases averaged 16 per cent of the population and medical charities 11 per cent. Hull provided a striking contrast, for there gratuitous treatment was supplied for only 7 per cent of its inhabitants. In Bristol, parochial provision amounted to 4·36 per cent of the population, in Coventry and Southampton to 7 per cent, and in Brighton it was under 3 per cent.[2]

Not only did the amount and method of the supply of medical relief vary in these towns operating under local acts, but the poor fared differently in places subject to the control of the Poor Law Commissioners. Illustrations can be drawn from several northern towns, each with large populations. In Liverpool and Manchester the supply of medical relief was regarded as liberal. Dr. Duncan estimated that in Liverpool, out of a total population of nearly a quarter of a million, 70 per cent or 175,000, belonged to the working class. Benefit clubs provided medical attendance for over 20,000, but Duncan deducted these from the great number requiring medical relief, not because the treatment they received was adequate or satisfactory, but because the clubs consisted chiefly of operatives and small tradesmen, who were able to provide for themselves by a better system. He therefore estimated that 150,000 needed to be cared for in sickness. From an extensive observation of statistics, he maintained, it was safe to assume that 60 per cent of the population was attacked by sickness or accident in a year. The total number of cases equalled 90,000 therefore, of which only 67,000 received gratuitous aid, leaving 23,000 without any settled provision. The numerous medical charities catering for every kind of suffering relieved 23 per cent of the population, and the destitution authorities 2·75 per cent.[3]

Manchester Union with a population of 197,000 (1847) gave medical relief to 4,000 paupers in the workhouse or general hospital in a year. But far more significant was the number receiving treatment from the many medical charities compared with that given under the Poor Law for the ratio was 20 per cent as against 2·5 per cent.[4]

Nothing like the relief afforded by these two towns was provided by other northern Unions. In Bradford only 823 of the poor received Poor Law medical relief out of a population of 132,000, i.e. one in 160. This was the lowest provision by any town from which information was received save Carlisle. But whereas in Carlisle there were excellent

<hr />

[1] H. W. Rumsey, Evidence to Select Committee, 1844. His is a long and extremely interesting report. His introduction points out the chaos in the information available, stresses the need for more accurate statistics, and gives a plea for reform.

[2] *Ibid.*

[3] *Ibid.*

[4] *Ibid.* A long report to Rumsey from Mr. Dorrington who obtained his information from the Clerk to the Board of Guardians and printed reports of the medical charities.

medical charities, affording relief to 11 per cent of the population, in Bradford less than 3 per cent of the population received help through these channels, so that only 3·5 per cent of the people were supplied with gratuitous aid from all sources. Huddersfield extended relief to double this number, but even so, the proportion of both parochial and charitable assistance was very small. More adequate provision was made in Sheffield, where 5 per cent of the inhabitants received medical relief from the Union, and 7 per cent from medical charities. In Stockport the supply was very defective, not 5 per cent of the people were provided for, and of these scarcely 2·5 per cent by the Union. In Sunderland 3·75 per cent of the population received Union medical relief and less than 2 per cent in York, but in both these towns, the medical charities supplied seven or eight cases in every hundred of the population with gratuitous relief.[1]

The provision of medical aid was still more meagre in smaller northern towns. Rotherham seemed to afford the largest amount of parochial relief, supplying 4·5 per cent of the population; while Lincoln gave the smallest, granting it to only 1·8 per cent. Other towns, such as Wrexham, Wakefield, and Beverley fell between the two. The total number of sick provided for, both by the Unions and by voluntary bodies in these towns, was under 5 per cent of the population.[2]

Although there was great variation in the supply of relief between the north and south, the midland and southern towns presented more uniformity. Bath was however distinguished for giving the same generous provision of charitable aid which characterized Liverpool and Manchester. Twenty per cent of the population was relieved annually at the hospital and several dispensaries, whilst parochial provision was extended to nearly 5 per cent, so that one-quarter of the population were recipients of gratuitous medical treatment. Other towns in the midland, western, eastern, and southern districts of England provided the following medical assistance: King's Lynn in Norfolk gave the highest proportion—11·4 per cent; this was followed by Reading offering relief to 10·5 per cent of the population; Bridgwater and Croydon to 9 per cent; Stroud to 8·5 per cent; Ipswich and Maidstone to over 7 per cent; Ludlow to under 7 per cent; Cheltenham and Gloucester to 5·5 per cent; Wolverhampton to 5 per cent; Hereford, Portsmouth, and Worcester to 4 per cent; and Yarmouth to 3·75 per cent. Patients attended by Poor Law Medical Officers in these Unions slightly exceeded in number those relieved by medical charities, and therefore in this respect contrasted with the northern towns.[3]

In rural Unions similar variations seemed to have occurred. In Stowmarket, for example, pauper patients formed 12·5 per cent of the population, whilst in Poole (Dorset) they were only 5 per cent. Neither had any medical charities, and agricultural areas were as negligent in their provision of medical aid for the poorer portions of their communities as were the towns.[4]

[1] H. W. Rumsey, Evidence to the Select Committee, 1844.
[2] *Ibid.* Here again the figures frequently conflict and are far from clear.
[3] *Ibid.*
[4] *Ibid.*

We have seen that there were many reasons for the differences in the supply of medical assistance throughout the country. On the whole, less restricted relief was given to the entire poorer class in towns not under the 1834 Poor Law Amendment Act, but everywhere the deficiency of an adequate provision for the sick poor was patent. If Bath, Exeter, and Shrewsbury, for example, towns which were not particularly poverty-stricken or insalubrious, found it necessary to supply a quarter of their population every year with gratuitous medical relief, what was the condition of the poor in those overcrowded and unhealthy industrial conglomerations, where only one in twenty of the inhabitants were so favoured? Rumsey therefore concluded in his evidence before the Select Committee of 1844 that, judging from the towns where medical relief was most adequately afforded, the proportion of the population which ought to have been provided for in sickness should have been not less than a half in towns where the working class was in a prosperous condition and not less than three-fifths in most towns. It was a brave suggestion, which the authorities never even attempted to consider. (See Appendix, Table 10.4, for statistical summary of Medical Relief afforded to poor.)

Through the failings and inadequacy of the Poor Law medical services, the great bulk of the poorer classes who could not obtain treatment in the legitimate way, or who from ignorance were compelled to resort to inferior sources for attendance, had recourse to druggists and quacks. 'Every town . . . [has its] unhonoured dabblers in physic, from the itinerant vendor of pills and worm medicines, to the dispensing druggist and more noteable bone-setter.'[1] Rumsey obtained returns from forty-two places, 36 per cent of which stated that illegal practices were carried on to an unlimited extent. In Hull for example a quarter of the population was affected; in Shrewsbury it was common for the poor to visit druggists in the early stages of disease, and later illegal practitioners. In Southampton half the poor were attended by druggists and half by doctors, and in Brighton as many people received treatment from druggists as from the hospitals, dispensary, and clubs together. From Wolverhampton it was reported that: 'A very large proportion of fatal cases among children were not seen by medical men, and often not even by druggists, the mothers merely applying for remedies at the druggist's shop.' In Reading this was also done to a 'lamentable extent', a third of the druggists even visited the sick when they thought it was safe to do so. Between 4,000 and 5,000 poor resorted to them in Wakefield, and in Lincoln all retail druggists had a considerable practice, both in chronic cases and in the early stage of acute complaints, and they frequently performed minor operations as well.

Access to the druggist's shop was so easy, and it vied with the gin palace in its tempting decoration. Therefore it attracted not only those who could only afford to spend a few pence, but also those who were apprehensive of encountering the formalities and the delay attendant on the application to a qualified Poor Law medical practitioner. The ignorant poor were also impressed by the speedy diagnosis of the druggist—a glance generally sufficing to satisfy him both as to the nature and treatment of a disease. None of the victims

[1] James Black, *Bolton and Neighbourhood*, 1837.

were in a position to comprehend the inevitable mass results of the fearful mortality and destruction of health!

A Manchester surgeon pointed out the danger to the community from this pernicious system:

It is perfectly frightful to contemplate the loss of life amongst young children and infants arising from the practice of numerous druggists in the poorest parts of the town. Any one who is much amongst the poor, and who sees as much of the disease of infants as I do, cannot fail to be horror-struck at the immense loss of life constantly taking place from this shameful practice. It is one of those crying abuses that deserves the most earnest attention of the legislator and philanthropist. Those who have been accustomed to life as it is in agricultural districts and small market towns, have no notion of the fearful extent to which human existence is played with in large towns, and in no way so barefacedly as in this. Adults may have a right to hazard their own lives by going to ignorant druggists or professed quacks, but they most assuredly have none to risk that of the helpless children . . . and as moral restraints are not sufficient to prevent this, legal ones of great stringency are imperatively needed. I speak decidedly and warmly on this point, because I am daily brought into contact with the miserable consequences of the present state of things.[1]

There is no doubt that a large proportion of deaths among children might have been prevented by substituting good medical care for treatment by illegal practitioners. The most serious effect of neglected or maltreated infantile sickness was that it laid the foundation for organic disease, ill-developed and deformed bodies, sickly constitutions and tuberculosis in the children who were to become the parents of the succeeding generation, and therefore entailed the dreadful results of early mismanagement on future millions. A great source of income for the druggist was that the working mother left her children in the care of a nurse who plied them with opiates, the most famous of which was 'Godfrey's Cordial'. Many cases of convulsions and nervous disorders resulted solely from maltreatment of this description. Chadwick, in his *Report on Interment in Large Towns*, quoted the evidence of a surgeon and registrar of Manchester as saying that a quarter of the registered deaths were due to incompetent and unqualified practitioners, when early attention by a doctor could have cured the child.

Infanticides found an able ally in the druggist. In the early 'forties there was a great increase in infanticide and Wakley impressed on the House of Commons the futility of punitive action, for the practice accompanied illegitimacy and both were increasing because wages were so low and employment irregular. His remedy was higher wages, cheaper food, better housing and decent sanitation, but he failed to advocate legislation to restrict the activities of the druggist to his proper function. Dr. Lyon Playfair in an inquiry he made in Staffordshire and Shropshire[2] pointed out the assistance druggists

---

[1] Mr. Dorrington, quoted by Rumsey, Select Committee, 1844.
[2] Quoted by Chadwick in his *Report on Interment in Large Towns*.

THE NECESSITY FOR MEDICAL RELIEF

afforded to infanticides. In the mining districts of these two counties, druggists' practices prevailed, and there had been an increase in the sale of opium in the form of a carminative for children. This had resulted in high infant mortality, 'sometimes suddenly, from an overdose, more commonly, slowly, painfully, insidiously'. The high death rate was coincident with a high birth rate, so that there was no decline in the numbers of children, only a diminution of their strength. 'Those who escaped with life became pale and sickly children', and it took a long time for an individual to overcome the effects arising from the noxious system, if indeed he ever did so.

But it was not only the children who suffered through the difficulty of obtaining efficient and adequate medical treatment. The evils consequent on the poor being driven to procure spurious relief can be deduced from District Registrars' notes which were appended to the quarterly returns made to the Registrar General. The following are extracts from some of them (the figures are for the whole population, not only the poor):

Period	Town	Remarks
Quarter ending 31 March 1843	Manchester (a) Deansgate district	. . . 119 deaths from 8 diseases, 30 ascertained attended by retail druggists, 4 no advice or attention. Number of first class very much below truth, as on direct enquiries no instance made to elicit information.
Quarter ending 31 March 1843	(b) Ancoats	. . . Out of total of 380 deaths, 180 attended by regular practitioners, 103 by druggists. Remaining 97 no attendance. 6 Coroner's Inquests.
Quarter ending 31 December 1843	Ashton (town district)	. . . 142 deaths, 95 attended by surgeons, 3 by druggists; 44 no attendance.
Quarter ending 31 March 1844	Stockport (Heaton Norris district)	. . . 86 deaths, 55 attended by surgeons, 5 by infirmary, 12 by druggists, 10 no medical aid. Remaining 4 Coroner's Inquests.
Quarter ending 31 March 1844	Halifax (Brighouse district)	. . . great child mortality; neglect of parents procuring medical aid, some none, others only assistance of druggists.
Quarter ending 31 March 1844	Leeds (North district)	. . . Infants die because of neglect of parents. Drugs often administered. No regular medical aid till unavailing. Half of the deaths under 5 years old.

It was to overcome the harmful effects of the deficiency in the supply of medical relief that many of the most eminent doctors of the time advocated the establishment of efficient and extensive provision for the sick poor. They appealed for a liberal view of the subject, not only on humanitarian grounds, but also in the interest of economy. Rumsey, as we have seen, demanded that the public should undertake to pay for medical assistance for the entire working class, for they were not in a position to provide it for themselves:— '*Medical and sanitary care,*' *he maintained,* '*like education and religious instruction, are matters which are beyond the means of the largest proportion of the population, and even if some of the poor temporarily provide for themselves in these respects, they are incompetent to provide adequately, properly, or continuously.*'

APPENDIX

In the following Schedules, Table 10.4, some figures do not correspond exactly with those quoted in the text. Here, as in all statistical data appearing in the volume, I have quoted the original work. The small discrepancies throughout are therefore due to the statements of the authors—who may have obtained their figures from different sources. The gathering of correct statistical information was in its infancy during this period—and indeed the requirements for the operation of the Poor Law medical service fostered its progress.

TABLE 10.4

Medical Relief afforded to Poor.—Three Schedules referred to by H. W. Rumsey, Select Committee on Poor Law Medical Relief, 1844: (Q. 9117)

SCHEDULE I—PLACES NOT UNDER NEW POOR LAW

Name of Place	Population in 1841	Number of Medical Officers	Number of Pauper Patients	Patients in Medical Charities					Total number of patients pro-vided for by public	Patients in 100 of population		
				Dispensary		Infirmary		Total		Paupers	Medical Charities	Total
				Out	Home	In	Out					
Brighton	46,660	2 1 w[1]	1,000	2,552	2,105	½447	½605	5,709	6,709	2·14	12·23	14·37
Chester with surrounding parishes	23,115 49,085	3 1 w	—	—	1,275	628	1,080	2,983	—	—	6·07	—
Coventry Exeter	30,743 31,334	4[2] 3 1 w	Av 2,000 Av 6,000	2,000 2,032	—	⅖16 ½576	½450 ½135	2,466 2,743[3]	4,466 8,743	6·83 19	8·02 8·75	14·85 27·75
Hull and Sculcoats[4]	41,609 16,346	1	Av 650	2,343	—	½386	½796	3,525	—	1·56	6·08	7·64
Leeds	152,054	2	2,000	3,234	1,607 (in-cluded) 100[8]	1,462[5] 326[5]	2,761	7,783[6]	9,783	1·32	5·12	6·44
Shrewsbury	22,575	2	(1843)3,726	130[7]	(in-cluded)	2	½1,886	2,620	6,346	16·50	11·60	28·10
Southampton	27,774	2	Av 2,000	1,280	—	130	—	1,310	3,310	7·20	4·80	12·00
Mean percentage of seven towns not including Chester										7·79	8·08	15·87
Bristol	64,298	6 hon-orary	2,663	6,229 14 dispen-saries		(2 infirmaries) 2,207	8,605	17,041	—	4·36	11·70	16·06
Clifton Union	64,231	6	2,934									
Bedminster Parish	17,862	—										

[1] W = Workhouse Medical Officers.   [2] Salaries £240 2s. 5d. per case; nearly twopence per head on population.

[3] Not including patients at Eye, Skin, and Lying-in Hospitals: returns not forwarded.   [4] Within Union.

[5] House of Recovery.   [6] No deduction made for non-residents.   [7] Eye and Ear Dispensary.

[8] Home Visiting provided by auxiliary society—no remuneration.

SCHEDULE II—NORTHERN TOWNS (classified according to amount of relief given)

Name of Place	Population — Town or city	Population — Parish or Union	Number of Medical Officers in Union	Average Population to each Medical Officer	Pauper patients, Annual Average	Dispensary — Out	Dispensary — Home	Infirmary — In	Infirmary — Out	Total	Total number of patients provided for by public	Patients in 100 of population — Paupers	Patients in 100 of population — Medical Charities	Patients in 100 of population — Total
CLASS A														
Liverpool and Toxteth	264,349	223,054	6 + 3 workhouse 6 honorary	37,175	6,131	37,076[1]	12,694[1]	5,875[2]	5,467[3]	61,112	67,243	2·75	23·12	25·87
Manchester,	192,408	3 Unions 356,159	7 + 6 honorary	27,487	5,994	25,459	10,135	2,783	—	} 46,579	—	3·11	19·95	23·06
Chorlton	70,228		4	17,557	1,595	3,863	1,800	—	—		—	2·28	} 13·10	15·38
and Salford	93,523		4	23,381	1,061	1,656 (30,978)	883 (12,818)	—	—			1·11		
CLASS B														
Bradford	34,560	132,164	11	12,015	823	2,494	1,260	50 (⅔114)	—	3,804	4,627	0·62	2·90	3·52
Carlisle	21,090	35,745	6	5,956	210	2,025	1,123		⅔551	3,813	4,023	0·59	10·66	11·25
Huddersfield	25,018	108,921	16	6,807	1,600	4,886	Av 700	319	—	5,905	7,505	1·47	5·42	6·89
Sheffield	67,967	85,074	5	17,015	4,311	2,543	—	871	2,716	6,130	10,441	1·46	10·80	12·26
Stockport	28,419	85,434	5	17,087	2,246	Av 1,004	Av 459	Av 162	—	1,625	3,871	2·63	1·90	4·53
Sunderland	52,898	55,783	4	13,945	2,073	Av 1,136	1,068[4]	33	—	2,237	4,310	3·72	4·01	7·73
York	29,435	44,011	9	4,879	814	Av 2,090	—	⅔266	Av ⅔334	2,690	3,504	1·84	6·11	7·95
									Mean percentage of seven Unions, Class B			2·27	5·46	7·73
CLASS C														
Beverley	7,574	18,957	6	3,159	419	500	—	none		500	919	2·21	2·64	4·85
Lincoln	16,172	36,110	7	5,158	664	750	818	Av ⅔224	Av ⅔147	1,939	2,603	1·84	5·37	7·21
Rotherham	13,439	28,526	7	4,075	1,292	700	—	none	—	700	1,922	4·53	2·45	6·98
Wakefield	29,922	43,481	11	3,952	1,282	294	399	35[5]	—	728	2,010	3	1·7	4·7
Wrexham	5,844	39,543	8	4,942	1,726	1,054	168	26	—	1,248	2,974	4·36	3·15	7·51
									Mean percentage of five Unions, Class C			3·19	3·06	6·25

49,770

[1] 39,872 in Northern and Southern
5,946 in Eastern
2,532 in Ladies
1,420 in Eye Dispensary

[2] 2,255 in Infirmary
1,550 in Northern
431 in Southern
749 in Lying-in
890 in Fever Hospital

[3] In Eye and Ear and Southern Hospitals.
[4] 788 relieved by four Charities. Supplied tickets for medicine and attendance, presented to certain doctors. Price of ticket only paid for medicine.
[5] House of Recovery.

SCHEDULE III—MIDLAND, SOUTHERN, EASTERN, and WESTERN TOWNS

Name of Place	Population		Number of Medical Officers in Union	Average population to each Medical Officer	Pauper patients, Annual Average	Patients in Medical Charities					Total number of patients provided for by public	Patients in 100 of population		
	Town or city	Parish or Union				Dispensary		Infirmary		Total		Paupers	Medical Charities	Total
						Out	Home	In	Out					
CLASS A														
Bath	53,209	69,232	9	7,692	2,898	3,856	880	Av 908	11,078	16,722	19,620	4·18	24·15	28·33
CLASS B														
Bridgwater	10,449	31,778	8	3,972	2,930	1,100	none	130	—	1,230	4,160	9·22	3·87	13·09
Cheltenham	31,391	40,221	4	10,056	2,460	3,954	—	276	—	4,230	6,690	6·11	10·51	16·62
Croydon	16,712	27,721	4	6,930	2,565	—	SSD 278[1]	none	none	278	2,843	9·30	1·0	10·3
Gloucester	14,152	26,838	2	13,419	1,500	Av 1,017	—	Av⅔445	Av⅔348	1,810	3,310	5·6	6·74	12·34
Hereford	10,921	25,289	3	8,429	1,102	250	—	Av⅔360	400	1,010	2,112	4·35	4·0	8·35
Ipswich	—	25,254	3	8,418	1,876	Av 474	none	Av⅔131	—	605	2,481	7·43	2·4	9·83
Ludlow	5,108	17,521	5	3,504	1,200	388	none	none	—	388	1,588	6·85	2·21	9·06
Lynn Regis★	16,039	16,489	3	5,496	1,976	388	SSD 1,200[2]	½97	½74	1,371	3,347	11·98	8·31	20·29
Maidstone	18,086	32,266	6	5,377	2,364	478	—	109	—	587	2,951	7·32	1·82	9·14
Portsmouth	9,000	53,036	5	10,607	2,201	Av 770	none	none	none	770	2,971	4·15	1·45	5·6
Reading	18,937	19,528	2	10,000	2,130	1,220	—	½150	½400	1,770	3,880	10·65	8·75	19·4
Stroud	8,680	38,919	6	6,486	3,364	304	350	38	35	727	4,091	8·64	1·87	10·51
Wolverhampton	36,189	68,425	6	11,404	3,403	1,071	269	42	—	Av 3 yrs 2,028	5,431	5	3	8
Worcester	26,306	27,130	2	13,565	Av 1,663	Av 736	—	⅔681	⅔742	2,159	3,322	4·28	7·96	12·24
Yarmouth	—	24,031	2	12,015	908	—	—	Av⅔52	Av⅔1,333	1,385	2,293	3·77	5·76	9·53
Mean percentage of thirteen Unions: Croydon and Lynn Regis omitted[4]												6·41[3]	4·64	11·05

[1] SSD = Self-supporting dispensary.
★ i.e. King's Lynn
[2] Patients estimated at 60 per cent of members with eight surgeons and one physician.
[4] Because they contained only self-supporting dispensaries.
[3] Contained SSD's

The Origins of the
National Health Service

PART II—1847-1871

CHAPTER 11

Outdoor Medical Relief, 1847–71

THE year 1847 was a watershed in Poor Law history, and particularly in the provision of medical services. The Poor Law Commission was the first 'expert' administration, but it was too weak to perform the new and onerous duties laid upon it. Benthamism was therefore comprised with more orthodox political views, which left reorganized parochial authorities in a position generally unassailable by the central authorities. Having no precedent for guidance, the Commissioners were however active in introducing the new principles, and when they relinquished their office the General Consolidated Order of 1847 showed how much they had attempted to achieve. These rules of Poor Law procedure drew into a comprehensive system the experience and regulations of the formative years. After 1847 the history of the treatment of the destitute falls into a study of how these principles were carried out, for they were the basis of rules regulating the work of Poor Law officers until the end of the century. Developments under the Poor Law Board could really have been achieved in the earlier period had the regulations of the central authorities been obeyed when they were first initiated. The rules of the Poor Law Commissioners were far more humane and adequate than the practice of the Guardians. Many of the suggestions of the Poor Law Commissioners showed greater interest in the welfare of the poor, especially the sick, than history has accorded to them.

The 'three Bashaws of Somerset House' were victims of the 'principles of 1834', and because they showed some alert activity they aroused opposition and hatred. The Poor Law Board profited from their predecessors' experience, and no odium surrounded Gwydyr House. In 1851 ex-Commissioner Cornewall Lewis wrote of the Poor Law Board: 'it has now become purely administrative and has no character or policy of its own, it therefore got from Parliament just what it asked for'—(nothing). Chadwick summed up the new authority with perfect acumen when he wrote that the Presidents of the Poor Law Board—who were the sole authority, for the Board was in practice non-existent—rested as quietly as they were permitted to do, on the fundamental errors of their system, 'letting the evil principles work themselves out at the expense of the public, and applying the rule—Never to act until you are obliged, and then do as little as you can'.[1]

This was a penetrating condemnation, but the fault lay at the door of the legislature who ceased to be interested in the problem of destitution, either because they believed the

---

[1] E. Chadwick, *Reorganization of the Civil Service*, 1855, p. 190.

267

problem solved, or because they realized peace could only be obtained by forcing forward a less aggressive policy for achieving the principles of 1834. Without criticism or initiative to offer, legislative powers were sparingly used, and as the Poor Law Board was apathetic and inactive, the enforcement of those principles gradually fell into desuetude, so that by 1871 they had been almost completely reversed. Therefore as the central authorities were dull, and deficient in experts to offer guidance, and as the appointed Inspectors were equally ignorant of requirements, more power devolved on the Guardians. The power of local authorities was sacred to orthodox minds in the nineteenth century, and ratepayers were the acknowledged check on central administration. The original policy of uniformity was achieved in general outline, but in the medical services particularly, greater divergence in the execution of Orders could not have been possible.

In 1847 the Assistant Poor Law Commissioners became a body of thirteen Inspectors. The type of man chosen is illustrated in an article of the *Lancet*: Lieutenant-Colonel Beckeford Ward of the Royal Artillery appointed Inspector in place of Walsham who resigned, ... what could he know of sanitary inspection, etc. etc., and of workhouses ... if he had had similar work in the army the appointment could be understood.[1] After years of office, Inspectors no doubt became knowledgeable in Poor Law administration, but the appointment of such men, with no medical or public health experience, to watch over medical services as well as general poor relief, was a great scandal. How much could have been achieved for the medical system if a body of Benthamite experts had been employed? Ignorant of standards by which to judge, Inspectors were easily overruled by Guardians. Only very occasionally were there adverse reports, and these appeared when a scandal had aroused public indignation; never was there a comprehensive outline of the mismanagement or inadequacy of sick relief which was fairly general. Poor Law Inspectors were poles apart from Factory Inspectors, who, although they also had no technical knowledge needed no prodding by a second party. No praise is too high for the Medical Officers, on whose shoulders fell not only the responsibility for therapeutic work, but also for the reform and development of the whole medical service.

The complacency of the Poor Law Inspectors which was the dominating cause and effect of the inactivity of the Poor Law Board was revealed most acutely in their reports and in their evidence to Select Committees. Inspector R. B. Cane, for example, who was one of the most voluble of the Inspectors, pointed out in the 'fifties how superior the medical system was, and how much more efficient it had become since 1847. The result of the regulations and the superintendence of the Poor Law Board and its Inspectors, he claimed, was that a doctor had been brought to the door of every poor man who was unable to pay for relief. A Select Committee was appointed in 1854, for the purpose of 'Inquiring into the administration of medical relief and to ascertain whether any additional facilities might be afforded the poor in obtaining medical aid'.[2] At the Inquiry, Cane maintained that 'the whole tendency of the regulations and correspondence of the Board

---

[1] *Lancet*, 1868, i, pp. 293–4. Article on 'Poor Law Enigma'.
[2] Hereafter referred to as the Select Committee of 1854.

and the supervision by themselves and by the inspectors in the districts, has been to improve medical arrangements . . . which have never been in a more efficient and satisfactory state than at the moment.' Giving evidence to the same Committee, Inspector Austin agreed, and said he failed to see how the system could be substantially amended. Inspector Weale similarly could not recommend any amendment, nor had he heard of any system which could be an improvement on the existing one. The growth in the number of Medical Officers in rural areas and the diminution in the size of districts had increased facilities for supplying medical relief. Many Guardians gave similar evidence, suggesting only minor alterations.

The Inquiries of 1861–64, originally instituted to investigate the adequacy of the Poor Law for meeting the needs of the exceptional distress in Lancashire and London, came to a similar conclusion. Cane evinced that the medical relief afforded to the poor since 1854, had been promptly given, and by the most skilful persons Guardians could engage: 'the poor were never so well attended as they are at the present time'. He did not think the question admitted any particular recommendation regarding an increase in efficiency in any direction, for he pointed out that complaints were rare from Guardians, rate-payers, or the poor. The few local objections raised were no reflection on the system as a whole. Inquiries had been held when Sotheron Estcourt was President of the Poor Law Board to ascertain the Guardians' views, but it had not been found necessary to alter the existing scheme, and the Medical Officers, Cane said, disagreed amongst themselves on the changes they sought.

The final resolution of the Select Committee of 1864 stated that evidence had revealed that there were no sufficient grounds for materially interfering with the system of medical relief, which appeared to be administered with general advantage. This then was the prevailing official opinion. In contrast to the early years of the new Poor Law, the development of the medical services after 1847 had to come, not only by forceful agitation from below, but it also had to evolve inconspicuously as circumstances altered, and these were coped with by *ad hoc* measures.

The inaction and complacency of the Poor Law officials allowed 1847 to become a watershed in an important and beneficial direction. This was the toleration of the provision of outdoor relief for the able-bodied—which was never legalized, and was not general in many rural areas—and the offer of institutional relief to the sick. The building of workhouses never caught up with the demand, and so authorities were compelled to offer the able-bodied employment in stoneyards, and later in public utility undertakings. Also, the gradual realization of the importance of institutional treatment for the sick led to a decline in the provision of domiciliary attendance. Therefore workhouses assumed more and more the role of hospitals. *The chief concern of the Poor Law administration in 1834 was the able-bodied labourer; by 1871 this administration had developed into the State medical authority for the poor.*

This was inevitable when in the middle of the century 72 per cent of pauperism depended on sickness. Statistics showing the alarming proportion of illness among paupers were given in the evidence to the Select Committee of 1854. In the Axbridge Union, for example, 2,300 paupers received poor relief in 1850–51, of which 1,800 were sick or had sickness in the family; in Bristol, 1,270 out of 2,200 received relief through sickness; in Clifton 1,700 out of 2,600; in Plymouth 793 out of 1,138; in Salford 1,126 out of 2,300; in Tewkesbury 1,385 out of 1,606; and in Bedford 1,050 out of 1,900. Further, these numbers referred only to 'casual' sick, and excluded those paupers on the permanent list such as the aged and the chronics. The Clerk of the Tewkesbury Union, where the proportion was 85 per cent pointed out that if an able-bodied man was taken ill, his wife and all his children were added to the category of paupers who received relief through sickness, and all were entitled to general relief.[1] In 1860 out of the 26,290 adult able-bodied males relieved out of the workhouse, 24,500 received assistance through sickness or accident. Of the total outdoor able-bodied of 314,000, 275,500 were relieved through widowhood, sickness, and accident, or were families dependent on sick men.[2] Proportions were similar every year. In the late 'fifties and 'sixties there were nearly three times as many 'non-able bodied' as 'able-bodied' in workhouses, and they formed the slightly larger class requiring out-door relief.[3]

The Poor Law Board however did not devote much care to the investigation of the component parts of pauperism, and it is important to observe that there was much apprehension about the class designated 'adult able-bodied'. Only a small proportion of the people receiving relief in this group were capable of earning their own livelihood at the time, for the vast amount of pauperism caused by temporary sickness was included in this class, as we have seen. Normally healthy persons given relief because of sickness and classified as able-bodied, led to misleading inferences from statistics. The problem was increased by a sick man's whole family being entered on the able-bodied pauper list, and the whole family being included as sick when one member required medical relief. Great divergence existed among Guardians as to the classification of their pauper population and hence their treatment, and it was not until 1869 that the Poor Law Board compiled a statement classifying the causes of destitution under four heads:

(A) old age or permanent disability;
(B) death or absence or desertion of husbands or fathers;
(C) temporary sickness, or want of work of male heads of families or single men;
(D) single women in receipt of out-door relief.

In the Metropolis in 1870 the total outdoor poor were classified by percentages as follows: Class A—31; Class B—34; Class C—34; Class D—0·8. Over the whole country Poor Law Board inquiries discovered that out of more than a million paupers, a very small proportion—less than 4 per cent—were adults destitute through unemployment; 30 per cent of indoor and 13 per cent of outdoor poor were actually on the sick list irrespective in

[1] Abstracts from evidence to Select Committee of 1854 by Dr. G. Wallis and Inspector Weale.
[2] Abstracted from figures in the Twelfth Annual Report of the Poor Law Board, 1859–60.
[3] Abstracted from figures in the Twentieth Annual Report of the Poor Law Board, 1867–68.

both cases of the vast number of old people disabled through age, but not actually on the sick list; 36 per cent of the paupers were children and 4·2 per cent lunatics, and about 35 per cent of pauperism was caused by death, absence, or desertion of the male head of the family.[1] But even these figures were inaccurate because of the overlapping of classes.

Slowly and inevitably, the sick and the children, who were the favoured classes of paupers, received a supplementary policy, which was not based on the principle of offering minimum relief as a deterrent, but on adequacy and efficiency of treatment—and in the case of children—education. Economic considerations provided the dominant influence, but the prevailing social philosophy and growth of humanitarianism had their effect on the welfare of the sick poor. The really destitute, in the absence of a lucid and guiding policy as to who was eligible for relief, were in many areas better off than the lowest of the labouring class when illness overtook them, but as this depended on the individual Boards of Guardians, less eligibility was not disavowed as general policy.

The drawing out of the sick from the morass of paupers and providing them with sufficient aid conducive to their recovery and independent existence was furthered by the gradually established practice of giving—as a right—outdoor general relief to whole families. In the early years, if a breadwinner fell ill or sickness in the family precluded him from providing food, the whole family was offered the workhouse.

> The workhouse test when applied to sickness, especially among children is often tanta-
> mount to the refusal of relief. A poor man cannot come into the workhouse and bring
> his family with him because his child is ill with measles or diarrhoea. Nor will a labourer
> who is ill usually accept indoor relief until he is seriously ill. So this workhouse test
> system as applied to sickness is positively silly.[2]

Many Guardians had deviated from this principle in the 'forties, but under the Poor Law Board official orders allowed specific exception to be made in the application of the work-house test, which gradually, through necessity, widened in scope. In 1848 the central authorities ruled that widows and mothers with illegitimate children were not to be refused outdoor relief if the children were sick.[3] The Outdoor Relief Regulation Order of December 1852 stipulated that outdoor relief might be given in cases of sickness in the family, if the head of the family was simultaneously earning wages. The panic caused by the cholera epidemic of 1866 induced the Poor Law Board to circularize Guardians empowering them not only to call in additional medical and other assistance, but also to provide whatever sustenance and clothing that might be required irrespective of 'destitution' and all previous orders to the contrary. It is important to note however, that all the circulars were permissive and not compulsory. The result can be easily illustrated from the variation which existed in the Metropolis alone. The Guardians of Poplar for example, appointed a special com-

[1] Twenty-second Annual Report of the Poor Law Board, 1869–70.
[2] Theodore Dodd, *Progress*, 'Social and Economic Advantage of maintaining Outdoor Relief', vol. iii, 1908.
[3] Official Circular, Nos. 14–15, 1848.

mittee to investigate cases of outdoor sickness in 1868, and this reported: 'In these cases Guardians appear to be absolutely unfettered . . . and the committee recommend that all such cases be amply relieved, on the recommendation of the Medical and Relieving Officers.'[1] In St. Margaret's and St. John's, Westminster, the total value of bread, money, and meat given to non-able-bodied paupers rose from £47 in 1844 to £93 in 1848. By 1851, 1,681 families were in receipt of outdoor relief. In 1852 a comparative statement was given of the number of able and disabled persons relieved with money in the last week in March 1845 and the corresponding week in 1852. There were forty-six able-bodied paupers relieved with money in the first year and only twenty-five in the second. Disabled receiving outdoor relief on the other hand had risen from 180 to 291, and this number increased to 800 per week in 1858.[2] Hampstead allowed no outdoor relief at all right up to the 'seventies.[3] In Eccleshall (Yorks.) the Board of Guardians automatically gave every sick person relief in money and bread, ranging from 2s. 6d. and five loaves to 5s. and ten loaves a week, according to the number of children in the family. Additional allowances were made if sickness was acute, and disabled old people received 2s. or 2s. 6d. and a loaf.[4]

Many Guardians however continued using ingenious devices for deterring applicants from applying to the Union for aid and by making entry into the workhouse of sick persons and their families compulsory. Atcham Board of Guardians adopted a system by which, if a labourer was ill, some of his children had to live in the workhouse during his sickness. 'The method . . . acts as a test of destitution for in almost every case where parties have refused to send children, they have gone without relief altogether'; and because fathers had refused to have their children incarcerated in a general mixed workhouse, the Guardians concluded they had other means of support and were not entitled to apply to the Relieving Officer.[5] But such policy became rare, and the sick were generally entitled to general outdoor relief if they required it in addition to medical relief. In 1854 Inspector Austin told the Select Committee that Boards of Guardians were occasionally inclined to afford outdoor relief to a family when one of them was on the sick list. By 1862 Inspector Cane could state that relief was always given to children out of the workhouse without the father being required to enter it, for although he continued working, it was realized that he might not be able to afford a doctor and necessaries. Money was seldom given, Cane said, and never to procure treatment—if it was given at all, it was for the purchase of necessaries. The proportion of poor who were pauperized by sickness whose families did not need additional aid for such emergencies was very small indeed.

Because outdoor relief to the able-bodied was officially disallowed by the General Outdoor Relief Prohibitory Order of 1844, where it was given for temporary sickness to any able-bodied person or family, the Medical Officer was required by the same order to keep a

---

[1] Minutes, Poplar Board of Guardians, 22 September 1868.
[2] Minutes of Governors and Directors covering several years.
[3] Minutes of the Hampstead Board of Guardians for several years.
[4] Minutes of the Eccleshall (Yorks.) Board of Guardians, 1853.
[5] Minutes of the Atcham Board of Guardians, 1871 (Webb MSS.).

strict account of the nature of the illness, and this the Guardians had to enter in their Proceedings for the purpose of check. A further controlling Order was issued in 1852[1] by which one-third at least of the out relief to the sick, aged, mentally infirm, or accident cases had to be given in food or fuel, or other articles of necessity. This was to prevent the misapplication of relief afforded. The fear of the abuse of the practice was voiced by a member of the Select Committee of 1854, who asked a Hampshire magistrate whether his Board of Guardians took the opportunity of fixing the amount of out relief to families. He also inquired whether it was true, that when a labourer with a large family complained of his inability to maintain his children, the first question was if he had anyone on the sick list, and if he had, his case would be considered and substantial relief given without reference to the immediate disorder of the sick person. Further, if not one individual could be found to be on the doctor's books, was it true that the application however urgent was refused. Although the inference was denied, such instances must have existed for the interlocutor to put the question, and probably Guardians were more liberally inclined to those temporarily pauperized through sickness than to those unemployed able-bodied who were still regarded as rogues and vagabonds.

Not only were families of the sick, or sick individuals only, given outdoor assistance, but they were also provided with food as medical 'extras'. These items constituted part of the medical service and so came under medical expenditure, whereas out relief given to the sick was classified as general relief. The granting of medical extras was universal, because general assistance was entirely inadequate to induce quick recovery or prevent disease from spreading. Starvation was habitual, particularly in London—as seen in the Registrar General's Reports—and in 1858, six clergymen wrote letters to newspapers on the great destitution in their parishes to elicit public subscriptions. One of the clergymen, giving evidence to the Select Committee of 1862, stated that in 1858 and 1861 women had died in St. George in the East, Stepney, because of the niggardly relief given to them. He said twenty-one out of the twenty-six deaths from starvation in the Metropolis at the beginning of 1862 were in parishes where rates were above the average, from which it could be inferred that relief was insufficient. A doctor of St. George's in the East told the Select Committee of 1854, that not only was general relief inadequate, but medical extras were often refused by the Relieving Officer, and this caused great suffering to the poor.[2] Inspector Cane admitted illness or debility arose from insufficient food, and that the poor applied to the Medical Officer even when they were not really ill. The doctor seeing their weak condition realized food was as beneficial, if not more so, than medicine, and ordered necessaries. Although this was shifting the expense from himself to the ratepayers, Cane did not think a doctor would do this if he did not genuinely believe that the effect of additional nourishment would be more salutary. There was, he said, no deliberate withholding of

---

[1] 25 August 1852.

[2] Evidence, Dr. Garrett to Select Committee, 1854. Dr. Garrett was a general practitioner, not a Poor Law Medical Officer.

medicines.[1] Dr. Griffin evinced to the Select Committee of 1862, that if a Medical Officer did not order meat and bread for the aged and infirm, they would die, for the 1s. or 2s. plus a loaf a week, which was usually allowed by Guardians was entirely insufficient. He gave illustrations from among his own old patients who were ill for eight months at a time with bronchitis and who would surely have died without medical extras.

In 1870 the Poor Law Board commissioned their Inspectors to inquire into the question of outdoor relief and the provision of 'extras'. Inspector Farnall reported that in the Eastern Counties 55·4 per cent of those receiving outdoor relief were not able-bodied and 43 per cent of the 'able-bodied' who were the Medical Officer's patients received food and stimulants on his recommendation. In eleven Unions which Farnall took as a sample, the fifty-two District Medical Officers had thirty-eight pauper patients a week, of whom only sixteen on an average were supplied with extras, and this was in districts where the wages of agricultural labourers were under 10s. The practice of District Medical Officers varied in different counties. One in the Eastern Counties, for example, recommended food for 5·5 per cent of his patients only, whilst another in the West Midland Counties recommended it for 100 per cent. But variation also existed within a county—in one Union in the East 22·6 per cent of the sick poor were given extras, whilst in another it was 52 per cent. The diversity of the practice of the Medical Officers in the same Union and between Unions created a strong impression in the minds of the Guardians that doctors abused the valuable authority which was given to them to recommend food and stimulants, which Relieving Officers and Guardians generally recognized as a command. Farnall maintained that in his experience he had never known a case in which either Guardians or officers had refused to make these provisions, and indeed Medical Officers' books contained a column 'Necessaries *ordered* to be given to . . .' and yet despite this heading—'a Medical Officer is not empowered by the orders of the Poor Law Board to order food or articles of diet . . . for his pauper patients'. Farnall advised the Poor Law Board not to disturb the power vested in the District Medical Officer generally, nor to deprive Guardians of the legal authority which they could exercise at their discretion disregarding either wholly, or in part, a District Medical Officer's certificate. Inspector Peel reported that in his region[2] only 37·4 per cent of the outdoor sick paupers received meat and stimulants, but there was considerable variation in the practice of Medical Officers. He had not heard of a single case where 'extras' had been substituted for medicines, but divergence was due to the different opinions held in the medical profession on the value of high, low, or moderate diets. The existing system, Peel said, offered a greater advantage to paupers than what the poorer class of ratepayers could command in sickness. Inspector Cane reporting on the Northern Counties[3] stated that one of the most constant representations made to an Inspector when attending the meetings of Boards of Guardians related to 'Doctors' Orders'. He also

[1] Evidence, R. B. Cane to Select Committee, 1862.
[2] District No. 3—Middlesex, Hertford, Bucks., Northants, Oxford, Cambridge, Bedford, Huntingdon. Report by W. A. Peel on Outdoor Medical Relief in General Report, 1870.
[3] Northumberland, Durham, Westmorland, and Cumberland.

showed that the extent and nature of orders varied in kind and degree in different Unions, and even in different districts of the same Union. In one district extras might be profusely given, whilst in a neighbouring Union a Medical Officer might be a supporter of the temperance principle and so systematically abstained from ordering stimulants, even if the patient required them. Cane said he had to remonstrate with such doctors as life was endangered. He also drew attention to the fact that doctors recorded cases as 'debility, requiring food only', and that this embarrassed and foiled the Guardians in their attempt to control relief, for much power and a great part of the expenditure virtually passed from their hands into those of the Medical Officer, who had no responsibility for financial outlay. Another evil, Cane maintained, was that necessaries could only be procured by sending long distances for them, so that a whole week's supply was ordered and procured at one time. Food was therefore frequently consumed at one meal by the entire family, instead of lasting a sick person, for whose exclusive benefit it was intended, a whole week. Cane summarized the three evils which arose from 'Doctors Orders' as: the transfer of a large portion of outdoor relief from responsible to irresponsible hands; the effecting of minimum benefit at maximum expenditure; the affording of constant opportunities for the evasion of regulations directed against the poorest form of relief in aid of wages; and the holding out of a strong and direct temptation to corrupt practices for private advantage.

Although the sick came to be regarded as the special and unfortunate class of poor, and although increased leniency was shown towards them, they were by no means treated with exceptional kindness, and often experienced great difficulty in obtaining medical aid. Early in the life of the new Poor Law a special definition of destitution had been given regarding eligibility for medical relief. This was inability to pay for medical attendance—and not absence of any possessions or means of income, which appertained to application for general relief. Paddington Board of Guardians even authorized the provision of a shed for the storing of furniture of people who entered the workhouse through sickness.[1] In furtherance of their policy, the central authorities declared in 1848 that sick servants who lived in their masters' homes and therefore had food and clothing, were eligible for medical relief because they were unable to pay for medical treatment when their wages temporarily ceased.[2] In 1854 Inspector Power stated . . . 'persons receiving medical relief are as a rule not on the Relieving Officer's books at all—nor are they considered destitute poor; in fact the Act of Parliament makes a difference between them; the Act calls those persons poor persons who receive medical relief, but all others receiving general relief from the poor rates are called destitute poor persons.'

One of the gravest omissions in the enactments of the Poor Law Board was their complete neglect in stipulating what connoted an insufficiency of earnings for the payment of doctors' fees. This fact was brought out clearly in the inquiry of 1854. One of the members of the Select Committee tried to ascertain what class of poor persons were held to be entitled to medical relief, whether, for example, a person in receipt of 8s. to 10s. a week was

[1] Minutes, Paddington Board of Guardians, 1858.
[2] Official Circular, No. 20, November 1848.

so eligible; in fact what would be the maximum wage which would disqualify a person from receiving medical relief. Inspector Cane gave the expected reply—the Poor Law Board were unable to lay down any rule as to the amount of wages which entitled a man to, or debarred him from, receiving such assistance. 'The decisions rest solely with the Board of Guardians . . . I do not know that any local Board . . . has laid down a scale of wages.' Circumstances therefore varied from Union to Union. Bristol had established a fixed rate: a man who received 15s. a week and who had three or four children not earning, was the maximum case allowed free medical attention for a wife and children—although not for the man himself. But here, as everywhere else, the question was generally left to the judgement of the Relieving Officer. The Relieving Officer of Clifton, giving evidence to the Select Committee of 1854, said it was the class just above the pauper who suffered most, for when he refused orders, these people went to druggists to obtain a little medicine, or to a cheap surgeon.[1] A Guardian of Dewsbury stated that in his Union only people already paupers before sickness set in, received medical attention. This policy had been adopted as the Guardians would not otherwise have been able to draw a line, and because there were many sick clubs in the area. He maintained local authorities should be very discriminating as to whom they offered gratuitous relief.[2] In Atcham, Shropshire, a woman who was refused sick relief because her husband was earning 9s. and they had no children, complained to the Guardians. The latter upheld the Relieving Officer's decision and agreed she was no case for medical relief.[3] The *Lancet* in 1858 printed an account of several areas, where the poor were dying or were seriously ill because the Relieving Officer refused orders on account of wages of 8s. or so being too high. The founder of the 'Society for the Relief of Distress', William Bromley Davenport, stated in 1862 that many cases of sickness occurring through insufficient food had come to his notice and that these people had been denied medical relief; one person in Lambeth had died because the Guardians refused medical relief.

Two categories of sickness were always granted gratuitous medical relief—these were midwifery and accidents. The Poor Law Amendment Act of 1848, Section 2, stipulated that medical attention was to be given on account of 'accident, bodily casualty, or sudden illness'. This was in fact already an established practice, as was the granting of relief to able-bodied men when their wives were confined. Inspector Cane went further, and said, in 1862, that no regulation actually existed whereby any able-bodied person was precluded from being attended, either himself or his family, by the District Medical Officer—'without reference to income, sickness is an exception to all regulations, so that the Board of Guardians can order medical relief to any person who they think is not in a position to employ a doctor'. Inspector Weale had also pointed out in 1854 that medical relief was never refused to any person entitled to relief; on the contrary, medical relief was given when it could have been withheld. The *Justice of Peace* had a leading article in 1857, in

[1] Evidence, G. Carter, Relieving Officer of the Clifton Union, to Select Committee, 1854.
[2] Evidence, J. Ellison, Guardian of the Dewsbury Union, to Select Committee, 1854.
[3] Minutes, Atcham Board of Guardians, 1851 (Webb MSS.).

which it was affirmed that the grievances of the Medical Officer were to a large extent caused by the great facility which was afforded to the labouring classes in obtaining gratuitous medical aid. The Guardians, the writer said, granted relief readily, because it cost them nothing more if the salary of the Medical Officers was fixed, and they hoped thereby to prevent the death of the head of the family, through which the remainder might fall on the poor rates. The article therefore drew the obscurantist conclusion that the poor rate could not be applied to prevent destitution—only to relieve it! Therefore the Poor Law Medical Officer should only be required to attend those already destitute: 'The Medical Officers cannot go on attending the labouring classes indiscriminately as they have hitherto done, unless they are legally bound to do so, or salaries are increased in the same ratio as labour.'[1]

Despite these assertions, the amount of untreated sickness was enormous. There must have been hundreds of such cases in every Union. The incidence of disease was increased and recovery retarded, either because the poor were reluctant to apply for Poor Law medical relief, or because it was withheld from them. The expectation of a man's working life was considerably shortened by retaining the medical services within the Poor Law administration. The period for which outdoor relief was given to the sick varied according to the Medical Officer's report, but there were very few Unions in which it was granted for more than three months at a time. Inspector Wodehouse reporting on the Metropolis in 1870[2] said that in Woolwich, for example, relief was ordered 'during sickness', and when medical attendance ceased, general relief ceased also. Chelsea, Camberwell, and Hampstead never gave relief to the sick for longer than a month. Bethnal Green granted medical relief for thirteen weeks. Old and infirm and chronic cases were sometimes granted assistance for as much as one year at a time in Camberwell, Greenwich, Hampstead, Lambeth, Wandsworth, and Clapham; in other Unions relief for these cases varied from three to six months. Medical Officers rarely attended meetings of Guardians while applications for out relief were being considered, so that everything was left in the Relieving Officer's hands. Only Poplar had adopted the practice, stated Wodehouse, and St. Pancras were about to introduce it.

The number of the District Medical Officer's patients depended very largely on how far the Guardians adopted a policy of deterrence. Sometimes the Relieving Officers considered it their duty to ward off applicants for assistance, others granted orders freely and indiscriminately, either to protect themselves from the risk of having an applicant die through lack of attention, or to rid themselves of a pauper by providing relief on the easiest possible terms. The Relieving Officer generally visited the sick once a week, and the old and infirm once a month. But in some Unions the sick were never called upon by the Relieving Officer and the aged only about twice a year. Application for orders to the Relieving Officer did not only apply to permanent paupers or the aged, for they held permanent medical orders as a matter of course, irrespective of whether they were ill or not.

[1] *Justice of Peace*, 27 June 1857. Article 'On Medical Relief to the Poor and the Poor Law Medical Officer'.
[2] Report on Outdoor Relief by E. H. Wodehouse (Metropolitan Inspector), 1870.

As in the early period the Relieving Officer and his functions in connection with the medical system came in for much criticism. Dr. Griffin[1] quoted to the Select Committee of 1861 some of his own cases, and also several taken from the 4,000 letters he had received from Poor Law Medical Officers, where Relieving Officers had granted medical relief to people earning wages of 15s. to 25s. This showed, he said, that the labouring classes were extensively supplied with medical orders, and the urgency for a law stipulating the class eligible for relief. He reiterated the necessity for legislation because neither the Poor Law Commissioners, nor the Poor Law Board had ever grappled with this point of relief as to whether poor or only paupers should receive gratuitous medical attention. He suggested the Act should divide applicants into two classes. The first was to consist of those entitled to free treatment—families with under 10s. a week income. These should be put on a list, redrawn every quarter, and inclusion would automatically mean an order had been granted so that no further application to the Relieving Officer was necessary. The second class of families—those with incomes of 10s. to 20s. should be granted relief on loan. These measures would mean all discretionary power would be removed from the Relieving Officer and would rest with the Board of Guardians, who could be compelled to inquire into each case of medical relief just as other cases were investigated. But the Poor Law Board in furtherance of their restrictive policy deprecated the loan system. In their Instructional Letter of 1852 they stated:

> what cannot be legally given, must not be lent, and the power of lending must only be exercised where Guardians think fit to do something less than absolutely give the relief applied for, in cases where application is lawful. In such cases, and in such cases only, may they lend it; and such loans may never be made without necessary steps for recovery being taken.

The Board did however recommend that as the fee paid to a Medical Officer for midwifery was an 'extra', relief of this nature could be granted by way of a loan, but repayment of part of the whole of it was to be rigidly enforced. Most Unions adopted this principle. But in very strictly administered Unions like those of Whitechapel and St. George in the East, medical relief was never given on loan under any circumstances. In fact, the position of applicants was scarcely ever found good enough to warrant granting relief by this means. Griffin admitted the objection to the loan system in the past had been the difficulty of recovery, but this was occasioned by Guardians attempting to apply it to incomes of 6s. to 7s., whereas he was advocating it for the 10s. to 20s. wage group. He insisted on the Guardians being responsible for granting orders and not the Relieving Officer—as was already the procedure in Norwich, Coventry, and Oxford—because of the important fact that in 1857, for example, well over one million sick, all with orders, had been attended by the Medical Officers.

The Inspectors and Guardians upheld the necessity for the casual poor obtaining orders

[1] The great leader in the campaign for reform of the Poor Law medical services. (See particularly Chapters 12 and 13.)

for medical relief from the Relieving Officer. As Weale said in 1854: 'If we had no system of obtaining a medical order . . . in a short time the whole labouring population would come for medical relief.' It was ironical on the other hand that the medical profession condemned the Relieving Officer for giving orders indiscriminately. The Metropolitan Poor Law Medical Officers voiced the opinion at a meeting in May 1861, that in London, Relieving Officers gave orders without due inquiry into the pecuniary resources of recipients. This, the doctors declared, not only injured them in the amount of work they were required to perform, but delegated to them the onus of proving the recipients' right to the order, for they then had to undertake the treatment or refuse it at their own discretion. The duty and responsibility of discrimination which was essentially the Relieving Officer's was transferred to the Medical Officer. When Charles Buller was President of the Poor Law Board in 1848–49, he stated that in his opinion, the Relieving Officer should not be allowed to judge on a pauper's state of health and his necessity for medical relief; and Robert Palmer, a member of the Select Committee of 1854 also recorded an individual resolution asking that Medical Officers should attend the sick poor without them previously obtaining an order from the Relieving Officer on the first application.

Sotheron Estcourt as President of the Poor Law Board in 1859 proposed to Medical Officers and Guardians a scheme by which the District Medical Officer's contract should include attendance without order on permanent list paupers, temporary paupers, and urgent cases of resident or casual poor. This was resisted by the doctors and was therefore abandoned. Strangely enough some of the Poor Law authorities showed more enlightenment than the Medical Officers on this subject, but the latter were thinking of the large amount of work they were expected to perform for the very meagre salaries. The British Medical Association put forward an argument very similar to the Metropolitan Poor Law Medical Officers in their petition of 1862, and demanded the duties of the Relieving Officer should be more strictly defined. But the petitioners also asked that other parochial officers besides the Relieving Officers should have the authority to issue orders so that the poor could have as speedy treatment as possible. Inspector Cane pointed out to the Select Committee of the same year that individual Guardians had no power to issue orders, and that it had been suggested that they should have this privilege. Many Boards of Guardians had introduced the system and overseers were already legally entitled to order relief in cases of emergency. As they were accounting officers, they could be surcharged if they granted orders indiscriminately, but no such control could be exercised over individual Guardians. Cane therefore deprecated the suggestion, pointing out further, that if the power were accorded to Guardians, many men would not accept office because it would entail the additional duty of being visited by the poor. He admitted however that the existing system caused delay in obtaining treatment as the Relieving Officer could often not be found when he was needed.

The opinion of most doctors was that the difficulty of obtaining medical relief by genuine cases was too great, and that the necessity of procuring an order from the Relieving Officer before medical relief could be given made for a narrow and inelastic system. The system led to the strange anomaly whereby a doctor who alone could determine whether medical treatment was necessary and its nature, came into conflict with the Relieving Officer who was the legal authority as to its necessity. A Guardian bore this out when he pointed to the fact that the poor could not be satisfied with the amount of medical relief they received, because Relieving Officers and Guardians were ignorant of medical knowledge and were therefore incompetent to distinguish whether treatment was necessary or not. He recommended that the consideration of an application should be left to someone conversant with medicine.[1] Rumsey in 1854 maintained that the serious objection against the obtaining of an order prior to treatment was that this practice hindered prompt treatment. He had met doctors, however, who refused medical aid if the sick person was not on the Relieving Officer's books first, because in such cases they were not constituted paupers. He deemed it important that the Medical Officer should visit the homes of the poor to detect the first signs of disease before the poor ever went to the Relieving Officer. For the intervention of the latter meant an illness might get worse or disease spread during the lapse of time. Dr. Livett of the Wells Union also wanted the poor to have permission to go directly to the Medical Officer. He did not think the supply of medical relief was sufficient for the wants of the population to prevent a great deal of illness. The poor, he said, disliked applying to the Relieving Officer first, because they believed he considered it his duty to make an order difficult to obtain, and often refused applications. In many cases great hardship was experienced because the granting of orders was delayed several days. Other doctors maintained that the difficulty of obtaining relief considerably swelled the list of paupers. The reformers found support in Lord Ashley. In 1848 he had moved a resolution in the House of Commons founded on the evidence taken before the Medical Relief Committee of 1844, of which he had been chairman. He recommended that 'every woman claiming medical assistance from the parish in consequence of being pregnant, shall be entitled in all cases to the aid of the Medical Officer, with her first child and also with others which may follow . . . at present medical relief can only be given in such cases on an order from the Guardians or Relieving Officer . . . and delay frequently occurs in granting orders.'[2] If this resolution were carried, said Ashley, some fraud would be certain, but this could be avoided 'by giving to Boards of Guardians the power of recovery by attaching the wages of those who had obtained relief to which they were not entitled'. The resolution had however been defeated.

It was Richard Griffin, Chairman of the Poor Law Medical Relief Association who gave the clearest evidence on the function of the Relieving Officer. To the Select Committee of 1861 he quoted cases of Relieving Officers still refusing orders for serious cases which often resulted in death, and he gave instances where Medical Officers refused to attend the sick if they had no order. Deaths had ensued after accidents because the Medical Officer had been afraid of giving treatment, although no order was necessary on such occasions. Griffin opposed investing the sole power of granting relief, when the Board of

[1] Evidence, Rev. Oxenden to Select Committee, 1854.
[2] *Hansard*, 3rd series, vol. 97, 16 March 1848.

Guardians was not sitting, to the Relieving Officer, for not only could he act capriciously, but he was never free from suspicion. In his own Union, a remarkable diminution in the number of patients he was asked to attend had occurred since a new Relieving Officer had been appointed, so that he was left to infer that orders had either been indiscriminately granted formerly, or that they were now improperly withheld. Either case proved the necessity of defining the class of persons entitled to orders and not allowing the Relieving Officer to give or withhold orders as caprice might dictate. Griffin also recalled the long journeys made by the poor to the Relieving Officer and demanded that they should be allowed to apply directly to the District Medical Officer, for the Relieving Officer was in any case no judge of the necessity for medical treatment. Dr. Fowler, another reformer, also recognized that in rural districts, distances between the poor and the Relieving Officer, and the Relieving Officer and the Medical Officer, were too great, so that the poor had to make long journeys for medical aid. He suggested that either the power of giving orders should be extended to other parochial officers, or that arrangements should be made for the Relieving Officer to reside, if possible, within a mile of the residence of the Medical Officer. The sick poor strongly objected to having to obtain orders from the Relieving Officer, first, because of the disgrace of becoming paupers thereby, and the uncertainty of success, and second, because of the difficulty in finding him at home and the long journeys it often entailed.

Not only were the poor discontented with having the Relieving Officer as an intermediary in their demand on medical attendance, but like the doctors, they realized that treatment was too difficult to obtain through the great extent of the medical district. The Medical Officer as well as the Relieving Officer was frequently a great distance away. Accounts given to the Select Committee of 1854 showed the situation had changed little since the earlier years and complaints of distances to be travelled by the poor or the Medical Officer run through the whole evidence. Rural areas only were affected, but the town dwellers had their own problem, for although the Medical Officer lived nearby, he could not see them as frequently as they wished because he had too many patients. Difficulties were enhanced in the country because Medical Officers often did not live in the area. This was the case in the Banbury Union where the Medical Officer said he had to travel 13 miles to and from a village, and a man coming for him to attend his wife or family would have to lose a whole day's work through the long journey. Inspector Austin in the 'fifties stated that there was less difficulty in obtaining a District Medical Officer because of the low salaries than because no doctor resided in the locality. He therefore suggested the rearrangement of districts, which, he asserted, had already been reduced in size, or the appointment of some medical man not fully qualified. He reported cases where, because of the scantiness of the population, Guardians had been obliged to resort to not fully qualified men, because no experienced practitioner would reside in these areas. Inspector Weale also confessed that in the West Country, although medical districts were smaller than the stipulated size, the poor had to send many miles for the Medical Officer who generally resided in market towns. But here the poor had adopted the system whereby, if they knew the doctor was coming to another home in the village they called there for him so that they and the doctor were saved long journeys. The 1842 and 1847 Orders restricting the size of areas were never applied at all to the wilder parts of the country in the North, or to Wales and parts of Devon and Lincoln. Inspector Cane informed the Select Committee of 1854 that no formal regulation had been issued on the arrangements to be made in rural areas—but the advice had been given that medical relief should be facilitated as much as possible. Complaints, he maintained, were few!

As on so many other subjects, Griffin lodged the strongest protest, and suggested an amelioration of the situation. He drew attention to the insufficiency of attendance in extensive rural districts. Where relief was given it was good, but there were far too few doctors appointed, and often the poor had to send three and four miles for the Medical Officer when two or three doctors resided in the village. He gave an illustration from one Union. Here the wife of an old and infirm man was ill, so he walked three miles to the Medical Officer, who was not in, so he walked home again. Late in the evening the doctor followed him and said he must return to the surgery for medicines. This was beyond the old man's strength and therefore he undertook his walk the following morning. Altogether 18 miles were walked by the doctor and the man before medicine was obtained. This case occurred frequently, said Griffin, although two qualified doctors lived within 200 yards of the poor man's house. He accused the Guardians of never considering the subject of convenience which a rearrangement of districts would effect, and suggested that all practitioners in an area, who were willing, should be employed by the Poor Law authorities. The poor should be allowed to choose from the panel, and as in all probability they would select the doctor nearest their homes they would enjoy more immediate and therefore more efficacious treatment.

As the Medical Officers supplied the medicines, the difficulty of procuring them in rural districts was the same as that for obtaining doctors' attendance. Some Guardians established a practice of making arrangements for the delivery of medicines to the poor at their own homes by the Relieving Officer, but there was no distinct regulation. Inspector Austin admitted the hardship of the sick, or a messenger, travelling many miles to a surgery and having to wait hours until a Medical Officer returned from his duty, before receiving them. Mr. Pigott[1] who questioned Austin at the inquiry of 1854, showed remarkable ability in drawing from witnesses accounts of the inefficiency of the medical system because he believed in reform. He told Austin that in rural districts hardly a case could be mentioned in which the medical area did not extend three to four miles from the Medical Officer's house. He had also, he said, never heard of arrangements for the delivery of medicines to the poor—either the doctor brought them or the patient had to wait a few days. Austin retorted that Pigott was taking extreme cases.

To overcome the difficulty in the supply of medicines in rural areas, Dr. Wells, another reformer, suggested that a deposit of drugs should be placed in dispensaries in villages.

---

[1] Later Sir Gillery Pigott (1813-75), lawyer and Liberal Member of Parliament, 1860-63.

This arrangement was already in operation in the colliery village of Abercarn in Monmouthshire. The poor, he said, were delighted with it. Wallis pointed out that there was no need for a new building to be erected because any empty cottage would answer the purpose or a room could be hired. These dispensaries, he said, could be run at little expense to the Guardians, and the cost of drugs stored in them, which they should supply, would only amount to sevenpence per head per annum. Pigott's Medical Bill of 1860 included a clause for the establishment of dispensaries, but that it should be illegal for Guardians to compel the poor living over six miles from the dispensaries to visit the Medical Officer there or send that distance for medicines. The British Medical Association in its petition of 1862 recommended Boards of Guardians should supply medicines and that they should set up dispensaries in the Metropolis and larger towns, provided the sick poor had not to send more than five or six miles at the utmost for medicines. The scheme was gradually being adopted in towns. Inspector Power told the Select Committee of 1854 that existing dispensaries were costing £7,114 in rent, and incidental expenses were quite high. They formed repositories of drugs, had a porter, caretaker, and in large towns apothecaries, whose salaries at that date amounted to £1,662 or £43 each on an average. But generally these stations were without dispensers and Medical Officers went to them periodically to dispense medicines. Inspector Cane said that dispensaries were a disadvantage and inconvenient when there was only one in a Union, because the distance to be travelled to it was often great. Expense deterred Guardians from establishing several stations, but Cane maintained there was an advantage when the Medical Officer himself took a room, kept the medicines, and dispensed them himself to the poor! He agreed the system was good for agricultural areas where no resident Medical Officer could be obtained. By 1870 Cane advocated that the drug stores should be connected with the relief stores. Some towns had undertaken this arrangement and Cane wished to see it extended to all large towns. In such combined stations, he said, a dispenser should attend daily and relief in kind should be given at prescribed hours. The poor would thereby be more 'promptly and effectually relieved, and many of the existing evils incidental to "Doctors' Orders" would be avoided'.[1]

Added to the disability of having to apply to the Relieving Officer, and suffering under the delay and neglect caused through extensive areas or overcrowded districts, efficient medical relief to the outdoor sick poor was impeded by the use of inferior drugs and the supply of poor quality food. The labouring class was affected by the scourge of food adulteration. The pauper relieved in the workhouse, or given bread and meat for home consumption, must never have been free from danger. Guardians generally obtained their food in bulk by tender, thereby acquiring the cheapest goods. In 1851 Wakley initiated a public investigation, and the results published in the *Lancet* are said to have constituted his greatest personal triumph. The work was an invaluable piece of microscopical and chemical analysis and brought to light amazing facts.[2] As a result of the inquiry and public

[1] Report by R. B. Cane on 'Outdoor Relief in Northern Counties', 24 November 1870.
[2] Undertaken by Dr. Arthur Hassall, the *Lancet*'s Analytical Sanitary Commissioner and later Inspector to the General Board of Health.

condemnation, the Select Committee of 1855 on the Adulteration of Food, Drink, and Medicines was appointed. Its findings were appalling and disgusting and 'no record of crime is more interesting'.[1] The agitation for the Select Committee had begun in Birmingham through Postgate, a lecturer in anatomy, and Scholefield, who with Briscoe and Pigott was responsible for the introduction of the Poor Law Medical Bill in 1860. They demanded public analysts should be appointed by Town Councils and County magistrates.[2] Through the awakening of the public conscience by the two inquiries, the *Lancet* found in 1858 that food adulteration had been reduced to one-tenth of what it had been in 1851. The workhouse inquiries of the 'sixties revealed that food in most institutions was 'genuine', even if it was of poor quality. Griffin told the Select Committee of 1862 that poor meat, for example, was universally supplied by butchers, and he suggested that inspectors should be established. Towards the end of the period Guardians set up their own bakeries, generally in the workhouse, and authorities eventually awoke to the realization of the necessity and economy of providing adequately nourishing diets.

The Poor Law authorities also interested themselves in the drug trade, and the Medical Inquiry of the Select Committee of 1838 had already taken a long account from a London doctor who carried out research into the subject.[3] Wakley had been his examiner and had drawn out valuable information as to the fraud in drugs and the remarkable amount of adulteration practised by drug houses. Reading through the report, scepticism is aroused of the so-called medicines having any effect on the sick at all. The public had no security against the widespread evil which drug grinders and wholesale druggists perpetrated. In 1857 the *Lancet* published an account of the deaths caused by poisoning through adulterated medicines at Woolwich, Gateshead, and Chorley, and in 1860 reported a death from Godfrey's Cordial. It was the quack doctors, to whom the poor had recourse, who committed the greatest crimes in selling deleterious medicines. The Society of Apothecaries should have carried out periodic inspection, but Medical Officers received no education in the composition of drugs. It was not until the Chemists and Druggists Act of 1865 that the qualifications of apothecaries and dispensers were regulated and that registration with the Council of the Pharmaceutical Society began. Constantly throughout the statements of the Poor Law Medical Officers there is a denial of the use of inferior drugs for the poor. Low salaries and the appointment of unqualified men, must inevitably have led to the practice, and indeed it was occasionally admitted in the Medical Officers' arguments for an increase in remuneration. The cheapening of medicines and the discovery of new ones or equally effective substitutes, was of the greatest consequence to the sick poor. The growth of this side of medical science in the nineteenth century was as important to the Poor Law medical

---

[1] H. W. Rumsey, *Essays on State Medicine*, 1856.

[2] Manchester Board of Guardians had already taken the pioneering step of appointing a Public Analyst in 1848. He was a Professor of Chemistry and received £80 a year for his work, which consisted in analysing all samples sent by the Guardians, writing a monthly report and furnishing himself with information regarding the food of the poor for the consideration of the Guardians.—Minutes, Board of Guardians, May 1848.

[3] R. D. Thomson, M.D., Physician to the Blenheim Street Free Dispensary.

service as the invention of Doulton's cheap earthenware drain was to the Public Health movement. In 1869 the *Lancet* investigated the supply of drugs for paupers. The report[1] revealed that the subject required the urgent attention of the Poor Law Board regarding regulation. Many Boards of Guardians provided drugs for the sick in the workhouse and by this time for the outdoor poor as well, by contract. To this the *Lancet* offered serious objection because it was impossible to secure freedom from adulteration by this practice. To determine the genuineness of tea and sugar was less difficult than to discover the purity of drugs, which required skill and particular knowledge. The price of scammony varied from 12s. to 40s. a pound (in 1838 this was said to have been adulterated from 20 to 90 per cent—chiefly with chalk). When the Guardians began to supply medicines in the towns, the *Lancet* asked that a Medical Officer should be assured of good drugs. There existed no orders or rules to guarantee this to a doctor, and as the false economy of the Guardians was conspicuous, the journal recommended that regulations should be published by the Poor Law Board, and that Poor Law Inspectors should be authorized to inquire into the kind of drugs supplied and the price paid. An inquiry was instituted, but the report was made under the Local Government Board.[2]

The effect of adulterated drugs had deleterious and sometimes fatal consequences for the sick pauper, but another tremendous obstacle to recovery was the absence of any nursing system for outdoor cases. One poor woman nursed another as district nurses were quite unknown, and only occasionally did Boards of Guardians allow a few pence to a neighbour to look after a patient. District Medical Officers sometimes engaged women as nurses on their own account. The *Lancet* in 1868 printed a letter from a doctor who did this. He stated that on several occasions he needed a nurse at operations or to give enemas, but the Guardians had refused to reimburse him on the grounds that they considered the Medical Officer should be capable of managing by himself. The doctor maintained that a Medical Officer should not be required to perform the duties which nurses could do, or ought to do. In the 'sixties, District Medical Officers who were also doctors to the workhouse, occasionally sent out workhouse nurses to attend district patients, which not only benefited the sick, but broadened the training of the nurse. In Hampstead the Board of Guardians in 1871 sent a letter to their Medical Officers regarding the practice of allowing wounds of paupers

---

[1] *Lancet*, 1869, i, p. 404.

[2] In 1872 the President of the Local Government Board, J. Stansfeld, received the result of the inquiry. F. W. Rowsell, Superintendent of Contracts to the Admiralty, was aided by Poor Law Inspector Corbett and a long report made, including detailed tables. The inquiry was to ascertain whether Guardians were receiving full value in food and drugs for their expenditure. Everything was dealt with from coal to coffins. *Re adulteration*—no deleterious or poisonous matter was found in milk for example, but dilution and adulteration was so great that it provided a completely unreliable food for infants and aged. Seven examples showed exactly half milk and half water. Butter also very inferior.—A great proportion consisted of animal fat—horse fat—shipped to Hamburg to be returned as 'bosh-butter'. Therefore inmates preferred dripping. *Re drugs*—These were generally obtained from excellent sources. Few exceptions existed because Guardians 'looked to the good of the parish' as well as to the quality of drugs. Many Unions' arrangements for the supply of drugs remained unaltered for 15–20 years. Some Guardians accepted the lowest tender, others took the highest contract. Some wines were wretched.

in receipt of outdoor relief to be dressed by infirmary nurses. They stated they did not consider such offices to fall within the duties of the nurses and therefore forbade it for the future. In rural areas the lack of district nursing was very serious, and many District Medical Officers stated that patients died unnecessarily because they had no one to attend them. If Guardians ignored unnecessary suffering they also neglected to apply the cynical principle of saving rates by curing a patient quickly.

The training and provision of nurses began in the 'fifties and 'sixties, and Dr. Sieveking devoted much attention to the necessities of the sick poor. He produced a plan for the training and employment of female inmates of workhouses as nurses for the poor in their own houses, and in this he was supported by the Epidemiological Society, of which he was Secretary. Rumsey opposed the movement, however, pointing out that the sponsors of the scheme little realized what class of women they had to deal with, and also there were no teachers in the institutions. He maintained it was a mistake to think the poor ought to be nursed by those equally low in habits and as depressed in circumstances as themselves. He believed only superior women should be used for the poor, so that they could influence the moral and mental improvement of the pauper, as well as their physical condition. Further, he desired to see the establishment of institutes of Nursing Sisters in every town, which should be the centre for the supply of nurses to the population of the surrounding district.[1] William Rathbone, the great Liverpool philanthropist, was attracted by the whole problem, and realized the miseries of the sick poor for whom no benefits of efficient nursing were available. In the early 'sixties as an experiment, he employed a good nurse for three months to nurse poor patients in their homes in a certain district of Liverpool. She was provided with equipment and was authorized to supply the sick with medicines and food when necessary. At the end of a month she asked Rathbone to release her from her engagement, as the misery and degradation she had witnessed was more than she could bear. She was induced to persevere, and after three months she declared that if Rathbone continued to employ her, she would never undertake any other work. 'Her achievements had reconciled her to the difficulty of her task.'[2] Many lives had been saved, and chronic diseases forestalled, and she had taught the poor the value of cleanliness and fresh air. Rathbone himself affirmed:

> She had helped to prevent the moral ruin, the recklessness, the drunkenness, and the crime which so often follow hopeless misery. Within the space of a few months she had had two cases in which a wife's sickness had thrown a household into disorder, and the husband, unable to face the wretchedness which he knew not how to remedy, had taken to drink. The nurse showed what might be done to restore order and lessen suffering. Husbands, who were well-meaning industrious men, took heart again, left off drinking and were saved, together with their families, from the state of utter

[1] *Essays on State Medicine*, 1856.
[2] Bickerton, *A Medical History of Liverpool*, 1936; see also William Rathbone, *Sketches of the History of District Nursing*, 1859.

wretchedness and collapse towards which they were fast drifting when the nurse came to the rescue.[1]

The institution of a training school for nurses in 1863 by Rathbone included in its object the provision of district nurses for the poor. But the work of district nursing increased more rapidly than nurses could be trained. In 1866 the whole of Liverpool was divided into eighteen districts, each under the care of a nurse and of a lady or group of philanthropists, who undertook to superintend the work of the nurse, pay her lodging, and provide food and medical comforts for the sick poor. The nurses' salaries were paid by the training school and a paid inspector supervised the purely professional part of the work.

It was not only nurses, however, but also trained midwives that were required for the outdoor poor and this important subject was again entirely ignored by the Poor Law Board and the Guardians. The Female Medical Society, founded in 1863 and of which Lord Shaftesbury was President, had as one of its objects the training of gentlewomen as midwives, but for many more decades pauper women remained the victims of the same malpractice and often of brutal treatment, as they had been in past generations.

It is not remarkable therefore that the poor should complain of the Poor Law medical service, although few grievances received official confirmation. Today, the opinions of the poor can really only be studied in the statements of doctors, or in occasional columns of the medical press, for they were never afforded the privilege of articulation. Doctors, handicapped in their work by the absence of intelligent nurses as assistants, knew it was useless to try many things in the homes of the sick poor, which could have been done if the requisite attendance had been at hand. As bandages, wool, and lint were hardly ever supplied by the Guardians, the evil was aggravated, for if the doctor was unable to supply them himself out of his meagre salary, rags alone were used. In the filthy homes with their putrid atmosphere, their lack of sanitation, and their absence of furniture, many District Medical Officers must have realized no medical aid could help a patient. What could he do in places devoid of any amenities to facilitate treatment? The poor were no doubt dissatisfied with the actual medical attendance they received, because they believed in their bottle of physic, or justifiably, because the doctor's insufficient salary did not permit him to provide drugs adequately, and they complained that they were not being given enough medicine. Many also objected to being committed to one Medical Officer, and would have liked to choose their own doctor. It was also detrimental to the sick to be sent to a hospital or the workhouse, not because their illness necessitated the transfer, but because medicines were becoming too expensive for the Medical Officer, or the disease was protracted and took too much of his time. To be bandied about when disease needed efficient and prompt treatment was to increase suffering, especially if there was a lapse in the time before admission to an institution could be arranged. Dr. C. F. J. Lord, Secretary to the Convention of the Poor Law Medical Officers, confessed to the Select Committee of 1854 that several cases of improper treatment and insufficient attendance had come to his knowledge. But generally, complaints

[1] *William Rathbone—A Memoir* by E. F. Rathbone, 1905.

about medical relief were not against the doctors but against the inadequacy of the whole system. A Dewsbury Guardian maintained at the inquiry that paupers received as much medical attention as small tradesmen and shopkeepers, and that he did not wish to see paupers rendered too comfortable. Pigott, as a member of the Select Committee, and at whose instigation it had been called, because he believed reform was necessary, asked a Hampshire magistrate whether the giving of insufficient medical relief increased pauperism. The reply was in the negative, with the exception made for cases which terminated fatally through neglect or malpractice.

The *Lancet* printed an article to illustrate the unsatisfactory state of medical attendance on the casual poor. A man staggered along a pavement as if intoxicated, fell, and struck his head on the kerb. A policeman took him to the police-station, where the man's wound was dressed, after which he was removed to the workhouse. Delirium followed and by the morning he was dead. No medical aid had been called, because the officials believed him drunk. The Coroner's jury passed a vote of censure on the man's companion! The *Lancet* concluded that as the symptoms of incipient apoplexy were closely allied to those of intoxication, there should be an order regarding the attendance of doctors, so that a recurrence of such an instance could be prevented.[1]

It was generally believed that the Poor Law medical services were more successfully administered in the provinces than in London. This was because Boards of Guardians contained a large number of clergymen and magistrates, who, as they resided near the poor and were personally acquainted with their wants, were regarded as being well qualified to exercise a 'wise discrimination' regarding relief. An account printed in the *Lancet* in 1869[2] showed this to be a complete delusion. The article was prefaced by the statement that an inspection of outdoor relief would reveal instances of hardship and inhumanity in the country which were not surpassed in the poorest parts of a town. In Guildford the Medical Officer complained that the Relieving Officer suddenly withdrew the supply of medical extras which had been ordered for a young girl suffering from anaemia and debility. The Board of Guardians considered the girl's father in a condition to provide nourishment for her, because an order had been given for the workhouse, which had been refused. The Medical Officer was also forbidden to continue his attendance on the girl as a pauper patient. The father was a jobbing gardener, and he and his wife and six children, one of whom was epileptic, had less than 10s. a week income, so that semi-starvation was the order of their lives. The Medical Officer stated the girl was too weak to remain in service, and was at a critical age when the continuance of insufficient food was certain to result in permanent disease. How could the father be expected to provide medical treatment and nourishment, the doctor asked? It was folly to force the workhouse test on a man who was doing his best to support a family, and there was neither policy nor justice in such treatment. The Medical Officer also complained that he had ordered nutriment for a man

[1] *Lancet*, 1867, i, pp. 344–46.
[2] *Lancet*, 1869, i, p. 336.

suffering from an eye disease which was granted, but because the Relieving Officer refused other relief the man shared his medical 'extras' with his family. This the Medical Officer stated might cost the man his eyesight and he would then become an inferior workman. But the Guardians offered the workhouse which was refused, and the patient then attended the County Hospital and subsisted on charity. Because of the workhouse test, the whole family had been forced to learn the art of begging, and if the doctor's prognosis was realized, the ratepayers he said, would have to support the family for years to come, and even in the workhouse the cost would be at least £1 a week. The *Lancet* pointed out that Guardians never visited the sick, nor took any real interest in curing them, so the least they could do was to support the Medical Officer. Such cases, it was concluded showed the necessity for the inspection of outdoor relief, for the vast subject was beyond the notice of the Poor Law Board. The *Lancet* therefore invited information on similar occurrences so that a campaign for inspection could be started.

Although the workhouses came in for much criticism and inspection at this period, nothing was done about the outdoor sick poor. This was because it was much more difficult to investigate domiciliary relief throughout the country and because no scandals roused public opinion to demand an inquiry. Outdoor medical relief was also comparatively neglected because institutional treatment began to assume far greater importance.

It is interesting to compare the medical services under the Poor Law and those provided by the Jewish community of London. The latter was described by Dr. J. H. Stallard, a leading reformer and member of the Poor Law Medical Reform Association, in his book on London pauperism published in 1867.[1] He devoted his attention to the outdoor poor, he said, because the evils described had neither been officially investigated nor mentioned in any reports. Many Boards of Guardians not only opened their meetings to him and allowed full inspection, but also authorized Relieving Officers to render every assistance. The miserable inadequacy of relief was revealed in the reports which Union officials themselves prepared for Stallard. The 18,000 Jews in London had their own Poor Relief system in the East End, with a separate Board of Guardians and medical staff. There was a strong contrast between their treatment of the sick poor and that of the Christian Boards of Guardians. The Jewish poor on the whole congregated in Whitechapel and St. George in the East, Stepney, and the paupers generally consisted of immigrants who arrived from the Continent in a wretched condition. The Jewish Guardians, recognizing the intimate connection between sickness and pauperism, had early appointed a committee to superintend the work of their properly qualified doctors and see that the recommendations made by them for the benefit of the sick were effected. Two Medical Officers attended daily at a station and visited patients in their homes. The Jews also had two lying-in hospitals of their own

---

[1] *London Pauperism amongst Jews and Christians—an inquiry into the practice of outdoor relief in the Metropolis*— dedicated to Baroness Lionel de Rothschild, philanthropist among the poor. Stallard also wrote another book on 'Workhouse Hospitals' and was physician to the Great Northern Hospital, and Dispensary of St. George and St. James, Westminster.

(which were described to the Select Committee of 1844) and subscribed liberally to other hospitals. Careful regulations were made to secure prompt and efficient attention to the sick, and the medical committee met once a month to receive doctors' reports and complaints from the poor. The latter were issued with tickets for institutional treatment, which were obtained by the subscriptions of the wealthy to the medical committee. The Medical Officers were responsible for the distribution of tickets and of cod liver oil, other expensive medicines, wine and brandy, and bedding. In addition Baroness de Rothschild had established a 'sick kitchen', because it was realized that food was as important as medicine. The sick obtained orders from their doctor to attend this kitchen and fifty patients were fed a day, every type of diet being supplied there. Orphans learnt to cook in the establishment as part of their training. As Stallard commented: 'If half the dispensaries of London were converted into food kitchens for the sick . . . a greater number of cures would be effected than by the physic they dispense.'

The medical committee was also engaged in the prevention of sickness. For example, in the spring of 1865 when fever was raging in the overcrowded dwellings, the true economy of sanitary precautions was realized. A special committee was formed to undertake sanitary inspection, and £100 was given for the purpose. The inspector appointed visited 1,400 tenements—half the dwellings of the Jewish poor—made representations to landlords, and also reported to local Boards of Works, so that in five months one-eleventh of the homes were improved. Only £39 was spent on the inspection. When cholera approached in 1866 the Board of Guardians and the medical committee met weekly to design measures for prevention and relief. A supply of pure water from stand-pipes was assured, house to house visiting was instituted, and people were removed from filthy hovels whilst they were cleansed and whitewashed, and their clothing fumigated. Meat, wine, and rice was distributed, and three houses were rented as a convalescent home. Therefore while cholera took its toll of lives from the surrounding community, the Jewish population escaped with comparative immunity. Meanwhile the general relief afforded was liberal. Cases of acute sickness received £1 a week, food from the soup kitchen, and other private assistance. The average amount of relief given to the sick was 10s. a week per family. Knowing the heavy responsibility of having widows and children to maintain, the liberality of relief was wise and economical.

Stallard compared this with the Poor Law arrangements and took St. George the Martyr, Southwark, as an example, for its population and circumstances equalled that of the poor Jewish community. Here the cramped, filthy, and furnitureless houses were proverbial, and no real care was taken to improve the condition of the poor. Fever and epidemic diseases were never absent, for they were inevitable where 'every law of health was systematically neglected', and 'where the floating mass of paupers were only kept from absolute starvation . . . by relief doled out from day to day in quantities barely sufficient for the maintenance of life'. Constitutions were gradually undermined and became daily less capable of resisting disease. In 1861 there were twenty-five deaths from fever in Southwark, in 1862—48, in 1863—88, in 1864—113, and in 1865—128. This represented, Stallard said,

3,400 illnesses of an average duration of three weeks. Not only had the parish to bear the cost of medical treatment, but also that of funerals and the loss of labour and health which inevitably followed. 6,800 people were assisted in six months in St. George the Martyr. In the first week of June 1866, eighty families were relieved through sickness of the male parents, and their dependants totalled fifty-eight wives and 209 children. For these the total relief amounted to £5 9s. 2½d. or threepence-three-farthings each, in food, for no money was given. In the same week nineteen families received relief because of the sickness of the mother or children, and the total relief was £2 13s. 3d. or three-farthings each in food.

Stallard gave many descriptions of the homes of the sick in Southwark. One example, taken from the *Evening Standard* of 11 July 1868, stated that a man and his wife and five children all had fever, and one of the children died. Relief consisted of 1½ loaves of bread and 1 lb. of meat three times a week. The people were in a wretched state of destitution and had only one room of 750 cubic feet in a horrible decrepit dwelling. Whilst they were ill with fever, the whole family had lain in one bed, without sheets or blankets and with no food for days, save some bread which was toasted for brewing tea. They had survived, but were described as wasted with want and illness. They had few clothes and none of them had shoes or stockings. The woman had also had rheumatic fever and tried to earn a little money by taking in washing. The children spent their day lying in a corner, hungry and pale and exhausted from the fever. Stallard described similar cases of illness and the great and cruel wasting of lives. People, he said, were left invalids because they were given no nourishment to facilitate recovery. Not daring to ask for more food, they became apathetic, and regarded their position as the normal routine of existence. This was social murder. Where lay the economy? Whole streets formed 'perpetual hotbeds of fever, pregnant with death'. Stallard suggested that visitors should go to see the horrors and arouse public feeling.—It must be remembered that he wrote his account in the late 'sixties, yet conditions in South and East London were then worse than twenty years previously. Houses were 'worse furnished, less clean, and therefore the inhabitants more dissipated'. Morbific agencies were less resistible, people got well more slowly and required more stimulants.—'Now the sick scarcely ever recover completely, even from the slightest illness.' Stallard was a doctor, but similar evidence had been given to him by independent observers, and universally by the poor themselves.

Of the 74,000 people relieved annually in the Metropolis, Stallard reckoned not more than 2,000 could be classed as 'able-bodied'—yet it was for them that the Poor Law had been devised. The poorest areas of London did not help one-third of the paupers in proportion to their population, compared with the City. This was because they could not afford assistance and because their workhouses were full. The amount of adult sickness publicly aided in the City was small, because the working classes were extensively provided with hospitals and dispensaries, and private charity was more active. Large firms there were more interested in the welfare of their dependants than they were in Whitechapel or Bethnal Green, but also whilst labour was monopolized by one district, the miseries and burdens were borne by others, for many City workers lived in Southwark, Whitechapel, and Bethnal Green.

Joseph Rogers, speaking at the meeting[1] of the Poor Law Medical Officers' Association, of which he was founder and President, gave a statistical account of the medical relief afforded in the Metropolis and a comparison between the years 1852 and 1867. Four examples given are shown in Table 11.1:

TABLE 11.1

Comparison of the Medical Relief afforded in the Metropolis for the years 1852 and 1867.— J. Rogers, President of the Poor Law Medical Officers' Association, 28 April 1869.

District	Population	In maintenance	Outdoor Relief	Total	Medical Relief
		£	£	£	£
Bethnal Green[1]— 1852	90,170	4,850	1,442	12,125	533
1867	105,101	17,294	5,137	36,801	1,006
St. Luke (City)[2]—1852	54,058	3,816	4,342	12,046	695
1867	57,073	10,664	5,382	23,037	849
East London Union[3]— 1852	44,407	5,224	8,240	18,287	556
1867	40,687	10,462	7,742	20,600	632
Whitechapel[4]— 1852	79,156	5,509	4,971	17,598	501
1867	78,187	11,059	7,477	36,089	968

[1] Very poor locality. Here the Medical Officer attended 1,213 cases in 1865; 1,871 cases in 1866; 2,198 cases in 1868. In-maintenance trebled because the Medical Officer was treated so badly. Only workhouse drugs found.

[2] All drugs found, therefore higher medical estimate.

[3] Medical Officers found all drugs.

[4] Guardians found all drugs.

Rogers contended that many District Medical Officers of the Metropolis were compelled to send patients to the workhouse who might have been treated in their own homes, if the doctors had been given higher salaries and had been supplied with drugs, and if the defective and insufficient system of medical relief had been reformed on the suggestions made to the Select Committees of 1854 and 1861. The position, he said, was the same over the whole of England and Wales. Birmingham furnished a special instance of the Guardians' mismanagement. (See Table 11.2, p. 290.)

This showed that there had been almost a sevenfold increase in institutional relief in fifteen years. The workhouse had developed into a huge hospital with nearly 700 beds, yet

[1] 28 April 1869.

medical relief and appliances for indoor and outdoor poor had increased by only £600—one-third, in the same period. Brighton, which Rogers described as a 'rich and thriving sea-side resort of opulence and fashion', only spent £460 on medical relief in 1852 and £870 in 1867, yet the total spent on poor relief was £19,000 in the former year and £35,340 in the latter; and the increase in medical expenditure had only taken place in the middle 'sixties. The Leeds Guardians, Rogers maintained, had taken an exceptionally just and intelligent view regarding medical relief. Here total relief had increased from £25,000 in 1852 to £34,000, and medical relief from £900 to £2,270. In-maintenance had trebled and outdoor relief diminished by a third.

TABLE 11.2

Comparison of the Medical Relief afforded in Birmingham for the years 1852 and 1867

Year	Population	In maintenance	Outdoor Relief	Total	Medical Relief
		£	£	£	£
1852	173,878	3,273	13,000	31,777	1,205
1867	212,000	21,470	33,135	83,440	1,807

The deduction to be made from Rogers' analysis was that there was an intimate relation between insufficient outdoor medical relief and a large increase in the workhouse population, and in the amount of taxation. Rogers attributed the short-sighted policy not to selfishness on the part of the Guardians, but to total ignorance of the importance of the subject: 'Unfortunately there has not been really anyone in office, with even the slightest pretension to professional knowledge of the intimate relation that subsists between neglected sickness of the working-class and the spread of pauperism ... and unfortunately for the community, the present medical advisers of the Poor Law Board [Smith and Markham] had not the slightest practical acquaintance with the Poor Law medical question before their appointment.'

This relationship between neglected sickness and the spread of pauperism had been pointed out unavailingly fifteen years before. Dr. Boyd, Inspector of Somerset Lunatic Asylums pointed out to the Select Committee of 1854, that if medical relief were given more profusely the poor would be prevented from eventually becoming paupers. He drew attention to the Marylebone Union where all the doctors were appointed to the workhouse, and only two of these had assistants. There were as many as 1,000 outdoor cases on the books at one time, so that the poor were compelled to attend as out-patients at the workhouse. He maintained that a vast number of people, if they were afforded adequate medical aid at the onset of illness, would not have to enter the workhouse infirmary at all. This was especially so with fever, when medical treatment should be provided at the time it was applied for, and questions regarding the ability to pay asked subsequently.

Liverpool was the only town which seemed to have learnt the truth of the principle. As we have seen already in the early years of the new Poor Law, medical relief was provided liberally. This was very necessary because of the vast number of poor immigrants who settled there or passed through the port. Inspector Austin had given a report on the special provision made for sickness, which had increased alarmingly in 1847 because of the great influx of impoverished Irish following the potato famine.[1] Between January and April of that year, nearly 200,000 Irish had landed in Liverpool. Special instructions were given to the Relieving Officers to visit every case of sickness which came to their notice without waiting for an application for relief. Reports had to be furnished immediately to a central office in order that appropriate medical attendance could be promptly supplied. Austin attended to this section himself. 'The vestry desired to give efficient relief as a necessary precaution against the threatened spread of disease, which would occur with increasing intensity in the crowded neighbourhoods, if the inhabitants were allowed to suffer from want and destitution.' The Relief Committee paid great attention to the subject of sickness. Six Medical Officers had existed up to 1847, and in that year twelve were appointed and all were allowed assistants to enable them to meet the rapid increase in sickness in the town. In April 1847 there were twenty-one doctors attending the outdoor sick poor. The Committee asked every Medical Officer to make a daily return of the number of patients under his care, distinguishing cases of fever and smallpox from ordinary cases of sickness. The want of unoccupied buildings, capable of being converted into temporary hospitals provided the most serious difficulty. One was obtained and was immediately filled with fever cases, the workhouse was enlarged, and finally, three large sheds, each capable of holding a hundred patients, were erected. The exertions of the Vestry and the Medical Officers were incalculable, and from January to May 1847 the average daily number of Irish given sick relief was 200 men, 300 women, and 600 children. The fever epidemic cost Liverpool £20,000 in outdoor relief for the Irish alone who were not in an institution. It was maintained however that the poor rates had been saved.

This was a time of epidemic, but other towns also visited by fevers and cholera failed throughout the period to make similar liberal provisions. For decades, Liverpool had the most enlightened Poor Law (and Public Health) authority in the country. The poor applying for medical assistance only, were not counted as destitute, but most of those applying for gratuitous relief were already paupers. In the middle of the century nine Medical Officers attended the outdoor poor and nearly £4,000 was spent on medical relief altogether. As an assistant overseer said in 1854: 'We consider the saving of life and the prevention of pauperism effected by this humane plan, fully compensates us for our outlay.'[2] In that year there were nearly 13,000 paupers, whereas formerly there had been 21,000. Referring to the constant fluctuation of pauperism in the city, because of the immense influx of strangers, the overseer stated that in the previous week fifty Germans en route for America had been

[1] Report, 1 May 1847.
[2] Edmund Gray, Assistant Overseer, Liverpool, evidence to Select Committee, 1854—still under Local Act but subject to Poor Law Board.

ill. On a previous occasion a vessel returned to port with 300–400 fever patients on board and the city had to look after them all and their dependants. Everyone going to and fro in the port fell to the care of Liverpool if they became sick, so that the poor rate was used not only for inhabitants of the town, but for all the world! Never had the Vestry, said the overseer, had any complaints from any quarter, and he recommended that the Poor Law Board should cause their liberal system to be adopted everywhere in England.

The position in the country was revealed in evidence to the Select Committee of 1861 and 1862. A table was published in 1861 showing that the ratio of the population which obtained gratuitous medical relief was scarcely larger in 1860 than it had been in 1838. In the former year it had been 2·16 and it had risen to 2·85 in the latter. There was, however, a decline in pauperism from 6·2 to 4·3 per cent of the population from 1849 to 1860, so that a larger proportion of paupers were in fact receiving medical aid. Also the average cost per pauper for medical relief had risen from 3s. 10d. in 1849 to 5s. 7d. in 1860.[1] This trend was commented on in the Report of the Select Committee of 1864[2]: 'whilst other charges for relief fluctuated and diminished in amount, the cost of medical relief steadily and largely increased from 1834. The increase of 1851 over 1841 was 36 per cent and of 1861 over 1851 was 13 per cent, whilst the number of Unions added have not increased to anything like a corresponding degree.'

Figures and expenditure were published annually by the Poor Law Board and Table 11.2 gives a statistical survey of circumstances affecting medical relief from 1849 to 1871.

The amount of medical relief afforded differed widely. No statistics were published for comparative purposes of the number of sick relieved, and the money expended on this account is the only guide available. Amounts spent by Unions on medical relief varied from one penny to sixpence per head. In 1844 the average per head of the population was two-pence-halfpenny and in 1854 threepence. In 1856 the Poor Law Board divided the country into Regions for statistical purposes, so that the divisions corresponded with the Registrar-General's classification. Figures for each Union which continued to be published showed diversity, but the averages computed for regions showed greater similarity.—Table 11.3.

The growing total expenditure on Poor Relief showed that the increase was in a much larger ratio than the number of paupers. The same number of paupers cost very much more at the end of the 'sixties than at the end of the 'forties.[3] This was because in all institutions, public and private, the scale of salaries had increased over a long period, and more officers had had to be employed in Unions, particularly Relieving Officers and Medical Officers. A paid nursing system had also been started in the workhouses. In 1870, for example, there was a £13,000 increase in expenditure on salaries, rations, and superannuation for officers. Further, there was a more liberal scale of relief in money and food.[4] Accom-

---

[1] Tables in Appendix, Select Committee on the Administration of Relief to the Poor under the Poor Law Commission and the Poor Law Board, 1861 and 1862 (six reports).

[2] Report of the Select Committee on the Administration of Relief to the Poor, 1864.

[3] Twenty-second Annual Report, 1869–70.

[4] Twenty-third Annual Report, 1870–71.

TABLE 11.3

Circumstances affecting Medical Relief from 1849 to 1871.—Compiled from Annual Reports of the Poor Law Board.

Year	Total Population	Total number of Paupers	Percentage of Paupers to Population	Total Expenditure on Poor Relief	Medical Expenditure	Average price of wheat per quarter	
				£	£	s.	d.
1849	17,534,000	1,088,659	6·2	5,792,962	211,181	49	1
1850		1,008,700	5·7	5,395,022	227,171	42	7
1851		941,315	5·3	4,962,704	209,993	39	11
1852		915,675	5	4,897,685	212,050	39	4
1853	17,929,000	886,362	4·8	4,939,064	215,053	42	0
1854		864,617	4·6	5,282,853	230,777	61	7
1855		897,686	4·8	5,890,041	231,682	70	0½
1856		917,084	4·8	6,004,244	231,872	75	4
1857[1]	19,207,000	885,010	4·6	5,898,756	231,623	65	3
1858		908,886	4·7	5,878,386	230,696	53	10
1859		865,446	4·4	5,558,689	233,124	42	9¼
1860[1]		844,633	4·3	5,454,904	236,339	44	9
1861[1]	20,062,000	883,921	4·4	5,778,943	238,233	55	10
1862[2]		917,142	4·5	6,077,927	242,200	56	7
1863		1,079,382	5·3	6,527,036	248,286	52	1
1864		1,014,978	4·9	6,423,383	253,204	43	2
1865	20,881,000	951,899	4·6	6,264,961	259,833	39	8
1866		916,152	4·3	6,439,515	264,052	43	6
1867[3]		931,546	4·4	6,959,841	272,225	53	7½
1868		992,640	4·6	7,498,061	272,341	67	6½
1869	21,760,000	1,018,140	4·7	7,673,100	282,115	58	3
1870		1,032,800	4·7	7,644,307	282,313	46	2
1871	22,200,000	1,037,360	4·7	7,886,724	290,249	49	8½

NOTE: In the last few years Poor Law Board reports said 'Medical Relief' figures given separately as indicating an important and special subject of Poor Law administration.

[1] Trade depression.

[2] Trade depression and Lancashire distress.

[3] From 1867 the Poor Law Board demanded economy in salaries because expenditure was rising.

modation in workhouse schools had increased, infirmaries and asylums had improved, and the prices of provisions, clothing, and buildings had risen. The Poor Law Board summed up the problem of expenditure in 1871 . . .

In the last few years, the higher price of corn, the higher standard of efficiency, increased sanitary regulations, the growing number of the more costly class of paupers, i.e., the sick and lunatic, and the augmented numbers and increase in salaries of officers, have together raised the cost of poor relief by 40 per cent.

Save for the price of food, these causes were more or less permanent, and 'could only be counterbalanced by a reduction in the number of paupers'.[1]

There is no doubt that the more humane views on the treatment of the sick poor which

TABLE 11.4

Amounts spent on Medical Relief—averages computed for Regions for the years 1856–57 and 1867.—From the Tenth and Twentieth Annual Reports of the Poor Law Board.

	1856–57			1867	
Region	Amount spent on Medical Relief	Percentage of Total Poor Relief	Rate per head of population	Expenditure on Medical Relief	Population 1861
	nearest £000		d.	nearest £000	nearest million
Metropolis	26,000	3	2·4	36,000	3
South East	35,000	4·8	4·9	42,000	2
South Midland	27,000	4·6	4·9	28,000	1¼
Eastern England	24,000	4·6	5·1	26,000	1
South West	28,000	4·1	3·6	31,000	2
West Midland	26,000	4·3	2·7	29,000	2½
North Midland	14,000	3·9	2·6	15,000	1¼
North West (Lancashire and Cheshire)	20,000	3·6	1·7	26,000	3
Yorkshire	14,000	3·4	1·7	16,000	2
Northern England	7,000	3·0	1·6	9,000	1
Wales	12,000	3·0	2·2	14,000	1¼
	233,000	3·9	2·9	272,000	21

[1] Twenty–third Annual Report, 1870–71.

prevailed during the last few years of the Poor Law Board's administration added most materially to Poor Law expenditure. Much of the money included in the total expenditure was directly or indirectly used for the medical services, but the sum is quite incalculable. In addition the amount spent on vaccination, a function which as we have seen devolved on the Poor Law authorities, steadily increased and was a substantial item.

When the Poor Law Board assumed office there was a falling off in vaccination because the poor neglected to avail themselves of the service. The Guardians were circularized by the Board asking them to publish notices pointing out the benefit of vaccination. The campaign was successful, and returns showed a great increase in proportion to births in the numbers vaccinated as a result.[1] In 1852, however, tables of mortality from the Registrar-General revealed that many deaths had been occasioned in that year through the neglect of parents to have their children vaccinated. The Poor Law Board called the attention of Guardians to the mortality arising from the epidemic and suggested that public vaccinators should take every opportunity of informing the poorer classes of the danger of leaving their children exposed to attack by smallpox, and the serious results which followed the neglect of vaccination. Guardians were again asked to print notices calling public attention to the arrangements made for the gratuitous performance of the operation. The Poor Law Board believed Guardians and public vaccinators had at last begun to co-operate in extending the practice of vaccination among the poorest classes in their districts.[2] The 1840–41 Acts were permissive but vaccination relied on persuasion. In 1853 the *Lancet* published an article on the inefficiency of vaccination. It pointed to the shocking prevalence of smallpox and the discreditable delay in vaccination.[3] Drs. Seaton and Buchanan had examined 50,000 vaccinated children in schools and found that only one-tenth had had the operation performed well. Dr. Ballard, a Metropolitan Medical Officer of Health, who later won a prize essay on vaccination, found similar results—an evil, he said, for which the profession was deeply responsible. The *Lancet* urged the Government to amend the Vaccination Act. It desired to see this Public Health service disconnected from the Poor Law and from all Poor Law arrangements. Further, better payment of public vaccinators and the appointment of inspectors was demanded.

The Act passed in 1853 made vaccination of children compulsory on parents, and penalties could be imposed if infants were not vaccinated within a few months after birth. Further obligations were put on Guardians to secure the means whereby the poor would have less excuse for not complying with the regulations. Unions had to be divided into districts for the purpose of affording increased facilities, and each vaccination area had to have a convenient station. Guardians had also to provide effectual means for giving all residents notice of days and hours when vaccination was performed. The minimum rate of payment for Medical Officers was fixed at 1s. 6d. per successful operation, as it had been previously, or 2s. 6d. if they lived over 2 miles from the station. The Poor Law Board

---

[1] First Annual Report, 1848.
[2] Fifth Annual Report, 1852 (in which no other reference is made to medical services).
[3] *Lancet*, 1853, i, p. 100–101.

had months of correspondence with Guardians regarding the alteration in arrangements and contracts, which the new Act rendered necessary. Successful vaccinations had to be registered by the Public Registrar, and the fee which was paid for registration was, like the fee for registering births, charged on the poor rate.

As a result of the Act a very great number of persons were vaccinated in the latter half of 1853. In 1858 the National Vaccine Board[1] published in its annual report that it was afraid of running out of vaccine because of the great increase in demand. The catastrophe was averted as it had to be, for in the following years the Privy Council circularized all Boards of Guardians of the Metropolis that they should encourage vaccination as smallpox was prevalent.[2]

Although vaccination was being furthered so extensively by the central authorities, the practice was not as salutary as might have been supposed. The *Lancet* was justified in calling for increased inspection for many towns were extremely lax in carrying out the policy of the central authorities. For example, Leeds and York, whose Boards of Guardians made no reference to any medical relief in their Minutes, only appointed a Committee in 1868 to consider the best means of carrying out the Vaccination Acts. In 1864 Dr. Stevens, Inspector of Public Vaccination for the Privy Council,[3] visited Manchester and reported that the Guardians practically declined to alter their system and were quite satisfied with the vaccination of 73 per cent of the births. They also refused to appoint a special vaccination officer as was suggested. The appointment of a Public Vaccinator to every district was, however, made imperative by the Act of 1867, which also reiterated the free and compulsory vaccination of children. The Poor Law Board issued a circular for the guidance of all Guardians, and asked that Medical Officers should keep a register of cases vaccinated. The Poor Law Medical Officers' Association suggested in 1869, that Public Vaccinators should also be the Registrars of Births. This was the practice in Ireland, and was said to have accounted for the great diminution of smallpox in that country.[4] In England the number of registered births increased from half a million to three-quarters of a million a year between 1848 and 1870, and the number of successful vaccinations from one-third to half a million. The percentage of successful vaccinations to the number of births fluctuated, but was generally between 60 and 70 per cent. The cost of vaccination to the Poor Law authorities was £18,000 in 1847, £20,000 in 1850, £46,000 in 1860, and £63,000 in 1870—it had therefore more than trebled. The number of Unions had in the twenty-three years risen from 627 to 647, and the number of vaccinators from 3,160 to 3,196.[5]

[1] Established at the beginning of the nineteenth century and consisted of Presidents of the Royal Medical Colleges, the senior censor of the Royal College of Physicians, and the Medical Officer of the General Board of Health—Simon at this time.

[2] Minutes of Governors and Directors of the Poor, St. George's, Hanover Square.

[3] The Public Health Authorities were responsible for the inspection side of vaccination.

[4] Quarterly meeting of the Poor Law Medical Officers' Association, 28 April 1869, reported in the *Lancet*, 1869, i, pp. 611–12.

[5] See annual statistics on numbers and expenditure in Annual Reports of the Poor Law Board, 1848–71, from which these figures were abstracted.

Not only was the cost of vaccination which the Poor Law authorities bore for the country a substantial item in expenditure, but another service, the treatment of venereal disease also fell to a great extent on their charge. The supplementary activities of the Poor Law medical service were continually increasing in number! As there were very few Lock Hospitals, and as most general institutions refused to treat the diseases, the destitution authorities were grudgingly compelled to include venereology in their provisions for relief. All patients were constituted paupers, however, and in several areas had to be paupers prior to seeking aid on this account. It was therefore not unknown for prostitutes to pauperize themselves deliberately by asking for general relief so that they might obtain medical treatment.

The problem was most acute in London and needed a gigantic remedy. A doctor read a paper to the National Association for the Promotion of Social Science in 1868, in which he stated that in the entire City there were not 200 beds for contagious diseases. St. Bartholomew's Hospital had 56, Guy's 30, the Royal Free 26, St. Thomas's 25, the Middlesex 8, King's 6, and the Lock Hospitals had the remainder. In the population of three million there were 6,000 known prostitutes, although in fact, there were actually three times this number. In addition, most of the Metropolitan Unions would not admit venereal disease cases into the workhouse, and if they did they were generally removed to Lock or other hospitals if beds could be found for them. Therefore in London, prostitutes were compelled 'to continue in sin and suffering to propagate disease for the purposes of procuring for themselves the common necessities of life'.[1] The state of affairs can be seen in the Boards of Guardians Minutes. In 1859 the Hampstead Guardians observed that 'the Medical Officer was attending two patients labouring under venereal disease, and that in the opinion of the Board it was incumbent on such patients to obtain medical relief from a hospital and not to resort to the parish Medical Officer.' This was written in reply to complaints on medical attendance, for even the poor objected to their Medical Officer coming into contact with a sufferer from venereal disease.[2]

In the provinces provisions were even worse. 'In Liverpool, and in fact in all towns there is no hospital accommodation whatever for syphilis as a disease, in such a manner that anybody can go to it who suffers from the disease. There are Lock wards in the workhouses, but they take in destitution, and then find destitution is also accompanied with syphilis, a very important distinction, . . . because it shuts out almost the whole of the prostitute class of Liverpool.'[3] Liverpool had a Lock Hospital connected with the Royal Infirmary, but admission was obtained by private subscribers ticket.

The *Lancet* had in the 'fifties drawn attention to the problem and urged that on the grounds of economy alone, the subject was worthy of consideration. The great expense of

[1] J. B. Curgenven, M.R.C.S., Paper on Contagious Diseases Acts, 30 March 1868: Sessional Proceedings of the Association.

[2] Minutes, Hampstead Board of Guardians, March, 1859.

[3] Evidence to House of Commons Committee in 1868 on Contagious Diseases Act of 1866 by a Liverpool doctor.

treatment for syphilis in Naval and Military Hospitals was recognized and the Contagious Diseases Act of 1864 ruled that in certain garrison towns and ports, prostitutes alleged to be infected with venereal disease were to be brought before the magistrates and medical examination ordered. The subsequent Act of 1866 strengthened this regulation and a Justice of the Peace could order periodic examination. The Government therefore tentatively initiated improvement in the right direction, but although preventive measures were introduced by the Acts, the therapeutic side was ignored. Heated controversy was aroused and the storm of protest was so enormous that the Acts were repealed in 1883 and 1886. The medical profession however applauded the legislation and many local authorities and Guardians desired to see it extended to the rest of the country, for it was claimed that it would scour the miserably diseased off the streets. A petition to the House of Commons in 1868 for the extension of the Act to Birmingham, stated that the workhouse contained 131 cases of venereal disease at the time, of which sixty-four were of hereditary form. The direct cost to the parish was £800 a year and at least as much more indirectly.[1]—Here lay the seed of future pauperism, for insanity and such diseases as ophthalmia were incidental to congenital venereal disease.

The Harveian Medical Society formed a Committee for the purposes of holding meetings and issuing propaganda to further the introduction of the Venereal Disease Acts universally. Circulars eliciting information were forwarded to all surgeons of hospitals, dispensaries, infirmaries, and workhouses in large towns. The amount of disease revealed was astounding. In St. Bartholomew's Hospital for example, half the surgical out-patients were sufferers from venereal disease, in Guy's two-thirds, in other hospitals one-fifth to three-eights, and in the children's hospital one-fifth.[2] No official statistics seem available on numbers attending hospitals and receiving treatment.

The *Lancet* had written in favour of the Acts from the beginning and pointed out that the absolute and relative gains were significant. There had been a steady decrease in disease at the protected stations, whilst numbers had been progressively increasing at the unprotected stations. The workhouses of Plymouth, Devonport, and Stonehouse had admitted an average of 706 women and 151 men with venereal disease for three years prior to 1866, yet in 1867, 1868, and 1869 there were only 55 men and 167 women. There had been a similar decrease in the inmates of prisons in those areas. The Government had increased the accommodation in its Lock Hospitals there, which in part accounted for the diminution of women venereal disease patients in the workhouses.[3]

The Poor Law Board however generally ignored this social problem and relief was left to the discretion of the Guardians. In small workhouses patients were mixed with the rest of the sick, in others they were segregated, but because they were recognized as the immoral class they were always provided with the most cramped and uncomfortable rooms in the institution. When cleanliness was of the utmost importance, these sufferers were left in the

[1] *Lancet*, 1869, i, pp. 414–15.
[2] Figures given by Curgenven, *supra*, p. 300.
[3] *Lancet*, 1869, i, pp. 404, 406.

dirtiest personal and environmental conditions. Treatment, or the lack of treatment, was appalling, and they were turned out of the 'foul' wards as soon as possible. Dr. Stallard[1] gave a horrifying description of these wards of the Farnham Union workhouse, where cases from Aldershot were sent prior to the Contagious Diseases Acts, and concluded: 'Throughout the country you will find conditions in the venereal diseases wards of workhouses a disgrace to civilization.'

There were some enlightened Unions however. The Preston Guardians, for example, resolved in 1868 that it was desirable that the Medical Officers should specify more particularly the peculiar symptoms of applicants suffering from venereal disease, so as to distinguish cases fit for any kind of outdoor labour or oakum picking from those where absolute rest was required. The Relieving Officer was instructed 'not to send to the workhouse those applicants certified to be fit for work, but to relieve them and employ them at such labour as they were able to perform'.[2] By the Poor Law Amendment Act of 1867, Guardians were given the power of compulsory detention in cases of infectious and contagious diseases, but it was seldom if ever acted upon with regard to syphilis. It was said that a Police Surgeon who attended the Lock wards of a London Union, explained in 1871 that he had only discovered when dealing with the epidemic of smallpox that he had compulsory powers of detention in cases of venereal disease as well. Therefore,

> unless a woman was fortunate enough to secure one of the very few hospital beds available, or unless she was so badly diseased that she was bedridden, in which case the workhouse would take her, the only chance of treatment was as an out-patient of a hospital, where, in Dr. Acton's words, she would be 'patched up by a voluntary charity in the morning, and continue to spread infection by plying her trade for a living at night'.[3]

To a great extent venereal disease was a Poor Law problem, for not only did it in its acute stages lead to unemployment and pauperism like other diseases, but it was communicable to the offspring of the sufferers. Gonorrhoeal ophthalmia was extremely widespread, and blindness or insanity often the lot of the children when they grew up. The prevention and efficient cure of the disease in its incipient stages would not only have been humane, but it would have led to a great decrease in pauperism and the poor rates.

What was never realized at the time by the central authorities was that the Poor Law medical services were assuming such important functions that a complete overhaul of the system was imperative. By 1871 they could no longer be regarded as insignificant and troublesome appendages to the general scheme of pauper relief. They had developed by unforeseen pressure into a necessary social service which required the prescience and generosity of statesmanship to make them really efficient and useful. The hospitals branch of the Poor Law could no longer be satisfied with converted old workhouses, but no less urgent

[1] To Royal Commission on the administration and operation of the Contagious Diseases Act, 1871.
[2] Minutes, Preston Board of Guardians (Webb MSS.).
[3] *James Stansfeld* by J. L. and B. Hammond, 1932.

302

was the necessity for drastic changes in the system of domiciliary medical relief. The Metropolis just succeeded in obtaining necessary and long overdue reforms before the Poor Law Board relinquished office, but the dimensions of the national problem were too overwhelming for the inadequate machinery of the obscurantist authorities to bring about similar improvements for the whole country.—The Poor Law medical system should have left its parent in order to reach salutary and effective maturity.

The Poor Law Board tried however to come to a decision on the best form of medical treatment, and in 1869 instigated an inquiry into the practice of Boards of Guardians in determining which cases among the sick poor should be treated as indoor patients in workhouse infirmaries, and which should be afforded domiciliary aid, to see whether any improvements could be made. But they found they could offer no advice, because no general rule could be 'safely or usefully laid down which would not interfere with Guardians exercising their discretion on the merits of each case'. (The deference to local authority during this period has already been noted.) By the Circular Letter of 13 December 1869, all Metropolitan and town Unions were asked to state what determined domiciliary or institutional treatment, and what stress was laid on the nature of a disease, the wishes of the patient or family, the condition of the home, the character and extent of infirmary accommodation, and the intervention of the District Medical Officer.[1] The replies showed much variety existed in the practice of different localities, but there were comparatively few Unions where sick paupers were sent by preference into the workhouse infirmary if the Medical Officer thought they could be safely and advantageously treated in their own homes. The Medical Officer's decision, it was seen, was based on housing conditions, nursing facilities and the illness itself. The family and the doctor decided without the Guardians interference whether a patient should be removed to the infirmary, but often because the workhouse was full, domiciliary relief had to be given, although the sick pauper would have recovered more quickly in the institution. It was shown that although institutional relief had become so important, the prevailing practice was still to give outdoor relief to the sick. In fact two-thirds received medical attendance in their own homes in 1870. Despite this revelation, no indication was given by the Poor Law Board that they entertained any policy for improving the system.

The development which should have been fostered and guided from above, but which was left to *ad hoc* invention and management as inclination dictated, was the institution of dispensaries. Large provincial towns began to find it was becoming increasingly impossible for Medical Officers to cope with the growing numbers of outdoor sick, and the obvious solution which presented itself was to provide central stations, which in practice were worked like the out-patients' departments of public hospitals. In fact, the new dispensaries and the new Poor Law infirmaries together, closely resembled the hospital system.

Three years after the Select Committee of 1864 reported that there were not sufficient grounds for materially interfering with the existing system of medical relief, came the

[1] For details of the replies see Twenty-second Annual Report, 1869–70.

revolutionary Metropolitan Poor Act of 1867. It was precipitated by the commercial crisis of 1866—which caused great distress in the City—by the cholera epidemic of that year, and by the three inquiries held in 1866 into the operation of the workhouse system by Inspectors Cane, Farnall, and Dr. Smith. The *Lancet* inquiry and its revelations, which gave rise to the three official investigations, deserves important recognition, as well as the strong and unflagging agitation for reform by the Poor Law Medical Officers' Association. Gathorne Hardy, President of the Poor Law Board, who introduced the Bill, also acknowledged his debt to Joseph Rogers from whom much of his information had been obtained.

By the Act, Unions and parishes of the Metropolis were combined into districts for providing 'asylums for the reception and relief of the sick poor'. For the first time all authorities operating under local or Gilbert Acts, of which there were eleven in London, were brought under the Poor Law Board. Administrative uniformity had at last been achieved. The new districts were all to come under a single central authority—the Metropolitan Asylums Board. Managers of each Asylums District were empowered, subject to orders from the Poor Law Board, 'to hold or dispose of land and property for the purposes of the Asylums District'. As each district was to provide separate institutions for every class of sick, the managers were also authorized to borrow money for building and alteration. In addition the new authorities were also to be responsible for providing drugs and medical appliances. Richard Griffin[1] however, writing in the *Lancet*, said that the question of the provision of drugs was of such vital importance that the central authorities, as in the Army and Navy, should supply them.[2] The Parliamentary Grant, he suggested, would be a convenient source from which the cost could be defrayed. The Act also established a Metropolitan Poor Fund for the purpose of equalizing over the whole of London, expenses connected with institutional medical relief. Unions were expected to contribute to this Fund according to their annual rateable value. Therefore the Consolidated Fund was entirely freed from paying a contribution towards sick relief.

An agitation immediately commenced against the injustice of these contributions, because the Metropolitan rating system was so unfair. The wealthy parish of St. George's, Hanover Square, supported 2,400 poor at a cost of £30,000 a year, raised at a rate of eightpence in the £, whilst Bethnal Green maintained nearly 5,000 poor at a cost of £43,000, by a rate of 3s. 11d. in the £. If the poor of Bethnal Green had been relieved on the same scale as those of St. George's, the cost to the Union would have been £64,000, so that the difference of £21,000 was 'wrung out of the sufferings of the poor, the majority of whom are the sick and aged'.[3] From another point of view, the 75,000 affluent inhabitants of Paddington (said by Stallard in 1867 to have consisted only of villas) contributed £20,000 a year, or 5s. 6d. per head, whilst the 56,000 poor persons of Stepney contributed £44,000 or nearly 16s. each, or £1 1s. if paupers were excluded from the population. At a meeting of the

---

[1] Griffin was an ardent campaigner for reform in the medical service and especially for the improvement of the Medical Officer's lot.

[2] *Lancet*, 1867, i, p. 301.

[3] *Lancet*, 1869, i, p. 296.

Poor Law Medical Officers' Association in 1869[1] it was stated that although poor Unions were to pay more to the Fund, the small amount they spent on medical services would not be altered, for the high rates permitted of only low salaries and inadequate medical relief. There was nothing in the new departure which would amend the system whereby Poplar spent £276 on 3,348 patients and Whitechapel £82 on 4,548, or less than a quarter of the sum per case. Some Medical Officers were paid less than 3s. a patient, others treble this amount. The Association therefore demanded that there should be a proper distribution of funds to be paid, and a system of inspection for outdoor medical relief which should also control the appropriation of money.[2] Legislators postponed the consideration of the ridiculous contrast, reform of which could have been the basis for providing adequate relief to the sick poor, fair remuneration to the doctors, and a more just treatment of indigent ratepayers. Equalization of rates was one key to the whole question of the medical system in the Metropolis and early in 1869, when Parliament was scarcely a week old, George J. Goschen as President of the Poor Law Board introduced a Bill for remedying the flagrant defects, and the amending Act of 1870 established Assessment Committees.

TABLE 11.5

Comparative Deductions of the Metropolitan system—published by the Select Committee of 1862 (average of ten years ending 25 March 1858).

Unions	Proportion of sick poor to population	Rate per head of population	Amount spent on District Medical Relief
		s.	s. d.
West London	1 in $7\frac{1}{6}$	4	1 $10\frac{1}{2}$
Holborn	1 in $11\frac{2}{3}$	$3\frac{11}{12}$	2 $2\frac{1}{4}$
East London	1 in $6\frac{2}{3}$	3	1 1
Strand	1 in $2 \cdot 5\frac{1}{3}$	$2\frac{10}{12}$	3 9
City of London	1 in $20\frac{2}{7}$	$2\frac{9}{12}$	2 6
St. Saviour's	1 in $11\frac{1}{2}$	$2\frac{7}{12}$	1 $11\frac{3}{4}$
St. George in the East	1 in $8\frac{3}{4}$	$2\frac{9}{12}$	1 $6\frac{3}{4}$
St. George's, Southwark	1 in 10	$2\frac{4}{12}$	1 $2\frac{3}{4}$
Bethnal Green	1 in 18	$1\frac{8}{12}$	1 $7\frac{1}{4}$
Whitechapel	1 in $6\frac{1}{2}$	$1\frac{11}{12}$	$11\frac{1}{4}$
Clerkenwell	1 in $15\frac{1}{4}$	$1\frac{5}{12}$	$8\frac{1}{4}$
St. Luke's	1 in 6	$3\frac{4}{12}$	1 $0\frac{3}{4}$
Stepney	1 in $8\frac{2}{3}$	2	1 $3\frac{1}{2}$
St. Olave's	1 in $4\frac{1}{2}$	$2\frac{8}{12}$	8

[1] Quarterly meeting, April 1869.
[2] See Table 11.4.

305

The Metropolitan Poor Act of 1867 also stated that the Common Fund was to provide the cost of indoor relief up to a maximum of fivepence per person a day.[1] No grant-in-aid was however to be made for district medical relief, save for drugs, and opposition was roused against Guardians being required to defray this charge out of local funds. No improvement could come, it was maintained, whilst burdens were unequally distributed and expenditure left to individual areas to meet as best they could.

Besides the establishment of Asylums Districts and the Common Poor Fund, the third great innovation of the 1867 Act was the authorization of the provision of dispensaries for the treatment of the outdoor sick poor. Either a new dispensary was to be built or part of the workhouse adapted in every Union. These institutions were to be established and managed by a Dispensary Committee elected by the Guardians from amongst themselves or the ratepayers. They were to be the central consulting rooms, where the District Medical Officer could see the sick, and where medicines and appliances could be supplied. District Medical Officers were, however, also to visit the homes of such of the sick poor as were unable to attend at the dispensary. Dispensers were to be appointed to each. This clause of the Act (42) gave official recognition to the distinction which had been gradually developing between prescriber and dispenser. It introduced another new element into the machinery of the Poor Law administration which was most significant in the reapportionment of duties. For the safety of the poor and for giving the Medical confidence in them, the dispensers were to possess special qualifications and be registered as Pharmaceutical Chemists. The defraying of the cost of drugs by the Common Poor Fund was extremely important, not only from the Medical Officers' financial point of view, but also because Guardians would be more willing to supply them. To effect the provision of dispensaries, the Poor Law Board 'could from time to time vary the medical districts, salaries, and contracts with the District Medical Officer'. This section of the Act subverted previous arrangements for the treatment of the district poor, because it placed such relief on an entirely new basis—the Dispensary Committees and not the Boards of Guardians were the new managers.

The Act did not specifically define who was to be entitled to relief, or who was to determine this. The omission caused the *Lancet* to comment: 'of all things that can be jobbed there is nothing like an "out-patients' department"'.[2] Probably referring to the experience of the old-established voluntary dispensaries, the writer maintained such a system could be constantly and seriously abused by the well-to-do, who would take advantage of it to evade payment for medical advice. It would also be possible and very easy, it was said, for a committee of such an institution to create fictitious sick and expenses on their behalf, and to send a bill to the auditor of the Common Fund who would never be able to check the statements. The *Lancet* believed that the whole machinery for regulating this department of outdoor sick poor relief was quite wrong and it wanted to see a General Board with its own inspectorate established by the Poor Law Board. Griffin also recommended that the entire medical system both in regard to asylums and dispensaries, should

[1] In force until 1927.
[2] *Lancet*, 1867, i, pp. 215–16.

be placed under the control of the managers of the Asylums Districts, so that dispensaries would become annexes of the asylums.[1]

Whilst an absolute epidemic[2] took place in the building or conversion of institutions, district hospitals for fever and infectious diseases, asylums for epileptics, idiots and imbeciles and district schools, there was little haste in the establishment of Poor Law dispensaries. It took fifteen months for the Secretary of the Poor Law Board merely to draw up a letter containing suggestions on the supply of expensive medicines. The *Lancet*, having welcomed the Act because the dispensary system was the only way of diminishing the number of patients in the densely-crowded sick wards of the workhouses, and because patients would have been enabled to receive treatment in their homes in the incipient stages of disease, condemned the delay in effecting the new arrangements. A revolution had been promised, which was to provide efficient assistance to the poor and raise the status of the Medical Officer 'from the undignified position of huxtering apothecaries dispensing their drugs at ruination prices, to the rank of honourable consultees, whose only possible object could be to cure patients as speedily as possible'. Faith had been placed in the Poor Law Board, said the *Lancet*, dispensaries were to have been formed without delay, and the central authorities had been given power to introduce them wherever the President pleased. Yet some Unions quietly ignored the regulations, others made independent arrangements with the existing medical staff, by which the dispensing of drugs was left exactly as before, whilst isolated Boards of Guardians, overwhelmed by the increase of sickness 'set about the work in their own fashion and executed it according to their own peculiar ideas'. The whole responsibility for the inaction, continued the *Lancet*, rested with the Poor Law Board. They could order dispensaries to be established (thirty-eighth Clause of the Act) and supervise the management; buildings had to be fitted and furnished to their satisfaction, and the number of porters, dispensers, and Medical Officers employed, and all the salaries had to receive their sanction. It would have been easy to obtain returns on the types of disease most prevalent so that the number of dispensaries required could have been ascertained. The *Lancet* called on the Poor Law Board, therefore, to issue regulations for the immediate adoption of the new schemes.[3]

Only through the constant agitation of the Poor Law Medical Officers' Association was a start made in establishing dispensaries. Rogers, to whom the chief credit for this part of the Act was due, wrote to Torrens, then Member of Parliament for Finsbury, asking him to inquire officially of the Poor Law Board the cause for the procrastination. This move engendered considerable alarm among permanent officials and an effort was at last made to institute the dispensary system. In their Twenty-first Annual Report, the Poor Law Board regretted that 'because of unforeseen obstacles in some cases, and legal impediments in others, little progress has been made in giving full effect to these provisions of the Act'. Guardians, it was admitted, were showing very strong opposition to supplying

---

[1] Letter to *Lancet*, 1867, i, p. 301.
[2] Rogers' expression in *Reminiscences of a Workhouse Doctor*.
[3] *Lancet*, leading article, 1868, i, pp. 351-2.

medicines and to Medical Officers examining and prescribing for the sick poor at a dispensary rather than at their own surgeries. The Poor Law Board concluded that they no longer considered it essential for Dispensary Committees to be appointed where Guardians objected, for the Metropolitan Poor Law Amendment Act of 1869 had relieved local authorities from the legal obligation of such action and offered them other inducements for the general establishment of dispensaries.

Nine Unions or parishes had such institutions for the supply of medicines only, before the passing of the Act. These were St. George in the East, St. George's, Hanover Square, Islington, Westminster, Mile End, Newington, St. Olave's, St. Pancras, Poplar, St. Saviour's, Stepney and Whitechapel.[1] In 1868 five others had begun to erect dispensaries, although not under the superintendence of Dispensary Committees. Long negotiations and tedious conferences with architects are common reading in the Minutes of the Boards of Guardians meetings at this time. In their Twenty-second Annual Report, the Poor Law Board confirming that progress had been made in nearly all districts, expressed much satisfaction in being able to state that: 'the provisions introduced by the Poor Law Board into the Metropolitan Poor Law Amendment Act for rendering the appointment of a separate Dispensary Committee unnecessary and for withholding repayment from the Common Poor Fund of salaries of Medical Officers and the cost of medicines, in those cases where Guardians neglected or refused to establish a dispensary, had the anticipated effect of promoting to a considerable extent, the general adoption of the system.' The Report stated that five Unions[2] possessed new dispensaries in comparatively full operation, and all these combined the indispensable requisites of a waiting-room for patients, a dispensing room, and a consulting room. Seven Unions had dispensaries where medicines were supplied to patients, but where no provision had, up to that time, been made for the attendance of a doctor,[3] and eighteen Unions and parishes had plans, more or less matured, for the establishment of such institutions.[4] A small group of Unions—Camberwell, Lewisham, Fulham, and Woolwich—had not adopted any definite scheme. The reason given was that the application of the system was difficult in consequence of the existence within them of large thinly populated areas. In 1869 however the Poor Law Board impressed on the Guardians the importance of establishing dispensaries immediately in their more densely-crowded districts. (Camberwell acquiesced in 1870.) The Guardians of Whitechapel decided to reduce their number of dispensaries from two to one, and while Bethnal Green began to erect three institutions, Mile End with a similar population had only one. Therefore it appears that the number of dispensaries bore no uniform relation to the area or popula-

[1] Parliamentary Accounts and Papers, 1868–69.
[2] Mile End, Stepney, Paddington, St. Margaret's and St. John's, Westminster and Poplar (2).
[3] St. George in the East, Islington, St. Luke's (Holborn later), Bloomsbury, Whitechapel (2), St. George's, Hanover Square (2), St. Saviour's (2).
[4] Bethnal Green (3), Shoreditch, Whitechapel, Islington, Hackney (2), Holborn (3), City of London (3), Hampstead, St. Pancras (3), Westminster, Strand, Kensington (2), Chelsea, Lambeth (3), Wandsworth and Clapham, St. Saviour's (2), St. Olave's (2), Greenwich (2). The institutions at Whitechapel and Islington were to be additional to those already in existence.

tion. The Poor Law Board did not think the discrepancy important, 'the point at which uniformity is most desirable . . . is not so much the number of dispensaries as the apportion-ment of work (taking into account population, pauperism, and area) in medical relief districts.'[1] As long as an adequate number of consulting rooms and a sufficiently large waiting-room were provided—as demanded by the Poor Law Amendment Act of 1869—the central authorities saw no inconvenience in several medical districts being attached to the same dispensary. Guardians in nearly all cases co-operated readily when the advantages of a joint dispensary were pointed out to them. Two limiting conditions were urged on the Guardians. The first, that the dispensary should not be more than one mile from the home of any patient, and the second, that there should be sufficient work in each dispensary to occupy the time of a dispenser.

It was for the first reason that the Poor Law Board in 1869 suggested to the Kensington Guardians, that besides having a dispensary at the workhouse, which was at the furthest extremity of the Union,[2] they should erect another in the centre of the town. The Guardians at first refused, but the Committee of the Notting Hill and Shepherds Bush Charitable Dispensary informed them that a great number of paupers were availing themselves of the Institution and crippling its resources. The Committee had never recognized parish paupers as fit objects for their relief, only the indigent sick poor, and urged that the evil would be remedied if a parish dispensary were established in the neighbourhood. It was on this recommendation that the Guardians in 1870 adopted a plan and purchased land for £1,500 for the erection of a dispensary.[3]

New buildings were not always erected; for example St. George in the East established a dispensary opposite the workhouse in a building which was enlarged and altered for the purpose. After a few months the dispensary waiting-room was turned into a vaccination station and it was twelve months before a resident dispenser was appointed for the indoor and outdoor poor at £60 a year, and before the Guardians began to supply medicines and appliances. In 1870 the Poor Law Board requested the Guardians to provide proper con-sulting rooms for the District Medical Officer, but they replied that there would be suffi-cient space in the new workhouse for this purpose. By 1871 however there were several dispensaries in different parts of the Union, where a District Medical Officer attended the district poor, instead of at the workhouse. They were all converted houses and all had their own dispensers. The doctors were required to attend for one hour a day, and three received salaries of £60 and a fourth £35. All of them were still elected annually, and a separate Medical Officer was appointed to the workhouse—an innovation in this Union.[4]

In Bethnal Green trouble arose between the Medical Officers and Guardians over the institution of the dispensary system. Here there were seven District Medical Officers who

[1] Twenty-second Annual Report, 1869–70.
[2] Map at County Hall, Westminster, Records Room.
[3] Minutes, Kensington Board of Guardians, 15 October 1869, and reports of meetings held in December 1869 and February 1870.
[4] Minutes, Board of Guardians, 1868–71.

received 10,000 medical orders a year and who were in consequence grossly overworked. As only three of them were permanently appointed the Guardians decided to divide the Union, which had a population of 120,000, into three dispensary districts, employing one of the Medical Officers in each and dismissing the remainder. Two offers were made to the permanent doctors, the first—a salary of £200 a year plus residence with £20 for a servant for full-time duties and the Guardians finding the drugs; the second—that the Medical Officers should reside at home and engage in private practice, but should attend the dispensaries every morning, the Guardians again providing drugs and a dispenser. The doctors declined with the support of the Poor Law Medical Officers' Association, which condemned the schemes as unjust to the Medical Officers and injurious to the ratepayers and the sick poor. A committee appointed by the Association to inquire into the case, reported that the doctors were already overworked and underpaid, and the proposed change offered no alleviation. Goschen, President of the Poor Law Board, was asked to veto the proposals. For a time the schemes were dropped, and the District Medical Officers engaged annually were reappointed for another three months. The *Lancet* took up the cause of the Medical Officers pointing out that it was impossible for seven men to do justice to the large number of patients let alone three. The doctors themselves had petitioned the Guardians for the introduction of the dispensaries, and in answer to their demands, the majority were to be dismissed, and the work of the remainder doubled. The proposals, the *Lancet* said, savoured strongly of 'minimum relief' in skill and medicine.[1] 'Sickness', the writer concluded, 'is the most costly form of pauperism. Inexperience and want of skill in those who treat it are dear at any price.' The problem of the Bethnal Green Guardians was that they had no special knowledge of what a dispensary should be, and that they would probably be ready to adopt a better plan if it were introduced to their notice. The outcome of the dispute was that the dispensaries were established and all the District Medical Officers retained.

The Holborn Union acknowledged their inability to deal with the new problem and invited the Poor Law Board's guidance. They affirmed their desire to fall in with a general system common to the whole Metropolis rather than attempt to adopt one exclusively their own. The Guardians had resolved over and over again that a dispensary ought to be introduced and asked for instruction as to how this might best be effected. But neither Dr. Smith, Medical Officer to the Poor Law Board, nor Dr. Markham, the Medical Inspector of the Metropolitan district, had shown any aptitude for dealing with the new system, and it was a reflection on both, that the Holborn Guardians were left to draw up regulations which ought to have issued from the central Board. The efficient development of the dispensary system depended on the central authorities laying down a general rule for making the scheme as uniform as possible throughout London. It was universally hoped by the medical profession that some comprehensive plan would be produced, for it was main-

---

[1] *Lancet*, 1870, i, pp. 17–18. The chief objection of the *Lancet* was that Medical Officers were to become the servants of the Guardians and were 'never to have the possibility of rising beyond a very paltry salary and very mediocre social status'. The *Lancet* always campaigned for the retention of private practice and against full-time Poor Law employment.

tained that no part of the Poor Law administration needed reform more imperatively. The *Lancet* made the request on behalf of the doctors generally, and said that on the introduction of this important measure largely depended the future welfare not only of the Poor Law Medical Officers, but of the general practitioner of the middle-class.[1] Many Metropolitan Guardians asked the central authorities to leave them alone, but the *Lancet* urged interference was necessary against the 'pettifogging jobbery of these would-be local magnates'. Further, it was said, pauperism had increased by $7\frac{1}{2}$ per cent in three years, with a great rise in expenditure, and it was impossible for the Poor Law Board to ignore this state of things much longer.

In these last years the central authority had awakened to a sense of its duty and had come to realize however reluctantly and hesitantly that Boards of Guardians sometimes needed supervision. Therefore in April 1870 the 'General Order on the management of Metropolitan Dispensaries' was issued. By the new regulation a Visiting Committee was to be appointed from the Guardians with a separate chairman. It was to meet once a fortnight, inspect books and forms and supervise the general working of the dispensary. Second, District Medical Officers were to attend at the institution every day at appointed hours, entering their arrival and departure in a book. They were also to keep a medical register which was to be open to daily inspection by the Medical Officer of Health, and were to certify all orders for drugs. For the future, two forms of medical order were required, one entitling the bearer to medical relief at the dispensary, and the other to domiciliary treatment. Relieving Officers were to place paupers on the permanent relief list for a maximum time of six months. Duties and qualifications of the dispensers were also re-iterated; he was to be engaged full-time, be in charge of the stores and help with the register, in addition to his normal work. This Order gave the first official recognition to the title of dispenser for this officer, and his supplementary duties meant that the Medical Officer would be relieved of much clerical labour. As was customary, the order was not immediately noted by the Guardians and it had to be recapitulated in a statement issued by the Poor Law Board in May 1871.

The *Lancet* continued to agitate for the wider adoption of the dispensary system so that the standard of the Poor Law Medical Officer could be raised. At the time, the writer said, 'their salaries were shameful, their work excessive and their position all but intolerable. . . . The best men of the district do not apply.'[2] Previously the *Lancet* believed that the adoption of the new system would have to be forced upon the Metropolitan Guardians, by the threat of the Poor Law Board to refuse payment of Medical Officers' salaries and the cost of drugs from the Common Poor Fund. This compulsion was not required, for considerable change gradually took place in the attitude of local authorities. From viewing an organized system of public medical relief with great distrust and suspicion, opinion veered to the conviction that ratepayers had a direct interest in the speedy recovery of every sick pauper. It was further realized that the old system failed to secure adequate domiciliary medical relief. The

[1] *Lancet*, 1870, i, pp. 124–125.
[2] *Lancet*, 1870, i, p. 125.

expenditure incurred by the Unions and parishes in these years is an indication of this change in attitude. From 1868 to 1870 the disbursements from the Common Poor Fund were as follows:

TABLE 11.6

Disbursements from the Common Poor Fund, 1868–70.—Twenty-second Annual Report of the Poor Law Board, 1869–70.

	Half-year ending Lady Day, 1868	Second Half-year, 1868	First Half-year, 1869	Second Half-year, 1869	First Half-year, 1870
	Total, nearest £100	nearest £100	£	£	£
Maintenance of lunatics	39,000	77,500	77,000	80,000	81,400
Medicine and medical and surgical appliances	2,800	3,700	4,400	2,600	4,700
Salaries of officers	44,300	45,700	58,000	39,500	59,300
Registration fees	2,600	5,000	5,000	4,900	5,000
Vaccination fees and expenses	1,000	2,600	2,800	2,800	2,200
Maintenance of pauper children	34,500	44,700	4,700	43,700	42,700
Expenses under Houseless Poor Acts	5,900	5,600	6,400	5,200	6,100
Total	130,100	184,800	158,300	178,700	201,400*

* These are actual totals. The published totals are only approximate.

In their last Annual Report the Poor Law Board made the magnanimous statement: 'Whatever is required for the proper care and treatment of the sick poor both medical and otherwise, . . . will be fully approved and granted . . . although expenditure requires to be watched.'[1]

The result of the growth of a more enlightened outlook was shown in a letter by a Kensington Medical Officer to the Westminster Union, which had enquired how Kensington managed to have so little pauperism.[2] . . . 'Every facility', said the doctor, 'is given to the poor to obtain speedy medical attendance in illness. . . . Illness one of the most prolific sources of pauperism is often cut short by prompt treatment, and whole families may be kept off the rates by the speedy restoration to health of the breadwinners. The Medical

[1] Twenty-third Annual Report, 1870–71.
[2] Minutes, Kensington Board of Guardians.

312

Officers are able to fulfil their duties with satisfaction to themselves and advantage to the poor. . . . They attend at the dispensaries daily . . . and none of their time is lost in the labour of dispensing . . . moreover they are able to prescribe the most suitable remedies in every case . . . not being deterred by considerations of cost which must necessarily influence them when they have to provide the medicines out of their moderate stipends. . . .'

The Holborn Guardians also stated the advantages of the new system. They appreciated the movement in the direction for relieving sickness out of the workhouse and stated that not only had treatment increased but also general relief to the sick which 'is essential to the repression of rapidly increasing pauperism, and will prove the truest economy in the end'. Homes once broken through entry into the workhouse were rarely recovered, and this contributed largely to the permanent charge on the Union for indoor maintenance.[1] The Poor Law Board, however, inferred from the answers received from Metropolitan Guardians to their inquiries undertaken in 1870,[2] that the expectation of dispensaries bringing about a reduction of workhouse patients was unwarranted. 'Such a result was never anticipated by the Poor Law Board in its efforts to establish the dispensaries. The sick poor are not sent into infirmaries through outdoor relief being inaccessible to them, but either an account of the character and condition of their homes, or because of some special requirement of their disease, or on account of the patients having no one to nurse them at home.' In concluding the report, the Poor Law Board pointed out: 'The result of establishing dispensaries will not be to remove the necessity for infirmaries, but to improve the existing arrangements under which medical relief is administered, by securing for the sick poor a prompter and better supply of all necessary and proper medicines and medical appliances, by abolishing the system of requiring Medical Officers themselves to supply drugs, by enabling those persons who are not confined within doors to obtain medical advice at fixed hours and within convenient distance from their own homes, and generally by organizing a more efficient control over the whole administration of outdoor medical relief.' This was a true statement, but on one point Joseph Rogers was more correct than the Poor Law Board, when he stated in a speech to the Poor Law Medical Officers' Association, that an array of figures (which he could produce), would show how economical a plan the dispensary system was, because it led to the cure of the sick before their disease made removal to the workhouse necessary.

It was at this meeting[3] that a resolution was adopted by the Association in favour of extending the dispensary system to the whole country. Even at the end of the 'sixties no part of the Poor Law medical service was conducted in a more slovenly fashion in the provinces than that relating to the outdoor sick. Medical Officers were disatisfied with their salaries, their overwork, and their lack of support by the Guardians. The poor suffered from neglect, insufficient medicines, and the absence of nursing. Because the doctor had no time

[1] Minutes, Holborn Board of Guardians, January 1868.

[2] See Twenty-second Annual Report on Practice among Guardians as to what determined domiciliary relief.

[3] Quarterly meeting of the Poor Law Medical Officers' Association, April 1869.

and because it did not fall within the scope of the Poor Law medical relief, he could not watch over a patient's convalescence, and through the inadequate general relief, a patient could not afford it, so that strength was never recovered before work was resumed. Many of the evils would have been remedied by the adoption of an efficient dispensary system, which, because the institutions were open to inspection, could also have safeguarded against noxious abuses. By 1870, nine Unions provided dispensaries in the provinces, some of which were used only for the supply of medicines. Where the new system had been tried, it was reported to be working satisfactorily. Inspector Peel dwelt a little on the advisability of establishing dispensaries in his report on outdoor relief in 1870.[1] He maintained it would be practicable to institute dispensaries, not only in large towns, but also in thinly populated and extensive rural Unions. In large towns one or two central dispensaries would be adequate, but in extensive rural Unions more numerous stations would be required because of the distances at which people lived. Expense would be considerable, but apart from the cost, Peel contended that they might have a prejudicial effect on medical clubs, and 'might be calculated from the additional facilities afforded for obtaining medical relief, to increase pauperism, and discourage habits of independence and self-reliance'. On the other hand, Peel suggested the universal establishment of dispensaries would ensure to the sick poor 'a more rapid and better supply of medicine, whilst it would tend to increase the remuneration of Medical Officers and remove from them any temptation which may now exist to prescribe medicine insufficient alike in quantity and quality'.

Rural areas, however, were practically left untouched by the dispensary system and district medical relief continued to be furnished as it had been over past decades—in-efficiently and inadequately. It was only the large towns which developed the same standard as London, and in the 'seventies places like Birmingham, Cardiff, Derby, Man-chester, Liverpool, Gloucester, Leeds, Plymouth, and Sheffield established one or more dispensaries. Early in 1871 there was a great preliminary struggle in Birmingham, but the new scheme when it was finally formalized was said to have been better than that of London. The *Lancet* commenting on it, recommended other towns to watch developments carefully. A medical member of the Board of Guardians drew up the scheme, and two Medical Officers instead of one were appointed to attend at the institution daily. A resident dispenser was also appointed at £90 a year plus his keep—a higher salary than that awarded by any Metropolitan Union.[2]

In the 'seventies, however, the Poor Law administrators embarked on an active crusade against all forms of outdoor medical relief, just when awareness of the necessity for its efficiency had taken root. Although the dispensary was such an admirable innovation it had several disadvantages. From the point of view of the Medical Officer and the sick poor the system was good—although several Unions like Paddington[3] refused to supply appliances through them—but the establishments themselves were bad. Premises were in most cases

[1] Report to Poor Law Board, 1870, on District No. 3 (Bucks, Northants, Bedford).
[2] *Lancet*, 1871, i, p. 796.
[3] Board of Guardians' Minutes, September 1869.

converted old buildings or even only a few rooms on the ground floor of a dwelling house. Seldom were they built for their purpose—and this condition still appertained in the early twentieth century. They were cold and unfriendly, and must have had a depressing effect on patients. Long hours of waiting not only entailed loss of earnings to the poor, but also the risk of cross-infection, especially as waiting-rooms were generally overcrowded and contained few amenities. No nurses were employed (an attendant was usual in out-patients' departments of hospitals), although one would have been of great assistance to the Medical Officer and the dispenser, besides having added greatly to the comfort of the patients.

In another sphere also, there was a great defect in the dispensary system. Although the institutions formed large centres for treatment, capable of indefinite expansion, no comprehensive reports were solicited. These could have provided invaluable accurate information as to the diseases which specially affected the poor and were conducive to pauperism. In this as in every other sphere, the Poor Law authorities failed to offer medical science and public health the service which they alone were able to render. The dispensary system was the first step towards the prevention of disease, but it was never carried to a logical conclusion. Its most flagrant defect was that from which the entire Poor Law medical system suffered— its scope was inadequate. To widen the application of the services was the greatest reform demanded throughout the life of the new Poor Law. When such a large proportion of pauperism was caused by sickness, prophylactic as well as therapeutic work was essential, but the efficacy of the former depended on affording gratuitous medical relief to a far larger class than came within the province of the Poor Law.

The two predominating arguments of the reformers were first, that medical relief should not constitute a recipient a pauper, and second, that all the poor should be eligible for gratuitous treatment.

As we have seen, the definition of those eligible for medical relief was far wider than that for those qualifying for general relief. But although the technical definition of destitution was not applied to the sick, those people who received advice from the Poor Law Medical Officer were termed paupers. In law, therefore, the recipient of medical treatment only was as much a pauper as the able-bodied inmate of a workhouse, and no doubt the designation was deliberatey made use of as a deterrent. The restrictive policy was even expressed in the standing orders of asylums. Griffin discovered that in many towns Poor Law Medical Officers were subpoena'd to produce their books at municipal revision courts, and the names of all voters found on them were struck off the register by one political party or another. The result was that voters refused to allow their children (because the whole family was 'pauperized' if one received sick relief) to have gratuitous assistance unless they were in the greatest danger. Yet, Griffin pointed out, many could have been cured if they had been treated early. He therefore suggested to the Select Committee of 1862 that medical relief if it were unaccompanied by other relief should not be deemed parochial aid, and that no person receiving it should be deprived of any right or privilege, or be subject to any disability or disqualification whatsoever. The most noxious result of pauperization through medical assistance was that the sick poor, unwilling to suffer from the stigma, tried to do without adequate attention. This often resulted in a deterioration in their condition and then in complete destitution. As one Member of Parliament said—the poor did not mind having scarlet fever in their homes, but they did mind having the parish doctor there. This was not because they disliked him, but because they objected to Poor Law relief and its consequences.

Another aspect of the effect of the principle was that the poor once recognized as paupers, gradually lost their feeling for independence and were no longer loathe to apply for general assistance. By immediate and non-committal treatment illness would have been quickly remedied and the fear of ultimate dependence on general poor relief averted. Rumsey in the 'forties and 'fifties constantly agitated for the disentanglement of medical aid from general aid. When dispensaries were formed, he also advocated there should be no connection between them and the workhouse, and that drugs and medical 'extras' should be supplied there with money obtained from a source distinct from the poor rate applied to ordinary outdoor relief. Inspector Austin admitted to the Select Committee of 1854 that it was impossible to calculate the number of persons pauperized by medical relief. In their final resolution, the Committee called the attention of Parliament to the evidence given on the considerable number of poor persons who had been placed on the pauper list through the receipt of medical relief in cases of sickness or accident, and from that cause alone. The Committee therefore recommended 'that persons so circumstanced be enabled to receive such medical assistance as their case may require, without being placed on the list of paupers', but that it should be left to the Guardians to decide 'in what cases medical relief be so given to persons who are not otherwise in want of, or in receipt of, parochial relief'. The abortive Medical Relief Bill of 1860 also contained a clause that medical relief was not to be deemed parochial relief and that the disabilities or disqualifications inflicted on the destitute should no longer be applied to the sick. Two years later the petition of the British Medical Association included a similar proposal, and further evidence was given in its favour to the Select Committee of 1861–64. Some of the members of the Select Committee of 1864 endorsed its predecessor's recommendations. Sir W. Miles proposed the resolution as he had done in 1854 and was supported by Sir Robert Cecil, but they were defeated by eight votes to five. The legislature and the Poor Law Board never gave the subject further consideration, and the report by Farnall, who was the most enlightened of the Inspectors, killed the discussion of the principle in 1870, when he wrote that the closest attention had been given to the subject but agreement with the reformers was impossible. He was convinced the working classes would as a rule eagerly accept gratuitous medical aid, and thereby not only seriously burden the rates, but rapidly pauperize themselves—for self reliance, 'which to a great extent animates them', would be destroyed. Farnall concluded: 'Such a national mode of meeting the medical wants of the people, would eventually destroy . . . those very valuable benefit and friendly societies which now exist in England the abandonment of which would incalculably increase pauperism.'[1]

[1] H. B. Farnall, Report on Outdoor Medical Relief, Eastern Counties, 1870.

At the same time as the agitation for the removal of medical relief from general parochial relief, there was a demand for all the poor to receive free treatment. The great unsolved question of this period was—who was eligible for sick relief? It was a question which could only be answered by the broad vision of statesmanship.—Unfortunately it was put to the Poor Law Board.—They in turn delegated it to the narrow and niggardly Guardians. Prescience was only shown by the more enlightened members of the medical profession. It was inevitable that their training and the nature of their work should convince them of the need for widening the scope of gratuitous relief, but they were also fortunate in that they never became absorbed into the Poor Law administration, and so remained unscathed by its obscurantism.

In 1840 the Poor Law Commissioners had stated their object was 'to provide medical aid for all persons who are really destitute and to prevent medical relief from generating or encouraging pauperism, and with this view to withdraw from the labouring classes, the administrators of relief and the Medical Officers, all motives for applying for or administering medical relief unless where circumstances render it absolutely necessary'.[1] These 'circumstances' were never defined, and as we have seen, rigid adherence to the technical connotation of 'destitution' was not resorted to for the sick. But because no statutory definition was ever given of who was sufficiently poor to be eligible for gratuitous medical relief, there was a marked lack of uniformity in the country. The inability of a labourer to afford a doctor's bill and medical 'extras' was left to the sole judgement of the Relieving Officer and the Guardians, who were guided by the cost incurred rather than by the prevalence of remediable ill-health in the district.

A just explanation of circumstances entitling a person to relief would have included the normal condition of practically all agricultural and unskilled labourers. Second, it would have embraced Engels's 'surplus population', which he said kept 'body and soul together by begging, stealing, street-sweeping, collecting manure, pushing hand-carts, driving donkeys, peddling and performing occasional small jobs', and which existed in multitudes in every large town.[2] This reserve army embraced an immense number during an economic crisis, and was large even during normal periods. These people later known as the 'submerged tenth', contained most of the prostitutes, defectives, low-grade criminals, and loafers of the community. Their numbers could have been greatly reduced had the Poor Law authorities shown any liberality. Some of the causes which lay at the root of the problem were medical and another was spasmodic unemployment. The medical factors were that these people suffered generally from a low intelligence quota or from minor illnesses such as debility, anaemia, and results of repeated childbirth, which weakened their constitution and made them incapable of standing the strain of normal life. Not only would efficient medical treatment and an adequate supply of 'extras' have reduced the constant threat that they would cross the line of demarcation into pauperism, but they

[1] Report of Poor Law Commissioners on Further Amendment of the Poor Laws, 1840.
[2] F. Engels, *Condition of the Working Class in England*, 1844.

would also have shielded the remainder of the community from much infectious and contagious disease.

The third class of people who should have come into the purview of automatic gratuitous relief, were those whose employment alternated between constantly recurring periods of slackness and earnings just sufficient to maintain the family. If economic conditions precluded them from maintaining health and strength, it was incumbent on authorities to ensure that it was quickly restored to them, before they fell on the rates altogether. In this class may also be included the widows of the poor, who lived by taking in washing, mangling, and needlework. The process of slow starvation was common to them and their children. In fact, however, the majority of those who did not desert their children to earn a livelihood by dissipation, did fall on the Poor Law—and in the 'sixties 35 per cent of London pauperism was made up of widows alone.

Yet another group were those workers who were affected by the trade cycle and had a claim to non-committal gratuitous medical relief. Not only had seasonal unemployment an effect on sickness, but also the great commercial crises of the nineteenth century. That the work of the Poor Law Medical Officer was increased at these periods can be seen from the statistics and read in the reports of the Poor Law Inspectors. One of them wrote in 1867 that because the shipping and shipbuilding trades in the East End of London had been so severely hit by the depression, all the District Medical Officers of Poplar had been allowed assistants for six months. The account also stated that 'all the best people' had already emigrated, affording the inference that the sick and the weak had been left behind.[1] In this area the evil of the lack of uniformity in the system of granting relief was vividly illustrated, for the people who had been pauperized by the cholera epidemic of the previous winter or by the prevailing commercial distress flocked to areas where there was most almsgiving. This resulted in overcrowding with its concomitant increase in disease. The part played by the crisis of 1866–67 in the passing of the Metropolitan Poor Act must not be overlooked. Much could have been achieved in the provinces if the depression in the late 'forties, which shook the manufacturing and mining areas of Lancashire, Monmouth, Glamorgan, the West Riding, Nottingham, Middlesex and Leicester, had had a similar effect on the legislative and Poor Law authorities.

The fifth group of people who should have received some attention from a State medical service were those workers who were liable to occupational disease. Wakley, through the medium of the *Lancet*, gave considerable assistance to Sir John Simon, in publicly ventilating the high incidence of tuberculosis, and the direct relationship of this disease to certain unhealthy trades and bad social conditions. The most startling accounts were given in the working-class press and in several books in the middle decades of the nineteenth century. Doctors also made investigations and published reports in which the high rates of mortality and disease consequent on some occupations was terribly revealed.[2]

[1] U. Corbett, Poor Law Inspector, Report, 1867.
[2] See for example Dr. J. C. Hall's various books particularly those on the Sheffield trades—knife-grinders mortality etc. (Inventions greatly aided the decline in occupational disease.)

The incidence of sickness in various employments was also shown in statistics published by the Poor Law Board, but these refer not only to occupational disease but also to the four broad trade groups in which ordinary sickness and pauperism were most common, and where gratuitous medical treatment had to be granted either because of unemployment or the inadequacy of wages. The four broad categories were commerce, agriculture, mining, and mechanical arts, and the predominant occupations of people receiving medical relief in the various Regions in 1857 and 1867 are listed in Table 11.7.[1]

TABLE 11.7

Predominant Occupations of People receiving Medical Relief in various Regions in the years 1857 and 1867.—Abstracted from the Tenth and Twentieth Annual Reports of the Poor Law Board.

Region	1857, per cent	1867,[2] per cent
Metropolis	Domestic service, Mechanical arts, Trade—47	Domestic service—41; Industrial—36
South East	Domestic service[1]—30; Agricultural—30	Domestic service—40
South Midland	Domestic service—28; Agricultural—25	Domestic service—35; Industrial—29
Eastern	Domestic service—27; Agricultural—26	Domestic service—38; Agricultural—26
South West	Domestic service—28; Agricultural—23	Domestic service—36; Industrial—28
West Midland	Domestic service—29; Agricultural—15	Domestic service—27; Industrial—37
North Midland	Domestic service—31; Agricultural—21	Domestic service—35; Industrial—34
North West	Domestic service—29; manufacture—21	Domestic service—34; Industrial—44
Yorks.	Domestic service—25; Manufacture—17; Agricultural—14	Domestic service—36; Industrial—41
Northern	Domestic service—27; Agricultural—16; Mining—12	Domestic service—39; Industrial—33
Wales	Domestic service—25; Agricultural—25; Mining—12	Domestic service—37; Industrial—28

[1] Domestic service included domestic industries.
[2] 1867 — Commerce and Agriculture had dropped to third and fourth places and were well below the other two classes.

Finally, the whole of the working-class might have been included in those who should

[1] Abstracted from Tenth and Twentieth Annual Reports of Poor Law Board.

have been eligible for gratuitous relief. A definition would have been impossible, but it should have embraced all those who lived in the insalubrious slums. In overcrowded and insanitary homes, filthy courts and alleyways, and where malnutrition was the accepted order of life, low fevers and illness of every type was never absent. The term malnutrition had not yet been coined, its effects as that of bad social conditions were however obvious to everyone. As the district medical services of the Poor Law had no conception of Public Health duties, it should have provided more adequate means for cure where it could or would not prevent. Insufficient medical care left the health of the poor damaged. Those who died were comparatively few, but those who became incurable or disabled for life were many. The effect on the young was important. Because parents refused to be pauperized by having their children treated by the Poor Law Medical Officer, or because Guardians refused assistance, common ailments had lingering after-effects. Defects of eyes, nose, throat, or malformations which could have been dealt with in infancy, remained untreated until cure became impossible. Much of the ill-health and defectiveness of the adult population could be directly attributed to the short-sighted policy of the legislature and the Poor Law authorities.

It cannot be said that all Poor Law Medical Officers were enlightened, for even Dr. Fowler as Secretary of the Metropolitan Association objected to the 'indiscriminate granting of medical relief'.[1] The Association had passed a resolution to this effect at a meeting at which the inadequacy of salaries was discussed, and the doctors believed justifiably that an enormous increase in their work would not lead to a proportionate increase in remuneration. The meeting also opposed indiscriminate relief because it would destroy the self-independence of the whole labouring population under the existing regulations—for they would all be classed as paupers. Apart from this single instance, all individual Poor Law medical reformers and the Associations agitated for a more comprehensive system for which the central authorities were to stipulate a definite maximum income up to which all families were to receive gratuitous relief.

One of the keynotes of the evidence given to the Select Committee of 1854 was that there would be decidedly less pauperism if medical relief were given more freely at the onset of an illness. The Superintendent Registrar of Bristol said that he had examined his five Registrars' books and found that fifty out of every 500 people died without any medical aid, 'partly from their poverty and partly from their unwillingness to go to hospital[2] for medical relief'. 'And I believe', the Registrar continued, 'that these cases would appear more numerous . . . because they take parties, especially children, to the medical man just on the last day or so . . . so that they may with greater ease, obtain a certificate of registration of death from the Registrar, and that is borne out by the fact that there is one medical man . . . who attends the poor almost for a nominal sum, and he has a greater number of poor cases than any other, and there are a greater number of medical certificates . . . from his hands than from any other . . . I cannot account for that from the

[1] Meeting of Metropolitan Poor Law Medical Officers, 10 May 1861.
[2] St. Peter's Hospital, Bristol, was solely for paupers.

320

fact that they only go to him just in time of extremity . . .' Referring to infant mortality the Registrar pointed out that because of the difficulty in obtaining medical relief, parents doctored children at home according to some old woman's direction, or simply took them to druggists who understood nothing of the sickness. Their quackery merely confirmed the illness and hastened the death of the children, many of whom died from curable diseases. He also spoke of the older people who were obliged to sell their goods in order to obtain medical relief. Although charitable hospitals existed, many poor could not obtain a ticket and therefore had to apply quacks' remedies, or gradually become pauperized by losing all their belongings to defray doctors' bills. The Registrar of Bristol therefore wished to see the establishment of a dispensary system which should include provision for all the poor, and without pauperization.[1] Dr. Leigh, a well-known Manchester surgeon and who was the Registrar, also spoke of the high infantile mortality in the country and maintained that half of these deaths were from curable diseases. Adults, he said, were better cared for because they were connected with societies, but even so a large proportion were not so provided for, and relief was only afforded after a considerable interval lost in obtaining a recommendation to a charity. Referring to Manchester, he stated that the great mortality of children there was attributable indirectly to mothers being absent at factories, but even this could not account for the larger proportion of infantile deaths in towns than in the country. The reason was the lack of medical attention. Parents, too poor to obtain medical aid, refused to become paupers for their children. Lack of proper nursing, clothing, and diet were contributory factors, but a doctor's advice at the early stage of an illness would provide, Leigh said, the greatest improvement in the prevention of unnecessary suffering and death. He suggested also, that a system of free dispensaries would be most advantageous to the poor. Manchester had an infirmary and six charitable dispensaries, all of which supplied free medicine to the poor. A Medical Officer, he maintained, would not refuse to visit a sick person if he were certain that a patient would obtain (free) medicine from somewhere. He also advocated that his proposed free dispensaries should not require tickets for admission, because subscribers who distributed them could know nothing of the circumstances of the person applying, and the practice would also lead to delay in treatment.

A Guardian of an agricultural area and seaport agreed that dispensaries should be established for the supply of drugs, and that the system should be extended to all labouring men generally who were members of a benefit club.[2] A Relieving Officer also evinced the necessity for increasing the scope of medical relief. He drew attention to the fact that it was the people just above the class of paupers who suffered most, and recapitulated that the poor pawned their belongings to obtain medical aid and that many died without having received any treatment. He had often, on an application for relief for burial, asked who had attended the person, and had received the reply, nobody, because there were no means. Experience led him to believe that there would be a great reduction in expenditure on poor

---

[1] T. F. Gilbert, Superintendent Registrar and Town Councillor of Bristol, in evidence to Select Committee, 1854.

[2] R. Wooldridge, Vice-Chairman, Fareham Board of Guardians in evidence to Select Committee, 1854.

relief if all the sick poor were attended gratuitously, and further, if they were not consti-tuted paupers thereby, the whole family would be precluded from falling on the rates.[1] Dr. Boyd, Lunacy Inspector in Somerset, and once a London Poor Law Medical Officer, stated to the Select Committee of 1854 that because medical relief was so scanty, and because people had to sell their possessions to pay for treatment, families became irredeemable paupers for two or three generations, and that a great deal of money would therefore be saved the public if medical assistance were afforded quickly and gratuitously. He advocated the giving of relief first and an inquiry into eligibility afterwards. This was particularly important in times of epidemics like cholera where a vast number of patients were lost through the want of early attention. Many cases of typhus, he said, resulted from the same cause because it was not until they were extremely ill that people would incur the stigma of pauperization. He produced figures showing that the cost to a poor person for several weeks' illness of typhus was great, and that convalescence, which required stimulants and medicines, was also expensive. The total prime cost of medicine, treatment, and extra food to people attended in their own homes was about £5. Rich and poor, he contended, should get like treatment and in all cases of urgency should be attended at parish expense.

Another doctor (Dr. Livett) from an agricultural area, stated that the profession charged on an average 5s. a visit including medicines. When the average labourer's wage was 9s. a week, he pointed out, it was quite impossible for him to obtain relief privately. Two-thirds of this doctor's cases were not paupers before they applied for treatment, but became so as a result, and through the pauperization of medical relief, became inured to losing their independence altogether.[2] An overseer from a Bristol suburb showed that a man earning the average wage of the district could not meet the contingency of sickness. As a rate-collector of the district for twenty-one years he understood a great deal of the social and economic conditions. A wage of 10s. a week out of which 2s. was paid for rent left little for the maintenance of a family. Formerly small dispensaries had existed, he said, which had been established by doctors and to which the poor contributed a small weekly sum. Since these had disappeared the poor had been left entirely to their own resources. He reiterated that the poor delayed applying for Poor Law medical relief until the disease had become serious because pauperization disqualified them from charitable aid, and many objected to becoming disfranchised. Some families apparently received as much as £6 from a charity at Christmas and most received 20s.[3]

One Guardian alone gave evidence to the Select Committee of 1854 opposing the suggestion that the scope of Poor Law medical relief should be extended. He prophesied deplorable results if the principle of affording medical aid to workmen, not paupers, however poor, were effected. It was impossible, he said, to draw a line of demarcation, and the system once established would have to be carried out to its full extent, and medical aid

[1] R. Carter, Relieving Officer, Clifton Union, in evidence to Select Committee, 1854.
[2] Dr. Livett, Wells Union, in evidence to Select Committee, 1854.
[3] G. Chick, Assistant Overseer, Suburb of Bristol, in evidence to Select Committee, 1854.

provided to the entire working class. This, he maintained, would be reverting back to the vicious principle which had been the main cause of the enactment of 1834, i.e., making the entire labouring population paupers. Not only would this lay a heavy burden on the rate-payer, as the whole cost of poor relief would have to be borne by them, but it would also destroy the self-reliance of the working classes.[1] Another Guardian (Rev. Oxenden) how-ever disputed these arguments. 'The importance of giving to every labourer, every work-man, an opportunity of receiving medical advice without any expense on his part is, I think, of the first consideration; because the absence of medical attendance at the very time when it is most needed frequently results in the individual becoming for a lengthened period ill . . . I should extend (free medical aid) to all the working classes, and I should except merely persons having a real or personal property of a certain amount, or an income of a certain amount . . . to all persons up to 25s. a week, I should be disposed to give gratui-tous medical aid. . . . I think it most important to extend it very far beyond the mere poor so as to prevent persons from becoming poor. . . . The doctor's bill is the bill which breaks down the labouring man.' The Rev. Oxenden concluded that he did not advocate that doctors under the proposed scheme should be paid out of parochial rates because he looked on medical relief as a 'national act'.

Rumsey, as we have seen in an earlier chapter, had always been the advocate of the extension of gratuitous medical relief. To the Select Committee of 1854 he reiterated that in his opinion half the working population should be eligible for it and that in this half, 25–45 cases of sickness actually occurred among 100 people every year. Under improved sanitary conditions, he estimated the number might be reduced by 50 per cent, therefore it was extremely important 'to prevent the occurrence of sick cases by proper sanitary management, rather than to adopt a system of medical relief which only has reference to the curing of disease'. He referred to the difficulty of defining the class of poor who were to receive gratuitous aid. It had never been done satisfactorily, he said, and never would be, because it depended on unforeseen casualty. There was still in the mid-'fifties a great difference between the North and South of England—although arrangements had im-proved in the former over the previous decade—regarding the proportion of sick people attended by the Poor Law Medical Officers. A discrepancy existed between wages, although these were on the whole not sufficiently high in the North to admit the provision of ade-quate private medical attention. But by tradition the Northerners found their own treat-ment by visiting unqualified doctors, and medical relief was through the same custom, given more sparingly by the Poor Law authorities. Because of the insanitary conditions of the towns and the paucity of medical relief, the greatest mortality occurred in the Northern industrial towns. But elsewhere also, Rumsey found the lack of medical attention a glaring abuse. In Gloucester for example, he found that one-third of the deaths returned by the Registrar had no medical certificates attached to them, and as no Medical Officer ever refused to furnish one, he concluded that this great proportion of cases died without medical

[1] J. Ellison, Guardian of Dewsbury Union, in evidence to Select Committee, 1854.

attention. He also pointed out the inevitable recourse to quacks and druggists by the poor. It was as much the case in 1854 as in 1844, because no legislation had been passed which would have altered, what Rumsey termed, the relation between the poor population and the medical attendants.

A great deal of evidence was therefore given to the Select Committee of 1854 in favour of extending the medical services of the Poor Law to a much larger section of the working class than the authorities ever envisaged. But the Committee ignored the suggestions which had emanated from every section of the Poor Law administration, from Guardians, overseers, Registrars, doctors, Relieving Officers, and clergymen. Only one member of the Committee, Mr. W. Miles[1] published an individual resolution. It was he who asked of every witness if it was because medical relief was so scanty and because it was accompanied by a stigma of pauperism, that a vast number of persons sold their goods and eventually became paupers, although a little timely aid would have saved them; and if any improvement would be effected in giving medical relief to all the poor of populous places. The answers he received led him to the conclusion made evident in his resolution: 'As a feeling of degradation arising from the application for medical relief, together with civil and political disabilities resulting from its reception, deter a great number of deserving objects from applying for Poor Law medical assistance, whereby a vast number of valuable lives are annually sacrificed, ... it is expedient that free medical and surgical assistance be given to the labouring population whose wages do not exceed a certain amount, to be determined by the Guardians.'

The most positive and comprehensive scheme for the reform of the Poor Law medical services during the whole of this period, was that outlined by Dr. Wallis of Bristol.[2] He had been a Medical Officer in that town for thirty-six years and had also been employed at the infirmary for twenty-six years, but he was not a Union doctor and therefore spoke without bias. It was as an 'advocate of the working-classes' that he had drawn up his plan. The resort of the poor to druggists, he said, had received such public notoriety that it left no doubt of its widespreadness, and the druggists themselves confessed to the great extent of illegitimate practice and quackery.[3] If the poor had the power of going to a legal practitioner this would cease, Wallis said, but they would also have to be furnished with free medicines from another source. Many Medical Officers offered to prescribe for the poor without fee, but druggists had no mercy on the sick if they discovered who the prescription came from. Therefore Wallis proposed the institution of free dispensaries. These should be established from the local rates, so that responsibility was not removed from the Boards of Guardians, who were also to find the materials and drugs in the dispensaries. The poor were to be allowed treatment without medical-aid tickets, for it had been seen that

[1] Later knighted; see p. 316, *supra*, for resolutions of 1864.

[2] Given in evidence to Select Committee, 1854, although he had published books and pamphlets on the subject since the early 'forties.

[3] The *Lancet* at this time printed letters on deaths which had occurred through the practice of quackery. See for example *Lancet*, 1855, i, p. 225.

this practice had led to the swamping of charitable dispensaries and infirmaries by people who could well afford to pay for treatment, and who received it gratuitously because they were friends of, or had influence on, the distributors of the tickets. The abolition of the ticket system would also prevent the inconvenience and delay occasioned by the poor having to walk to the Relieving Officer and then to the Medical Officer. Fit applicants were to be chosen by their income, and Wallis suggested a wage of 10s. a week with additional allowances for the size of families. Medical relief was to be given to all on their own responsibility, but the Relieving Officer was to scrutinize the register of patients daily and all those not entitled to benefit were to be fined by the magistrate. This would act as a deterrent to those who knew their means exceeded the limit set down by the Guardians.

The Medical Officer was to attend at the dispensary at certain times of the day to examine patients and dispense medicines. He was to keep case-books rigidly but all kinds of additional fees were to be forbidden. His salary was to include compensation for all services so that there would be no disputes with the Board of Guardians. Gratuities were to be granted only for midwifery and consultations. Surgery was excluded so that no operations would be performed unnecessarily. All patients requiring operations were to be examined by another doctor unconnected with the Medical Officer. Every woman was to be allowed to be confined in the dispensary, but she was to obtain a ticket from a Guardian, to be produced at an early date to the doctor, so that he would be prepared for a difficult case. All normal deliveries were to be attended by midwives only. They were to be employed by the Guardians, who were to pay and supervise them. Supervision was emphasized because of the allegations frequently made at the time that midwives concealed births to influence settlement.

The dispensaries were not to be connected with the Medical Officer's residence and were to be conveniently situated for the surrounding working classes. A dispensary committee was to be set up of Guardians and ratepayers, who besides attending to management would also listen to complaints from the poor. Wallis was particularly insistent on drugs being supplied by the dispensary and not by the doctor. This would deter a Medical Officer from sending a patient to a hospital or the workhouse, or ordering extra nourishment, because medicines were too expensive for his meagre salary. Wallis confessed that for the sake of cheapness doctors were administering Epsom salt in peppermint water for gastric fever! Therefore if the interests of the country were to be considered it would be advisable to incur a considerable outlay on the provision of free medicines rather than to permit drugs to be supplied by the Medical Officer. Although the initial expense for the dispensary would be high, Wallis pointed out the average cost per patient throughout the kingdom would not be more than sevenpence a case with strict management.

Many Medical Officers, Wallis believed, would give their advice without fee, and therefore the poor would be greatly assisted if they could obtain medicines free at the dispensary. On the other hand some of the working class could afford to pay for medical advice but not medicines, so that if dispensaries supplied the latter, not only would the sick benefit, but also the Guardians would be relieved from providing a doctor. Wallis did not

325

wish to interfere with the Poor Law Board and general pauper relief, therefore his plan did not include the provision of medical 'extras'. For these the poor were to apply separately and distinctly to the Guardians, and by obtaining them they would become paupers in the ordinary way.

The advantages Wallis claimed for his scheme were that there would be first, greater security for the indigent section of the population, and because there would be no intervention between the Medical Officer and the sick any poor person would be able to receive immediate attendance, so that speedy recovery would be fostered. Second, the sick poor would remain independent, although they obtained gratuitous relief. A distinct and clear demarcation was to be effected between medical aid and pauper relief. Third, those just above the class of paupers would be able to receive treatment without becoming destitute, and this was extremely important when 72 per cent of pauperism depended on sickness. If medical relief were provided for this class, they would have more to spend on necessaries, the absence of which often drove them to the parish. Wallis also pointed out the saving to the rates, for free medical relief to the non-pauper would cost one-tenth the amount that food and general relief would cost if families became destitute.

At the Inquiry of 1854 the Rev. Oxenden supported the scheme. Expenditure, he admitted, would be increased tenfold but it would be compensated by the decrease of pauperism. Country practitioners, he said, would dislike the project because it would entail daily travelling over long distances to the dispensaries and also affect their private practices. Oxenden did not believe the disappearance of medical clubs would be of great consequence because a great many members denied themselves necessary things to afford their contributions. Dr. Livett of Somerset, like Dr. Cooper of Suffolk, maintained it would not be possible to establish free dispensaries in areas where populations were scattered. He agreed with Wallis's plan for gratuitous medical advice, but said the rest of the scheme was superfluous, if salaries were augmented. A small room hired for the purpose of dispensing medicines where a Medical Officer could attend at special times to distribute drugs would be sufficient. Charles Kingsley, although he desired to see an increase in medical relief, contended that the system of universal gratuitous medical relief to the working class would be much abused.

The obscurantist attitude of the central authorities to the revolutionary proposal was shown by Wallis himself. In 1848 he had had an interview with Charles Buller (then President of the Poor Law Board) at which he outlined his scheme. Buller, as all the members of the Government with whom Wallis had interviews, admitted the question was a very large one, and alleged the difficulty of entering upon so vast and important a subject, which was a great national problem. Lord John Russell had also given a similar opinion. Lord Palmerston had been equally vague and unwilling to embark upon considering the reform. At the same time, Wallis said, 'my views have never been contravened by any member of the government, or even by the Poor Law Board'. In 1859, Sotheron Estcourt, when President of the Poor Law Board, included in his abortive proposals free medical relief for 'urgent cases of resident or casual poor', but the subject was never really raised again after the inquiry of 1854, and the Select Committees of the 'sixties were silent on the subject of providing free dispensaries or increasing the range of gratuitous medical relief.

Rumsey in 1856 aptly summed up the situation as it had been and as it continued. The labour of the Medical Officer among the poor, he said, was uselessly increased 'by the multiplicity of media through which that aid could be procured'. He gave a typical description of the confusion existing in a large town:

> Take for instance, one of the thickly-inhabited lanes or courts of this city during any prevalent sickness. Some of the families succeed in obtaining orders for the attendance of Union officers; others, with almost equal difficulty, procure recommendations to some of the medical charities, several physicians or surgeons of which may have patients in the same spot, at the same time. A few labourers and artisans belong to sick clubs and are supposed to be attended by the medical contractors of their respective societies. Another portion of the residents receive gratuitous advice from private sources, or otherwise recklessly demand professional services, with the promise of remuneration, seldom if ever fulfilled. A still larger proportion probably more than half the population, frequent druggist's shops; diminishing their chances of recovery, and wasting their scanty resources on improper remedies boldly administered by ignorant and unqualified persons.[1]

Rumsey then offered his own scheme, which went even further than Wallis's and carried the district medical relief system to a logical conclusion. The Boards of Guardians, he suggested, should be relieved of the power of appointing Medical Officers and controlling medical relief, and local bodies should be established for managing the proposed public dispensaries. (He agreed with Wallis's plan.) The cost was to be borne by the Union poor rates and so Guardians were to nominate a proportion of the dispensary committee members. Voluntary subscriptions were to be encouraged by conferring on subscribers the privilege of electing another portion of the committee. Therefore as in County Lunatic Asylums, Rumsey proposed the combination of voluntary contributions with public taxation. The third part of the dispensary committee was to be limited to a number of well-known local people—doctors, lawyers, clergymen, magistrates, and philanthropists. One or two medical assessors were also to be included in the committee, nominated by the profession of a wider area. The dispensary committee was to meet weekly, maintain stocks of medicines and appliances at the institution, supply doctors of remote parishes with drugs, appoint a dispenser and inspect his books, examine registers of patients, employ nurses for the sick, under the direction of the Medical Officer and regulate the financial affairs of the institution. In times of epidemic the dispensary committee would be the ablest authority to provide additional medical assistance if required by the District Medical Officer, and to form supplementary depots open day and night for the immediate supply of medicines. All complaints made to the committee by the poor, were to be recorded and

---

[1] H. W. Rumsey, *Essays on State Medicine*, 1856.

investigated, and opinion solicited from a proposed Superior Sanitary Court and Medical Inspector of the Circuit. Rumsey stressed the need for ridding medical relief of its Poor Law connection and linking it with Public Health services. He wanted to see an 'efficient national establishment for cure and prevention' without degradation or pauperization affecting those who benefited. The institution of free elementary education, public libraries and museums for example, had not diminished the independence or self-reliance among recipients of the benefits, said Rumsey, 'neither then will medical attendance and sanitary advice have such an effect when freed from their pauperizing concomitants and association'. The real cure for the perverted idea and practical evils to which it had led, was to 'connect medical duties among the poorer classes with preventive visitation of districts, . . . to separate drug provision . . . and to place the renovated office under professional supervision, co-operating with highly qualified central and local Councils of Health.'

In 1867 the Metropolitan Poor Act could have introduced far reaching improvements. Although it established dispensaries in London, it did not widen the scope of medical relief to include all the poor. The Act stated that 'Guardians shall provide proper medicines . . . to such of the poor in receipt of relief as require the same'—therefore they had to be paupers. This as Griffin commented, meant that one-third of the sick poor in the Metropolis would be deprived of medical relief at the cost of the rates: 'the line confining medical assistance to paupers only is far too stringent', and in his pamphlet 'Evidence on Poor Law Medical Relief' (1867), he urged the widening of the scope of gratuitous assistance. In the spring of 1869 the *Lancet* wrote that matters were coming to a crisis. 'The intimate relation between sickness and pauperism, has received too many proofs to be any longer ignored. Pauperism and therefore sickness has prodigiously increased. The physical condition of the labourer is degenerating; his children die or become weak and unhealthy cripples, and he himself is too often reduced to impotence by neglected trifles, which drive him to the workhouse sick ward, when by a little timely help he might have been restored to work.'[1]

Ten days after this statement the House of Commons debated the subject.[2] One speaker[3] pointed out that the expenditure on poor relief had increased out of all proportion to the population despite the fact that the capital of the country had increased enormously and the number of members of benefit clubs had more than doubled. He maintained that all good effected by the new Poor Law had ceased by 1844 and from that time there had been a steady increase of pauperism. There were, he continued, half a million sick and aged to whom the system of repression could not be applied, and workhouses had become hospitals without being fitted for the purpose. He recommended the funds of endowed charities should be applied for the relief of this class. In London there were 242 institutions with annual funds of £2,100,000 devoted to the relief of the poor. He suggested these societies and institutions should be rate aided to provide medical and general relief and old age pensions for all the poor. In large towns, this Member of Parliament wished to see the

[1] *Lancet*, 1869, i, p. 612.
[2] *Hansard*, 10 May 1869.
[3] Mr. Corrance.

establishment of the Irish dispensary system. Dr. Lush, the advocate of the Poor Law Medical Officers in Parliament and an experienced parochial doctor himself, spoke of the need for providing the sick poor with adequate treatment. Other members of the Commons, like W. H. Smith, showed their awareness of the intimate connection between medical relief and pauperism, and one said that the figures of the Poor Law Board failed to reveal the truth. George Goschen however maintained that it would be striking at the root of independence if medical relief were to be regarded as a right of the poor.

The Poor Law Medical Officers' Association at this time began to interest itself in the need for altering the medical relief system by widening its scope and increasing its expenditure. As Joseph Rogers, the President reiterated, a more liberal administration of poor relief meant true economy to the rate-payers, for if the sickness of the poor were curtailed and if the mortality among breadwinners were diminished, the ultimate result would be an economy of expenditure and outdoor relief. He led the Medical Officers in their demand for the adoption of the Irish system in England. Wallis had taken much of his scheme from this, such as the free dispensaries open to all the poor, dispensary committees, free medicines, and no provision of medical comforts. Early in 1870 Rogers drew attention to the fact that the alarming increase in pauperism in England had no parallel in Ireland. He had in the two previous years been in Ireland several times to study the system and obtain complete insight into the way the medical system operated there. He brought back with him such papers and documents as enabled him to popularize the subject in England.[1] He revealed that one-sixth of the total expenditure on the poor in Ireland was for medical relief, whereas in England it was one-twenty-seventh. A comparison between mortality in the two countries showed similar divergency, and Rogers pointed out that if the rate in England were the same as in Ireland there would be an annual saving of 120,000 lives.[2] W. H. Smith, on the instigation of Rogers obtained Parliamentary Returns in 1870 on mortality rates in England, Scotland, and Ireland. These showed the vital superiority of Ireland.

General Rate of Mortality	Zymotic Mortality
England 1 in 43	England 1 in 190
Scotland 1 in 44	Scotland 1 in 194
Ireland 1 in 60	Ireland 1 in 308.

Yet the cost of pauperism per head was 6s. 11½d. in England, 5s. 7½d. in Scotland, and 2s. 11¾d. in Ireland. Rogers credited the advantage of Ireland to the operation of the dispensary system, and concluded his analysis by again urging the adoption of a similar scheme in this country as being beneficial to the poor and economical to the public.

[1] J. Rogers, *Reminiscences of a Workhouse Doctor*, 1889. Rogers also spent much time in examining records and statistics of the Poor Law Board.
[2] Quarterly meeting of the Poor Law Medical Officers' Association, January 1870. Reported in *Lancet*, 1870, i, p. 173.

Since the passing of the Medical Relief Charities (Ireland) Act[1] in 1851, any sick poor person not necessarily a pauper had the right in Ireland to free medical advice and medicine, and such attendance was not deemed poor relief. Outdoor medical relief was not administered by the Guardians but by Dispensary Committees consisting of Guardians and ratepayers of the several dispensary districts into which a Union was divided. Members of the Committee, Relieving Officers, and wardens, were each authorized to issue tickets without restriction as to numbers, and the bearers were entitled to receive treatment either at their homes or at the dispensary. There were 720 dispensary districts in Ireland with an average population of 10,000, and 776 Medical Officers attended at the 968 institutions.[2] Medical Officers also acted ex-officio as the Medical Officers of Health under the sanitary authorities. The Committee of management appointed the doctors and there were five medical inspectors. Guardians supplied all the medicines, which were provided at the dispensaries, but no extra medical comforts were furnished. The dietaries which were given to the poor in hospitals and workhouse infirmaries were however much larger than in England.[3] The salaries of Medical Officers averaged £73 a year in the 'fifties and drugs cost Guardians about £30 a year per dispensary. No additional fees were paid to the doctors and all operations were performed in a hospital or in the infirmary. There was also a fever hospital in every town to which all fever cases had to be sent, so that this relief was effective, and coupled with a more liberal offer of medical relief, was probably an important factor in checking the spread of epidemic diseases. The elimination of smallpox in Ireland was mainly due to the efficiency and zeal of the Poor Law Medical Officer—who was also the Registrar and could keep a check on vaccination—and the good organization of the dispensary committee. The social position of the Medical Officer was much superior in Ireland than in England, and this with the higher average remuneration had salutary economic results. Salaries were still regarded as inadequate however, for in the 'sixties an agitation began not only for superannuation (which was introduced in 1869—a year before England) but also for a Poor Law Medical Officers' Widows' Fund. By this time there were 781 dispensary doctors with an average salary of £86, but Dr. Phelan, originator of the new proposal gave instances of the hardship caused to widows who were left unprovided for, as the Royal Medical Benevolent Fund was completely inadequate to meet even a small proportion of the cases.[4]

The *Lancet* had frequent references to the Irish system and its superiority and supported the English Poor Law Medical Officers who advocated the introduction of the scheme here. The doctors' association believed it was impossible for Goschen to refuse serious consideration of the powerful arguments which were being pressed on him for complete reform in organization and remuneration in the English Poor Law medical service. In 1862 Inspector Cane had maintained that it would be impracticable to introduce the Irish system unless

[1] 14 and 15 Vic. c. 68.
[2] Rumsey in evidence to Select Committee, 1854.
[3] Select Committee on Dublin Hospitals, 1854.
[4] The Indian Medical Service had such a provision—*Lancet*, 1864, i, pp. 141-42.

there were great restrictions and modifications in the method of bestowing general relief in England! He had also pointed out that Guardians would raise very serious objections. Five years later however the Poor Law Board had sent Inspector Lambert to investigate into the working of the Irish system. On his return he explained not only the nature and accommodation which buildings intended for dispensaries were capable of affording and the general arrangements adopted in order to ensure efficient management and supervision, but also the great advantage of the Irish system. The sick poor, he said, were offered facilities for treatment at fixed hours at a convenient distance from their homes, and were assured of a sufficient supply of all necessary medicines and appliances. Vaccination was carried out at well-known places where a Medical Officer had to attend at stated hours. Records of medical treatment of every case were preserved and these furnished a test of both the skill and attention of the doctor. The supply of drugs prevented a conflict between interest and duty which might arise in the mind of the Medical Officer when he was required to provide them out of his salary. Finally, the Irish system offered an organization which was always ready and capable of expansion to meet any outbreak of epidemic disease promptly, whilst it was at the same time calculated to prevent disease becoming epidemic, by early treatment and by procuring the adoption of precautionary measures in any threatened locality. This was especially realized in Ireland regarding cholera.

The Poor Law Board republished this account in their Twentieth Annual Report but they omitted to add Lambert's conclusion:—the dispensary system was admirable for larger and densely populated communities in England, although the abuse of obtaining tickets which was widespread in Ireland would have to be removed. In 1870 the Poor Law Board issued their own account of the Irish dispensary system giving their opinions why it would not be practicable to introduce it here. Comparing the two countries, the Board said the cases were not parallel. In Ireland, the public dispensaries were supported partly by subscription and partly from rates. The existing system was also founded on established custom whereby not only the destitute, but people considerably above this class were enabled to obtain medical relief gratuitously. Therefore the statistics of medical poor relief in the two countries could not be fairly contrasted without bearing in mind that the dispensary system in Ireland embraced a larger class, which in England did not receive gratuitous medical relief at the expense of the rates. In 1867–68 over three-quarters of a million dispensary tickets were issued, whilst 340,000 paupers were relieved by the Guardians. Of this number only 50,000 received outdoor relief. This showed that the overwhelming majority of dispensary patients were not in receipt of real poor relief at all. In England on the other hand, the Poor Law Board said, instances were comparatively few where the sick were given medical relief only. A far greater proportion of actual paupers in Ireland were indoor patients, as they exceeded outdoor patients by two-thirds, whilst in England the proportion of indoor sick was only one-fifth of the whole. In this country the total number of outdoor poor was nearly fifteen times as great as the number of indoor sick, whilst in Ireland the numbers were almost equal. A comparison between the total number of sick admitted into workhouses in Ireland and of the outdoor poor of all classes during

1868 furnished an even more striking result, for there were 112,000 in the former category and only 50,000 in the latter. Therefore in connection with the general administering of relief a much greater proportion of sick paupers went into the workhouse infirmaries in Ireland, with its dispensary system, than in England, without it. Probably this was accounted for by the realization of the necessity of removing the sick from their wretched homes, where there was no chance of recovery.

The Poor Law Board did not discuss how far it was advisable from the social or public health point of view to extend gratuitous medical relief in England beyond the actual pauper class, or the merits of not pauperizing the recipients of such assistance. They pointed out the difficulties of introducing such a scheme.—The additional charge on the public would have to be seriously considered, they said, and how far the system would be compatible with existing arrangements under which medical practice was conducted in this country. Further, to what extent would it have a pauperizing tendency by diminishing self-reliance and competing with existing self-supporting organizations? Irish statistics, they believed, proved that the additional burden on ratepayers would be considerable and a very small proportion of the cost of medical attention was actually for paupers. The introduction of the scheme here would result in a transfer of many private patients to a public officer which would materially affect the proportion of cases between public and private practitioners. In Ireland the dispensary system owed its origin chiefly to the paucity of doctors in rural districts where populations were too sparse and too poor to afford remunerative practice to a general practitioner. In England, however, the Poor Law Board maintained that the medical wants of the people were supplied by a doctor at a charge adapted to the circumstances of all but the very poor. Three-eighths of the doctors in Ireland were dispensary or workhouse Medical Officers, and there was one doctor to every 2,500 of the population, whilst in London, the Poor Law Board's figures showed there was one to every 1,000 (an unjust comparison). The difference between medical practice in the two countries was, it was maintained, not occasioned by Poor Law regulations, but depended on social causes which were not common to them both. There were also few Benefit or Friendly societies in Ireland, whereas in England a considerable portion of the working class were members of such organizations, who would have to choose between contributing to the additional taxation required for the establishing of a system of public medicine, whilst still retaining their separate associations, or, more probably, of abandoning them and resorting to the public Medical Officers.[1]

The Report of the Poor Law Board was concluded with what was perhaps the most startling statement the central authorities ever made between 1834 and 1871. It revealed that a tremendous change had taken place in their views—just at the time when their term of office was almost over. After ending the discussion of the differences between England and Ireland and the difficulty of adopting the new system here, Goschen wrote:

At the same time, the economical and social advantages of free medicine to the poorer classes

[1] From Twenty-second Annual Report, 1869–70, from which figures were also abstracted.

generally, as distinguished from actual paupers, and perfect accessibility to medical advice at all times under a thorough organization, may be considered as so important in themselves, as to render it necessary to weigh with the greatest care all the reasons which may be adduced in their favour.

The Poor Law Board therefore relinquished office with an admirable sentiment, but in their last year did nothing further towards examining their own criterion. The only part of the Irish system which they actually put into effect, besides having copied in a modified version the dispensary for pauper relief in London, was to issue a new form of medical relief book in 1870 modelled on that of the Irish Poor Law Commissioners.

Public provision for the medical attendance of the outdoor sick poor remained in England restricted and inadequate, and unlike that of any other country in Europe, a branch of the Poor Law.

APPENDIX
Brief survey of Medical Relief Systems in other European Countries

In Belgium as in other countries no civil disabilities were attached to the receipt of medical relief. The supply of medicines and medical attendance was separated. A competent body of well educated men were appointed by law to superintend the administration of medical relief. There was no impediment to the direct application to the Medical Officer—there was no Relieving Officer. The office of Medical Officer was considered particularly honourable so that doctors were content with salaries lower than those of general practitioners, although they were higher than those of English Poor Law Medical Officers. This opinion was different from that in England where there was a general feeling of degradation both on the part of the profession and the community.

In France Medical Officers did not provide drugs, which were supplied at a certain regulated cost at the pharmaciens' shops. From the time Louis Napoleon assumed the throne Paris was divided into medical districts, and since the cholera epidemic Medical Officers were required to make house to house visits for sanitary purposes. Medical relief was chiefly 'sanitary', there was little other in the greater part of France.

In Italy each province established a council to superintend medical and sanitary affairs which met three times a year. Each district had a physician and surgeon for the poor. The Roman States were divided into 800 Communes, each with a doctor appointed annually. *All* inhabitants when ill had a claim to gratuitous relief, although the rich did not avail themselves of it. In France, Italy, Germany, and Austria the public Medical Officers were also the Sanitary Officers, although in Italy little was accomplished in sanitary engineering.

In Germany Medical Officers were appointed everywhere for attending paupers and those too poor to afford medical advice. Here again medical attendance and the supply of drugs were divided. Districts were united under a superintendent who inspected the medical service and the 'sanitary' condition of schools, hospitals, prisons, public baths, vaccination stations, and other public

23

institutions, as well as the apothecaries' shops. The District Officers made post-mortem examinations for courts, reported on medical topography, meteorology, agricultural statistics, diseases of animals, epidemics and the cause of disease generally, and on all matters injurious to public health. They also attended to the registration and organization of the profession. Above these superior provincial physicians was a director of a Provincial Council, who stood in communication with the Central Supreme Council. This was the highest court of legal medicine and public health, and immediately under the Minister of the Interior. Salaries of public doctors were fixed by the Medical Councils of districts and provinces and had to receive government approval. In Prussia the Medical Officer was paid directly by the government. Medicines were supplied by apothecaries who had to pass a very stiff qualifying examination and who were far superior to the English druggists.

Austria had almost the same system, save that the doctors were paid from a Poor Fund raised by taxation and voluntary subscription combined.

CHAPTER 12

The Poor Law Medical Officers, 1847—71

THE difficult formative years of the new Poor Law had seen the inception of a special and distinct branch within the medical profession—the Poor Law Medical Officers. In the next twenty years they developed into a compact and influential body, with articulate organizations of their own, and they began to take their place, important and indispensable, in the irrepressible movement towards a Welfare State. Their demands over the past dozen years had not all been complied with, and expressions of discontent, by individuals or by organized associations, about the anomalies concerning their own position or about the Poor Law medical system in general, continued unabated. They were to face a similar apathy or obscurantist opposition in this period of consolidation, but most of their ideas gradually seeped into the Poor Law administration and were introduced piecemeal, without acknowledgement to their sponsors. Therefore, by the 'seventies, demands which had been made decades previously, were to a great extent satisfied, but as the reforms came tardily and as they were not introduced when they would have shown enlightened prescience on the part of the administrators, they came in answer to existing demand and so were often too late to avoid the emergency which made their introduction imperative.

By their two important Orders, the Medical Order of 1842 and the General Consolidated Order of 1847 the Poor Law Commissioners had attempted to establish greater uniformity in the administration of relief, and many improvements had taken place. We have seen how they attempted to abolish the system of appointment by tender, and how they tried to obtain better qualified doctors and make their position permanent. By the reduction in the area of a medical district and the size of its population, the work of the Medical Officer was alleviated, and from 1842 he was intended to receive fixed payments for certain operations and midwifery. But these reforms were only imperfectly effected, for tender was not actually abolished while Guardians were at liberty arbitrarily to fix the price of medical duties, and reduce it from time to time at their pleasure. Areas were insufficiently limited, or Guardians refused to observe the Orders, as they did respecting Medical Officers' qualifications. The 'fifties and 'sixties, however, saw almost universal adoption of these improvements and the ironing out of the infinite variations in the treatment of the Poor Law doctor.

Much depended on the growing self-consciousness of the medical profession, and on its putting its own house in order first.[1] The belated medical reform, whereby definite standards of qualification became recognized, facilitated the efforts of the Poor Law authorities in laying down rules as to the eligibility of practitioners for office. Prior to 1858, no unified medical profession as such, can be said to have existed. There were physicians, surgeons, and apothecaries of various degrees, who scarcely recognized their affinity. To become a member of the Royal College of Surgeons it was necessary to sever connections with the Royal College of Physicians and vice versa. The Medical Act of that year[2] was a decisive landmark, and ensured the distinction between qualified and unqualified. It was important that degrees and diplomas from Scottish and Irish Universities and medical schools were given equal status with the English. The General Medical Council was established and a Medical Register was compiled in which every qualified practitioner might be enrolled. This was not compulsory, but in fact, only those registered were regarded as duly qualified in the eyes of the law and could hold public appointments. The disciplinary powers entrusted to the General Medical Council were a great factor in maintaining and developing the traditions of medical practice.

As soon as the Council was formed, the Poor Law Board deemed it advisable to issue a Circular Letter addressed through the Boards of Guardians to Medical Officers warning them to take prompt steps to qualify themselves for holding their offices. On 10 October 1859, the Board framed an order regarding the qualifications of Medical Officers, requiring that besides being registered, they should possess a legal qualification to practise both medicine and surgery in England and Wales, issuing from some competent legal authority in Great Britain or Ireland.

The Poor Law Board were always anxious to obtain the services of the most efficient doctors, and in 1853 considered that the qualifications of Poor Law doctors 'ought to be such as to ensure for the poor a degree of skill in their medical attendants equal to that which can be commanded by the more fortunate classes of the community'.[3] As a matter of fact the Poor Law Medical Officers were better qualified after 1842 (when double qualifications were required) than the general practitioners who attended the non-destitute, for a single degree was sufficient to establish a practice.

An interesting controversy arose in 1849 over the right of a homeopath to continue in office, and it became the subject of a Parliamentary inquiry. The Poor Law Board stated that they did not know homeopathy[4] was practised at all by any Poor Law doctor, and refused to allow it, because the system had not been recognized by any of the medical authorities in the country. The Honiton Board of Guardians were informed that if the doctor in question was not willing to change his mode of practice, he should be asked to relinquish his office. The Guardians had however received reports that no

[1] Charles Newman, *The Evolution of Medical Education in the Nineteenth Century*, 1957.
[2] 21 and 22 Vic. c. 90.
[3] Mr. Baines, President of the Poor Law Board, *Hansard*, Vol. 129, p. 138, 12 July 1853.
[4] This system of therapeutics was founded by S. C. F. Hahnemann (1755–1843) and was a new idea in medical practice at this time.

person who had been attended by the homeopath had ever complained of his method of treatment, and he had held office for over eight years. His results, the Guardians pointed out, had been equally successful as those of any other Medical Officer of the Union, and that to deprive him of his medical district would be most unjust and cruel both to him and to the paupers. The doctor maintained that he had carried out his duties punctually and to the best of his ability, and that he had searched the regulations of the Poor Law Board to ascertain their right to interfere with the mode of treatment any medical practitioner chose to adopt, or on what principle they constituted themselves as judges on such a subject. On 8 August 1850 the Poor Law Board wrote to the homeopath: '... If a peculiar system of treatment opposed to that practised by the faculty generally, dis-avowed and disapproved by the College of Physicians and unsanctioned by any legally constituted medical body, is systematically and exclusively adopted by a Medical Officer, the Board consider themselves bound to prohibit such a mode of treatment, and to prevent the sick poor from being subjected to it, by removing if necessary, the Medical Officer who continues so to practise in defiance of that prohibition.' They continued that they had already removed the Medical Officer of the Wells Union because he declined to abandon the practice of homeopathy and would repeat the action if the Honiton doctor refused to give an assurance that he would give it up. After some months an individual Guardian again reported the Medical Officer, and the rest of the Board for retaining him despite the Poor Law Board's decision. The poor themselves memorialized the Guardians, stating that they were satisfied with their treatment, and the Guardians themselves voted by great majority in favour of the doctor. The Medical Officer wrote a long and interesting letter to the central authorities on homeopathy and maintained that many deaths were caused daily through wrong medical treatment. He said that 4 to 6 grains of calomel were given by physicians to infants so that 'can we wonder at the frightful number of deaths that take place under seven years of age?'—'If you refer to the bills of infantile mortality and consider the quantity of calomel children take, you would be compelled to declare—not how little medicine has achieved for the prolongation of life, but how much it has done to shorten it.' He continued with a fervent attack on the Royal Colleges and the ignorance which existed in the medical profession. It is interesting to read between the lines and see how backward and undeveloped medical science was. He appended an analytical statement of his work over eight years and this provides a source for discovering the diseases to which the poor were most subject and the ages of the patients—see Table 12.1.

The outcome of the controversy was that the homeopath agreed to treat the sick poor in the routine way and conform to the demands of the authorities. He must have needed his pauper practice or he would have resigned without compromising his principles.

Despite the attempted strictness of the Poor Law Board, evidence was given to the Select Committee on Medical Relief of 1854 and reports were made to the central authorities

TABLE 12.1

Analytical Statement of Homeopath, Honiton Union, of work during the years 1842–49. Forwarded to the Poor Law Board, 1850.

Date	Number of Cases	Nature of Disease		Results		Disease of those who died	Age
		Acute	Chronic	Recovered	Died		
1842	134	111	23	130	4	Dropsy of pericardium	88
						Colliquative diarrhoea	80
						Rheumatism of heart	70
						Natural decay	88
1843	140	105	35	134	6	Scirrhus of stomach	69
						Dropsy	80
						Whooping-cough and debility	70
						Dropsy	64
						Paralysis (discharged from Exeter hospital)	25
						Consumption	23
1844	164	129	35	156	8	a) Decay; b) Decay	87;99
						a) Apoplexy; b) Consumption	70;30
						a) Convulsions;	3 wks.;
						b) Measles,	10 mths.
						Whooping-cough and inflamed lungs	2
						Typhus fever	3
1845	114	107	7	109	5	Consumption (2)	27;23
						Bronchitis	74
						Burnt to death	39
						Diseased heart and natural decay	93
1846	176	150	26	172	4	Disease of bladder	66
						Decay (2)	80;84
						Apoplexy	36
1847	178	45	33	172	6	Influenza; Consumption	19;22
						Decay (3)	81; 71;87
						Diseased liver	70

338

Date	Number of Cases	Nature of Disease		Results		Disease of those who died	Age
		Acute	Chronic	Recovered	Died		
1848	376	343	33	363	13	Fracture of neck of thigh-bone	93
						Decay (4)	88;80; 81;85
						Whooping-cough	3
						Paralysis (2)	28;65
						Atrophy	1
						Severe burn	70
						Dropsy	65
						Typhus	20
						Neglected inflammation of lungs	67
1849	428	389	39	423	5	Diseased heart (2)	76;60
						Softening of brain	60
						Consumption	36
						Decay of nature	75
Total	1,710	1,479	231	1,659	51		

in the following years, that inadequately or even unqualified practitioners were still being appointed. This was particularly so in thinly populated areas where very few Medical Officers existed, and to which no doctors could be attracted to accept Poor Law appointments because of the paucity of the remuneration. In 1861 Griffin told the Select Committee on Poor Relief that Medical Officers' assistants were often appointed to a neighbouring district when they only held a single qualification, and therefore he requested that there should be a law stipulating that no doctor should be elected to public service who was an assistant to another man and who was not practising bona fide on his own account. In 1868[1] the Poor Law Board found it necessary to issue a Circular regarding unqualified assistants, because it was widely alleged that the system of doctors employing such men prevailed. The Circular pointed out that by the Consolidated Order of 1847 (Article 199) every Medical Officer was required to visit and attend patients personally and was responsible for their treatment. The delegation of duties to unqualified assistants defeated the objects of the regulation requiring medical and surgical degrees and the Poor Law Board urged Guardians to co-operate in discouraging the practice. Even in the 'seventies it was maintained that there were hundreds of cases in the country in which doctors in large practices and

[1] 2 April 1868.

with high reputations retained Poor Law appointments which were worked principally by the help of assistants, frequently unqualified.

Medical Officers were however requested to name suitably qualified deputies who could act for him should he fall ill or be absent from home. If a doctor failed to nominate a substitute, Boards of Guardians were empowered to appoint a temporary Medical Officer and pay him for his services by separate fee. The Poor Law doctor was frequently slack in attending to this demand, as was shown by a serious instance of neglect in Kensington in 1859, where no deputy had been found to take over urgent cases. The Guardians severely admonished the Medical Officer to name a regular substitute to prevent a recurrence of the scandal.[1] One Union in an advertisement for a District Medical Officer in the *Lancet*, 10 June 1865, mentioned that the successful candidate had to provide one assistant or more for Poor Law duties if he proposed having a private practice as well. The Poor Law Board issued a Circular in 1868 saying that a Medical Officer should, soon after his appointment, name to the Guardians some legally qualified medical practitioner to whom application for medicines or attendance could be made if the Medical Officer should be absent or unable to attend patients for any other reason.[2]

As the Poor Law authorities demanded high qualifications from their doctors, they wished in return to secure for them permanent appointments. The Poor Law Commissioners had already attempted to make this universal, as we have seen. But in several instances, Boards of Guardians refused to comply with the demand, because they maintained they had a stronger check on a Medical Officer's efficiency if they kept the control of his appointment in their own hands. The *Bradford Observer* for example, printed an article in 1851 revealing that the Guardians of the town still elected doctors annually.[3] In the 'fifties one of the Metropolitan Unions, St. George in the East, was also still electing Medical Officers annually and so were Islington and Bethnal Green in 1870.[4] But when a doctor was subject to re-election, he was nearly always reappointed as a matter of course.

Charles Kingsley giving evidence before the Select Committee of 1854 stated that there were 1,600 permanent Medical Officers in England and Wales and 1,500 temporary. He believed a new element was coming into the Poor Law medical service. The profession was exceedingly overstocked, he said, and since the introduction of the payment of extra fees, which made midwifery the most lucrative part of an officer's work, many young men, who were qualified in this subject only, struggled by every means to get into a district and withdraw work from older and established doctors. He maintained that they regarded Union work as a complete loss, but it provided a lever for building a midwifery practice, whilst they remained ignorant of the other fields of medicine. Kingsley had overheard doctors' conversations regarding this, both in his district and in the hospital. Over a

[1] Minutes, Board of Guardians, 1859.
[2] 2 April 1868.
[3] 6 February 1851.
[4] Minutes, St. George in the East, Board of Guardians, and *Lancet*, 1870, i, pp. 592–93 and 1870, i, p. 494.

period of years he had recognized that as more and more young men obtained appointments so the older men became afraid of them and played into the Guardians' hands to retain their positions. Although annual election was suitable in the 'thirties, because the efficiency of Medical Officers left much to be desired, Kingsley held that permanent engagements had become desirable because the education of doctors had greatly improved and it would put an end to the deleterious development of overcompetition by young men.

Several suggestions were put before the Select Committee. A Guardian of Dewsbury, J. Ellison, recommended that appointments should be for fixed periods, and in no case were they to exceed three years, for if legitimate and wholesome control were once withdrawn, neglect of duty would follow. He pointed out that if Members of Parliament were subject to re-election every three years, why should doctors enjoy a privilege from which the former were debarred? Actually, Dewsbury had tried the triennial election system but had reverted back to the annual system, Medical Officers being reappointed if they had performed their duty well. The Guardian stated that the old system had been adopted again because the poor liked a change of doctor. At one time a Medical Officer had held his post for many years and the poor began to refuse to take his medicines. But the effect of employing a temporary doctor was also revealed. Every year candidates canvassed the Guardians for appointments and there was such keen competition especially among the younger men, that the six practitioners of the town were 'at daggers drawn for the vacant appointment'. Robert Weale, a Poor Law Inspector, admitted there were some reasons for annual election such as ensuring a Medical Officer's efficiency, and he also pointed out its disadvantage in that doctors could be intimidated in their ordering of extras or in acting independently of Guardians. But all the members of the medical profession giving evidence to the Select Committee—and there were eight out of a total number of seventeen witnesses[1]—advocated permanent appointment, and so did the Convention of Poor Law Medical Officers. One of the resolutions of the Select Committee therefore recommended that practitioners engaged after 25 March 1855 should continue in office till they died or resigned, became disqualified or were removed by the Poor Law Board.

On 15 February 1855 the latter issued a General Order on the subject of permanency, repeating what had been stipulated in 1842 and 1847 and in sixteen other Orders to individual Unions between 1849 and 1854. Besides confirming their earlier regulations, the Guardians were authorized to appoint temporary Medical Officers in times of emergency such as in cholera epidemics. It was not long before this General Order was found to have left some doubt as to its construction, and it was also said to be inapplicable to some cases. Therefore it was rescinded by the General Order of 5 May 1857. Once again the new Order only confirmed earlier regulations securing permanency of office to duly qualified Medical Officers who resided in their respective districts. Save in exceptional cases, they were appointed temporarily if they fulfilled neither of these conditions, and could only hold office for the time approved by the Poor Law Board. Medical Officers could also be

[1] Eight Medical Officers, one Justice of the Peace, one Town Councillor, one Rates Collector, one Assistant Overseer, one Land Surveyor, one Relieving Officer, and three Clerks to the Guardians.

changed, after the permission of the central authority had been obtained, if the size of the district was altered and the Medical Officer declined to acquiesce in the new arrangements. Guardians could engage non-properly qualified or non-resident practitioners on a permanent basis without re-election if they satisfied the regulations within two months of their appointment. Clauses as to qualification and permanency were recapitulated in the abortive Medical Relief Bill of 1860.

Much evidence however was given to the Select Committees on Poor Relief of 1861–1864 that the Order was not being put into effect universally. Dr. Griffin of the Poor Law Medical Reform Association stated in 1861 that the previous regulations on qualifications and residence were not being observed, and that a great number of Medical Officers could not be permanently appointed for this reason. From a Parliamentary Return of 1857[1] he quoted that 632 medical men were in office who had not double degrees and eight had not stated their qualification; and in 1858, 1859, and 1860, 85 were elected who similarly had not the required qualifications. In the first six months of 1861 twenty doctors were engaged with only one qualification and nine were unregistered. Griffin had brought the subject to the attention of the Poor Law Board but no notice had been taken. He maintained that half-qualified men, who had interrupted their studies, came straight from medical schools to fill a vacancy. In order to check irregular appointments he desired the Poor Law Board to print in their Annual Reports a list of all appointments made contrary to their rules and to state their reasons for confirming these appointments. Many were not allowed however, as was seen from the complaint of the Hampstead Union that the Central Board refused to sanction their application for the appointment of a Medical Officer for a period of six months.[2]

Griffin also pointed out that the Parliamentary Returns of 1857 showed 1,045 Medical Officers, one-third of the whole, to be non-resident in their districts; that 875 of them had patients who lived from six to twenty miles from their surgery; and that 507 of them were permanently appointed. This caused great inconvenience to the Medical Officer, and the poor were not ensured close proximity to medical aid. On the other hand there were 175 non-resident Medical Officers who lived only one mile from their districts and the furthest extremity of which was not over two miles from their house. Griffin himself was in such a position, but his colleague who lived in the Union had patients ten miles away. The latter was permanently appointed and Griffin was not, and this instance brought to light an anomaly which the regulations in many cases had to maintain in the interest of uniformity. The situation arose because Unions were generally situated round a town, where doctors congregated; the towns then formed one medical district with a permanent Medical Officer, and the other practitioners who also lived in it had to attend the surrounding districts. They could not become permanent Poor Law Medical Officers because they did not reside in those areas, although only a road or river might lie between. Griffin therefore

---

[1] Abstract of Accounts 1857–58, xxix, Pt. I.
[2] Evidence, 1861, by Rev. John Ayre, Chairman, Hampstead Board of Guardians.

proposed that the Orders should be altered, and mileage substituted for residence, with the right to claim permanent appointments being confined to those Medical Officers who lived one mile from the nearest patient. Annual appointments should be conferred on those whose district was situated more than six miles from their residence.

Griffin reiterated the fears of practitioners who were only engaged on a temporary basis. He had himself suffered under the system, for the Guardians had tried to dismiss him by altering the district, and only failed because they feared he would make the affair public. He had as Chairman of the Poor Law Medical Reform Association received several letters from which he deduced that Medical Officers were in danger of losing their appointment if they failed to please the Guardians, however faithfully they performed their duties to the poor. To prevent the arbitrary exercise of power by which doctors could be dismissed by the amalgamation of districts, Griffin suggested the Poor Law Board should make it a rule that if areas were redivided the former Medical Officer should be allowed to retain the one nearest his residence.

Medical Associations also stressed the need for the permanent appointment of Poor Law doctors, and the Royal College of Surgeons concurred in their demand. The Association of Metropolitan Poor Law Medical Officers at a meeting held in 1861,[1] stressed the importance of the measure, and the Executive Council of the British Medical Association sent a petition[2] in 1862 on behalf of its 2,100 members, the Poor Law Relief Association and the Metropolitan Poor Law Medical Officers, in which the subject of permanency and double qualification formed one of the clauses. The *Medical Circular* in the same year[3] printed an article on the reform of the medical system which contained a suggestion for triennial appointments—for this it was maintained would rouse competition, talent, and energy, and if the Medical Officer had done his duty well, he need not fear the election. Competition was the only safeguard against the *laissez-faire* system of practice which was engendered in most professions where permanency was the rule. The author failed to recognize the greater advantage of having doctors who had had years of experience in practice amongst the poor, compared with young men direct from hospitals. The *Lancet* however continued to print long articles in favour of permanent appointments. One out-spoken leader condemned the 'insolent tyranny to which gentlemen belonging to a liberal profession had been subjected at the hands of the Guardians', and that this was a 'disgrace to the administration of the country' as every other salaried Union office was permanent.[4]

The problem was almost solved, however, for little more was heard of Guardians retaining the annual system of election for Medical Officers who fulfilled the qualification and residence requirements. The temporary office actually meant permanency until a

[1] 10 May 1861—The Association had 175 members from thirty-eight Unions and Parishes in the Metropolis.
[2] Signed by Sir Charles Hastings, its President, and P. H. Williams, its Secretary.
[3] 21 May 1862, by E. T. Meredith.
[4] *Lancet*, 1855, i, p. 223.

doctor who would satisfy the regulations could be found to accept the salary and the duties. The Select Committeee of 1862 was told by R. B. Cane, Poor Law Inspector and Keeper and Auditor of Poor Law Accounts, that in that year there were 2,841 permanent Medical Officers and only 711 subject to re-election, either because they were non-resident or not qualified or neither, and that the latter existed chiefly in very thinly populated areas where no doctors would settle. Cane reiterated the complaint frequently made by Guardians as to the undue independence of Medical Officers permanently appointed, a system which had proved advantageous to the poor but not to the ratepayers, because many ordered food and wine in profusion. Dr. Fowler, Secretary to the Metropolitan Poor Law Medical Officers' Association, restated Griffin's case that permanency depending on residence was an anomaly with no advantage, for it did not ensure proximity to patients, and the requirements only gave Guardians the power of recommending the dismissal of Medical Officers who had incurred their displeasure.

Various alternative suggestions were made by other witnesses in 1862 as to the length of tenure of office. Poor Law Inspector A. Doyle maintained it would be a great improvement if Guardians had control over medical appointments by making them renewable every three years. As a case in point he quoted the instance of the Medical Officer of Macclesfield who had never given any trouble until his office became permanent, since when, Doyle had had to investigate three or four complaints against him for overcharging. In 1861 he had submitted a bill for £180 for extra fees. In his experience Guardians had always been liberal in sanctioning fair expenditure by the Poor Law Medical Officers, therefore he saw no reason why they should not be more closely controlled by them. The Guardians of Macclesfield themselves had sent a petition to the Poor Law Board regarding increased control, for they found it difficult to make out a case to the central authorities recommending a Medical Officer's dismissal. Because doctors were engaged on a permanent basis, they could only be dismissed for inefficiency—and appeals on this account received ratification only with great difficulty, save for flagrant neglect. Therefore many Boards of Guardians desired their doctors should be entirely subject to dismissal by themselves. The Chairman of the Chelsea Guardians wanted this power and wished to revert back to the annual election system. Chelsea had succeeded in having an incompetent District School Medical Officer dismissed, but the Chairman objected to having to appeal to the Poor Law Board first.[1] The Clerk of the Camberwell Union also said in 1862, that one of their doctors was frequently extremely rude to the Board of Guardians, yet he could only be removed if a case of inefficiency were brought against him.[2] But for the central authority to have delegated this power would have had a deleterious effect, because the Guardians were inevitably bound up with local interests and party feeling, so that doctors would have been placed at a serious disadvantage. This was illustrated by two letters to Dr. Lord, Secretary to the Convention of Poor Law Medical Officers.[3] In Warwick, it was

[1] T. H. Walker, evidence to Select Committee, 1862.
[2] Irvine, evidence to Select Committee, 1862.
[3] 11 March 1849.

stated, permanent appointment was opposed by the bulk of farmer Guardians in direct opposition to the more intelligent members of the Board, who showed interest and ability in conducting the business of the Union, and who were solicitous for the fair treatment of Medical Officers. In Surrey the Guardians were overpowered and outvoted by a large number of farmers, who flocked to special meetings and secretly planned who should be the next Medical Officer. A letter from Wiltshire in 1854 suggested to Lord that appointments should be taken out of the local authority's hands for similar reasons. Therefore in direct opposition to the Guardians' demands, many Medical Officers, especially those in the Metropolis, desired that their responsibility should be solely to the Poor Law Board and that they should not be liable to suspension or dismissal except at their command. Further, the central authority should be an independent and uninfluenced body and all complaints of neglect or malpractice should go straight to them.[1] The Lancet which generally reported kindly on the Poor Law Board also maintained that the Boards of Guardians should never be given absolute power of dismissal. In an article published on 1 January 1867, the journal recognized the shortcomings of the central authority but maintained that it always treated Poor Law Medical Officers in a 'truly equitable spirit'. As a court of appeal from the decisions of the Board of Guardians, it had frequently thrown a shield over a doctor who had been unjustly suspended and 'we know of no instance in which it had condoned any flagrant offence'.

The removal of local control over Medical Officers had been suggested earlier, in 1854, by M. B. Garrett, a general practitioner in St. George in the East. He had been a Poor Law doctor for seventeen years and had had constant clashes with his Guardians and with the Relieving Officer who tore up his orders for 'necessaries'. He had lost his post through being too independent for he had a large private practice. This freedom of action he maintained was essential, if the poor were to receive adequate treatment. Ceely had earlier recommended that ratepayers should nominate Medical Officers who should work in conjunction with his proposed local Boards of Health.

Two suggestions were very current in this period. The first, generally advocated by the medical profession, was that all the doctors of an area should be employed by the Guardians. In one Union in Norfolk there were six practitioners, and all had been engaged on Poor Law service since 1839 and all were permanent.[2] One doctor suggested Guardians should appoint all qualified practitioners of a Union as Poor Law Medical Officers and that the poor should be allowed to choose whom they wished from the list. This would involve payment 'per case', but it would probably result in the underpaid doctor receiving higher remuneration and the poor obtaining better treatment, as competition would be engendered.[3] A magistrate from Hampshire proposed a similar scheme, the poor being given the option of going to any practitioner in the Union with their tickets and the salary being divided

[1] Dr. Edward Moore, Medical Officer of Bethnal Green.
[2] Evidence to the Select Committee, 1854, by the Rev. Howman, one of the Guardians of Downham, Norfolk.
[3] Dr. J. Gilbert, Banbury Union, evidence to Select Committee, 1854.

between the doctors according to the number of tickets each held. This had had to be adopted in his particular Union as there were only three practitioners, one of whom refused to associate himself with the destitution authorities because of the salary. As the area could not be subdivided, the two remaining doctors attended the whole Union for salaries of £75 and £100 each, with £8 for extras, paid according to the number of patients seen per week.[1] Dr. Griffin on behalf of the Poor Law Medical Relief Association recommended in 1854 that every year, Boards of Guardians should invite all duly qualified men in one district willing to undertake medical relief for the poor on stated terms to forward their names, and if they were approved by the Board as to qualification and character, they should be appointed as Medical Officers to the whole Union, the poor being given the privilege of sending to any practitioner within a certain limit of distance. He also advocated payment 'per case' to increase competition and efficiency. Six years later he proposed a law for the benefit of the poor, whereby in all Unions which already had dispensaries it should not be legal for Guardians to compel the sick living over six miles from the institutions to visit the doctor there or send such a distance for medicine if a registered Medical Officer lived nearer who was willing to attend them on regulation terms. Dr. Garrett suggested all practitioners should take Poor Law office for a period of five or seven years. They might be engaged in alphabetical order or according to seniority, but all should take their turn in performing their duty to the destitute sick. Dr. Fowler of the Metropolitan Poor Law Medical Officers' Committee desired that the poor should be able to employ any doctor and go to him before they became pauperized.

The other proposal current at this time was that Medical Officers should be given full-time duties. A few Unions had already adopted this sytem. In a letter to the Poor Law Commissioners in 1843[2] the Nottingham Guardians had suggested that in towns where doctors had a large number of sick under their care, the Guardians should have their entire services, and in order to ensure regularity of system as well as uniformity and co-operation in practice, Unions should not be divided into medical districts. Medical Officers whose whole time and ability were at the disposal of the Union gained advantage in experience of work among the poor, and the latter were always sure of immediate attention. Nottingham, like Liverpool, had two resident surgeons, under the direction of an Honorary Board, and they supervised the nursing and the entire care of the sick. Birmingham also employed one full-time resident doctor, and in 1851 Manchester had appointed two whole-time Medical Officers, paid by fixed inclusive salary instead of fees 'per case'. The Guardians stated their reason for the introduction of the system as being in the interests of 'economy and more attention'.[3]

Inspector Cane agreed in his evidence to the Select Committee of 1854, that in densely populated areas Medical Officers should not have private practices. The Rev. E. J. Howman, Chairman of a Norfolk Union, proposed a scheme which was in operation in

[1] G. Taylor, Alresford Union, evidence to Select Committee, 1854.
[2] 17 February 1843: Poor Law Commissioners' correspondence.
[3] Minutes, Board of Guardians, 13 November 1851.

some districts and which had years previously received Charles Buller's sanction. This was to establish a Medical Staff to be engaged solely in pauper practice. As an illustration he outlined a plan for his own Union which was twenty miles in diameter, had a population of 21,000, and a workhouse situated centrally. Here would be required one surgeon at £180 and one assistant at £120, the Guardians would supply drugs costing about £100, forage for horses £75, and board for the surgeon and his assistant £100. The total expense would amount to £575 whereas the average expenditure of the Union over the last eight years had amounted to £657 and in the last year £766. A saving would therefore be achieved and vested interests would not be touched in any way. As a general scheme he recommended a chief surgeon should be engaged with a sufficient number of assistants, who should travel from one district to another, attending at a different one every day. Unions should find drugs and residence and maintenance for the medical staff. The doctors should take pupils, which might form a very fine school, and these should be allowed to attend the poor. This, as Howman pointed out, was already being done—'a great many things are done that are not allowed'—but in future pupils engaged in Poor Law work should be supervised by their principals. Further, the Guardians should not choose the medical staff, but they should be appointed by the Home Office, which could exercise a better control. No man should be selected until he had undergone an examination before a Medical Board, as was required of military and naval medical men. As the doctors under this arrangement would be well qualified, all discretion regarding medical relief should be left to the medical staff, although supreme supervision for cases of negligence would be left with the Board of Guardians and the Poor Law Board—an anticlimax!

Griffin in 1862 was also in favour of debarring Poor Law Medical Officers from private practice, but in 1866 Dr. E. Smith, Medical Officer to the Poor Law Board, stated the case against practitioners being solely employed by the destitution authorities. If they were engaged full-time, he maintained, it would generally be young and inexperienced men who held office, and they would resign as soon as the way was clear for them to enter private practice. Actually, the majority of Poor Law Medical Officers were not young, despite arguments to the contrary. As Sir Benjamin Brodie, the famous surgeon, pointed out, young men had more time and a stronger desire to advance their interests, and would therefore be more valuable Medical Officers than older men, largely established in private practice already. Smith believed the disadvantages of full-time Poor Law medical duties lay in the fact that the doctor would lose the incentive of ambition and remain content with his work. He would withdraw his association with the profession, read little, become fixed in his ideas, and soon lag behind. Also when a doctor had been engaged solely in Poor Law duties he would become unfitted for private practice. His means of livelihood would be at the mercy of the Guardians and so he would become more and more submissive to their views. Therefore he might hesitate to discharge some of his functions with proper independence, such as the ordering of 'extras', and the removal of obstreperous lunatics. On the other hand it might be possible for a prudent man to gain the esteem of his Guardians and thereby increase his influence. Smith thought this very unlikely, but did not entirely condemn the idea, because many Medical Officers could not succeed in private practice but were 'admirably fitted to discharge the duties of a public appointment'. If they were permanently employed, Smith concluded, it would be more economical to live in the workhouse, where the Guardians could provide accommodation at much less cost. But where the system already appertained, the institution frequently had no accommodation, as at Mile End for example, where the Medical Officer was also married and lived in his own home.[1]

The *Lancet* in 1870 produced a long leading article opposing the appointment of a special Poor Law medical staff.[2] It was replying to a suggestion, which had appeared in the *Pall Mall Gazette*, that full-time destitution doctors should be instituted to prevent Medical Officers from subordinating the welfare of the sick poor to other considerations. The *Lancet* believed the scheme quite impracticable, particularly in rural areas, where Unions could scarcely remunerate the doctors, a difficulty which would be increased if they had to engage one specially for attendance on the poor. Permanent staff entailed an enormous expense, and the condition of service would be such as not to secure the best man, for payment for medical treatment of the poor could never go beyond the verge of very rigid economy. Also there would be no prospect of promotion and the retirement allowance would be insufficient to enable anyone to live on it. The duties, the *Lancet* continued, were too disagreeable to tempt any man to devote his life to them and an interest in professional advancement would be destroyed. Private practice supplied an 'incentive to industry, professional zeal, and reputation . . . the very best guarantee that public duties would be properly performed'. Like Dr. Smith, the writer maintained that the Poor Law Staff would consist either of very young and inexperienced members of the profession, who would only remain long enough in the service to suit their own purposes, or on the other hand, of older practitioners who had failed to secure the confidence of the public whilst in private practice.

Three years earlier an advertisement in the *Pall Mall Gazette*[3] gave an illustration of this. Only one suitable candidate presented himself to the St. Pancras Guardians for the position of workhouse doctor. But he was rejected because he was thirty-five years of age, for the Guardians considered that if he had been clever he would have done better before reaching this age than be forced to take a workhouse appointment! The *Lancet* even deprecated the employment of a special staff for the workhouse :

> The practice of placing several hundred patients under the charge of a single resident Medical Officer is entirely wrong . . . he is the servant neither of the Guardians nor of the Poor Law Board . . . he is subject to no immediate control and is to a large extent beyond the influence of public opinion.

The writer agreed there should be resident surgeons in large hospitals, but such institutions

[1] Dr. E. Smith, *Report on Metropolitan Workhouses*, 1866.
[2] *Lancet*, 1870, i, p. 592.
[3] January 1867.

should be visited by doctors with experience, whose social position would secure or enforce the efficient treatment of the poor. In conclusion it was maintained that there was already too great a division in the public services and too wide a separation of the public medical department from civil practice:

> All would be benefited by consolidation and freer interchange, and we should welcome proposals which would tempt earlier retirement from naval and military services in order that Poor Law, criminal, police, and civil practice might reap some of the many advantages those services secure, but which cannot be obtained in civil life.

Whole time employment by the Poor Law authorities was not introduced for District Medical Officers but by the end of the 'sixties became more general for those engaged in workhouse duties. This was particularly so in small institutions in the Metropolis where the Medical Officer was both resident and engaged full-time. It was infrequent here in the larger workhouses, and where accommodation was provided it was generally not fitting for professional men.[1] In Marylebone, for example, two junior Medical Officers begged the Guardians in 1853 to allow them to have quarters outside the workhouse as their sleeping rooms were 'dangerous to health'. The senior surgeon stated that the rooms were so ill-ventilated that the doors had had to be bored to let in the air! The subject was referred to a committee, and it was suggested that paupers should be placed in the rooms if they were vacated by the doctors. To this the latter retorted that if the rooms were not fit for them, they were not fit for the paupers either![2] But in the country it was only in the large workhouses with many patients that Medical Officers were resident, so in consequence the system of attendance was invariably that of visits by a medical practitioner at stated periods.

With the increase in the number of cases requiring medical relief, and with the workhouse assuming more and more the nature of a hospital, not only were separate workhouse Medical Officers engaged, but they were also generally solely employed there. The dividing of the functions of Poor Law doctors into District Medical Officers and Workhouse Medical Officers was one of the most pronounced developments of this period. It was an inevitable and necessary step, although Cane pointed out that to divide their spheres of duty might lead to different treatment for a single patient with evil consequences. In the 'sixties workhouses generally employed one Medical Officer, in the Metropolis generally two. Sometimes they were allowed private practice, and often district pauper practice as well, but this became less common. Parliamentary Returns of 1857 gave 130 doctors as being employed for institutional duties only, 582 in workhouses conjointly with a district, and 2,695 districts were unattached to workhouses.

Smith in his Report on Metropolitan Workhouses stated it was essential for workhouse Medical Officers to live very near, if not in the establishment, and they should not be so much engaged in other duties as to render them unable to answer a call to the institution

---

[1] Dr. E. Smith, *Report on Metropolitan Workhouses*, 1866.
[2] *Lancet*, 1853, i, p. 419.

speedily. He therefore concluded that a large private practice should debar a doctor from being engaged for the workhouse. Further, he maintained that Medical Officers should attend all institution cases personally, and that an assistant should not be employed, for the poor should have only one person treating them to ensure that responsibility was not divided and the sick receive the consideration their illness required. If an assistant was engaged because the doctor was indisposed to do the work, or other pecuniary means rendered him independent of the appointment, or if it was because he was largely engaged in private practice, he should resign. If it arose from old age or because the doctor had a partner, the Guardians should appoint the substitute or partner as joint Medical Officer at a separate salary and with absolute responsibility. To engage a doctor to devote his whole time to workhouse duties and at an adequate salary, would probably ensure that no assistant would be employed to whom the care of paupers could be delegated.

As other doctors had spoken of the District Medical Officer so Smith said of the workhouse officer, that great advantages would accrue if their whole time were devoted to the destitute sick. If he was industrious and efficient, he was, or might become general superintendent of the sick-wards and exert direct control over the nursing and feeding of patients. Because of his knowledge and position he could more than any other officer exert an influence and gain minute acquaintance with detail, so that organization would be improved and the efficiency of the institution increased. Although this arrangement would entail the Guardians losing much of their responsibility, they would find an able assistant and adviser in a full-time resident Medical Officer. (On another occasion Smith suggested that when Poor Law doctors had become efficient and enjoyed a high status, they should sit on Boards of Guardians with the right to debate and deliberate, but not to vote!) He advocated that wherever there were 500 inmates, a number which would contain a relatively high proportion of sick, the appointment of a resident full-time Medical Officer was warranted, and it would be wise of Guardians to give him a large amount of liberty regarding the arrangement of sick-wards, the necessity for appliances, furniture, and conveniences, and particularly of the nursing system. Such an officer would be of little value if he were fettered by details and subject in every move to the Guardians.

But Smith was merely outlining again what was already becoming the tendency of the day, for the increase in the number of resident, full-time workhouse Medical Officers was strongly marked.

The trend towards dividing Poor Law doctors into District Medical Officers and workhouse officers also brought about a clearer demarcation in their functions. We have seen in the early period after the passing of the Act how the Poor Law Commissioners laid down elaborate rules, but because one Medical Officer generally attended a district and its institution, there was difficulty in putting them into effect totally or efficiently. Also, throughout the history of Poor Law administration, a long interval always elapsed between the promulgation of an order and its universal adoption. The salutary ideas of the Poor Law Commissioners and their orders, only came to fruition under the Poor Law Board, and it was this that made 1847 a watershed in the development of the Poor Law Medical Service.

As the 'principles of 1834' regarding who was to receive domiciliary aid and who was eligible for outdoor relief became reversed in practice, so heavier work fell on the workhouse doctors. The services required of them were comprehensively explained in the Consolidated Order of 1847. They were to attend all the sick in the institution at an interval arranged by the Guardians or when cases required it, provide medicines, order the diet of patients, and recommend alterations in the diet of a whole class, or any individual among the remainder of the inmates. They were to look generally into the sanitary condition of the establishment and make suggestions to the Guardians on improvements necessary for the health of all paupers. Further, they were requested to make full reports, give health certificates to children who were to be apprenticed and to certify as to the fitness of a pauper for work. They were empowered to order the removal of any dangerous lunatic maintained in the workhouse, and in 1862 Rogers proposed Medical Officers should invariably be required to give certificates on all cases of lunacy under their care. With so much responsibility it was only natural that workhouse doctors should regard their authority in the institution's infirmary as paramount. In 1852 the *Lancet* reported great confusion in the St. Pancras workhouse because the attempt of the master to arrogate to himself jurisdiction over the infirmary was resisted. The subject occupied the Board of Guardians for months, and it was finally settled by a vote of censure being passed on the master. 'The Medical Officers were placed in their proper position which gives them uncontrolled power in the treatment of the sick poor in the house.'[1]

In practice there was much diversity of action among workhouse Medical Officers as to the frequency of their visits, the time devoted to their duties and the nature of their work. It is interesting to recall what was required of doctors in the best workhouses to illustrate the high standard that most of the smaller country institutions, and also many of the urban ones, still had to attain. In Liverpool[2] the house surgeon resided on the premises and never left it without acquainting his assistant. He was required to obey every order of the central authorities strictly, and was responsible for the good conduct of the sick-wards and the proper care of all sick throughout the establishment. Sick-wards were visited at 9 a.m. every morning and between 6 and 9 p.m. each evening, and as frequently in the interval as the condition of patients required. He attended every new admission promptly and kept a journal regularly of case histories and plans of proposed treatment, and he also placed a case card over the bed of each patient. In his weekly return he entered the hours of the day at which each patient had been visited, and also prepared statistical returns on the workhouse. Once a week he held a parade in the day-room of all the inmates of the house, children as well as adults, save the bedridden, and carefully examined them to ascertain whether they were free from itch or other eruptive disease, and from ophthalmia, so that the affected might be separated immediately from the healthy portion of the community. He was required to give all information to the master and matron as to the clothes and bedding of those suffering from any infectious or contagious disease so that it might be

[1] Leading article 12 April 1856 referring to January 1852: *Lancet*, 1856, i, pp. 408-9.
[2] Evidence to Select Committee, 1844.

properly cleansed and fumigated. The care of surgical instruments, bandages, and splints belonging to the corporation were his responsibility, and he also had to prepare medicines in the absence of the apothecary. Lastly, he informed the master whether relatives should be admitted to the sick and whether a person was dangerously ill so that he might receive religious rites.

But such efficiency was only usual—and where it was most necessary—in large towns such as Manchester, Birmingham, Nottingham, and some of the extensive Metropolitan areas. Joseph Rogers stated that he often visited the Strand workhouse five times a day. In the country it was general for a Medical Officer to attend sick patients only once or twice a week, and the aged and infirm at much greater intervals. Witnesses to the Select Committee of 1854 therefore recommended that he should be required to visit the workhouse at least three times a week, and that there should never be a lapse of over two days in his attendance. In 1860 the 'Consolidated Orders Respecting Medical Relief' (Article 207) determined that doctors were to make a personal daily attendance at the workhouse or workhouse infirmary. Later in the 'sixties Dr. Smith maintained that it was still necessary for proper regulations to be framed regarding the duties of a workhouse officer, and that he should be required, as were officers of Lunatic Asylums, to attend at least once a day, if not twice, at a convenient hour, and that he should not wait to be called to see a particular case.[1] He should also attend all cases of midwifery and receive a fee equivalent to that paid by the non-pauper poor, at least in workhouses where there was not a properly qualified resident midwife. Smith pointed out that the idea was prevalent that the attention of the Medical Officer was due only to the sick and that this was an argument for congregating them together to facilitate his visits, but in fact, he should regard the whole workhouse as an asylum and should visit every ward and see every inmate more frequently than was usual. Even when a Medical Officer visited the institution several times a week, the time occupied there was too short.[2] This was probably because too much clerical work was required of him—in Shoreditch for example, over twelve hours was spent weekly in keeping books and the usual time was two to six hours. Also, much of his time was occupied in ordering separate diets, and Smith claimed that much of the disagreeable work would be rendered unnecessary if a general dietary was established which suited the wants of the aged and infirm. Rogers instituted this after a struggle in the Strand workhouse.

Smith also desired the Medical Officer to consider as his department all the subjects on which he was particularly capable of expressing his opinion, and which would be of greatest importance in Poor Law medical relief administration. These included not only nursing and diet, but also the serving of food, the classification of inmates, the supply of furniture and clothing, and the cubic space allowed per inmate. He should not fail to advise the Guardians on these matters. The doctor should also inspect the whole workhouse at least once a week in order to correct the defect, which was very general, of the infrequent

[1] Dr. E. Smith, *Report on forty-eight Provincial Workhouses*, 1867.
[2] Dr. E. Smith, *Report on Metropolitan Workhouses*, 1866.

visits of the Visiting Committee. In provincial workhouses, Smith discovered stocks of medical appliances were very deficient and this question was within the direct sphere of the Medical Officer's functions. He also maintained that the doctor was not occupying the position of a sanitary officer which had been indicated by the Consolidated Order of 1847 and which would have proved useful to Guardians as well as being conducive to his own position. Therefore Smith insisted it was not enough for doctors to rush through sick-wards and omit the remainder of the workhouse. They should more directly control sanitary arrangements and see that there was adequate ventilation and warmth, and that baths and lavatories were provided, reporting defects to the Guardians. By attending to these matters, Medical Officers would not only be discharging their duty to the Union, but also to the Poor Law Board, who represented the public (by whom half their salaries were paid through the Grant-in-aid). That it was necessary to reiterate these functions twenty years after most of them had been ordered, showed that either the Medical Officers were negligent or had insufficient time to pay attention to them, or more probably, that Guardians disregarded their advice and intimidated doctors from giving it. Therefore Smith advocated that the Poor Law Board should require a copy of all recommendations made by Medical Officers to Boards of Guardians to be sent to the Inspectors, with a report of the Guardians' action regarding them.

The District Medical Officers discovered that they were no more successful than the workhouse Medical Officers in appealing beyond the Guardians to the Poor Law Board, for the central authorities were intended to be unassuming administrators of the Poor Law and not energetic initiators of new schemes. Experience of twenty to thirty years of Poor Law medical service was bound to bring forward new fields of activity for the District Medical Officer, and point out others where his special training was no longer necessary and where laymen might be employed as efficaciously. But no new duties were officially assigned to him save a tentative proposal that he should be engaged in the Public Health field under the Nuisances Removal Acts. And in 1848 a resolution had been brought before the House of Commons asking that an additional practitioner should be employed for midwifery if an operation on the mother necessarily involved the death of the child. But this had been withdrawn on the assurance of Charles Buller that everything that could be done by instructions from the Commissioners would be done.[1] The Medical Relief Bill of 1860 merely recapitulated the duties of the District Medical Officer, but these duties varied throughout the country, both as to whom he was to attend—whether patients were to be strictly paupers or the poor as well—and what he should provide. Some Medical Officers complained that they were not given sufficient power and discretion and that medical relief was not given in sufficient profusion. But Cane cynically advised the Select Committee of 1862 that this allegation was never made unless it was accompanied by further allegations that payment was altogether inadequate. Some Guardians imposed additional duties on the District Medical Officer, as in Poplar, where they acted like the Relieving

[1] *Hansard*, Vol. 197, 3rd series, 16 March 1848.

Officers and were always present at meetings of the Relief Committee. Their suggestions were invariably adopted as to whether applicants were to be treated in the workhouse, in their own homes, or in the infirmary. In Worcester, the Medical Officers were one of the groups of people supplied with registry tickets to be given to convalescent labourers who wished to avail themselves of the services of a Labour Exchange[1] after they had lost employment through accident or illness.[2]

The duties of the District Medical Officer had also increased since the Vaccination Acts of 1840–41. The further Act of 1867 recapitulated the Order for free, compulsory vaccination of children, the Medical Officer being required to keep a register of all persons vaccinated. Payment, for successful operations only, remained the same at 1s. 6d. if people attended at a station, or 2s. to 3s. if the doctor had to travel any distance. Public Vaccinators, generally the District Medical Officers, were established under the Act, and were to be resident in the newly-formed Vaccination Districts, not necessarily the Union. In 1870 many places, even in the Metropolis, had not appointed a Public Vaccinator. St. George in the East only engaged one in this year, at a fixed salary of £50.

In one field alone was there an alleviation in the duties of the Medical Officer. Not only were nurses becoming more widely employed, but they were also receiving training and salaries, so that duties could be safely delegated to them. They therefore could be of invaluable assistance to the doctor in administering medicines and generally looking after the welfare of the sick. The midwifery service had also improved. Dr. Wallis[3] for example, stated that in his Union one midwife never had occasion to call the Medical Officer, and another only required the doctor's help seventy to eighty times a year. He maintained that only midwives needed to be employed, under the Guardians' control, and that doctors should only be called in difficult cases. This was no doubt the prevailing practice, especially since the introduction of extra fees for the service, but in some Unions, as in Hampstead, the Medical Officer still did all the midwifery in the 'sixties. Lying-in charities and hospitals, particularly in large towns and the Metropolis took some of the work off the hands of the Poor Law doctors.

But apart from the additional duties assigned to the District Medical Officers and the alleviation they obtained from some quarters, the actual amount of their normal general work increased enormously. The ordinary duties varied according to the activity and opinions of the Relieving Officer. In some cases, as Wakley stated in a speech to the House of Commons: 'the Relieving Officer gave an order to anybody who applied and they thus created wholesale pauperism . . . they would not pay the Medical Officer an adequate salary, but compelled him to attend all those for whom he received an order.'[4] Therefore many Medical Officers desired to be free from the control of Guardians because they alone

[1] Labour Exchanges had been established in 1856. *Worcestershire Chronicle*, 24 December 1856 (Webb MSS.).
[2] Board of Guardians' meeting, 22 September 1869 (Webb MSS.).
[3] Dr. Wallis, Clifton Union (Bristol), evidence to Select Committee, 1854. Dr. Wallis was the originator of the scheme for free dispensaries.
[4] *Hansard*, Vol. 97, 3rd series, p. 655.

were able to judge the necessity of cases both as to treatment and its nature, and whether extra food were required.[1] A Guardian of Hampshire agreed, but said control over doctors was necessary so that the Union might order repayment if it was thought that a poor patient could afford his treatment.[2] The petition of the British Medical Association in 1862 maintained that Relieving Officers issued orders indiscriminately, throwing an additional burden on the Medical Officers, and it therefore desired to see the duties of the Relieving Officer more strictly defined, or judgement on applicants left to the District Medical Officer.

It was generally in the large towns that the most flagrant injustices existed. Liverpool was an example of great liberality, and here nine District Medical Officers were appointed, four workhouse doctors and one for the industrial school, for a population of a quarter of a million. All nine District Medical Officers had private practices and averaged 350 pauper patients a week. Although there were so many medical charities they did not afford the Poor Law doctors much relief, because there was an understanding that paupers should not be sent there for treatment save in cases of accident. In Bradford there were only three Medical Officers to attend 2,440 medical cases on an average in a year, excluding midwifery and operations.[3] The Metropolis employed 157 District Medical Officers and workhouse officers who in 1865–66 attended 206,600 patients. In St. Margaret's and St. John's, Westminster, one Medical Officer had over 2,500 pauper cases a year, and St. James's, Westminster, engaged only one doctor, who treated 4,500 workhouse and 2,400 outdoor patients in a year! In Marylebone one of the five Medical Officers had 4,100, and another nearly 4,000 patients, in St. Pancras four of the six District Medical Officers attended nearly 3,000 cases each. Similarly, in Holborn, St. Luke's, Whitechapel, Mile End, St. George the Martyr, and Stepney, an average of 3,000 sick paupers were consigned to each District Medical Officer. Stepney Guardians in the early 'fifties attempted to entrust the medical treatment of the poor to the exclusive care of three Medical Officers unconnected with private practice, thinking this number sufficient if they were engaged full-time. The plan completely miscarried, for one of the doctors very shortly after his appointment applied to the Guardians for assistance as on some days he was obliged to neglect between thirty and forty patients. The subject was discussed by the Board of Guardians several times until at one meeting the Rector said: 'I thought the surgeons treated us badly, but now I feel we treat them shamefully'! On one occasion a District Medical Officer was summoned to attend six cases of midwifery requiring immediate assistance in distant parts of the district in one day. It did not take long for one Medical Officer to resign, and only a single reply was received to the advertisement for a successor, and this candidate withdrew as soon as the duties were fully enumerated. At a Coroner's inquiry in 1868 it was revealed that an Islington Medical Officer attended 200 paupers weekly and often 250.[4]

[1] Dr. Garrett, evidence to Select Committee, 1854.
[2] Wooldridge, evidence to Select Committee, 1854.
[3] *Bradford Observer*, 24 February 1848.
[4] *Lancet*, 1868, i, p. 825; also 1868, i, pp. 351–52.

The numbers of 'patients' and 'cases' are both given as reported; there is no uniformity in the statistics available.

The *Lancet* investigations showed that the single Medical Officer who was appointed to the Bethnal Green workhouse had an average of 600 patients in the institution. This evoked a comment by the journal that in a London hospital there would be fifteen doctors for so many sick.[1] In 1868 a Return was made to Parliament of the number of sick on the books of each District Medical Officer on 7 January and 7 July distinguishing between the number of persons labouring under (1) fever and zymotic diseases, (2) acute diseases, (3) chronic illnesses. It showed that 159 Metropolitan District Medical Officers attended an average of over 100,000 patients in each half year—or 630 each. But the total number was unequally distributed. Some doctors had very little to do whilst others were grossly overworked. In the Clapham Union for example, the ten Medical Officers averaged 2,158 patients per half year or eight each in a week. Whitechapel on the other hand employed only four District Medical Officers to attend an average 7,686 cases in six months or a weekly average of seventy-two new cases; 10,000 patients were actually under treatment at any given time—2,000 fever and zymotic, 3,500 acute and 4,500 chronic, requiring constant care. But the Medical Officers' duties were no less unequally divided regarding the treatment of these classes of patients. On the previous January the Paddington doctors had not a single patient in these categories, and in July only one, whilst in Marylebone on the same days, one doctor had 385 patients on his list—over 100 being zymotic and acute cases. Similar inequality regarding the amount of work existed between doctors of the same Union. In Poplar one Medical Officer had 400 pauper patients and required four assistants; in Lambeth one had 176 patients and another only seven; and in St. Pancras one doctor had 120 patients while a colleague had twelve.

Dr. Griffin in his evidence to the Select Committee of 1862 gave a detailed summary of the duties he performed as Medical Officer of Weymouth, showing that in country districts the situation was little better than in the Metropolis, Table 12.2.

District Medical Officers were absolutely responsible for their cases and were not bound by any regulation as to when, and how often, their patients were to be visited. Therefore, unlike the workhouse doctors, much depended on their own conscience and efficient discretion. Inspector Austin was asked by a member of the Select Committee of 1854 (Palmer) if it would not be practicable and an improvement, if each Medical Officer were to make a circuit through his district in the same way that the Relieving Officer did, and attend in every parish at stated times. Austin replied that this idea was not new,[2] but the difficulty regarding its adoption lay in the fact that diseases were sometimes of such a nature as to require attendance more than once a day. Confinements frequently necessitated several visits, and if the doctor was attending the various parishes at fixed times, he would not be in a position to see other patients when he was needed. Austin's interrogator then suggested the Medical Officer might visit every parish once a week, whether there were any sick there or not, so that anyone might have the opportunity of consulting him. But

[1] *Lancet*, 1867, i, p. 346.
[2] *Bradford Observer*, 24 February 1848, suggested the Medical Officers of the town should work the different districts in rotation.

TABLE 12.2

Summary of Duties performed as Medical Officer of Weymouth: Total for six years 1856-61.—Dr. Griffin in evidence to Select Committee, 1862.

Number of orders	2,216
Half-yearly Return of Patients to Poor Law Board	2,559
Number of weekly entries of patients	12,154
Average duration of illness	5 weeks 3 days
Number of visits to each patient's house	18,439
Average number of visits to patients' homes	8·3
Number of attendances at surgery	2,973
Average number of attendances by patients at surgery	1·3
Average number of times each patient seen	9·6
Number of mixtures given to patients	10,853
Number of bottles of lotion	960
Number of bottles of liniment	298
Number of draughts	87
Number of boxes of pills	1,460
Number of packets of powders	621
Number of boxes of ointment	619
Number of blisters	82
Total supply of medicines	14,980
Average supply of medicines to each patient	6·7
Number of cases of childbirth	16
Amputations	4
Fractures and dislocations	8
Salary including extra midwifery fees	£210, i.e., £35 a year
Average payment per patient	1s. 10d.

the Inspector advised that arrangements had best be left to the Medical Officer, and suggested that no excuse should be provided for allowing him to be absent from his house by a mere mechanical contrivance.

The extent of medical duties and the frequency with which patients were attended, were recorded in the doctors' case books. Complaint regarding Medical Officers was generally one of neglect rather than malpractice, and this could be checked by reference to the books. From them, Guardians could see how often a patient was visited, when medicine was sent, and whether attendance had been at the patient's home or at the surgery. But in many Unions, Medical Officers did not send their books to the Board of Guardians, and Austin suggested in 1854 that it should be the duty of the Poor Law Inspector to see that this was done. If the Medical Officer failed to comply with the demand he should be reported to the Poor Law Board. Dr. Wallis advocated the inspection of case books at irregular and unexpected intervals like the principle followed regarding lunatic asylum officers. He also suggested that treatment should be recorded by doctors, and he tried to get the Guardians of Bristol to adopt this scheme. It was put into operation in one district, but the Medical Officer refused to allow Wallis to inspect it, because he objected to supervision. Wallis believed it was 'too bad to be looked at'. In any case, he pointed out, lay Guardians were not competent judges of whether patients received suitable treatment.

In many Unions no medical books were kept at all. Dr. Lord, Medical Officer of Hampstead, did not believe, in the light of his experience as Secretary of the Convention of Poor Law Medical Officers, that a strict writing of records was generally followed. He confessed he did not keep his own books according to the regulations of the Poor Law Board, and in the workhouse they had never been kept in detail. As he had never been requested by the Guardians to do so, he had not considered the orders of the Poor Law Board as imperative. A sick dietary table was not outlined in his accounts because the Guardians did not require it, and therefore he had not deemed it expedient to spend time on it. The workhouse dietary was written in the margin of each book every Sunday for the master, because he found it gave him less trouble to write it up according to a schedule. No record was made either of the number of visits paid to patients or to the workhouse; this, Lord said, was a part of the vexatious system of management which had passed into disuse in his Union. If he were requested, he would compile these figures, but they were already in the workhouse account book, in which doctors' visits were recorded, and in the House Committee's Visiting Book. Infirm cases scattered over the workhouse could not benefit by the doctor paying them a formal visit and recording their cases. A book was kept at the door of the wards, and whenever the Medical Officer visited his attendance was recorded, but there were many old and infirm paupers that were not seen every time—this was the rule everywhere.

In such cases the Guardians were as much to blame as the Medical Officers, for as Lord affirmed, he would have kept his books if the Guardians had asked him to do so. It was noteworthy that in one of the worst administered Unions in the Metropolis, St. George the Martyr, Southwark, where the minimum relief was afforded, and where workhouse conditions were intolerable, the Guardians regularly reported: 'medical officers' books read and approved'. Save for these few words the Board of Guardians had in twenty years only one other reference to Medical Relief—it asked a Medical Officer to resign because he had moved from his district.[1] In the field of supervising the doctors' book-keeping the Union was at least obeying regulations.

It was found necessary to embody a clause ordering Guardians to examine medical books in the Medical Relief Bill of 1860. But the method of keeping accounts of cases was outlined in the early period, and as we have seen, the information required was insufficient to be of any real use. It was pointed out in a question by a member of the Select Committee of 1854, that it might be advantageous for books to be so arranged that not only disease was recorded, but the method of treatment, and that Guardians should then have a medical

---

[1] Minutes, Board of Guardians, from 1842 to 1860.

inspection to determine whether the treatment was being carried out. The question contained no suggestion that Guardians were unfitted to judge on medical matters and that it would necessitate the appointment of a Medical Supervisor.

An alteration was authorized in the method of medical book-keeping in 1857, but only in the direction of simplification. The Poor Law Board asserted that they regarded the statements recorded as of great importance, but they desired to diminish repetition of entries and to save labour for the Medical Officers. The modified District Relief Book (Form P) therefore had to contain weekly facts of name, age, residence, parish, disease, days when attended, necessaries ordered to be given, existing state or termination of disease, and doctors' observations. It did not increase the value of the medical records, and the Medical Relief Bill of 1860 recommended that not only should an account of the numbers of patients be recorded, but half-yearly calculations should be made of the amount of sickness in each class. These should be published in the Annual Reports of the Poor Law Board, with the number of deaths, and the total figures on diphtheria, cholera, diarrhoea, fever, scarlet fever, measles, whooping cough, and smallpox in each Union. The Poor Law Medical Officer was in a particularly important position to assist the growing demand for statistics by the increasing number of associations interested in Public Health and the progress of scientific knowledge. The 1862 Petition of the British Medical Association signed by Sir Charles Hastings stated that as 1,349,452 sick poor were attended by Poor Law Medical Officers in 1857, it would be of incalculable value for the removal of preventible disease, if a medical register of the diseases of the sick poor were established (as Griffin had suggested), under the superintendence of a proposed Medical Officer attached to the central authority, and by him annually presented to Parliament. The Epidemiological Society urged the Select Committee of 1864 to recommend that Medical Officers should give monthly statistics of all cases attended. The information required appertained to the nature of diseases, age and sex of patients, deaths, and remarks on dwellings, occupations, and food. As no comprehensive statistics of the incidence of disease among the poor existed, this would have been an inestimable duty of the Poor Law Medical Officer. The subject seems to have been ignored, and doctors' book-keeping remained of value only to Guardians, and for a less worthy cause.

The only sphere in which the Union doctor was used for the positive maintenance of health, and not for Poor Law relief purposes only was that he was permitted to order food and 'necessaries' for the sick pauper. In many instances much was achieved for constructive ends by the Medical Officer giving recommendations for 'extras' even if the patient was not in need of actual treatment. Again, this, which was in many cases 'preventive' activity by the doctor, varied from Union to Union, depending sometimes on the Medical Officer but generally on the Guardians. Thomas Wakley, the doctors' battling voice in Parliament, gave an account of the system in a speech in 1848[1] . . .

In many districts, in a great majority of cases, when he [the Medical Officer] visited a

[1] *Hansard*, Vol. 17, 3rd series, 16 March 1848.

destitute person, he found him in a state of disorder arising not from any positive disease, but from want of food. The duty of the Medical Officer then was . . . to order proper nourishment. He gave in such instances order for food and frequently a poor person had to walk twenty miles . . . before that food could be obtained . . . If a Medical Officer was what was called 'liberal' of these orders for nourishment, he speedily lost favour with the Guardians . . . Before a poor person could receive the food he required the order had to be confirmed by the Relieving Officer, or in other words the Relieving Officer stood above the Medical Officer in reference to an order given medically and given too for food.

In 1852 the Paddington Board of Guardians wrote to the central authorities requesting a statement as to when and by what authority a Relieving Officer could refuse the 'orders' of a Medical Officer for the sick. The Poor Law Board forwarded an Official Circular of June 1850 as a reply. This showed that Guardians did not always pay attention to the commands of their superior authority. The communication only reiterated previous orders; a Medical Officer was not empowered to order authoritatively the supply of food or articles of diet to any sick pauper under his care, but might certify to the Relieving Officer what particular necessaries he considered the pauper to require. The Relieving Officer was then to act as he deemed right. If he refused to supply food in the intervals between Guardians' meetings, he did so on his own responsibility and had to be prepared to justify the refusal.[1] In 1857 the minutes of the Board of Guardians showed that the 'orders' of both parish doctors for 'extras' of meat, beer, or wine, were to be immediately attended to, and any question arising as to the propriety of such orders were to be waived until the subsequent meeting of the Board. Again in 1867 the Relieving Officer was ordered to supply promptly all articles of nourishment prescribed by the doctors for the outdoor poor, although in 1864 he was asked to report periodically on any cases of unusual costliness that occurred in outdoor medical relief. Regarding the workhouse, the Medical Officer in 1869 agreed to fall in with any suggestion of the Board on the ordering of beer, wine, and food to certain classes of inmates on his Medical Relief list.

The conflicting evidence which the Select Committee of 1854 heard on the subject illustrates the diversity in the arrangements throughout the country. It was stated that some Boards of Guardians were too liberal in giving orders, and a Hampshire magistrate (W. Taylor) commented that these had doubled in many places over the past few years, although his Guardians, for example, never refused to comply. Inspector Cane also stated he occasionally received complaints that Medical Officers were ordering too expensive diets and comforts. On the other hand, Charles Kingsley said that an insufficient quantity of medical comforts were being provided. From his experience he quoted cases where Guardians selected Medical Officers whom they knew would order the least amount. Therefore others were afraid of making recommendations because they were apprehensive of annoying their employers. He directed attention to the continuous jealousy and irritation which

[1] Minutes, Paddington Board of Guardians.

existed in almost all rural areas, because it was felt that Medical Officers were ordering too many necessaries and were substituting them for medicines. One doctor in his Union was superseded because he was acting too liberally, but he was recalled after three years, only for the quarrelling to start again. Kingsley did not think that Guardians believed extra food to be a real necessity.

Inspector Weale, however, reported that it was a rare occurrence for Guardians to disallow extras ordered by the Medical Officer, although he admitted some doctors were influenced by a desire to oblige their employers. Inspector Austin had not found any disposition on the part of the Board of Guardians to disallow or discourage doctors from ordering meat and wine to convalescents or fever patients. He found that isolated Guardians murmured, but rarely Boards collectively. Odd cases of refusal occurred regarding individuals, but it was nowhere maintained as a principle. He had known two or three cases however, where Guardians reported the Medical Officer to the Poor Law Board for giving orders too liberally. Inspector Cane confirmed the generosity of Guardians, and that Relieving Officers everywhere generally obeyed recommendations implicitly. Dewsbury Guardians, for example, never disallowed extras,[1] and the Relieving Officer of Bristol[2] said he never complained of a doctor's liberality in his ordering of extras. Far more wine and food was ordered in the neighbouring parishes which had much smaller populations, illustrating the lack of uniformity even within a few miles. Dr. Cooper of Suffolk also affirmed that in his Union no complaints were made against him, and Guardians gave all the extras the doctors ordered. A Hampshire Guardian[3] suggested it was desirable for Guardians to supply additional medicine rather than comforts. In his Union necessaries ordered in 1853 had amounted to £270—only £30 less than the total Medical Officers' salaries—yet the Guardians never complained. But he recommended extras should be given on loan, so that expenditure on this account might be recovered. In Barham, Kent, the private medical charity supplied all the extras and were far more liberal than the Guardians would have been, for nearly all the poor were included.

Some Medical Officers had fixed diet schedules which they ordered for various types of patients. At Greenwich a Committee of Inquiry held in 1864 into a case of scandal regarding medical relief, heard in the evidence the amount of extras given by the Medical Officer. The latter—Dr. Moore, who was responsible for a scheme for reform and active in the Medical Officers' Associations—generally ordered wine, beef for tea, milk, and bread. For debility and abscesses caused by malnutrition he ordered 1 gill of milk, 2 eggs, 2 oz. of arrowroot and 1s. 6d. worth of beef for tea daily. For general debility and consumption, he recommended milk, beef for tea, eggs, and arrowroot in varying amounts. He had his own sick club from which he provided some of these necessaries, pending the Guardians concurrence in giving them to the paupers in question. His orders had never been objected to previously, although the remark had occasionally been made that he was too liberal

---

[1] J. Ellison, Guardian, evidence to Select Committee, 1854.
[2] G. Carter, evidence to Select Committee, 1854.
[3] Wooldridge, evidence to Select Committee, 1854.

and that it was impossible to imagine how the patients ate all the food. The Relieving Officer however made it imperative for people for whom the extras were ordered to call for them personally, save under very special circumstances, such as severe illness. But in the 'sixties the Relieving Officer occasionally refused Moore's recommendations, so he suggested that all orders for necessaries should be made imperative on that officer.

Apart from doctors ordering food for invalids, cases were common where meat and wines were ordered as a means of preventing starvation. It was clearly nothing more nor less than an eking out of relief, because the doctors believed the Guardians were not supplying people with adequate food or money to live by. This was especially so regarding the aged, and the increase in expenditure on this account was very large in some areas. A witness in 1854 stated that in his Union in Norfolk expenditure on extra diet had risen from £180 in 1846 to £228 in 1853 and the average over the last eight years was £205 a year.[1] Wages in the district were 10s. a week, and some account had to be taken of the rise in food prices. In one Union a Medical Officer gave a recommendation for 2–3 stones of mutton a week for a list of twenty to twenty-five patients, but he withdrew his request after remonstrance from the Guardians. Generally Guardians uniformly confirmed this Medical Officer's orders, and it seemed as if doctors were reverting to the old system of poor relief. Dr. Garrett of St. George in the East, Middlesex, stated that every morning he gave thirty of the forty patients in his surgery orders for food and extras. The daily average over the year came to twenty-five and they received these because they were destitute or unemployed. He had therefore set himself up in the Relieving Officer's place, and his antagonism with the latter was continuous and eventually caused his dismissal. He was convinced, however, that he had done good to the poor, who were definitely undernourished, and who often came to him when they were not ill but just needed food. This was the system of which it was said in 1873: 'The doctors' mutton and brandy is a fertile origin of permanent pauperism.'

Many Medical Officers persisted in an agitation that their recommendations should carry the weight of definite orders, and indeed they were generally so called. Both the Select Committees of 1854 and 1862 heard demands that notes for extras should be carried out unquestioned. The Medical Bill of 1860 stipulated that Medical Officers should have the power not only to order necessary diets, but also that all meat, wine, and brandy should be kept at the workhouse for their disposal. Dr. Fowler stated that the Guardians of the East London Union treated his recommendations for food and necessaries, such as cod-liver oil, like orders for drugs, and they were therefore imperative. He pointed out that the Association of Metropolitan Poor Law Medical Officers, of which he was Honorary Secretary, advocated that District Medical Officers and workhouse Medical Officers should have the power to order any necessary food or clothing and that it should be the duty of the Relieving Officer to obey. One doctor had suggested to the Select Committee of 1854 that Medical Officers should be empowered to give certificates or orders to tradesmen for relief. He

[1] Rev. E. J. Howman.

had himself taken this step and given orders on publicans in an emergency, paying for them himself although he had not been reimbursed. He demanded in the interest of fairness that Relieving Officers should obey all doctors' recommendations for relief.[1] The Poor Law Medical Relief Association, supported by the British Medical Association and the Metropolitan Poor Law Medical Officers, included in its proposals put to the Select Committee of 1854 the right of doctors to give imperative orders for the supply of any articles of food, and any kind of stimulants that they might consider necessary for their patients. Also, stores and stations for the deposit of such articles should be established from which Medical Officers might order without restriction. But the Select Committee concluded that the distribution of food, wine, and other articles of nutriment, left to the unchecked discretion of the Medical Officer would increase expenditure, and to a serious degree, diminish the extent of control exercised by the Guardians.

There is no doubt, however, that the amount of extras given was very large in most Unions, and the scheme was assuming an important position. In 1868 the Hampstead Board of Guardians, for example, urged the Relieving Officer not to waste any time in providing food ordered by the doctors for the outdoor sick, and any queries were to be settled afterwards at the subsequent Guardians' meeting.[2]

Dr. Smith in his report of 1867 stated that extras were generally the only source of disagreement between Guardians and Medical Officers. He himself had been astonished when visiting Unions throughout the country at the quantity ordered, and therefore he recommended the Poor Law Board should institute an inquiry. If some of the causes of pauperism and sickness had been understood, this suggestion would have been superfluous. In 1854 a Manchester surgeon realized that under an improved system of general relief only a slight percentage of people would require medical comforts. Similarly, if medical relief were given early and generally, before a labourer was pauperized, he believed only 5 per cent of all diseases would require extras to assist in their cure.

One of the evils of allowing Medical Officers to order extra diets was continually pointed out, and this was in the accusation that food was often substituted for medicine. It was asserted that doctors handed over their cases as soon as they could to the Guardians, so that extras were frequently improperly given and in too great quantities. A Guardian stated that medical men ordered necessaries when they really should have provided expensive medicines. He had never heard of cod-liver oil being given, additional diet always took its place, with the result that patients, especially children, suffered because the whole family consumed the food. Dr. Cooper of Suffolk agreed that Medical Officers should not order extra diets in place of expensive medicines, and Rumsey himself admitted that doctors were under the temptation to order comforts instead of drugs. The Rev. Oxenden did not object to Medical Officers granting extra medical relief because he believed a conscientious man would never give it in place of medicine or to save expensive drugs. He regarded the evil as lying in the Medical Officers' attempt to obtain popularity among the poor by it, and

[1] Dr. Cooper, Medical Officer in Suffolk.
[2] Minutes, Hampstead Board of Guardians, 1868.

confessed he had had cases of complaints where doctors had constituted themselves into irresponsible deputy Relieving Officers.

Strangely enough it was the Poor Law administrators who exonerated the doctors. The Relieving Officer of Bristol (G. Carter) said he had never heard of any instance where inferior drugs had been supplied by Medical Officers and in his parish they only received inclusive salaries of £70 each. Inspector Austin maintained that complaints of Medical Officers avoiding furnishing expensive drugs like cod-liver oil[1] and quinine, and substituting wine and meat, were only allegations made by people ignorant of the matter. He admitted the abuse of giving inferior medicines existed, but maintained that a narrow view of the motives which actuated medical men should not be entertained, for a doctor saved expense and time by curing patients as quickly as possible with the aid of good medicine. Inspector Weale also said he had never heard of Medical Officers supplying paupers with drugs inferior to those administered to private patients, and he had looked into the question extensively. Both were arguing that Medical Officers should remain responsible for the supply of drugs, and against the doctors who demanded Guardians should furnish them—both ignored the fundamental issue, that it was impossible for Medical Officers to supply drugs out of their low salaries.

It was often because the doctor did not supply sufficient medicine that the poor preferred going to a quack. As a member of the Select Committee of 1854 said: 'the feeling of Englishmen is that they do prefer quacks'! Kingsley stated, as a clergyman, he had observed when visiting the sick, that the poor had not the advantage of a higher class of medicine, which would be particularly beneficial to their complaints. Diseases arising from malnutrition and bad social conditions—ague and fever—needed quinine; and lung affections, so common among the labourers and the submerged class, required cod-liver oil. It was the inadequate or inferior medicines as well as the absence of medical knowledge that caused the extraordinary long duration of even minor ailments. Kingsley realized that it was impossible for Medical Officers to afford expensive medicines. He had listened to many complaints that salaries were too low and had inquired round England by letter. Almost every reply stated that remuneration was inadequate, and that even in areas where payments were higher the cost of drugs was barely covered, so that Medical Officers were precluded from administering quinine and cod-liver oil. Where the doctor received only 1s. on an average 'per case' he was always out of pocket through supplying medicines to permanent patients. He quoted an example from Newton Abbot Union where the salary was relatively not low. Here the Medical Officer asked the Guardians for assistance in giving cod-liver oil to an urgent case, for it was costing him twopence-halfpenny to threepence a day and he had been administering it for three weeks. His salary was calculated at 2s. 6d. per case and he was therefore working at a financial loss. The Poor Law Board was referred to, and replied that if the cod-liver oil was being given as a medicine the Medical Officer was bound to pay for it out of his salary, but if it was being

[1] Cod-liver oil was a new 'medicine', very much in vogue in the mid-nineteenth century, therefore it is constantly mentioned. It assumed great prominence in the nineteenth century pharmacopoeia.

supplied as a food it would be a different matter. The Guardians took the former to be the case and refused to pass an order! Kingsley also quoted an instance where a pauper chronic patient had lain on a doctor's hands for thirteen years, during which time he had continued to supply him with medicines. Here also the Guardians refused additional remuneration.

It was not surprising therefore that many witnesses to the Select Committee of 1854 urged the necessity for a change in the system. The Rev. Oxenden, as a Guardian, evinced that the class of medicine given to the poor was unsatisfactory and that the way in which it was dispensed was objectionable. Another Guardian (Wooldridge) recommended that Boards of Guardians should supply expensive medicines because the Medical Officers always failed to do so, and cod-liver oil was never given. Also, if the local authorities ensured an adequate supply of drugs they would be relieved of much expenditure on extras. A Manchester surgeon (John Leigh) likewise objected to the system of contract which was then general because it afforded a strong temptation to supply inferior drugs. If disease was widespread and in periods of epidemics, the administration of expensive drugs was impossible. Even in Manchester, he said, where the Poor Law doctor was paid the relatively high amount of 5s. a case, it was impossible to furnish quinine save at serious loss, so the Medical Officers agitated for Guardians to take over this duty. Six years later in 1862 the Manchester Guardians were finding drugs in one division and it cost them 2s. 2¾d. for each case. In the other nine divisions the old system of contracting with the Medical Officers to find the medicines still appertained, and the average payment to them including drugs had fallen to 1s. 11½d.—threepence-farthing less than the cost of the medicines alone where they were found by the Guardians!

The argument that the Medical Officer was supplying inferior drugs was probably used for the purpose of inducing the employers to increase salaries, for only in the most exceptional cases was this true, as the inference in the charge was that the doctors were cruel and dishonest. In 1866 Smith pointed out that there was both an economical and luxurious method of dispensing which made no appreciable difference in the effects of the remedy. A Medical Officer he said, could give ammonium carbonate at tenpence or compound spirit of ammonia at 3s. 6d. a lb.—whichever was chosen was of no moment to the patient. But to avoid the occurrence of a doctor withholding the necessary drugs he agreed it would be more satisfactory if Guardians provided them. Rumsey advocated, as he had done for twenty-five years, that the supply of medicines should be entirely separated from medical duties. He realized however that under the existing system it would be better if rural doctors continued to provide them, but where Union dispensaries had been established in the rest of the country, Guardians should be made responsible. The Poor Law Inspectors regarded this agitation with disfavour. Austin in 1854 maintained that he had not found the new system more satisfactory where it had been tried, and that the transfer was no guarantee that medicines would be of better quality.

The Registrar of Bristol who was also a Town Councillor (T. F. Gilbert), gave evidence to the contrary and asserted that there were great advantages in the system of drugs being supplied by the Guardians. He quoted the experience of Bristol, where the Corporation was able to deal with some of the first drug-houses in the kingdom and so obtained the finest supplies because it could buy in bulk. For this reason the system was of particular advantage in thickly populated places, and in the middle 'fifties Guardians of such towns as Leeds, Liverpool, Nottingham, Manchester, Hull, Rotherham, Fulham, Norwich, Chorlton, Sheffield, Sunderland, and West Derby, supplied or began to provide medicines. The system was also introduced into a large number of Metropolitan areas, and by 1860 local authorities were assuming this responsibility in Stepney, Paddington, Marylebone, St. Pancras, City of London, St. Giles, St. Leonards, Whitechapel, Poplar, St. Olave, Lambeth, Wandsworth, Islington, and Shoreditch. The latter Union's Quarterly Estimate of Poor Rates are still extant and these show that in 1857 the Guardians were paying £14 a quarter for drugs and £10 6s. a quarter in 1862 for the workhouse. Fowler stated in this year that the average rate for medicines when they were supplied by the Guardians in the Metropolis was elevenpence-farthing a case, and that this was fourpence more than what he received from his inclusive salary.

Several large rural Unions were following the example of the towns and drugs were provided in such places as Bromyard in Hereford, Cleobury Mortimer, Leominster, Kingston in Surrey, Bangor, and Beaumaris. Therefore at the end of the 'fifties the system was no doubt becoming more widely adopted, to the advantage of doctors and paupers in many parts of the country. In 1857 there were forty-six Unions in which medicines were provided by the local destitution authorities—of these twenty-six supplied them for workhouses only, sixteen for all the sick, three for medical districts only, and one Union for only a portion of the outdoor cases. This diversity probably caused the great differences in cost, which varied from twopence-halfpenny a case in Nottingham to 15s. 7½d. in the Islington Infants' Poor House. On an average drugs varied from sixpence to 7s. 1¾d., proving all absence of controlling power by the Poor Law Board. The extreme cost was however exceptional. In 1862 the total expenditure of the forty-six Unions on medicines was £8,387 for 134,000 cases. The amount of drugs supplied for each case of illness varied according to the views of the doctors, and this was another factor accounting for the variation in costs between the Unions. On an average they amounted to 1s. 3d. 'per case' according to Griffin's statistics, and 1s. 5¾d. by Fowler's estimates. The latter maintained that the cost for medicines to the independent poor was much higher, and concluded that those supplied to the paupers were therefore inferior or inadequate.

The Poor Law Medical Relief Association, the British Medical Association, and the Metropolitan Poor Law Medical Officers' Committee, included in their proposals for reform that a general law should be enacted applicable to all Unions. The British Medical Association in its Petition to the Select Committee of 1862 demanded that Boards of Guardians should furnish all medicines like cod-liver oil, linseed, and leeches. Griffin told this Select Committee that thirty years previously he had been one of the honorary surgeons at the Norwich Dispensary and had later been elected one of the Guardians of the poor. He maintained, therefore, that he understood the advantages of a public body finding medicines to be used on behalf of paupers. Medical Officers, he affirmed, did not so much think of the cost as of the advantage to the patient. He gave the heavy demand for cod-liver oil by consumptives as an example, where the invalid suffered because the inadequacy of a doctor's salary did not allow this medicine to be provided save at a great loss. He also stated that the cost of a leech—sixpence—was often the entire sum or even more than was allowed for attendance on a case. Speaking on behalf of the Poor Law Medical Relief Association he recommended in 1862 and in 1864 that cod-liver oil, leeches, quinine, linseed, and sarsaparilla should be excluded from doctors' contracts. Fowler concurred for the Metropolitan Poor Law Medical Officers' Committee. Griffin suggested the average cost of drugs to the Guardians should be calculated at 1s. to 2s. per patient if the expense of a dispenser were included. Above all, he stressed the need for uniformity, so that arrangements, whereby a Union like Bury St. Edmunds which found leeches only, or Plymouth which supplied leeches, bandages, linseed, and trusses, but no medicines, might be abandoned and superseded.

On behalf of the workhouse Medical Officers, who suffered under a similar lack of uniformity, Rogers demanded that Guardians should find drugs for them also. In the workhouses as in the districts this would get rid of the temptation of using cheap drugs, especially where salaries were small and duties exacting. Rogers admitted to the great difference in the quality of drugs where Medical Officers supplied them, cheap substitutes being commonly used. He believed that the suspicion of doctors ordering extras for inmates would also be removed, and pointed out that the new system worked well in the Army and the Navy. He advocated it particularly strongly for Metropolitan institutions because they were becoming receptables for a huge number of incurables, such as those suffering from cancer and phthisis. Many people were under the impression that drugs cost the workhouse doctor nothing, yet opium, chiefly used for alleviating intense pain cost 32s. a lb. so that there was a very strong temptation for a Medical Officer not to see the suffering. By 1862 the Metropolitan workhouses of St. Giles, St. Pancras, and St. Mary, Newington were being supplied with drugs by the Guardians. Rogers himself was allowed £27 by the Income Tax Commissioners as a deduction from his salary for drugs, but he said he had to prescribe very carefully to keep inside this estimate. Many of the Guardians would have liked to have increased his salary, but he preferred them to find drugs instead. He did not believe salaries would be reduced if Guardians provided medicines. Smith also stated that it was rarely fitting for workhouse doctors to dispense medicines themselves and suggested that all surgical instruments and appliances should be found for them.

The arguments for the provision of drugs by the Union were unshakeable. The Medical Bill of 1860 had contained a clause that the supply of expensive medicines should not be included in the Medical Officer's contract, and Sotheron Estcourt, when he was President of the Poor Law Board, had also proposed a list be drawn up by the central authority with the help of the Medical Council, of the most expensive drugs and appliances. These were to be excluded from contracts as well as 3 gallons of wine, duty free, for every 100 patients attended yearly. The latter, he suggested, was to obviate the use of methylated spirits. The

Select Committee of 1864 after hearing the copious evidence on the subject recommended that cod-liver oil, quinine, and other expensive medicines should be provided at the expense of the Guardians subject to the orders and regulations of the Poor Law Board. The latter agreed to the principle and a circular letter was issued on 12 April 1865. This letter stated that the Board had repeatedly considered the recommendation of the Select Committee with a view to determining what measures should be taken by them to carry it into effect. But true to the weak and vacillating nature of their policy, the Board maintained that they could not issue a general and positive Regulation on the subject, for they were afraid of the 'difficulty and embarrassment [which] might arise from a compulsory interference with arrangements for medical relief, which are in force under existing contracts'. The Guardians were therefore requested to consider whether alterations in the arrangements respecting the supply of medicines could not be made whenever a new appointment was necessary, or with the consent of the existing Medical Officer during the continuation of his contract. The Poor Law Board suggested a store of cod-liver oil and other medicines should be kept at the workhouse or other convenient place, and that the sick poor should be supplied on the prescription of the doctor through the Relieving Officer, in the same way as food and clothing was being provided. Medicines should be obtained either by the order of a Medical Officer on a chemist, the cost being defrayed by the Guardians, or the doctor might supply them and send in the account quarterly to his employers. The Poor Law Board suggested the former would be more expedient in towns and the latter in the country. In reply to this circular 401 Unions stated that the Guardians would act wholly or partially on the recommendation and 225 stated that they were not acting on it. The Minutes of the Boards of Guardians at the time bore reference to the new proposal. The Bradford Guardians, for example, resolved 'a store of cod-liver oil be deposited at the workhouse and placed under the care of the pay clerk, and be supplied by him on the prescription of the Medical Officer through the Relieving Officer in the same way as wine is supplied'. Cod-liver oil was the article most generally supplied even if other medicines were not provided. Bakewell appointed a special committee to consider the supply of cod-liver oil, quinine, and disinfectants, and the means of distributing them, with wines and spirits, to the paupers. On the Committee's recommendation a resolution was carried for the provision of 9 gallons of cod-liver oil, and 3 oz. of quinine, 4 doz. bottles of port wine and 2 doz. bottles of sherry, which were to be kept at the workhouse to be distributed exclusively by the master on orders from the Medical Officers. In 1869 a doctor wrote to the Guardians asking that patients might obtain quinine without obtaining the Relieving Officer's signature as well as his own. The attention of the former was however called to the stipulation in the General Consolidated Order (Article 216)—whereby the Relieving Officer was really the authorizing power in the supply of 'extras'.[1]

This instance clearly illustrates that the difficulties of the Poor Law Medical Officers in obtaining a supply of drugs were not over. In this field too, the power of the Relieving

[1] Minutes, Bakewell Board of Guardians (Webb MSS.).

Officer had to be circumvented. But taken generally, the Poor Law Board's Circular was no finite solution of the problem of the provision of medicines by local authorities. Agitation and debate continued for many years. In 1870 Inspector W. A. Peel could still report[1] that the supply of all expensive medicines by the Guardians should be made compulsory. He believed it would probably have little effect in diminishing the amount of extras ordered, but because they would not be supplied out of the scant salaries of the Medical Officer it would be advantageous to the pauper, as they would be administered more frequently. This showed there was much diversity in the country, but by the 'seventies the Metropolis and the large towns had on the whole agreed to the scheme, and it was in the rural areas where the Medical Officer was still responsible for supplying medicines from his own low salary.

Where Guardians supplied drugs some abuse occurred. In a few Unions for example, it was said that the doctors charged their employers for medicines which they had never delivered or used. This could only have happened rarely, for the system which generally appertained was for Guardians to contract with drug-houses who delivered them to the Medical Officers or workhouses themselves. Some doctors began to complain that they were supplied with inferior drugs, because the Guardians, with an eye to cheapness, obtained them by tender contracts. Probably the strongest objection to Poor Law medical relief by the local authorities was the large cost of drugs.

Rumsey and several other Medical Officers had many years previously drawn attention to the small average cost for drugs 'per case' which could be effected by an economic system of dispensaries, and the Provincial Medical and Surgical Association had advocated the institution of dispensaries for the supply of medicines from 1836 onwards. In 1854 the Rev. E. J. Howman, a Norfolk Guardian agreeing with these early proposals, outlined a plan of his own. He suggested small medicine chests containing common drugs should be deposited in stations, in certain places throughout a Union, so that people would always know where to obtain medicines. He estimated the cost of drugs would be about £100 a year and the Medical Officer would do the dispensing. The late 'fifties and 'sixties saw the beginning of a more comprehensive and efficient scheme. Dispensaries were established in many large Unions with a qualified dispenser. Liverpool had always had the system and engaged two qualified licensed apothecaries at 23s. and 25s. a week. But salaries varied everywhere when the practice became adopted and were not based on any recognizable principles.

It was naturally advocated that the system should become universal and that one or more dispensaries should be established in every Union. As in so many other fields of Poor Law medical reform, Griffin was one of the foremost agitators. He laid great stress on the importance of these dispensaries being established everywhere, save in purely rural areas where it was not possible to do so. The poor would benefit because they would not be kept waiting for hours for their medicine, which was frequent where the Medical Officers had

[2] In Report on 'Outdoor Relief in District 3'—Oxford, Cambridge, Bedford, Herts, Bucks, Hants.

large districts to visit. Griffin believed one of the reasons why Guardians procrastinated in setting up dispensaries was the expense, and he was convinced local authorities would not agree to the scheme unless they were compelled. He pointed out that the Poor Law Board had the power to order the institution of dispensaries and demanded they should exercise their authority by withholding Parliamentary Grants from recalcitrants. On the other hand, he suggested that Guardians should be encouraged to find drugs and supply them from dispensaries, by the central authorities defraying the entire cost out of the Parliamentary Grant. The Poor Law Board might even furnish them themselves, like the Army and Navy authorities, and so ensure that adulterated or inferior drugs were not supplied.

In country districts Guardians were not convinced of the practicability or the economy of the idea. Dispensaries could in fact have been established in these areas for if distance provided the obstacle, several small ones could have been set up with an itinerant dispenser on duty for a few hours at each in turn. Unions could also have combined for this purpose. Dr. Smith interested himself in the subject and suggested that a committee consisting of Poor Law Medical Officers should undertake the supervision of a dispensary and the recommendation to Guardians of drugs required. Some dispensaries, he thought, might also be used as surgeries where the District Medical Officers might attend at fixed hours or they might be used for vaccination stations. In discussing the question in 1866 with the workhouse doctors of the forty-eight Metropolitan Unions, Smith was told that they all desired the Guardians to provide the drugs and a dispenser both for indoor and outdoor patients. Paddington paid a druggist to dispense medicines, but generally it was maintained that the system whereby Guardians purchased drugs from wholesale houses at wholesale prices and had them dispensed in the workhouse was a preferable plan. The Medical Bill of 1860 had suggested that in no instance should Guardians be allowed to enter into contracts with druggists for the supply of medicines, but that they should be obtained through the Medical Officer or made up at the dispensary. In addition it contained a clause whereby Guardians should employ a dispenser. Smith also advocated that if Guardians were to find drugs it would be wise to pay a dispenser and engage his spare time in other duties, such as superintending nurses, or acting as clerk to the master, or as storekeeper. It was generally found however that the dispenser's time was fully occupied in attending to his special work, even when two were appointed—one for the outdoor poor and the other for workhouse patients.— The dispensaries which were established in these years were generally in the workhouse and were only for the provision of medicines. This was their distinct function, but where Union dispensaries were established by Guardians for the treatment of the outdoor sick poor by the District Medical Officer, these places were often used for the purpose of a drug dispensary also.

Another reform which was advocated to alleviate the work of the Poor Law doctor was a reduction in the size of medical districts. We have seen that agitation in the early years after the passing of the 1834 Act had led to the diminution in the size of districts by the Medical Order of 1842. Many Unions had either been granted exemption from these orders or had ignored the regulations. However efficient Medical Officers might be, districts remained too large and an insufficient number of doctors were engaged, particularly in rural areas. Hardship inflicted on the poor through long journeys to the Medical or Relieving Officers continued to be pointed out, but doctors also suffered from having to travel as much as 12 to 20 miles to visit their patients. Many of them gave evidence to this effect to the Select Committee of 1854. Inspector Austin maintained that Guardians did not generally like areas as large as 15,000 acres. He had found that the average area of all medical districts formed in the centre of England was 8,000-9,000 acres. His advice to Guardians, he said, had always been to make districts in rural areas as small as possible, and he asserted that there had been a considerable diminution over the previous ten years, accompanied by an increase in the number of Medical Officers. Inspector Weale admitted that a decrease in the size of medical districts was the only improvement he knew of in the Poor Law medical services, and he believed the situation was constantly changing for the better as superintendence grew more vigilant. But one of the final resolutions the Committee had to recommend was that the Poor Law Board should continue to direct their attention to the extent of medical districts, to the reduction of areas where they were inconveniently large, and to the appointment of additional Medical Officers in such cases.

In 1857 Returns were made on the subject to the House of Commons. An enormous list was prepared giving data on every Poor Law doctor in the country. From this can be seen that the population of medical districts in 1856-57 was 17,913,873, the acreage 35,093,821, and the number of medical officers 3,307. Of these 251 doctors held appointments in two Unions, and nineteen in three—therefore the actual number of medical officers was 3,018, of which twenty-seven were precluded from private practice. There were one-and-a-quarter million patients, so that this meant all but these twenty-seven had private practices to attend to as well in their large areas. The Medical Bill of 1860 contained clauses by which districts were to be changed where necessary. No Medical Officer was to be appointed to districts which extended 6 miles beyond his residence. Wherever a doctor had over 1,500 patients on his list in a year (save during an epidemic) it was to be the duty of the Guardians to reduce the size of the district or to appoint additional medical staff.

Griffin gave extensive evidence on the subject to the Select Committee of 1861 from facts which had been collected by the Poor Law Medical Reform Association. In England there were 583 districts exceeding 15,000 acres and three which extended from 70,000 to 100,000 acres each. The South West and Midlands were the worst regions: 291 Medical Officers had 629 appointments, and eighty-six of these united districts contained over two-and-a-quarter million acres, or an average of 26,000 acres each. The excess above the 15,000 acres legally allowed would have provided employment for sixty additional doctors. There were at least twenty-three Unions which were each attended by only one Medical Officer, and only in nine was the acreage less than the extreme limit fixed. In Wales where the 15,000-acre limit did not apply, but where no medical district was to be assigned to any practitioner residing over 7 miles from any point in the parish, the law was also evaded. In England and Wales 120 districts contained populations exceeding 15,000, some extending to 40,000 people. Of these forty-three were in the North-West, twenty in the Metropolis, and fourteen in the West Midlands. There were 875 other districts which because of their irregular shape extended to over 6 miles from the residence of the Medical Officer, although they were within the acreage and population limit.

There was another feature of the medical service which never received the consideration of the Poor Law Commissioners or the Poor Law Board. There were so many poor residing in some 266 areas that each Medical Officer had to attend from 1,000 to 6,000 patients in a year. Griffin believed it would be a salutary reform if the number of patients as well as the size of the district were limited. It was impossible for one man to attend such a vast number of cases—the result was inevitably neglect or delegation of duty to assistants. These abuses illustrate the lax way the Poor Law Board allowed Guardians to conduct the medical service. As Griffin pointed out: 'that but little regard has been paid to the welfare and comfort of the poor there can be no doubt, for with such extensive districts, how can a medical man visit his patients so often as the nature of complaints require?', and he continued: 'how is it possible for the poor to send these long distances for their medicines, 10–15 miles out, and as many home again . . . This is trifling with the lives of the poor.' When the Medical Officer suffered there was the danger of the poor suffering also; therefore Griffin demanded that there should be a law that no man should be elected to a district whose furthest limits were 6 miles from his residence.

The Metropolitan Poor Law Medical Officers at a meeting in 1861 (10 May) also pointed out that districts, particularly in rural areas, were too large. The *Medical Circular* of 21 May 1862 printed a scheme proposed by E. T. Meredith. He maintained districts should be limited in extent by the number of patients. His own experience had taught him that 1,200 bonâ fide cases of sickness were as many as any practitioner in private practice could conscientiously and efficiently attend, and that a country area of 50 square miles was as large as anyone could work over if it had more than 600 cases in it.

But the situation had improved regarding the reduction in the size of districts since the 'forties, demonstrated by comparing the increase in the number of Medical Officers with that of areas. In 1840 there were 2,376 Poor Law doctors, in 1861 3,479, an increase of 46 per cent, whilst the area under the Poor Law authorities had grown by only 5 per cent. (Pauperism had decreased by about 2 per cent.) The increase in the number of doctors taking pauper appointments was very necessary and was quite marked. This was because the office was rising in status, and the Poor Law Medical Officers were becoming publicly recognized as a body of importance to the profession and the community. Also the post was becoming more attractive by a definite upward trend in salaries.

While there can be no doubt that there was an overall rise in salaries, either because Guardians acknowledged the increase in the work of the Medical Officers, or recognized that they had been unjust, or because they were forced to advance emoluments in order to obtain the services of a practitioner who possessed the necessary academic and residential qualifications, remuneration varied throughout the country. Because the central authorities neglected to establish any system, uniformity, equality, or definite principle was absent, and the income of the doctor depended entirely on the attitude of Guardians. The Poor

Law Commissioners had repeatedly affirmed in their first years of office that, although in principle they desired to see increased uniformity in the methods of remuneration, they wished to authorize and permit the adoption of different systems in various parts of the country, in the expectation that trial and error would enable them, after a period, to ascertain the most advantageous form of payment. Despite the fact that the 1847 Order (Article 172) directed that Guardians should pay 'to the several officers and assistants holding any office or employment under this Order, such salaries or remuneration as the Commissioners may from time to time direct or approve', twenty years later the Medical Officers were still waiting for the central authorities to come to a decision.

The only definite rule laid down for the guidance of Guardians was the 1835 Order whereby salaries were not to exceed the amounts formerly paid, and which advised the abolition of appointment by tender because this would tend to lower them. In 1839 the Commissioners had hoped 'at no distant period to ascertain the most advantageous form to be finally established', but because they and their successors took no firm stand, and in the absence of regulations, Unions adopted several methods of payment. Some paid 'per case' with the additional fees ordered in 1842 and 1847, some 'per case' for casuals with fixed salaries for the permanent 'pauper list' and additional fees, others entirely 'per case' without any fees, although this was rare. In various parts of the country Unions gave fixed salaries with or without extra fees, and some Guardians reduced remuneration in consideration of their supplying the drugs. Occasionally fixed salaries were paid exclusive of extra fees or sums for various duties, and in one instance the Medical Officer was on a scale which varied in amount with the number of cases attended, his salary fluctuating by £10 for every twenty-five patients. Some Unions commuted fees prescribed by the Orders for a definite annual payment, the Guardians taking the average of fees over a period of years and adding the sum to the fixed salary. This however could not be done without the concurrence of the Poor Law Board and the consent of the Medical Officer. Doctors under suspension received no salary, and the period was often of many months' duration.

The system which generally appertained was a fixed salary with the prescribed additional fees, without any reference to the duties performed. As we have seen the Poor Law Commissioners had stated their preference for the per case system for casuals, with a fixed salary for the 'pauper list', but this had only been put into practice in a few instances, such as at Weyland in Suffolk from 1841 onwards. Here the total annual fixed salaries for three doctors before the change of system was £240 for 566 cases; under the recommended method, fixed salaries amounted to £105 and the 'per case' payments to £129 15s.—346 cases at 7s. 6d. each, a total sum of £234 15s., which did not therefore vary very much from the former system. The 'pauper list' was revised every year, and salaries included all journeys, medical appliances, and the signing of certificates. In Bradford a peculiar system existed. Here the township desired to pay by fixed salary while the surrounding districts desired to continue the 'per case' method. In 1848 the Guardians representing the town centre wished to redivide the Union into four districts in order that the payment to Medical Officers could be equalized—and reduced. The cost of medical relief had risen from £100 in 1844 to £527 by 1848, and in one district cases had increased from 49 to 12,774. The Union therefore desired to appoint four doctors—two at £120 and two at £100 each. The out-townships wished to continue payment 'per case', because under this system fees were paid by the respective townships. This had resulted in the central district which desired the change being burdened with high expenditure, as sickness there was four times as great in a population which was only double the size. The Poor Law Board increased the difficulty of the situation by refusing to agree to the appointment of four Medical Officers, maintaining three would be adequate, although they sanctioned the total salary of £440. Therefore the Guardians continued with the 'per case' system of payment. In 1848 the Poor Law Board was again approached to sanction the payment of doctors by fixed salary, the Guardians maintaining that the existing system tended to increase pauperism.[1] This time the suggestion was accepted on condition that the salaries were paid out of the Common Fund of the Union. The Guardians then wrote to the Poor Law Board[2] that they could not understand the principle 'which excluded them from the arrangement of permitting each township to pay for its own Medical Officer by fixed salary out of its own funds, when they had in the past agreed to each township paying its own officer according to the number of cases attended'. The reply of the central authorities is interesting.[3] It referred to the regulations by which salaries were required to be paid out of the Establishment Fund, adding that treatment given on the 'per case' system was regarded as medical relief paid to the pauper (like the provision of extra food), and therefore was properly charged to each township. The Guardians called this 'regular humbug'! In 1850–51 another attempt was made to get the doctors paid by fixed salary, this time on the grounds of alleged corruption among them. To reduce salaries, the Guardians ordered that in future Poor Law doctors were to dispense their own medicines and payment for cases was reduced from 6s. 6d. to 3s.[4] But the Poor Law Board would only sanction a reduction to 5s. in two districts and 5s. 6d. in others (13 February). In the following month the Medical Officers went on strike against the reduction, and as they were appointed by annual election, new doctors were engaged after advertisements had been widely circularized and included in the *Lancet* and the *Medical Times*. In 1858 the Finance and General Purposes Committee reported to the Guardians that their attention had been drawn to the large emoluments of the District Medical Officers.[5] The Committee had caused several cases out of every district to be visited and 'the result of such visits had shown that in some districts it was very common for Medical Officers to attend indiscriminately without orders, persons who may approach them, . . . out of twenty visited in one district, eight had been attended for the first time without an order . . . One person stated he had never applied for a medical note, that he had sufficient income to maintain his family, and always paid his own surgeon's

[1] Minutes, Board of Guardians, 1849.
[2] 2 August, *Bradford Observer*, and other references 24 February, 14 December 1848.
[3] 28 August 1849.
[4] *Bradford Observer*, 6 February 1851.
[5] Minutes, Board of Guardians.

bills.' The Committee recommended that the system of payment by cases was bad and that doctors should be paid by fixed salary. The Poor Law Board was again requested to sanction the alteration. The reply received was that in the case of officers already appointed prior to the issue of the Order of 25 May 1857, Boards of Guardians could not make alterations in the remuneration of Medical Officers against their will. The doctors were consulted and they refused to agree to the change.

In 1861 there were only eighteen 'per case' paying Unions. Besides Bradford, these included, St. Neots, Peterborough, Barton-on-Irwell (Lancs.), Newmarket, Bedford, Chester, Todmorden and Swaffham (Norfolk). The fact that each Union was allowed to follow its own system, shows that the Poor Law Board exercised little control. Liberal minded Guardians paid 10s. 6d. for an order, others 5s., independent of distances to be travelled. The Poor Law Commissioners had recommended 6s. in 1839, but the average for the country in the 'fifties was only 3s. Those casual sick who were paid for by the case generally required much more treatment and more frequent visits and medicine than those on the permanent list, who were generally aged and infirm or chronics. Remuneration for the latter varied from eightpence to 5s. a patient, and Griffin gave illustrations to the Select Committee of 1861 of the disgraceful scales operating in Todmorden. Here cases of fracture received a fee of only 16s. and midwifery 6s. instead of the £1 to £5 for the former, and 10s. to £2 for the latter. Griffin accused the Poor Law Board of having failed in its duty in permitting it. Amongst these Unions there was also considerable variation in the duration of an order—some lasted till the termination of the illness, others twenty-one to thirty days after recovery, some for three months and others for twelve months. No fixed principle existed.

Charles Buller as first President of the Poor Law Board expressed many advanced opinions before his untimely death in 1849. He admitted that there was great room for improvement in the administration of Poor Law medical relief, and contrary to the opinions of his predecessors, suggested the advantage of payment by fixed salary. The Poor Law Board continued in the following years to agree with his view. Poor Law Inspectors informed the Select Committee of 1854 that they preferred the system of fixed salaries. Weale stated that Guardians frequently complained, when they paid by case, of the multiplication of patients by the Medical Officers. In Bedford, one of the Unions in his region, Guardians had told him that if the doctor called to attend one member of a family, he invariably found some complaint in another member. Weale also pointed out that the system was no more satisfactory to the poor. This was illustrated by a Guardian of Dewsbury (J. Ellison), who advocated that payment 'per case' should be withdrawn officially, for the system afforded every inducement to the Relieving Officer to deal out medical orders sparingly in order to keep down the pressure on the rates. A fixed salary would induce him to be liberal and so avoid the greater expense of prolonged sickness.

Another Guardian however advocated the universal adoption of the payment 'per case' system. This was the Rev. Howman of Norfolk, who as we have seen had formulated other plans regarding the medical system and who was quite well known by the Poor Law medical reformers. He maintained that the prevailing system was detrimental to all parties, and both Medical Officers and poor were discontented. A fixed salary tempted Guardians to inflict as much duty on the doctor as possible for a smaller payment, and the poor were also induced to get as much out of him as they could because they realized the parish did not pay for them individually. Howman pointed to the constant grumbling of the Medical Officers and believed the only reason which prevented them from resigning was the wish to exclude new doctors from the district. He stated that in his Union fixed salaries and extra fees had been paid, but as no satisfactory arrangement could be reached the details had been amended several times, six varieties of schemes having been tried altogether. As the Guardians could never agree as to who was a fit subject for relief, he had suggested that a list should be compiled of paupers to whom tickets should be issued, and the Medical Officers were to be paid according to the number held from a total fixed sum. As in clubs, each pauper was to be allowed to choose which doctor attended him. But the Guardians defeated the idea, and Howman also failed in his suggestion that a Committee should be set up on payment 'per case'. The Guardians of Wolverhampton took the unusual step of changing to the 'per case' system as late as 1852. Scales were fixed at 2s., 2s. 6d., 3s., 3s. 6d., and 5s. 6d. a patient, depending on the illness—the existing salaries averaged 1s. 4½d. a case. The question of whether Medical Officers should be appointed to districts, or whether the poor should be allowed to employ any Poor Law doctor was also discussed. The Relieving Officers were against the latter suggestion because they believed the doctors would give more orders for food and necessaries to the poor to win popularity. They pointed out that they had given 578 such orders, and the Medical Officers 1,985, in the preceding year.[1]

Union doctors were decidedly in favour of receiving fixed salaries. The Convention of Poor Law Medical Officers considered it essential, and Lord mentioned it as one of their resolutions to the Select Committee of 1854. Dr. Gilbert also gave evidence in its favour and in 1862 the Petition from the Executive Council of the British Medical Association contained a prayer for fixed salaries. By this time there were only ten Unions in England which paid by case solely, and only ten more which paid partly by case and partly by salary. The Clerk of the City of London (John Bowring) thought the 'per case' system had decidedly failed and would always be regarded as distasteful by Medical Officers.[2] Inspector Cane drew attention to the general objection which had arisen amongst the Guardians to payment 'per case' because they believed it increased the cost of poor relief. The most important factor in influencing Guardians, however, was the grant paid by the Treasury since 1845 for half the cost of medical salaries. It was obvious that Unions would change to fixed salaries to obtain the grant. Salaries of doctors were derived from the Common Fund of the Union, the particular parish to which a pauper belonged, and the Parliamentary Grant. The latter was limited to a moiety of the fixed salaries, medical and surgical appliances, and where a dispensary was established to half the cost of drugs and the dispenser's salary. In the first two years of office of the Poor Law Board counties were

[1] Report in *Lancet*, February 1852.
[2] Evidence to the Select Committee, 1862.

THE POOR LAW MEDICAL OFFICERS, 1847-71

receiving the amounts shown in Table 12.3; the list of payments incidentally presents a picture of the salaries of the Medical Officers, the variations in the country, and the relation to the population.

TABLE 12.3

Parliamentary Grants showing amounts received by counties and Medical Officers' salaries.—Compiled from (a) 'Return showing Manner in which £110,000 for salaries ... is spent in Poor Law districts and parishes', (b) 'Return showing Number and Description of officers employed ... amount of salaries and Parliamentary Grant ...', B.P.P. 6, 1849 and 1851.

County	Population, 1841	Number of Unions	Number of Medical Officers, 1850–51	Salaries, 1850–51	Grant, 1850–51	Grant, 1849 (to show rise in two years)
				£	£	£ (nearest £)
Bedford	112,379	6	26	1,895	940	928
Berks.	190,367	12	51	3,687	1,826	1,776
Bucks.	138,255	7	50	2,608	1,341	1,370
Cambridge	171,848	9	46	2,766	1,382	1,358
Chester	344,860	9	45	3,366	1,218	1,230
Cornwall	340,728	13	71	2,280	1,127	1,123
Cumberland	177,912	9	35	968	484	479
Derby	242,786	9	47	1,534	737	729
Devon	430,221	17	164	5,422	2,558	2,543
Dorset	167,874	12	56	3,361	1,549	1,543
Durham	326,055	14	60	1,648	844	801
Essex	320,818	17	114	6,620	3,308	3,279
Gloucester	330,562	16	60	3,763	1,863	1,857
Hereford	110,675	8	25	1,854	890	862
Hertford	176,173	13	59	3,495	1,658	1,712
Huntingdon	55,573	3	15	1,143	634	576
Kent	534,882	27	113	7,091	3,542	3,445
Lancaster	1,719,306	28	186	8,887	5,559	5,550
Leicester	202,232	11	48	2,641	1,302	1,320
Lincoln	356,347	14	110	4,006	2,026	2,017
Middlesex	846,207	22	129	10,039	4,448	4,279
Monmouth	150,222	6	27	1,027	511	501
Norfolk	343,277	21	120	5,764	3,073	3,046
Northants	199,104	12	54	2,727	1,527	1,493
Northumberland	265,988	12	65	1,761	919	914
Notts.	270,719	9	54	2,036	1,109	1,165
Oxford	143,510	8	43	2,861	1,453	1,453
Rutland	23,150	2	8	368	160	160

TABLE 12.3—*continued*

County	Population, 1841	Number of Unions	Number of Medical Officers, 1850-51	Salaries, 1850-51	Grant, 1850-51	Grant, 1849 (to show rise in two years)
Salop	191,052	13	61	2,615	1,274	1,242
Somerset	454,446	17	114	5,925	2,994	2,961
Southampton	268,989	23	95	5,767	3,056	2,925
Stafford	443,982	16	76	3,110	1,554	1,555
Suffolk	314,722	17	98	5,085	2,540	2,539
Surrey	523,238	19	97	6,118	3,154	2,956
Sussex	223,623	20	93	5,255	2,465	2,439
Warwick	358,244	12	63	3,626	1,927	1,921
Westmorland	56,469	3	17	559	279	278
Wiltshire	223,246	17	67	4,504	2,345	2,324
Worcester	336,108	13	64	3,294	1,661	1,593
Yorks—E. Riding	221,847	10	54	1,590	744	760
N. Riding	180,643	15	64	1,960	965	958
W. Riding	917,033	22	165	4,961	2,931	2,807
Wales	884,173	42	147	7,507	3,694	3,656
Total	14,307,845	605	3,156	156,494	79,571	78,425

This was how the grant was applied and not as stated in the Thirteenth Annual Report of the Poor Law Board: 'in the improvement of medical relief, and in facilitating in remote places the residence of a medical officer'. If the latter had been the intention in providing the grant, it should only have been given to Unions which needed it for this purpose, or in varying proportion. The grant rose steadily. By 1857–58 it reached £90,000, in 1858–59 it remained the same, in 1859–60 it was £93,000, and also in 1860–61. In 1862 the Chairman of the Court of Governors of Norwich (W. Wilde) suggested that the whole charge for medical relief should be thrown on the Consolidated Fund. In the 'sixties it was the desire to obtain an increased Parliamentary Grant that induced Guardians to commute extra fees.

The commutation of extra fees was a scheme to which Medical Officers found strong objection. It was introduced by several Unions in this period and threatened to become widespread. Guardians also resorted to it because of their desire to get rid of charges on particular parishes to which paupers belonged. Although the Poor Law Board sanctioned its adoption by Guardians, no legal right really existed, for the Order of 1847 (Article 177) stated: 'no salary of any District Medical Officer shall include remunerations for operations, etc.' Often Medical Officers were coerced by Guardians to agree to the system. In Banbury Union, for example, extras were compounded by taking the total fees over the previous five years and the average was added to the salary. This was unfair because numbers of patients were rising every year. In 1854 the fees were £18 yet the average over the previous five years only amounted to £13. The Medical Officer only gave his assent to the scheme under protest, particularly with regard to the inclusion of midwifery fees. As a result far more orders were given, for the Guardians could send as many cases as they wished. The Poor Law Board was appealed to, but no decision was reached.

Sometimes Medical Officers acquiesced willingly if they did little operating or if they had been receiving large sums previously, also if there had been a high accident rate in the period from which the average was being computed. In the City of London extra fees were compounded in 1858 on the average for the previous three years. Formerly four Medical Officers received salaries of £75 and subsequently £100, including the supply of medicines. The Clerk to the Guardians affirmed in 1862 that the system was working satisfactorily to both parties, as the doctors had enjoyed little benefit from extra fees, because there were so many hospitals and other charities for the poor in the neighbourhood. He advocated giving doctors a fixed inclusive salary, which should be liberal, even if it were higher than salaries plus fees, for it allayed the suspicion that cases were made for the additional remuneration, and this acted as a deterrent to the giving of orders. There were seventy-nine Unions where fees were commuted, yet salaries remained very low. In six of these Unions collective emoluments averaged less than 1s. a patient; in ten it was between 1s. and 7s.; in fifteen between 2s. and 3s. and in fifty-nine less than 5s. Dr. Moore in his proposed scheme for a new system of remuneration (1862) voiced decided objection to cases of midwifery being included in salaries. When he was first appointed to a parish in Bethnal Green he had thirty cases of midwifery a year, by 1862 this number had risen to 150. Therefore, he asked, on what basis should salaries be fixed? The actual amount of work was incalculable in advance and no fair averages could be computed for obstetrics. Much depended on the district. Near London, pauper women were generally delivered by students if they went to hospitals, but even if lying-in institutions were taken advantage of, tickets for admission were limited.

Griffin also demanded that Guardians should not be allowed to compound additional fees. But Inspector Cane held that where fees had been commuted, arrangements were satisfactory to both Medical Officers and Guardians, and therefore suggested in 1862 that it would be an improvement if fixed allowances were made for extras, which should be included in the salary. He believed £10 would be adequate. The *Lancet* often voiced its objection to the commutation of fees and issued a strong protest in 1870 when the Poplar Board of Guardians adopted the scheme with the acquiescence of the Medical Officers and the consent of the Poor Law Board. The journal predicted that the Relieving Officer would be careless in the giving of orders and that the doctors' work would therefore be increased. It had already done so over the past few years, and it was pointed out that doctors had no right to limit the fees which their successors would be legitimately entitled to in the future.

Extras, the writer continued, could not be fairly commuted because services inevitably varied, in fact the word 'extra' of necessity had to apply to exceptional cases.[1]

More controversy was aroused, however, over the actual payment of additional fees, and as much variation existed in this sphere as in the method of paying salaries. But increasing uniformity and acquiescence in the rules were becoming apparent in the 'sixties. The Orders of 1842 and 1847 had made the payment of fees for midwifery and surgery obligatory on Guardians, although surgery fees depended on the success of the operation and the consent of a higher medical authority to its performance. In 1854 Griffin admitted that the scales laid down were perfectly satisfactory to the profession, but pointed out that not all operations were listed in the Orders, so that Guardians were at liberty to use their own discretion in the interpretation of them. Therefore niggardly authorities gave nothing for operations not specifically mentioned. Fowler, speaking for the Metropolitan Medical Officers, desired the rates of fees to be increased all round.

Some Unions offered Medical Officers payment for additional duties like visiting Lunatic Asylums or Poor Law Schools. Chelsea, for example, gave its four doctors a total of £2 2s. 6d. a year for quarterly attendances at the Lunatic Asylum,[2] Shoreditch remunerated the Medical Officer who attended its subsidiary workhouse in which lunatics were maintained with £10 a year, and the surgeon who attended Brentwood School with £10 a quarter. Bedford Union allowed two guineas a year for the keeping of the Medical Book and Dr. Cooper of Suffolk received £8 for travelling. But this was not the usual procedure and most Unions were disposed to meet only their minimum obligations, frequently not recognizing the additional services of the Medical Officers and not remunerating them. In 1856, for example, the *Lancet* stated that 95 per cent of the death certificates were furnished gratuitously for the public benefit.

In 1861, 571 out of the 667 Unions allowed extra fees, and returns were given four years previously showing these amounted to nearly £34,000 or a halfpenny per head of the population. But the number of cases varied for which orders entailing additional expenditure were given. Extra fees in the Metropolis averaged threepence-three-farthings a patient, in the North Midlands and Northern Divisions elevenpence-farthing a patient. Even within the regional divisions there was great diversity—one Metropolitan Medical Officer received an average of 1s. in fees, while another got 104s., and in Wales it varied from 3s. to 156s. If the doctors' remuneration is taken collectively, from less than a farthing per patient to sixpence was paid in 165 Unions; from sixpence to 1s. in 235 others; from 1s. to 3s. in 156; and from 3s. to 7s. in seven Unions. If the fees paid per patient are examined for doctors individually, they range from a farthing to 13s.; 868 Medical Officers receiving a farthing to sixpence; 736, sixpence to 1s.; 868, 1s. to 3s.; and 122, 3s. to 13s. This remarkably great variation proved incontestably the entire want of system in this department of expenditure and the absence of control by the Poor Law Board over the activity of Boards of Guardians. Griffin, who was responsible for collecting so much of the statistical material pointed out

[1] *Lancet*, 1870, i, p. 133.
[2] Board of Guardians' Abstract of Accounts, 1864.

that accidents did not alone account for the diversities. He admitted that in colliery, mining, and manufacturing districts the need for emergency operations frequently arose, but in purely rural Unions the frequency of accidents ought to have been alike, yet here there was equal dissimilarity among Unions in the payment of fees. Midwifery cases were a great cause of the variation, some Unions giving orders freely, whilst others practically abstained; also there were great differences in the payments to midwives.

The Select Committee of 1854 heard evidence from Inspector Cane that many cases of complaints occurred where Guardians refused to pay Medical Officers for attendance on urgent cases without an order. The latter possessed the authority to go to accidents or confinements without an order but they were required to use discretion wisely. They had either to give credit to a person, or trust the Guardians to recognize the destitution of the patient after treatment had been rendered and to reimburse them accordingly. Cane believed destitution authorities were inclined to be liberal, but pointed out that, without a legal order, there was no legal remedy if the Guardians chose to refuse. He explained that extras were only paid for outdoor cases, because fractures, for example, necessitated daily or special visits for many weeks and caused a great deal of additional trouble and expense to the doctor. If accidents were brought into the workhouses Boards of Guardians had the power, which Cane maintained was frequently resorted to, of voting the doctor a sum for extra aid which was not contemplated at the time the salary had been fixed. Cane asserted that many payments were made every year to Medical Officers for rendering services which it was not supposed they would be required to perform when they were appointed.

It was the duty of the Poor Law Board to investigate claims and recommend Guardians to pay them, but the responsibility rested with the local authorities and they did not always obey. In one Union in Derbyshire, for example, an order had been given to a mother for medical relief, when one of her children also had an accident. The Medical Officer attended but was refused an extra fee for the fracture because the order had been given for the mother and not the child, and the Guardians stated that she alone had been recognized a pauper. The doctor appealed to the Poor Law Board, who ordered the Guardians to reimburse him, but the latter upheld their refusal and the central authorities did no more about the matter. Because of this experience the Medical Officer waited with a man who had fractured both his legs and refused to treat him until an order had been received. Such instances must have resulted in much unnecessary suffering. Another illustration came from the Medical Officer of the Wells Union. Dr. Livett recalled that he was once refused a fee for setting a boy's broken arm, because no order had been obtained. The father's wages were 9s. a week and he was quite unable to pay for medical treatment, yet the Guardians refused to reimburse Livett. He had come to the conclusion that the local Boards tried to evade paying fees whenever they could, and the most common and easiest way was to refuse them when no order had been previously obtained. The Medical Bill of 1860 included a stipulation that in cases of emergency a doctor was to be remunerated as if the sick person had been granted an order, and that he was to be entitled to the same fees if he had to perform an operation.

St. George the Martyr, Southwark, did not allow Medical Officers any fees for additional duties unless patients had been seen by the Relieving Officer first.[1] Liverpool paid no extra fees at all—the authorities had done so originally, but the practice had been abandoned because of the difficulty in determining whether bills sent to the Relieving Officers were correct. A Hampstead surgeon received £85 for services and medicine and was only offered an additional fee of 10s. for midwifery cases. Kensington Board of Guardians paid one of their doctors £98 which included vaccination, midwifery, and the examination of lunatics.[2] But in St. George in the East £40–£50 a year was allowed for extras.[3]

The Rev. E. J. Howman, although he advocated in his evidence in 1854 that Medical Officers should always be remunerated if they attended an emergency without an order, believed additional payments opened the door to an immensity of evils. Doctors might be induced to keep cases in their own hands instead of sending them to a hospital. On the other hand, Griffin maintained (1861) that Relieving Officers often forced people to go into hospitals to save the fees. Therefore to obviate the drain on the funds of charitable bodies he recommended that Guardians should pay these institutions the same fee as they would have had to offer the Medical Officer. Fowler also said he received no fees from the East London Union, because there was a tacit understanding that all midwifery and surgical cases should be sent to a hospital. He believed the real reason for sending people away was to get round the payment of extra fees, for the suspicion that a Medical Officer would perform an operation for the sake of the fee was spurious, as no one was entitled to additional remuneration without a certificate from a higher medical authority saying it was 'right and proper' to carry out the operation.

Howman stated that abuse was most likely to occur in midwifery. He believed the system had reached a point where, almost universally, women who could afford to pay postponed calling in a midwife until the last moment, and then in the emergency they applied to a Relieving Officer who immediately granted an order for a doctor to attend and the Union to pay. Instances had occurred, Howman said, where orders arrived too late and payment had still been asked for. In his own Union the cost of additional fees amounted to an average of £75. They had risen from £50 in the 'forties to £108 in the 'fifties and had generally been for midwifery. A Guardian of Dewsbury stated that the only complaint his Board had ever had to make to the central authorities regarding the Medical Officers had been over the question of payment of fees. Here the doctors presented bills annually and one of them contrived to make a great many surgical and midwifery cases. For two years in succession he had tendered an account which amounted to almost as much as his general stipend, and on investigation a great number of frauds were discovered.[4] But such occurrences were not often mentioned and in this field it was general to hear far more

[1] Minutes, Board of Guardians, St. George the Martyr.
[2] Minutes, Board of Guardians, Kensington.
[3] Minutes, Board of Guardians, St. George in the East, 1853.
[4] J. Ellison, evidence to Select Committee, 1854.

complaints from Medical Officers, either on the variation which existed in the giving of fees, or on their inadequacy.

Griffin, on behalf of the Poor Law Medical Officers' Reform Association, recommended that a new table of fees for midwifery, surgery, and consultation should be drawn up by the Poor Law Board with the advice of the General Council of Medical Education and Registration, and that a revision should be made every seven years if it were thought necessary by the Poor Law Board, the Guardians, or any twenty Medical Officers. Sotheron Estcourt, when he was President of the Poor Law Board, included in his plan for reform (November 1858) a suggestion that a new table of fees should be compiled by the central authorities and the Medical Council, and that this should include more operations and expensive drugs and appliances. The Medical Relief Bill of 1860 contained a clause identical with Griffin's proposal, and included Estcourt's recommendation that medicines, apparatus, and splints should also be covered, but it excluded the provision of wooden legs, crutches, and trusses. All three schemes advocated the prohibition of compounding of extra fees and remuneration for consultation.

No law existed for payment for consultation on difficult cases, or for advice and assistance at operations. Some Guardians were generous and others refused to acknowledge the justice in reimbursing doctors for such additional aid. Assistance at major operations was imperative and Medical Officers generally helped each other gratuitously, but this was unfair when the low salaries were taken into consideration. Dr. Wallis gave evidence to the Select Committee of 1854 on how he was refused fees in Bristol for coming to the aid of a doctor in difficulties. Griffin informed the same Committee that a surgeon required three assistants at an amputation, and on one occasion the Guardians in Weymouth agreed to pay for these. Then Inspector Gulson called and pointed out that the regulations declared that the Medical Officer must provide assistants for operations at his own expense. The Guardians were therefore powerless, although they subsequently returned the three guineas to him, and also paid him two guineas several times for giving advice on obstetrical questions to another Medical Officer. Griffin objected to the lack of security afforded to doctors on this point. In some Unions doctors, if they consulted each other, shared the fee the Guardians paid for the extra duty in order not to occasion the Board any further expense. He concluded that a case clearly existed for making a ruling for the payment of consultants and assistants—a scheme which the British Medical Association had recommended as far back as 1839. The Medical Bill of 1860 required that advice should always be obtained by a doctor when necessary and that the Guardians should pay for it. If a patient resided within 1 mile of the consultant a fee of 10s. should be paid, if he lived from 1 to 3 miles away £1, and if over this distance £2. The Bill also stipulated that in cases of sudden death where no registered medical man had attended and an inquiry had to be instituted, a Medical Officer should receive 5s. plus 1s. per mile travelling expenses from the Guardians.

A unique experience befell Joseph Rogers in 1867. He had a severe midwifery case at the Strand workhouse and called in another doctor for consultation. Because the operation entailed $2\frac{1}{2}$ hours of difficult work, Rogers asked the Guardians for additional remuneration. They not only offered him a guinea, which was the usual midwifery fee paid in the Strand Union for workhouse and district cases but also £3 13s. 6d. to pay £3 3s. for the consultant, and 10s. 6d. to another doctor for assisting. Rogers stated that the Strand Union in acceding to his request had established a very important precedent, and he asked the *Lancet* to publish the incident so that other Poor Law Medical Officers might be encouraged to make similar applications.[1] In the same year the *Lancet* printed another letter which showed the variation in the actions of the Guardians. A doctor of Settle Union asked for a fee of £2 for a difficult obstetrical case. The Guardians refused the request and allowed him £1 only, demanding that in future he should call in another Medical Officer to endorse the application for the extra fee. The doctor said this injured his pride, and as there was only one other qualified practitioner in the district, it would be unjust to them both to have to consult each other at any hour of the day without a fee being offered, in order that one of them might claim the extra remuneration for the work.[2]

The diversity which existed in the method of computing salaries, in the extra fees given, and in the supply of drugs inevitably resulted in an infinite variety of actual rates which Medical Officers received throughout the country. The absence of positive provisions for medical aid before 1834 in the 15,000 districts which administered poor relief under the uncontrolled discretion of parish officers had made it difficult for the central authorities to establish any uniform rate of payment in town and country Unions. We have seen how the Poor Law Commissioners usually deferred to the opinion of the Guardians concerning remuneration, for they maintained that as salaries were paid by the local ratepayers, the central authorities were placed in a delicate position in enforcing an increase in opposition to their opinions. The Commissioners affirmed that the rate of remuneration was as high as could be obtained under the prevailing circumstances without Parliamentary interference, and while Medical Officers complained that they were deprived of adequate remuneration, Guardians asserted on the contrary that they were required to pay excessive salaries. Amid these objections, Nicholls wrote, the Commissioners had to pursue a medium course, 'that they succeeded', he continued, 'can be inferred from the fact that both parties continued to complain of the other being unduly favoured'.[3]

The amount of the salaries really resolved itself on the question of competition, and the first central authorities stated that they found it exceedingly difficult to keep up a rate beyond that which Medical Officers were willing to accept. They believed that doctors expressed their satisfaction in the practical way by accepting office on the terms offered them, and although, as we have seen, there was much agitation against inadequate salaries in the early years, doctors were to blame to a great extent for the way in which they were exploited. In the 'thirties there was a disposition to acquiesce in the remuneration, because they believed this would lead to a good private practice, and less than a covering salary was

[1] 9 January. Letter printed in *Lancet*, 1867, i, p. 99. 19.1.67.
[2] Dr. Edwin Green, Settle Union. Letter in *Lancet*, 10 December 1867.
[3] Sir George Nicholls, *History of the English Poor Law*, 1854.

accepted. Active competition for practices existed[1] which had ceased by the 'sixties, but the scales of payment remained regulated by earlier ones.

In 1848 a Member of Parliament informed the Commons that 'it was well known that medical men were generally ruined in their profession if they did their duty to the poor'.[2] In looking at the statistics (Table 12.4) offered to the Select Committee of 1854 a steady rise in the total salary expenditure to Medical Officers between 1838 and 1853 can be seen, but since the number of Medical Officers had increased from 2,000 to over 3,000 their individual salaries were reduced.

TABLE 12.4

Salaries and Fees paid to Medical Officers between the years 1838 and 1853.—Statistics supplied to Select Committee, 1854: Abstract of Accounts, 1857–58, B.P.P., xlix, Pt. I.

Salary, including extra fees		Salary		Midwifery and Surgical fees	Total
	£		£	£	£
1838	136,000	1847	139,340	40,186	179,526
1839	148,652	1848	155,784	42,170	197,954
1840	151,781	1849	156,850	54,331	211,181
1841	154,054	1850	159,210	67,961	227,171
1842	153,481	1851	159,656	54,337	209,953
1843	160,726	1852	162,858	49,192	212,050
1844	166,330	1853	165,198	49,856	215,054
1845	174,330				
1846	175,190				

Inspector Cane maintained that Union doctors were much more satisfied with the rates of payment than they were previously. The Regulations of 1842 and 1847 had led, over a great part of the country, to extra medical fees and gratuities, and vaccination fees had been introduced. In 1857 a special Return to the House of Commons showed that net salaries were £177,270 (as compared with £156,500 net in 1850), and that extra medical fees amounted to £36,386, fees for certifying lunatics to £3,458, and for vaccination to £33,847. Guardians had also begun to find drugs and were subscribing to hospitals and infirmaries to lessen the work of the Medical Officers; the forty-six Unions which were

[1] Cornewall Lewis, 1844—said there was a superfluous number of doctors at the time. (Competition for Poor Law office was also great because in many areas it was the only means of obtaining the large proportion of working class as patients.)

[2] Captain Pechell, 16 March 1848. Hansard, 1848, vol. 97, p. 603.

providing medicines spent £8,387 on this item. In 1862 Cane admitted that frequent complaints from Medical Officers were still received regarding the inadequacy of their salary, but they were not so loud or well-founded since 1854. By this time medical extras had risen to £40,000, vaccination fees to £40,000–£50,000 and compulsory payment for certifying lunatics had been introduced, the fees totalling well over £3,000. Guardians in the early 'sixties were also beginning to give special gratuities more frequently for rendering extraordinary services during outbreaks of fever or in consideration of lengthened attendance on particular cases. Even the Clerk to the City of London Board of Guardians did not believe doctors were being adequately paid, and suggested that this was short-sighted policy, for medical expenditure was augmented by the increased ordering of food and necessaries for the poor, the cost of which might just as well have been paid in a higher doctor's salary. But he recognized the general tendency for Guardians to increase emoluments; some had advanced them by 10 per cent and one Union[1] by 40 per cent.

The Inquiry of 1864 brought to light that more than one-third of the salaries of Union officers in England and Wales was paid exclusively to the doctors. A comparison of Poor Law officers' salaries is interesting and was given in 1850—see Table 12.5. By 1868 net salaries of Medical Officers had risen to £208,057, extra medical fees to £45,563, and

TABLE 12.5

Comparison of Poor Law Officers' salaries in the year 1850 covering 604 Unions and thirty under Local Acts.

	Number	Average salary per annum		Number	Average salary per annum
		£			£
Clerks	634	110	Nurses	248	14
Chaplains	466	47	Labour		
Medical Officers	3,156	50	Superintendents	69	38
Relieving Officers	1,377	82	Collectors	3,042	24 (plus
Masters and Matrons	1,359	37			commission)
Schoolmasters	383	31	Treasurers	622	(Paid by
Schoolmistresses	501	21			poundage)
Porters	442	18	Order Officer	505	26
			District Auditors	49	268

Total number 12,853—£43 average—Total £548,690

[1] This was the Union to which Charles Villiers belonged; he was Chairman of the Select Committee and was later to become a President of the poor Law Board. As Member of Parliament for Wolverhampton, he was interested particularly in the Free Trade Movement and the Repeal of the Corn Laws.

nearly £19,500 was paid by Guardians for medical appliances and drugs.[1] In ten years therefore salaries had increased by £30,787 or 17.4 per cent and additional fees by £9,177 or 25.2 per cent.[2]

Apart from official opinions, the Medical Officers' Associations collected much evidence on salaries. In a petition from the Convention of Poor Law Medical Officers to Sir George Grey in 1848 many anomalies were revealed. When the Poor Law Board assumed office Medical Officers were exposed to low rates and wide disparities in their payments. Flagrant inconsistency caused great individual hardship and inflicted grave injury on the poor as well as on their doctors. In 1848 the rate 'per case' varied throughout the country from threepence to 14s. 4d., and the average rate of payment for each case of sickness, which the Convention had ascertained from returns of 805 Medical Officers, was 1s. 6¾d. per case in the Metropolis and 2s. 7d. in the country. Yet, it was pointed out, the average cost of drugs for a single case in the dispensaries for paupers was 2s. 0d. and for hospital patients 4s. 4½d. There was great variation within Unions and many illustrations were given; in the Axbridge Union the Medical Officer of one district who attended only 200 cases of sickness in a year and had a district of only 7,100 acres received an average of 3s. 1d. a case, whilst a colleague in a neighbouring area treated 1,404 patients scattered over 17,420 acres for only elevenpence per case.

The successors of the Convention, the Poor Law Medical Officers' Reform Association, sent a petition to the House of Commons ten years later containing a great analysis of salaries and anomalies deduced from statistics which Griffin had laboriously collected. Some 500 medical men were taken at random and their salaries averaged 2s. 9¾d. a case, payment varying from threepence to £1 16s. 8d. including drugs. The following table was included in the Petition. Of the 500 doctors:

28 received	3d. to	1s. 0d. per case	7 received	6s. 6d. to	7s. 0d. per case
35	1s. 0d.	1s. 6d.	12	7s. 0d.	8s. 0d.
48	1s. 6d.	2s. 0d.	10	8s. 0d.	9s. 0d.
69	2s. 0d.	2s. 6d.	8	9s. 0d.	10s. 0d.
71	2s. 6d.	3s. 0d.	3	10s. 0d.	11s. 0d.
55	3s. 0d.	3s. 6d.	2	11s. 0d.	12s. 0d.
49	3s. 6d.	4s. 0d.	3	12s. 0d.	13s. 0d.
32	4s. 0d.	4s. 6d.	4	13s. 0d.	14s. 0d.
24	4s. 6d.	5s. 0d.	2	14s. 0d.	15s. 0d.
14	5s. 0d.	5s. 6d.	1	15s. 0d.	16s. 0d.
10	5s. 6d.	6s. 0d.	1	16s. 0d.	17s. 0d.
10	6s. 0d.	6s. 6d.	1	17s. 0d.	18s. 0d.
			1	£1 16s. 8d.	

[1] Twenty-first Annual Report of the Poor Law Board.
[2] Total expenditure on medical relief had increased by about 10 per cent.

Griffin also gave detailed evidence on the subject at the Inquiry of 1861. Admitting there had been a rise in salaries, he did not believe Medical Officers enjoyed any material gain, because although total amounts had increased, work had grown more in proportion. He pointed out that in 1843 the total population of Unions had been 13,750,000, and Medical Officers salaries £139,784, so that doctors received twopence-halfpenny on the entire population. This had been so unequally applied that some Unions paid only a farthing per head (Glossop) whilst in others it was 1s. 2¾d. (Thetford), and there was every possible intermediate stage. By 1860 the population was estimated at nearly twenty million and medical expenses amounted to £236,339. The sum per head of the population was practically the same as formerly—it was still less than threepence, varying from a farthing to ninepence, which was the highest sum paid, and showing a decrease therefore over 1843. This decrease was accounted for by medical expenditure including more than salaries. The cost of medicines, wines, medical appliances, vaccination, and subscriptions to hospitals were all added to the net salaries, and as more Guardians were providing for these items a greater proportion of the expenditure had to be deducted from the total figure. This was particularly marked in the Metropolis; in 1857, for example, the Poor Law Board credited the St. Pancras Medical Officers with £2,786 when they had only received £1,085 according to a separate Return made by Lord Elcho and Abel Smith to the House of Commons in that year. The St. Marylebone doctors were said to have received £1,980, whereas the separate return gave only £1,441 and in St. Mary, Islington, Poor Law figures gave £1,500 compared with £634. The Poor Law Board had promised an inquiry into these discrepancies after Griffin had made several representations but nothing was done.

Such errors in statistical computation must be ignored for comparative purposes, and great similarity existed in payments in the two periods. In 1842, 411 Unions were paying less than threepence per head of the population and in 1857, 399. In 1861, twenty-one Unions were offering the same salary as in 1842, despite the increase in population. Twenty-two Unions had reduced salaries by an average of nearly £16, although the expenses of medical treatment had risen, and forty-one Unions, even with extra fees added to the salaries still paid Medical Officers less in 1857 than in 1841 by nearly £3,000. Eleven of these however increased the remuneration in the next four years. Sixteen Unions paid their doctors collectively, salaries so low that they averaged only eightpence to 1s. per patient. At the opposite extreme were Unions which paid as high a salary as 16s. a case on an average. Between these gradations there were in the 667 Unions, 239 which remunerated Medical Officers with eightpence to 3s. a patient, 348 who paid from 3s. to 7s., and 51 from 7s. to 16s.

There was similar blatant diversity in the emoluments of individual Medical Officers within a single Union. In 1862 3,509 Poor Law doctors were employed, and their individual income ranged from threepence to 68s. a case. (The latter was very exceptional, and probably arose because not all cases had been recorded for dividing into the salary.) There were 140 Medical Officers whose salaries were so low that they averaged less than 1s. a patient, and of these eighty-nine had had to find their own medicines. Griffin pointed out that such doctors would have to substitute methylated spirits for wine, quassia for quinine, and blisters instead of leeches. 'But', he declared, 'it is a wretched system which compels the Poor Law Medical Officer to be obliged to have recourse to such means to make his salary meet expenses . . . it is unjust to the medical man, cruel to the poor, and anything but a saving to the ratepayers.' There were 595 doctors with less than 2s. a case, 1,173 with less than 3s., 1,716 with less than 4s. and 2,150 with under 5s. Above these there were 931 doctors who received the princely sum of 5s. to 10s. a patient, and 313 were given 10s. to 68s. Nothing could account for this diversity. Griffin maintained that the more travelling a doctor was compelled to do, the less he was paid, and in urban areas this could not account for the dissimilarity. In Kensington, for example, two Medical Officers received 1s. 6d. and 2s. 5d. respectively. In Fulham one doctor was paid elevenpence while another received 4s. 3d., the latter having the more compact district. Payment per patient in Lambeth ranged from fivepence to 9s. 6d. for its two Medical Officers, and in Wandsworth and Clapham from 1s. 6d. to 7s. 1d.

Nor could the diversity be accounted for by the amount of work performed, for by this criterion, Medical Officers in poverty-stricken areas of Unions, although they had no long journeys, ought to have been entitled to the highest rewards. Taking the three City of London Unions,[1] the average amount of salaries and extra fees combined, in East London for the three years ending 1859 were 1s. 1¼d. a case, in West London 1s. 11¼d., and in the City of London 2s. 7¾d. In the latter one out of nineteen people came annually under the care of the District Medical Officer, in West London one in seven-and-two-thirds and in East London one out of every six-and-one-third. The density of population also varied—in the East there were 290 people to the acre, in the West 240, and in the City 106. Therefore it was logical to conclude that the East London Medical Officers had far more work, and as this was indisputably the poorest neighbourhood the doctors had a far more dangerous occupation and treatment for patients was more prolonged. Even within this Union there was lack of uniformity, one Medical Officer receiving ninepence-halfpenny a case and another in the adjoining parish 2s. 8d. The District Medical Officers of the East London Union collectively made an application to the Boards of Guardians for an increase in salary, enclosing Tables 12.6A and 12.6B, which showed the Guardians how much more their neighbouring colleagues were paid.[2]

The agitation was led by Dr. R. Fowler, Secretary of the Metropolitan Medical Officers, and Drs. Lobb, T. Lloyd, and H. Hadlow. They demanded that their salaries should be augmented to equal those of the District Medical Officers in the other two Unions—which meant an increase of £200. To further their application the four doctors pointed out that half the increase would in any case be furnished by the Consolidated Fund.

Jealousy also existed among the medical profession itself, and this sometimes stood in the way of an increase in salary being achieved. For example, in 1859, one of the three Kensington Medical Officers applied for a rise in remuneration, but the other two wrote to

---

[1] R. Fowler, evidence to Select Committee, 1862.
[2] Letter, 6 July 1859.

TABLE 12.6A

Table showing the Amount per Case produced by Sums paid as Annual Salaries to the District Medical Officers of the three City Unions.

Union	Total number of cases treated*			Total of the three years	Mean number of the three years	Total amount paid as salaries†	Actual amount per case
	1857	1858	1859			£	s. d.
East London	7,361	7,133	6,516	21,010	7,003	320	10¾
West London	3,953	3,940	3,123	11,016	3,672	220	1 2¼
City of London	2,751	3,357	2,766	8,817	2,939	280	1 10¾

* Total number of cases treated by the District Medical Officers of the three City Unions during the three years ending 25 March.
† Total amount paid to the District Medical Officers as annual salaries.

TABLE 12.6B

Table showing Average Amount per Case paid as Extra Medical Fees to the District Medical Officers of the Three City Unions, for the year ending 25 March.

Union	1857	1858	1859	Total of the three years	Average of the three years	Average annual number of cases treated	Actual amount per case
	£ s. d.	£ s. d.	£ s. d.	£ s. d.	£ s. d.		d.
East London	79 10 0	78 9 6	70 16 4	228 15 10	76 5 3¼	7,003	2½
West London	152 6 0	134 15 6	129 9 6	416 11 0	138 17 0	3,672	9
City of London	65 15 6	132 5 0	135 17 0	333 17 6	111 5 10	2,939	9

the Board of Guardians stating that this was quite unnecessary and unfair, and asked them not to consider the application, as their duties were equally arduous. In 1868 the Medical Officer, Dr. Guazzaroni applied again for an increase in his salary—he received £250 a year for attending the workhouse, a district, an average of 130 midwifery cases, and for vaccinations. (A doctor of St. Margaret's, Westminster, received £250 for the workhouse alone.) Guazzaroni had been the Union doctor for twenty years without a rise in salary, although as he stated his work had greatly increased. Replying to his request, the Guardians complained of his supply of medicines and asked him to establish a dispensary at his own house where the poor could call for drugs and obtain treatment. If this were done, an increase in remuneration might be considered. In 1869 Guazzaroni conceded to the demand

and his salary was augmented by £25. This year he applied for an increase in his stipend for workhouse duties which had grown to an unprecedented degree. In 1859 he had attended 283 patients a quarter in the institution, in 1865 421. By 1868 this number had risen to 623 and by 1869 to 834 a quarter, and yet he still received only £85 for duties which had trebled. It was the same with his district duties where he was now receiving £100 compared with his colleagues who were getting £125 a year. In 1870 Guazzaroni died, and it is significant that although he had been a Union Medical Officer for so long the Board of Guardians gave no mention of his death in their Minutes.[1]

Turning to the remuneration of workhouse doctors, we see that diversity in payment existed here also. The extreme variation was threepence-halfpenny to 16s. a patient, the average amounting to 2s. The Poor Law Medical Officers blamed the Guardians, but Griffin condemned the Poor Law Board, because the law had charged them with the power of regulating salaries and therefore they were bound to see that the Guardians did their duty. In conclusion he exclaimed: 'Make it do its duty; if not sweep it away, and let not a sham power continue in existence.'

As Medical Officer to the Poor Law Board, Dr. Smith reported in 1866 that, as it was still not possible to formulate any principle regarding the payment of salaries which would 'commend itself to the judgement of all', emoluments of Union doctors, as of all other workers, had to rest on the relation between supply and demand. He pointed out that it had always been the practice of the profession to perform a very large amount of duty without fee and to attach more value to the work than to direct remuneration. Medical men took public appointments without salary or with a completely inadequate salary because there was no working agreement between them by which they could act together, and in the past they had been ready to underbid each other. In reference to the Poor Law Medical Service, legislation had to some extent mitigated this evil by rendering it illegal to receive tenders and by requiring Guardians to fix salaries before appointments were made. (But even in 1865 an advertisement appeared in the Lancet from the Bromyard Union, asking medical practitioners to send tenders and testimonials to the Clerk of the Union.[2]) Smith was of the opinion that beyond this, interference could not go, and the profession must be allowed to undersell its services if it thought right to do so. The increase in salaries had been progressive, but he confessed that no principle had been evolved to ascertain when a Medical Officer was being fairly remunerated. In the case of resident doctors, Guardians could look to the example of other institutions like the hospitals, and regarding full-time District Poor Law doctors, to the payment of assistants by private practitioners, but no analogy existed for the case of those who were engaged in private practice as well as in destitution work, save that of the usual fees charged to independent patients.

The Clerk to the City of London agreed with the central authority's decision that the Guardians were the best judges of remuneration. He maintained that the medical admini-

---

[1] This account abstracted from the Kensington Board of Guardians' Minutes over a period of several years.

[2] Lancet, 1865, i, p. 641. Article re advertisement of 3 June in issue of 10 June.

stration of the Poor Law was the most difficult and could not be settled by legislation or by sub-legislation of the Poor Law Board. It had to depend entirely on local circumstances and the basis of salaries had to be calculated by local men, for no uniform system could be laid down. The danger in this principle was illustrated in Stowe Union, Suffolk, where in eight years the Medical Officers had been changed four times through the constant quarrelling between the doctors and the Guardians over remuneration. In the Alresford Union in Hampshire, the Guardians themselves could not agree although the majority of them were of the opinion that the Medical Officers were adequately paid.

Medical Officers were aware that the ultimate determination of their salaries rested with the Poor Law Board, and that theoretically, if they did not agree with the stipends they could always appeal to the higher authority. In practice the Central Board had never increased a salary by order and had never altered a scale which Boards of Guardians had forwarded to them for approval on the appointment of a new doctor. They did occasionally however refuse to sanction a decrease in remuneration. Guardians in some areas were still trying to reduce salaries, as in the Hungerford Union where the Medical Officer received £80 a year—an average of sixpence a visit or 2s. 6d. per case. Here the Guardians voted the reduction of the payment to £70 in 1853, and on the Poor Law Board asking them to reconsider the proposal they replied that they were unanimous. They put their scheme into effect and ignored the Central Board. In 1856 a Medical Officer of Cockermouth wrote a letter to the *Lancet* describing his Guardians' activity. Two years previously the Poor Law Board had desired to see an alteration made in the size of the districts. This was resisted. Eventually four were made into five, but little alleviation was brought to the doctors' duties. Following this move the Guardians decided to reduce salaries from £35 to £30, regardless of population or the differences within the districts. The Medical Officer thereupon wrote to the Poor Law Board pointing out that in one year, after deducting expenses, he had received £11 1s. 6d. which included his extra fees, for making 1,786 visits and covering 1,417 miles. He averaged three-halfpence a visit whatever the distance or illness. His salary was reduced without warning, and again he communicated with the Poor Law Board without receiving a reply. His third letter brought an answer after twelve months, and in this the central authorities confirmed the Guardians decision![1] Many similar letters of complaint were reprinted in the *Lancet* at this time.

On the other hand Inspectors Cane and Austin reported that the Poor Law Board sometimes defined higher salaries than the Board of Guardians. In Wigan, for example, the Union was unable to obtain a Medical Officer who resided in the district because of the inadequate remuneration offered. The Central Board therefore urged (not ordered) that the salary should be raised to attract local practitioners to the appointment. Inspector Peel in a report in 1870 proposed that where Guardians could not obtain the services of a resident doctor through the paucity of the stipend, the Poor Law Board ought to *enforce* the offer of a higher salary. Dr. Gilbert stated in 1854 that in his Union of Banbury, no resident Medical

[1] Dr. Joseph Pearson, Medical Officer of Maryland District, Cockermouth Union. Letter, 15 March 1856: *Lancet*, 1856, i, pp. 297–98.

Officer could be obtained because of the low salary and the long journeys required, and Griffin pointed out that one of his colleagues had resigned from office because the Guardians of Weymouth contemplated the reduction of his remuneration although he had performed his duties well for eight years.

The *Lancet* thought quite highly of the Poor Law Board because they often refused to sanction reductions, and praised them in 1853 for baulking the intentions of the Bishop's Stortford Guardians.[1] In 1850 the same journal had printed a letter from the Manchester Medico-Ethical Association with the comment that it did so with 'extreme satisfaction' and because it showed the sagacity and humanity of Baines, the President of the Poor Law Board.[2] The Manchester Association praised the central authorities for refusing to sanction the Chorlton Board of Guardians' attempt to reduce the Medical Officers' salaries, and it further urged all members of the medical profession to give cordial assistance to the Poor Law Board by supplying them with statistics and information.—'Experience has shown it is to them that the profession must look for support and protection in any contests that may arise out of the growing tendency of local Boards to depreciate medical services.'

In 1851 the Tewkesbury Union (Gloucester) proposed to alter the stipends of the four Medical Officers. In the first district there was to be a reduction from £90 to £75, in the second from £45 to £40, in the third from £45 to £40, and the fourth was to remain at £35. The reason offered was that remuneration had increased considerably over the previous years because of the additional fees and the cost of vaccination, and that fixed salaries had remained unaltered. The Guardians maintained that the doctors had formerly agreed to perform additional duties without extra fees, and also that there had been a general reduction in salaries in the region because of the distress among the ratepayers owing to the decline in agricultural prices. One of the Medical Officers therefore complained to the Poor Law Board that his stipend was already inadequate for the care, labour, and expense demanded. The area he covered was 30 square miles and contained a population of 2,000–3,000, living very scattered in ten to twelve different villages. The roads in winter were quite impassable and yet the average distance of patients from his house was 4–5 miles. To overcome this great obstacle he had, at his own expense, established a dispensary in the centre of the district, where he attended three days a week to prescribe and dispense, and where the poor at all times could obtain medicine. Much time and trouble was saved the poor, though his own labour was increased. He received an average of 2s. 4d. a case, but pointed out that the great number of minor cases were not entered in his books. In the town dispensary, druggists received 2s. 6d. for medicines alone and worked at hours to suit themselves. They were paid separately for leeches and cod-liver oil, and only had the additional outlay of an apprentice. He asked how he could be expected to pay for a horse, medicine, and the rent of the district surgery and still obtain remuneration from his allowance. He had to keep two horses because he travelled so extensively—in winter this amounted to 100 miles a week for an average sum of a guinea. When cholera had broken

[1] *Lancet*, 1853, i, p. 518.
[2] Letter, 18 February 1850: *Lancet*, i, p. 254.

out he had not asked for additional payment, and he maintained that the introduction of cod liver oil into general use incurred new heavy expenditure. The proposed reduction in salary he regarded as a great insult:

> It diminishes the respect in which the medical man must hold his labour to do it effectually, it informs him that the poor may be pressed down to an unjust state, and that the saving of a few pounds is the highest and only object of those appointed his masters, no matter how it be obtained.

The Guardians' letter explained that the reason for the proposed reduction of salaries was that the cost of necessary articles of consumption had been reduced through the fall in the prices of agricultural produce. But the Poor Law Board replied that they

> never recognized the principle that the price of articles and of the produce referred to is to be a criterion by which the amount of salaries should be liable to vary as the prices of food fluctuate. The price of food and necessities of life are important and should be considered in fixing the remuneration of labour—but the nature of the office and the services to be performed, the character, position and qualification which should be possessed by a candidate for office, the adequacy and certainty of remuneration sufficient to ensure such candidates is also important and unconnected with prices and variations, which cannot be disregarded without danger to many interests involved in the judicious and efficient administration of the Poor Law.[1]

Therefore the Poor Law Board refused to sanction the contemplated reduction in salaries.[2]

On other occasions the central authorities were not so generous or wise, and although they gave early and repeated assurances of sympathy, and affirmed their desire to ameliorate the status of Union surgeons, in the case of the Holborn doctors they not only sanctioned a reduction in salary to an average of eightpence a case, but actually made suggestions to the Guardians which would have diminished it further and increased the work of the Medical Officers.[3] The York Guardians wished to raise the salary of a doctor from £70 to £100 a year, but the Poor Law Board demurred, saying the increase was excessive, and only agreed to the proposal in 1866 after the Guardians had persisted in their demand.[4] In St. George in the East, where Medical Officers were still engaged by annual election, salaries in the 'fifties were still the same as they had been in the 'forties. One doctor received £35, three £60, and a fourth £80 which included payment for visiting the Plashet Poor Law School. They continually applied for an increase in remuneration, particularly the workhouse doctor who was receiving £45 a year although his duties had increased enormously.[5]

---

[1] Letter from the Poor Law Board, 24 February 1851.
[2] Accounts and Papers, House of Commons, December 1852.
[3] C. F. J. Lord, evidence to Select Committee, 1854.
[4] *Lancet*, 1867, i, p. 261.
[5] Board of Guardians' Minutes over a period of years for this account.

It was only in 1869 that the Board of Guardians asked the Poor Law Board for permission to increase the salary of the Medical Officer who attended the Plashet School. They wished to offer him £120, but the central authorities required them to reconsider the application. The Guardians replied that the doctor in question attended the children with great vigilance, he tried to detect the first symptoms of disease, gave careful treatment and devoted a long time to the school, so that they considered the increase in salary as reasonable. The Poor Law Board was however adamant, stated the salary was sufficient, and finally declined to discuss the subject further. Dr. Garrett, one of the Medical Officers of this Union which contained 42,000 people, a very high proportion of whom were poverty stricken, said in 1854 that he had accepted office seventeen years previously when he was young. It had been a question of a drowning man catching at a straw: 'When young men commence practice they are very glad of these appointments, it was so in the days of my youth.' At first his motive had been to bring him into prominence so that he could build up a private practice, but the experience of later years had changed his ideas.

Where Medical Officers had held office and were appointed for a fixed period only, they often refused to accept further employment unless their salaries were raised. But it was rarely difficult to obtain the services of fresh practitioners and there was frequently more than one candidate. Inspector Cane maintained in 1854 that keen competition still existed, and that he had heard sincere disappointment expressed by those who had failed to obtain a post. Representations were regularly made to the Poor Law Board because these men conceived injury and injustice had been done to them. Therefore Cane concluded:

> ... looking at the facility with which Medical Officers' services are obtained, the avidity with which such offices are sought for, the tenacity with which they are held, and the reluctance with which they are given up ... these offices afford very considerable attractions to the whole medical profession.

He did not believe Medical Officers were inadequately paid in the 'fifties and refused to entertain the idea that doctors accepted Poor Law office for ulterior motives. Salary, he suggested, was the predominant consideration, not keeping others out of private practice. But Inspector Austin at the same Inquiry stated that salaries were only a portion of the return or compensation Medical Officers looked for, as work amongst the poor gave them a reputation leading to practice amongst the wealthier sections of the community. He hedged on giving actual figures of remuneration, and when asked whether Medical Officers were compensated for drugs, loss of time, and expense in travelling, he did not know— although he was an Inspector! He said this was less important than the other reasons for taking office. He also could not supply any data on whether the salaries earned afforded a doctor a profit, but merely generalized that in his opinion compensation was adequate to the duties, otherwise they would not be undertaken. This sentiment was re-echoed by Inspector Peel in his Report on Outdoor Relief in 1870. He maintained that although salaries were undoubtedly too low in many instances, Medical Officers accepted them voluntarily with full consciousness that a rigid performance of duties would be exacted.

Dr. Cooper of Suffolk stated that his reason for accepting an appointment as Poor Law Medical Officer despite the slight remuneration attached to it, was that his predecessor had lived such a great distance away that he (Cooper) was performing most of his duties in any case. He kept an account of all journeys made and all medicines supplied to the district. The salary he received was £40, and yet according to the usual scale of charges to private patients for treatment, journeys, and medicines this should have amounted to £302. The payment he should have received for attending the local medical club of sixty members amounted to £24, but he only received £9, but even so, while he was attending club patients for three-eighths the usual charges he attended Union patients for one-eighth. He declared the attention which he paid to the sick paupers was nevertheless as efficient as that which he afforded to his private patients, and he gave the poor no cause for complaint.

In a rural area in Derbyshire, Medical Officers received £20 and £22 for attending scattered populations of 8,000–9,000. In Norfolk £50 was usual as the Rev. Howman stated to the Select Committee of 1854, and his Union paid £300 to six doctors. In Plympton, Devon, two District Medical Officers received £45 and £40 for districts 7 miles square, which were thickly populated and contained a high proportion of paupers. The workhouse generally contained about 200 inmates and the doctors' salary was only £10, a sum insufficient for medicines and leeches alone. In the Wells Union, the District Medical Officers attended an average of 500 cases a year for a salary of £55, and the workhouse doctor received £40, all were paid an average of £15 in extra fees. Although this rate of remuneration was comparatively high for rural areas, the doctors complained that it was inadequate for the efficient execution of their duties. One Medical Officer believed this was the reason for the Poor Law medical system not working well, as doctors were compelled to link private practice to Poor Law duties, to the detriment of the latter. In 1851, in an epidemic which lasted six months, he had attended eighty-nine cases and made eighty-six journeys to a parish 5 miles away. For these journeys totalling 860 miles he had received £1 4s. 6d.

Rural officers had the disadvantage of having to travel long distances; doctors in practice amid the squalor of industrial slums had to contend with immensity of numbers and patients who lived in the receptacles of disease. But with the spread of these forbidding wildernesses, salaries were higher here than elsewhere, for where great poverty and sickness prevailed, there was also to be found wealth. In the provincial conurbations therefore but not in the Metropolis, ratepayers could afford higher remuneration for their Medical Officers. It was both these factors—the growth of new seats of poverty and of wealth, which caused the ironing out of the general differences in the supply of medical relief and its cost between North and South, which, as we have seen, existed earlier. In this later period dominant variations between urban and rural communities replaced regional diversity, although within these classifications no uniformity was ever achieved either.

In Bristol, the Medical Officer of the Clifton Union received £140 a year, divided equally for district and workhouse duties. He was the sole Poor Law doctor engaged for a population of 25,000, living for the most part in densely crowded courts and streets. In the naval town of Devonport the pauper doctor received £120 a year. Liverpool in 1854 paid its nine Medical Officers—half of whom were engaged solely on Poor Law duties—£2,069 with £40 to £50 per doctor for vaccination. Drugs were supplied at the city's expense and had risen from £1,039 in 1851 to £1,218 in 1852, and £1,320 in 1853, so that nearly £4,000 was spent on salaries and drugs in a year. But as the Assistant Overseer and Superintendent of Relief (Edward Grey) pointed out, the saving of life and the prevention of pauperism by this humane procedure fully compensated the Board for the outlay, and ratepayers did not complain.

Nowhere was the economic importance of liberal remuneration to Medical Officers realized so strongly as in the Metropolis, where a large percentage of poverty had always been a problem. Paupers were said to constitute one-thirtieth of the population, and the rise in doctors' salaries, though nowhere sufficient or startling, showed there was an increasing awareness of the importance of medical relief. In Chelsea, for example, the District Medical Officer who also attended the workhouse, received £130 and £35 for extras in 1850, and the other doctors £70 plus £4 7s., £67 plus £17 11s. and £30 plus £25. In 1852 the salaries were still the same but extra fees had risen to £150 and vaccination fees amounted to £40. Three years later the four districts were redivided into five, carrying salaries of £92, £82, £70, £30, and £24 with a total of £150 for extras and £41 for vaccination. In 1863 vaccination fees amounted to £340 and extra fees to £91. In 1865 salaries were raised to £150, £90, £80, £50, and £30 with £113 for extras and only £38 for vaccination fees, and the Guardians paid £12 for all trusses and surgical instruments. Medical extras in 1869 amounted to £140 and vaccination fees to £92 and in this year the Guardians began to supply drugs to the value of £23 and they also paid £8 for trusses and surgical instruments. In the year following extra fees totalled £135 and vaccination £69, and an inspector of vaccination was engaged at £25 10s. a year.[1]

In St. Leonards, Shoreditch, four District Medical Officers were paid £100 a year between 1857 and 1861, and the workhouse surgeon £126 for attending 650 people on an average in the institution. By 1867 there were six District Medical Officers receiving £100 and the workhouse doctor was paid £200 and his new assistant £63. Four years later another District Medical Officer was appointed at £100 and the institution officer had his salary raised to £220 with board and lodging.[2] Before 1867 one Poor Law physician was in charge of all the sick of Greenwich workhouse, estimated at between 400 and 800, and he received £200 a year including all fees and vaccination and the supply of medicines. In that year an additional doctor was engaged, so that there was one for the male wards, who was to receive £160, and another for the female wards at £100; the Guardians also began to find the drugs.[3]

Bethnal Green workhouse which housed 600 sick had only one Medical Officer who

---

[1] St. Luke's, Chelsea, Board of Guardians' Abstract of Accounts for several years.
[2] St. Leonards, Shoreditch, Quarterly Estimate of Poor Rates for several years.
[3] *Lancet* Inquiry, 6 March 1867.

also did the dispensing, and he was paid £160 a year.¹ St. Pancras advertised for a new workhouse doctor in the *Lancet* in 1867 at £160 rising to £200 with vaccination fees, board, and lodging.

By the Metropolitan Poor Act of 1867, officers' salaries became a common charge over the whole of the Metropolis, therefore the Poor Law Board endeavoured to secure as far as practicable a uniform basis of remuneration for all officers of a similar class. In a Circular issued to Guardians on 10 November 1869 they requested that before any subsequent additional appointment was made, or any existing salary altered, the proposal was to be communicated to the Central Board for consideration and approval. Existing salaries were to be reconsidered as vacancies occurred. Table 12.7 illustrates the amount of salaries and the number of Medical Officers employed in 1867 and the changes effected by 1871, after the four years of active reform.

Much attention was focused on the enormous burden of pauperism and the increasing amount of medical relief required in the Metropolis in the late 'sixties, and no doubt the authorities recognized it was a sound investment to afford efficient treatment to the sick, which in turn necessitated the employment of more doctors at higher salaries. The official view was always circumspect, however, and probably more reforms were due to the constant and insistent agitation of the Medical Officers than to the growing enlightenment of their employers.

Throughout the country also there had been a shift of balance in the provinces where relief for destitution was required, and the scales weighed heavily on the side of the sick and the aged. There was not however a similar universal rise in the numbers of Union doctors or their salaries. In Birmingham, for example, the District Medical Officers had made a representation to the Guardians in 1861, drawing attention to the great increase in the number of cases requiring medical relief and the neglect to increase salaries proportionately. They included a table showing that for the period 1852–60 their duties had doubled:

Annual average of new cases for the three years
1852, 1853, and 1854 = 6,432 being 2s. 9¾d. per case;
1855, 1856, and 1857 = 10,097 being 1s. 9¾d. per case;
1858, 1859, and 1860 = 11,621 being 1s. 6½d. per case.

A Wiltshire doctor wrote a letter to the Convention of Poor Law Medical Officers in 1854 saying he was still receiving £45, the same as he had received when first appointed, so that the average payment per case had fallen to ninepence-three-farthings.

Demand for redress by the medical profession was naturally widespread, and because remuneration bore no intelligible relation to the amount of work performed, one of the dominant themes was that salaries should increase proportionately with the work done. One of the leaders of the reform movement was Dr. R. Fowler, Honorary Secretary of the Association of Metropolitan Medical Officers. He himself as a District Medical Officer of East London attended an average number of cases in the Bishopsgate district of 2,805 a

¹ *Ibid.*

TABLE 12.7

Comparison between the years 1867 and 1871 (the period of reform) in the number of Poor Law Medical Officers employed and their salaries in Metropolitan Unions.—Most of the material was included in a Return to the House of Commons, 1872, B.P.P. LI, from which this table has been abstracted. More Unions were given; also there were similar statistics for Nurses in the Metropolis.

Union or Parish	Number of Medical Officers	Salaries KEY: 1867 data in roman type 1871 data in italic type
Greenwich	10	1 workhouse Medical Officer at £160 and Assistant at £100; 8 District Medical Officers at £160 a year each
	7	*1 workhouse Medical Officer at £300; 6 District Medical Officers at £120 a year each*
Woolwich (new Union 1868)	4	*2 at £125; 1 at £120 and 1 at £100*
Bethnal Green	5	1 at £160; 3 at £120; 1 at £100 + board and lodging
	8	*6 at £120; 1 at £160; 1 at £100 + board and lodging (workhouse)*
Fulham	6	1 workhouse Medical Officer at £50 + £12 12s. extras; 5 District Medical Officers at £50 each + extras averaging £16 a year
	6	*1 workhouse Medical Officer at £50 + £22 16s. extras; 5 District Medical Officers at £50 each + extras averaging £22 a year*
Hackney	6	1 at £180 + £37 11s. extras; 3 at £85; 1 at £76; 1 at £65 + extras of varying amounts
	7	*1 at £180 + £22 11s. extras; 1 at £85; 2 at £80; 1 at £120; 1 at £70; 1 at £65 + extras varying from £17 to £37*
Holborn (1869 parishes of St. James and St. Luke added)	4	4 at £125
	5	*3 at £75; 1 at £40; 1 at £130*
	5	£150; £125; £75; £70; £60
	15	*4 at £125; 1 at £150; 8 at £105; 1 at £130; 1 at £40*
Kensington	3	1 workhouse Medical Officer who was also District Medical Officer at £160 + £169 11s. extras; 1 District Medical Officer at £75 + £7; 1 District Medical Officer at £105 + £100 extras
	4	*1 workhouse Medical Officer who was also District Medical Officer at £185 + £205; 1 District Medical Officer £100 + £15 extras; 2 District Medical Officers at £125 and £95 + £68 extras*

TABLE 12.7—*continued*

Union or Parish	Number of Medical Officers	Salaries KEY: 1867 data in roman type *1871 data in italic type*
City of London added 1869	4	1 at £275 + 10s. 6d. for cases of midwifery; 3 at £100—no extras
E. London added 1869	5	1 at £125; 1 at £145; 1 at £140; 1 at £120; 1 at £75
W. London	3	£110 each
	11	*1 at £275 + midwifery; 1 at £125; 5 at £140; 1 at £190 + midwifery; 2 at £40; 1 at £10*
Mile End Old Town	2	2 at £200 and dispenser at £135
	3	*2 at £250; 1 at £200 and dispenser at £135*
Paddington	3	1 workhouse Medical Officer at £100 + £88 extras; 2 District Medical Officers at £150 + £120 in extras
	3	*1 workhouse Medical Officer at £100 + £74 extras; 2 District Medical Officers at £150 + £120 in extras*
Poplar	6	5 at £100; 1 at £105
	7	*3 at £170; 1 at £190; 1 at £160; (these 5 had fees commuted); 1 at £100; 1 at £150*
St. George in the East	5 + 1	1 workhouse Medical Officer at £100, and 1 District Medical Officer at £35 with £144 extras shared; 1 Medical Officer, Plashet School, at £100 3 District Medical Officers at £60 each with £72, £58, and £26 in extras.
	5 + 1	*1 workhouse Medical Officer at £100, and 1 District Medical Officer at £35 with £123 extras shared; 1 Medical Officer, Plashet School, at £100* *3 District Medical Officers at £60 each with £41, £71, and £81 in extras*
St. Leonards	8	1 workhouse Medical Officer at £200 + 1 assistant at £63; 6 at £100—no extras Medical Officer, Brentwood School, at £50
	1 *7 + 1*	*1 workhouse Medical Officer at £220 + lodgings; 7 District Medical Officers at £100 including dispenser*
St. Pancras	8	1 workhouse Medical Officer at £160 + assistant at £85—both board and lodging + 1 dispenser at £80 + meals; 6 District Medical Officers—4 at £150; 2 at £100

TABLE 12.7—*continued*

Union or Parish	Number of Medical Officers	Salaries KEY: 1867 data in roman type *1871 data in italic type*
St. Pancras— *cont.*	9	*1 workhouse Medical Officer at £150 + board and lodging—no assistant; Infirmary Medical Officer at £175 + board and lodging and dispenser at £80 + meals; 6 District Medical Officers at £150* *1 school Medical Officer at £100 + board and lodging*
Stepney	4 3	I workhouse Medical Officer at £220 + 10s. per case of midwifery 2 District Medical Officers at £120 + 1s. 6d. per vaccination I temporary District Medical Officer at £163 10s. I dispenser at £150 + assistant dispenser at £60 *1 workhouse Medical Officer at £220 + 10s. per case of midwifery* *2 District Medical Officers at £240 each—no extras* *1 dispenser at £150 + assistant dispenser at £32 10s.*
Whitechapel	4 I 5	2 at £125; 2 at £110 + 2 dispensers—I at £100 and I at £78 Medical Officer Forest Gate School—£110; became District School 1868 supported by Poplar, Whitechapel, Hackney *2 at £125; 2 at £110 + 2 dispensers—1 at £100 and 1 at £78* *Medical Officer, Forest Gate School—£110.*
Lambeth	12 I 13 + 1 I	10 District Medical Officers—4 at £80; I who had 2 districts £315; 2 at £75; 2 at £70; I at £50 I workhouse Medical Officer at £300; I assistant at £80 + I dispenser £40—both board and lodgings Medical Officer for Schools—£50 *10 District Medical Officers—4 at £80; 1 who had two districts at £315; 2 at £50; 1 at £75; 1 at £110; 1 at £70;* *1 workhouse Medical Officer at £300 and 1 temporary at £50; 1 assistant at £80—no workhouse dispenser but dispenser for 'outdoor sick' dispensary* *Medical Officer for Schools—£50*
Wandsworth and Clapham	9 9	I workhouse Medical Officer at £135 + £57 extras 8 District Medical Officers—2 at £110; I at £100; £50; £80; £30; £20; £25 *1 workhouse Medical Officer at £250 + lodging—no board* *8 District Medical Officers—at £75; £50; £110; £80; £40; £20; £25; £110—extras varied from 30s. to £80*

year, so that his salary came to sevenpence-halfpenny per illness which lasted an average of sixteen days. This fee included drugs, and paupers were supplied from the same stock as his private patients. He maintained that Metropolitan District Medical Officers should receive not less than 2s. 6d. a case excluding extras. Dr. Moore, another influential member of the Association said his salary was the same in 1862 as sixteen years previously, yet the population had doubled in his district of Bethnal Green. He stated that the Bethnal Green Poor Law doctors had once a year for the past five years applied for an increase in salary, which had fallen from 2s. to elevenpence-halfpenny a case.

The Rev. Oxenden giving evidence to the Select Committee of 1854 agreed that doctors should be remunerated in proportion to their duties, and proposed that Medical Officers should be paid £5 for every 100 people in rural areas. In his Union of Barham, with its population of 12,000, this would mean £600 a year, including extras, yet in 1853 only £258 was paid. The local Medical Charitable Society spent far more on medical relief for the poor, so Oxenden pointed to the logic of the argument in ratepayers paying £600 to cover the cost of medical relief for all the poor, as £586 was spent already on club members and paupers. Dr. Wallis, who propounded the free dispensary scheme, suggested at the same inquiry that salaries should be calculated in relation to population and area. Griffin acquiesced, but dwelt on the importance of the Poor Law Board settling the amount to be offered. Dr. Lord, speaking on behalf of the Convention of Poor Law Medical Officers, advocated the necessity for a more equitable scale of salaries, and that payment should be proportionate to duties. He gave further evidence of the vicious state of the existing system whereby some Medical Officers received threepence a case and others as much as 19s., and showed that Unions like Canterbury could still offer one doctor 2s. and another 10s. a case on an average. He did not desire to see fixed salaries generally, but that they should vary according to the population, area, and degree of pauperism. Workhouse doctors should also be paid a separate salary if they held a district appointment as well, and this should be based on the average number of inmates. This system operated to some degree in the Alresford Union (Hants.) where the salary of £100 was larger than usual for rural areas, because it was based on the number of cases seen in the past weeks. But even here only an average of 1s. to 1s. 3d. a visit was paid including drugs and extras, and Medical Officers were discontented and the poor dissatisfied.[1] The Select Committee, however, merely included in its resolutions that the Poor Law Board should direct their attention to the salaries of the Medical Officers 'which in some cases appear inadequate to the duties they are required to perform'. Even Pigott, who was a member of the Select Committee, and known for his sympathy towards the doctors' cause, only included in his individual resolutions that Poor Law Medical Officers should be paid liberally, mentioning no specific details. As Member of Parliament for Reading, it was he however who introduced the Medical Relief Bill of 28 March 1860, 'with a view to improving the position of Medical Officers and secure a more efficient relief to the poorer classes'.

[1] W. Taylor, Magistrate, Hampshire, evidence to Select Committee, 1854.

Regarding salaries, the Bill contained clauses whereby remuneration was to be based on the number of acres and the number of paupers in receipt of relief on an average in the first week in January and the first week in July each year, on an average of the last three years, and on the average number of patients over the last three years. Fresh calculations were to be made every year based on the past three years' averages. Any disputes were to be settled by the Poor Law Board. The Bill suggested salaries should be calculated at one penny per case plus 1s. 6d. per head on the average number of persons in receipt of relief in the three-yearly average plus 2s. 6d. for each patient attended by the Medical Officer on an average over the past three years, when a doctor supplied the medicines, and 1s. 6d. if the Guardians found them. Workhouse Medical Officers were to be remunerated on the same basis, but instead of receiving an average rate, they should be given 1s. for each attendance at the institution, infirmary, lunatic asylum, or schoolhouse, where these were situated less than 1 mile from his residence, or 2s. 6d. if over 1 mile and under 2, and 5s. for further distances.

Hundreds of petitions were sent both for and against the Bill. A mass petition was sent in its favour from the Poor Law Medical Officers' Reform Association at the instigation of Griffin. No less than 697 members sent him 5s. each to help his work for the Bill, and on 19 May the *Lancet* reported 246 petitions including 2,622 doctors' signatures had been sent to the House of Commons. One Medical Officer wrote a letter to the *Lancet* asking all doctors, not only those employed in pauper service, to petition the Commons. He said his own salary had been doubled since his appointment, and begged other favoured Medical Officers not to be apathetic, for all should join in the cause to help the less fortunate. He had encouraged well-known London physicians and all the staff of a hospital to sign a petition, and concluded his letter with a plea for them to rally round Griffin and Pigott: 'Up then and doing. Petition! Petition! Petition!'[1] One workhouse doctor sent a letter to the *Lancet* saying 25 per cent of the inmates were on his sick list. His duties entailed 5,406 personal visits a year and the administering of 10,000 doses of medicines. He was required to make lengthy weekly reports and had to examine all paupers on admission to the institution— which averaged 152 cases. For all this he received £15 salary, with £4 10s. for extras, generally for midwifery, for which he visited the workhouse at all times of the night. He had got many ratepayers to join in a petition and a Guardian, Chaplain, and solicitor had also signed.[2]

A total of 301 petitions, of which 265 were signed officially under seal, including 831 signatures were sent against the Bill. Pigott in a letter to Griffin on 4 May wrote that the feeling of the House of Commons had been well in favour of the Bill although it had been against some of the details, but Members of Parliament had been gradually converted by the storm of letters from the Guardians of their constituencies. The outcry against the measure had been immediate. Eccleshall (Yorks.) sent a Petition in which it was maintained doctors' salaries were sufficient.[3] The Hampstead Board of Guardians held a meeting at

[1] Anonymous letter, 3 March 1860: *Lancet*, 1860, i, p. 223.
[2] Anonymous letter, 24 March 1860: *Lancet*, 1860, i, p. 297.
[3] 2 May 1860: Minutes, Board of Guardians.

which letters from Cambridge, Wisbech, and other Unions were read, calling attention to, and pointing out the objections to the Bill. They passed a resolution that: 'The Poor Law Medical Relief Bill is open to various objections and is in many respects inapplicable to a Metropolitan parish,' and that a petition for its withdrawal should be presented to the Commons.[1] The Bill had little chance of success, neither the clauses nor the debate on the first reading were mentioned in *Hansard*,[2] and it was withdrawn on 5 May before the second reading.

In the following years Griffin worked for the introduction of legislation which agreed in part with the Medical Bill. He based his scheme on cases of sickness only, and not on population or pauperism, for he maintained that payment made according to population was impracticable, as the amount of medical relief afforded by the Poor Law authorities varied considerably in different parts of the country. It ranged from 1·6d. in the North to 5·7d. in the East, with other areas falling between the two. Even within a Union this difference existed. In his own Union of Weymouth, for example, the population of one district was 3,271, one in nine of which were the Poor Law doctors' patients; in the other area there was a population of 6,499, and only one in twenty were pauper patients. He also argued against remuneration being made proportionate to population because the average amount of sickness amongst indoor and outdoor paupers varied remarkably. The average of indoor and outdoor was nearly the same for the country, but it varied considerably between different regions; for example, in the South Midlands it was 1·9 and in the Eastern Counties 4·4 for the outdoor poor—see Table 12.8.

Griffin suggested that the inordinate amount of sickness in the South Midlands might be real or only apparent; if the latter, it was because medical relief was offered to all the labouring class, whilst in the East it was only given to paupers. With regard to workhouse inmates who were all paupers, like disparity existed in the amount of sickness amongst the poor, but it appeared in other geographical divisions. In the North-west nearly all would obtain institutional relief—an average of 1 in 1·8, whereas in the South-east, East, North Midlands, and North, only 1 in 3 patients would enter the workhouse. Therefore to remunerate Medical Officers according to the number of paupers would be to pay some three times as much as others, and also questions like the greater preponderance of fever in some areas would not be considered.

Griffin, after taking these factors into consideration, suggested salaries should be fixed according to the number of patients attended on the average of the last three years, with triennial recalculations. The rate should be not less than 5s. for each patient up to 300, and 2s. for each additional one, plus a sum for mileage—1s. for the first mile and 2s. if over this. He pointed out that members of Tradesmen's Clubs paid 5s.–6s. a year, and this afforded the basis for calculating the amount to be paid per case. Alternatively, he suggested a total sum for stipends might be allocated by Unions, which could be divided among the

[1] 3 May 1860: Board of Guardians' Minutes.
[2] *Hansard*, cxv, p. 163, 28 March 1860.

TABLE 12.8

Statistics of Illness amongst Paupers in 1857.—Griffin, evidence to Select Committee, 1862
(calculated from a Return moved for by Lord Elcho, 1857).

Region	Outdoor Poor	Cases of Illness	Average amount of Sickness	Indoor Poor	Cases of Illness	Average amount of Sickness
Metropolis	604,188	200,092	1 in 3·0	220,760	89,675	1 in 2·4
South-Eastern	301,437	143,642	1 in 2·6	82,604	22,996	1 in 3·5
South Midlands	224,241	115,189	1 in 1·9	44,753	15,172	1 in 2·9
Eastern	523,855	117,770	1 in 4·4	56,060	17,210	1 in 3·3
South-Western	298,418	147,907	1 in 2·0	48,085	17,114	1 in 2·8
West Midlands	282,902	113,857	1 in 2·4	48,027	20,049	1 in 2·3
North Midlands	144,329	54,914	1 in 2·6	29,639	8,901	1 in 3·3
North-Western	262,726	84,701	1 in 3·1	64,634	35,488	1 in 1·8
Yorkshire	149,033	42,273	1 in 3·5	29,191	11,483	1 in 2·6
Northern	100,320	25,881	1 in 3·8	27,981	8,381	1 in 3·3
Wales	203,129	48,713	1 in 4·1	15,756	5,539	1 in 2·8
Total	3,122,578	1,094,939	1 in 2·8	667,490	252,008	1 in 2·6

Medical Officers according to the number of tickets each held. This system worked success-fully in clubs and should have done so under Poor Law administration, although Griffin had never heard of a Union experimenting with the scheme. The salaries of doctors em-ployed in workhouses, infirmaries, lunatic asylums, or schools should be fixed on the same basis as that of the District Medical Officer, and he agreed with Pigott's scheme that the mileage fee should be replaced by 1s. for each mile travelled for every attendance. Medical Officers, like clergymen, should also be exempt from tolls on roads, and be free of the tax assessed on one horse, a carriage, and a manservant. He gave a lengthy account to the Select Committee of 1861–62, justifying his schemes on the grounds that not only were medicines costly but salaries should take into account the expensive education, the length of study, the amount of experience and reading necessary, besides the severe mental strain and trial of patience to which a doctor was subjected. He maintained that Medical Officers with the least work to perform and the shortest distance to travel were the best paid. His own salary averaged 2s. 6d. per patient, although the average duration of illness was over five weeks. His predecessor had resigned after three years' service. So did another doctor who received £116 and who had practically no private practice.

Griffin further asserted that almost every word of the British Medical Association's protest to the Commissioners in 1839 regarding the lowness of salaries and the method of determining remuneration without consultation with the Medical Officers was applicable in the 'sixties. He had been a magistrate for twenty years and Medical Officer of Weymouth for six, so he realized no redress could be obtained from the Board of Guardians or the Poor Law Board. He had therefore suggested to many Poor Law Medical Officers that they should put their case before Parliament, and when the Poor Law Medical Relief Association was formed in 1856, a petition had been sent to the House of Commons praying for reform of the doctors' position. As Chairman of the Association, Griffin had had ample opportunity of inquiring into the medical service of the Poor Law and he could unhesitatingly say 'it cannot be in a worse state than it is in at the present'. He was speaking on behalf of the Association's 1,780 members to the Select Committee of 1861, and 4,135 subscriptions had been sent to him to enable him to make a detailed study and present a case. A total of 129 practitioners unconnected with Union service had sent him 158 subscriptions in addition, and the two together amounted to £170. 'The subscriptions from the Poor Law Medical Officers . . . prove how they suffer, otherwise they would not have sent the money voluntarily.'

In the following year, 1862, Griffin suggested that in order to encourage the fixing of salaries according to the number of cases attended, it would be expedient for new legislation to be introduced, so that payment for medical relief could be removed from the respective parishes and be distributed in equal shares over the whole Union and the Parliamentary Grant. One Board of Guardians suggested it should be a county charge. In most towns, Griffin pointed out, there were certain parishes where there were scarcely any poor, whilst in others, they constituted the entire population. As the labourer worked in the richer parishes, or for those who resided there, he deemed it only fair that the more fortunate areas should contribute to the support of the poor ones. The Poor Law Board agreed to this principle when they stated in their Fourteenth Annual Report: 'the unequal distribution of a common burden is inconsistent with a policy of justice'.

The Executive Council of the British Medical Association presented a petition to the Select Committee of 1862, on behalf of its members, the Poor Law Medical Relief Association and the Metropolitan Poor Law Medical Officers, recommending both for the welfare of the poor and their doctors that salaries should be made more just and equitable, and proportionate to the amount of work done. It demanded that Guardians should not make cheapness the ruling guide in the selection of doctors, and that 2s. 6d. should be the average payment per case in the Metropolis and 5s. in the provinces, with extra fees and travelling expenses.

Dr. Fowler told the 1862 Inquiry that after a meeting of the Metropolitan Poor Law Medical Officers the Committee deemed remuneration inadequate. According to the scheme which he proposed, travelling expenses were to be paid from a certain gross sum fixed by the Guardians, and these were to be in the nature of compensation for the size of districts and not according to the journeys made. A Medical Officer should receive so much per head of the total number of paupers for attending the sick and so much for travelling. Every half-year, Boards of Guardians were to calculate the salary for the following six months on the basis of not less than tenpence per head of the total number of paupers relieved during the previous half-year, in districts or in the workhouse. His plan therefore differed from Griffin's scheme of payment for the sick only. When the total number of paupers amounted to 250 up to 600, double the minimum rates were to obtain. An additional sum per head of the same number should be paid when cases of illness in the district or workhouse in the preceding six months exceeded 25 per cent of the total number of paupers relieved. In London 2s. 6d. and in the provinces 5s. were to be the minimum rates per case. Strangely, he also advocated that one-third of the Medical Officer's salary should be deducted if the Guardians found the drugs, and that paupers falling ill more than once during the half-yearly period should be counted as only one case for that period.

Fowler based his scheme on the amount of pauperism rather than on the actual cases of sickness, because he had the idea that the administration of the Poor Law was an extension of the functions of ordinary benefit and sickness societies. He believed the objects were the same, although the means for procuring the end were essentially different. One derived its finances from voluntary subscriptions and the other from compulsory payment of the poor rate. He thought that the method by which these societies remunerated their doctors was capable of adoption by the Poor Law authorities. The former paid the doctor so much a year per member whether sick or well, and members of the 'Poor Law Benefit and Sick Society' were the whole pauper population. The total indicated the individuals who had been, or were, entitled to be recipients of the services of the Medical Officer. Fowler believed (though erroneously) that Benefit Society surgeons were content with the basis of computation and were satisfied with the sums paid per member. The system had also been adopted by many large private firms, as for example, the Sugar Refiners in Whitechapel, who paid their staff doctors 10s. a year for all employees, sick or well. The scheme, Fowler concluded, was an improvement on the 'per case' system of payment where there was always an imputation that doctors manufactured cases. Endless squabbling with Boards of Guardians would be avoided where figures were compiled independently of the Medical Officers. The latter were however to have access to the books recording the number of paupers, so that they would be able to check on the Clerk, the Relieving Officer and the master of the workhouse. The Order of 1847 had not stated that doctors could examine the Permanent Pauper List, and the destitute were only given tickets to bring to them. Fowler insisted that his scheme would benefit both ratepayers and poor. The poor would be assured of the best medical attention and drugs, and the ratepayers would gain by paupers being cured more quickly.

Dr. Moore of Bethnal Green outlined a scheme to the Select Committee of 1862 which took up one of Griffin's earlier suggestions that a medical sum should be fixed by a Union and then divided out each year among the parish doctors according to the number of cases attended. The sick would be allowed to obtain the services of any Union Medical Officer and would not be tied to the particular one appointed to their district. His plan differed from the payment 'per case' system—which existed in some Unions and which resulted in limiting the number of recipients of gratuitous medical attention, because each case meant additional expenditure—as a previously fixed total sum would allow unlimited orders being given. He further recommended a medical rate to be levied in each parish to facilitate the increase of the gross allocation to salaries. A census should be taken every five years of the number of ratepayers and the increase in pauperism to enable the rate to be revised. He believed an average of 2s. per case would constitute a tolerably fair payment for Metropolitan Medical Officers, although popularity and industry would affect the determination of the total salary.

Dr. George Ross, another well-known figure in the Reform Movement, outlined a scheme in 1862 very different from the others. His chief objection also was that salaries bore no relation to the amount of work performed. But he pointed out that ratepayers of heavily pauperized districts, where doctors were worked the hardest, were themselves usually in needy circumstances and burdened with rates, so that they were not only unwilling, but also often unable, to remunerate doctors adequately. He produced a table (Table 12.9) showing the wide discrepancies which existed between population, pauperism, and sickness. In the Eastern Counties, for example, 4½ ratepayers contributed to pay for one case of sickness, but in Yorkshire it was 29 ratepayers.

TABLE 12.9

Table showing discrepancies existing between Population, Pauperism, and Sickness.

Divisions	Rates of Paupers relieved annually to population	Ratio of sick cases to paupers	Calculated ratio of sick cases to ratepayers
Metropolis	1 in 3	1 in 3	1 in 6
East	1 in 2	1 in 4½	1 in 4½
South-East	1 in 4	1 in 2⅔	1 in 7
South-West	1 in 5	1 in 2	1 in 8
West	1 in 5½	1 in 4	1 in 18
North	1 in 7½	1 in 3⅔	1 in 24
North-West	1 in 7½	1 in 2½	1 in 15
Yorkshire	1 in 10	1 in 3¼	1 in 29
Average of Total	1 in 4⅔	1 in 2⅘	1 in 10

The average payment was 2s. a case in the Eastern Counties, and 3s. 9½d. in Yorkshire. In the Metropolis six ratepayers discharged the same liability as the twenty-nine in Yorkshire and payment on an average was only 1s. 1d. per case. The grant-in-aid received from the Consolidated Fund was only sixpence-halfpenny therefore, whilst in Yorkshire ratepayers were assisted to the extent of 1s. 11d. Ross showed that the rate of pauperism to the population was 1 in 4⅔, and of sick cases to pauperism 1 in 2⅘, therefore the ratio of sick cases to ratepayers was 1 in 10. Further he calculated, that if a patient was worth 3s., of which half was paid by the Consolidated Fund, each ratepayer contributed about one penny-three-farthings. He proposed the minimum payment throughout the country should be 3s. a case, excluding a mileage fee, and in order to facilitate uniformity of remuneration, contributions from the Consolidated Fund should be paid on cases attended in the several Unions in amounts graduated according to the ratio of sick cases to ratepayers. Half the payment, 1s. 6d. a case, should be considered the medium sum, and the Poor Law Board should contribute less or more, in proportion as the ratio of ratepayers to sick cases increased or diminished, each ratepayer being required to pay an average of three-halfpence a case. By this means the central authorities would effectually relieve needy and distressed Unions, both urban and rural, whilst paying no more than the existing contribution. Local Boards should be at liberty to pay as much more than this three-halfpence a case per ratepayer as they pleased, but the government contribution should be less. Ross suggested the following gradations in payments out of the Consolidated Fund:

1 sick case to 4 ratepayers —	2s. 6d.
1 sick case to 4–8 ratepayers —	2s. 3d.
1 sick case to 8–12 ratepayers —	1s. 9d.
1 sick case to 12–16 ratepayers —	1s. 3d.
1 sick case to 16–20 ratepayers —	9d.
above this ratio —	6d.

Additional payment for mileage was to be proportionate to the square mileage of the district—he suggested £20 for 4 square miles. There were 54,834 square miles in the divisions, which, estimated at £1 per square mile, would give an additional 1s. per case on all outdoor cases. Urban doctors were not to receive a mileage fee, so that aggregate payment would not amount to half this sum. The Consolidated Fund, it was proposed, should be responsible for these fees. Ross concluded that it was fruitless to expect fair remuneration in special cases, or any equalization of salaries throughout the country generally, so long as by an inverse process the heaviest liability fell on the poorest districts. He believed this incongruity was and always would be, the cause of the failure of every attempt to establish a better system. He deprecated the inconsistency of the existing scheme whereby the Consolidated Fund paid 5s. to aid a healthy Union and only sixpence to an impoverished one; there was neither reason, fairness, economy, nor good policy in it. Workhouse doctors were to receive two-thirds of the value of outdoor cases and salaries were to be revised every three years. The plan offered a corrective for an anomaly which other reformers overlooked, and it is interesting for throwing light on another angle of Poor Law administration.

Joseph Rogers, who gave such valuable service to the cause of workhouse reform, was authorized by the Metropolitan Poor Law Medical Officers' Committee to give evidence to the Select Committee of 1862 as the representative of the workhouse doctors. He reported the objection to the method of remunerating workhouse Medical Officers by fixed salary for a variable amount of work done. He desired the institution of the payment of 5s. per head on the average number of inmates during a year. The average of the number of sick should not be taken, he maintained, because workhouse Medical Officers were called to perform many duties relating to the able-bodied and the sanitary condition of the establishment. Griffin had called to notice the unfairness of the regulations whereby institution doctors were not to receive additional fees, for so many poor-houses were becoming hospitals. Rogers therefore demanded that workhouse Medical Officers should be offered the same fees for operations and midwifery as the District Medical Officer.

The Metropolitan workhouse doctors reiterated this desire to Dr. Smith in 1866. In some Unions the scheme had been introduced, and in others in part, with the permission of the Poor Law Board. In discussing the question of salaries with all Medical Officers of the forty Metropolitan workhouses, only three or four were satisfied with their emoluments. Marylebone and St. Pancras doctors desired no change. Smith agreed with Rogers that to take the number of sick as a basis for comparing salaries in different workhouses, as was the custom, was unsuitable. First, the number of sick poor had increased by fully a third in most workhouses—generally to obtain a better diet for the aged and infirm. Little or no further treatment was required for these people and therefore the amount of work could only be fairly estimated from numbers from which these had been excluded. Second, it was becoming desirable for a Medical Officer to pay attention to all the inmates of the institution and to assume the duties of a sanitary officer, which would demand a great deal more of his time. Finally, the diversity in the arrangements regarding lunatics prevented an accurate comparison between services of several doctors.

Smith deemed it expedient for the Medical Officers to come to some agreement as to the sum they regarded as fairly adequate. He himself advocated, if Guardians provided the drugs and a dispenser, that the salary should be calculated at 10s. per adult on the average maximum number of inmates in the institution at one time, two children under 16 years of age equalling one adult for the computation. This would have necessitated a considerable increase in nearly all salaries, particularly in the larger workhouses, and would probably have induced the Guardians to appoint one or more resident full-time doctors to each workhouse. Finally, Smith recommended that all Medical Officers who were solely employed in pauper work should be entitled to a superannuation allowance and that they should be placed by the legislature under the provisions of the Superannuation Act.

A superannuation scheme had been demanded by the Poor Law doctors since the early 'forties. In 1844 the Poor Law Commissioners had expressed their opinion in favour of establishing a fund for superannuating workhouse masters, to be created by receiving a proportion of the salaries of these officers.[1] In the following years more comprehensive schemes were contemplated by Union officers in England, and in 1846, 1,030 salaried

[1] Tenth Annual Report, Poor Law Commissioners, 1844.

employees signified their assent to the formation of a Superannuation Fund on the principle of deductions from their remuneration.[1] Twenty-two Boards of Guardians passed resolutions in favour of the arrangements and several petitions were presented to Parliament praying for legislation on the subject. The 1845 Act to 'Amend the laws for the provision and regulation of Lunatic Asylums' (8 and 9 Vict. c. 126) had provided that superannuation annuities payable out of county rates were to be granted by Justices of the Peace to any officer of a lunatic asylum on their becoming incapacitated from confirmed sickness, age, or infirmity. The amount to be paid was left to the discretion of the magistrates and was to vary according to what they deemed proportionate to merit and service, but were not to exceed two-thirds of the salary at the time of retirement. Therefore as Parliament seemed to favour the general principle, the Poor Law Commissioners proclaimed their readiness to assist in the preparation of a scheme for destitution officers, but nothing further was accomplished until the Poor Law Board directed their attention to the subject in 1849. The latter fully approved of superannuation, but maintained it could only be effected by means of contribution or deduction from the salaries of officers themselves, without any resort being had either to the poor rate, or to any other fund of public character.[2]

On this principle a plan was framed by a Committee of Union officers and was submitted to the Board as the groundwork for legislation. The proposal suggested the deduction of £2 10s. per cent a year from salaries and that the Poor Law Board should invest the total sum. Officers were to have served a minimum period of fifteen years before they could draw a third of their previous salary per year. Over twenty years' service entitled a man to half his former stipend and over thirty years to two-thirds. A minimum age for retirement was fixed at 55. In 1859 the President of the Poor Law Board submitted a Bill to the House of Commons on superannuation, but the session was over before it could be debated.

Pigott had also included a clause on superannuation in the Medical Bill of 1860, and the Poor Law Medical Officers' Association was carrying on a virile campaign at this time. It was on the Association's behalf that Griffin spoke on the subject at the Inquiry in 1862. He pointed out the Poor Law doctors were often more impecunious after a life's work than when they started their careers. Medical practices throughout England did not average £400 a year, and in many country districts they were not half of this. One Medical Officer, strongly supporting superannuation, wrote to Griffin that his Poor Law appointment remunerated him with £30 a year, and that he had little private practice. The doctors' objection to the stipulations of the previous Superannuation Bill was that they could not afford to pay contributions out of their inadequate salaries. Also, many of them did not remain in the Poor Law service long, because they were treated so badly, and therefore they did not wish to subscribe. Griffin therefore desired to see a scheme introduced independent of doctors' contributions. Apparently, the mortality among Poor Law Medical Officers was great—figures for 1861, for example, showed that there were sixty-four deaths

[1] Twelfth Annual Report, Poor Law Commissioners, 1846.
[2] Third Annual Report, Poor Law Board, 1850.

in that year. Few practitioners retained their appointments long enough to entitle them to superannuation, and this caused Griffin to point out that claims on the Fund would be light. Probably the sickness rate was as high as the mortality, and so it was proposed that if a Medical Officer resigned through illness, after not less than ten years' service the Guardians should pay an allowance of one-third of the salary.

Dr. Fowler also demanded superannuation because of the personal risk and the low remuneration. He suggested it should resemble the scheme laid down by the Civil Service Superannuation Act, and as was proposed in the Report of the Select Committee on Irish Poor Relief in 1861. The British Medical Association in its Petition of 1862 seconded this proposal. The Select Committee of 1864, although it had been instituted to inquire whether the Poor Law was adequate to meet the needs of the exceptional distress in London and Lancashire, passed a resolution on Superannuation. The inquiry had revealed that officers continued working beyond a reasonable age, so that through infirmity they could not perform their duties efficiently. Therefore the Committee recommended that power should be conferred on Boards of Guardians to provide at their discretion for the superannuation of Union officers, subject to the control of the central authorities. The Statute of 1864 (27 and 28 Vict. c. 42) was only permissive legislation as was the following one in 1867 (30 Vict. c. 113), and they were not put into practice regarding the doctors.

Joseph Rogers was a great campaigner for superannuation and advertised in the *Lancet* for information from any Medical Officer, showing how he had been compelled to cling to his appointment long after his power to discharge his duties efficiently had ceased.[1] The Council of the Poor Law Medical Officers' Association, of which he was then President, sent a Petition to the House of Commons in 1870 and a copy was sent for signature to all Poor Law Medical Officers. The Royal College of Surgeons also petitioned Parliament on behalf of superannuation for Poor Law doctors in 1870, and in that year Dr. Brady introduced the required Bill. The Act which followed (33 and 34 Vict. c. 94) extended the power of Guardians to provide superannuation allowances for Union Medical Officers and included doctors who did not devote their whole services to paupers. A sum not exceeding two-thirds of the amount of the emoluments of the Medical Officer was to be granted him. In their Twenty-third Annual Report, the Poor Law Board made known that in the first year of the operation of the Act, the total sum allotted by the several Boards of Guardians, slightly exceeded half the amount of officers' remuneration, and in that year eighty-two Poor Law officers were superannuated, a figure which included four doctors and five nurses. It was another innovation which increased the expenditure of the Guardians on the Poor Law medical service, and it was also a further victory for the Medical Officers. It had taken them thirty years to achieve!

Of equal duration, but attended by less success, was the Poor Law Medical Officers' agitation for the establishment of a Medical Department or Medical Inspector—with powers either extensive enough to withdraw all medical work from the Poor Law Board,

---

[1] *Lancet*, 1870, i, p. 323.

or attached to them as an influential counsellor. We have studied the various schemes proposed to the Poor Law Commissioners, and they were equally diverse and also as insistent, under their successors. The latter had scarcely assumed office when Lord Ashley moved in the House of Commons:

that it is expedient that Medical Inspectors be appointed by the Poor Law Commissioners or by the Secretary of State, or with his sanction, to each district to which an Assistant Poor Law Commissioner or Inspector is attached at a salary not exceeding £600 a year, exclusive of travelling expenses, and exclusive of all allowances of a clerk if the duties should require one. That the duty of a Medical Inspector should be to inspect and report on the medical treatment of the poor of different Unions, and on the fitness of medical men appointed by the Unions, to inquire particularly into the treatment of the sick poor within them generally, together with such other sanitary duties of every kind as may be required of them by the Secretary of State or by the Poor Law Commissioners, and particularly with respect to the number of Medical Officers who ought to be employed in each Union, and under the sanction of the Poor Law Commissioners to fix salaries which ought to be awarded to them for their resources in each particular Union or part of the Union in the district.

Charles Buller, as President of the Poor Law Board, objected to the appointment of medical inspectors on the grounds of expense, and maintained that the scheme would diminish local initiative and entrust too much power to the inspectors. The House divided with 101 against the proposal and 19 for it, so the resolution was not put.[1]

Much evidence was afforded to the Select Committee of 1854 on the question of medical supervision. Dr. Rumsey confirmed the statements he had made ten years previously, that doctors should be subject to medical supervision. Dr. Wallis commented that non-professional men were not judges of medical efficiency, and that Union practitioners would raise no objection to a system of inspection. Dr. Livett of Wells also favoured the proposal because laymen could not judge medical treatment. Similarly, Dr. Leigh asserted that no proper check existed and that only medical men could supervise the profession efficiently. He suggested the appointment of a number of itinerant Medical Inspectors, who should not be in practice in the districts allocated to them. They should examine all books, and occasionally houses, like the Medical Officers of Health. These Inspectors would rarely interfere with a doctor's work, but they would be able to determine disputed cases, and also give decisions on who was eligible for gratuitous relief. Dr. Cooper differed from Leigh in that he believed Inspectors would be only a slight advantage unless they were located in a district.

The Poor Law Inspectors denied the need for appointing additional men. Weale recognized the increasing importance of superintending the Medical Officers because they were growing more numerous, but he, Cane, and Austin did not believe that new posts

[1] *Hansard*, Vol. 197, 3rd series, p. 608, 16 March 1848.

should be created. Cane maintained that the practice of the Poor Law Board of calling independent medical advice and assistance for disputes was sufficient and made superfluous any new permanent officers. The Rev. Howman recommended that if his scheme was adopted of having a medical staff simply for pauper practice, no medical supervisor or inspector would be necessary, because it was not right for one doctor to supervise another. Everything could be left to the discretion of the medical staff of the Union if the services of a well-qualified chief surgeon were obtained, and the Guardians and Poor Law Board would still enjoy powers of supreme supervision against negligence. The majority Report of the Select Committee ignored the subject, but Pigott gave an individual recommendation that Medical Officers should be subject to the interference of medical inspectors. Robert Palmer, another member of the Committee, likewise stressed the importance of medical inspectors.

The controversy continued for another six years, when the Commissioners of the early 'sixties listened to a reiteration of former arguments. Dr. Fowler, on behalf of his 175 Metropolitan Poor Law Medical Officers, guaranteed in 1862 that no conscientious doctor would object to supervision, but that if he were going to be made liable to inspection, he should be given increased payment for duties which were to be well performed. Speaking for the workhouse Medical Officers, Rogers welcomed fixed inspection of the institutions and agreed to it as a matter of general policy. His interrogator, Mr. Lyall, who was favourably inclined to the medical reformers on many schemes in later years, told him that there were many inefficient medical men in the country who would be found out in a general inspection and who would probably not be permitted to retain office. Rogers refused a retort and asked not to be required to libel his own profession.

For the official viewpoint, Inspector Hawley thought it would be a great disadvantage for Medical Inspectors to visit workhouses and infirmaries. It would be a superfluous duty because Guardians were quite capable of undertaking their own supervision without interference. He also believed it would lead to friction—for Guardians, Medical Officers, and Inspectors would never agree—whereas, he asserted, there was harmony at the time.

The majority of doctors who demanded the innovation did not wish to see a group of Inspectors established as servants of the Poor Law Board and Guardians. Experience had taught them that the central and local destitution authorities were incompetent to deal with the medical services. Although Fowler advocated that the powers of the Poor Law Board should be consolidated and extended to facilitate the introduction of reforms, medical associations and individuals, particularly Rumsey and Guthrie, recommended, as they had done in earlier years, that there should either be a central medical authority attached to the Poor Law Board, or a completely independent body.

In 1854, Dr. Gilbert, who had had experience of the Poor Law medical system since 1837, argued that it would be beneficial if a central medical inspector were appointed, or sub-inspectors under the existing Poor Law Inspectors. Charles Kingsley stated that, as so many queries constantly arose as to whether medicines or food were required, and on the duties of the Medical Officer, it would be advantageous to have them settled by a central medical authority rather than by the existing destitution officials. Griffin, as in 1854, suggested an appointment similar to that of the Assistant Poor Law Commissioner, who exercised this function inefficiently, should be made with powers to investigate abuses, and he should be employed full time. The 1860 Medical Bill proposed the institution of an additional Commissioner by the central authority. He was to be a registered doctor and have been a Union officer for at least three years, and was to be nominated by Poor Law Medical Officers' votes. His duties were to consist in conducting medical correspondence, in preparing a Medical Report to be laid before Parliament every year, and in adjudicating in all matters regarding the Union doctors subject to the confirmation of the Poor Law Board.

Two years later Griffin had become convinced that a Medical Secretary should be appointed, attached to the central authority but not under them. He admitted that some doctors opposed having a medical man in such an influential position, for they felt he would be like a policeman. But he favoured the idea because there were already over 3,000 Medical Officers engaged in the services of the Poor Law. The diplomas and licences of 300 practitioners on an average had to be considered every year and the appointments confirmed. With so many employees it was imperative to engage an adjudicator and an official to answer inquiries, who understood the problems and who was subject to his own knowledge rather than to the Poor Law Board. He would be even more indispensable if the suggestion for reports on diseases were adopted, for nearly 1,500,000 sick poor would be affected, and the increase in the amount of correspondence between the central and local authorities regarding the causes of disease affecting particular localities would necessitate control by a medical man. His appointment would also increase in importance if the central authorities were to find the drugs, for he could be made responsible for their purchase, distribution, and use. All the anomalies in the medical service regarding the Medical Officers which had been pointed out over the previous years, arose, Griffin maintained, because the Poor Law Board refused to assert its authority to institute a uniform system, and from having men 'ignorant of medical affairs placed over the great medical department of the State'.

Dr. Moore, in his plan for reform, agreed with Griffin's scheme. He suggested the Inspector at the Central Board should be an eminent man who would do justice to the Medical Officers, shield them from insinuations, and investigate charges. He should be responsible for the work of the doctors, examine their books regarding treatment and should also inspect the workhouses. Such duties, Moore did not believe would be unpleasant, because he did not feel that there were many incompetent doctors. The Inspector would be the medium of communication between the Poor Law Board and the Guardians on medical matters, and he should therefore be completely independent of local and personal influences.

The Petition of the British Medical Association of 1862 asked for the appointment of a Medical Officer in connection with the Poor Law Board. His duties were to consist in the arranging and enlarging of the table of extra fees, conducting the medical correspondence, and reporting annually to the House of Commons. The adjustment of medical remuneration and districts were also to be his province, as well as arbitration in disputes.

Dr. Wallis and Dr. Lord were responsible for outlining more ambitious schemes whereby the medical services were to be taken out of the hands of the destitution authorities altogether. In 1854 Dr. Wallis in his detailed plan for the establishment of free dispensaries also mentioned the necessity for Medical Inspectors. He recommended the appointment of six highly qualified and skilled doctors under a chief Medical Officer in London. They should constitute a Medical Department separated from the Poor Law Board and probably under the Home Office, although the president was to have contacts with the Central Board. They should form a court for complaints and have the power of dismissing doctors. They were to be responsible for inspecting Medical Books every three months and were to have entire control over expenditure. These seven would be the most competent judges of salaries—based on population and areas—and their own was to be paid out of the Parliamentary Grant. Wallis wished to give a further duty to his proposed Medical Board; they were to constitute a Sanitary Authority as well, dealing with all questions of Public Health and quarantine, for he considered the existing Board of Health a failure.

Dr. Livett fully concurred in this scheme and agreed that Medical Officers would greatly prefer being under the control of a Central Medical Authority. Inspector Austin however, regarding medical relief as satisfactory as it could be, refused to acknowledge that any improvement would be achieved by the establishment of a Medical Board. Nor did he believe the medical profession would benefit by having recourse to their advice on difficult problems. He insisted that the Poor Law Board was perfectly capable of dealing with any question requiring scientific treatment and pointed out that properly conducted inquiries were always held in cases of doubt.

Revolutionary and prescient was the scheme proposed by Lord on behalf of the Convention of Poor Law Medical Officers in 1854. He suggested placing the entire cost of the medical services of the poor on the Consolidated Fund and establishing a State Medical Board. All control would be removed from the destitution authorities. The Government would appoint the Director-General of the Poor Law Medical Department, which would exercise supervision over medical practice in the manner of other public services. The Government was also to engage the medical inspectors, chosen preferably from those with experience in the Poor Law service, and they were to act under the orders of the Director-General. Part of their duty would be to regulate the appointment of Medical Officers, who were to receive fixed salaries, and were to be permanent to obviate competition, but local responsibility would not necessarily be destroyed because the doctors were to be engaged by the Guardians. The district Inspectors would examine the infirmaries of workhouses, scrutinize the reports of the doctors, and inquire into alleged negligence and matters of dispute regarding salaries or treatment.

The Convention of Poor Law Medical Officers also desired to see the fusion of the Union doctor and the sanitary inspector, so that the proposed Medical Board might assume the management of preventive and curative medicine. If the Poor Law Medical Officer were removed from the destitution authorities he might serve the entire public, performing sanitary duties and establishing a separate practice apart from his private practice. The Convention had circularized the profession and the replies were singularly unanimous on the possibility and desirability of effecting this fusion. The comprehensive Medical Relief scheme, it was estimated, would cost about £500,000, including vaccination and increased salaries to doctors, therefore expenditure would be double what the Poor Law medical service was costing at the time.

The connection between poverty, sickness, and Public Health was recognized by the Poor Law Medical Officers, but the legislature ignored their far-seeing demands for reform. Very tentatively however, the Poor Law Board made a half-hearted concession to the proposals for engaging Medical Inspectors. Early in 1865 Dr. E. Smith[1] was appointed a Poor Law Inspector with special reference to Medical Relief. Immediately, the Lancet begged him to undertake a general inquiry into workhouse hospitals, and as we have seen, the Poor Law Board commissioned him to undertake investigations into the Metropolitan and Provincial institutions in 1866 and 1867. His detailed reports were extremely valuable and no doubt stimulated further and more revealing inquiries. In his official capacity he placed Poor Law dietaries on a scientific and practical basis. He did much work for reform in the interests of hygiene, the structural arrangements of workhouses and workhouse infirmaries. In their regulations on the subject of cubic space the Poor Law Board adopted Smith's opinions, although they differed from those generally accepted by the medical profession.

At the end of December 1867, a change was made by the central authorities—they took a step in the right direction—relieving Smith of his inspectoral duties and ordering him to devote his whole time to the creation of what the Lancet called the 'Medical Department of the Poor Law Board'. Whilst acting as an Inspector and medical adviser, Smith had been in an equivocal position. As he was the only member of the medical profession attached to the Poor Law Board, he had often been called on to give an opinion or to assist at investigations in conjunction with colleagues, who in all matters of the administration of the Poor Law were more experienced than himself. It must also have been difficult to criticize the treatment of the sick in the face of his fellow Inspectors' apathy and contentment. In his own district he had however invariably made suggestions for reform, although he had been

[1] Dr. E. Smith, F.R.S. b. Derbyshire 1818, d. 1874. 1851 F.R.C.S., 1863 M.R.C.P. Physiological chemistry occupied much of his attention. In 1844 went to North Texas to examine its capacity as a place of settlement for emigrants. Great deal of writing and research. 1853, Lecturer and Demonstrator, Charing Cross Hospital School of Medicine. 1861, Assistant Physician to the Brompton Hospital for Consumption. Dietetics were his great interest in later years, and in 1862 he reported to the Privy Council on the 'Food of the lowest fed classes in the Kingdom', as an Appendix to Simons' Sixth Report. In consequence he was consulted by the Government on Poor Law and Prison dietaries and this probably caused his appointment as a Poor Law Inspector. Publications: *Practical Dietary for Families, Schools, and Working Classes*, 1864; *Report on Dietary of Lancashire Cotton Operatives and Other Low Fed Populations*, 1862–63; *Manual for Medical Officers of Health*, 1873; *Manual of Inspectors of Nuisances*, 1873.

unable to persuade the Guardians to carry them out because he lacked sufficient influence and authority. On the change in his functions the *Lancet* wrote:

> Being released from his invidious position and placed in one of considerable responsibility and power, he will have the opportunity for rendering the most valuable services to the sick poor, and to the members of his own profession. . . . No man of our day has greater opportunities for doing good . . . . [His] method and perseverance in several scientific investigations, [his] experience gained in the workhouses of the Metropolis and later still in those of every class in every part of England . . . guarantee he will suggest to the Poor Law Board an organization worthy of the gigantic social duty involved in the care of many thousands of sick, and the supervision of medical officers who now attend them.

The *Lancet* continued by hoping that Smith would receive the same assistance from the President of the Poor Law Board (Lord Devon) as that which the Commander-in-Chief accorded to the Director-General of the Army Medical Department. From Smith, the writer of the article expected

> a speedy issue of official regulations for the construction of infirmaries and sick wards, for dietary and the nursing of patients, for dispensing medicines . . . for salaries and duties of the Medical Officers, and for the manner in which the duties be reported and performed.

It was supposed that Smith would have a staff of professional assistants, qualified to see that instructions were carried out, and, as in the Army, workhouse hospitals would be inspected by a double staff, the medical and the general inspector. The *Lancet* also thought it was important for medical inspectors to be sent here and there as occasion required, conducting inquiries where medical questions were involved and reporting to their chief adviser, reforms which appeared necessary. As sickness first began in the home, and as a cure was most likely to be effected by early intervention, it was essential, that whilst workhouse patients were properly taken care of, those who remained in their homes should not suffer from neglect. Inspection of domiciliary medical relief was difficult, but the establishment of dispensaries meant a check on outdoor treatment would be facilitated. The *Lancet* believed that:

> Should the new department of the Poor Law Board expand itself to its legitimate dimensions and act in harmony with the other departments of State, such as those of registration, and of health, . . . the highest services will be rendered to the entire community. Reports from pauper dispensaries and hospitals will give the truest measure of the State of Public Health, and yield the first indications of approaching epidemics.

In conclusion the *Lancet* maintained that the importance of the new department from the point of view of the public was that it afforded the best guarantee of kindly treatment for the sick poor. It was equally important to the doctors, who for the first time would be able to appeal to a member of their own profession against their miserably inadequate salaries, the vicious system of finding and dispensing drugs, and the continual annoyance to which they were subject, if they acted independently of the Guardians. Smith was looked upon as a chief who would protect their interests and gradually obtain for them reasonable reforms. He had a right however, the *Lancet* said, voicing its own opinions on medical solidarity, 'to stipulate that members of the profession shall respect themselves and not quarrel, or offer to take appointments at insufficient salaries'. It was the duty of Smith to see the work was well done, and that of the profession to demand and support adequate remuneration.[1]

It was a noble eulogy and, as often before, its aspirations were full of prescience, but of little consequence to the moment. By the time Smith was transferred to the Medical Department of the Local Government Board as 'Assistant Medical Officer for Poor Law Purposes', Union doctors had still no superior to whom they could report. On the simplest and first question, that of inquiry into medical treatment, little had been done by 1871. Official inspection was out of the question and so there was a curious lack of comprehensive and useful medical statistics on diseases, prophylaxis, method of treatment, the frequency of attendance, drugs or appliances supplied, or the results effected by the Poor Law medical service. It would be grossly inaccurate to say Smith achieved nothing, but through no fault of his, great opportunities were lost by the Poor Law administrators in not embarking whole-heartedly on the establishment of a Medical Department.

The medical reforms which were introduced in this period came not through guidance from above, but through the agitation and sheer hard plodding of the Medical Officers. By 1871 their own position was still most unsatisfactory and it was shameful but typical of the speed with which social reforms were introduced, that a speech made at the Poor Law Medical Officers' Conference in 1876 contained practically identical words to those used in the Memorial to Sir George Grey a generation before. Referring to the Union doctors, Dr. Child said:

> Their work is harassing and exacting, and very difficult to do with a due regard equally to the requirements of the poor, the orders of the Guardians and the rights of the rate-payers. Their pay is confessedly cut down to the last possible sixpence . . . It is easy further to see that the evils of this state of things have a tendency to get worse in direct proportion to the skill, reputation, and success of the individual practitioner.[2]

When such conditions appertained over forty years it was little wonder that cases of incompetence should occur. In 1854 Inspector Cane stated that rarely a year had passed without it being necessary for the Poor Law Board to dismiss formally some Medical Officer. In the previous year, for example, the central authority required the resignation of seven doctors, but not a single case of gross misconduct had occurred to render it impera-

[1] Leading article, *Lancet*, 1868, i, p. 16.
[2] Poor Law Conference, 1876, West Midlands. Dr. Child on 'Sanitary Legislation and its Relation to Poor Law Medical Science'.

tive for them to issue an order for public and formal dismissal. This, Cane maintained, was very creditable to the profession, considering the onerous and highly responsible nature of the duties of a Poor Law Medical Officer. Complaints were generally made by the Boards of Guardians for neglect, by the poor for insufficient attendances or inadequate supply of medicines, by the ratepayers that they were too heavily burdened with charges for medical relief and that districts were too large, and by the Medical Officers that they attended more patients than was just at the salary. Nearly all cases of complaint against doctors were centred on neglect rather than malpractice. Inspector Austin assured the Select Committee of 1854 that he hardly remembered a case of unscientific treatment, save one at Liverpool. Here a Medical Officer at the workhouse operated on a pauper inmate for an affection of the throat arising from syphilis. He performed the operation by applying a caustic, and the patient died. The surgeon was charged with ignorance and carelessness. Austin had to investigate the case and as he himself possessed no medical knowledge, took with him a reputable Manchester surgeon who proved the innocence of the doctor and he was exonerated. Austin had also had to make some inquiries where medicines had been prescribed without the patients being seen by Medical Officers, and where death had ensued. Dismissal had been ordered on one occasion, but at other times remonstrance had been found sufficient. In 1870 the Liverpool workhouse committee produced charges of neglect against two doctors and they were ordered to attend at the institution at least twice a week.[1]

Inspector Weale affirmed that he had never found it necessary to call in the assistance of an independent medical man. He investigated promptly all complaints which the poor reported to the Guardians or to the Relieving Officers, and he had never experienced difficulty in obtaining evidence for inquiries. It was in the interest of the Guardians that the poor should recover by receiving efficient attention, and they therefore watched their doctors closely, with the result that there were few complaints. Inspector Cane found many accusations baseless on inquiry, and then they were for inattention. He maintained there had been a general improvement consequent on the revised regulations of 1847, and that since then there had been far fewer complaints of neglect. He also agreed that vigilance over the activities of the Medical Officers had increased. The Rev. Howman said in 1854 that he heard many complaints by the poor, but they were never substantiated. He had received notice of one case however in his Union of Downham, where a woman employed a private practitioner to complete the treatment of her son, whose case had been grossly mismanaged by the Union doctor. She had been intimidated from carrying her grievance to the Board of Guardians by a violent tempered farmer who was a friend of the doctor. Her husband who was employed by the farmer was threatened with dismissal if she gave evidence to the Board. W. Taylor, the Hampshire magistrate who gave evidence to the Select Committee of 1854, stated that he often received complaints of inattention. One death occurred because the Medical Officer did not attend a case promptly. The Guardians held an inquiry but there was no inquest. The doctor was exonerated and no further

[1] *Lancet*, 1870, i, p. 565.

medical witness was called to give evidence. On another occasion the same officer did not go immediately to an accident and he was only censured. Taylor proposed that Medical Officers ought to be dismissed after several censures, but the difficulty always arose of finding a substitute. This negligent doctor had been dismissed, but had had to be reinstated.

The Relieving Officer of Bristol maintained that the poor were receiving as efficient medical attention as the class above them. They had themselves told him they were being treated well, and the overseer also affirmed there were no complaints against the Medical Officers. Attention was particularly good in the town where doctors lived nearby. Charles Kingsley, who as we have seen gave much valuable information to the Select Committee of 1854, asserted Poor Law doctors did their duty 'at a loss of time and pocket to themselves, very bravely and well'. He believed practitioners were motivated by feelings of humanity and not merely by remuneration. They knew the eyes of non-paupers were on them. If they established a good character they would be repaid by getting farmers and small tradesmen as patients. He had known Medical Officers buy new instruments which cost two or three guineas simply to deliver a pauper woman in the particular way which it was thought the case necessitated, and they were never reimbursed by the Guardians.

The Select Committee of 1862 heard only one instance of incompetence regarding a Union doctor. This was in relation to the North Surrey District School, where the Medical Officer was dismissed because the school was affected with itch and he was a long time in curing it.[1]

The *Lancet* in 1865 printed an article in which it was maintained that the public were often too apt to criticize severely any neglect on the part of the Poor Law Medical Officers: 'They think little of the labours of those who become the objects of their ill-feeling', nor was any consideration given to the low salaries and the hard work, to perform which, candidates for office had to hold high qualifications and produce testimonials of their character and fitness for the duties.[2] Years before, the *Lancet* had written of the feuds between Medical Officers and Guardians which sometimes led to the dismissal of doctors on the slightest case of neglect. The article gave one instance where an application was made to Wakley, Coroner of Middlesex, to hold an inquest on a pauper who died during her confinement, as her friends said, from brutal and cruel neglect by the Medical Officer, amounting to murder. Wakley on inquiry was satisfied with the doctor's conduct and refused to hold an inquest. The Guardians thereupon appointed a medical committee who came to the same conclusion as Wakley. But two of the Guardians recommended dismissal, therefore a second inquiry was held and the doctor was only retained because of the difficulty experienced in obtaining a successor.

Charles Dickens wrote an eloquent and fair-minded account in *Household Words* in 1854. He gave the experience of a Poor Law doctor defending himself and his colleagues as a class against the charges of neglect and inhumanity, and expressing the grievances and

---

[1] Chelsea children were sent to this school. T. H. Walker, Chairman of the Chelsea Board of Guardians, evidence to Select Committee, 1862.
[2] *Lancet*, 1865, i, p. 184.

difficulties under which they suffered. This was reprinted as a long article in the *Journal of the Provincial Medical and Surgical Association* (later the *British Medical Journal*) under the title, 'Medical Practice among the Poor'.

Very few public medical inquiries were found to be necessary in these years and in the 'fifties and 'sixties only three cases came to the notice of Parliament, two in 1857 and the other in 1864. In the first year an inquiry was instituted regarding the alleged neglect of two dangerously ill patients by the Medical Officer of Bridgwater (Somerset). From the correspondence between the Poor Law Board and the Guardians it seemed that the poor were very satisfied with the doctor and that there was a feeling of respect and goodwill towards him. A patient suffering from severe heart trouble was under his care from April to November 1857, but he only visited his home once, although he lived nearby. The patient himself called at the surgery six times a month and was given digitalis to take without supervision. Excessive dosage caused his death, and at an inquiry the doctor's neglect was proved. Similarly he attended a man with an inflamed knee only twice in two months, although he sent medicines by the man's daughter very frequently. The man had been a valued worker at a brickyard for twenty or thirty years and his fellow workers took his complaints to their master. Subscriptions were raised to obtain the assistance of another doctor and the senior surgeon of Bridgwater Infirmary was called in, who, because the knee was in such a bad condition, advised the man to be removed into the workhouse. The workhouse doctor testified to the precarious condition of the man's limb, and neglect was proved against the doctor. He kept no real books and stated his pauper work was conducted from memory. Inspector Gulson, investigating the case, called on the Poor Law Board to demand the Medical Officer's resignation, but the poor collected a testimonial with a long list of names of people opposing this move. Therefore the accused doctor refused to resign and demanded a further hearing. The case was re-opened and again he was asked to resign by the Poor Law Board. On his refusal they threatened to dismiss him publicly by order, but gave him a few days to reconsider his decision, because public dismissal by formal orders disqualified any doctor from further practice. He still declined and said if he were dismissed he would appeal to a higher tribunal—'as it is quite impossible to obtain justice at your (Poor Law Board) hands'. This doctor attended over 1,000 cases a year for a salary of £65 with £16 for extras, and was appointed annually as he was non-resident in the district.[1]

A unique case of dismissal occurred in the Greenwich Union in 1857-58. The Incumbent of Deptford said he had received numerous complaints against the Medical Officer, but had waited for the proof to accumulate. He accused the doctor of using vulgar and insulting language against him and also stated that several patients were not attended for weeks, despite the fact that they were seriously ill and had obtained orders. The Incumbent also found fault with the dispensary and its Medical Officer, although the latter asserted the poor never complained. Inspector Farnall who conducted the inquiry found little evidence

[1] Dr. Symes, M.R.C.S., L.S.A., District Medical Officer of the Bridgwater Union: Information from Returns relating to Medical Poor Relief in England and Wales, 1857, *Accounts and Papers*, xlix, Pt. I.

of neglect and said opposition to the doctor came only from the Clergy, because he insulted them during their visits to the sick. On this charge and not on medical grounds he was asked to resign, after Farnall had had to hold a second inquiry. He had been a Union Medical Officer for more than seventeen years, whilst the new clergymen were utter strangers to the district. All the Poor Law doctors and private practitioners of the area signed a petition expressing their regret at the resignation. They maintained that no medical man would be found who would perform his duties with greater efficiency or benefit to the poor, and begged for his reinstatement. Several Guardians concurred in this wish and a memorial was sent by 150 ratepayers. The poor also expressed their great regret. During his term of office the doctor had been presented with many gifts in gratitude for his good service, especially for his work during the cholera epidemic. The Guardians resolved to re-elect him, but the Poor Law Board refused to sanction the re-appointment, and the doctor asked for an inquiry to be opened by the Home Office.

A great deal of public attention was focused on the third official inquiry of this period. This concerned Dr. Moore, also of Greenwich, one of the foremost members of the Poor Law Medical Reform Movement, who was called to give evidence at the Parliamentary Inquiry in 1862 on his schemes concerning the remuneration of Medical Officers. The case actually opened in 1862 when the Guardians had tried to force him to resign because of the large quantities of food he ordered for the poor. But public opinion was in his favour and the *Lancet* accorded high praise to him for warding off starvation.[1] Two years later the Guardians wrote to the Poor Law Board that the *Daily Telegraph* had reported on the dreadful state of the poor in Bethnal Green and the alleged death of a child through blood poisoning. 'The Guardians cannot help feeling grieved that so much scandal should have been brought on the parish (as they believe unnecessarily) by one of their medical officers— Dr. Moore.' They therefore resolved that they had lost all confidence in him because of his neglect of patients; his extraordinary claims for vaccination and midwifery fees, which were 'six times the amount of ordinary medical statistics'; his determined opposition to, and public slander of the Board of Guardians; his bringing of contempt on the Poor Law system by public appeals to benevolent people; for neglecting and refusing to keep books as ordered; and for demanding unnecessary inquests. On these charges the Guardians asked for the dismissal of Moore.

At the inquest on a death attributed to Moore's neglect, the Coroner found the mother of the child had been to blame. During the inquiry into the alleged overcharging for extra fees it was discovered that the midwife had been telling untruths and her incompetence was revealed. In addition she always failed to call in Moore for fear of losing her 2s. 6d. On the question of overcharging for vaccination it was found that Moore had written up forty-seven non-existent addresses, but the Guardians in the past had never bothered about the matter. These two charges were therefore quashed. Regarding the claims for surgical fees, Moore proved that in every case where he thought an operation necessary he had consulted

[1] *Lancet*, 1862, i, p. 180.

another doctor who had confirmed the difficulty and dangerous nature of the operation. On the charge of degrading the Parish by demanding inquests, Moore was also acquitted as the Coroner confirmed the necessity for the inquests because deaths had been caused by the insanitary nature of the district. Questions asked regarding the accusation against Moore that he brought the Poor Law system into contempt by appealing to the benevolent, showed that he had written letters to *The Times* asking for a bed and mattress for a 97-year-old woman, and the awful conditions in her house had been described. Subscriptions obtained through *The Times* amounted to £146, half of which was used for buying necessaries and medical appliances. For ten years the Guardians had refused to provide Moore with a fracture apparatus, they now objected to his obtaining one through charity because of the inference that they were indifferent to suffering. Moore had also received contributions through the *Daily Telegraph* to enable him to have the parents of a child who had died from blood poisoning removed from the 'poisonous district'. Only one charge against Moore was upheld—his neglect of book-keeping and the delegation of a great deal of work to his substitute. The crux of the case was the great ill-feeling between the Guardians and the Medical Officer. The inquiry proved Moore had not neglected the poor, but on the contrary, he had brought to light the foul sanitary conditions which were tolerated, and had exerted himself to improve the health of the district. This work had incurred the hostility of the authorities who naturally desired to be rid of him, and they succeeded in inducing the Poor Law Board to ask for his resignation![1] In February 1865 the Guardians advertised for a new Medical Officer at a salary of £100 inclusive (extra fees had been compounded) with 1s. 6d. per case for vaccination.[2]

In the case of Dr. Moore there was little ground for dismissal for incompetence, and the few instances where it was justifiable, only throw into clearer relief the large amount of good work accomplished by the Medical Officers. Many of the salutary services the Poor Law doctors rendered never received recognition. It was not the staff but the medical system which was generally at fault, which by overworking and underpaying the doctors had led to negligence, where such existed. 'We do not complain of the Guardians for adopting a system for which they have the sanction of the Poor Law Board,' wrote the *Lancet*, 'but we do complain of a system which acts unjustly both to the medical profession and to the poor.'[3] In 1869 the Poor Law Board began to publish figures of dismissals of its officers. Statistics referring to the medical staff were: 1869—3,906 Medical Officers of whom sixteen resigned voluntarily, five were forced to, and four dismissals; ninety-eight male nurses, of whom one resigned voluntarily, three were forced to, and five dismissals; 689 female nurses of whom seven resigned voluntarily, six were forced to, and eighteen dismissals. 1870—3,950 Medical Officers of whom twelve resigned voluntarily, five were forced to, and one dismissal; 114 male nurses of whom three resigned voluntarily, five were forced to, and seven dismissals; 770 female nurses of whom eleven resigned volun-

---

[1] Correspondence between Poor Law Board and Greenwich Guardians, *Accounts and Papers*, 1864.
[2] *Lancet*, 1865, i, p. 184.
[3] *Lancet*, 1865, i, p. 185.

tarily, six were forced to, and twenty dismissals. The number of doctors dismissed was therefore negligible, and as Cane had already asserted of the trend up to the mid-'fifties, dismissals were continually decreasing, whilst the number of Medical Officers engaged was steadily rising, Table 12.10.

TABLE 12.10

Table showing the Number of Poor Law Medical Officers engaged from the year 1838 (the first year medical statistics were published).
From the Annual Reports of the Poor Law Commissioners and Poor Law Board in which figures were given.

Year	Medical Officers	Year	Medical Officers	Year	Medical Officers
1838	2,091	1844	2,825	1861	3,479
1840	2,376	1848	3,000	1862	3,509
1842	2,530	1853	3,151	1869	3,906
1843	2,709	1858	3,307	1870	3,950

In the early years of the new Poor Law, Dr. Arthur Wilson informed Lord John Russell in a deputation to him that: 'he felt it his duty to caution students not to disgrace themselves and the profession by having anything to do in their outside life or ever afterwards, with so degrading and cruel a system as the present mode of medical relief.' Nearly thirty years later the Select Committee of 1864 found that under the existing system there was no practical difficulty in securing the services of a competent practitioner, and that

looking at the large number of Medical Officers that are now employed to attend the sick poor, the progressive diminution in the extent of districts inconveniently large, the care that has been taken to ensure the engagement only of properly qualified medical men, their augmented remuneration, and their improved status, arising from their tenure of office and from other causes . . . the Committee believe the system under which medical relief is administered has been greatly improved, and the poor were never so promptly attended to, or so effectually relieved during sickness than at the present time.

From the official point of view, no doubt the position of both the sick poor and the doctors had greatly improved. No progressive orders or regulations could however compensate for the moral influence of Poor Law work. The doctors had to battle constantly with the evil effects of bad housing, malnutrition, unskilled nursing, and inadequate amenities. They suffered under the frustration of being powerless to secure better environmental conditions for the patients whom they were trying to cure. Amongst filth and squalor and in the homes where there was little furniture or food, the Medical Officer had to diagnose disease, knowing full well that his efforts would be rendered nugatory by the awful state of the houses. In the absence of any knowledge of hygiene or the importance of ventilation and cleanliness, the doctor had often to perform a nurse's duties, which in many cases were more necessary than his own skill. Many of these conditions were ameliorated over the forty years following 1834, but the disheartening nature of medical work among the destitute increased in another direction. As the able-bodied began to require less relief than formerly, so a greater proportion of the aged and infirm, the chronic sick, and the dregs of the submerged class—the super-ignorant and intemperate—needed attention. Salaries had risen perhaps, although much of the Medical Officers' work remained unpaid, unrecognized, and unrecorded, but never could they be adequately recompensed for the zeal and humanity they showed for the welfare of the sick poor.

The problem of, and for, the Poor Law doctor, set in 1834 was still there in 1871. Its wide ramifications, coupled with the prevailing social and political philosophy made it insoluble in the nineteenth century. The twentieth took up its heritage reluctantly, and in 1910 Beatrice Webb was still able to write what Rumsey, Ceely, Griffin or Lord, Chadwick or Shaftesbury, could have written generations before. About one of the most important functionaries in the development towards a Social Welfare State she wrote:

Of all branches of the public service, that of the Poor Law Medical Officer seems . . . the most hardly treated, the least appreciated, and the most depressed. . . . The miserable pittances . . . that a nation allows to thousands of fully qualified practitioners, for laborious duties of the highest importance to Public Health, at a rate which often works out at a few pence per attendance. . . . The degradation of having to balance the cost of drugs . . . against the prospect of having to spend on a case out of his own pocket far more than he is paid for it. . . . The total absence of any professional stimulus, the lack of any encouragement by competent inspection, the absence of professional records, the complete indifference of the Boards of Guardians and Local Government Board to any results, as shown by the failure to ask for any reports, or to inquire whether patients live or die. . . . As to the future of a Poor Law Medical Officer . . . year after year he goes on in the same round of uncomfortable Poor Law practice, without any prospect of promotion, usually without the slightest chance of rising out of the narrow rut into which fate has thrust him. . . . Has any mark of distinction or any sort of public honour ever been given to a Poor Law Medical Officer, [as such] even for the most meritorious, most zealous, most useful, and most prolonged official service. . . . There was nothing with which I was more impressed [when on the Poor Law Commission] than with the amount of devoted work, really quite unpaid for, that the Poor Law Medical Officers were as a class, giving to the poor, or than with the utter lack of official appreciation and encouragement, which that work secured. . . . What many members of the Poor Law Medical Service feel most . . . is not the miserable payment, nor the lack of official appreciation or encouragement, nor even the absence of honours and dignities, but the extraordinary narrow scope that under the necessary limitations of the Poor Law they find for useful work.

Illustrating this remark, Beatrice Webb concluded that it was not encouraging for a doctor to have one-third of all deaths from phthisis pass through his hands without seeing a single curable case.

> It breaks the spirit of a man who cares anything about his professional work to have to go on year after year merely pretending to deal with cases, which have come to him only when destitution has set in, and therefore are usually too late for any permanently remedial treatment, under the structural and other conditions which he knows will prevent a cure, but which he, as a mere Poor Law doctor has no power to prevent. . . .[1]

If the Medical Officers were hardly treated and suffered under a feeling of frustration, their oppression was alleviated by the increasing recognition that they had become indispensable. The State might accord them no honours, but they had become an integrated body and a distinct and important branch of the medical profession. In the 'thirties a practitioner who accepted office was considered of inferior ability or character, or as young and inexperienced, willing to accept a public appointment with a view to obtaining a private practice. Because he was underpaid he was accused of discharging his duties carelessly. By the 'seventies these views had become an anachronism. The advance in medical knowledge and the improvement in medical teaching had been enormous, almost beyond conception to the preceding generation and this had extended to the lower branches of the profession, so that the position of these members increased remarkably in the estimation of the public, and its own higher ranks. Many famous physicians and surgeons were engaged voluntarily in Poor Law work, but this became increasingly less necessary. As early as 1847 the Manchester Board of Guardians passed a resolution thanking the honorary Medical Board for their former services, but stated that in future they would only be required to render assistance as consulting physicians and surgeons rather than in their more active capacity of the past.[2]

In 1866, Dr. Smith pointed out that Poor Law doctors were generally the advisers of the middle-class in the surrounding neighbourhood, and often of the Guardians themselves. He maintained that it would scarcely be possible to find a body 'of Medical Officers who could excel those now in office, or who could discharge their duties more kindly'. Turning his congratulations on the institution doctors, he said it would be difficult to meet Medical Officers of the Metropolitan workhouses without 'perceiving and acknowledging the high position which they hold by character and attainments' and without recognizing the direction as well as the ability with which they discharged their duties. A workhouse doctor regarded the institution as his hospital and his position 'with as much pride and

[1] Pamphlet—*Poor Law Medical Officer*, 1910. Beatrice Webb speaking of her experiences on the Poor Law Commission, 1906-9.
[2] Minutes, Manchester Board of Guardians, April 1847.

pleasure as is felt by a hospital physician; whilst with few exceptions the public regard the appointment as honourable, and as evidence of the ability and integrity of the Medical Officer'.

After this praise, Smith concluded:

It only remains to reconsider the duties of the office and the time devoted to it, with a view to its increasing efficiency, and to award such a salary as shall remove just grounds of complaint, increase the value with which the Medical Officer regards it, and be an inducement to the most able, industrious, discreet . . . and most efficient medical men to compete for it . . . When this is attained, both physicians and general practitioners of high positions will seek the appointments, and within a few years the appointment may rank as high before the public and medical profession as that of hospital consultants.[1]

---

[1] See also 'Poor Law Medical Officers of England', by Ruth G. Hodgkinson in *Journal of the History of Medicine and Allied Sciences*, 1956, Vol. XI, No. 3, pp. 299–338.

CHAPTER 13

The Poor Law Medical Officers' Demand for Professional Standards

THE Poor Law Medical Officers individually or collectively achieved much over the period of forty years by their agitation and by the evidence they gave before Select Committees. It is of interest and of no little importance therefore, to trace briefly how they became an organized body and to examine the work of the associations.

The parent of the Medical Officers' movement was the general professional organization, the Provincial Medical and Surgical Association. This was founded in Worcester on 19 July 1832 by Dr. (later Sir) Charles Hastings, a physician of great reputation. The general urge for political and social reform was making itself felt in the medical profession also. Unorganized and ill-defined opinions needed regulation, and Hastings' Association found permanency, becoming the British Medical Association in 1856. He was its first secretary and in 1843 became permanent President and Treasurer until his death in 1866. We have seen that a British Medical Association interested in the reform of the Poor Law Medical Services existed earlier and into the 'thirties, but this was a short-lived association centred on London.

As well as having a national professional organization, the Poor Law Medical Officers also enjoyed the support of local medical associations. Liverpool, which ran an efficient public medical service, was also the scene of important activity among doctors. The Liverpool Medical Society had been established in 1833, and although regulations limited it strictly to the 'promotion of medical and surgical knowledge', it was not indifferent to the public interests. It invited discussion on medical relief, and the relation of medicine with the State, and petitioned the House of Commons regarding tenders and the inadequacy of the remuneration of Medical Officers. In 1833 it had asked for doctors to be included in the Poor Law inquiry 'so that the Bill might be more useful to the poor and more honourable to the profession'. This Society amalgamated with another in 1837 to become the Liverpool Medical Association. Some of the topics debated were the 'discussion of all questions affecting the health of towns', and the 'dissemination of information affecting the welfare of the community'. In 1850 the Medico-Ethical Society of Liverpool memorialized the Poor Law Board and requested the aid of the medical colleges in demanding the redress of the Poor Law Medical Officers' grievances—'fully intending to follow them by further steps'. Liverpool was always strongly connected with the Provincial Medical and Surgical Association and later the British Medical Association.[1]

The Provincial Medical and Surgical Association beginning with fifty members had 1,700 by 1844, and the Association extended over the greater part of England and Wales. Its objects were wide and varied, and of great significance to Public Health, the Poor Law, and the relation between the public and the doctor. In 1835 and in 1838 two special committees were established for inquiring into the Poor Law Medical Services, and we have already studied the Reports of 1836, 1840, and 1841. These were of such importance that they were published separately from the annual Transactions which became the *British Medical Journal* in 1857. It was at one of the meetings of the special Poor Law Committee in 1846 that the Convention of Poor Law Medical Officers was founded. The connection with the general professional organization was not entirely severed, for the largest proportion of members of the British Medical Association were the public Medical Officers. The Association retained a great interest in State medicine and Public Health and offered valuable aid in securing salutary legislation. An example of the collaboration may be seen in the career of Ernest Hart. Famous in the Association's history because he founded its library and was one of the first editors of the *British Medical Journal,* he is also well remembered in Poor Law history for his invaluable work for the improvement of the workhouse infirmary and as one of the *Lancet* Commissioners in 1865–66.

The last meeting of the Provincial Medical and Surgical Association's Poor Law Committee in 1845 passed a resolution on the qualifications, districts, remuneration, and the arduous and repulsive work of the Medical Officers. The Convention at its first meeting in 1846 pointed out that it did not seek the furthering of professional interests alone, but that it also wished to bring to public notice the evils which existed in the administration of poor relief. Lord Ashley presided over the large gathering and took the opportunity of stating that the interests of the poor and the Medical Officer were identical. Since he had been Chairman of the long Inquiry of 1844 he had realized, he said, that 'no class of men are more aggrieved and ill-treated by a rich and benevolent nation, than the Medical Officers. As they suffer so the poor must suffer.' He wished the Convention 'God Speed' to 'bring the crying evils under the notice of the legislature, . . . to enlighten the ignorant and remove prejudices'. The celebrated pathologist of Guy's Hospital, Thomas Hodgkin was the Chairman of the new movement until its dissolution ten years later, and although he did much valuable work and wrote pamphlets on the medical service, the *Lancet* in writing his obituary in 1866, failed to mention his Poor Law activities and his association with the Convention. C. F. J. Lord, a Poor Law Medical Officer from the beginning, was the efficient Secretary and spokesman of the movement, and in this position he had extensive opportunities to learn the opinions of the profession and the general requirements of the sick paupers and working class.

The first effort of the Convention for amending the medical system was to issue questionnaires to all doctors in the country. From the 900 returns received, details were derived

[1] T. H. Bickerton, *A Medical History of Liverpool,* 1936.

which were embodied in memorials to Sir George Grey,[1] the Poor Law Commissioners, the Royal Colleges, and the Society of Apothecaries. After another meeting in February 1849 over which Lord Ashley presided, a statement was issued from the 300 doctors present to the effect that as Union surgeons had rendered their organization complete, they would not fail to press their claims on the legislature—not as a matter of bounty but as a right. Therefore a comprehensive petition was sent to Parliament with which the Provincial Medical and Surgical Association associated itself. To strengthen the petition fifty shorter versions with many signatures were forwarded from various well populated districts of England and Wales to the Central Committee for presentation. Similar petitions were also obtained from rural areas and some came from clergymen, magistrates, and Chairmen of Boards of Guardians, as well as from the Medical Officers. These were presented to Parliament by the members for the constituencies from which they had emanated, while the general petition was entrusted to the care of Talfourd, Forster, Aglionby, and Lord Ashley. The details were the same as those embodied in the Memorial to Sir George Grey and embraced permanency of appointment, payment proportionate to duties, and responsibility to a professional authority consisting of a Medical Board and Inspectors. The latter clause was particularly strongly worded, for Medical Officers pertinaciously believed that lay supervision and control were invidious and oppressive. An objection was included against the non-payment of Medical Officers for the considerably heavy sanitary duties which had been imposed on them during the cholera epidemic. It was stated further, that under the existing system the duties of the Medical Officer were a 'source of great anxiety, vexatious, harassing and oppressive, and therefore cannot be exercised with that full measure of benefit to the poor which a better system would not fail to secure'. In conclusion the Medical Officers condemned the entire medical system as inefficient and unjust—opinions which were shared, the petitioners claimed, by the majority of doctors in the kingdom.

Efforts were subsequently made to establish a Poor Law Medical League with branch associations in the principal cities and towns. Some 3,000 circulars were accordingly issued to ascertain the opinion of every Union Medical Officer, but only 263 answers were received. Letters were sent inviting co-operation of those favourably inclined to the scheme and they were asked to become local organizing secretaries. Most of them however had insufficient leisure and confessed they would be unable to sustain an effective movement. Therefore the idea of forming the Association was reluctantly abandoned by the Convention. The three medical corporations were again addressed and further deputations waited on Lord John Russell and Baines, the President of the Poor Law Board. Another petition was formulated containing the grievances of 3,000 Poor Law Medical Officers. The Committee of the Convention attended the annual meetings of the Provincial Medical and Surgical Association and solicited resolutions favourable to their cause and support for the Parliamentary petition.

[1] Home Secretary, Memorial, 28 March 1848.

The regulations of the Board of Health during the cholera epidemic gave occasion for protest by the Union doctors against the imposition of unrequited services, and a third deputation waited on the President of the Poor Law Board. Hodgkin asked for salaries to be based on 6s. per case and for the union of Poor Law duties and sanitary obligations under a new General Board of Health.[1] The complaints were recognized and sympathy expressed, and the petitioners thanked for their 'valuable suggestions', but no redress was promised and the practicability of effecting the recommendations was scarcely admitted. The Committee drew public attention to their problem in *The Times* and other journals by an article entitled 'The Poor Law Board, the Sick Poor, their Medical Attendants, and the Ratepayers'. Subsequently, 1,000 copies of the article were printed and one was forwarded to every Member of Parliament calling their attention to the subject of Poor Law Medical Relief. The *Lancet* published a supporting account concluding 'Unity is strength' and asking all Medical Officers to stand together.[2] Simultaneously advertisements were inserted in the London and provincial daily press revealing current cases of hardship and injustice, and how the poor and their doctors suffered together through the terribly inadequate salaries. This activity formed only a part of the exertions of the Committee of the Convention, but they were not matched by an equivalent effort on the part of the majority of Poor Law Medical Officers. In 1850 the Committee said it was reluctant to recommend the dispersion of the Association, but that it could only continue if doctors pledged a more uniform co-operation. Up to April 1851 Committee meetings were held regularly and then it was resolved that the state of public opinion was unfavourable to further efforts at that time. Indefinite adjournment was decided upon 'until some important public movement should arise to warrant the re-assembly of the Committee'.

For four years activity was discontinued because it was felt that no effectual measures could be achieved under the prevailing public apathy. In 1853 the *Lancet* called again for action. Guardians, it was said, were 'little tyrants' and an appeal to Somerset House at best a solemn farce.

> We [*Lancet*] have battled on many occasions on behalf of the Poor Law surgeons both with the Guardians and the Commissioners . . . Had the profession been true to itself what might not have been achieved?[3]

On Pigott obtaining the Parliamentary Inquiry in 1854, meetings of the Convention were again summoned, and the House of Commons was petitioned to hear evidence from several members of a Committee specially organized for the purpose. Great efforts were made to secure a report for the benefit of the Poor Law medical staff and the sick poor. Lord pointed out that doctor and patient were still discontented, and that ratepayers were affected by illness becoming severe through delayed medical care. When disorder passed to disease, he said, and then became chronic, it became the source of permanent and pro-

[1] *Lancet*, 1850 report.
[2] *Lancet*, 1850, i, p. 739.
[3] *Lancet*, 1853, i, pp. 518–19.

tracted expense. He emphasized that the redress of grievances and the more equitable remuneration of the Medical Officer would be received favourably by all classes of people, for these would increase the efficiency and usefulness of the doctor.

In December of 1854 Lord retired from the Secretaryship of the Convention, and the *Lancet*, giving an account of the tributes he received for his services, concluded by calling Medical Officers

> Village Hampdens . . . who have stood forward as the champions of those who have 'no friends beside' and been marked out for destruction . . . by those whose tyranny they had the virtue and manliness to oppose. . . . The pages of this journal have for the past thirty years abounded in instances of this kind.[1]

In 1855 the inherent vices of the Poor Law Medical Services found a fresh denouncing voice in Richard Griffin of Weymouth. The Poor Law Medical Relief Association was organized and was met with 'cheerful and manly advocacy by the medical press . . . The Committee of the Convention watched with deep interest the rise and progress of these combined exertions, and have gladly acted in furtherance of them'.[2] The measures proposed by Griffin's association differed only in matters of detail from those put forward by the Convention in the late 'forties. Its activity was reported closely in the *Lancet* and often in the *British Medical Journal* and letters from Griffin and Lord constantly appeared appealing for unity. The *Lancet* published several long and often leading articles expressing satisfaction with the movement and the progress made. 'Already meetings are held in several districts of the country, and we fervently trust that these examples may be followed in every district of every Union in the kingdom.' Resolutions which appeared were passed unanimously on every occasion, which, the *Lancet* maintained, were bound to lead to speedy and good results.

> It is by local influence that victory must be won, by petitions . . . and by urging on members of Parliament . . . not only the importance of the subject to the public, but to an influential section of their constituents. . . . We feel assured Mr. Griffin will not relax in the efforts he is making for the benefit of the large number of his oppressed and injured professional brethren.[3]

Griffin, thanking the journal for the powerful advocacy of the cause, appealed to readers not to delay in joining the movement so that reforms could be achieved quickly.

Provincial branches were formed, for example, at St. Albans, where a resolution was passed that salaries should be paid by the Government, and suggesting subscriptions of 5s. a quarter should be made, half of which was to defray local expenses and the remainder for Griffin's. A similar resolution was passed in Weymouth. The *Lancet* began to publish the names of all branches which arose in the country. The first were: Whitechapel, Newing-

---

[1] *Lancet*, 1854, ii, p. 514.
[2] *Lancet*, 1856, i, pp. 636–37.
[3] *Lancet*, 1856, i, p. 137.

ton, Chelsea, in London; all areas around Reading; Rugby, Chorlton, Northleach, Plymouth, Wells, Bedford, Blything, Tewkesbury, Manchester, York, Bury, Halifax, Ashton-under-Lyne; and many places in Norfolk, Sussex, and Somerset. All voted a quarterly subscription of 5s. and that salaries should be increased and paid by the Government. In February 1856 Medical Officers of fifty Unions sent addresses professing adherence to the Poor Law Medical Relief Association, in March fifty-seven Unions were involved, and by May 284 Unions.[1] Every day, wrote the *Lancet*, was signalled by new meetings of surgeons and new adherents to the central organization against the 'degrading subservience to Guardians'. It was pointed out that the answer Pigott had received when he asked the Commons whether the Poor Law Board contemplated acting on the recommendations of the Select Committee of 1854, showed that the Government would not resist 'any just and reasonable amendments in the present system that *may be urged by the united body of Poor Law surgeons*'.[2] Griffin thanking the *Lancet* again for its support admitted that without the press individual efforts would have been fruitless, and that he could not have persuaded 350 practitioners to render their support. He again appealed through the journals for help because there was still much apathy, although more and more of the labouring class were falling under the Medical Officers' care. He believed half the working class (Mayhew had estimated the total as four million) were now covered by them. One District Medical Officer, he suggested, should canvass all his colleagues to join the local and national association, and the backing of the entire medical profession was solicited for a huge meeting to be held at the end of May 1856. The *Lancet* wrote it was essential to the success of Griffin's movement that the Convention of Poor Law Medical Officers should also give its assistance. 'Let the conduct of those who assemble on the 30th give such an answer to these enemies of our profession as will effectually silence them for the future.'[3]

To obtain a large and influential gathering the Convention and the Association co-operated over the London meeting. Lord Shaftesbury[4] once again presided and spoke to the 300 Poor Law Medical Officers of the importance of their movement and the necessity for unanimity. He pointed out that the battle cry of the opponents to the rights of the doctors had been 'disunion in the profession'. Lord drew attention to the great public outcry which would be raised if 'the quiet walk of the Union surgeon could be prominently brought forward and the injurious effect of the present system on ourselves and on the suffering poor could be graphically given through the daily press'. At this meeting the Poor Law Medical Officers formed themselves into the Poor Law Medical Reform Association, with Griffin as Chairman and Lord and Rogers on the Committee. A petition was sent to Parliament from the meeting and was presented by Sir John Trollope. Sotheron Estcourt, later a President of the Poor Law Board, expressed his readiness to bring the cause of the Poor Law Medical Officer before the House of Commons. The petition spoke

[1] *Lancet*, 1856, i, pp. 216, 242, 246, 613.
[2] *Lancet*'s italics, 1856, i, p. 236.
[3] *Lancet*, 1856, i, p. 561–62.
[4] Lord Ashley had succeeded to his father's title in 1851.

of the 876,000 paupers and the great proportion of the working class which came under the care of the 3,000 Medical Officers; of the long education, the arduous services, and the danger to health which such duties entailed. A uniform rate of payment was demanded and a fixed salary based on the average number of cases attended over three years, with not less than 5s. per case and 1s. per mile for travelling. An extended scale of extras was also asked for and that a workhouse Medical Officer should receive fees as well as the District Medical Officer. Commutation of fees was condemned. Further, medical orders were to continue in force for each case for no longer than three months, and if they were renewed they were to be counted as fresh orders. Medical men conversant with Union practice were to have a seat on the Poor Law Board and control over the medical department; and finally, the Poor Law Board was to be requested to define the class of persons entitled to medical relief, as this should not be left to the discretion of the Relieving Officer. A memorial was also forwarded to the Poor Law Board stating that it was well known that the Board had the legal power to effect reforms without the intervention of Parliament, but that the utter failure of the numerous and urgent applications to the central authority led the memorialists to infer that the Board desired to have authorization by direct legislative interference—hence the petition to Parliament.

Following this, the movement continued its agitation in the country. In February 1857, students of King's College Hospital, London, passed a unanimous resolution in favour of the Poor Law Medical Reform Association and Griffin, and a subscription fund for aid was opened. Other medical schools in London co-operated. Students of the London, Charing Cross, University College, St. George's, Guys, St. Bartholomew's, Westminster, and St. Thomas's hospitals all desired to assist the association. Provincial Medical Schools also joined, as for example, those in Hull, Manchester, Liverpool, and Bristol. Medical students were keenly interested in public appointments, and their support of the movement showed how far progress had been made since a famous medical teacher cautioned his pupils not to disgrace themselves and the profession by having any connection with the Poor Law. At the end of March the student branches of the Association held a large public meeting in Edinburgh at which resolutions were passed on the inadequacy of Poor Law relief for helping the poor, the grievances of the Medical Officers, and a warm eulogy on Griffin. A petition was also formulated.

Meanwhile the *Lancet* had again been urging unity, and on 28 May 1857 a great public meeting of Poor Law Medical Officers and private practitioners was staged for the purpose of sending another petition to Parliament. Lord Shaftesbury as on previous occasions presided. In his address he concurred with the petition, and deprecated the inadequate status of the Medical Officer when the condition of the working class and their badly drained and ventilated homes were taken into consideration. He regarded the position of the Poor Law doctor as disgraceful: 'If you want a sober, healthy, loyal population . . . means must be taken whereby the poor people will be able to obtain that proper medical treatment to which they are entitled.' He promised that he would not fail to advocate unceasingly in Parliament that the Medical Officer should occupy the position necessary to the onerous duties which he had to perform. Griffin dwelt with particular emphasis on the various anomalies existing under the Poor Law Board regarding surgery—for example, no remuneration was allowed where a doctor had been able to preserve a limb, yet he was paid for an amputation. The petition to the House of Commons pointed out how much higher rates of payment were for attendance on prisoners than on paupers, and that 72 per cent of the latter were receiving medical relief. It also stated that the doctors' awareness of the injuries they suffered was illustrated by the number of resignations—in 1855 for example 290 had relinquished their posts, and in 1856, 249. (Griffin deprecated the readiness of some practitioners to fill the vacancies because this was detrimental to the cause.) The petition was very lengthy but the chief demands were similar to previous ones. The absence of members from the medical corporations was noted at the meeting, but in June the Royal College of Surgeons sent a petition to Parliament in agreement with the Association's, and the Society of Apothecaries did likewise.

Early in 1858 Griffin published a pamphlet summarizing the grievances of the Poor Law Medical Officer and the social evils entailed on the poor and the ratepayers by the existing system of medical relief. It was written in the form of an address to the legislature and included the draft of a Bill. The Lancet reporting on this work praised Griffin as the 'resolute champion of the rights of the poor and of his professional brethren'. It stated also that in and out of Parliament, even amongst the Boards of Guardians, there was a strong and growing conviction that a comprehensive measure of reform could not be delayed.[1] Griffin's proposed Bill dealt with eligibility for office, mode of election, tenure, duties, remuneration, and superannuation. The Bill was followed by a compendium of all orders relating to Medical Officers since 1847, and therefore embodied a vast amount of information. It formed the most valuable digest existing on the position of Poor Law doctors and supplied a want which the central authorities should have filled.

In April 1858 Griffin, who was at this time being continually thwarted in his appeals for improvement in his own Union because the Guardians were supported by the Poor Law Board—led a deputation to Sotheron Estcourt, President of the Central Board in 1858–59. Rogers and Lord were members, as well as Medical Officers from all over the country, and twenty Members of Parliament including Pigott and Slaney. The President agreed that the method of paying salaries was bad and freely admitted that the system of Poor Law medical relief required alteration. If he could see his way to the adoption of a good measure he promised to introduce it, but pointed out that Parliament would object to interfering with the Boards of Guardians.[2] He introduced a scheme with which the Medical Officers were dissatisfied and a second deputation visited him in February 1859. The deputation was led by Lord John Russell and again included many Members of Parliament. As a result of this and subsequent correspondence with Griffin, Estcourt dropped his plan. The scheme included proposals whereby all existing contracts were to terminate at a cer-

[1] Leading article: Lancet, 1858, i, pp. 391–92.
[2] The nineteenth-century fear of the central authorities interfering with the power of local government must again be remembered

tain period, to allow a fresh start to be made. (This met the chief objection of the Poor Law Medical Officers.) Two Medical Officers were then to be appointed for each district, the poor being given a choice of doctor. Contracts were to be for three years and renewable, and salaries were to be fixed on a basis of 1s. 6d. per case on the average number of patients attended for a year for a three-yearly average, and a sum per case was to be paid for mileage. The table of extra fees was to be redrawn by the Poor Law Board and the Medical Council. Permanent cases were to be counted as new cases every three months. Many Medical Officers sent alternative schemes to the *Lancet* in reply to Estcourt's, and the journal contained another long leading article on the reform of salaries.[1] The *British Medical Journal* in 1859 and 1860 also published many letters and reports of meetings of the Poor Law Medical Reform Association.

When Pigott introduced his Medical Bill of 1860, Griffin wrote a thirty-page summary adding commentaries and statistics. A copy of the pamphlet was sent to each Member of Parliament and to all Medical Officers, and the latter were urged to petition for the Bill. Griffin continued an unwearying agitation and made countless appeals to doctors through the medical press recommending energetic activity. On one occasion he quoted the Poor Law Commissioners as saying:

> Here and there an individual candidate well-fitted for a Union Officer may from peculiar circumstances be willing to accept it for an inadequate salary, but even he will, probably, after a short while become dissatisfied, and will desire to transfer his services to some other Union, or to seek some other employment.[2]

This, he said, had come true, for from 1856 to 1860 there had been nearly 1,500 resignations. A great mass of petitions were forwarded by the Medical Officers on the Bill and a public meeting was held in April 1860 at which Rogers was one of the foremost speakers. Student members of the Poor Law Medical Reform Association were also active and meetings were held by all branches in these months. The *British Medical Journal* published a leading article in which it was stated:

> It must be understood that we have to fight the Boards of Guardians for every penny of increased remuneration we wish to give to the miserably underpaid Poor Law Medical Officer. Those engaged in this struggle should remember that as far as its opponents are concerned, the battle will turn on the mere question of £ s. d. . . . It may be all very well for us to descant upon its human aspect as regards the poor, but neither the Poor Law Commission nor the Boards of Guardians will view it for one moment in this light.[3]

At the end of 1860 Griffin drafted and published proposals of a new Bill, but the Association deferred the introduction of an independent Bill until the result of Villiers' Inquiry was

[1] *Lancet*, 1859, i, pp. 220–21. See also p. 224 for Medical Officers' reply.
[2] 31 October 1840.
[3] *British Medical Journal*, 1860, i, p. 363.

known. Petitions to the Select Committee which was about to be held were drawn up and in March 1861 the Association appointed a sub-committee, of which Fowler was Honorary Secretary, to collate facts and prepare a statement on which to base the evidence to be laid before the Commissioners. The Metropolitan Poor Law Medical Officers, of which Fowler was Secretary, held a meeting (10 May 1861) and drafted a list of suggestions to be sent in evidence. These included the following points: cheapness was not to be the ruling guide in the appointment of Medical Officers; permanency of office; the power of ordering extras; the reorganization of districts; remuneration should be 2s. 6d. in the Metropolis and 5s. a case in the provinces; fees for extras should be reconsidered; superannuation; and the powers of the Poor Law Board should be consolidated and amended.

In 1861 Griffin was crippled for funds and was working at his own expense. Another meeting was held in February at which Rogers was again the dominant speaker. Fourteen months later Griffin started a new campaign and asked for more funds so that the Association might continue. He addressed the Royal Colleges and the medical schools in England, Scotland and Ireland for aid for the cause, and Sir Charles Hastings promised on behalf of the British Medical Association to memorialize the Select Committee. The *British Medical Journal* reported Griffin's speeches but pointed out the hopeless task of asking Parliament for the redress of grievances. Nothing, it maintained, could be expected from a *laissez-faire* and Free-Trade House of Commons. A great united movement would have to arise, for as long as a number of candidates came forward to take Poor Law appointments at unremunerative rates, there could be no hope for the improvement of salaries. It was the old story of the lack of union in the profession.

Unfortunately there was a rift over schemes between Fowler and Griffin which continued throughout 1862. Griffin accused Fowler and Rogers of suggesting plans which would injure country Medical Officers, whereas his ideas were advantageous to both urban and rural doctors. The rival proposals were outlined in the medical press in June 1862, and comparative statistics were given. Fowler suggested that as there were five schemes for reform before the Select Committee, their originators should constitute a Committee to watch over the interests of the Poor Law Medical Officers during the inquiry. The men in question were Griffin, Meredith, Lord, Rogers, Fowler, and Ross, whose ideas have been studied, and Wills and Nicholas. Griffin however would not agree as five of the doctors were from London and would represent only 175 Medical Officers, whilst nearly 3,000 provincial practitioners would be represented by only three men. In the end no Committee was formed because the Select Committee was chary of hearing medical evidence.

In 1864 the medical press had again to advertise for subscriptions to the movement. One Medical Officer wrote to the *Lancet* that doctors were dilatory in sending contributions because they had come to regard their case as hopeless. In March, Griffin stated that if the Select Committee did not give a favourable report it was time for him to resign. As we have seen, the recommendations were not propitious to the cause of the profession and the Committee refused to reopen the question by examining further witnesses. The *Lance* published an angry argument asserting that claims had been just and should be effected, and the writer failed to comprehend why the Select Committee had ignored them.[1] In June Fowler wrote to the *Lancet*:

> Poor Law medical reform is virtually ended. The period has therefore now arrived for giving practical expression to our gratitude for all that mass of time, energy and exertion which Mr. Griffin has for years so perseveringly bestowed on our cause.[2]

Fowler opened a subscription for defraying the outstanding expenses pertaining to Griffin's fund and presenting him with a testimonial. Over £150 was collected. The *Lancet* disagreed with the proposal for abandoning the cause. It insisted that the movement had been unsuccessful through the want of unity and the lack of liberality in supporting Griffin's schemes. After a eulogy the journal suggested that the time was opportune for rallying round the leader.

In the following year Griffin was still attempting to get a Bill introduced in Parliament, but no Member of Parliament was willing to undertake the task. The *Lancet* called for unity and campaigned against the apathy of the Poor Law Medical Officers. Griffin turned his attention to the supply of drugs and asked for the doctors' support for obtaining determination on the meaning of 'expensive' drugs. In June 1865 he appealed again through the medical press to the Poor Law practitioners, for the Continuance Bill had been introduced,[3] and he believed this to be a vital opportunity to make a final attempt to secure the amending of the medical system. He circularized Members of Parliament with a pamphlet and tried to get important clauses inserted in the Bill, but in vain. During the next two years he continued with the Association, obtaining subscriptions for the introduction of a Private Member's Bill and for the amendment of the Vaccination Bill in which he desired to see the fee of 1s. 6d. raised to 2s. 6d. But he was constantly short of funds for publishing and circularizing his pamphlets. In May 1866 another deputation waited on the Poor Law Board regarding a Medical Relief Bill.

During this year the Metropolitan Poor Law Medical Officers were taking measures to form an association for the purpose of uniting isolated Medical Officers into a compact body 'to afford each other mutual help and support, and to interchange opinions in regard to duties, position, difficulties, and requirements'.[4] As we have seen they had held meetings in 1861 and the Association of Medical Officers of Health formed an excellent precedent. The leadership of the Poor Law Medical Officers' movement in the late 'sixties passed into the capable and persevering hands of Joseph Rogers. His work has been made known to posterity through his autobiography[5] which not only furnishes a good illustration of the

---

[1] *Lancet*, 1864, i, p. 397.
[2] *Lancet*, 1864, i, p. 710.
[3] The continuation of the Poor Law Board for a further three years—this did not become a permanent body until 1868.
[4] *Lancet*, 1866, i, p. 695.
[5] *Reminiscences of a Workhouse Medical Officer*, 1889. Edited with a preface by Thorold Rogers, his brother, the well-known economist.

arduous duties of Medical Officers and the frustration of their attempts to carry out improvements for the sick poor, but also of the later movement for bettering their own position. Coming to London soon after qualification, Rogers began his life's work—the reform of the Poor Law medical services. For this, in the words of his brother, he 'surrendered all prospects of professional success, fortune, popularity, and health . . . he literally wore himself out by his labours'. The sordid and indolent nature of London vestrymen, the vacillation and timidity of the Poor Law Board, formed no mean deterrent to progressive Medical Officers, whose impatient struggles were regarded as meddlesome and odious, and a danger to retrenchment. Rogers constantly proposed changes which would relieve rates in the end, but great courage was needed to attack the abuses which were such a scandal and dishonour to humane principles. In 1844, Rogers came to Soho and the first reform he undertook in conjunction with G. A. Walker was the closing of burial grounds in the city and the prohibition of future intramural interment. He succeeded in establishing the first public mortuary in London, an important innovation because the dead sometimes lay a week in the overcrowded and insanitary homes of the poor. Helped by Lord Duncan he succeeded in getting the window-tax repealed in 1851, although the agitation had been originally started 20 years before by Southwood Smith on sanitary grounds. As a doctor Rogers recognized the effect of light and air on disease, and attempted to get drainage improved; he therefore revealed his interest in the preventive as well as the therapeutic side of medicine.

The outbreak of cholera in 1855 saw him working among the poor and the epidemic seriously affected his private practice. He successfully applied for the position of Medical Officer to the Strand workhouse and was offered a stipend of £50 a year, including the supply of medicines. This appointment was the beginning of his systematic and courageous struggle on behalf of the sick poor and the medical profession. He immediately became an active member of the Convention of Poor Law Medical Officers, and then of Griffin's Poor Law Medical Reform Association. His evidence before the Select Committee of the 'sixties has been noted and his particular championship of the proposal that Guardians should supply drugs and appliances. He felt the sick were not given adequate or appropriate medicine in the workhouse, and his struggle for public provision of drugs linked to his campaign for the complete charge of the doctor over his patients was the initial move for the establishment of real workhouse infirmaries.

Griffin's evidence before the Select Committee had taken months and Fowler's a few days. We know that the former had worked assiduously for years to call attention to the grievances of the Poor Law Medical Officer but he failed. 'Facts which he collected with such pains were traversed by Inspector Cane, who by statistics made out to the Committee with satisfaction, that medical men had no great cause for complaint.'[1] Fowler's efforts were similarly snuffed out, but the Committee compromised on Rogers' proposal and suggested that expensive medicines should be found—they probably dreaded the cost of the provision of all drugs.

[1] Rogers, *Reminiscences of a Workhouse Medical Officer*, 1889.

In the spring of 1865 the *Lancet* embarked on its momentous investigations. Dr. Anstie called on Rogers, because he believed he would be able to suggest the best course to follow in obtaining admission to workhouse infirmaries. Rogers arranged a dinner party to facilitate discussion of institutional abuses. Among his guests was John Storr of Covent Garden, one of the wealthiest and most respected members of the Strand Board of Guardians. Rogers' personal friend Ernest Hart was also present. As a result of the party a meeting was held in Storr's office in January 1866, and the Association for the Improvement of Workhouse Infirmaries was launched. Storr gave £100 to float the Association, lent his own offices free and became the first treasurer. Anstie, Rogers, and Hart were honorary secretaries. The Society prospered beyond anticipation, and was joined by Louisa Twining, the Earl of Carnarvon, Earl Grosvenor, and the Archbishop of York. Money poured in. Farnall, the Metropolitan Poor Law Inspector, was deputed by Villiers, then President of the Poor Law Board, to give information to the infant Association. He attended all Committee meetings and afforded much valuable assistance, for he was by this time a convert of Florence Nightingale and interested in the efficient medical relief of the poor. In May 1866 the superintendent nurse of the Strand workhouse went to a general hospital, but before she left, Hart questioned her on the prevailing conditions in the institution of which Rogers had been speaking at a Committee meeting. Hart forwarded her statement on the mismanagement she had witnessed to the Earl of Carnarvon so that he would press Villiers for an official inquiry. Rogers' evidence denouncing his Board of Guardians was reported in full in the press, as was his rider that although the Strand had been singled out for inquiry, conditions were no worse than in the other workhouses of the Metropolis. The Inspector gave a remarkable statement on the conditions he had witnessed, but the President of the Poor Law Board put it aside and wrote his own.

At the same time a questionnaire was sent to the forty Metropolitan Workhouse Medical Officers—in order, Rogers maintained, to trap them into contradictory answers. He therefore felt it imperative to take immediate action and a meeting was arranged so that a single form of reply could be worked out. It was also decided to establish an Association of Metropolitan Workhouse Medical Officers which would be able to deal promptly with any similar departmental trickery. Rogers was elected President, an office which he held until the Association was merged in the Poor Law Medical Officers' Association, of which it was the nucleus. During the following two years the Workhouse Medical Officers' Association played an important part in the settlement of many questions regarding the administration of institutional medical relief—'which without the practical knowledge of medical men, would have been wholly left in the hands of officials at the Poor Law Board ... who at this time ... showed singular unwillingness to face the facts.'[1]

Rogers' official life after the Strand inquiry was an unpleasant one because he was accused of trying to bring 'his masters into contempt'. The Derby–Disraeli premiership which followed soon afterwards promised to deal effectively with the scandals that had

[1] Rogers, *Reminiscences of a Workhouse Medical Officer*, 1889.

been revealed in connection with workhouse infirmary administration. Gathorne Hardy, the President of the Poor Law Board had been Chairman of a Quarter Sessions and an ex-officio Guardian of a Kent Board. One of his first acts was to punish Farnall for his activity in aiding the Workhouse Infirmary Association by sending him to the Eastern Counties. Dr. Markham was appointed as Poor Law Inspector and so-called medical adviser. He had been editor of an obscure journal, had never seen the inside of a workhouse and had had no connection with public health work. 'The popular explanation given for this appointment was that he spent the larger portion of the day looking out of the windows of the Carlton, Pall Mall, and Mr. Hardy gave him something to do'. He proved to be one of the most difficult officials of the Board. Dr. Smith, the other medical adviser of the central authorities, also maintained at this time that the suggestions of the Workhouse Medical Officers' Association regarding the cubic space required for each sick inmate were excessive, and that area was of no consequence so long as the roof of the sick-ward was high enough. A meeting of the Association was therefore convened and the support of Dr. Parkes, an eminent professor of hygiene, was obtained. He and three secretaries produced a paper stating what in their view were the minimum area and cubic space requirements. This activity forced Hardy's hand and induced him to appoint the Cubic Space Committee to settle the question.

During the Conservative Government numerous and influential deputations on behalf of the Workhouse Infirmary Association waited on Hardy. They included such men as Lord Shaftesbury, the Archbishop of York, and Earl Grosvenor, who urged extensive alterations in the system. Rogers advised Hardy that in regard to any scheme which might be under consideration he hoped the President would be guided by his own judgement and not by that of permanent officials. This intensified the ill-feeling against Rogers. The Workhouse Infirmary Association drew up a scheme for a general dietary for all Metropolitan institutions. Rogers, as we have seen, had for many years been interested in this and had introduced an amended dietary at the Strand workhouse. He now successfully urged the Poor Law Board to issue a general order to all London Boards of Guardians relating to a uniform dietary, which excluded only the acutely sick. This measure was important because dietaries in some workhouses were niggardly in the extreme whilst others were absurdly liberal.

While Hardy was engaged on drafting the Metropolitan Poor Bill, Rogers was in constant contact with him. One of the subjects he pressed was the advisability of turning the vast field for clinical observation which the workhouse infirmaries afforded to some practical purpose by throwing the wards open to medical students as the Marylebone Infirmary had done thirty years before. He also urged that the hospitals about to be established should be staffed by resident doctors who, however, should not be in sole control, for their work should be superintended by external physicians and surgeons. Rogers' proposition regarding the turning of the infirmaries into teaching hospitals was overruled by the doctors of the general voluntary hospitals, who thought that the educational opportunities suggested would interfere with their own institutions and students.

Finally, Rogers asked for the consolidation of Poor Law schools and that permanent juvenile paupers should be separated from those constantly going in and out of the workhouses. Hardy, introducing the Metropolitan Poor Bill, mentioned that he had resolved to adapt the reforms Rogers had advocated. Although the Bill was quickly passed, it took up to six years for the implementing of the dispensary clauses. This was in great measure due to the appointment of Lord Devon as the new President of the Poor Law Board, for he had previously supported all the worst parts of the old system, and as a Poor Law Inspector had always yielded to the Boards of Guardians. While he was President he deferred entirely to the permanent staff, but he did institute a new order of officials—the Assistant Inspector.

In this year, because he had protested against the hideous malpractice of the Strand workhouse officials, and because he was the champion of the sick poor, Rogers was dismissed from office after a quarrel had been planted by the Board of Guardians. He called another meeting of the Metropolitan Poor Law Medical Officers at the end of April 1868 because, as he maintained, the election of a new Parliament was a time for renewed united action. Griffin sent £20 for the funds of the Association, for by this time he was too ill to take any further active part in the movement. Drs. Anstie and Stallard, the workhouse reformers, were also present at the meeting. Resolutions again advocated the payment 'per case' system—3s. 6d. was suggested, exclusive of medicines. The remuneration of the medical staff at Marylebone workhouse, approved and sanctioned by the Poor Law Board, was taken as the basis for the equalization of salaries. Further, the doctors opposed the imposition of additional duties on them (regarding sanitary measures), for this brought them into frequent collision with Guardians. Fowler maintained that the Metropolitan Poor Act had been an equivocal boon to medical men. The rating clauses, on which salaries depended, were permissive and therefore of little value. Medical Officers were to appoint qualified assistants, yet salaries did not permit it, and 200–300 assistants would result in greatly increasing expenditure. Fowler stated that the practice of some Union Medical Officers of employing unqualified assistants had for the past twenty years received the implied sanction of the Poor Law Board, and that if it were the intention of the central authorities to enforce the appointment by doctors of legally qualified assistants, it would be an imperative necessity for the Board to supplement such an order with a compulsory and considerable increase in the existing inadequate salaries of the Medical Officers.

The meeting ended by reviewing the treatment of Poor Law doctors. One said he had been forced to resign from the Cambridge Union because of his persistent endeavours to carry out improvements for tramps and the other inmates of the workhouses, and for his attempts to suppress fever by drawing attention to public health requirements. The Guardians had constantly been supported by the Poor Law Board. Rogers' enforced resignation, it was said, also showed that a Medical Officer was doomed, however well he might perform his duties, if he dared to oppose any of the numerous abuses of the Poor Law. Because he was no longer a Poor Law Medical Officer, Rogers resigned his position as Chairman of the Metropolitan Workhouse Medical Officers' Association at this meeting and was elected an honorary member and President. The *Lancet* powerfully took up his personal struggle with the Guardians and the Poor Law Board, although the *British Medical Journal* opposed him. Many letters of sympathy were printed in the former journal and one Metropolitan workhouse Medical Officer who was not a member accused the Association of being at the feet of the *Lancet*.[1] The *Lancet* did not however agree with payment 'per case' because the number of sick poor was too large. In the Metropolis alone, it was stated, there were 200,000 medical orders in a single year and 10,000 patients were always under treatment. At 3s. 6d. a case this would have amounted to a total expenditure of £36,000 excluding additional fees, a sum, the *Lancet* said, it was unreasonable to expect ratepayers to pay.[2]

But outside support was widespread. William Farr, and Sir Charles Hastings until his death, for example, were keen advocates of the demand. Another doctor wrote that isolated as the Poor Law Medical Officers were, and powerless as a body, yet they had the encouragement and the good wishes of the public and were supported by the Press. It had become recognized that greater liberality towards them would promote the welfare of the numerous poor.[3] A Birmingham hospital physician wrote to the *Lancet*:

> The payment for the services rendered by the Parish Medical Officer is so thoroughly contemptible as to be a disgrace to us (doctors). Over and over again this matter has been the subject of indignant leading articles and still more indignant letters in the *Lancet*. . . . Medical Officers are requested to resign . . . if they utter 'insolent' remarks . . . Are the Poor Law officials to abuse the patience of a noble profession?

Pamphlets, he continued, had been written in vain.

> Mr. Griffin has given a life to his oppressed brethren. The medical press tells them of their sufferings with the regularity of the seasons . . . But medical men do not know how to obtain the objects they aim at . . . There is no machinery whereby common action can be secured.

The writer was a champion of the doctors employed by public dispensaries and medical clubs, and was a staunch advocate of boycott by them at this time in the furthering of their demand for increased remuneration. He therefore advocated the combination of all publicly employed Medical Officers in the style of the Incorporated Law Society, although he opposed the Trade Unionism of working men. The only effective means for securing adequate salaries, he maintained, was by all Medical Officers abstaining from taking office where remuneration was too low.[4]

The need for reviving the national movement was also felt among Poor Law Medical Officers at this time. Freed from his public duties, Rogers in 1868 turned to making the

[1] Dr. Vallance, West Ham Workhouse Poor Law Medical Officer since 1834. (Dr. Vallance had been called to give evidence to the Select Committee of 1844.) *Lancet*, 1868, i, p. 574.

[2] *Lancet*, 1868, i, p. 596.

[3] R. Grimbly, Banbury: *Lancet*, 1868, i, p. 673.

[4] T. P. Heslop, M.D., *Lancet*, 1868, i, pp. 229–31. (The interest of many eminent doctors of the day in Poor Law medical problems was of great importance and its significance must be stressed.)

permanent officials do theirs. The Poor Law Board was only nominal, for it never met, and documents requiring members' signatures were taken to their private residences, where, Rogers asserted, they were often signed without the contents being read. Therefore he called a meeting in June to discuss the composition of the Poor Law Board and the grievances of the Poor Law Medical Officers. It was an immense success, with a large attendance, for the first time in many years, of doctors from all parts of the country. The central authorities were therefore given the opportunity of learning how the officials were watched and criticized in every region. The *Lancet* reported on the vigour and intelligence which had been shown in the speeches, the unanimity of feeling, and the notable advance since Griffin 'the father of Poor Law Medical Reform' had called the first national meeting twelve years previously. The journal expressed hearty appreciation that Medical Officers were at last alive to the absolute necessity of pressing on Parliament and the country a radical reform in the constitution of the Poor Law Board: 'which shall render that body a real, and not a mythical and irresponsible body, and which above all, shall constitute a medical department for the general supervision of all Poor Law medical matters'. The parliamentary power of the profession was quite considerable by now. This, the *Lancet* stressed, should be used 'unceasingly and unflinchingly till the most important and primary objects are obtained, . . . and there must be perfect Union and unflinching resolution.'[1]

At this meeting Rogers formed and became the President of an all-embracing Poor Law Medical Officers' Association, which was to further the perfection and extension of the organization already existing in the Metropolis. Its activity showed the change in policy which had gradually been developing under Rogers' leadership. He had come to the conclusion, he said, that the course followed previously by his friend Griffin in continually calling attention to the grievances of the Medical Officers would 'never eventuate in the improvement of their position, because the general public never cared for our class in any way'. He therefore tried to demonstrate to the public the shortcomings of all the arrangements and attempted to prove that an amended system of medical relief would diminish the duration of sickness and therefore the cost to the ratepayers. Through illness, Griffin's activity had ceased in 1868, although he continued to write letters to the medical press and to send subscriptions to the Poor Law Medical Officers' Association. Rogers made several journeys to Ireland and highly commended the dispensary system there. He discovered that where medical relief was abundantly and generously given, pauperism decreased and the rates diminished. It was due to his efforts that many provincial towns voluntarily adopted the principles of the Metropolitan Poor Act. Because the full effect of the dispensary system could be studied in Ireland, Rogers was asked by the Council of the Poor Law Medical Officers' Association to propose to the Council of the Irish Medical Association, the 'mutual interchange of good offices to further the object of the respective associations' and mutual aid.[2] The Irish Medical Officers succeeded in obtaining a Superannuation Act in

[1] *Lancet*, 1868, i, p. 824.
[2] *Lancet*, 1869, i, pp. 25–26.

1869 under the leadership of Dr. Brady, who was also a spokesman for all Poor Law doctors in the Commons. Rogers assisted the movement by drawing attention to it in medical journals, and induced his Association not only to petition, but also to interview Members of Parliament for the Bill. In 1870 Brady undertook to attempt to get the enactment of a similar measure for the English Medical Officers. Rogers opposed superannuation on principle, but realized its necessity when inadequate remuneration made insurance against old age impossible. Without his aid Brady's success would have been impossible.

From 1869, the Poor Law Medical Officers' Association, under Rogers' presidency, rose in importance. It grew in prosperity and became a well-organized permanent movement calling upon a large amount of Parliamentary support. Eighty-nine Members of Parliament declared their intention in this year to give the subject of medical relief for the poor attentive consideration. They also expressed their conviction that the Medical Officers were unjustly treated. At a quarterly meeting in January 1869 Dr. Fowler in a long speech pointed out that the general increase in medical expenditure was no proof of a similar rise in salaries, for wines, drugs, appliances, and subscriptions to hospitals were included in statistical enumerations. Rogers at the meeting continued to press for the universal supply of drugs by Guardians—which would have amounted to an increased annual outlay of £86,000. He also desired salaries to be paid entirely out of the Consolidated Fund. Further he drew attention to the fact that Ireland was spending £118,000 for 5,500,000 people on Poor Law medical relief, whilst in England, with four times the population only £272,000 was so spent. He therefore pressed for the nation-wide establishment of dispensaries and for an additional outlay of at least £500,000.[1] Other doctors at the meeting, at which Edwin Chadwick was also present, gave further lists of inadequate salaries which they said had not increased in the same ratio as the number of patients. One Medical Officer who had seen fourteen years service at Bethnal Green, estimated that his salary should have risen from £120 to £1,600 if the growth in the number of cases had been taken into account, and this omitted the great increase of work in times of cholera and fever epidemics. A member of the St. Giles Board of Works, who was not a doctor, impressed on the Association the necessity of making all facts known to the public. He said William Torrens[2] and Sir John Gray were powerless to act in the Commons unless they had the sympathy of the people. The meeting therefore moved for the President's speech to be printed and extensively circulated, and a petition was sent to Parliament.

In March 1869 a memorial was presented by Rogers on behalf of the Workhouse Medical Officers regarding the regular 'statement' required of them by the General Order of 4 April 1868 on the condition of the institutions. The doctors desired other officers to undertake this duty, or else they should be granted additional remuneration for becoming inspectors. In May Goschen was presented with another memorial containing 122 signa-

---

[1] Report of a meeting of the Poor Law Medical Officers' Association, 23 January 1869: *Lancet*, 1869, i, p. 210.

[2] For William Torrens (1813-94) see D.N.B. He was a barrister who served as assistant-commissioner on the Irish Poor Law Commission in 1835 and later as Liberal Member of Parliament, 1847-1885.

tures of Workhouse Medical Officers. The deputation was led by Dr. Lyon Playfair[1] and included Dr. Brady and Dr. Lush, all Rogers' firm friends and advocates of the cause in Parliament. Sir John Gray, Sir George Jenkinson, and Rogers himself completed the deputation. At the end of April 1869 several Members of Parliament were present at the quarterly meeting of the Association and heard how inadequate payment and unjust treatment of Medical Officers had led to an increase in poor rates. Resolutions were passed for the introduction of the dispensary system throughout the country. Reporting on the meeting the *Lancet* wrote: 'The increase [in poor rates] of late years has been due to neglected sickness among the poor, which would have been properly treated had not the medical service been systematically starved and maltreated'.[2] But the journal feared there was little chance of an increase in salaries or the effecting of permanent appointments under the existing form and constitution of the Poor Law Board.

In January 1870 the Association demanded a Royal Commission on the administration of the Poor Law, and all Medical Officers were urged to communicate with their Members of Parliament on the question. The doctors congratulated themselves on the introduction of dispensaries in the Metropolis and on the success of the Superannuation Bill. The Act for the Registration of Disease had also been passed—this had been an object of the Poor Law Medical Officers throughout the 'sixties, and the British Medical Association and the medical colleges had written strongly in its favour. In the last year of the Poor Law Board the Association helped to bring about greater activity there. This was what the Poor Law Medical Officers had striven for and Rogers always regretted that so much power should have been given to the Boards of Guardians.

> It is generally believed that the Poor Law Board has not the power of initiative; that it can do nothing besides make suggestions. This notion must be practically incorrect; for if it be compulsory on local boards to submit their resolutions to the central office for confirmation, it is evident that the Poor Law Board could control many matters which they now leave the Guardians to decide.

On the question of dispensaries Rogers asserted it was incumbent on the Board to lay down general principles for the guidance of Guardians, who had no practical knowledge on the subject of efficient treatment of the outdoor sick. Regarding remuneration of doctors, he said the Poor Law Board should have established the principle of uniformity of payment, as half the amount of the salaries was drawn from the parliamentary grant. Goschen, Rogers recommended, should submit this important subject to a commission of experts, and suggested it consist of two medical inspectors, two or three experienced Medical Officers, and some Chairmen of Boards of Guardians. A precedent had been established in the Cubic Space Committee.

---

[1] Despite his work for public health and the Poor Law medical services, Lyon Playfair (later Sir Lyon Playfair, first Baron Playfair of St. Andrews) was not medically qualified but a Ph.D. in chemistry of Giessen University. See D.N.B.

[2] *Lancet*, 1869, i, p. 580.

The question of engaging the whole services of Poor Law Medical Officers was also under discussion, for at this time Chadwick was advocating they should not have a private practice in addition to their public duties. In a speech to the National Association for the Promotion of Social Science, he stated, 'in the Poor Law administration I early arrived at the conclusion that medical relief to the destitute . . . should be attended by professional men who were kept out of . . . competition and independent of private practice'. He maintained that through private practice 'the public curative is impaired, and . . . the sanitary preventive service is, by general declaration, obstructed and frustrated'.[1] Other people also favoured the idea hoping it would lead to a reduction in the public medical staff. Speaking for the Poor Law Medical Officers' Association, Dr. Benson Baker its Secretary proposed that it was inexpedient to reduce the number of District Medical Officers or to appoint resident Medical Officers only, to an institution. He asserted that personally, he would not be exclusively a pauper doctor for £500 a year because it entailed loss in professional and social advancement.

Before the dissolution of the Poor Law Board, the Council of the Association issued its future programme and deplored the absence of any allusion to Poor Law Reform in the Queen's Speech. There were nine reforms for which the Association would work: permanency of appointment and entire payment of salaries out of the Consolidated Fund, so that as State officers the doctors would be enabled to act with greater freedom and efficiency; adequate remuneration, as far as possible on a uniform basis, thus making the Poor Law medical service a branch of the civil service, with superannuation chargeable to the Consolidated Fund so as to render it free from the caprice of local influences; increased salaries for length of service and promotion in the service to higher inspectoral appointments, as obtained in the Army and Navy; consolidation of the various offices of registrar, vaccinator, Medical Officer, and Medical Officer of Health, with fitting remuneration; all drugs and surgical instruments to be found by Guardians, and dispensers and dispensaries wherever practicable; provision of a basis for consultation and united action in case of difficulty; payment for surgery and midwifery in the workhouses as obtained in districts and an extension of the list of operations for which extra fees were paid; and finally, the raising of the status of the Poor Law Medical Officers so as to increase their influence and usefulness and consequently their remuneration, with the provision of a channel through which all the defects of the Poor Law medical service might be brought to light and discussed with a view to their removal or amelioration. The plan was sent to all Poor Law Medical Officers and they were asked to reply giving illustrations of their difficulties and the disadvantages of the service. All facts were to be recorded—

in order that the public may know that we are a united but discontented service; and when we receive the position and remuneration which we have long earned, we shall the more zealously and efficiently labour for the public weal, the less will zymotic

[1] Sessional Proceedings, 30 May 1872.

diseases afflict all classes of society, and the smaller will be the burden on those who support the pauper population.[1]

Simultaneously with this enlightened statement, the *Lancet* reported that the Association was entering into the discussion of matters of great public interest, and regarding which it was high time the medical profession as a whole showed the sense of its own responsibility. It was not enough, it was pointed out, for medical reformers to elucidate abstract principles of hygiene or humanitarian progress on the one hand, or that doctors should struggle to improve their own social and pecuniary position on the other. The faculty of statesmanship had been especially lacking—the power of looking at medical science and medical interests as they were connected with politics and the social life of the entire nation. The Poor Law Medical Officers' Association, the *Lancet* maintained, had done good service in showing that professional and public interests were identical.

By 1871 the Association was fully-fledged and recognized. In succeeding years conferences were held annually and reports were printed and put on record. Griffin had died at the end of 1869 and Rogers had not many more years in which to influence the movement for which he had laboured so unsparingly. After his dismissal at the Strand, he continued to work among the poor at the Newport Market Refuge, where he had already been doing so much for the poorest. In 1872 the Westminster Union appointed him to its workhouse infirmary, and his career there was one of 'incessant and unavailing remonstrance' and his troubles recommenced.[2] He tried to reform conditions for the sick in relation to diet, clothes, the cheating of patients of their food, ill-treatment, and brutality.

On the passing of the Local Government Act Rogers appealed, on behalf of the Poor Law Medical Officers' Association, through the medical journals to provincial doctors for information as to the arrangements made in their respective localities. From the replies he received he drafted a paper entitled 'Chaos', in which he ridiculed the provisions and pointed out that the Central Department, faithful to tradition, had brought about complete confusion in local administration. He called the act a 'disastrous and ludicrous failure'. The paper was read at a meeting of the British Medical Association in Sheffield and attracted a great deal of attention both in the medical and general press. But of its effects he himself wrote: 'It materially acted in evolving order out of chaos into which the subject had drifted owing to the indifference and incompetence of those who had drafted the measure.'

An assessment of Rogers' work is not difficult. By the end of his active career it was said he had added £18,000 to the incomes of the Poor Law Medical Officers in the Metropolis and it was alleged, this, with other changes, had saved ten times that amount in the London poor rates. He was the noblest reformer of the Poor Law medical system, because he genuinely had a dual purpose. He performed great services for his profession, a class of men who did so much, from whom so much was expected, and who were so scantily recompensed or recognized. On the other hand, by his advocacy of Poor Law dispensaries,

[1] Report of Benson Baker's speech to Quarterly Meeting of Association.—*Lancet*, 4 February 1871.
[2] Thorold Rogers: Preface to J. Rogers, *Reminiscences of a Workhouse Medical Officer*, 1889.

separate sick-wards in the infirmaries, public provision of medicines, adequate staffs of medical attendants and efficient nurses, he saved thousands of poor from suffering and misery or incipient pauperism. To form an association of doctors and to assist its development into a permanent and influential institution, needed great qualities of leadership and perseverance. He provided the necessary guidance, but he was also favoured by finding so many able and enlightened colleagues. Another aid must not be overlooked. This was the loyal and stalwart support given by the *Lancet* to the cause of reform. Faithfully all complaints were recorded and meetings reported, and in this way, Wakley himself must rank as a great Poor Law medical reformer. Although he died in 1862, the interest of his journal in all causes of social improvement, of which the Poor Law, Public Health, hospitals, sweated labour, and slavery are only outstanding examples, had been firmly established. Other medical journals, particularly the *British Medical Journal* also gave assistance, but without the *Lancet* it would have proved extremely difficult to establish a national movement of Poor Law Medical Officers, for neither Griffin nor Rogers could have circulated information as quickly, as widely or as cheaply.

Rogers' work in building up a movement was in one respect easier than that of Griffin's and the earlier reformers, for the medical profession was becoming yearly more self-conscious. Reforming activity increased with the rise in professional standards, and this was one of the most decisive factors in the history of the Poor Law medical service. Refusing to tolerate what they saw around them as medical science progressed, and becoming aware of the importance of their work, doctors at last united to improve their professional status and social position. In this general movement the Poor Law Medical Officers played a dominant part, which has failed to receive recognition by medical or social historians. Had it not been for the pressure of the first public doctors, sometimes individually but generally collectively through their associations, it is doubtful whether many of the developments would have come in the country's medical system. Their work was bitterly hard, and as all pioneers, they must have suffered from desperate frustration. They had to force the hands of Guardians, Inspectors and the central authorities—all laymen, ignorant of conditions and requirements. It is these doctors, now all forgotten and unrecognized, who were the fathers of the twentieth century State Medical Service.

CHAPTER 14

The Workhouse Infirmary, 1847—71

BEFORE 1834 the destitute sick were left in their own homes with a pittance of outdoor relief. In 1834 there was no mention of giving them institutional treatment as the sick wards of the workhouses were intended for cases of the able-bodied who might fall ill while in the establishment. Between 1834 and 1847 the practice arose of admitting sick paupers into the workhouse either because there was no one to attend them or because home conditions were too bad to allow recovery. After 1847 there was a silent revolution in policy—the able-bodied were evicted from the workhouse because of the overwhelming necessity for admitting the sick. And by 1871, the Poor Law institutions had become the first public hospitals.

In consequence and at the same time another change of the utmost importance took place. Although far from being a revolutionary change in extent the workhouse infirmaries began to lose their deterrent quality. Overcrowded and insalubrious ramshackle buildings retarded recovery, indeed by cross-infection disease was often propagated. Doctors from a medical point of view demanded improvement and the Poor Law authorities, unable to ignore public agitation when scandalous conditions were revealed, tried to effect some amelioration. The story is long because events moved slowly, so it is impossible to give an examination of, or accord recognition to the effect of the great influence of social philosophers and humanitarians. Ideas irresistibly and constantly seeped in from outside, but what was achieved and what was neglected is predominantly the work of those engaged in, or connected with, Poor Law administration. This chapter in the development of the Poor Law medical service is one of the outstanding landmarks in nineteenth-century social history.

By 1871 the Local Government Board had the opportunity to put into practice the many reforms and ideas which had remained as salutary suggestions in the preceding period of transition. They had remained suggestions because the principles so firmly impressed by the 1833 Royal Commission and the new Act died hard under governments which were influenced by orthodox economics, and whose executives consisted of men on the whole lacking in prescience, imagination, and forceful determination. But much was achieved under the Poor Law Commissioners and the Poor Law Board, for although in the eyes of the twentieth century, conditions in the workhouses of 1871 were outrageous, they were markedly different from those in 1834. Parliament and public ignored the hospitals branch of the Poor Law until the 'sixties; no better illustration can be afforded than the absence of any reference to it in the 1854 inquiry into medical relief, and very little is mentioned in the 1861–64 investigations. From 1847, however, the Poor Law Board was, through force of circumstance, impelled to introduce regulations, at first only spasmodically, but later in increasing regularity. Most of the early orders were to individual Boards of Guardians dealing with local workhouse conditions, until in the late 'sixties piecemeal admonition was quite inadequate, and General Orders and Regulations were issued. Likewise the history of the workhouse infirmary in the 'fifties can only be obtained from local sources, for no comprehensive investigation was undertaken during this decade.

There was always throughout the life of the new Poor Law much complacency about the provisions that were made by the individual Union Guardians. In Bradford, for example, the Medical Officer in 1848 certified that the 'idle workhouse' (where venereal disease patients, fever cases, and some lying-in women were kept) would accommodate 100–120 inmates, but the Poor Law Inspector (Lambert) maintained that only eighty-five should be housed there. This excited great expressions of disapprobation on the part of several Guardians, who alleged that the inmates were far better off and more comfortable than two-thirds of the poorest ratepayers. It was in vain that the clerk reminded them that the way to remove poverty and suffering from the community was to set the paupers in the workhouse a good example in cleanliness and general hygiene so that they—and the poor generally—would no longer tolerate the filth and degradation in which they lived.

In the following year the Guardians wanted to take over another building which had previously been a school, as an additional workhouse. Outbreaks of fever had been common there, the drains needed attention and it was in a very unhealthy situation. The Guardians again expressed strong resentment at an Alderman's protest, but eventually a new workhouse was promised in which adequate provision was to be made for the infirm, aged, sick, and children, and a dispensary was to be attached to the infirmary. In 1850 the Poor Law Board wrote a letter to the Guardians giving extracts from the Inspector's report on the workhouse. This showed that the refractory ward was used as a mortuary, that the Medical Officer was not seeing inmates on admission, and that he was not entering a sick dietary in the workhouse books or making correct reports on the causes of death. The Guardians failed to attend to these and many other requirements which the Poor Law Board had stipulated.[1] In Leeds Inspector Lambert condemned the workhouse up to 1857, when the Board of Guardians finally voted in favour of building a new one, but it was not until 1871 that they agreed to erect a new infirmary and then they had to be advised to modify their plans to meet the requirements of the Poor Law Board.[2] In 1866 the Inspector recommended the Eccleshall (Yorks.) Guardians to supply mattresses to all beds appropriated to the sick and infirm. The Guardians remonstrated that no complaints had ever been

[1] *Bradford Observer*, 17 August 1848, 17 May 1849, and Letter from Poor Law Board to Guardians, January 1850.
[2] *Leeds Intelligencer*, October 1857, and *Leeds Mercury*, 1871.

made that the existing beds were not comfortable. Although they acceded to the suggestion they refused to order mattresses for the ordinary wards of the workhouse.[1] The auditor's statement that the 'health, comfort, and morals of the paupers are well attended to', must therefore be accepted with some scepticism.

Nor were the Guardians alone complacent. In the 'forties the mortality among those treated in the Marylebone infirmary was 15 per cent, whilst it was only 7 per cent among those treated in their own homes, and this was when 640 paupers on an average received institutional medical relief daily. Yet Dr. Boyd told the Select Committee of 1854 that there was no parish in England where the sick poor were better off and only condemned the children's dormitories which had never been improved and which were the cause of a high death rate whenever there was an epidemic of measles and scarlet fever. No inquiry was ever instituted here into the high mortality of infants in the lying-in wards.

But generally it was the doctors who shook complacency, and demanded and often obtained improved conditions in the workhouses in the 'fifties and early 'sixties when local situations tell the history. In 1848, for example, the Kensington Board of Guardians built a new workhouse and on examining it the Medical Officer pointed out that the sanitary arrangements were quite wrong and offensive, so that if the poor were moved there, their health would be jeopardized. He suggested immediate alteration, for part of the sewer was open. The Medical Officer also frequently recommended the removal of idiots and sick out of the institution. As a result the stable behind the workhouse was converted into a lunatic ward.[2] As the accommodation for sick and infectious diseases was also inadequate the Medical Officer continued for years to press on the Guardians the need for providing additional wards. In 1855 his suggestions were still unheeded, so he wrote repeated letters pointing out that there were no convalescent wards, no sick wards for children, and insufficient space for infectious cases, added to which the wards were very objectionable because of the overcrowding and the lack of sanitation. The Guardians therefore held a special meeting to discuss the infirmary. Inspector Hall attended and he supplied the information that Poor Law records showed that the sick constituted 16 per cent of the workhouse inmates on an average. This meant that in Kensington 70–80 beds would suffice and therefore the infirmary was large enough. If more beds were conceded, Hall maintained, the Medical Officer would soon fill them, as the number of sick increased in the same ratio as the size of the infirmary. The Medical Officer continued his agitation, until in 1860 the workhouse infirmary was enlarged and two extra wards were added to each floor at a cost of £300.

In 1854 the *Lancet* reported that a Medical Officer had been dismissed in a Union because he had endeavoured to secure for the inmates of an overcrowded workhouse the improvements in sanitary conditions which were absolutely necessary. The workhouse had been built when the population in the Union was only one-tenth of what it was in the 'fifties and the doctor asserted that the wards were fertile hotbeads of sickness. Because he

[1] Minutes of Board of Guardians, February 1866 (Webb MSS.).
[2] Minutes, Kensington Board of Guardians, August 1849.

imperatively demanded improvement and also the classification of the sick, and because he forwarded his proposals to the Poor Law Board as well as to the Guardians, he was debarred from making further trouble by dismissal![1]

Some Guardians improved workhouse accommodation for the sick of their own accord. In 1847 the Bakewell (Derbyshire) Board of Guardians appointed a Committee to obtain plans for attaching a hospital to the workhouse and also for altering some detached buildings of the Institution for a male hospital. The Duke of Rutland in the following year gave the Union some free land, and it was resolved to appropriate £150 for the erection of a new hospital on it.[2] In 1862 the Hampstead Guardians appointed a Committee to examine the arrangements in the workhouse for the accommodation of the sick poor, with a view to affording more space to patients and for improving ventilation. The recommendations were all put into effect, and in 1866 further improvements were made and the lying-in ward extended.[3] The Poplar Guardians in 1864 enlarged their workhouse to hold 1,000–1,200, provided increased accommodation for harmless idiots and lunatics, and also added an infirmary for the sick. In St. George in the East the number of acute or chronic sick rose from 121 in 1860 to 250 in 1866, excluding the aged, infirm, and lunatics, but here only a piecemeal effort was made to meet the need, and a needlework room was adapted for a sick ward. When there was an outbreak of scarlatina and measles in the workhouse in 1866, a workshop was converted to hold those affected.[4]

The increase in overcrowding in the Metropolitan workhouses as well as the proportionate rise in the number of sick inmates can be deduced from the Official Returns made in 1866. In St. Marylebone, for example, the institution had originally been constructed to hold 1,000 paupers. In 1837 three were 257 sick and 1,100 'others'. In 1848 there were 351 sick and 1,709 'others'. In 1856 there were 215 sick and 1,712 'others'. In 1866 there were 291 sick and 1,454 'others'. Similarly, the Strand workhouse had originally been erected to hold 282, yet in 1837 there were 482 inmates and in 1848 596 (no separate classification between sick and 'others' was effected until the 'fifties). In 1856 there were in the same institution 105 sick and 461 'others' and in 1866, 188 sick and 350 'others'.[5]

The Poor Law Board occasionally intervened in an attempt to solve the growing problem of inadequate and insalubrious infirmary accommodation. In 1849 papers and diagrams were circularized to Unions in the Metropolis on the efficient ways of ventilating workhouses. Epsom Union built a new hospital and receiving wards at a cost of £1,500 under an order of the Poor Law Board of April 1852. In their report of that year the central authorities stated that most of the workhouse sick wards, particularly those for infectious diseases, were insufficient, but pointed out that the new workhouses which were springing

---

[1] *Lancet*, 1854, ii, p. 514. This was probably Dr. Semple of Islington of whose dismissal Rumsey also wrote in his *Essays on State Medicine* in 1856.

[2] Minutes, Bakewell Board of Guardians, June 1847 (Webb MSS.).

[3] Minutes, Hampstead Board of Guardians, 1862–66.

[4] Minutes, St. George in the East, October 1865–March 1866.

[5] *Accounts and Papers*, 1866, lxi.

up everywhere would provide increased accommodation for the sick. A long article in the Manchester press in 1866 roused the attention of the Poor Law Board. This described the deficiencies in the workhouse hospital, the rough diet, the employment of only one night nurse for six wards with 100 patients, and the dipping of half-a-dozen patients in the same bath. The Board asked the Poor Law Inspector to hold an inquiry. Soon afterwards the papers printed similar allegations but the Medical Officer contravened them. Although the Poor Law Board pronounced judgement in an exculpatory tone they admitted there was much truth in the complaints, and recommended that more nurses should be appointed and censured the master.[1]

The most outstanding inquiry instituted by the Poor Law Board in the 'fifties and early 'sixties was that on the St. Pancras workhouse. Not only did this have a great and salutary effect on the Union in question, but it also awakened the conscience of the public, the Poor Law Board, and the medical profession. It therefore paved the way for the spate of investigations and reforms which began in the middle 'sixties. Dr. Henry Bence Jones,[2] physician to St. George's Hospital was deputed to carry out the investigation which was to reveal conditions common to all large Poor Law institutions. In 1856 the St. Pancras workhouse contained 300 more inmates than in 1846, yet a new building had only added space for 150 beds. The three principal wards of the men's infirmary had 121 cases with from 570 to 650 cubic feet per person and the six principal women's wards had 152 cases with 600-650 cubic feet per person. Yet, Dr. Jones pointed out, the College of Surgeons refused to recognize as medical schools hospitals which afforded less than 800 cubic feet to each patient on the ground that less space, even with good ventilation, was injurious to the sick. He described the foul and offensive atmosphere in all wards, where means for ventilation were entirely disused or out of repair. The least noxious room had windows which opened on to the adjoining burial ground. In four out of the six women's wards all air coming from outside had to pass through a privy first. The Medical Officers considered overcrowding and not the absence of ventilation the cause of the slowness of recovery, because patients frequently had to be put on the floor. The doctors themselves were nauseated by the excessive offensiveness of sinks and urinals in the wards and pointed out that many patients contracted additional illnesses like dysentery and ulcerative stomatitis through the terribly bad sanitation. A nurse giving evidence said people were ill at night with headaches and sickness, and she herself complained of giddiness, vomiting, and loss of appetite—the symptoms of low fever—through the foul air. She also drew attention to the danger to patients of suffocation, and the threat to the life of all female inmates because 'casual' women slept in the receiving wards and introduced fevers and other diseases into the house. Dr. Jones stated that the room where lying-in women slept at night, and night-nurses during the day, were the most badly ventilated of the whole workhouse. He collected a specimen of air and this contained 2·75 per cent of carbonic acid. In the infant

---

[1] *Manchester Examiner and Times*, 31 January 1865, 1 February 1866, 22 February 1866, and 3 March 1866.
[2] See 'Henry Bence Jones, 1814-1873', by Ruth G. and Robert Hodgkinson in *Medicine Illustrated*, Vol. 6, pp. 134-48, March 1952.

nursery mesenteric disease was common and children were always ailing because the old nurses refused to have the windows open and the children could not stand the atmosphere.

Outdoor-relief applicants waited in 'pens'—underground. There were always between 300 and 900 people and the atmosphere was so offensive that a doctor had to be constantly on duty to attend those who fainted. Sometimes these people waited all day without food and often broke the windows to let in some air. The Relieving Officer stated that his predecessor died from typhus caught in the workhouse, and he himself always felt ill when he visited these 'pens'. One Medical Officer compared them to the Black Hole of Calcutta and attributed much of the disease of the parish to the crowded state and suffocating atmosphere of these underground rooms, where people caught diseases and then spread them outside. The conditions led Dr. Jones to conclude:

> I cannot sufficiently strongly express the opinion I have formed of the evils which result from cold, wet, foul air and fasting which the poor endure. Whilst endeavouring to obtain outdoor relief . . . they are exposed to disease and even death. Such state of things ought not to be tolerated by the Government . . . That disease and death has come out of them is certain . . . I know no word more suited to them than horrible.

On the workhouse infirmary proper he concluded that disease was greatly increased by the lack of ventilation and overcrowding. No attempt had been made, he said, to prevent the entrance into any room of polluted air from privies, sinks, drains, urinals and 'foul' patients. Also there were one fourth to one third more patients in the infirmary than there should have been and even if they were removed, unless ventilation were improved, the atmosphere would still be worse than in any London hospital. He urged that there should be greater classification between casual and receiving wards, that no open urinals should remain, that underground dormitories in which there were 123–175 people and underground day rooms in which there were between 140 and 200, should be closed, and that because all insane wards were ill-adapted for lunatics and were unwholesome and unsafe the insane should be removed. Children should also be sent from the institution. Finally Dr. Jones recommended that an entirely new infirmary should be built for the sick.

A considerable amount of indignation both public and official was hurled against the St. Pancras parochial authorities. The *Lancet* wrote that the wealthy Metropolitan rate-payers who cried out against the scandals were themselves in part to blame for the defective conditions and suffering of the inmates in this area, for both Paddington and the City had expelled their poor who now flocked to districts like St. Pancras. The Bishop of London had raised the value of his Paddington estate and the City had obtained vast commercial buildings by this move and had increased sickness and pauperism in the East and North. A uniform Metropolitan Poor Rate the *Lancet* maintained would have precluded this.[1] In 1858 St. Pancras refused to allow the Metropolitan Inspector to obtain measurements in, and dimensions of the workhouse, to enable the Poor Law Board to fix the limit of inmates. The Court of the Queen's Bench had to be applied to, in consequence of which the

[1] *Lancet*, 1856, i, pp. 408–09.

Directors of the workhouse withdrew their opposition and the Poor Law Board were able to determine and regulate the number of inmates to be admitted.[1] In 1862 Inspector Farnall reported that great improvements had taken place in the St. Pancras workhouse since Dr. Jones's report and that it had been almost entirely rebuilt. The Director of the Poor of the parish told the Select Committee of that year how well the sick poor were being treated. Ignoring the subject of infirmary accommodation, he drew attention to the chops, eggs, broth, wine, brandy, and port which patients received to any limit the Medical Officer ordered. The dispensary in the workhouse, he said, was 'replete with everything which can be conducive to establishing the health of the inmates'. The salutary effect of the 1856 inquiry was patent, and if the Poor Law Board had been roused to action previously reforms would have come much earlier, for conditions were bad long before the middle 'fifties.

A predominant reason for the inactivity of the Poor Law Board was that the system of inspection instituted by the central authorities was radically defective. Visiting Committees were to have been appointed in the 'thirties to supervise workhouse management, but this order was either neglected, as at Bradford where none was instituted until 1857, or they were entirely inefficient. In their Seventeenth Annual Report the Poor Law Board stated that cases of neglect had been brought to their notice regarding the treatment of the sick inmates of the workhouses. The Board reaffirmed their readiness to institute an inquiry promptly and to remove any officer guilty of neglect—if cases were pointed out to them. Therefore they seemed anxious to provide systematic supervision of workhouse sick wards. As the Poor Law Inspectors were only able to visit institutions at long intervals, the central authorities reiterated their previous order on the appointment of Visiting Committees whose duty it should be to inspect the workhouses at least once a week and furnish a report in writing to the Guardians. By the Poor Law Amendment Act of 1849[2] this had been made obligatory, and the Poor Law Board had been empowered to engage a paid Visitor to a workhouse in every case where Boards of Guardians neglected to appoint the special Committee. In 1866 Dr. Smith in his report on workhouses could still condemn the visiting and inspecting of institutions by the Visiting Committees as the most defective part of the workhouse system and to which many of the existing faults could be justifiably traced. The conduct of Committees he had discovered varied greatly, but on the whole they were too hasty and too much disinclined to recommend changes. He suggested they should go at least twice a week to the workhouses, keep records, and make written reports. The inspection of hospitals was more efficient, he said, because one or two members of the managerial staff visited them two or three times a week, going through every ward and inviting complaints. Moreover these were frequently men connected with, or knowing of, the practice in other hospitals and who took a deep interest in discharging their duties. Smith urged that workhouse Visiting Committees should forward recommendations or

---

[1] Eleventh Annual Report of the Poor Law Board, 1858.
[2] 10 and 11 Vic. c. 109, s. 24.

complaints to the Poor Law Inspector. In 1866 the Poor Law Board again issued Orders on inspection because, as they stated, infirmaries were engaging their very serious attention:

> With a view of securing proper management of this important branch of workhouse administration . . . the general orders of the Board make it the duty of Visiting Committees of workhouses to inquire and report weekly to Guardians whether regular attendance is given by the Medical Officer, whether inmates of sick wards are properly tended and whether nurses are efficient . . .[1]

In 1868 a circular was issued to all Boards of Guardians requesting Visiting Committees to undertake their investigations efficiently. A long list of questions to be answered was given relating to Medical Officers, nursing, diet, cleanliness, infectious disease, lunatic inmates, and numbers in the workhouse.[2] But an unpaid body drawn from Guardians or ratepayers could have little interest in examining wards, beds, linen, clothing, sanitary arrangements, nursing, or seeing that the sick were properly attended. Principles of deterrence and economy precluded efficient inspection on a local scale. Improvement did not come until the late 'sixties and from 1869 critical reports of Visiting Committees appeared in some of the Minutes of the Metropolitan Guardians, from which can also be seen that inspection was being undertaken weekly.

In 1848 a new regulation of the Poor Law Board ordered Medical Officers to report defects in diet, drainage, accommodation, overcrowding, ventilation, nursing, and in the general arrangements of the infirmary or sick wards. These reports were to be forwarded twice a year to the central authorities, but this important stipulation was waived the year following and reports were to be made only once a month to Guardians. Here also salutary arrangements introduced by the Poor Law Board were abortive, for Medical Officers were either too busy to attend to the reports or where they were made the local authorities ignored them. Dr. Smith in his report on Metropolitan workhouses said that it was obvious, however often doctors had made reports, Guardians had disregarded them. Because of the grave defects which existed in ventilation and overcrowding he advised a return to be obtained of the actual representations which had been made in writing during the previous years. Smith further desired exact reports to be furnished stating how conditions compared with the 500 cubic feet per person required by the Poor Law Board—

> When as at Clerkenwell nine out of twelve and at the Strand workhouse nineteen of twenty-four wards containing sick offer less space than required, and when as at the latter, excellent means of ventilation might have been readily adopted and applied, and when the obvious impediment is not removed, it appears that a serious responsibility rests on the Medical Officers.

That they should carry out the terms of the Consolidated Order, he continued, was of the utmost importance, not only because of the great questions involved, but because they

[1] Nineteenth Annual Report, 1867.
[2] Circular of the Poor Law Board, 6 July 1868.

possessed the monopoly of sanitary and scientific knowledge. Only by repeated, urgent, and precise recommendations in writing to the Guardians could defects be remedied. In 1868 the Poor Law Board recapitulated their early recommendation. But on this occasion the doctors themselves raised strong objection. Memorials poured into the central office stating that their low salaries and arduous duties would not permit of such additional duties. They desired other local officials to be given the responsibility, for even if doctors could send reports to the Poor Law Board they would have to fear the consequential action of the Guardians, and if they made false reports they would have no value. In 1869 Goschen altered the rule, and as in 1849 Medical Officers were requested to make reports only to the Guardians—and with similar results. Their object was completely destroyed. The British Medical Association, however, as in 1862 and 1868, sent a deputation to the central authorities to urge that additional inspectors be appointed to form a special department of the Poor Law Board. The medical profession continually agitated for medical inspectors because they realized that neither local officers nor regional Poor Law Inspectors would bring to light the glaring abuses which demanded reform.

The Poor Law Board had to rely on their regional Inspectors, but these were no greater aid in the medical field than the local committees. They were men whose education and profession had not qualified them for their duty. One of their most important assignations was to examine the disposition of the workhouses. Elaborate instructions had been issued to them in 1841:

> The points to which your attention should be principally directed at such visits [once every six months] are the following: You should in the first place, carefully inspect every part of the workhouse; and in making this inspection you should not content yourself with examining merely its principal parts, but should look carefully into its minutest details. Its general state of repair; its drainage and ventilation; the cleanness of the house and its various offices, and especially the beds and bedding. The orderly arrangement of stores; the proper arrangement of meals; the state of the probationary wards, and of wards appropriated to the confinement of refractory paupers; the sufficiency of the infirmary and sick wards; should each be the subject of your examination. The health and general welfare of the inmates you will of course diligently inquire into.

Further the reports of the Visiting Committees were to be rigidly scrutinized and explanations called for, and any complaints from the inmates were to be received and investigated.[1]

Special scientific knowledge and practical acquaintance with the sick were required for the efficient performance of these duties connected with the infirmaries, and only medical men possessed these necessary qualifications. In lunatic asylums and prisons the necessity for special knowledge and experience in their inspectors was recognized, and a medical commissioner always attended the inspection of an asylum. If the Poor Law Inspectors had been experienced medical practitioners they would have detected the

[1] For this long and in many ways excellent list of instructions see Seventh Annual Report, 1841.

defective conditions in workhouse infirmaries long before the middle 'sixties, when because of their ignorance and neglect, a whole spate of investigations were instituted revealing conditions which could and should have been remedied years before.

In the 'fifties for example an Inspector reported Holborn workhouse to be in good sanitary order and that it could safely accommodate more inmates, yet there was a fearful infant mortality rate, a sensitive index of the sanitary condition of a locality. This excited attention and led to inspection by the Medical Officer of Health who discovered vast over-crowding and inadequate ventilation. Similarly the Inspector found the workhouse of St. Margaret's and St. John's in Westminster, in excellent condition, with 'cleanliness, order and regularity', yet in 1863 a Commissioner in Lunacy forwarded a letter to the Poor Law Board complaining that the mentally defective were kept in two small gloomy rooms and asked for them to be removed to Hanwell Asylum. Inspector Farnall gave evidence to the Select Committee of 1862 that the forty-two workhouses in London would hold over 30,000, and that therefore there were vacancies for 9,000 paupers. He did however suggest that sixteen of the forty-two were too small and that through this there was no proper classification of inmates. Most of these defective institutions were under the Poor Law Board although there were some areas operating under local Acts where interference was rejected. Inspector Lambert informed the Committee that he visited the sixty-one Unions under him (in Cambridge, Derby, and York) twice a year, and he wished to see improved classification for the sick and other inmates. An ex-member of the Manchester Board of Guardians maintained that the Poor Law Inspector could be more useful and offered the suggestion made to him by the Guardians of a nearby town that the office of Inspector should be abolished altogether and the duties should be undertaken by local magistrates. The Clerk of the City of London Union recommended to the Select Committee that as all workhouses had infirmaries or sick wards attached, there should be Medical Inspectors and agreed with his questioner (Lyall) that great improvements could be effected in conditions if workhouses were inspected like lunatic asylums.

In 1867 the Inspectors' general reports stated that in the majority of cases workhouses themselves were adequate, save in the manufacturing districts where there were some serious defects and abuses as there were generally in the arrangements of the institutions' hospitals. These arose chiefly from the problem of accommodation. This had become inadequate because of the rapid increase in population and the pressure of commercial and manufacturing distress, and in some cases by the failure in the discharge of their duty by workhouse officers who neglected the regulations. In certain instances the Inspectors reported the absence of efficient supervision on the part of Guardians and Visiting Committees. When these examples were the only evidence of Poor Law Inspectors' original investigations, an amendment in the supervising system was imperative. Either the Inspectors should have been selected from those who had had wide experience in the direction and treatment of the sick in hospitals or workhouses, or the inspection of infirmaries should have been entrusted to the Medical Officer of Health.

The National Association for the Promotion of Social Science, which drew many members from the Poor Law Medical Officers and the Workhouse Infirmary Association, had since its inception shown great interest in Poor Law problems. A meeting was held in 1867 on the question of workhouse infirmaries. Ernest Hart, who had already become famous as one of the *Lancet* Commissioners and as a leading member of the Workhouse Infirmary Association, and who was to be the undaunted agitator for reform in the next decade, read a paper on a 'National Scheme for the better organization and management of workhouse infirmaries'.[1] His dominant theme was that intolerable conditions had arisen through the inefficiency of the Inspectorate. Coroners' inquests, he said, had revealed the unsatisfactory condition of the London workhouse infirmaries. The writings of Louisa Twining and the records of the Ladies' Workhouse Visiting Association had shown that nursing and the treatment of the sick and the children needed systematic reorganization. It was not until the *Lancet*'s inquiry that anyone suspected the real state of the Metropolitan institutions, and not until Dr. Smith's report of 1867 was it evident that the same assertions were equally true of country workhouses. The reason for this long ignorance, Hart maintained, lay in the fact that there was no technical authority attached to the Poor Law Board to undertake medical investigations. Dr. Smith had been appointed as Medical Adviser but no distinct duties had been assigned to him, and he had no definite relation to the other Inspectors. When each district Inspector was responsible for fifty to sixty workhouses it was only possible to make a cursory examination. Even if they had possessed any technical knowledge they would have laboured under a considerable disadvantage in obtaining actual information, for they were given no detailed code of instructions as to the standard they were to be allowed, or what was regarded as necessary and useful. No technical authority existed for comparative purposes and from whom information could be obtained in case of difficulty—therefore one Inspector tolerated a variation of 200 to 900 cubic feet per person in different wards of the same institution. In Leicester, Hart said, the three workhouses showed the utmost variety as to space and arrangements. In some rooms floors were badly boarded, in others bricked. Some had lockers and cupboards, others none. One of the infirmaries had recently been put into a comparatively satisfactory condition, another was left without repair and was to continue so. The Inspector ignored this diversity, and his report allowed the inference that he was as satisfied with the workhouse in the wretched state as with the other where amenities had been provided.

Besides the absence of any code of regulations or any central authority to whom he could appeal for guidance, the Inspector, Hart reiterated, was precluded from discharging his duties efficiently through his ignorance of technical questions. As a comparative stranger to the workhouse, a master could show him the most salubrious places only, or first, whilst he sent a message to other wards to have windows opened or to have some patients temporarily removed out of the rooms. With regard to the Medical Officers' duties, an important part of his supervising work, he was completely at a disadvantage. 'Nothing was so well known to doctors', said Hart, 'as that the Inspectors knew absolutely nothing of their

---

[1] Sessional Proceedings of National Association for the Promotion of Social Science, 18 December 1867.

work as inspectors of infirmaries, ... [and that they were] absolutely ignorant of principles on which an infirmary ought to be conducted and inspected ... If this were not so ... nothing could excuse the present state of things.' Lord Devon as President of the Poor Law Board had recognized the inadequacy of the inspectorate and had hoped to remedy it by increasing the power of the central authorities over the Boards of Guardians. This proposal, Hart maintained, was shown by existing facts not to be sufficient. It would be necessary to alter the relation of the Inspectors to Guardians and of Guardians to the Poor Law Board completely. The Guardians were unacquainted with the duties of the Inspectors towards them and the Inspectors reciprocated the doubt. No existing regulation solved the question with whom initiative should rest, and if it were taken, how the proposal should be pressed. Many an Inspector appeared to consider himself as a kind of censor over the Guardians; that arrangements were to be initiated by them, and that he was to accept their standard and to suggest amendments only where flagrant flaws were apparent according to the Guardians' own definitions. This was the only explanation which could account for the absolutely diverse arrangements which existed in a single Inspector's unit. In Gloucester, for example, the Inspector called attention to untidiness and broken drains, but did not consider it part of his duty to initiate a scheme for improvement or lay down a standard of requirements.

> Had the Inspectors had any kind of agreement as to the standard they should require, had each considered it his duty to inform Guardians of the character of arrangements ... which he thought they were bound to make, and to fill up an outline for them to adhere to ... a very different state of things would have existed.

In any alteration of the relationship Hart insisted that it would be necessary to define more distinctly what should be done with the reports of the Inspectors, how they should be brought to the notice of Guardians and when. He gave an illuminating illustration of the type of circumstance which existed. A Guardian of Bedminster, Sir Arthur Elton, examined the infirmary in 1865 and found it deficient. He informed the Poor Law Board and an Inspector was sent to investigate, who agreed with the complaints and asked the Guardians to prepare plans for affording additional accommodation. Two schemes were prepared, the cheaper being adopted, and it received the confirmation of the Poor Law Board. When the altered buildings were examined by a doctor commissioned by the *British Medical Journal* they were found to have no closets or lavatories and were so extraordinarily badly constructed that they were entirely unsuitable for an infirmary. The *British Medical Journal*, writing further of the scandalous defects and the inefficient nursing, roused a public outcry and an inquiry was instituted by the Inspector in October 1867. Dr. Smith was asked to make a report and his conclusions were similar to the original ones of Elton's. They were not shown to the Guardians who felt grieved that a report so necessary for their information was withheld from them for twelve months. When they asked the reason the Inspector (Gulson) replied that he had considered himself relieved from all responsibility because Smith had inspected the house. When the question was put in the House of

Commons, the President of the Poor Law Board (Lord Devon) stated that the report had not been sent to the Guardians because the Inspector's investigation had not been considered sufficient. This illustrated admirably how the Guardians waited for the Poor Law Board, and one Inspector for another, whilst a workhouse was left in an unsatisfactory condition for eighteen months. It was equally unsatisfactory that the Poor Law Board sanctioned inadequate plans, the adoption of which only necessitated further immediate improvements.

Hart also drew attention to the great public grievance that such difficulty existed in getting a special inquiry into any particular complaint. Sclater Booth, a former President of the Poor Law Board, had stated to the House of Commons that such a proceeding was very costly and ought not to be undertaken unless an overwhelming case existed. Hart maintained that the obstacle in the way of instituting a special investigation should be removed, nor should it be a matter of great expense and inconvenience. The results of such inquiries were demonstrated in London when the many investigations of 1866 produced important changes in the conduct of Metropolitan workhouse infirmaries. Hart was convinced that the Poor Law Board was afraid of public inquiries, not for themselves, nor immediately for their officials, but because a number of such investigations would produce a scandal that would be intolerable to a government department. Inquiries, he added, had been repressed at Shoreditch, Lambeth, Clifton (near Bristol), and elsewhere, and information had been withheld which the public had a right to possess, and which no thoroughly well-organized administration would have desired to suppress. In any new scheme Hart recommended there should be an Inspector whose duty it would be to institute inquiries when necessary, in any district.

In his plan for reform he further stipulated that a staff of technical Inspectors should be appointed. Not only doctors, but architectural experts were to be included with a thorough knowledge of hospital construction. The eleven existing district Inspectors who were supposed to possess encyclopaedic knowledge, were not too many for administrative purposes, but these could be abolished and an entirely itinerant body substituted capable of moving anywhere according to particular requirements. Alternatively, the mobile technical staff might be added to the district inspectorships.[1] This new departure in the regional field would also necessitate a medical or hospital department of the Poor Law Board to which new Inspectors could send their reports and from whom instructions would emanate. It would be the duty of the central authorities to act immediately on the reports of the Inspectors and to ensure that Guardians maintained the prescribed standard instead of each setting up their own. A complete code of instructions would be essential to the efficient working of the new system of inspection. Hart, in conclusion, drew attention to the already existing medical department of the Privy Council and that the functions of the Poor Law Board and Privy Council overlapped in many spheres. He therefore proposed, as many

---

[1] This is an illustration of the growth of the expert, a marked feature in the nineteenth-century Poor Law and Public Health services. Problems grew to such dimensions that functions had to be separated and specialization became imperative.

other people had done, that a Central Board should be drawn out of the two authorities for health purposes.

Rumsey sent a letter to the Social Science Association's meeting in which he agreed that Hart had hit at the weaker part of workhouse management. He suggested that to secure a thoroughly efficient inspectorate and a permanent reorganization of administration, the reformers should strive to obtain a more rational and complete organization of local sanitary authorities aided by skilled superintending officers. He concurred in the reforms recommended for the central office but also urged the importance of establishing really effective district organizations, which would apply as beneficially to the superintendence of infirmaries as to the not less weighty matters of sanitary administration. The country, he maintained, would never submit to a purely central executive. There should be a public doctor who would direct a staff to inspect every public institution. He had already propounded this scheme in his *Essays on State Medicine* in 1856, and in a paper, 'Comments on the Sanitary Act', 1866. He reiterated that large local Boards should be established embracing all existing small ones, which should form a court of a few selected persons of special qualifications.

> Once obtain such an organization and we should have an administrative machine, which could be available for directing all measures for the scientific relief of pauper sickness, for maintaining public health, for investigating the causes and prevalence of disease and mortality, and for ameliorating the social conditions of the working classes.

Chadwick, who presided at the meeting, pointed out that because prejudices were in favour of local self-government and because the central administration vacated their office on the change of government, in consequence of which they were induced to maintain their popularity with the Boards of Guardians, the Poor Law Board were paralysed and were checked from efficient inspection. He hoped however that public opinion would grow sounder and that the belief in the superiority of the system of employing Medical Officers solely for public service would become more popular. The greater part of necessary inspection, he agreed, was medical in character, and he therefore favoured a medical inspectorate. The Irish Poor Law administration, he stated, was most in accordance with the principles originally laid down, and this was chiefly because it recognised the specialities of medical inspection and of superior inspection. He had himself written an article on the 'Medical Inspection of Outdoor Relief in 1866'.[1]

Dr. Stallard, an ardent reformer, gave evidence to the meeting that the inspection of outdoor relief was more efficient than that of institutional relief. He also favoured the establishment of medical inspectors and in 1865 had had an interview with the Secretary of the Poor Law Board to point out the necessity of a supervisory medical inspectorate. An adviser at the Poor Law Board was not sufficient for detailed supervision, he said, for he could never discover cases familiar to local doctors. An entire special department was

[1] *Frazer's Magazine*, September 1866.

required. Dr. Smith had on many occasions recommended important improvements but had always experienced the strongest opposition from the Boards of Guardians. The new executives and public opinion had to be the mainspring of any influence to be brought to bear on them. In Ireland, Stallard continued, Boards of Guardians who failed to do their duty could be superseded by paid Guardians, but in England, as they were an irremovable, unpaid, elected body, they were dangerous to quarrel with. Inspectors should be able to suggest modifications of carefully weighed central orders to adapt them to local circumstances, which was the only means to ensure they would be carried out.

William Rendle complained of the inaccuracy of the returns of disease. He had often found 'fever' put down when not more than one case in four was such. For efficient supervision accurate statistical reports were also necessary.

The question of correct returns was an important factor. However inaccurately Guardians or Inspectors might have given them, they could not hide the dominant theme which was running through the Poor Law Medical Service. Official statistics however defective were revealing the enormous number of sick and aged maintained in the workhouses. As the problem of the workhouse infirmary raised such acute controversy between 1865 and 1868 Parliament and the Poor Law Board collected a mass of statistics on the subject of sick inmates, for ordinary annual returns did not include the number of paupers on the Medical Officers' books. The first returns (312 session 1865) showed the number of beds occupied on 28 January 1865 in the Metropolitan institutions, the number of people suffering from acute and chronic disorders, and the number of aged and infirm (excluding those in the sick wards) requiring occasional attendance. The second return was Dr. Smith's report in 1866 on Metropolitan workhouses (372 session 1866) which gave an analysis of the number of sick. The third made to the House of Lords in 1866 (216 session 1866) showed the total number of sick in workhouses in the whole year 1865, and those who might benefit from a better diet. It revealed also the actual diseases which Medical Officers had to treat in four specified weeks. The fourth was the report of Dr. Smith on forty-eight provincial workhouses in 1866 (4 session 1866). This not only gave the number of sick in workhouses but dealt with existing arrangements for the treatment of the sick poor. The fifth return made to the House of Commons in 1868 (445 session 1868) showed the total number of poor in all provincial Poor Law institutions and the number who were on the Medical Officers' books on 1 July 1867 and 1 January 1868. The sixth was a census undertaken on 18 January 1869 of all inmates of Metropolitan workhouses; and lastly there were the returns collected by the Poor Law Board, through the Clerks of Unions, from workhouses and Medical Officers.

The general result of these inquiries showed that in London, where children were not as a rule in workhouses but in district schools, the incidence of sickness was greater than elsewhere. It appeared that in the Metropolis there was a larger proportion of sick paupers than in the provinces. By the first return, of the total number of inmates of 26,296 there were 12,670 sick or others requiring medical attention, i.e. 48 per cent. The return made to the House of Lords revealed there were 8,754 sick or 34 per cent. Dr. Smith's report of

1866, again allowing for a slightly different period showed that there were nearly 9,000 inmates ill out of a total of 24,000, a proportion of 38 per cent. The inquiry by the Poor Law Board in 1869 stated there were 11,000 sick out of a total number of inmates of 28,600, or 39 per cent. Therefore allowing for differences which varying definitions of sickness must have entailed, paupers receiving indoor medical relief amounted to between 34 and 48 per cent of the total inmates. The general proportion of the various classes composing the bulk of inmates in Metropolitan workhouses in January 1869 were:

> 6,000 ordinary sick, including lying-in cases,
> 5,000 old and infirm people requiring medical care,
> 1,700 imbeciles,
> 2,400 children,
> 10,500 healthy old people, *and only about*
> 3,000 *able-bodied.*

The sick, old, and infirm requiring medical care therefore constituted 39 per cent of the total number. (In outdoor relief it was 13·8 per cent, i.e., 10,348 sick in a total of 70,889.) Imbeciles accounted for 6 per cent, children 8 per cent, and 'healthy' old people 37 per cent —and the adult able-bodied only 10 per cent.[1]

In provincial workhouses the proportion of sick was not quite as high as in the Metropolis. The return of 1868 showed that there were 33,855 sick out of a total number of inmates of 120,000, i.e., 28·2 per cent. Dr. Smith's report listed 5,810 sick inmates in the forty-eight institutions surveyed, out of a total of 19,237—30 per cent. This proportion varied greatly in different districts and with the season; for example, it was 48 per cent in midsummer and 43 per cent in midwinter in Cumberland. In July there were fifteen counties in which the proportion was over 30 per cent while the number was reduced to 14 per cent in January.[2] This divergency was probably caused by the number of able-bodied requiring relief at the two seasons, whilst the aged and infirm which constituted such a large portion of the sick remained stationary. Smith's returns showed that there were 12,260 able-bodied inmates in July while there were nearly 20,000 in January, an increase which largely affected the number of sick which could be admitted, who formed a more stable class in relation to the whole number. The result of the returns made by workhouse Medical Officers to the Poor Law Board in 1869 revealed remarkable similarity to the previous inquiries. There were 159,000 paupers in workhouses of whom 47,213, or 29·7 per cent were sick. Therefore in the provinces nearly one-third of the inmates of Poor Law institutions were receiving medical care, while in the Metropolis numbers ranged from one-third to one-half.

In 1867 a return, Table 14.1, was made to the House of Commons similar to the 1865 Inquiry on the number of indoor poor on the workhouse medical relief books on 1 July of that year. This also classified the sick.

---

[1] Figures do not include children in Poor Law schools—only those retained in the workhouses.
[2] See Smith's Report for list of Regions' and Counties' percentages in July and January.

TABLE 14.1

Number of Indoor Poor on the Workhouse Medical Relief Books on 1 July 1867.—Return made to the House of Commons.

	Male	Female	Total
Fever and zymotic	472	486	958
Venereal cases	223	512	735
Acute cases	2,048	2,125	4,173
Chronic cases (excluding aged and infirm)	4,997	4,938	9,935
Aged and infirm requiring medical treatment	3,652	3,265	6,917
Inmates requiring extra diet only	3,015	3,080	6,095

Total number of cases in workhouse medical relief books 29,178—30 per cent.

Total number of lunatics in workhouses   8,372

Total number of paupers in workhouses   96,079

Therefore over the whole country 30 per cent of the total number of indoor paupers were receiving medical relief. When Smith stated in 1867—'the number of inmates in a work-house is not necessarily an indication of the number of sick . . . yet there is a certain relation between them', he could have been even more forceful and definite.

Because of the inadequacy of domiciliary treatment and the insalubrious living conditions workhouses were being converted into extensive hospitals, and expenditure on indoor relief had more than doubled in England generally, and in some areas, particularly in London, had trebled. Much institutional sick relief could have been prevented by a more liberal supply of general relief. This particularly applied to the aged, who on being offered 1s. or 2s. a week had to enter the workhouse to obtain an adequate diet, and here their feebleness and natural infirmity were an additional burden to the medical staff. Sufficient maintenance allowances would have saved workhouses from being filled to their utmost limits, and could have assured the poor that they would not have to look to the Poor Law institution as the natural termination of their lives. Inadequate general relief for the young also helped to swell the numbers in the workhouses. Fever arose out of poverty, broken constitutions and low living. In 1862 the Chairman of the Board of Guardians of South-wark stated that there was so much sickness in the Union that the workhouse had become more like a hospital. There were on average, he said, 400 in the institution, two-fifths of whom were ill, and there was always a large influx of fever cases from the overcrowded dwellings and from the lodging-houses where a bed could be had for threepence—and an illness gratuitously. As poverty increased so the demand for them grew. They were generally brothels and the Chairman of the Union was himself a lodging-house Inspector. He stated that sometimes forty to fifty patients entered the workhouse at a time and that in May 1862 there were twelve deaths from fever in a week. He himself admitted the complete inadequacy of the seven sick wards of the workhouse for the increasing number of sick and lunatics.

Although those designated 'able-bodied' formed a small proportion of the workhouse inmates, a great number of these were far from healthy and were unable to work. Parliamentary Returns of 1861 printed the names of all paupers in every institution and the reason for their being there; those not included among the sick were many who should by stricter definition have been so. There were numerous cases of pauperism through bad eyesight, idiocy, weak intellect, and minor deformities. If they were not ill, they were incapable of undertaking employment and helped to swell the numbers of infirm receiving institutional relief, and reduced even further the class of 'able-bodied'. A glance through the 'Remarks' column of admittance books of Boards of Guardians reveals the overwhelming proportion of people admitted to workhouses through illness, lunacy, childbirth, or infirmity. Medical Officers' books are no longer extant but their letters to Guardians reveal the increase in the numbers of sick to able-bodied at that time. In Kensington, for example, the workhouse Medical Officer had on 24 December 1859, 283 patients, and on 24 March 1865 he had 428—the workhouse was accommodating about 500 people at this time. Exactly three years later there were 623 sick inmates and on the same date in 1869 there were 834. In the first three months of 1869, he attended nearly 1,000 patients in the workhouse.[1] The workhouse Medical Officer of St. George in the East had 121 cases on an average on his books in 1860, and 134 in 1861; by 1865 there were 133 acute and chronic sick alone, and in 1866 there were 250 in this category. The total number in the institution at this time was nearly 800.[2] Bethnal Green Workhouse contained 318 'sick' in 1856 and 959 'others'; ten years later the 'sick' had risen to 425 and the 'others' fallen to 883. In Whitechapel there were 360 'sick' and 338 'others' in 1866, and in Stepney 1,164 'sick' in 1856 and 255 'others' while in 1866 there were 767 of the former and 269 of the latter. (The total number had fallen because inmates were boarded out on other institutions because of the overcrowding.[3])—In Leeds the average weekly number of inmates in the workhouse in 1868 was 600 and the number on the medical relief list over 200.[4]

When the workhouses contained so many sick and aged of the half starved and weakest part of the community it was to be expected that they should have had a high mortality rate, but figures published by the Registrar General showed that it was very abnormal. In 1866 10·5 per cent of all deaths in London occurred in the forty-six workhouses, whilst the total number of deaths of the 116 public institutions including the workhouses was 18·2 per cent of the total. Therefore all other establishments had only 8 per cent of the Metropolitan deaths, and these seventy institutions included hospitals which took the most acute surgical, medical, and accident cases, and the special hospitals for fever and smallpox. They also had a much larger and quicker intake of patients, while the workhouses took the chronic and

[1] Minutes, Kensington Board of Guardians.
[2] Minutes, St. George in the East Board of Guardians.
[3] See Table 14.2 for details of Metropolitan workhouses, pp. 573–74.
[4] *Leeds Mercury*, 28 January 1869.

468

lingering diseases. On an average 4–5 per cent of paupers died in the workhouses every year and the proportion was gradually rising. When it is remembered that the sick and infirm accounted for one-third to one-half of the inmates, excluding the fit aged, and that the mortality rate was chiefly applicable to them, about one in ten must never have left the institution alive.

It was the conditions that were conducive to this high death rate and which were to a great extent remediable that evoked the great outcry for the improvement of the workhouse infirmary in the middle 'sixties. The public outburst over the scandalous deaths of two sick paupers brought about the famous *Lancet* inquiry, the most important in its revelations and its results of the whole spate of investigations.

> The intimate relation between sickness and pauperism which had for many years been well known at the Poor Law Board was never fully recognized by the public or Parliament till the condition of the Metropolitan workhouses was described by the *Lancet* Commissioners, and the masses of sickness and infirmity therein contained, held up to view. . . . For the first time it could not be denied that the character of workhouse inmates had completely changed, and that a harsh and repulsive regime intended for the repression of idleness and imposture had been and was still applied to persons suffering from acute diseases, permanent disability, or old age brought on prematurely by sickness, starvation, intemperance and neglect. . . . The national sense of humanity was deeply shocked, and arousing from its usual apathy on pauper misery, society united in a determined effort to redress the evil . . .[1]

Dickens had in the 'fifties popularized the workhouse atrocities with his graphic descriptions in *Oliver Twist, All the year round, Martin Chuzzlewit*, and *Household Words*. Rumsey had in his *Essays on State Medicine* in 1856 revealed the serious mismanagement in some institutions. He had pointed out that the workhouses planned in the late 'thirties were a terrible negation of the first principles of hygiene. Rural workhouses in Kent, for example, had adopted the plan devised by the eccentric Sir F. B. Head, brother of the Assistant Poor Law Commissioner, which allowed only 117 cubic feet of breathing space to each inmate. Even larger and better contrived workhouses, Rumsey had pointed out, provided only 160–200 cubic feet for ordinary dormitories and 300–400 cubic feet in sickwards. At the same time foreign writers were recommending 800–1,000 cubic feet for each hospital patient, and English Prison Inspectors allowed 1,000 cubic feet for every prisoner. Rumsey had also drawn attention to the neglect of cleanliness and ventilation and the unsatisfactory dietaries.

But it had been Thomas Wakley the 'Great Medical Reformer'[2] who had prepared both the public and the medical profession for the dreadful revelations. He had in the late 'twenties and 'thirties denounced the maladministration of hospitals. As they were supported by the public and were public places they should have publicity, he remarked.

---

[1] *Lancet*, leading article, 1868, i, pp. 351–52.
[2] *Lancet*, obituary, 1862, i, pp. 605–7; for life of Wakley see Dr. (Sir) Squire Sprigge's biography, 1895.

Week by week he had recorded the activities within the jealously guarded walls of the Metropolitan hospitals and had printed scathing attacks on surgical malpractice. His aim in entering Parliament had been definite—he became the 'Member for Medicine'. His indignation at the regulations concerning the medical care of the sick poor under the new Poor Law eventually spread to the whole Act. He had general sympathy with the destitute no less than with the sweating of doctors. The workhouses he called 'death-traps and foci of disease', and pointed out that they were totally inadequate for the relief of the sick. He promised that the *Lancet* which he had founded in 1823 with the co-operation of William Cobbett the Radical political reformer would reveal the scandalous conditions. His son kept his word. Long before Wakley's death in 1862 his son, who had taken over the editorship, planned to make a complete investigation into the treatment of the sick poor in workhouses, and when the tragedies of St. Giles and Holborn were revealed James Wakley seized the psychological moment and instituted the inquiry.

On 15 April 1865 he wrote in the leading article of his journal that the public disclosures of the scandals of Gibson and Daly,

> of the terrible defects of dietary, of nursing, of medical supervision of the long cure, of the general fittings, and indeed of all parts of the workhouse hospital, affords a stern commentary on the cold neglect, varied by harsh refusal with which successive Poor Law Commissions and Committees have met and repulsed constant and earnest appeals of the medical profession. The pertinacity and unanimity with which a more liberal regard for the wants of the sick poor have been refused . . . are one of the most notable circumstances in the internal administration of this country.

The two scandals were not exceptional, they had only been more thoroughly investigated.

> Such examples of neglect, of suffering, of insufficient care, bad nursing, and cruel privation, are the necessary incidents of a scheme which aims solely at escaping public ignominy by a bare fulfilment of necessary public duties, but thinks only in doing so of saving the farthings. . . . The workhouse hospital system is a disgrace to our civilization. Compare it with that of the public hospitals. In the latter there is everything provided which can ensure the well-doing of the sick inmate: the constant care of skilled nurses; the administration of all remedies which may be useful irrespective of cost. . . . The workhouse hospitals sin by their own construction, by their want of nursing, by their comfortless fittings, by the supremacy which is accorded to the question of expense, by the imperfect provision made for the skilled attendance on the sick, the immense labour imposed on medical attendants, and the wretched pittances to which they are ground down. . . . This state of things cannot continue. It is necessary that public opinion should be fully enlightened and deliberately directed.

To supply the requisite materials the *Lancet* appointed Commissioners 'well acquainted with hospital management and whose whole ability and direction were beyond doubt'. They were to compare the system of the workhouse infirmaries with that which prevailed in the public hospitals in the Metropolis.—'The sick poor in the Metropolitan infirmaries have a right to the same advantages of pure air, food, baths, efficient ward arrangements, skilled nursing, sufficient and unfettered medical attention which is supplied to the inmates of the voluntary hospital.' The Commissioners were instructed not to set too high a standard nor to 'execute their mission in a spirit of hostility to Guardians or others. . . . It is the system which is blameable', the working of which, it was later pointed out, was rapidly coming to a deadlock. James Wakley realized the inquiry would be criticized minutely and severely, and he recognized the serious responsibility involved in the undertaking, so the intention of the investigation was far higher than detecting faults—it aimed at reorganization rather than destruction.

The three Commissioners were Ernest Hart of St. Mary's Hospital, who suggested and laid down the scheme of the inquiry, Dr. Anstie of the Westminster Hospital and later editor of *The Practitioner*, who took the largest share in examining the infirmaries and to whose able pen the general summary of the results and recommendations which prefaced the reports were due, and Dr. Carr of Blackheath. Of the seventeen accounts on sixteen infirmaries, thirteen were written separately or jointly by Dr. Anstie and Dr. Carr, one by Hart and Carr, and three by Hart alone. All reports were printed unaltered in successive issues of the *Lancet*, and the whole of the general survey was written by Anstie. He made it clear that as the task was arduous, the Commissioners only hoped to break the ground.

The General Survey opened by pointing out that the Metropolitan workhouses had a character of their own regarding the class of inmates and the kind of accommodation. For example, the workhouse of the City of London Union at Mile End was a pretentious building with every sanitary requirement, yet the institution of St. George the Martyr, Southwark had every amenity wanting. The workhouses therefore illustrated in a striking way the two distinctive features of London life—comfort and luxury close to filth and misery. The Commissioners were convinced however that when it was discovered that institutions with conditions conducive to health cost less to the ratepayer, Guardians would cease to waste the wealth of the nation 'in misguided parsimony or mean extravagance'. Yet the Guardians were magnanimous enough to open their doors to the investigators. Chairmen had the sole power of granting permission to a stranger to enter a workhouse and special application had to be made to the Local Boards. Of the thirty-nine Unions and parishes, thirty-six readily admitted inspection and only Westminster refused. This operated independently of the Poor Law Board through 'one of those admirable contrivances for favouring mismanagement, called "Local Acts"'. The Commissioners found much goodwill, especially from Inspector Farnall. Medical Officers were of great assistance and showed their books as did the masters of the workhouses.

To examine the efficiency of the infirmaries the Commissioners outlined the general desiderata for hospitals. These were: convenience and salubrity of site and surroundings; efficient drainage, water supply, and ventilation; isolation of the sick, especially those suffering from contagious diseases; constant supervision by superior officers and superintendent nurses; a competent nursing staff; a sufficient number of Medical Officers; proper classification; and intelligent liberality of management. These requirements needed certain additions for workhouse infirmaries because of the particular type of applicant for medical relief. Besides the growing inferiority of the number of able-bodied inmates the sick-wards themselves contained only a small proportion of the type of case normally admitted to the hospitals. It was the chronically sick, especially the prematurely aged who crowded into the infirmaries and who were regarded by officials as an 'anomalous but unavoidable nuisance'. Their position was ill-defined and they should have been regarded as patients and obtained strict attendance not merely perfunctory medical supervision. The Commissioners pointed out the advantage which would have accrued to society and the ratepayer from giving the infirm medical treatment, for a large percentage could have been cured.—'Negligence and mismanagement inflicts severe penalties for short-sighted blunders.' The Medical Officers were exonerated from the charge of giving insufficient care to less acute cases which were allowed to become chronic, because they were grossly overworked, and here also there was great contrast between the voluntary hospital and the workhouse infirmary. Turning to the workhouse in general the Commissioners recapitulated the growth of the institutions, how they had been built for the 'custody of sturdy ne'er do wells', and how the necessity of providing for the genuinely sick and feeble had come as an afterthought and as an appendage to the main scheme.

> The present workhouse system is a thing of shreds and patches, which has slowly grown up to its present form with all manner of miscellaneous additions and alterations from time to time. . . . How comes it that the public . . . and the profession . . . have nearly ignored these *real hospitals of the land*, while lavishing princely munificence on the splendid institutions which ostensibly supply the national hospital requirements?

The scandalous inequality in the treatment of the two classes of sick-poor was a difficulty which had to be surmounted. The voluntary hospital, said the Commissioners, could but 'lightly touch the surface of the wide field of London misery'. The eighteen in London provided nearly 4,000 beds, the workhouses nearly 8,000 for the sick and 7,000 for the infirm, although the latter number was in fact much larger. With efficient management, they maintained, the infirmaries could become magnificent clinical hospitals from which patients, public, and medical science would draw great advantages. The practical study of chronic forms of insanity for example, could be undertaken because workhouses contained such a vast number of these cases which were lost to the service of medical research.

The Commissioners divided the practical side of their inquiry into eight sections. First they dealt with the general character of the infirmary buildings, their position, aspect, form, drainage, water supply, number of inmates and the proportion of these to the accommodation provided, and gave a critical appreciation of their fitness for hospital purposes and particularly for the hospital requirements of the districts. Second, they inquired into the wards with regard to ventilation, light, warmth, aspect, beds and furniture, provision for personal cleanliness, closets, etc., and tried also to give a 'general estimate of their management with a view to comfort and health of the inmates'. Nursing, the quality of food and its cooking, and dietaries were also investigated. Medical officers, their duties, responsibilities, remuneration, and liberty of action were examined, as were the mortality rates. Finally, the Commissioners took a history of the epidemic diseases of the workhouses.

It was discovered that the infirmaries in their position as vast district hospitals were badly and inconveniently situated, for many were close together leaving large districts uncovered. Defects in site and construction were so serious that it was found necessary to divide the institutions into three classes. The worst were reported to be entirely unsuitable for the sick and even for the able-bodied: these were the Strand, Clerkenwell, St. Martin in the Fields, St. Giles, St. George the Martyr, and Smithfield. The second class were those which might be used as establishments for chronic diseases and infirmity if improvements were effected: the infirmaries of St. James, Westminster, Chelsea, St. Luke, Lambeth, Lewisham, Camberwell, Holborn, East London, and Bermondsey came into this category. The third class of infirmaries were those in a really good situation, which had been built on the principles of scientific hospital construction and which, it was stated, might be developed into first-rate hospitals, capable of serving all the needs of large districts for the treatment of the more important and acute diseases, both medical and surgical. This class included very few of the workhouses which were situated in the most thickly populated and therefore the most diseased districts: they were Fulham, Hackney, Kensington, Marylebone, Paddington, St. Pancras, Stepney, Newington, Richmond, Wandsworth, City of London, Mile End, and Bethnal Green.

The worst fault in the general character of the infirmaries in the first two categories was the mixing of sick-wards in the body of the workhouse where separation was impossible. Such buildings, the *Lancet* Commissioners recommended should be condemned for infirmary purposes. They described the repulsive picture of Clerkenwell, saying it was difficult to imagine a more dreary and unhealthy life, although the officials were kind. There was a total absence of the quiet and privacy found in a hospital, which was the first necessity for patients. Storeys were piled one on another linked by narrow cramped staircases which allowed little penetration of air. St. George in the East offered similar conditions. The sick-wards were objectionable and the infirm women lived under the roof where the heat was oppressive. Also the sick and infirm were scattered all over the house. In Greenwich the Commissioners condemned the 'roof-wards', and in St. George the Martyr, Southwark, the surroundings. Here as at Clerkenwell, the Strand, and St. James, Westminster, bone-boilers and grease and catgut manufacturers carried on their trade in the environs of the workhouses. The closeness of other buildings also totally impeded any circulation of air through the institutions—and many of these were often the property of the parish. The position was worst at the Strand where the Guardians supplemented the nuisances of the neighbourhood by carrying on a carpet-beating business in the yard immediately below the windows of the sick-wards. Remonstrations were ignored because £600 was received by the Union through it—and by choking the patients with dust.

Part of the Greenwich workhouse site, and the entire sites of those at Rotherhithe, St.

473

Olave and Bermondsey were below high-water mark and occasionally flooded. Drainage was however reported as being good on the whole by this time as the deep system of sewers had been instituted. Many workhouses were condemned for overcrowding, particularly those in thickly populated districts. Classification was stated to be inefficient in the first two classes of workhouses. The insane, for example, were not separated from the body of the house. There were generally insane wards, but patients were allowed to mingle freely with ordinary cases. Although the chronic lunatics who were dangerous were in the main sent away, a considerable number of acute maniacs were found to be retained from four to ten days because of the difficulty of removal. In Chelsea there was no padded room nor provision for temporary seclusion of even the most violent lunatics, and these with thirty chronic insane wandered 'in a melancholy objectless manner about the house and yards. . . . It is quite an oasis in the desert, when, as at Marylebone, Newington and some other houses, we find a garden with swings, birdcages, and rabbit hutches for the amusement of these poor creatures, and a number of pretty pictures pasted upon the walls of their day-room.' Classification was neglected in some workhouses to the extent of mixing contagious fevers of the most dangerous type with other patients in wards containing not more than 500 cubic feet to each bed. (This was also a common hospital practice and had been advocated by some physicians.) The greatest apathy was shown towards scabies and other contagious skin disorders which were the curse of institutions like workhouses at that time. The master of Paddington, who was described as an intelligent and active official, told the *Lancet* Commissioners that there were very few workhouses where itch (scabies) was discovered and cured promptly. He maintained that it always should be got rid of within forty-eight hours of the patient's admission.

The Commissioners' description of the character of the infirmary wards themselves gave a good picture of what these must have looked like in the 'sixties of the last century. Great variation existed in the form of the wards, but the long rectangular shape predominated, especially in older institutions, in which there were from fourteen to thirty or even more beds. The new workhouses had two rows of opposite windows which allowed the provision of adequate light and ventilation, but the older institutions with their single row of windows were defective in these requirements. Almost in every case there was an insufficient allowance of space per bed. Hospitals required from 1,000 to 1,200 cubic feet for each patient and more for fever cases, but in five infirmaries less than 500 cubic feet, the 'wretched state sanctioned by the Poor Law Board' were provided. In all but a very small minority, it was stated, at least some of the wards transgressed the laws of hygiene. Even where sick-wards were comparatively presentable, the infirm wards were miserably cramped. Some of the newer houses were as defective as the old regarding space. In most infirmaries attempts had been made to assist ventilation by a series of gratings above and below, but it had been found impossible to keep the atmosphere clean where only 500 to 600 cubic feet of space was allotted to each bed. As in St. Martin in the Fields some of the very bad workhouses, through their inconvenient construction, had discouraged the authorities from putting in gratings, but at Clerkenwell, which was of equally bad con-

474

struction, the master and the Medical Officer had done a great deal to mitigate the evils of deficient ventilation.

When they turned to the general superintendence of the wards the Commissioners were astonished at the hopeless state of the infirmaries. The walls, for example, were painted with 'hideous drab' up to the middle and were finished off with 'glaring white-wash'. Only a few had coloured prints or cheap engravings. Bedsteads were nearly always of iron and the majority were of adequate length. In Lewisham however the framework was double and had a wooden separation so that there was under 2 feet for each occupant and were as a rule only 5 feet long. Although the bedsteads were long enough the beds were usually 18 inches shorter in half the infirmaries. Officials remained entirely unconscious of the great discomfort so caused. The crucial test of good ward management, stated the Commissioners, was cleanliness, and here they were horrified.

> There is (to the superficial observer) rather a special air of *bescrubbedness*, rather a power-
> ful odour of soap and water, about the wards of the workhouse infirmaries. So much
> for the surface; now for the inside of the cup and platter. In several infirmaries the
> nurses of one or more wards admitted, with very little compunction, that the bed-
> ridden patients habitually washed their hands and faces *in their chamber-utensils*; and in
> one of the first-class houses, where such a disgusting practice was repudiated, we saw
> whilst in the company with the Medical Officer—at least a dozen women in the very
> act, and, on expressing our surprise, were told that they preferred it!

The Commissioners found only one instance—at Lambeth—where a separate hand-basin for each bedridden patient was provided. Only at the new Stepney infirmary and at one or two others were bathrooms in sufficient numbers attached to the sick-wards. The supply of towels was also inadequate. One nurse of a syphilitic women's ward distinctly told the Commissioners that there was only one round-towel a week for the use of eight inmates. Much had still to be done in regard to water-closets. In the old houses these were inside the wards, and in St. James's there were two or three in one ward. Because of their defective flushing arrangements they were a dangerous nuisance. The Commissioners protested against the public closets and asked for screens to be placed between them.

The general impression the Commissioners obtained from the inspection of wards was that they were inefficiently managed through the want of proper hospital organization. Even excellent workhouses like those at Kensington, Paddington, and Newington could not be excluded, although the intention of Guardians and officials was good. The small value of lay inspection was revealed, for the worst faults were seen in the workhouses which were regularly inspected by the Guardians.

Surveying the nursing system, the Commissioners found that the principle of paid nursing had taken root. 'One by one the Boards of Guardians are giving cautious assent to at least a partial trial of the plan of paid nursing.' Marylebone had fourteen such nurses in 1865 and paid them a total salary of £250 a year. St. Pancras had sixteen and paid £280 a year, nine other Unions or parishes had between two and four, and fourteen employed one.

Two or three workhouses employed an assistant matron in that capacity. The Commissioners listened to conflicting arguments not only from laymen but also from doctors. They believed 'with those of real experience', that the employment of a full staff of well-trained paid nurses offered the only possibility of a thorough and genuine execution of duties, which were at the time 'so perfunctorily discharged'. The majority of pauper nurses, they pointed out, were aged and feeble, or had strong tendencies to drink. Even the opponents of paid nurses admitted that as a rule the only method of managing pauper nurses was by confining them to the institution, a practice which undermined their health and unfitted them for their duties. Their inefficiency was evinced by the character of their ward work and the majority only managed their patients by inspiring them with fear, and consequently their conduct was often brutal. The problem of obtaining good paid nurses at salaries which were not exorbitant was one which authorities would have to solve by having girls at the district schools trained. (This was Inspector Farnall's idea.) One of the greatest scandals of the workhouse infirmaries, in the eyes of the Commissioners, was the inadequacy and inefficiency of night nursing. Hospitals laboured under the same difficulty of not being able to secure the efficient performance of night duties, and in the infirmaries the investigators had uniformly failed to obtain any satisfactory report of the paupers' conduct as night nurses.

The quality of provisions was generally found satisfactory when food was expressly ordered for the sick, and the Commissioners only complained of the house diet, which was in the majority of cases supplied to the infirm also. Separate kitchens situated in the infirmaries as at Stepney were recommended. Extras for the sick were always provided on the doctors' recommendations, and the practice of the voluntary hospitals was closely followed in the amount of nourishment and wines given. The infirm and feeble were however often underfed as they could not eat the tough boiled beef—'clods and stickings'—the pea soup and the suet puddings with which they were supplied. The uniformly insufficient diet was conducive to 'ward fever' among this class of inmate, and Rogers was praised for his efforts and agitation to induce the Strand Guardians to adopt a special dietary for the infirm.

When the Commissioners came to consider the Medical Officers of the infirmaries they found these had two or three times as many patients as they could cope with, so that adequate treatment was impossible. Because of the enormous amount of overwork, doctors could not give their attention to many details of hospital management which rightly fell into their province. As a body, the Medical Officers, the Commissioners said, 'applied themselves with a zeal and an amount of success' which was surprising. And in the majority of cases they also fought the 'battle of the poor with terrible earnestness against the prejudices and gross material interests of the worst members of the Boards of Guardians'. Reforms which the Commissioners recommended were: higher salaries paid out of the Consolidated Fund, public provision of drugs, and the appointment of dispensers. Further, Medical Officers should have sole control of the infirmary and not be subject to the interference of the master and matron regarding patients.

If the history of epidemics which had fallen on the workhouses could have been obtained the Commissioners believed this would have been an interesting study, but epidemics, they said, were a thing of the past. The great curse of the infirmaries had been their liability to the introduction of typhus from the neighbouring crowded districts. The danger of mixing these patients with others had become obvious and the practice of removing them to the Fever Hospital was nearly universal. An example of the previous state of affairs was given. St. Luke's infirmary was situated near a part of Shoreditch where typhus (probably typhoid) was always rife and where there was a refuge so perennially infected that everyone who lived there for a week caught the fever. In the winter of 1864–65 the disease spread so rapidly that the matron and other workhouse inmates caught it and died. Therefore the practice of receiving typhus patients was abandoned, but not before twenty-eight deaths had occurred. In Marylebone, however, case after case of small-pox was admitted to the workhouse in 1864, but the extreme care of the Medical Officer, who made arrangements for the effective isolation of the patients, resulted in not a single inmate contracting the disease. It was difficult to obtain good records of epidemics generated by sanitary nuisances. One account existed and this was of the Newington workhouse which was situated by an open tidal ditch fed with sewage. Typhoid fever never occurred in the house between 1858 and 1864, but the following extracts appeared in the Medical Officer's book:

1858:	19 August	—diarrhoea very troublesome amongst inmates
1859:	13 January	—tendency to puerperal fever
	31 March	—six cases of chicken pox
	7 April	—six cases of chicken pox and three cases of scarlatina
	21 April	—many cases of deranged liver function
	28 April	—several cases of sore throat and one fresh case of scarlatina
	28 July	—nine cases of diarrhoea
	7 August	—twenty-seven fresh cases of diarrhoea
1860:	30 August	—diarrhoea severe
	October	—diarrhoea amongst children
	13 December	—diarrhoea still prevalent, attributed to ditch
1861:	22 August	—diarrhoea five, choleric
1863:	July	—diarrhoea prevalent
1864:		—purulent ophthalmia prevalent

The average mortality of the Metropolitan workhouses, the Commissioners found to be very high. The special reason to which they attributed this was the great number of feeble aged people and the hopelessly diseased who entered the institution, as well as to the number of sickly infants who were born there. The majority of deaths were found to have been caused by factors which induced debility such as old age and want (combined often with a long-standing hopeless disease), and by the congenital feebleness of tubercular or syphilitic infants. Only in special circumstances was the influence of zymotic disease on mortality large. Therefore the only field in which deaths were to any considerable extent preventable, the Commissioners admitted, was in regard to infants. The enormously high proportion of infantile deaths in the workhouses was notorious, and this was attributed to the unhealthy nurseries and the lack of supervision over the supplementary food administered. The greatest harm was done by the abuse of giving arrowroot and other starchy foods to the newly-born. The extraordinary benefit of wine in many infantile cachetic conditions[1] was almost ignored, said the Commissioners, and cows' milk was insufficiently supplied.[2] The children's wards were also described as very defective and there was often no day-room and no means of occupation or amusement. There were also few baths and despite the prevalence of ophthalmia and cutaneous affections little segregation was attempted.

In concluding their General Survey the *Lancet* Commissioners maintained that the difficult problem of improving the Metropolitan workhouses could only be solved by the immediate appointment of one medical and one surgical inspector by the government. They should inspect and report on the infirmaries as to their fitness for hospital purposes, and should consider the best way of converting the workhouses into hospitals if able-bodied paupers were in future to be separated from the sick and infirm by being sent into the country. It was also recommended that they should be instructed to prepare a plan for the organization of suitable hospital medical staffs, by which pauper in-patients might receive, in addition to the visits of the existing Medical Officers, the advantage of advice from consulting physicians and surgeons.

Following the General Report detailed accounts of the individual workhouse infirmaries appeared in successive editions of the *Lancet*. The Institution of St. George the Martyr, Southwark, for example, was entirely condemned and demolition suggested. In St. Giles, Bloomsbury, the infirmary was overcrowded, there was no classification of patients and the rate of mortality was high and increasing. Food was good but bedding was worn-out and dirty. The Shoreditch workhouse inmates were said to have lived in an atmosphere of desolation and there were 'herds of lunatics, gibbering and moping'. The Commissioners denounced the cruelty of keeping them there, and the total absence of classification or effort to afford treatment. The lying-in wards were filthy and so were the sick-wards. The inefficient pauper nurses neglected to administer medicines and food, and left patients filthy and horribly neglected. There was no furniture in the infirmary yet the external structure of the building was good and a new one was in the process of being erected. The Islington workhouse offered a great contrast. The external structure was terrible and inadequate, yet the master and the officials had established within these very unpromising premises an excellent infirmary system. The wards were low, small, ill-lighted, yet they were cheerful and comfortable because of their coloured walls, prints, and flowerpots. Books were also circulated. The linen was clean and was changed every week, stomach and feet warmers

---

[1] General ill-health and malnutrition.
[2] If it had been, bovine tuberculosis would have been rife—for the 'danger of the cow' had not been discovered. Diagnosis, treatment, and medical terminology are given throughout as in the original.

and shawls were provided. The patients were cheerful and grateful, medicines were given regularly and dressings were well applied. Small dinner-cloths were supplied for the bed-ridden and they also had pieces of muslin to protect their faces from flies in hot weather. The pauper nurses received only 1s. to 1s. 6d. a week but were well-dressed and most were 'well-conducted' and 'well managed'. The Medical Officer encouraged visits from hospital doctors and invited professional publicity. There was a shortage of day-rooms and con-valescent wards, and an absence of bathrooms, but this was a defect of the building which was only fit for demolition—a new one was being erected. Only the maternity ward was objectionable, this was cheerless and wretched and devoid of furniture. The walls were bare, the bed and personal linen dirty and the women unkempt. The midwife and nurse were responsible to the doctor but the patients were not as well attended as the other sick. These conditions were attributable to the impression (common in most workhouses at the time) that the women were mostly profligates so that discomfort was a measure for reform-ing them. The *Lancet* Commissioners condemned this approach. Nevertheless the Islington infirmary offered a great contrast to Shoreditch because by good management the defects of a bad house had been partly neutralized, whilst at Shoreditch which had an admirable institution bad management counterbalanced its potential efficiency.

In St. Martin in the Fields the workhouse was a 'gloomy, prison-like structure', and the infirmary was only separated from the National Gallery by a narrow court. The atmo-sphere was terrible, and the sick were grossly overcrowded. Nash, the famous architect, had once offered £30,000 for the site and to rebuild the workhouse at his own cost in any other place. In the 'sixties the site was worth £60,000 so the Guardians could well have erected a new institution elsewhere. The *Lancet* Commissioners condemned the terrible sanitary conditions and recommended the immediate removal of all inmates of the work-house. In Clerkenwell 'the lowest point in the scale of Metropolitan workhouse hospitals' was touched. There was no trace of a separate infirmary and as the building had been erected in 1729 it was cramped and decrepit. The special feature of the house was the shrieks of laughter from noisy lunatics. Yet the master was said to have been an excellent officer, accustomed all his life to the management of the sick, and a paid experienced nurse was also employed. Although the wards were 'sanitary abominations' the Guardians here also refused to sell the site and rebuild elsewhere. With them lingered the early policy of the Poor Law Commissioners and the workhouse test.

In conclusion, the conditions in the St. Pancras infirmary in 1866 might be compared with those Dr. Bence Jones described ten years earlier. The workhouse had become the largest in London and accommodated nearly 2,000 inmates, it was important also because such a large number of sick were being treated there. In 1866 a separate infirmary existed— a four-storey building on one side of the workhouse site, and another two-storey block housed the infirm. The insane wards occupied the lower storey of another block with further infirm wards above them. In January 1865 there were 232 inmates in the infirmary, 746 in the infirm wards and 116 insane—a total of 1,094 people under medical care. A later visit of the *Lancet* Commissioners discovered a far greater number than this and the house was overcrowded. As the infirmary alone was equal in size to the Middlesex and St. George's Hospitals, and as a large proportion of the acute cases were treated, the first question the Commissioners tried to determine was whether the Guardians provided a staff of doctors and skilled nurses to correspond with the needs of a hospital of this size. However, the strength of the medical staff consisted of two resident Medical Officers, who besides attending to their infirmary duties were responsible for the maternity department and over 700 infirm, many of whom were seriously ill. In addition they were required to exercise medical superintendence over the whole workhouse. But neglect was not patent when the institution was inspected. It was well situated and adequately ventilated, drainage and water supply were good and the infirmary wards were light and cheerful with a double row of windows. Several of the infirm wards were however low and very dark and this block contained the maternity department and the nursery. The whole section was unhealthy and was situated immediately behind other buildings. The furniture of the hospital was insufficient and the bedsteads were too short, the mattresses had had their flock content reduced from 40 to 25 lb. for the sake of economy. The average allowance of space was 530 cubic feet in the male and 615 in the female wards. In the winter months overcrowding was so great that people were bedded on the floor and the nursery was similarly over-crowded. Hot and cold water was laid on to every ward, but there were no bathrooms and there was a great deficiency in towels.

St. Pancras workhouse had formerly obtained notoriety for harbouring fatal forms of fever but sanitary improvements had been effected since Dr. Jones's inspection. Zymotic diseases had also been excluded as far as possible from the workhouse, and if they were accidentally admitted they were removed to the Fever Hospital. Because of the many attacks which had formerly been made on the institution, sixteen paid nurses were engaged in 1866. These were reported as being neat and efficient and as having a salutary influence. There were still no skilled or paid night nurses. The Commissioners recommended an increase in the nursing and medical staff and in the quantity of furniture and conveniences. They also desired to see the abolition of the large insane department, for St. Pancras, like some other Unions, had begun to attempt the treatment of all cases of insanity, rather than incur the large expense of maintaining pauper lunatics in County Asylums. This was quite impossible with the organization found in the workhouses, where there were no means of secluding the violent and no opportunities for outdoor recreation or work. The Commissioners said the practice was a 'superficial and mischievous imitation' of asylum treatment and repeated the protest of the Lunacy Commissioners against the 'cruelty and shortsighted folly of the Guardians in attempting to charge their meagre establishments with the additional responsibility of maintaining insane wards for any but the most harmless and incurable cases of imbecility'.

The general conclusion of the Commissioners on the St. Pancras infirmary was that it might with certain modifications of structure and improved management be developed into a good pauper hospital.—But the institution was not retained, for the propery was sold to a railway company.

After the General Report was written and before all the detailed accounts were published, the *Lancet* realized that it was hopeless to expect the government to take the workhouses under their care and classify them into good and bad for the purpose of putting into effect the schemes suggested. Therefore in concert with the Committee of the Association for Improving Workhouse Infirmaries a scheme was adopted which the Association presented to the public and to the Poor Law Board. When all reports had been studied as a comprehensive whole, the *Lancet* maintained that arguments seemed even stronger for a complete remodelling of the institutions. The main features of the scheme for reform outlined by the Infirmary Association and which Ernest Hart set out in detail in the *Fortnightly Review* of 1 April 1866, were identical with the projects published in the *Lancet*:

The sick poor were to be separated from able-bodied paupers and treatment was to be placed under a distinct management; in place of sick wards annexed to each workhouse, consolidated infirmaries were to be provided, where the following rules of hospital management were to be adopted under skilled supervision. [These were generally accepted in this and other European countries.]

(1) Buildings be specially devised for the purpose, suitable construction and healthy sites. Rules laid down by Barrack and Hospital Commission (1861) be consulted.
(2) Not less than 1,000—and for particular classes of cases 1,200 to 1,500—cubic feet of air should be allowed to each patient.
(3) Nursing be conducted entirely by a paid staff; not less than one day nurse, one night nurse, and one assistant nurse for each fifty patients.
(4) Resident Medical Officers to be appointed in proportion of not less than one for each 250 patients.
(5) Medical Officers not to have any pecuniary interest in medicines supplied, nor be charged with the duty of dispensing them.
(6) A judicious classification of patients be strictly observed. Epileptic and imbecile, acutely sick, aged and infirm to have separate wards.
(7) Aged, infirm, chronically sick and convalescent be provided with day-rooms separate from dormitories.

The scheme was signed by Thomas Watson, M.D., President of the Royal College of Physicians, George Burrows, M.D., President of the General Medical Council, James Clark, M.D., William Jenner, M.D., Edward Sieveking, M.D., William Fergusson, M.D., and James Paget, M.D., F.R.S.

These desiderata were revolutionary for Metropolitan workhouses. A few had some of the conditions, none had them all, and a large number existed nowhere. Most institutions could not be improved up to the standard necessary.

Patch up the present system as we may, and it will still continue to be a scandal and a reproach. Foreigners coming over are not slow to discover that the public hospitals of London, of which we boast so much, accommodate but a small portion of the sick. *The*

State hospitals are in the workhouse wards. They are closed against observation, they pay no heed to public opinion; they pay no toll to science. They contravene the rules of hygiene; they are under the government of men profoundly ignorant of hospital rules. They are separated from the world of medical observation, and from the sphere of benevolent and voluntary visitation and aid. The doctor and the patient are alike the objects of a pinching parsimony. There is neither uniformity, nor liberality, nor intelligence in the management. If all were present they must still be badly conducted. For there can be no worse type of hospital steward than the workhouse master; no worse influence under which sick-wards can exist than side by side with the wards for able-bodied paupers. To perpetuate thirty-nine bad hospitals where half a dozen good ones will suffice will be an act of grave and dangerous misgovernment.[1]

In February 1867 *The Times* stated that for the past two years the world had heard more than enough of London workhouses and that it was strange so little had been heard of them before. The writer pointed out that workhouse reform began with the scandals of Holborn and St. Giles and implied that no one had previously suspected anything amiss in the treatment of the sick poor until these two cases came to light. Had the pages of the Workhouse Visiting Society's Journal, which had been issued continuously from 1859 to 1865, besides many pamphlets, been publicized, similar revelations to the *Lancet*'s Reports would have been discovered. Individuals had for years striven against great obstacles to improve conditions, and women had played no mean part. The Women's Movement which grew up in the latter half of the nineteenth century was closely linked to the genesis and growth of modern social services, and Ibsen could prophesy that women with the working men would dominate the history of the twentieth century. Pamphlets were issued on prison reform and every other reform, and the books of Mrs. Wightman and Mrs. Henry Wood which sold in thousands of copies stirred the clergy so much that temperance reform became closely allied with the evangelical revival. It was inevitable that women should get involved with the Poor Law medical service. Not only were there in this field the great philanthropists like the Baroness Lionel de Rothschild, Lady Alderson, Miss Augusta Clifford, and other ladies of wealth, but there were particularly the reformers such as Frances Power Cobbe, Mrs. Gladstone, Mrs. Jameson, and Louisa Twining, who attacked the social system itself which made philanthropy imperative. Of these it was Louisa Twining who stood out as the most determined, energetic and prescient.

Women, [she said] have been the first to enlist public sympathy on behalf of the better management of our workhouses, as they have already done for the better management of our hospitals, and in matters connected with the poor, the sick, and the aged, it would seem to be especially the mission of women to work a reformation.[2]

[1] This is the concluding paragraph of the 'Introduction' to the *Lancet*'s monumental collective report of 1865–66 entitled 'The *Lancet* Sanitary Commission for investigating the State of the Infirmaries of Workhouses'.

[2] *Recollections of Workhouse Visiting and Management*, 1880.

Louisa Twining devoted years of her life to the amelioration of the lot of the workhouse sick and in the early twentieth century she was still campaigning for the reform of nursing in the infirmaries. It was her initiative that started the agitation for the abolition of pauper nurses, and the numerous letters to the Press besides the pamphlets she produced, particularly in the 'fifties and 'sixties, are an indication of her tremendous activity.

She began visiting workhouses in 1854 and aroused the interest of a host of other women. Not only did they bring the philanthropic alms to the sick and aged and teach them how to read and sew in order to make them useful citizens, but they were also the first independent body to be allowed, after a struggle, inside the institutions to study conditions. The type of information these Visitors obtained was recorded by Louisa Twining in her diary. An entry in 1856 reads:

> Went to see J.T. in the [St. G. St. Giles, Bloomsbury?]. He was in a ward partly under-ground, with a stone floor; beds, sheets, and shirts were dirty and grey. Said he had not seen the matron more than once during four months, only the chaplain and Guardians occasionally; nurse was an old R.C., with bloated face, above 70. To get in I had to wait with a crowd at the office door to obtain a ticket. Visitors to the sick are only allowed once a week, for one hour.

The diary abounds with references to the feelings of despair that used to come over her when she visited the sick and saw their 'abject and lifelong misery'. Of a visit to one of the largest infirmaries she wrote:

> 'We hardly think any sermon could be preached which would so eloquently plead the cause of labouring for the welfare and elevation of the lowest classes, both physically, morally and spiritually, as a visit to those homes of pauper children. Their ill-grown bodies, low and debased countenances, weak eyes and all the other various signs of disease, the dullness of many, almost approaching to idiocy, speak but too plainly of the condition of those masses of our population from which they have sprung—of homes unfit for human habitation, of the drunken habits, induced probably by the state of those homes, and of all the sin and misery of the parents which are thus entailed upon a new generation, and which years of training and wholesome living are unable wholly to eradicate.

In 1861 the verdict of a jury on the death of a sick pauper was recorded:

> They think the said ward deficient in lighting, ventilation, and proper accommodation for patients, as well as its very bad position, and ought to be closed. They also think more paid nurses should be appointed to attend the sick, and are of the opinion that the neglect of the nurses to change the linen is severely reprehensible.

In 1857 Louisa Twining read a paper to the Social Economy department of the National Association for the Promotion of Social Science on 'The Condition of Work-houses'. At the meeting it was decided to form a central society for the promotion of workhouse visiting. It developed under the presidency of William Cowper and had a large committee consisting of well-known men and women, philanthropists and reformers, and included noblemen, bishops, clergy, and doctors. Louisa Twining was the first Secretary, and the society was affiliated to the Social Science Association.[1] Its objects were to enlighten the public, educate the paupers (many grants were made for establishing workhouse libraries), and to campaign for the institution of efficient nursing. Destitute and orphan children were also befriended and comforts brought to the sick and aged. The *Journal of the Workhouse Visiting Society* was begun in 1859 to bring pressure on the Poor Law authorities, for it was believed that by printing information obtained from individual knowledge and experience the public would demand an amelioration of conditions.

In 1862 Louisa Twining was called to give evidence to the Select Committee on Poor Relief. She stressed the overcrowding of workhouses, particularly in the Metropolis, but the thirty or forty she had seen in the provinces were equally as bad. New institutions were more salutary, she admitted, because they were larger. She had been through workhouses with Medical Officers who had expressed astonishment that people ever got well, or how they managed to survive in such crowded atmospheres. Many Guardians, she said, had thanked the Society for their suggestions, which had been circulated round the country, and some had promised to try to put them into effect. The Clerk to the City of London Union told the Select Committee that his Guardians refused admittance to the Visitors, because they believed their mission was fruitless. The Visitors, he said, only wanted to interfere and this would lead to disagreements, and as they knew nothing of the poor personally their interference was pure meddling. Because she realized this attitude on the part of the Guardians, Louisa Twining tried to limit the number of Visitors and only used ladies known to the authorities. She also recognized relief could only be given with the co-operation of the Medical Officer and that nothing could be done without him. But the Medical Officer also needed the help of the Visitors, for although he could report defects and recommend additional diet himself, he was always apprehensive of becoming unpopular with the Guardians if he advocated what he thought necessary. Louisa Twining gave proof of this when she stated that it was obvious to all Visitors that Medical Officers did not suggest everything they should have done.[2]

An important branch of the Workhouse Visiting Society's work was begun through Frances Power Cobbe's pamphlet on the state of the chronic sick.[3] The 'plea for the destitute incurable' was made through pamphlets, letters to the Press, and papers read before the Social Science Association, and finally by an appeal to the Poor Law Board. Lord Shaftesbury, the Bishop of London, and Miss Burdett Coutts were closely associated with this

[1] In 1861 the work of the Society was brought before the Social Science Association at Dublin and met with much sympathy. Local Committees were formed for visiting two large workhouses there.

[2] Louisa Twining also gave evidence to Select Committee of 1862 on the Industrial Home for Women she had started in Great Ormond Street. Girls were taken there from workhouses and trained as domestics or seamstresses and situations were found for them.

[3] 'Plea for the Destitute Incurable', 1861: F. P. Cobbe for Workhouse Visiting Society.

movement. The 'plea' was that the chronic sick should be separated from the inmates of the workhouse and given additional comfort. There were about 80,000 helpless sufferers of this category in institutions, and the petition to the House of Commons was signed by the leading physicians and surgeons of London hospitals, who as doctors agreed that an incurable should not be kept for more than a brief period in any hospital established for the cure of the sick. In 1865 a plan of campaign was formulated at Mrs. Gladstone's house and twenty-one Members of Parliament and many doctors attended the meeting. In May a deputation of the Society waited on the President of the Poor Law Board with a statement and a petition as to the general condition of the sick in workhouse infirmaries. Dr. Stallard led the deputation which included such men as Charles Buxton, Kay Shuttleworth, Dr. Sieveking, Dr. Markham, Abel Smith, M.P., Lyall (who had been a progressive member of the Poor Law Select Committees), and Sir T. Watson (President of the Royal College of Physicians). The petitioners stated that workhouses had to a great degree become institutions for the reception of the sick poor, but that hospital accommodation had not increased in proportion to the needs of the population. They pointed out that workhouses as then constituted were not fit places for treatment because there was generally only one Medical Officer who was also underpaid and often had to find the medicines; there was no adequate inspection or control over the Medical Officer; nursing was inefficient; the construction of the workhouse was defective; ventilation was bad and there was an absence of furniture and amenities. The petitioners further recommended the admission of voluntary benevolence to the sick-wards so that the rates would not entirely have to bear the cost of the improvements. They desired also to press the government on the necessity for a medical element in the inspection of workhouses, which should also advise the Poor Law Board on all sanitary and medical questions and help to reorganize the whole system both in relation to construction and management. The petition concluded:

> Should the evidence already given not be considered sufficient for the establishment of the above facts, we beg to suggest that a few members of the medical profession in London . . . should be appointed to visit and inspect on the condition of the workhouse infirmaries and give a report on them. . . . The projected removal of some of the workhouses from London seems to offer an opportunity for making improvements, and we suggest the question whether it would not be desirable to separate wards for the sick and incurables from the workhouses, so that they can be arranged on different principles without encouragement to pauperism.

Charles Villiers,[1] now President of the Poor Law Board, agreed with the petitioners as to the propriety of at least occasional inspection by an eminent physician but pointed out the main difficulty of the Poor Law Board lay in the operation of the Local Acts which enabled Guardians to resist their authority. He promised to give the question of inspection serious

[1] Villiers had some sympathy for Poor Law reform and had been Chairman of the Select Committees for the years 1861 to 1864—therefore, his political and economic views must be remembered, for his colleagues opposed many of his principles on social questions. (See also p. 386.)

consideration and hoped to introduce a Bill to remedy other defects, for he admitted he had 'yet to learn that there was any exaggeration in the statements'. But as there was a change in government, Villiers was relieved of his office, and Gathorne Hardy had the satisfaction and credit of introducing and carrying the Bill for remedying the grievances which had been brought forward. The work of the Society therefore did much to prepare the way for further action by enlightening the public and officials. It undoubtedly affected the inception of the *Lancet* inquiry and with the latter gave the necessary pressure for the institution of the Poor Law Board's own inquiries in 1866.

Closely connected with the *Lancet*'s investigations and the Workhouse Visiting Society was another society which was formed in February 1866. The leading reformers were members of, or associated with, all three, and these movements demonstrate that public awareness had reached the climax when reform could no longer be withheld. While the *Lancet* inquiry was in progress Joseph Rogers held a dinner party at which the Association for Improving Workhouse Infirmaries was launched. Dr. Anstie, Ernest Hart, and Rogers were the three able honorary secretaries. Kay-Shuttleworth, Charles Dickens, the Rev. F. D. Maurice, and John Stuart Mill were among the members, and the Association had the influential support of the Earl of Carnarvon, Earl Grosvenor, and the Archbishop of York. Indefatigable social workers like Shaw Stewart and Louisa Twining also joined. Public meetings were held and the investigations of the Association widely publicized. Villiers deputed Farnall, the Metropolitan Poor Law Inspector, to render assistance with any information desired. The object of the Association was to enlighten the public, to appeal to the legislature to separate the care of the sick poor from that of the able-bodied and to establish a certain number of workhouse hospitals in London to which existing Poor Law Medical Officers would still be attached, but where the patients would have the advantage of the service of paid resident assistants, an efficient staff of nurses, properly fitted wards, dispensaries and dispensers, under a system of organization such as existed in the voluntary hospitals. A scheme was also outlined for a general dietary for all the London workhouses which was to replace the varying ones that existed.

At the initial public meeting in March 1866 the Archbishop of York proposed the first resolution on the unsatisfactory nature of the infirmaries. One of the Guardians of the City of London Union supported the views of the Association and wished that the whole Poor Law system might be revolutionized. Ernest Hart recommended that the proposed consolidated infirmaries should be supported by a general Metropolitan rate and should be placed under a uniform management connected with the Poor Law Board. He suggested there should be six district hospitals each with 1,000 patients, and Guardians of each district should nominate two representatives to constitute the governors of the hospitals. A number of paid inspectors should be appointed by the Poor Law Board to assist the governing body in their deliberations. A Member of Parliament—Bromley-Davenport—advised that a deputation should wait on the central authorities to urge the introduction of a Bill, and if they refused a private Bill should be brought in. The deputation, including forty Members of Parliament, among whom were T. Hughes and J. S. Mill, was well received and consideration promised. The plan for reform which the Association produced was identical with that of the *Lancet* and has already been studied. It was forwarded to all Metropolitan Unions, and the Guardians held a meeting to discuss the Association's activities and proposals.

In 1866 in consequence of the *Lancet*'s and the Association's condemnations nearly every local authority in London began to take active measures for improving their infirmaries. There were few changes in buildings, although the West London Guardians removed their institution to the country. Others, said the *Lancet* in its second inquiry,[1] would have seen great advantages in doing likewise, reserving some central and convenient receiving house in town. This policy was imperative on the Guardians of St. George the Martyr, South-wark, but here nothing was done, and no amelioration could be attempted until some relief was afforded to the overburdened ratepayers. In the infirmary of 'Little Dublin'—St. Giles, Bloomsbury—where one-fifth of the population were paupers, patchwork conversion and remodelling was undertaken. The itch ward was removed altogether from the infirmary but this alleviated the overcrowding little, and of equal result was the installation of perforated glass to assist ventilation. The whole building was so miserably constructed that the Guardians were finally convinced of the necessity for a new workhouse. Internally some good was affected. Filthy and ragged bedding was replaced and armchairs, basins, towels, and shelving for books and medicines were supplied. The walls were hung with pictures and texts, and books and periodicals were circulated. Hot and cold water was laid on to the infirmary so that baths could be given. The nursing staff was improved; formerly there was one paid nurse and fourteen assistants and in 1867 there were five paid ($£8–£25$ a year) and twenty-five assistants. The dietary was also changed, especially for the aged and infirm. Yet the wards remained unfit for hospital purposes.

Great structural changes were made in the suburban infirmaries of Greenwich and Lewisham. In the former, many thousands of pounds were spent on new wings because overcrowding had been so dangerous and ventilation and lighting defective. Two paid nurses were appointed and three lunacy nurses to supervise forty assistant paupers. Lewisham spent $£2,000$ in 1866 on structural alterations, ventilation, lighting, and water supply. Beds and furniture were improved and abundant linen was provided. Two paid nurses were employed at $£25$ and $£22$ a year, and the dietary was also improved. Camber-well had made alterations in the workhouse, but 600 paupers were still accommodated when the recognized complement was 250. Of these 150 were sick but some attempt at classification was made, acute cases were separated from the chronic and infectious from the others. The beds were good and clean and sufficient lavatories were installed. Three paid nurses were appointed, two of them for night duties at salaries of $£10$, and the day nurse received $£20$. The dietary was also amended. In Rotherhithe the *Lancet* Commissioners found no change had been made and explained this by the poverty of the Union. In Bermondsey changes were made in the wards but there was no space for enlarging the

---

[1] *Lancet*, 1867, i, pp. 344–46.

buildings. The wards which had been condemned on the first *Lancet* inquiry had been converted into day-rooms. In 1867 there were still 610 inmates occupying accommodation for 500, of whom 100 were sick. Classification had been attempted and the acute sick removed from the incurables. Bedding, ventilation, and furniture had been improved, and armchairs, basins, towels, brushes, and combs had been provided. Three paid nurses were employed at £25, and there were eighteen pauper assistants. Shoreditch also began to appoint paid nurses and Marylebone engaged two for night duties. In St. Pancras more nurses were employed and other minor improvements had been effected. In the vastly overcrowded but large infirmary of Bethnal Green little improvement had been made in the two years because the Guardians had not the means. No medical treatment was of any avail in the defective sick-wards. One Medical Officer had 600 patients, a number which in the voluntary hospitals would have claimed the attention of fifteen doctors. Added to this the Poor Law Medical Officer had the duty of dispensing—all for a salary of £160 a year. Holborn made a number of changes in the internal arrangements of the infirmary. Drainage and water supply were reconstructed, ventilation and lighting were improved, and fireplaces installed in many wards. Three paid nurses were added to the staff and the diet was amended (to include roast beef). On these improvements the *Lancet* commented: 'So far our labours have been rewarded by such considerable and important amelioration in the condition of the sick poor as are in themselves a splendid compensation.'

The Strand Union however was alone in taking measures for the building of a new infirmary in the suburbs. Credit for this must no doubt be given to Joseph Rogers. Not only was he a foremost member of the Workhouse Infirmary Association and leader of the Poor Law Medical Officers, but as the doctor of the Strand workhouse he did everything in his power to publicize the conditions which existed in his infirmary and to obtain alleviation of the dreadful conditions for his patients. To build proper hospitals for the sick and to supply them with paid and skilled nurses and adequately paid Medical Officers was his life's work. In his *Reminiscences of a Workhouse Medical Officer* he gave a clear picture of the state of infirmaries in the 'fifties and 'sixties by the description of the Strand institution. He explained how the sick could not sleep nor have any windows opened because of the Guardians' carpet-beating business carried on in the yard underneath the wards, and how the place was always filled with steam from the laundry below the hall where the washing for seven voluntary hospitals was done. For twelve years he strove to get the nuisances removed but the Guardians' opposition was so fierce that he had to abandon it. At the back entrance to the workhouse a converted carpenter's shop had been turned into a mortuary and opposite was a tinker's shop with a forge and unceiled roof. This was the means of communication to an odd ward containing beds for fever and 'foul' cases and only a lath and plaster partition 8 feet high separated it from the tinker's shop. The Guardians made no attempt to alter these conditions which Rogers described as unfit for any human being, however degraded. Paupers had to be bribed with beer, gin, and steaks to wait on the sick there and a patient's death was generally quickly followed by the attendant's. Rogers was always in dread of a 'horrid catastrophe' occurring in the male insane ward and he said he gained valuable surgical experience from constantly stitching the wounds of a single epileptic case. Yet it took him three years to get this patient removed to an Asylum. The female insane ward was immediately below the lying-in ward so that this was never free from disturbances. The Guardians, Rogers maintained, never considered the patients' feelings or needs, only the question of housing them. Of the wretchedly damp, overcrowded, and miserable nursery, he wrote: 'That death relieved these young women of their illegitimate offspring was only to be expected, and frequently mothers followed in the same direction.' He always dreaded entering this room and commented on the scores of distinctly preventable deaths which occurred because inmates were housed in 'this horrible den'. Infectious diseases were always rampant and the number of recoveries were very few. Rogers had laid down the most stringent regulations for isolation and disinfection, but as his orders could only be given to pauper women no attention was paid. The majority of Guardians regarded this den as a perfect paradise and called Rogers an 'irreconcilable fellow' for troubling them with complaints about it.

The nurses were more or less infirm paupers or 'broken-down pot-men', frequently under the influence of drink in the morning because the master issued their allowance at 7 a.m. Also many inmates sold their allowance. When Rogers reached the house they were always wholly or partly intoxicated and he could not get this system altered until he appealed to the Board of Guardians. His success made the master his enemy. For years he had one nurse who muddled everything. She showed great contempt for him because he introduced 'new-fangled' notions of having medicines administered correctly, and patients well attended. When he told her he had obtained linseed for tea she expressed great surprise and exclaimed: 'My God—linseed tea in a workhouse!' She died worn out by the effects of habitual intemperance aided by stealing wine and brandy from the sick! Occasionally Rogers received the help of a strong young woman who was a temporary inmate, but she always left when he had trained her to be useful, and he was forced to fall back on the broken-down inmates, the selection of whom did not rest with him but with the master and matron. They were rewarded by a pint of beer and an amended dietary, and for laying out the dead and other duties they were given a glass of gin by the master.—This however had to receive Rogers' permission.

The master of the Strand workhouse, George Catch, became a notorious figure. He had been a policeman in Clare Market and had made himself useful to the Chairman of the Guardians who had a beef shop in that locality. Through the latter's influence he became a porter in the workhouse and when the master fell ill he succeeded him. He was at first so ignorant he could only write his name with difficulty—yet he was appointed with the sanction of the Poor Law Board. The Chairman of the Guardians was himself little superior and visited the workhouse on Sundays unshaven and dressed in a 'dirty, greasy jacket' in which he had been serving beef the night before—and thus he went to Chapel with the paupers. During this man's term of office all Rogers' recommendations were resisted. Through his success in getting the cellar enlarged for the better accommodation of casuals, the increase in his miserable stipend was delayed for two years. He quarrelled with the Board because many of the young women who came into the infirmary for their confinement had to receive treatment afterwards because they were suffering from extreme exhaustion, and some were hopelessly consumptive. Rogers found that the practice in the lying-in wards was to keep single women on gruel for nine days, at the end of which they were dismissed to the nursery ward on the house diet. He asked the Poor Law Board for permission to introduce a more generous diet and received the reply that this was completely in a doctor's hands. His employers condemned his writing to the Poor Law Board as reprehensible because it 'traversed the deliberate action of the Guardians, who had established a starvation dietary for parturient women, as a deterrent against the use of the workhouse as a place in which to be confined'! Rogers' unpopularity with the Guardians grew because he demanded the enlargement of the infirmary. He asked the Poor Law Inspector for support, but the Guardians upheld the obstruction of the master and matron and the inquiry was closed. The master's hostility was then increased to sending for him on the most frivolous pretexts. He was forbidden to attend any woman recently confined unless he was called either by the master or matron or midwife, and it was so arranged that no order was given until nine days had elapsed after childbirth, when he had to take charge of her as an ordinary patient so that he could not claim any fee. Eventually the Board of Guardians entrusted him with the duty of certifying lunatics. Previously it had been thought hazardous to entrust such a function to the workhouse Medical Officer in case he might be tempted to eke out his salary by certifying healthy persons to secure the fee.[1]

The mismanagement of the workhouse by the Guardians and the outrageous conduct of the master, at length aroused the attention of the ratepayers. An influential Committee recommended a new list of Guardians and the 'whole old gang were ejected' from office. It was under the new officials, the Chairman of whom however was motivated solely by personal interest, that improvement came. Catch was dismissed through Rogers because he had refused to supply a patient with crutches for three months and because he opposed the transfer of patients to and from wards. Farnall inquired into the case and the salutary outcome revealed that a Medical Officer could get an inefficient master discharged by making a complaint. Catch however immediately obtained an appointment at Lambeth. Here he and the Medical Officer caused a scandal in 1869 by fumigating a chimney to bring down a sick woman who was hiding there. Both were dismissed by the Poor Law Board— but the Guardians appealed for the reinstatement of the master. The *Lancet* raised an outcry against this.[2] But after Catch's dismissal from the Strand reforms were introduced there. The new master and matron were kind and educated. The house was well managed and the inmates treated with consideration. One of the earliest activities of the new master was to inquire into the previous occupations of the sick and when they recovered he used them in the trade they had followed for the improvement of the institution. But as he could not alter the structural deficiencies of the building nor make it larger, nor prevent the fearful

[1] Joseph Rogers, *Reminiscences of a Workhouse Medical Officer*, 1889.
[2] *Lancet*, June 1869.

overcrowding, nor improve the wretched system of pauper nursing, 'the curse of that and all similar institutions . . . which Whitehall made no genuine effort to change' persisted.

Rogers achieved some improvement in his own position, and in twelve years succeeded in getting his salary raised from £50 to £100, but he continually complained of his large outlay on medicines particularly because he had so many chronic patients. He had also been allowed to take some pupils; it was a great pity, he said, that 'such a vast field for clinical observation and study which the sick, nursery, and lying-in wards of large urban workhouses afford . . . is utterly thrown away . . . there are certain diseases which can hardly be seen anywhere else'—(particularly in the field of paediatrics and geriatrics).

The widespread distress in London in the years 1862 to 1865 led to the filling of all the workhouses beyond capacity. Overcrowding in the already vitiated atmospheres led to a considerable outbreak of fever. Rogers stated that he was absolutely perplexed on how to deal with them, and there were no facilities for sending so many cases to the special hospital. He had also to cope with a great influx of fever-stricken boys from a nearby school. A clergyman had opened a home for orphan boys in an old disused slaughter-house and he called Rogers to see cases—four or five lying on straw—which could not be admitted to the overfull workhouse. The two men decided to establish a real school, and Mrs. Gladstone was a frequent visitor. The Newport Market Refuge Industrial School was for several years under Rogers' medical care and never once had a case of fever although it was located in a densely-crowded and repulsively-degraded neighbourhood.—'It affords a striking instance . . . of what can be done in keeping schools free from epidemic disease—if only persons having control adopt and strictly carry out judicous sanitary arrangements.'

Rogers' dismissal from the Strand workhouse aroused great interest and was given much publicity by the reform movement. In 1867 he sent a girl convalescing from rheumatic fever to the school in Edmonton giving the matron instructions not to employ her in hard or damp occupations. This was ignored and the girl after cruel treatment was returned to the workhouse with a severe relapse. Rogers asked the Poor Law Board for an inquiry. Dr. Markham, Medical Officer to the central authorities, sent for the matron to come to his private home in Harley Street and then reported that Rogers' complaint was 'vexatious and frivolous'. The report was sent to the Guardians, whereupon a man who had asked at the inquiry 'whether mesenteric disease was something to eat' moved for Rogers' suspension. The Clerk compiled a letter to the Poor Law Board including all the past hostile resolutions of the Board of Guardians. Later Sir Michael Hicks-Beach admitted that the Poor Law Board had desired the discharge of Rogers for some time. The latter asked for an official inquiry and was supported by a few Guardians and some influential ratepayers. But the Earl of Devon on his return from his few months winter holiday in Southern France immediately dismissed him. The reason given was that he could not get on with the Guardians! The *Lancet* printed the whole case in full and invoked a loud outburst against the injustice. It is interesting that the Medical Officer of the Poor Law Board acquiesced in the Guardians' mismanagement of the workhouse, and he was the proximate cause of Rogers' suspension and subsequent dismissal.

The active part Rogers had taken in the *Lancet* investigations were no doubt a contributory cause to his dismissal. He had conducted Dr. Anstie through the whole workhouse, pointing out its defects and reporting the animosity he had incurred in his attempts to improve them. He had also shown Anstie the list of fever cases which revealed how disease had always been most prevalent when overcrowding was greatest. Anstie's article was written 'with marvellous clearness and fidelity' so that Rogers was accused of having written it himself and a great storm burst over his head from the Guardians. As a result, however, he was empowered to send some of the acutely sick to Guy's hospital. His action met with hostility—he was accused of having sent them away to rid himself of the trouble of attending them and it was seriously proposed that he should have £20 deducted from his salary for the cost of the cabs.[1] Rogers had won his greatest victory in 1865 when a superintendent skilled nurse was appointed by the Guardians. He himself gave the credit for her institution to Louisa Twining's[2] evidence before the Select Committee of 1862 and to the *Lancet* inquiries, because his own repeated demands had been constantly ignored. Her appointment however had become imperative because the numbers of the sick had increased so tremendously that the ceilings of some of the infirmary wards had had to be removed to increase the cubic feet allowance. Beds had been put so close together that patients could only get out at the end. Rogers said it was beyond the new nurse's strength to supervise so many patients but she could check some of the graver abuses connected with pauper nursing.

It was through the allegations of this nurse that two official inquiries were held in 1866. She brought her cases to the notice of the Workhouse Infirmary Association and they demanded investigations from the Poor Law Board. Matilda Beeton had been employed at Rotherhithe workhouse before going to the Strand and her charges were concerned with the terrible nursing system, the negligence of the master and the matron, the lack of cleanliness of the patients—who were 'crawling with vermin'—the total absence of amenities for the sick, the 'foul smell of the beds' from which maggots crawled in their hundreds, and the inadequate food of the patients. If they wanted nightdresses they had to pay for the laundry themselves for which they sold their food, and milk had been unheard of in the infirmary until her arrival. To her complaints the master had replied she must 'get used to all that, as workhouses were not like hospitals'. The evidence at the inquiry revealed that the master and the matron had never met any of her requests, nor had the Medical Officer taken any steps to procure efficient nurses or reported in writing any defects which he was required to do by the Consolidated Order of 1847.[3]

When Matilda Beeton came to the Strand Workhouse she made similar allegations against the treatment of the sick and Inspector Cane was deputed to investigate. Several

[1] Evidence at inquiry held by Inspector Cane, June 1866, on the 'Treatment of the Sick in the Strand Workhouse'.

[2] Louisa Twining had begun her workhouse visiting in the Strand.

[3] Report of Inquiry held by a Metropolitan Inspector (Farnall) into complaints regarding the management of the Rotherhithe Workhouse Infirmary, August 1866.

members of the Workhouse Infirmary Association attended the inquiry, as they had done at Rotherhithe. Evidence was given that Louisa Twining and other Visitors had stated the Strand workhouse was 'clean and sweet' and that arrangements and cleanliness were superior to other institutions. Rogers however confirmed Matilda Beeton's charges. Ernest Hart was also asked to take evidence and to him Rogers condemned the plans for the new workhouse at Edmonton, for no provisions were being made for through-ventilation nor were any sleeping wards being included for nurses. The architect said the plans were not his—he had only been asked to draw them to scale. Only 500 cubic feet were being allowed for acute patients and only 390 cubic feet in the womens' wards for infectious diseases. Rogers demanded at least 1,000 cubic feet, paid day and night nurses, and baths and kitchens for each ward. Two Guardians wrote to Inspector Cane asking for their views to be communicated to the Poor Law Board.—One of these was John Storr, the wealthy business man who had financed the initial outlay on the formation of the Workhouse Infirmary Association and who was an active member.—They pointed out that the workhouse was always overcrowded, that inmates were for the most part sick, aged, or infirm, and that it was in fact an infirmary though it was called a workhouse. They corroborated Rogers' criticisms and urged the building of State hospitals in and around London, which should be under the immediate direction and control of the Poor Law Board provided ratepayers' interests were represented.[1]

Two more inquiries were held in the summer of 1866. The first was into accusations of cruelty by an inmate of Clerkenwell infirmary who pointed out the untruths contained in the evidence given at a Coroner's inquest on the death of a patient. He maintained that the deceased—a harmless imbecile of dirty habits—had been treated like a beast. Farnall however reported that the patient had died from injuries received from falling out of bed accidentally. Much correspondence followed between the Poor Law Board and the Guardians, and the question was never settled, for other paupers' statements were denied and some were afraid to speak for fear of being ejected from the workhouse.[2] When Farnall made his second investigation into a complaint by a pauper he took Ernest Hart with him, and Hart wrote a letter on his experiences at Whitechapel to the *Daily News* and *The Times*. The Guardians denied the allegations of cruelty, filth, and inefficiency, but Farnall corroborated Hart's evidence and his report described the terrible state of the sick poor, their dirty condition, their neglected bandages, and their semi-starvation. Only three kinds of medicine existed in the Whitechapel workhouse—'House medicine', 'Cough Mixture', and 'Saline Mixture', there were only three patients receiving any other. Farnall was emphatic in getting the facts publicized and obtaining redress.[3] Immediately afterwards the Poor Law Board commissioned Farnall to investigate the allegations made by a paid

[1] Report of R. B. Cane, Poor Law Inspector, on Inquiry into Matilda Beeton's allegations regarding treatment of sick in the Strand Union Workhouse, June 1866.
[2] Correspondence between the Poor Law Board and the Clerkenwell Board of Guardians, July 1866.
[3] Correspondence between the Poor Law Board and the Whitechapel Board of Guardians and Report of Inspector Farnall on the Whitechapel Union, July 1866.

nurse of Paddington. Her case had been brought before the notice of the central authorities by the Earl of Carnarvon on behalf of the Workhouse Infirmary Association. She complained that the sick-wards were scattered throughout the house; that as many as three children, some with infectious diseases, slept in one bed; that the sick were not classified, and aged, young, infirm, chronic, and acutely sick were all mixed together, even noisy lunatics were allowed to disturb wards full of sick people; and that bed sores were common because patients were left in a filthy state lying on hard straw mattresses. She described the plight of many acutely sick because they had no night nurses and that infants could not be washed because the soap was always stolen by the pauper attendants in the maternity wards. Guardians, she said, frequently visited the sick wards and asked for complaints, but no one dared to speak, although when they had left, questions were discussed loudly. Because of the scattered nature of the wards and her many extraneous duties, the nurse said she was unable to give all her attention to the sick and so she had to rely on the incompetent, cruel, and venal pauper nurses.—She had been dismissed for 'inefficiency', although she possessed certificates for qualifications in three subjects. Farnall corroborated her charges and stressed the inefficiency of treatment and the dreadful condition of the sick wards. In his report, he begged the Poor Law Board to point out to the Paddington Guardians the need for sufficient cubic space allowance, an adequate nursing staff, the separation of infectious cases, and that the Medical Officer should keep his books efficiently and that he, rather than the nurses, should do the dispensing.[1]

The reports from these official inquiries into individual cases, the work of the *Lancet*, the Workhouse Infirmary Association and the Workhouse Visiting Society, as well as the pamphlets and papers of individuals like Dr. Stallard who covered the ground of the *Lancet* inquiries again in articles to the *Standard*, could not be ignored by the central authorities. Public opinion was roused and the Poor Law Board was forced into action. In 1865 and 1866 they instituted their own investigations into Metropolitan workhouse infirmaries.— 'With every desire to remedy any abuses that existed and to place arrangements for the treatment and care of the sick poor on a proper footing, we still considered that we should not be justified in taking any measures for this purpose without a special inquiry being undertaken by the officers responsible to the Board'. Before Farnall and Smith undertook their investigations the Poor Law Board issued a detailed circular to the Medical Officers of London workhouses asking for accurate information on salaries, duties, time occupied, space required for patients, numbers accommodated in the existing building, and alterations and improvements judged necessary. The doctors held a meeting under Rogers' chairmanship to formulate a uniform reply. Only one Medical Officer present was satisfied with pauper nurses and with the 500 cubic feet of space which the Poor Law Board required for each patient. The resolutions passed at the meeting were sent as a comprehensive report to the central authorities and included the recommendations of paid nurses, the

---

[1] Report of H. B. Farnall, Poor Law Inspector, on 'Inquiry into Alleged Mismanagement of the Sick Poor in the Paddington Workhouse, July 1866'.

employment of night nurses, resident Medical Officers at increased salaries, day rooms for the infirm, and 1,000 cubic feet and 80 square feet of floor space for each sick person.[1]

The reports of Farnall and Smith formed a curious contrast to that of the Select Committee of 1864. It was significant of the general ignorance and indifference to the condition of the sick poor which prevailed, that only a year or two before this epidemic of scandalous revelations, no evidence was given or allegations made relating to the Metropolitan workhouses, or that medical attention or nursing was insufficient, or that the sick were neglected. Therefore the Select Committee of 1864 had reported, 'the poor have never been so promptly attended to or so efficiently relieved as at the present time', and that no interference was necessary. Farnall[2] in the new inquiry described conditions similar to those which we have already outlined but stated that the infirmaries were clean although he had given no warning of his visits. Regarding space, he said the Poor Law Board's order as to the complement of each institution was correct, but there was an insuperable obstacle to its being effected, for it would mean that nearly half the beds occupied by the sick would have to be withdrawn. The same difficulty would be experienced if more nurses were appointed —there would be no accommodation for them. Classification was also impossible because in the forty-two Metropolitan workhouses which were calculated to hold 28,550, there were over 6,100 old and infirm, 6,000 temporary disabled, and 1,800 idiots, besides the able-bodied and children. There were over 4,300 chronic sick, 1,500 acute sick, 200 fever and zymotic patients.[3] Farnall was given twenty-four subjects to inquire into regarding the workhouses, and in dealing with them he described the improvements required by various infirmaries. On the Strand workhouse he wrote: 'Every improvement has been carried out that could be thought of, except hot and cold baths, which would greatly limit accommodation.' About half the Guardians were supplying drugs and he gave a long list of workhouses where paid nurses were employed or absent, their numbers, ages, and salaries, and the number of pauper nurses engaged, stating their duties. He reiterated that the employment of paid nurses was a policy which the Poor Law Board always warmly advocated and which he himself as Inspector had frequently and earnestly urged on the Guardians. Many of the conditions he reported had been known for years, he said, yet most of them the Poor Law Board had not the power to remedy. He drew attention to the situation that the Poor Law Board could not compel Boards of Guardians to build infirmaries for the sick poor or oblige Guardians to elect and pay resident Medical Officers. Nor could the public provision of drugs be enforced. Therefore, until these and other powers were conferred on the central authorities by the legislature, sufficient infirmaries for the sick poor were not likely to be built. The advice of the Poor Law Board as well as the recommendations of the Inspectors would remain generally inoperative as long as their adoption would result in unusual, although necessary, outlay of poor rates. As an Inspector, Farnall admitted he

[1] Communication to the Poor Law Board, 26 May 1866.
[2] May 1865: Farnall was the only enlightened and progressive Inspector.
[3] In 1866 there were in July 2,500 fever and zymotic cases (and cholera in the winter), 3,300 acute and 4,500 chronic cases.—*Abstract and Accounts*, 1866, lxi.

frequently failed in inducing Guardians to build a new workhouse—there were always two arguments: either times were too bad for ratepayers to afford the outlay, or they were too good to necessitate a new institution because pauperism had decreased. The Poor Law Board, he recommended, should be empowered to order the building of an adequate number of sick-wards which should be paid for from a Metropolitan rate. They should also be able to institute in these sick-wards and out of the rate, a sufficient staff of Medical Officers and trained nurses, and supply such drugs and appliances as they considered necessary—without the Guardians' consent. Further, Farnall recommended that hospitals should be built wholly apart from the workhouses, and that the cost of the building and the maintenance of the sick should be defrayed by a common rating of the Metropolis, as the existing pressure of rates was intolerable. 'No ingenuity or contrivance can render the majority of the present sick-wards in any way equal to the just requirements of sound medical science.' There was nothing new in his proposition, Farnall concluded, for twenty-six years previously the Poor Law Committee had framed a Bill containing provisions of a similar character. By one clause the central authorities could unite Unions for the management of any class or classes of infirm or infant poor.[1]

In 1866 came Dr. Smith's long and famous report. Had his inquiry preceded the work of the *Lancet* and other investigators he would have discovered an infinitely worse situation. Patchwork improvement, as we have seen, had been made and many of the minor, though essential, reforms which could be effected immediately under the existing organization had already been carried out. Smith prefaced his report by stating: 'The subject of the medical care of the inmates of workhouses is of so great an importance and at present so diverse that its discussion is attended with much difficulty.' The individual reports from which he gave an introductory résumé are very illuminating though considerably more circumspect than the *Lancet*'s accounts. In his general observations he instanced the difference between a workhouse infirmary and a hospital in the type of patients admitted

> ... Inmates of a workhouse usually remain there for many years, or until the end of life and even the chronic sick are not turned away after a few months' treatment, as at hospital, but are retained till death or recovery occurs. Old age and infirmity are, for the most part, beyond medical skill, as is also the large majority of cases of tuberculosis and other chronic diseases which are found in workhouse wards.

Smith traced the development of institutional relief and showed how advanced the two newly-erected establishments of Mile End and the City of London were. Here whole complexes had replaced the single workhouse. Fever and smallpox patients were sent to hospital and noisy and dangerous lunatics to asylums. Nearly all venereal disease cases were sent to the Lock Hospital and children at Mile End occupied a large detached building enjoying all the conveniences of an independent institution. There was also a separate and

---

[1] Poor Law Amendment Act, 1838, section 8: it was a long time before the central authorities realized these powers to the fullest extent.

detached hospital for sick children. Imbeciles and lunatics were placed in two large detached buildings with their own officers and every convenience was provided for the treatment of the sick. The infirmary was also a detached block, so that only the aged and infirm were left in the main building with a few able-bodied and the administrative offices of the institution.

Surveying the arrangements made for the classification of the sick in the workhouses, Smith pointed out the advantages in sending fever and smallpox cases to the special hospitals where the payment of 1s. a day per patient lessened rather than increased the cost to Guardians. He also recommended the removal of venereal disease patients who were a source of 'moral contamination' to other inmates. The difficulties which arose however, were that the special hospitals were generally full. Therefore the Guardians of St. Pancras asked the Poor Law Board to establish several fever and smallpox hospitals in various parts of the Metropolis. Smith predicted these might not be necessary because the decline in the epidemic diseases resulting from sanitary reforms would make the existing hospitals sufficient. He agreed however with the proposed erection of a Lock Hospital for the poor, whilst regretting that voluntary hospitals refused to admit venereal disease. Where offensive diseases remained in the workhouse infirmaries he stressed the need for making further arrangements for segregation. All dangerous lunatics he found were generally sent to asylums, and wards for 'quiet' cases he discovered were often far better in construction, decoration, and size than those provided for the sick, as were their washing and water closet accommodation. This he attributed to the activities of the Commissioners in Lunacy and the sympathy of voluntary helpers, but in some workhouses conditions were still very unsatisfactory, particularly in regard to special provision for treatment. Smith also pointed out that there were far too many children retained in the workhouses that consequently their health was bad and some were constantly ailing. A sick nursery and isolation ward should have been provided in every institution. The wards of the aged and infirm were described as very depressing, particularly where the ill were mixed with the comparatively healthy. Many maternity wards were inconvenient and some scarcely decent, so Smith concluded that there should be a reshuffle in workhouses—the largest and best rooms being used for the sick whose numbers were constantly increasing.

On the construction of workhouses, Smith condemned the ventilation and sanitary arrangements and said that in each of nineteen institutions there was at least one ward totally unfit for the sick. All workhouses needed alterations in floor space and cubic space, which rarely met with the Poor Law Board's standards, and he gave suggestions for their improvement, including diagrams. He paid great attention to hygienic requirements and also to the brightening of the wards by coloured prints. He regarded ventilation as important as space but pointed out that there was scarcely a public building which was decently ventilated and that architects generally designed without any reference to this requirement. Hospital wards were equally defective, and nurses had died from fevers at St. Bartholomew's and the Westminster. Surgical cases also still contracted some infection. But scientists and physicians like Dr. Todd, Dr. Bence Jones and Dr. Sutherland had made detailed investigations into ventilation and cubic space requirements so that sufficient information existed for improvements to be made. Workhouse doctors had also agreed on the necessity for 1,000 cubic feet per patient and Smith himself produced diagrams on means of ventilating and warming the infirmaries.

For the comfort of patients he recommended: rugs in gay colours; three blankets, three sheets, an under blanket and spare sheets for each person; more furniture; means of amusement such as illustrated periodicals and books, religious tracts, games, sewing kit; spectacles for the aged; pottery; foot and chest warmers; bath chairs; and lifts where there was a steam engine for taking aged inmates up and down stairs. He also urged the necessity for providing suitable carriages for conveying the sick to the workhouses. Dietaries should also be augmented and separate cooking facilities attached to the sick wards. More efficient cooks should also be engaged and special food supplied to the aged and infirm, imbeciles and lying-in women. Smith found a tremendous amount of food wasted and said it was lamentable to see the swill tub at the East London workhouse for example, in which was a solid mass of excellent bread and other food that might have fed many poor every day. Smith made many other recommendations for reform similar to those pointed out by previous investigators.[1]

On all these reports a daily paper commented:

If we affirm that all these reports disclose the most lamentable deficiences and the most radical errors in every one of the departments of management, we shall only say that which repeated proofs of the isolated shortcomings have led everyone to anticipate ... The subject is one which deeply concerns the honour, and touches the conscience of the people ...[2]

The Poor Law Board realized there was general agreement over the defects of workhouse infirmaries in the Metropolis, but opinions over one remedy differed—the amount of cubic space desirable. The question was therefore referred to a Cubic Space Committee consisting of eminent physicians (the first Committee of experts) and Inspector Corbett and Dr. Markham, Medical Officer to the Poor Law Board.[3] The Committee stated that diseases caused by overcrowding were not common, but that more space should be provided. They also pointed out that the workhouses were only such in name for there were few able-bodied inmates. They recommended no less than 850 cubic feet with a clear space of 6 feet across each bed should be allotted to each patient. Wards appropriated to offensive cases should have not less than 1,200 cubic feet per person. For chronic and infirm wards occupied day and night 500 cubic feet was found sufficient and 300 cubic feet for healthy adults and children in night wards.

[1] Dr. E. Smith, Report on Metropolitan Workhouse Infirmaries and Sick Wards, June 1866.
[2] Quoted by Louisa Twining in *Recollections of Workhouse Visiting and Management*, 1880.
[3] The experts were: Sir T. Watson, President of the Royal College of Physicians, Dr. Acland, Regius Professor of Medicine, Oxford University, Dr. Sibbon, F.R.S., Mr. C. Hawkins, F.R.C.S., Mr. T. Holmes, F.R.C.S., Dr. Randall, a workhouse Medical Officer, Dr. Smith, and Capt. Galton, R.E. (member of the Hospital and Barrack Improvement Committee).

Inspector Corbett and Dr. Markham were deputed to undertake a further examination of several workhouses in London. They reported that twenty-four of the existing workhouses needed partial reconstruction or additions to make them adequate for all requirements of a workhouse. The other fifteen were incapable of adaptation and could only be properly used for the reception of one or more separate classes of poor. The necessity was pointed out for removing all cases of fever, smallpox, imbeciles, and harmless lunatics and also the children, and that separate hospitals or asylums should be established for them. Further, dispensaries should be erected for administering outdoor relief, as well as additional buildings in all Unions and parishes where workhouses were inadequate and incapable of enlargement. These objects, the two Inspectors concluded, could not be effected without special legislation.

On the receipt of their reports on individual workhouses, the Poor Law Board immediately drew the attention of the Boards of Guardians to the points stated to be defective. Direct action for remedy was requested and for limiting the number of beds as previously recommended by Dr. Smith. For example, St. George in the East was urged to build a new workhouse in the suburbs or in the country, a suggestion which had earlier been made by the Commissioners in Lunacy.[1] Until this was established, the Poor Law Board advised, all venereal disease cases should be sent to the Lock Hospital; all children to the District School; the centre building should be used only for female imbeciles, nursing mothers, and infants; chairs, baths, and lavatories should be supplied in greater quantity; a mortuary should be provided; ventilation improved, and a resident Medical Officer appointed. In the Nineteenth Annual Report the Poor Law Board stated that the recommendations had generally met with favourable consideration and much was being done to improve arrangements for the treatment and care of the sick, so far as existing accommodation admitted of it. (The second inquiry of the *Lancet* confirmed this. Nevertheless it was added—'But it appears to us that to place matters on a perfectly satisfactory footing further legislation is required.') The existence of Local Acts regulating the administration of relief in many of the larger parishes of the Metropolis was an obstacle to the introduction of a uniform system of administration which could only be removed by the authority of Parliament. The Select Committee of 1864 had reported the necessity for the central authorities to have the same powers in parishes operating under the Gilbert or Local Acts as they exercised over those under the Poor Law. Because of the necessity for uniform action the Poor Law Board impressed on the Government the imperative need for further legislation.

Such authoritative confirmation of all that had been written and said on the subject could not but have great weight in influencing Parliament, and led by an able and energetic Minister it hastened to legislate on the subject. *The Metropolitan Poor Act*[2] *of February 1867 was the starting point of the modern development of an efficient State Medical Service.*

Gathorne Hardy, President of the Poor Law Board, introducing the Bill, said he felt himself supported by public opinion and was satisfied that the care of the sick was in-

[1] Minutes, Board of Guardians, August 1866.
[2] 30 Vic. c. 6.

efficiently carried out by the Guardians. The thoroughness of the reforms suggested were conveyed in his explanation of the provisions of the Bill. He prefaced it by an elaborate review of past legislation and acknowledged his debt to the various inquiries into the subject, especially those of the *Lancet* and the Cubic Space Committee. These, he said, had shown that the chief improvements required were greater cubic space, increased ventilation, and a more complete classification of the sick and the poor generally. Assuming he had to deal with 34,000 people including children, he proposed to obtain these improvements by placing all imbeciles in separate establishments, by removing all children over two years of age to separate schools and by providing new accommodation for 2,000 lunatics and for 700–800 fever and smallpox patients, either by erecting new buildings, or hiring old ones. (It is interesting to reflect that the Royal Commission of the 'thirties had intended not the establishment of large comprehensive workhouses, but separate institutions for different classes.) The infirmaries for the remaining sick poor would be placed under separate management because so many of the evils had sprung from their being regulated under a system originally intended for the able-bodied pauper. By this means Hardy hoped to secure more efficient inspection and to provide facilities for training nurses and medical students. His recommendations as to space were 1,200 cubic feet for offensive cases, 500 cubic feet for the infirm, 850 cubic feet for surgical cases, 1,200 cubic feet for maternity cases, 300 cubic feet in general wards, and 2,000 cubic feet for fever and smallpox cases. As he believed ventilation was more important than cubic space, he desired to enforce classification into these categories.

In the ensuing debate Villiers, Hardy's predecessor at the Poor Law Board, dwelt strongly on the incompetence of the local Boards, who whilst they expressed admirable sentiments, 'allowed the most abominable abuses to flourish under their very noses'. He desired to see the central authorities invested with more power. The Member for Norfolk (Read) provided the only dissentient note. 'Reflecting no doubt, on the scanty convenience of the independent labourer's cottage for the accommodation of sickness, and on the impossibility of charging the agricultural interest with the cost of fully equipped hospitals', he said Parliament was legislating in a panic. He was directing his attention to the provinces, but there was some truth in the statement if applied to the poorest parishes of the Metropolis.

Because it was recognized that single Unions and parishes (which now all came under the Poor Law of 1834) would be unable to face the expense of classification into separate buildings individually, the Act provided for the creation of district asylums for the sick, insane, or infirm by a combination of districts. The principles of the first Royal Commission were re-introduced by these Asylums Districts being required to provide special institutions. Not only were the managing committees to erect hospitals, but they were also to be empowered to adapt any building already in use at the discretion of the Poor Law Board. Guardians might also rent buildings from other Unions and pay them such amounts as the Poor Law Board agreed to. The asylums were also to be used for medical instruction and for training nurses, and because medical schools would be subject to constant supervision, not only from responsible Medical Officers but also from the numerous body of students, public attention would be attracted immediately to any neglect or malpractice. The Asylums Districts were to come under the central authority of the Metropolitan Asylums Board, which was to consist of sixty members—forty-five elected by the Guardians and fifteen nominated by the Poor Law Board. (The first site of the offices was where the County Hall, Westminster, now stands, and at the time of its inception the Board controlled an area of 118 square miles with a population of over three million.) The Poor Law Board was therefore to have a direct connection with the management of Metropolitan sick relief and in addition could determine or vary any contract with a Medical Officer, or any other workhouse officer and direct the Guardians to pay a doctor an increased salary or a gross sum. This was to facilitate the appointment of resident workhouse Medical Officers and to further the better classification of the sick in separate hospitals or infirmaries distinct from the workhouse.

The Poor Law Board was also to be charged with the duty of assessing the contributions of each Union to the Common Poor Fund. The rate levied was to be one-eighth of a penny on the rateable value of property and was expected to yield £8,000. The Fund was to be applied to the maintenance of lunatics, fever and smallpox cases, the provision of medical appliances and medicines, salaries of officers, fees for the registration of births, deaths, and vaccination, maintenance of pauper children in schools, and the relief of casuals. But the classes to be helped by the new institutions were only a proportion of the sick, and little hope of aid was given to East End Unions when the supply of treatment for the ordinary sick and outdoor poor was left to be provided for by a local charge. This hindered the consolidation of workhouse infirmaries for the purpose of saving expenses and separating patients from the able-bodied.[1]

On the day the Bill was introduced *The Times* included an article endorsing all the views of the reformers and advocating all they had striven for.[2] The Bill it was said,

> opens questions which have engaged the attention of thinking men and experienced administrators for a long time, and which, as the spirit of humanity increasingly pervades society, will tend to become more and more matters of public concern. It is an attempt to remedy a deeply felt evil, a national disgrace, a too real grievance of the Metropolitan poor . . .

The Times had itself printed a letter on the subject of workhouse nurses in 1858 outlining the great abuses in the treatment of the sick and the consequent need for investigation and reform. It concluded its review of the new Bill:

> It is proper that the sick, and even those incurably disabled, should have some special provision made for them, for although the workhouse is rightly made uninviting to the able-bodied pauper, it is inhuman as well as impolitic to deny the weakly and suffering

[1] We have already studied the clauses for the introduction of a dispensary system for outdoor medical relief in Chapter 11.

[2] At last Chadwick's early ideas for medical reforms were also beginning to make an impression.

501

the means of recovery. The chief hindrance to a proper management of sick wards seems to be the want of space, the next, the want of sufficient paid attendance. . . . By the establishment of district infirmaries on such a scale as will give each patient air enough to breathe, with a doctor who knows and will attend to his business, a proper nurse, and necessary medicines, and by supporting these institutions partly out of a general fund, the legislature may guard against a repetition of the late abuses.[1]

The *Lancet* also provided comment on the Bill.[2] It was pointed out that in general terms Hardy had accepted every principle laid down in the plan for reform produced by the Workhouse Infirmary Association and the *Lancet*. The classification of the sick, the provision of special institutions for particular classes, the separate management of these establishments, and the principle of paid and skilled nursing had all been entirely adopted. (The difficulty regarding the latter was the impossibility of finding enough trained nurses to supply the demand.) Not only had the principle of resident Medical Officers been agreed to but one doctor was to be appointed to every 150 sick. (The reformers had suggested 250.) Yet the *Lancet* saw no valid reason for Hardy stopping short at removing only lunatics, fever, and smallpox cases from the general workhouse management. The *whole group* of the severely sick should be treated in separate hospitals maintained out of the Common Fund. The reason given for this not having been proposed was that there might be a tendency to create 'fictitious' sick, which could not be checked, whereas it was impossible to job lunacy or smallpox. The *Lancet* also criticized the machinery for regulating the Asylums Districts as being entirely inadequate. It objected to the constitution of the Metropolitan Asylums Board whereby the nominees of the Poor Law Board could always be out-numbered, and said experience would soon show 'the indifferent disgust with which all unpaid officers regard the duties which expose them to the necessity, not only of working hard, but of strenuously opposing the selfish clamour of persons who have real material interest in the questions to be discussed'. The district boards would be unsatisfactory, not only because of the character of the effective working majorities of their members, but also because of the 'want of harmonious and uniform action'.

> *The presence of a properly paid responsible servant of the Poor Law Board at each of the district boards* would do ten times as much to produce intelligent agreement in their system of management as could be produced by the feeble and uncertain action of a fluctuating number of unpaid nominees whose degree of interest in their work will be constantly varying.

Therefore the *Lancet* suggested Hardy should reconsider these proposals. He was praised for establishing the principle of common payments for the expenses of the Metropolitan sick, but he was urged to push it to its natural limits and to discard all the cumbrous machinery which he had been obliged to devise, by separating infirmaries altogether from the management of Guardians and workhouse masters.—'Let the Common Fund which is to pay the

---

[1] *The Times*, 9 February 1867.
[2] *Lancet*, 1867, i, pp. 215–16.

common expense be administered by a board or boards at which a paid officer of the Poor Law Board shall sit, whose duty it will be to see that reports and recommendations of the Poor Law Inspectors are carried out.' It was pointed out that Hardy would spend a sum of money on an incomplete and fragmentary scheme, which could have been made to suffice for the erection of consolidated infirmaries in which *all* the sick inmates of the workhouses might have been attended.—'He is about to throw on the already deeply distressed poorer parishes an amount of local expenditure which almost, if not altogether, would counterbalance the relief which other parts of the scheme would afford.' In conclusion, Hardy was commended for adopting the *Lancet*'s scheme for the establishment of medical clinics for the study of chronic diseases in the 'asylums': 'A more important benefit could not possibly be conferred, either on the profession itself, or on sick persons, who would thus be placed under an inspection infinitely more calculated to detect abuses of management than any other which could be devised.' (Unfortunately this clause was repealed in 1869.)

A month later the *Lancet* wrote: 'Society demands the inmates of our workhouses should have the same domestic comfort and professional care as is so universally bestowed on patients of ordinary Metropolitan hospitals.' For the future . . . 'if we can read aright the promised legislation, the infirmaries of our workhouses will be a credit alike to our profession and our Christianity'. The doctors would also benefit because the plan of appointing Medical Officers to infirmaries would not be so executed as to make the resident officer the sole attendant of the institution. This would have involved the displacement of some of the ablest workhouse doctors who could not have held resident appointments. It was expressly stated by Hardy that there was to be for each workhouse a house surgeon and a visiting doctor of superior grade—the latter engagement falling to the existing Medical Officers. All the new measures were however merely tentative—Hardy did not wish to be supposed to have entertained the notion of radical reform! The *Lancet*'s verdict on him however was: 'he has made deep cracks in the mass, the extent of which will speedily become apparent when the new system is tested by actual working'.[1]

The Bill provoked a thinker of logical and uncompromising disposition to take a prominent part in the discussion. John Stuart Mill, the philosopher and Member of Parliament for Westminster, strongly attacked the local bodies, demanded an increase in central power, and administration by experts. Although he did not oppose Hardy's scheme he suggested amendments on the means of securing an efficient Poor Law medical service. Something of a far wider character than the proposed changes would quickly be required, he prophesied. He pressed the argument that it was impossible to expect duties of a difficult and arduous character like those appertaining to the supervision of the sick in the workhouses to be performed by numerous bodies of men, especially of ill-educated men. He proposed, like many members of the Workhouse Infirmary Association that the functions of the Guardians like those of the committees of voluntary hospitals should be strictly limited to more general supervision. The executive, stated Mill, should consist

[1] *Lancet*, 1867, i, p. 338.

of a small body, highly skilled and well paid, strictly responsible to a Central Board (which might be elected) and to the Poor Law Board, and devoting their whole time to their duties. Mill also urged the efficiency of the executive would be improved, not only by increasing the power of the inspectoral staff but also if necessary by largely augmenting the salaries of the Medical Officers who would do the actual work in the infirmaries, asylums, and dispensaries. Amidst cheering, he concluded that large sums of money devoted to providing really first-rate medical attendance for sick paupers would be well and economically spent.

The whole Metropolitan Asylums District was responsible for providing lunatic asylums and isolation hospitals. Two asylums were projected, each with 1,500 beds, at Leavesden near Watford and Caterham near Croydon—therefore both were to be far out of the city. Three isolation hospitals were planned, one in the North-East, one in the North-West, and the third in South London. The Hampstead project was however abandoned shortly afterwards.

Immediately the Act was passed, the Poor Law Board wrote to the Guardians of the following Unions and parishes requiring them to provide infirmaries on sites detached from the workhouses and under separate management: Bethnal Green, Camberwell, Chelsea, Clerkenwell, Fulham, St. George in the East, St. George's, Hanover Square, Hackney, Holborn, St. Luke's, Middlesex, Lambeth, Marylebone, Mile End, Paddington, Shoreditch, Whitechapel, and Wandsworth and Clapham. In consequence some began to build new infirmaries, others new workhouses with infirmaries attached, and the remainder to adapt part of their workhouses. They added lunatic wards and fever wards, for example, as an additional infirmary. Many temporary buildings were erected because of the great overcrowding in the workhouses. Kensington established a temporary infirmary for 200 patients, St. George in the East converted the men's workshops for fever cases and the workhouse committee recommended three houses adjoining the institution be acquired. The Poor Law Board sanctioned their temporary use for infectious cases provided not more than one patient was put in each room.[1] Many other Unions made temporary arrangements either for the infirm or able-bodied, infectious and venereal disease cases, lunatics, or casuals.

Very often space for the sick was made in the workhouses, which became infirmaries, by splitting up other classes of paupers and sending them to new accommodation. For example, the City of London's new workhouse at Homerton became an infirmary and the old infirmary was turned into the workhouse because it was smaller. Also the Strand workhouse in Covent Garden was in 1868 converted into an infirmary by the Central London Sick Asylums District and the able-bodied poor were sent to Holborn workhouse. When Islington opened a new workhouse in 1870 the old one was taken over by the Metropolitan Asylums Board as a Smallpox Convalescent Hospital. Guardians used it also as a school for children in quarantine. Bow infirmary however went in the opposite direction and in later

[1] Minutes, St. George in the East Board of Guardians, October 1868.

years became a workhouse. Because of the absence of open spaces in the city most of the new institutions were erected in the suburbs or in less crowded parishes. The Strand Guardians branched out to Edmonton where the school and nursery were situated. St. Giles, Bloomsbury, also sent its sick to Edmonton. In later years the St. Marylebone authorities had to occupy premises in Kensington, Southwark Infirmary was built in Camberwell, and the Holborn Infirmary in Islington. But within the city there was great activity in enlargement and conversion as well as in the erection of new permanent institutions. In 1868 Marylebone for instance began constructing new wards at the work-house in which 240 female chronic and convalescent patients were to be housed.[1]

In the same year the six Sick Asylums Districts were formed—Rotherhithe, Newing-ton, Kensington, Poplar and Stepney, Central London, and Finsbury. Some Unions or parishes were never included like St. George's, Hanover Square. In a letter from the Poor Law Board in August 1868 it was stated that although Unions had been asked to combine into districts to secure the establishment of separate hospitals, in the case of St. George's the Board did not contemplate it would be necessary to annex it to any adjoining Union because of its extent and large population. The parish adapted its two workhouses to meet the requirements of the Act, and on the recommendation of the Poor Law Inspector retained one of them for the sick only, with two lunatic wards attached, and the other for all other classes of paupers.[2] The Poor Law Board later reported that other Unions which had not been included in a Sick Asylums District were taking steps for improving infirmary accommodation, either by erecting new buildings or by making additions to existing wards. The completion of projected alterations in some institutions had been postponed until imbecile inmates who occupied some of the wards required for the sick, could be removed to the new asylums which were being erected at Leavesden and Caterham. The Holborn, Strand, and Westminster Unions amalgamated into a new Holborn Union and St. Pancras joined them in 1869.[3] St. Pancras only came under the Poor Law authorities by the Act, and it was at once evident that although it had the largest workhouse, this was in-sufficient for the requirements of the parish. As it was impossible to extend the buildings on the existing site, a new one had to be purchased elsewhere for the erection of a distinct hospital for the sick. Thus, $3\frac{1}{2}$ acres were bought at Highgate, within the parish, and a design was selected which the Guardians hoped would prove to be a model hospital although the estimated cost was less than £60 per bed.[4]

In 1868-69 the Poor Law Board authorized the expenditure of £15,000 by the Kensing-ton Sick Asylums District on an infirmary to be erected at West Brompton, Middlesex, and an expenditure of £8,250 was allowed the Newington Sick Asylums District for a workhouse or infirmary at Lewisham, Kent. Lewisham had had a pauper hospital since 1817 and there had always been an interchange of patients, many of the Lewisham cases

---

[1] From Records at the County Hall, Westminster.
[2] Minutes of the Directors of the Poor from August 1868.
[3] Poor Law Board Orders, 23 November 1869.
[4] Letter, W. H. Wyatt, Chairman of Board of Guardians, 1868.

going to Newington before 1869. The Poplar and Stepney Sick Asylums District was also permitted to spend £7,200 for a building at Bromley by Bow, Middlesex. Of this expenditure Rogers wrote: 'An absolute epidemic took place regarding the building of asylum hospitals, district hospitals for fever and infectious diseases, asylums for epileptics, idiots and imbeciles, district schools, etc.' This he partly attributed to indifference on the part of the permanent officials, but to a greater degree to their 'complete ignorance of the necessary details required for economic building'. Rogers stated emphatically that it had never been his desire in striving to amend the system, to substitute the absence of any organized medical relief with the reverse policy—so that architects, surveyors, and builders should be at liberty to extract all the money they could get from the pockets of the Metropolitan ratepayers. Because the absence of all efficient control was resulting in an enormous outlay, the public, he maintained, was getting not only alarmed but indignant. He therefore wrote to Torrens, Member of Parliament for Finsbury, asking him to question the President of the Poor Law Board on the subject of what he called 'profligate expenditure', and to move for a return of what had already been spent and what was proposed to be spent on such buildings. Considerable alarm was caused among permanent officials and a curtailment in the amount of contemplated expenditure resulted as well as greater control over it.

When the six Sick Asylums Districts sent in their proposals regarding the purchase of sites and the erection of new hospitals the estimated cost for each institution was between £45,000 and £50,000. The Poor Law Board, influenced by Rogers and the returns procured through Torrens, thought this amount would greatly increase the burdens of the ratepayers. They thought it necessary to review the plans in order to ascertain whether requisite separate facilities for the sick poor might not be provided in some other way, equally efficient, but not involving so serious an expenditure. A full inquiry was made into the accommodation available in existing workhouses. From this it was deduced that if each workhouse in the Unions forming the Sick Asylums District were appropriated to a separate class, the requisite classifications would be secured, besides being conducive to economy in space. The Poor Law Board then recapitulated the recommendations of the Royal Commission of 1833 that the central authorities be empowered to cause any number of parishes to be incorporated for the purpose of workhouse management and for providing new workhouses where necessary, and to assign to those institutions separate classes of poor, although they might come from distinct parishes: . . . 'Requisite classification and requisite superintendence may be better obtained in separate buildings than under a single roof . . . each class might then receive appropriate treatment.' Therefore the Poor Law Board reported that they intended buildings to be utilized in this manner, and that it was of great importance that all workhouses within a district should be placed under one management.

It meant that the Boards of Management for the Asylums Districts and their staff would no longer be required and that in place of separate Boards of Guardians in each Union forming the district, one Board only would be necessary for the entirely new districts to be established. Similarly one Assessment Committee could be substituted for several and this would secure uniformity of assessment throughout the extended areas. The enlarging of the rating area, it was maintained, would prove a boon to the poor because they would be less liable to removal and there would also be greater uniformity in the administration of outdoor relief. Therefore the Poor Law Board formed three of the Sick Asylums Districts —Rotherhithe, Newington, and Finsbury—into Unions for all purposes. Newington had from the beginning been antagonistic to the establishment of the Sick Asylums Districts and had memorialized the Poor Law Board. The Medical Officers had spoken in favour of maintaining the arrangement but had been beaten in the division. The *Lancet* was also against the break up of the scheme because Newington workhouse was so overcrowded that beds were arranged on the floors in the aisles of the wards.[1]

The Kensington and Central London Sick Asylums Districts remained under considera-tion. The Poor Law Board also stated its intention of placing the whole area of the City of London under a single management and of appropriating to different classes the several existing workhouses. The Metropolitan Poor Act passed in 1868 amended the Act of 1867 to permit the alterations. This principle was really no new departure, for London parishes and Unions had always sent out patients and children to other infirmaries and workhouses before they were amalgamated in 1870 or at later dates. If there was desperate overcrowd-ing, prevalence of, or reason to fear any epidemic or contagious diseases, the Poor Law Amendment Act of 1849 (section 14) permitted the boarding out of paupers on other workhouses on terms to be agreed between the local authorities and with the consent of the Poor Law Board. The Act of 1851 allowed children to be so sent away for education if the institution was not more than 20 miles distant. The Poor Law Amendment Act of 1867 (section 21) stated that Guardians could provide for the adult blind, deaf, and dumb in any hospital or institution established elsewhere for the needs of these cases, and by the Poor Law Amendment Act (section 13) of the following year idiots, imbeciles, or insane paupers could be sent to another workhouse or establishment of any other parish.

In 1869 the amalgamation of Unions for *all* purposes in place of the Sick Asylums Districts was effected to further the policy of using the several workhouses for separate classes of paupers. The number of Boards of Guardians was reduced from thirty-nine to thirty, and the six Boards of Managers of the Sick Asylums Districts were dissolved. The already-united Holborn Union had St. Luke's, Middlesex, and Clerkenwell added to it and it was made coterminous with the late Finsbury Sick Asylums and Schools District. The East and West London Unions were annexed to the City of London Union. When the Kensington Sick Asylums District was dissolved the parishes of St. Margaret's and St. John's, Westminster, which had been included in it were added to St. George's, Hanover Square. Kensington Union had all along objected to being included in an Asylums District because of the increased expenditure it would have entailed. The Guardians had maintained they had sufficient land for extending the workhouse and a deputation had waited on the Poor Law Board who had however refused to sanction the withdrawal of the Sick Asylums

---

[1] *Lancet*, 1869, i, p. 218; also records in the County Hall, Westminster, London.

District because plans had already been approved for the erection of an asylum. The Guardians struggled hard.[1] A meeting of representatives of Kensington and St. Margaret's had been held to see if a new hospital could not be built more cheaply by the conversion of the former's workhouse, and the Poor Law Board had been asked to stay its activity until the deliberations were over. Kensington had offered to extend its workhouse to hold 900 and to attach an infirmary; the whole project was estimated to cost £15,000. The Poor Law Board had replied that the question rested with the Sick Asylums Districts and desired the problem to be solved by Kensington selling part of the land adjoining the workhouse to the Sick Asylums Districts and St. Margaret's doing likewise with some contiguous ground, so that a new asylum could be built. After consultation both Boards of Guardians had maintained they had ample land to provide for their own sick and the Poor Law Board had again been asked to rescind the formation of the Sick Asylums Districts. After a further deputation the Guardians had been successful and the Poor Law Board suggested sick wards should be built in front of both the Kensington and the Westminster workhouses, which were adjoining, and this infirmary was to be placed under the control of a joint Committee of both authorities in place of the Sick Asylums Districts. This suggestion was favourably received and building was begun in the summer of 1869. As a temporary arrangement a hall was hired in Fulham to accommodate 100 patients.

Of the other amalgamated Unions which replaced the Sick Asylums Districts in order to reduce expenditure and appropriate individual workhouses for different purposes, the Guardians of the City of London Union secured the Bow workhouse exclusively as an infirmary, the one in Holloway for the aged and infirm, and that in Homerton for the able-bodied. The Holborn Guardians used their own workhouse for the able-bodied and that of St. Luke's, Middlesex, for the sick and infirm.[2] The *Lancet* protested against this and pointed out that the building was ill-arranged, the rooms low, dark, and badly ventilated, and it was totally unsuitable for an infirmary.[3] But additional wards were planned on land forming part of the workhouse site and these were to accommodate 450 aged and infirm inmates. The Plashet School was also attached to Holborn in 1869 when the Guardians bought it from St. George in the East.[4] The Guardians of the enlarged St. Olave's Union proposed to provide the necessary accommodation for the sick by adding wards for 160 beds to the existing separate infirmary at Rotherhithe workhouse. The workhouse at Bermondsey was to be appropriated to the chronic sick and infirm of both sexes, the old workhouse at Rotherhithe to the able-bodied and healthy males and the St. Olave's institution to the healthy women and infants. The Bermondsey children were sent to Camberwell, and Bermondsey itself later sent its sick to Lewisham. The St. Saviour's Union had a detached infirmary at Newington and this was enlarged so as to provide for the sick. The workhouse of St. George the Martyr, Southwark, was to be used only for able-bodied males and the

[1] See Minutes, Kensington Board of Guardians from January 1869 onwards.
[2] Twenty-second Annual Report of the Poor Law Board, 1869–70.
[3] *Lancet*, 1869, i, pp. 268–69.
[4] Minutes, St. George in the East Board of Guardians.

Newington for able-bodied females. The St. Saviour's workhouse was to hold the infirm cases of both sexes. Both Holborn and St. Saviour's experienced immediate pressure on the existing accommodation and it was found impossible to wait for the completion of the planned arrangements. Temporary steps were taken to meet the emergency. The Holborn Guardians hired the old French Hospital in City Road for housing 200 aged and infirm cases and the Guardians of St. Saviour's obtained permission from the Trustees of the Peabody Fund to occupy temporarily, free of rent, Magdalen Hospital, Blackfriars Road, which afforded accommodation for 150 inmates. Supply could not keep pace with demand, although frantic endeavours were made. Kensington also had to ask the Poor Law Board at the end of 1869 whether the Metropolitan Asylums Board could give any assistance as the workhouse was overcrowded. The Poor Law Board replied however that this body was only empowered to provide asylums for the reception and relief of the insane and those suffering from infectious diseases.

The circumstances of St. Pancras at the end of 1869 pointed to the expediency of joining it to the Central London Sick Asylums Districts, which had not been dissolved. The areas were contiguous and St. Pancras had loaned one of its two infirmaries to the District Managers previously. This became a workhouse proper under the new amalgamation, and the large St. Pancras hospital at Highgate was acquired by the Sick Asylums District later in 1870. (It was purchased back in 1883 when St. Pancras resumed its independence.) The addition of so large a parish to the Sick Asylums District necessitated the reconsideration of the general arrangements for the further classification of paupers. The overcrowding of St. Pancras workhouse was relieved by the removal of 160 patients from the infirmary there to the Highgate Hospital. The Asylums District had to go even further afield for additional hospitals and proposed to build one at Hendon. (This went to the Westminster Guardians in 1913 when the Central London Sick Asylums District was dissolved.) The other remaining Sick Asylums District, that of Poplar and Stepney, comprised only those two Unions. They began the erection in 1869 of a hospital to hold 560 patients. When these were removed from the workhouses the Unions adapted one of the institutions for the aged and infirm and the other for the able-bodied. Poplar in addition already owned a large house out of town since the 'forties, where all severe cases of smallpox and fever were maintained and which also had a convalescent ward.

Almost in every case where Unions remained independent, the Poor Law Board tried in 1869 and 1870 to induce Guardians to take active steps to relieve serious overcrowding and to make further arrangements for the accommodation of the sick. Most of them responded. Bethnal Green began the erection of a new wing adjoining the infirmary, which was at the workhouse, to provide for ninety additional sick. In September 1869 the Poor Law Board approved plans for the building of a detached infirmary by St. George in the East. Land was bought adjoining the workhouse and the new establishment was to hold 200–300 patients. (St. George in the East had had a hospital at Wapping from 1844.) At the same time money was voted for the building of a new dispensary and the addition of several amenities to the workhouse. The latter at this time had over 900 inmates but this was not the number reported to the Poor Law Board for it was vastly overcrowded, its legal complement being 693.[1] Hampstead Board of Guardians also had their plans approved for the erection of a new infirmary at the workhouse for the accommodation of eighty-five additional inmates at a cost of £8,500.[2] Hackney adapted the main building of its workhouse for an infirmary, and the block which had been occupied by children, who were removed to the Forest Gate School, was enlarged to provide room for 350 adult able-bodied inmates. Paddington had in 1867 appointed a Committee for considering the enlargement of the workhouse infirmary but this had reported in favour of the erection of a new infirmary of 200 beds as the increase in the number of patients over the previous six years averaged 10 per cent per annum. After some hesitation and deliberation with the Poor Law Board the Guardians decided on a new building because of the heavy estimated cost of enlargements. The new infirmary was opened in 1869 and held 150 patients and the existing infirmary had two extra wings added.[3] Wandsworth and Clapham also started to erect a new infirmary in 1869 and this in conjunction with the old one, which had been materially altered and connected with the new buildings, was to afford accommodation for 400 patients. (This became the St. John's Hospital and the entire workhouse was added to it in 1885 when a new workhouse was built.) Lambeth planned to adapt the existing workhouse as an infirmary and to erect a new workhouse for the able-bodied; temporary buildings were obtained meanwhile. (But already by 1878 this new workhouse had to be added to the infirmary for the accommodation of the sick.)

Shoreditch contemplated adding to the separate building occupied by the imbecile inmates as soon as that class was removed to one of the new asylums, so as to effect the separation between the sick and the infirm and the able-bodied. (This was finished in 1872 and later became the St. Leonard's Hospital.) Fulham referred the question of additional infirmary accommodation to a committee, and in the interim pressure on the workhouse was relieved by the removal of the children to the Central London District School. Chelsea contemplated building a separate infirmary opposite the workhouse but legal difficulties in the purchase of a leasehold interest in the required land delayed proceedings. Whitechapel began the erection of a new workhouse for 300 able-bodied and when this was completed the existing building was to be appropriated for the sick and infirm. (In the following years constant adaptations had to be made to the latter.) Islington proposed the establishment of an entirely new workhouse in Holloway for the accommodation of 850 inmates of which 350 were to be sick and infirm and for these a separate infirmary was to be attached.

The new buildings which were completed in 1869–70, including asylums for imbeciles and temporary supplementary workhouses, afforded accommodation for 6,320 inmates. In the three years 1868–70 nearly £1½ million had been obtained in loans for these projects, whilst at the same time expenditure on maintenance rose as a result of the increased

[1] Minutes, St. George in the East Board of Guardians.
[2] Minutes, Hampstead Board of Guardians.
[3] Minutes, Paddington Board of Guardians May, 1867 and September and October 1869.

pauperism engendered by the commercial crisis of 1866.[1] In 1862 in-maintenance had accounted for 18·7 per cent of the total Poor Law expenditure, outdoor relief for 51·9 per cent, and the care of lunatics 7·9 per cent. By 1869 the former had risen to 20·2 per cent, outdoor relief had fallen to 48 per cent, and the latter had risen to 9·3 per cent.[2] New buildings to be finished in 1870–71 were to provide for the accommodation of a further 5,000 inmates. This did not mean that the activities of the past three years had brought 11,000 more paupers to the workhouses for 5,000 of them constituted the number to be housed elsewhere if overcrowding was to be avoided. The increase in institutional accommodation had not kept pace with the rise in the number of paupers, and the determination of the legislature and the Poor Law Board to provide more indoor relief for the sick as well as more space, inevitably entrenched to a considerable extent on the room previously available for other classes. The pressure of demand always exceeded supply.

In 1870–71 further considerable progress was made in the Metropolis for providing separate accommodation for the sick and in the arrangements for relieving the crowded condition of the workhouses. The Bethnal Green Guardians found that besides building a new infirmary, they had to acquire a four-storey building for receiving wards and for housing 450 males. Camberwell built a separate infirmary for 200 patients on land adjoining the workhouse. Fulham proposed the addition of two new wings to the existing infirmary. The new infirmary of St. George in the East was finished and the wife of the resident Medical Officer was appointed matron for a year without remuneration. The Medical Officer continued to complain that the workhouse was overcrowded, as it had 150 above the permitted number, and the Guardians inquired of neighbouring Unions whether 80–90 paupers could be taken from the parish for a few months.[3] Whitechapel, Hackney, Hampstead, Wandsworth and Clapham, and Islington had their new arrangements working in 1870; the latter housed over 1,000 people in its workhouse infirmary. In Kensington the new infirmary for 350 patients which was to be shared with St. Margaret's and St. John's, Westminster, was still under consideration at an estimated cost of £30,000. The old workhouse was also to be converted to hold over 400 able-bodied and additional wings were to be added for the sick in accordance with the architect's proposal to relieve the existing overcrowding. Inspector Corbett and Dr. Bridges attended a Guardians' meeting and complained against the new infirmary and the workhouse extensions. They were not satisfied with the proposed ventilation arrangements and wanted still more space for the sick. Dr. Bridges suggested the whole existing workhouse should be adapted for the sick and a small institution should be erected elsewhere for the able-bodied. He also advised a new infirmary of about 210 beds for acute cases should be added to the converted workhouse when it was finished. We have seen that Whitechapel and Lambeth had already erected new small workhouses for the able-bodied. The Poor Law Board communicated

[1] Twenty-third Annual Report of the Poor Law Board.
[2] Twenty-second Annual Report of the Poor Law Board.
[3] Minutes, St. George in the East Board of Guardians.

with the Guardians on the complaints of Dr. Bridges regarding the serious overcrowding in the sick wards, female itch ward, and the venereal disease ward. But the Guardians had already abandoned their own projects and decided to adopt Bridges' proposals, the Poor Law Board authorizing an expenditure of £32,000. The new infirmary (the old work-house) with its small annex for the able-bodied was opened in 1871 and later became the St. Mary Abbott's Hospital.[1]

The Strand Union had in 1870 nearly 1,000 people in its new workhouse in Edmonton, and Westminster found it necessary to make extensive additions to its institution. Wool-wich had completed a new workhouse for 440 paupers and the Guardians were about to erect on the same site a detached infirmary for 200 patients. Arrangements for the classifica-tion of inmates in the institutions of amalgamated Unions were proceeding slowly because of the delay in acquiring workhouses. The Strand, Westminster, St. Pancras, and St. Giles, Bloomsbury, which had been included in the Central London Sick Asylums District had begun to send their patients to the Highgate Hospital. St. Pancras retained its workhouse attached to the hospital and also built a subsidiary one at Wandsworth. In the Poplar and Stepney Sick Asylum District, Poplar had by 1870 reconstructed the old workhouse (for the able-bodied) and had made large additions, and the Sick Asylum in Bromley, Kent, was completed in 1871. This hospital was to receive four classes of patients: those suffering from acute diseases and injuries, chronic cases requiring regular medical treatment or trained nurses, venereal disease cases and those suffering from skin diseases including scabies. A relief committee was established to determine at which institution the patients of the Sick Asylums District were to receive treatment. The sick were however to be discharged after four weeks unless the Medical Officer considered they should receive relief for a longer period, in which case fresh orders had to be obtained.[2] At the same time the Central London Sick Asylums District's hospital at Hendon was opened for over 250 patients.

The Poor Law Board paid great attention in these years to the provisions being made in the Metropolis, and strictly supervised the adequacy and suitability of the new accommo-dation. In 1868 they wrote:

> It is highly important that workhouses should be supplied with all reasonable and proper appliances for the treatment of disease of every kind, and there should be no question of the necessity of cleanliness, sufficient space, good nursing, and of the adoption of everything which may tend to promote a cure or alleviate suffering.[3]

To give effect to the provisions of the Metropolitan Poor Act, they certified the maximum number of paupers each asylum or workhouse was to accommodate. The managers and Guardians were also furnished with statements showing in detail for what class it was contemplated by the central authorities each ward was to be reserved and the number of patients it was to contain. In fixing the accommodation scale the recommendations of the

[1] Minutes, Kensington Board of Guardians.
[2] Minutes, Poplar Board of Guardians, 1871.
[3] Twentieth Annual Report.

512

Cubic Space Committee were adopted.[1] If there was any change in circumstance such as an unusual pressure of sickness, through which Guardians might desire to transfer sick or bedridden people into rooms assigned to the able-bodied, the situation was to be reported to the Poor Law Board so that the accommodation of wards could be reviewed and the certificate revised. The Board drew the attention of the Guardians to the fact that the maximum number they had certified was in many cases below the number in the institutions and they hoped new building would remedy the overcrowding. As a deterrent to overcrowding, payment to local authorities from the Central Fund was given according to the number stated in the certificates—so that additional inmates were not paid for! False returns were however given by some Unions where the complement of the workhouses was exceeded, and the local rates defrayed the additional cost. In their circular of September 1870 the Poor Law Board pointed out that

> ... it is in all cases most desirable and in some cases quite indispensable—that Guardians should secure additional temporary accommodation to meet the acknowledged deficiencies till new buildings are completed. Where this course is taken Guardians shall receive repayment of fivepence a day in respect of every adult inmate adequately accommodated in supplementary or temporary buildings.[2]

The total number of inmates for which the several Metropolitan institutions had been certified in 1870 was 27,140 (the total number of paupers receiving indoor relief was about 29,000).

The Metropolitan Asylums Board was established by the Act of 1867 because of the necessity for a single central authority to make provisions for the insane and for those suffering from infectious diseases. The Act of 1869[3] authorized the Metropolitan Board of Works to lend money up to half a million pounds for the erection of new hospitals. The construction of the two asylums at Leavesden and Caterham was begun immediately and each was to provide for 1,500 patients. Directly on the formation of the Mile End Union, the Guardians informed the Metropolitan Asylums Board that as they were harbouring a dangerous lunatic in the workhouse for whom they could not secure admission to a lunatic asylum, they would be glad to know when the new asylums would be ready. The Board replied that they were proceeding with all possible speed—but that they had no power to provide for the class of lunatic referred to.[4] Only the harmless 'insane' were to be catered for—and these were not defined until 1875. The two asylums were opened in 1870 and children and adults were admitted together, although in 1873 children were separated so that they could be given training. The facilities for the relief of imbeciles formed a salutary contrast to what had previously been offered in the mixed workhouse. The asylum authorities asked for statements from all Unions as to the numbers, ages, and health of this

[1] Circulars including the individual statements, 29 September 1870.
[2] Guardians also received repayment of the cost of rations for officers, e.g. masters, matrons, schoolmasters, and Medical Officers where resident at 12s. a week.
[3] 32 and 33 Vic. s. 37.
[4] *The Metropolitan Asylums Board and its work, 1867–1930*, compiled by Sir A. Powell, C.B.E., 1930.

class of pauper which they were maintaining, so that their removal could be arranged. In August 1870 St. George in the East for example, sent twenty-five males and nineteen females to Caterham and Leavesden.[1] Lunatics were however still retained in workhouses for a short period—although separate wards or even a detached building had to be provided —before they could be transferred to an already existing lunatic asylum, which catered for the dangerous cases. In 1869 the Commissioners in Lunacy visited St. George in the East lunatic ward and reported it to be satisfactory. Bethnal Green had an asylum to which lunatics from other parishes could be sent but 16s. per head per week was charged and in 1870 this was raised to 17s. 6d. The St. George in the East Guardians stated that they preferred sending their cases to Colney Hatch or Hanwell—the Middlesex County Asylums, where the cost was just under 10s. The City of London established its own asylum, Hoxton House, in 1868 and the Guardians were charged 15s. per patient, increased to 16s. in 1869 because of the rise in the cost of living. This high charge to the Guardians necessitated constant inspection of workhouses to prevent lunatics being retained longer than the legal fourteen days. Kensington for example spent £710 a quarter on maintaining lunatics in Hanwell and in 1870 the Commissioners in Lunacy found forty-seven lunatics in the workhouse. Five dangerous cases were ordered to be removed to an asylum; of the rest some went to one of the Metropolitan Asylums Board's institutions and others remained in the infirmary.[2]

Another important service which the Metropolitan Asylums Board were to undertake was the provision of ambulances. Wakley, soon after he became Coroner of West Middlesex in 1839, cautioned the public on the use of street cabs for the removal of infectious cases, and the *Lancet* in the succeeding generation urged the need for special conveyances for all classes of sick. In an article in 1856 the journal pointed out that for public safety and on grounds of humanity for the sick each workhouse should be provided with an ambulance in which a patient could be conveyed in a horizontal position.[3] Shoreditch already had such a vehicle in the 'fifties, but a return made to the House of Commons in 1863 showed that there were only thirty-five cabs, carriages, wheelchairs, or hand ambulances for the whole of London, rich and poor. The divergence which existed in the provisions made for the workhouses was remarkable. Holborn, for example, had no vehicle, and the workhouse hired a van from the Fever Hospital, which was paid for on a mileage basis. Kensington had none in 1868, although there had been one in 1847 for it was mentioned by the Guardians. Whitechapel Union had two and so had Stepney. Islington had five vehicles of various kinds. In Lambeth the workhouse officers had to apply to the Relieving Officer before the ambulance could be used. Unions that hired conveyances paid from 5s. to 10s. 6d., or sometimes for a horse only. In other places they were lent free of charge. In Unions that owned their own vehicles, these were usually kept in the workhouse. No uniformity existed in the type of conveyance, in the price the Union paid to one of its

[1] Minutes, St. George in the East Board of Guardians.
[2] Minutes, Kensington Board of Guardians.
[3] *Lancet*, 1856, i, p. 409.

parishes to whom it belonged, in the number available, or in the class of sick for whom it was used. Some parishes allowed the non-destitute to be removed to hospital in their ambulance. Invalid police carriages existed from 1860 and in that year an Order was issued for the disinfection of carriages used for transporting cases of infectious disease. The police carriages were used for carrying the sick poor from the common lodging-houses to workhouse infirmaries and not the Unions vehicles.[1]

This was the situation when the Metropolitan Asylums Board was formed. Attention was immediately drawn to the defects in the arrangements for removing patients to hospital. The new Board found no alteration had been made in the system whereby Guardians could use their own initiative in methods of transport. Nothing was done however before the Poor Law Board was dissolved. Ambulances were either the property of Guardians, the local sanitary authorities, or hired. It was pointed out that vehicles were often quite unsuitable in themselves and were housed in a dangerous way—for example, the carriage after being used for transporting smallpox was placed in a yard amongst tradesmen's carts. Complaints were frequently made that carriages conveying patients to hospital stopped at public houses into which the driver and the patient's friends went for refreshment. Nurses were seldom provided and a carriage was often difficult to obtain when required. The attention of the Metropolitan Asylums Board was attracted when, during the epidemic of 1869–71 urchins ran behind the slow-moving vehicles shouting 'fever'! Nothing tangible was attempted during this period although reform was more imperative than ever when the epidemic raged. The beginning of an efficient ambulance system had to wait until 1879, but the authority which was to organize it on a comprehensive basis for the entire Metropolis was established in 1867.

The work which the Metropolitan Asylums Board especially developed after 1867 was the provision of isolation hospitals. Before 1867 organized removal and isolation of infectious diseases in the Metropolis hardly existed and there was particularly no effective means of prevention. Little was done by the Guardians and other local sanitary authorities and there was no central body to arrange and control supervision. There were two voluntary hospitals in the Metropolis for infectious diseases which were intended for paying patients to which the Guardians subscribed for a limited number of paupers; there were none for the poor whose insanitary and overcrowded homes imperatively demanded the prompt removal and isolation of the sick. The workhouse also in the 'sixties tried to exclude as many fever patients as possible, so that only domiciliary relief was generally available. From the outset the Metropolitan Asylums Board was empowered to deal with fever, diphtheria, and smallpox occurring amongst paupers; later this limited scope was widened until they became the authority for providing public isolation hospitals for all classes. *The origin of public hospitals was in the Poor Law, and the Metropolitan Asylums Board developed an enormous range of functions from this nucleus.*

In 1867 it was decided to erect two permanent fever hospitals each with 200 beds, and

[1] Return of number and description of carriages suitable for conveyance of sick and distressed persons within Metropolitan Police District, May 1863.

two permanent smallpox hospitals each with 100 beds. Temporary accommodation for cases of emergency was considered and sites were acquired for this. Land was bought at Homerton and Stockwell for the hospitals, and Hampstead which had originally been chosen for a third hospital, was to provide the ground for the temporary erections if required. Delay in building was occasioned by opposition to the acquisition of sites and appeals had to be made to the Poor Law Board. The outbreak of relapsing fever early in 1870 afforded additional proof of the great necessity for the fever hospitals and the central control of the Metropolitan Asylums Board. The permanent institutions were not finished but the existence of the Board rendered it possible for immediate and effective steps to be taken. Contracts were made with the London Fever Hospital for the erection of temporary wooden huts in its grounds for the reception of sixty patients. But this additional accommodation did not suffice and a temporary structure was raised on the Hampstead site for ninety more patients. Arrangements were made with the contractors that the building should be capable of easy extension to hold 180 at an additional cost of £3,000. Accommodation for 150 patients was secured, although in the first month the women's wards were filled to capacity.[1] The Poor Law Board could congratulate itself however on the speedy intervention, for it materially assisted in checking the spread of the disease.

This intervention which had been so beneficial in the winter of 1869–70 was subjected to a far more severe strain towards the end of 1870. In autumn the first case of what proved to be a formidable epidemic of smallpox occurred. Previously, the Poor Law Board reported it found no cause for alarm, scarlet fever was above the average, but other infectious diseases had been confined to their usual level. Typhus and typhoid fevers had been less prevalent because of this state of comparative quiescence. The Poor Law Board therefore, in the interest of the ratepayers, recommended to the managers of the Metropolitan Asylums District in July 1870, that only one of the two isolation hospitals should be opened for patients, although the other buildings were to be completed. At the end of October admissions into the general Smallpox Hospital in Upper Holloway became more frequent, all the beds were filled and many patients were refused admission. The difficulty of disposing of smallpox cases weighed heavily on the Boards of Guardians. Dr. Bridges, Medical Inspector of the Metropolis, pointed out the importance of local officials in areas which were the principal seats of the disease, doing everything in their power to co-operate with the Metropolitan Asylums Board in providing temporary shelter. In the first week of 1871 over 600 cases of smallpox were treated in their own homes. In the workhouses more nurses (paupers) were attached to the isolation wards, and in St. George in the East for example, orders were given that no attendant on infectious cases was to have any contact with the rest of the institution. All sufferers from smallpox in this Union were removed to the workhouse and in addition the Guardians had to provide treatment for their lunatics who were sent back from Colney Hatch Asylum when they contracted the disease there.[2] Of the activity in the Unions Dr. Bridges wrote: 'Every possible precaution was taken to

[1] Twenty-second Annual Report of the Poor Law Board.
[2] Minutes, St. George in the East Board of Guardians, 1870–71.

isolate cases; credit is due to the Medical Officers and the authorities for the fact that save in a very few instances has there been even a suspicion that disease may have spread from the smallpox wards to other inmates of the workhouses . . . but the inconvenience and difficulties caused were very great.' The Poor Law Board suspended the orders for the return of the poor to Ireland for the epidemic period. In November 1870 the Medical Officers were requested to forward weekly returns of the number of smallpox cases under treatment to Dr. Bridges.

It was obvious that active measures for isolation were necessary, and the returns made it possible to estimate how far these should be carried. Dr. Bridges maintained that great value would have accrued from a systematic registration of contagious and infectious diseases if this had been done by parochial Medical Officers under the supervision of the Poor Law administration. Three weeks, he maintained, could have been gained for preventive measures. The vigour and promptness of the action of the special fever committee of the Metropolitan Asylums Board enabled the Hampstead temporary iron hospital to be reopened for smallpox cases pending the completion of the Stockwell and Homerton institutions. Although it had been originally built for ninety fever patients, the Hampstead hospital was considered capable of accommodating 130 cases of smallpox, because such a large proportion of the victims were children and because the convalescent stage was reached rapidly. The provision was increased to 200 beds by the removal in January 1871 of an iron shed from the grounds of the London Fever Hospital to the Hampstead site. As the epidemic was still increasing four additional iron sheds were obtained and this raised the number of beds to 450. Fifty-two patients were housed per acre, which was not regarded as excessive or dangerous. From 1 December 1870 to 1 January 1871, 354 patients were admitted but in February the temporary fever hospital in Homerton was opened for smallpox cases. The East Grinstead Sisterhood supplied the nursing staff, as it had done the previous winter during the fever epidemic, and a doctor of great experience and ability was appointed.[1] Within a short time the Eastern Fever Hospital in Homerton was completed and later the temporary one was merged with it.

Meanwhile the Stockwell Smallpox Hospital was opened in January 1871. It was constructed on the pavilion plan and had two parallel wings each with four large wards and two smaller ones for special cases. A large and spacious corridor connected the two wings and each ward had a nurses' room and a scullery. The hospital also provided two reception rooms. It was erected on a healthy site and ventilation and heating were efficient. The Medical Officers' sole complaint was the lack of vehicles for transporting cases. Day and night nurses were appointed to each ward and they were selected on their previous experience. There were also two head nurses and the night superintendent. Duty hours were from 7.30 a.m. to 9 p.m. and 9 p.m. to 7.30 a.m.[2] The 100 beds of the hospital were filled so rapidly that the number was increased to 130 by the day rooms being converted into

[1] Dr. J. H. Bridges, Poor Law Inspector: Report on Epidemic of Smallpox in the Metropolis, 1871 (Greater London Council Records).

[2] Report of Medical Superintendent in First Annual Report of Management Committee, 1871–72.

dormitories. In March the Fever Hospital at Stockwell had to be appropriated to smallpox cases, the number of beds having been increased from 176 to 224. This was also filled within a few days and here again thirty patients were put in the day-rooms. The recourse to using both fever and smallpox hospitals at Stockwell and Homerton together was possible on only this one occasion, because all four had not been officially opened for the reception of the special classes. The Poor Law Board said they acted on the advice of the most eminent and experienced sanitary authorities in placing the two types of hospital together—it proved very useful in 1870–71. They had however adopted the most stringent precautions against any intercourse whatever on the part of the nurses, stewards, matrons, and even Medical Officers of the smallpox and fever hospitals. Erection on the same sites had been dictated by the consideration of economy and by the extreme difficulty with which the purchase of numerous sites was attended. But in every other respect they were to be totally distinct establishments. During the smallpox epidemic the necessity for observing these precautions was waived as all four hospitals contained only the one class of patient.

Application was also made to the London Fever Hospital to continue receiving patients sent by the Guardians of Unions, until the epidemic subsided. This request was granted. By the end of February 1871 the total number of beds available for smallpox cases in Metropolitan Asylums Board establishments was 1,250: 450 at Hampstead, 400 at Homerton, and 400 at Stockwell. The disease still showed no signs of abating. The weekly mortality from it, which in the first week of the year had been seventy-nine, had by the last week in February risen to 227. The number of new cases in that week coming under the notice of the Relieving Officers was 571. As each case was allotted four weeks' duration, over 2,000 required isolation under the Metropolitan Asylums Board. Therefore the Poor Law Board took 'several important and decisive steps'. As delay would have been involved in building a fresh hospital, the Board asked the managers of the Poplar and Stepney Sick Asylums District whether they would be willing to grant the use of their infirmary, which approached completion, for smallpox patients.—'To divert a workhouse from its ordinary purpose and occupy it with inmates affected with infectious disease . . . was obviously a course which nothing but the strongest necessity could justify.' Second, the old workhouse of Islington which was partly empty and partly occupied by smallpox patients for whom the Guardians had not been able to obtain admission into the hospitals, was temporarily handed over to the Metropolitan Asylums Board by the order of the Poor Law Board. It was old and ill-adapted for cases of acute disease but it was regarded as suitable for convalescent cases. Three hundred beds were provided for recuperating patients from the Hampstead Hospital and it was opened in March 1871. Another convalescent home was opened in Clapton.

While the Poor Law Board was offering the Metropolitan Asylums Board this accommodation, they pointed out the importance of obtaining fresh sites on which temporary buildings could be placed at short notice, either in existing or future emergencies. The Poor Law Board justified its policy on the grounds that emergencies should be met promptly and without the accumulation of too large an amount of infection on the same site. Further, isolation, which was so essential for preventing the progress of an epidemic, was impossible through the opposition of patients to being removed a great distance from their homes. The Poor Law Board therefore recommended as the best policy the establishment under the superintendence of the Metropolitan Asylums Board of a local hospital in every Union. The expense and the machinery of administration as well as the difficulty in securing appropriate sites, were the dominant objections. So, as the more practicable alternative, the Poor Law Board suggested one or two additional sites in carefully chosen localities should be procured. The first land the Metropolitan Asylums Board obtained under this proposal was that of the dissolved Sick Asylums Districts. The Poor Law Board also urged[1] the Metropolitan Asylums Board to occupy temporarily land adjoining Battersea Park which had been placed at the disposal of the central authorities for a limited time by the First Commissioner of Works. Plans for the erection of iron sheds capable of accommodating 400 patients were prepared with the assistance of the engineering staff of the War Department. But they were never executed because of the considerable expense entailed and the shortness of the period during which the land in question could be occupied. The Admiralty also offered the use of the Dreadnought Hospital Ship at Greenwich and a second ship if it were needed. The Metropolitan Board of Works had not at first permitted the erection of wooden huts and tents, and had therefore impeded the rapid provision of beds. This prohibition was temporarily suspended and huts and tents were placed on the Hampstead Hospital site and were supplied to Stockwell and Homerton by the War Department. The Poor Law Board asserted that these answered well for convalescent patients. Their cost was small and they could be set up in less than a week. The huts at Hampstead cost only £8 for 1,000 cubic feet—which was recognized as sufficient for the accommodation of ten patients. In April the demand for beds had increased so much that at Stockwell for example, the 384 had been increased to 500 by placing convalescents in corridors and landings. One hundred and twenty were then removed to the camp which was built in front of the Fever Hospital from ten army hospital marquees.

In May the disease was at its height—600 patients were being treated at Stockwell, with a weekly admission of nearly 150 fresh cases. From January to May 2,000 patients had passed through the two hospitals there. Altogether 2,140 beds were at the disposal of the Metropolitan Asylums Board in May, and in the last week in April there had been a total of 780 new cases. The provisions made by the Metropolitan Asylums Board were to some extent supplemented by the local action of the Boards of Guardians and vestries. But accommodation varied greatly in character. In Paddington and Rotherhithe, Guardians obtained large sites on which to erect temporary iron sheds. As the Poor Law Board wrote: 'The experience of the epidemic has shown the extreme importance to the Boards of Guardians of possessing a small building of this kind in which cases of great urgency can be at once placed pending removal to an asylum.' The Poor Law Board directed their

---

[1] Letter from the Poor Law Board to the Metropolitan Asylums Board, 13 February 1871.

attention to the subject of the removal of patients to hospitals and Medical Officers were cautioned against recommending such transfers where the sick were unfit for the journey. The Board also stressed the importance of providing a sufficient number of appropriate ambulances.

By the end of September 1871 the epidemic was nearly over. The fever hospitals were emptied of patients, and cleansing and disinfection for the reception of fever cases began. No sooner were these operations completed, than at the end of December a fresh outbreak of smallpox occurred in the Southern district. Once again the Fever Hospital was opened for smallpox cases to avoid sending acute cases up to the Hampstead Hospital—from January 1871 to February 1872, 4,000 patients had passed through the Stockwell establishments of which 700 or 17·6 per cent died. Nine hundred convalescent patients had been sent from them elsewhere. The daily cost per head for maintenance and clothing had been 2s. 2½d. and for the maintenance of a Medical Officer 2s. 1d. This was reduced during the latter half of 1871 to 1s. 2½d. and tenpence per head. The greatest difficulty that was experienced throughout the epidemic was in the obtaining of suitable nurses. The Committee of Management of Stockwell Hospital reported that the loathsome and infectious nature of the disease deterred the better class of nurses, but through re-vaccination the staff of the hospitals enjoyed almost complete immunity. Very suitable women had come forward from time to time so that the managers were able to weed out those with whom they had at first to be contented. Within the first year there had also been a complete change of the principal Medical Officers. The Committee stated that they had regularly inspected the wards and had held weekly meetings at which all patients due for discharge were interviewed and asked if they had any complaints. The replies, it was said, generally expressed satisfaction.[1]

The Metropolitan Asylums Board was therefore severely tested as soon as it was established, and the provisions made form an amazing contrast to the Poor Law authorities' activity of earlier decades. The medical services had made gigantic strides forward in the realm of ideas and principles, as well as in practical measures. The Metropolitan Asylums Board gained considerable experience at the outset to help them develop the hospital and ambulance system. The virulence of the epidemic brought about the simplification of formalities which had been prescribed for admission to the hospitals, because it was evident that a large proportion of patients were not those who normally obtained pauper relief. Greatly increased provision had to be made for the non-destitute because they could not be safely isolated and efficiently nursed in their homes. Many public sanitary authorities made urgent representations on the necessity for making the hospitals available to all classes. These bodies pointed out that as a central authority supported by the rates existed to deal with infectious diseases among one class of the community, it would be more salutary for sanitary and financial interests if their power were extended to enable them to

[1] Reports in Twenty-third Annual Report of the Poor Law Board, 1870–71, and First Annual Report of the Committee of Management, Stockwell and Homerton Fever and Smallpox Hospitals, 1871–72, and Return to the House of Commons, 1871, No. 184.

provide for everyone, rather than that action should be taken by the local authorities themselves. Admittance to a hospital on a Relieving Officer's order only was impracticable when non-paupers were taken, and also the need for prompt intervention made it necessary to admit patients on the receipt of information (even a telegram) from any Poor Law official, subject to subsequent confirmation. From 1870 to 1872 16,000 cases of small-pox were admitted to the Metropolitan Asylums Board hospitals—but this was only one-third of the number for whom accommodation was required. The deaths in the Board's hospitals were over 3,000 and 6,600 died in their own homes. At a Poor Law Conference in 1883 it was said that the Metropolitan isolation hospitals were pauper institutions, although they were in practice used by the non-destitute whom it was necessary for public safety to remove from their homes. In 1882 persons suffering from infectious diseases admitted to the Metropolitan Asylums Board hospitals no longer suffered from any disqualification or disability as a pauper.[1] The procedure found imperative in time of epidemic had come to stay.

The results of the Metropolitan Poor Act are best shown in the evidence given to the Select Committee in 1888. Before 1867 the sick in the Metropolis were nearly always in sick wards of the general mixed workhouse, by 1888 there was scarcely a Union in London which had not got its separate infirmary, many of which later became public hospitals. The differentiation between them and the voluntary hospitals became ever narrower and with the lapse of twenty years, 11,000 beds were provided in the separate infirmaries. In 1866 there were 111 paid nurses and only three night nurses. In 1888 there were over 1,000. It was also general before the Act for the workhouse Medical Officer to be in private practice attending the institution daily at stated periods; he also very often found his own drugs and appliances. Resident Medical Officers, with assistants, and who had their medicines supplied for them was the universal custom twenty years later. By this time the Metropolitan Asylums Board had six isolation hospitals, three lunatic asylums, convalescent homes and a hospital-ship to augment the provisions made by the London Fever Hospital and the London Smallpox Hospital before its inception. It must also be remembered that pauperism slightly decreased in these years and the percentage of sick to the total pauper population had fallen to 50 per cent—although this number increasingly received institutional relief.

Florence Nightingale's admonition in the sixties had been effected.

The sick [she said] can never be properly treated in the same establishment as the able-bodied pauper ... there is absolutely no more real connection between an infirmary and a workhouse than between an infirmary and a railway establishment.

She had strongly advocated the separation of management:

good hospital governors, good superintendents and head nurses, good hospital officials

[1] Mr. Bousfield on 'Medical Relief', Poor Law Conference, 1883.

are not only rare but expensive articles—one of each could answer for 500 to 1,000 sick just as well as fifty.[1]

The selection and training of such people was a long and difficult process, and changes were not immediately apparent everywhere in the Metropolis.

In 1871 a movement began for the resuscitation of the Association for Improving Workhouse Infirmaries and the *Lancet* gave it support. It recapitulated its object—the erection of large hospitals at public expense for sick and infirm paupers and an alteration in the system of relief for such people. Rogers resumed his leadership and until the 'eighties continued to agitate for the reform of the conditions of the sick regarding diet, clothing, the cheating of patients of their food, and against their maltreatment which he claimed was often brutal. From his own experience he realized conditions were still bad in some institutions, for in 1873 when he was appointed to the Westminster Infirmary he found no conveniences were supplied for the infirm or paralytic patients. This had not been discovered by Inspectors or by previous Medical Officers—or no steps had been taken to rectify the situation. The master derided Rogers when he pointed to the bugs in the corners of some wards, but eventually he had these swept into the fire in their hundreds. There was great laxity in discipline and patients were allowed to get drunk, and no special dietary had been adopted for the sick and infirm. The chief illnesses in the infirmary were consumption and bronchitis. Rogers asked for the acute sick to be removed to the Highgate Hospital as Westminster belonged to the Central London Sick Asylums District, but the Guardians objected although the infirmary was full and was inadequately staffed with nurses. The nurses were not responsible to the Medical Officers but were selected by the Guardians, so that Rogers had no power to dismiss them. Some paupers cheated the doctors—one woman had for years simulated dumbness and had received presents of sweets and books from visiting ladies. She only gave herself away when threatened with removal to the insane ward. Also a man had for years pretended he could not walk because he was too lazy to work and preferred staying in bed. In this infirmary the insane were liable to imprisonment for crimes committed whilst demented. The lunatic wards were a menace because both dangerous and harmless cases were kept together until the latter could be moved to one of the institutions of the Metropolitan Asylums Board and the former to a County Asylum. The master had calmly let things slide, despite the new activity of the Poor Law authorities. To Rogers he stated he had been in the Poor Law service long enough 'to be fully aware that no good would accrue to him by too much zeal in the performance of his duty!'[2]

Meanwhile, the reformers were no less active in the provinces, and with like effect. When the *Lancet* instituted its inquiry into the metropolitan workhouses questionnaires were also sent to all provincial Unions. Information was sought on the general

[1] Quoted by Dr. J. H. Stallard, M.P., *London Pauperism amongst Jews and Christians*, 1867.
[2] Joseph Rogers, *Reminiscences of a Workhouse Medical Officer*, 1889.

character of the infirmary buildings, the wards, the system of nursing, the quality of provision, the dietaries, the Medical Officers, the history of epidemics to which the institution had been subject and their results, and finally the mortality, average and special. Great interest was aroused and many Medical Officers in the country forwarded reports to the *Lancet*. A terrible account was given of the Farnham (Hants) workhouse by Dr. Anstie and Dr. Stallard, and the latter also wrote an article on it for *The Times*. Each year every pauper, male or female, who could crawl left it to go hop-picking, and the abandoned state of the institution made it impossible to be cleaned in these weeks. The *Lancet* gave it the usual description—'a marvel of bad construction'. It had been built in 1790 and additions had been made to it ever since. The infirmary had been erected in 1846 for one-sixth of the number which it held twenty years later when one-third of all the inmates were sick. Syphilitic and fever cases were housed in a separate building, originally intended for the aged. The *Lancet* described each ward in turn, and the inefficiency of the pauper nurses—there was one paid nurse and many of the patients themselves had to assist her. Few towels were provided and the house was filthy—'a dirty hole was the larder'. The Visiting Committee never answered the required questions in the Visitors' Book and deaths occurred through neglect. The *Lancet* charged the Poor Law Board, the Inspector, and the Guardians for allowing such evils to exist. Thereupon the central authorities asked for a Report on Farnham workhouse from Inspector Lambert and Dr. Smith. This was merely descriptive however with little comment, and the only recommendations made were that separate infectious wards and proper vagrants' wards should be provided—the building should remain and be further adapted. The Inspectors concluded by pointing out the vast cost this would entail (thereby admitting the truth of the *Lancet*'s allegations) and that this would be a great handicap.[1]

Dr. Stallard also reported to the *Lancet* on the Walsall workhouse. Of the venereal disease wards he wrote: 'In all our experience we never saw patients in a more wretched state.' There was neither fireplace nor ventilation and only 567 cubic feet per person, and the fever patients were in little better condition. The Poor Law Board again instituted an inquiry.[2] The Medical Officer in his evidence remarked:

> What would Dr. Stallard have to be done with the filthy and miserable dregs of habitual vice that again and again resort to the workhouse, not to be cured, for they will not stay to be cured, but to be rid of the filth and vermin, and loathsome and offensive odours of their habits and diseases, which they import at each return. Does he [Dr. Stallard] advocate any more for them than the necessary food, shelter, and medicine? Would he put them on a par with the respectable destitute and invalid inmates of the workhouse?

Stallard's accusations he concluded were sensational but not practical, the Guardians subscribed liberally to several hospitals in Birmingham and Wolverhampton, so that many of

---

[1] *Lancet*, 1867, ii, pp. 496-98, and Report to the House of Commons, 1868, No. 134.
[2] *Lancet*, 1867, ii, pp. 585-86, and Poor Law Board, 20 January 1868.

the sick inmates were removed from the workhouse. Stallard pointed out that he had searched through the Visitors' Book for twenty years, before he found reference to one complaint, and there was no notice of the abuses and defects which must have arisen in this time. Not a single suggestion appeared for improving the condition of the sick wards or for the benefit of patients. Many improvements he agreed had taken place. Baths had been installed and at one time all the closets had been stinking cesspits. The supply of linen had formerly been so scanty that a pair of sheets could scarcely be found for every bed, or a change of clothes for the inmates. Once there had not been a cupboard or shelf in any ward, and the chapel had been used as a common thoroughfare. The sick had also been scattered all over the house. Improvements had been effected through the activity of the master and the Medical Officer, but there was still in 1867 only one basin for washing in the establishment. All the rest of the inmates used buckets, even the bedridden, so there was a high danger of infection. Only two towels were allowed for every ten patients per week, again conducive to the spread of contagious diseases. An offensive smelling water-closet opened out into the fever ward. Epileptics and imbeciles were not segregated. The nursing staff was insufficient and there were no night nurses at all. Yet Stallard declared that he had visited another workhouse near Walsall in comparison with which the former was a palace. In the sick wards there ten out of twelve water-closets were permanently nailed up and the other two depended on rain-water from the roof.[1] He told the Poor Law Inspectors at the inquiry that he had seen no provincial workhouse as good as that of Wolverhampton nor any management superior to that of Walsall. Although he had drawn attention to the faults in the latter workhouse, he said the bedsteads were large and good, the bedding clean, comfortable, and sufficient, the walls of the sick wards were painted and the floors polished, clean, and matted down the middle, and the windows were curtained. He made it clear that in writing his account in the *Lancet* he had had no intention of choosing the worst or the best. He had wished to take a sample, pointing out the good and the bad points.

Dr. Smith and Inspector Graves were sent to investigate conditions in the Cheltenham workhouse which also came in for criticism from the *Lancet*. They reported that the insufficient accommodation could only be remedied by the erection of a new institution, but as the Guardians were building a school they believed there would be ample space in the workhouse in the future, and that the arrangements for the sick would be put on an entirely satisfactory footing. The provincial press had meanwhile been taking up the work of the *Lancet*. For example, the *Manchester Examiner* printed a long report revealing the serious deficiencies in the local workhouse sick wards.[2] Inspector Cane held an inquiry and suggested improvements but the Board of Guardians and the Medical Officer insisted that conditions were satisfactory. After fifteen months the Poor Law Board censured the master and asked that alterations be made and more nurses appointed.

[1] These instances were also given at a meeting of the National Association for the Promotion of Social Science, 1867.

[2] *Manchester Examiner*, 31 January 1865, and Minutes of the Manchester Board of Guardians (Webb MSS.).

These revelations of independent and official inquiries influenced the Poor Law Board to request their Inspectors to furnish reports on all the workhouses in their regions. They were presented to the House of Commons on 2 December 1867. Inspector Cane seemed to have undergone conversion for he made the important statement that the arrangements for the reception of infectious and contagious diseases, medical attendance, nursing, and the general care of the sick, as well as the ventilation, drainage, water-supply, bedding, food, and clothing of inmates were most unsatisfactory in his new district of Derby, Lancashire, the West Riding, and part of Cheshire. After describing the bad conditions of the able-bodied inmates of the Stockport workhouse, he said the sick wards did not admit the classification of cases—old and young, aged, able-bodied and children were all together in the same wards. In a single ward there was a case of accident, asthma, scabies, venereal disease, and infirmity from age. There were no fever wards and the insane were kept in great numbers. There was also no separate diet. In another workhouse, that of the Caton incorporation, there were no insane wards, no infirmary or even separate sick wards, no water-closets, lavatories, or baths. The sick and well occupied the same dormitories and the Medical Officer lived 6 miles from the workhouse. Only pauper nurses were employed who were so feeble and inefficient that several lunatics committed suicide. In Preston, Cane said the horrors of the workhouse were especially disgusting. The practice of putting two sick people in the same bed prevailed and had increased, and he gave a long list of patients with different diseases who were sleeping together. Even the bedridden and infirm were not kept apart and aggravated each other's condition. In Huddersfield there was an entire insufficiency of accommodation especially for the sick. Here 'puddings were boiled in the same copper as the foul linen was washed and boiled in'. The truth of this could not be denied when the Inspector reported it and the *Lancet* called it 'barbarous beastliness'. Cane also endorsed the inefficiency of the pauper nurses—they could not read the labels on medicine bottles, yet they were entrusted with the administration of drugs. He also gave evidence of cruelty and tyranny. In general, Cane condemned the large majority of workhouses in his extensive district as almost entirely unfit for the reception and care of the sick. He did this by a naked statement of facts which were more serious and shocking than those of the *Lancet* Commission. His businesslike official descriptions were more 'sensational' than the *Lancet*'s.

Inspector Gulson's reports on the south-west were more placid—he had not yet been converted. 'Few improvements required'; 'nursing generally satisfactory' were the statements which were included in tabular form, showing that he had probably sent a questionnaire to all the Unions, which only required a monosyllabic answer. No real investigation could have been undertaken for there was an entire absence of complaints in all the accounts on fifty-eight workhouses. That Gulson's reports were incorrect was revealed by the *Lancet*'s revelations on such workhouses as those of Clifton and Bedminster, and Dr. Smith's on Totnes. Inspector Hawley in the south-east remonstrated against the worst defects of workhouse management and pronounced nursing in particular as unsatisfactory. But even so the faults of the institutions escaped his notice as he failed to mention Farnham workhouse on which an inquiry had just been held. The official reports taken together formed a curious mixture. Those Inspectors who had had their eyes opened complained seriously, but others who had not been startled out of their apathy by being brought unexpectedly in personal contact with a scandal found no faults and spoke with complacency. The comprehensive report was very long and amounted to almost seven hundred pages.[1]

In consequence of the increased interest being taken in the state of the provincial workhouses, the Poor Law Board in 1867 deputed their Medical Officer to examine forty-eight workhouse infirmaries in selected districts so chosen as to embrace institutions of all kinds and to afford a fair indication of the state of infirmaries of all Unions throughout the country.[2] Dr. Smith was requested to report on the classes of sick cases; the officers in charge; the sites of the workhouses and their character; the construction of wards and whether these were detached; sanitary appliances; nurses' apartments; medical appliances; dietary, cooking, and distribution of food. He found generalization difficult because of the variation in areas, population, and occupations in town and country, but he produced a general survey from the individual accounts. On the classes of sick, he found that in country districts the number of males greatly exceeded females, whereas in towns the opposite situation appertained. This caused great inconvenience, for while the total provision might be adequate, that for the more numerous sex was often deficient and there could be no transfer. The ordinary sick constituted about five-sixths of the patients and to them nearly all the sick wards were appropriated. These consisted first of the aged and infirm who were in the workhouse chiefly to enjoy the advantage of nursing, warmth, and a bed. Because they were generally not offensive cases and because their facilities for observation were inactive, it was supposed they did not require as large a space, or as light and bright rooms as the second class of patients—the sick. In the country there were fewer of this category than in the towns and then they generally suffered from chronic diseases such as consumption and debility. In larger towns the sick class was more numerous and varied, and in the localities where voluntary hospital accommodation was deficient or non-existent, acute cases were always found in the workhouse. It was the special requirements of these patients as well as the necessity for warmth, quiet, cheerfulness, good ventilation, good nursing, and efficient medical attendance that entailed difficulties for the institutions. The number of patients in the larger workhouses was sufficient to enable a Medical Officer to appropriate some wards to the aged and infirm and others to the sick. In the smaller and the majority of workhouses an acutely sick person was placed in a room alone, which deprived him of many comforts, and if the illness were protracted must have appeared like imprisonment. In larger institutions patients were further divided into medical and surgical, but the definition was in most cases arbitrary and, as in nearly all general hospitals, the same ward was occupied by both medical and surgical cases. In a few Unions, surgical and accident cases were in separate wards and here, Smith said, care was especially necessary

[1] Presented 16 October 1866.
[2] Inquiry instituted by the Poor Law Board, 15 April 1867, and Report by Dr. E. Smith on forty-eight Workhouse Infirmaries in the Provinces, November 1867.

that the sanitary conditions of larger wards should be afforded. Wounds and fracture cases placed in small rooms for technical classification conduced to pyaemia and erysipelas, which it was pointed out, prevailed in the surgical wards of general hospitals, but from which workhouses were almost exempt! Therefore in country workhouses all the sick—aged, infirm, medical, or surgical—were placed in the same ward, and even this, Smith confessed was not as universal as it might be.[1] Another question arose, which was seldom answered satisfactorily—should persons acutely ill or dying be separated from others? This separation was not effected in the general hospital and if it had been deemed beneficial it would have been introduced in them. Many workhouses provided screens and some had separate rooms for isolating the seriously ill, but the practice was rare.

The remaining one-sixth of the patients in the workhouses were lying-in women, children, and those with venereal and infectious diseases. One or more wards in every workhouse Smith found appropriated to midwifery, but great variation existed as to when expectant mothers should enter the maternity ward and at what period after the confinement the mother was to mix with ordinary cases. In large workhouses Smith recommended day rooms with efficient ventilation and warmth, and rocking chairs should be supplied. He also advised that beds should be at least 3 to $3\frac{1}{2}$ feet apart. Referring to children, he said that if there were many in the workhouses they should have a separate ward to facilitate supervision, but this was only practicable and useful in large institutions. When diseases were neither severe nor contagious he agreed with two being placed in one bed, but nowhere three. Mackintosh sheeting, small armchairs, toys, pictures, and other amusements should be provided. He drew special notice to the prevalence of skin diseases among children and stressed the importance of increased attention being given to this problem. Venereal disease cases he advised should, wherever practicable, be warded separately not because of the treatment required, but on account of the moral issue. He found it very repelling on entering venereal disease wards at some seaport workhouses to find mere boys and men of over 50 years of age together. Prostitutes, he said, should also be segregated. Similar conditions obtained in several parts of the country, particularly in large towns and around barracks and army camps. The number of cases was sufficiently great to warrant the authorities appropriating special wards and yards for their use. But in the majority of country workhouses the number rarely exceeded one or two at a time and separation was therefore difficult. As there were or ought to have been itch and other isolation wards in every workhouse, Smith saw no reason why venereal disease cases should not be placed there. For offensive and disagreeable cases he suggested one isolation ward was sufficient in small workhouses for either sex, but in large ones these patients, generally the aged, should be segregated. Progress had been made in providing separate wards but '*much further improvement may yet be effected*' (his italics). The character of the isolation wards was generally inferior to that of the ordinary sick wards and they had the worst bedding and

[1] Smith made the astute observation that when surgical patients were housed together in a small ward the septic cases infected the non-septic, whereas if the surgical patients were spread among the other sick in larger general wards this cross-infection was less likely to occur.

furniture. In regard to ventilation they should have been the best in the workhouse, and they should have been at the end of the infirmary or on a floor by themselves—'*much improvement is needed*'.

There were three classes of patients for whom provision was usually made in the provincial workhouses—itch (generally scabies), fever, and smallpox. Numbers varied greatly in districts and at different periods, and bore no necessary relation to the size of the workhouse nor affected the special provision that should have been made for them. The itch wards were generally low, dull, and wretched, and were often an outhouse or small lean-to building. They were dirty and repelling and there was little furniture and very inferior bedding. This was not only because of the general sense of disgust at the nature of the disease but also because it was feared that the treatment by sulphur ointment spoilt the linen. This treatment was in itself entirely inefficient. In other workhouses where patients were treated correctly scabies cases were cured in two to three days. Smith wished to see much improvement in the way of proper nursing, avoidance of the ointment, a supply of sheets, decent bedding and furniture, and isolation. Fever and smallpox cases which occurred in the country were nearly always placed in the same wards. But in these rural areas there were few instances of Guardians admitting patients who had contracted the diseases outside; this was only done in great emergencies or if the afflicted were tramps and homeless. Outdoor cases were generally treated in their own homes, but in some of the large country towns special provision was made for fever and smallpox in the County Hospitals, and to these a certain proportion of district paupers were sent. Large country workhouses also had special fever wards, which were generally separate or in a detached building. In extensive urban areas practically every workhouse had fever wards or a distinct fever hospital attached to it. These were in themselves important institutions and occasionally had a special class of officer. Practice therefore differed, but Smith pointed to the essential factor that there was an unusual number of fever and smallpox cases among the population. He doubted whether the course pursued by the Guardians of country workhouses was wise. Life and cost could be saved if a greater number of fever patients were admitted, for the domiciliary conditions of the poor were unsuited to treatment and only propagated the disease. Yet results of domestic relief compared favourably with those of hospital treatment! Smith however advocated an extension of public assistance during epidemics where fever was spreading in families, where there was destitution and deficiency of ordinary care, where accommodation at the workhouse was sufficient with regard to nursing and space, and where removal could be effected early and safely. Permanent organization, he said, on a large scale was not desirable because of the variability in occurrence and incidence of the disease. The existing arrangements in workhouses also rendered such provision impracticable because without a certain number of sick cases it was impossible to maintain a paid nurse. As an alternative Smith suggested Guardians should everywhere subscribe to general and public hospitals for the maximum number of cases which could be admitted. Where this failed further arrangements should be made by the extension of fever wards in the workhouses and by a more liberal attitude to admission. He sympathized with the

Guardians in their fear of admitting fever cases, and with the Medical Officers who objected to a considerable number being introduced unless salaries were raised, because they were regarded as the District Medical Officer's patients. The question of isolation was arousing controversy in the medical world at this time and although its necessity was not generally admitted by the leading hospitals, Smith advocated there should be complete segregation in workhouse infirmaries. If possible he wanted separate buildings, because the chief danger lay in cross-infection by nurses or other people passing from one ward to another. Isolation wards, he further contended, should be exposed to wind and sun and ventilation should be perfect.

Referring to lunatics, he said that all the dangerous should be removed to asylums, although there was general complaint of the insufficiency of their numbers. The remaining harmless cases were only classed as sick if they were ill and were generally treated in the ordinary infirmary wards. Smith desired much better accommodation for this category.

He also reported on the function of the master and matron of a workhouse. The supervision of the infirmary was their duty, and there were extremely few institutions which engaged a special master or matron. Both were presumed to visit the sick wards daily—the master to inquire into their general state, the state of the building, and the nursing arrangements on the men's side, the matron to supervise the women's wards and to inquire into cleanliness, linen, food, and supplies generally, the state of the patients, and the efficiency of the nursing. She was practically a superintendent nurse, and in workhouses where no paid nurse was employed, she had direct responsibility for the nursing. As the duties of the master and matron were onerous and many, it was impossible for them to discharge them adequately—they could only have the merest general supervision over the sick in all but the smallest institutions. Efficiency therefore varied greatly. Smith contended that they should have '*greater liberty . . . in supplying minor wants and remedying small defects without waiting for direct instructions from the Guardians*' (his italics).

As to the sites of workhouses, Smith reported that the new provincial institutions were universally 'unexceptionable in reference to salubrity', because they were usually built on raised ground and in many districts outside the towns. There were very few instances as in Sheffield, where they were situated on low lying land as the workhouses had been before 1834. Drainage, light, air, and water supply, he maintained were therefore good, although quantity was often lacking. Country workhouses had land attached which offered facilities for employment and recreation—privileges which should be extended. The site of the infirmary was, however, always in the rear of the main building if it was separate so that it was not exposed to the sun. Attention had not been paid to this disadvantage. Besides the chief sick wards, others for special cases were placed in every possible position. With the concentration of these and the erection of a single infirmary a suitable site could be selected. Smith noticed a great evil regarding sites, for in numerous instances the buildings had been erected on the edge of land belonging to the Guardians, and this had prevented the insertion of windows and ventilators in the outer wall and the extension of the buildings in that direction. This he stressed should be forbidden in the future. Yards for exercise were always small and badly situated. No sunshine ever penetrated the high walls which enclosed them and they invariably had a drain in the centre. In the country, however, some workhouses had flower gardens surrounded only by railings and with seats in them to which the sick inmates had access at stated times. Smith advocated that much should be done in this direction.

Reporting on the wards themselves, Smith said every possible variety existed. In country workhouses they were deficient in width although generally sufficient in height, and often had windows along two opposite sides to provide better light and ventilation. In towns the workhouse sick wards were much larger and not generally lighted from two sides; also from the nature of their site they were less cheerful and had fewer means of ventilation. Smith found generalization difficult because of the entire absence of uniformity in construction throughout the country. The best infirmaries were equal to any sick wards in the kingdom, and the worst were far better than the homes of the poor.[1] But thinking of the new infirmaries which were to be built in the future, he recommended that some general principle should be established to be applied universally. He forecast great difficulty would be experienced in effecting this as long as the preparation of plans was left with the Guardians and their architects, for they were inevitably imperfectly acquainted with the requirements of sick wards and usually continued with schemes of construction adopted many years previously. Also their activity was too much restricted by existing legislative limits on expenditure. Smith therefore drew up some of the principles which the Poor Law Board should adopt and impress on the Guardians:

> The site of the workhouse was to have a southerly aspect; yards were to be paved and have seats, large walls were to be dwarfed or replaced by railings; in country workhouses gardens were to be accessible to the sick daily; the ground floor of an infirmary was to consist of offices and the officers' apartments, the first floor was to be given to the sick; all sick wards were to have windows on two sides, and be not less than 20 feet in width and 10 feet to 12 feet high, the length was to be determined by 6 feet of wall space being allowed to each bed; the entrance was to be in the gangway; windows were to reach near to the ceiling and extend to 3 feet off the floor; ventilators were to be small and sufficient in number; there were to be means of distributing warmth throughout the wards; and finally, day-rooms were to be provided.

The number of beds to be put in each ward presented a difficulty because of the infinite variation in the size and form of the existing wards. The rule should be, Smith advised, that at least 3 feet was to be allowed between each bed. Wards were untidy because some patients had their heads to the wall and others their sides. There was much diversity regarding ventilation. Birmingham workhouse, for example, one of the most extensive in the country, had a special system of flues and so had Portsea and Birkenhead.[2] Smith

---

[1] Inspector Cane had made a similar assertion to the Select Committee of 1862.

[2] Birmingham had a separate infirmary attached to the workhouse which Inspector Weale said in 1854 was one of the best arranged and best managed in the country. By that time a full-time resident workhouse

noticed ventilation was not particularly defective in rural institutions, but stated that the novelty and importance of the subject demanded it should receive careful and extended attention.

As to sanitary arrangements, Smith reported very few instances in which cleanliness was not a marked feature of the sick wards, and this extended to linen, floors, and furniture. He pointed out that in the past few years there had been so few able-bodied women in the workhouses that matrons found it difficult to obtain labour. The Guardians would not pay servants and often had to adopt the indefensible course of requiring a paid nurse to clean the wards. Smith believed that it would not be long before paid servants would have to be engaged. He also desired to see separate laundries attached to the infirmaries—this was not possible in the smaller workhouses but many larger institutions already had them. Great diversity existed in the supply of clean linen and its quantity. Much variety also existed in the provision of water-closets; some workhouses had none, but newer and larger infirmaries almost always had them, so that the defect was really a problem of the small country workhouses. Many infirmaries had good hot and cold water supplies, in others arrangements were most defective. In the ordinary sick wards of small workhouses fixed baths were rarely seen, but they were commonly found in newly-constructed fever wards. Although many moveable baths were used, there were many problems, for even in large new infirmaries hot and cold water was often not laid on to the sick wards. Smith recommended that this should now be installed for the entire institution, although the cost would be considerable. Sick inmates should also always have clean hot water for making tea—a statement which implies that this was not usual.

Smith also reported the great diversity in the supply of furniture and medical appliances and the desirability of uniformity. Bedsteads were universally iron, but only a few had racks by which the upper part of the body could be raised. Wooden cribs should also be supplied for epileptics and very aged and offensive cases. Lengths of beds varied tremendously, but the average width was $2\frac{1}{2}$ to 3 feet. The bedding generally consisted of two blankets, often very old and thin, and cotton rugs. Mattresses were made of flock, coir, chaff, or straw, generally sufficiently full and good. He believed the provision of chairs and benches on the whole sufficient. Lockers were often supplied in infirmary wards but there was a great deficiency of cupboards. Screens, prints, and religious books were commonly supplied in small numbers. In half of the infirmaries, Smith found illustrated papers and he hoped some kind of library would become more general. Very rarely were towels issued to every patient; pots, plates, and mugs were seen, but in too many instances tin or pewter plates were used, and tin pannikins were common. Woollen caps were sometimes provided for sick women and woollen nightgowns were found in some infirmaries. So great was the diversity that in some wards Smith saw nothing beyond beds, chairs or bench and a nightstool, whilst in one ward at Loughborough each female sick inmate had for her own

Medical Officer was employed and the Guardians supplied medicines. The new system of ventilation by tubes which was being introduced in many workhouses was invented by Sir John Walsham, Poor Law Inspector, 1834–67.

separate use a teatray, tray cover, towel, cup and saucer, spoon, clothes basket, slippers, woollen cap, comb and brush, and a wash hand-basin. In some workhouses, as for example in Derby, the supply of furniture and conveniences equalled that of the best furnished hospital. Because of this great variation Smith advised the Poor Law Board to make recommendations on the matter and induce the Guardians to furnish wards with a greater regard to accepted standards, and in many cases particularly in rural workhouses, with greater liberality. He then listed forty-two proposals on the supplies to be provided.

He also outlined the inefficient system of pauper nursing, and in advocating the employment of paid nurses and the better class of pauper women, he suggested nurses' apartments should be more comfortable. They were to be in the centre of the building and each nurse was to have a bedroom and sitting-room. Bells should be placed between all the wards and her bedroom. Great variation existed—in a few workhouses nurses had no room at all and in others only one. More commonly however the paid staff had two. The situation of these rooms differed widely because they had been appropriated to their use after the infirmaries had been constructed and had not therefore been originally built for the purpose. Some newer institutions however had admirable arrangements.

Speaking on sick dietaries Smith referred to these being left to the Medical Officer's discretion because medicine and food went together in the treatment of disease. He suggested much trouble would be saved if workhouse doctors prepared certain general forms applicable to the majority of cases. If the Poor Law Board were to suggest a special dietary for the aged and infirm class as well as a low dietary and convalescent dietary, greater uniformity would result, and the practice in the workhouse hospital would then be more akin to that in general hospitals. Further, the lack of skill shown by nurses and matrons in cookery might be tolerated for the able-bodied but not for the special diets of the sick; therefore, in large establishments Smith suggested the appointment of paid and skilled cooks. Cooking for the acutely sick should be done in the infirmary kitchen as at Portsea and some larger workhouses. But generally in extensive workhouses food was cold before it was served to patients, so as an interim measure Smith recommended the use of an insulated box as was the practice in Wolverhampton and the City of London.

He concluded his long report by pointing to the great transformation that had taken place in the condition of the pauper, the views of the Guardians, and the opinion of the public during the past thirty years, and how the workhouses had been built for the able-bodied who had practically disappeared from them by the 'sixties. Most of the institutions were still comparatively new and yet their structure was so ill-adapted to the changed circumstances that they needed radical alteration. Three great problems therefore presented themselves.—First, whether a large part of the body of the workhouse could not be converted into infirmary wards; second, whether existing sick wards could not be enlarged and reorganized and made suitable for the accommodation of the majority of the inmates; and third, whether outdoor relief could not be more generally given to the aged and infirm. Smith believed that the best rooms in the workhouses would be comparatively wasted, whilst much expense would be entailed in enlarging and concentrating the sick wards. He advised the wisest course in a considerable number of cases would be to convert the greater part of the body of the institutions into wards for the two chief classes—the aged and infirm and the sick—and if required the existing outbuildings could be appropriated to the able-bodied. He stated that many of the workhouses which had been erected during the preceding thirty years were not deficient for existing requirements because old sick wards had been pulled down and replaced by a good infirmary. Also in many other areas the special needs of the Union had increased so much that the excess of accommodation in the body of the institution, which had been brought about by the diminution of the number of able-bodied, had been appropriated to the growing wants of other classes, and thereby left the Guardians free to remodel the sick wards by utilising the vacant space in the main building. The time had arrived however, maintained Smith, 'when the Poor Law Board should hesitate to sanction the erection of new sick wards in workhouses without having been informed as to the general fitness of the whole, as to the necessity for a general concentration or remodelling of the whole'. Where workhouses were built near towns, where space was restricted and where fragmentary additions had been made from time to time, he suggested the moment was expedient for reconsidering whether money should be spent on a site which was unsatisfactory and new buildings added to a series which demanded modification, as at Wolverhampton and Liverpool. Smith ended by recapitulating the great diversity which existed on every subject embraced in his survey. The differences in the size and circumstances of the workhouses were matched by those in the opinions of the Guardians and by the views and capabilities of the officials.

It is proper that any defects which exist should be removed and that the state of the sick wards in the workhouses and the treatment of the sick should contrast not unfavourably with the arrangements of a fairly conducted general hospital.

The Poor Law Board forwarded a copy of Smith's report to all Unions for the Guardians to consider the recommendations, adding that they were giving continued attention to the question of providing in infirmaries all requisites for the adequate care and treatment of the sick. They pointed out however that workhouses were not State Hospitals in which all the sick poor of the country could be received for treatment and that at least two-thirds of the sick poor were receiving medical advice in their own homes.[1] Ernest Hart in 1867[2] outlined a scheme for provincial infirmaries similar to that which the Workhouse Infirmary Association had produced for London in the previous year and which in the main had been adopted in Hardy's Bill. The principles which should be effected were: the laying down of a minimum cubic space for the sick; their separation from the able-bodied; the appointment of Medical Officers for life; the appointment of trained nurses; the choosing of sites for workhouses in accordance with definite principles, and the suitable equipment of wards. Hart also demanded that visitors to the aged and infirm and the sick should not be

[1] Twentieth Annual Report.
[2] Meeting of the National Association for the Promotion of Social Science: Sessional Proceedings, 1867–68.

liable to exclusion and provision should be made for what Hardy had advocated in his speech, but which was not secured in the Metropolitan Poor Act, namely that under proper regulations and at appropriate times, the workhouse infirmaries should be open to medical visitors as hospitals were, and also to members of the Ladies' Visiting Committee. He insisted that it was absolutely necessary for legislative protection to be given to such lady visitors. At Bedminster the ladies had confirmed the report made by the *Lancet*, and the Guardians had immediately passed a resolution excluding them. (Paddington Guardians had excluded members of the Workhouse Visiting Society after Hardy's Act.) It was, Hart maintained, extremely desirable in the interests of the sick and the public, that visits of doctors and the ladies should be continued.

In the 600 provincial workhouses there were 40,000 inmates, consisting as we have seen, chiefly of the sick and the aged and infirm. Yet it was not until 1867 that their condition was made known, and as in the case of the Metropolis, again through the pioneering work of the *Lancet*. After the Poor Law Board's official reports *it was recognized as imperative that something should be done regarding the State Hospitals—a designation given to the workhouses by Hart in 1866 and which was afterwards generally adopted.* Therefore the Poor Law Amendment Act of December 1867 applied similar principles to the country as had been embodied in the Metropolitan Poor Act.[1] From then onwards the central authorities carried out a campaign for the reform of provincial workhouses, and where Guardians refused to improve conditions they ordered the institutions to be closed after a certain day, and even threatened to dissolve recalcitrant Unions. The further history of the workhouse infirmary was one of continuous if slow progress. In June a Circular was sent by the Poor Law Board to the Guardians—the sick were to occupy a separate building and in large workhouses were to be divided into seven classes: the ordinary sick of both sexes, lying-in women, itch cases, dirty and offensive cases, venereal disease cases, fever and smallpox cases, and children. Accommodation for imbeciles if they were retained in the workhouse was to be in accordance with the regulations of the Commissioners in Lunacy. A detached building was to be provided with separate rooms for fever and smallpox cases. Infectious wards were not to be inconveniently distant from the paid nurses' apartments and there were to be communicating bells. Infected linen was to be washed in a detached washhouse. The length of wards was to be calculated according to the following minimum wallspace for each bed: for dormitories only—4 feet; for ordinary sick wards—6 feet; for maternity, fever, and smallpox—7–8 feet. Day rooms for the sick were to afford accommodation for at least half of those who occupied day and night rooms. Stipulations were also made regarding corridors, windows, and ventilation. Sick wards which were to hold two rows of beds were to be at least 20 feet wide, 10–12 feet high, and have windows on opposite sides. The gangway was to be down the centre. In the infirmary one room or a suite of rooms communicating by a gangway was not to exceed 90 feet in length. Where there were two or more blocks of buildings they should be placed so far apart as to allow for free access to

[1] 30 and 31 Vict. c. 106; also the Poor Law Board was for the first time made permanent by this Act.

light and air and also have, where possible, such an aspect that they might enjoy direct sunshine for several hours of the day. Arrangements were also to be made for supplying hot and cold water to bathrooms and sick wards. If hot water were not laid on to the sick wards, stoves were to be provided with a boiler and gas was to be installed in wards where practicable. Suitable kitchens and sculleries were to be attached to the infirmary wards. The sanitary requirements were also to be well attended to. The walls of the sick wards were to be plastered internally, and yards for the sick, aged, and children were to be enclosed with dwarf walls and palisades where practicable.[1]—Altogether the Poor Law Board made sixty-three proposals in this Circular—a veritable revolution from their earlier policy and activity.

At the same time another Circular was sent out desiring uniformity in the furnishing of workhouses. While the Poor Law Board believed 'only a few simple conveniences were necessary' for the ordinary wards, the sick wards were to be more carefully furnished and all necessary medical appliances supplied. Articles were to be kept in stock and Guardians were not to defer procuring them until the moment they were needed. It was to be the duty of the Medical Officer to suggest from time to time what things were required, and the Poor Law Board hoped the Guardians would comply. A long schedule was enclosed of the articles in question such as furniture—armchairs for two-thirds of the number of sick, bed tables, cheerful looking rugs—appliances, and other amenities.[2] One of the clauses of the Poor Law Amendment Act of 1868 (House of Lords) extended the powers of the Poor Law Board to order surgical and medical appliances and furniture for any workhouse, and also to order drainage, sewers, ventilation, fixtures, and conveniences to be altered or fitted. The Poor Law Board had however no direct powers to enforce expenditure on the erection of new institutions, but they were active in inducing Guardians to improve conditions. This was evinced in 1869:

> Being unable to sanction any longer the continued use as workhouses of buildings totally inadequate and unfit for the purpose . . . we have been compelled to issue orders on several occasions directing the closing of these buildings after a certain day.[3]

They succeeded in their object. They closed the Madeley workhouse in Shropshire and the Guardians built a new one, and they also closed the Clitheroe and Crickhowel institutions. Todmorden (Yorks.) never had a workhouse because of the great opposition to the new Poor Law on the part of the local authorities and workers. (Fielden the great industrialist Free Trader, and factory reformer led the Anti-Poor Law agitation here.) At last in 1869 the Poor Law Board forced the issue, by threatening, under the powers of the 1834 Act by which they could separate a parish from a Union, to dismember Todmorden and include its parishes in Rochdale and Halifax. A workhouse was built—and it had taken the central authorities thirty-five years to realize their powers!

[1] Official Circular, 15 June 1868.
[2] Official Circular, 13 June 1869.
[3] Twenty-second Annual Report, 1869–70.

The Poor Law Board were aware that the reforms demanded inflicted high increased costs on local bodies—'The hospital branch of the Poor Law administration is of comparatively recent origin, workhouses designed mainly as a test for the able-bodied, have especially in large towns been of necessity gradually transformed into infirmaries for the sick. . . . The higher standard for hospital accommodation has had a material effect on expenditure' —therefore it had been considered necessary to allow separate fever wards to be attached to the workhouses, but wherever possible these wards were to be isolated by the erection of separate buildings. In 1869–70 considerable progress was reported in the provision of isolation wards. During the first year plans for such wards were submitted to, and approved by the Poor Law Board for fifty Unions in which no similar provision had existed previously. The absence of this accommodation had in former years led to deplorable results and new building was hastened by the spread of relapsing fever and smallpox from London in 1870.

The fever epidemic was particularly virulent in the large slum towns of Lancashire, and Guardians took immediate steps for providing additional accommodation. Inspector Cane reported the 'serious labours and responsibilities which fever imposed on the Guardians and officers', and the 'zealous and satisfactory manner in which the duties were performed'. When smallpox followed fever the temporary accommodation was made available for the new patients. But the Poor Law Board pointed out the establishment of hospitals and measures for preventing the spread of infection, except regarding pauper cases, were problems which really came under the jurisdiction of the sanitary authorities. Fever had been particularly widespread in Liverpool, but the Select Vestry possessed an extensive and well-arranged Fever Hospital connected with the workhouse. There were also two other smaller hospitals and one Poor Law school which had been converted for the emergency. In one week in June 1870 there were 138 patients in the hospitals—by October this number had risen to 1,373. After this the epidemic abated. Domiciliary relief had been given to eleven fever patients in the first week in June and to 287 in the last week in October. (Altogether nearly 2,000 paupers were afforded district medical relief in Liverpool every week.) Fever was also severe in Manchester, Salford, and Chorlton. The Manchester Guardians possessed a Fever Hospital, which was generally adequate, but which was found wholly insufficient for the epidemic. A neighbouring Union received some of the Manchester cases and the Guardians also hired an old mill, once used as a cholera hospital, and this they shared with the Manchester Infirmary Board. But as the epidemic proceeded the voluntary hospital was asked to erect its own temporary wards. The town corporation also erected a temporary Fever Hospital and some wards in the House of Industry were converted. Cane inspected and approved them all. The sick wards of the Chorlton workhouse were adequate, and their excellence and efficient management were well-known at the time. Commenting generally on this region, Cane said some of the wards of the workhouse infirmaries were full, but otherwise every requisite was provided. The mortality rate in these hospitals was comparatively low—under 5 per cent. The Medical Officers of Manchester, Salford, and Chorlton resided in the workhouse and performed their duties well.

Cane pointed out the serious and additional work inflicted on the Guardians and officers, who had often succumbed to the fever and lost their lives. The Guardians' service was gratuitous and other officers received no additional remuneration.

With regard to the improvement of workhouse hospitals, the Liverpool Vestry proposed a conference to the Guardians of other large towns in order to represent to the Government 'that the expense of what is required for sick paupers beyond the ordinary cost of maintenance should be provided for by county or national funds after proper inspection'.[1] In December 1867 Manchester suspended the operations on the enlarging of its new workhouse until the Government's arrangements for the maintenance and care of imbeciles, epileptics, and the insane in national institutions were made known. The Conference of Guardians was held on 11 February 1868 in Manchester—and Birmingham, Bradford, Chorlton, Leeds, Liverpool, Manchester, and Warrington were represented. William Rathbone, the Liverpool philanthropist, presided, and the two proposals of grants-in-aid of pauper hospitals and the Government provision for lunatics were discussed. The Guardians affirmed their interest in good medical treatment because they recognized sickness was a potent cause of pauperism. One obstacle was however pointed out—the fear that efficient provisions might attract the sick poor from other areas. This had always been very evident in Liverpool—'yet the speedy cure of the sick labourer is a national gain, and it is unfair that those districts which specially exert themselves to discharge their duty efficiently should be pecuniary losers in the bargain'.

The Manchester Guardians sent a memorandum stating that they had voted against the Liverpool resolution as

the defrayal of attendant expense of such a measure even if practicable out of a county or national rate would be objectionable, . . . as it would greatly enhance cost and increase the centralizing power of the Poor Law administration, by necessitating the appointment of an additional staff of officials . . . It would lessen the sense of responsibilities of the Board of Guardians and increase improvident expenditure from the knowledge that it would be partly defrayed out of the national purse.

Further, the Manchester Guardians believed

a much higher system of medical treatment and nursing . . . sought to be introduced into workhouse hospitals by the proposed measure, would tend to discourage the provident habits and self-reliance of the industrious poor by providing them therein with better accommodation and treatment than they can usually secure for themselves in case of sickness.[2]

Manchester recognized many improvements had still to be made, but suggested each Board of Guardians should separately submit to the Poor Law Board from time to time its

[1] Minutes, Manchester Board of Guardians, 28 November 1867 (Webb MSS.).

[2] This sentiment is very typical of nineteenth century northern industrial areas. Both masters and men believed in the sanctity of 'self-help'. The former quotation is also very typical of nineteenth century political thought.

own particular requirements and views, leaving it to the Board to embody them in 'well-digested practical measures calculated for general application'. Other delegates had some objection to increasing the centralizing powers of the Poor Law Board and to the suggestion of grants being made after periodic inspection as to efficiency. The Leeds Guardians, however, were unanimous in their support of Liverpool; here sick paupers cost about 5s. a week in the workhouse. The final voting was sixteen for and two against the resolution.[2]

A deputation from the Conference waited on the President of the Poor Law Board, the Earl of Devon, to urge on him the desirability of grants-in-aid to workhouse infirmaries similar to those made towards primary education and the police force. Their plan was that the average cost of healthy paupers and the average cost of sick paupers in a well-conducted workhouse and infirmary should be ascertained, and that the Government should be prepared to make grants of the difference in amount to those establishments where a certain standard of efficiency was reached. Lord Devon received the deputation favourably but gave no promises. He admitted the proposals would facilitate the improvement of infirmaries and would ensure cordial co-operation between the Poor Law Board and the Guardians. The subsidy however, he pointed out, would necessitate official inspection 'which might interfere in local management more than the Guardians would like', and the deputation had previously expressed their opposition to increased centralization. On the question of providing for the insane poor, Lord Devon stated that he was shortly to introduce a Bill in the House of Lords proposing amendments to the Lunacy Laws whereby Unions were to be authorized to combine with a view to the erection, *out of the county funds*, of asylums for the insane poor. Such institutions were to be under the inspection of county magistrates, and were to be used by Unions where it was impracticable to establish asylums of their own.

In 1870 many Poor Law Inspectors reported on the alterations and additions being made to the workhouse infirmaries in their regions. There was activity everywhere. Of Cambridge, Essex, Kent, Norfolk, and Suffolk, Farnall stated that over 2 per cent of the destitute were lunatics and over 48 per cent aged and infirm, practically all of whom were in workhouse infirmaries, besides the sick. In their Twenty-second Annual Report the Poor Law Board drew attention to the changes that had taken place:

> The extreme parsimony displayed by the Boards of Guardians of the older school has in some of the larger Unions given way to a desire to conduct all the duties devolving on Guardians upon a somewhat grand and liberal scale. . . . In many cases the Poor Law Board are now compelled to intervene to check the outlay which Guardians would be willing to incur in the more ornamental part of the various structures which they propose to erect.

Several examples were given of the plans for ornamentation and the elaborate Victorian edifices which local authorities wished to build and how they were going to embellish them. The Poor Law Board vetoed them all as unnecessary. No doubt many of the pro-

[2] *Leeds Mercury* 14 March 1868.

vincial infirmaries equalled or were superior to those of the Metropolis. Birmingham, for example, had a huge infirmary, which was one of the finest in the country. Most famous of all was perhaps the Chorlton infirmary. In 1867 Dr. Stallard had written of this: 'Chorlton provides the sick with a hospital which altogether shames the provision of the London workhouses . . . Enlightened liberality has accepted the services of two trained nurses.'[1] The Poor Law Board also affirmed that this Lancashire infirmary was one of the best in the kingdom. The main offices of the workhouse, 3 miles distant, were connected to it by telegraph line and a greenhouse was built in the late 'sixties to supply the sick with flowers. It was also the first infirmary to be built on the pavilion system,[2] which was later adopted by most new infirmaries and hospitals. Dr. Robertson, one of the most prominent members of the Manchester Statistical Society and a great local Public Health reformer wrote papers in 1856, 1858, and 1860 on the new scheme for hospital construction, and in 1866 an article on the 'Pavilion System at the Chorlton Workhouse' described its great advantages and urged its adoption universally.[3]

That many abuses continued to flourish in the provinces as in the Metropolis was only to be expected in these years of transition and the Inspectors pointed to the overcrowding which still existed. Of the workhouses in the late 'sixties Louisa Twining wrote: 'Many mistakes made even in the recent buildings of our new infirmaries, prove only too clearly the incompetency of those who had the matter in their hands.' Because of the narrow and short-sighted policy and insistence on economy, controversies, she said, were frequent between Guardians and Medical Officers, who were not consulted as they should have been on matters connected with the welfare of the sick poor. She suggested a medical superintendent should be the head of the infirmary and have a seat on the Board of Guardians. One of the most important recommendations which had been brought forward and which she urged Parliament should institute, was the opening of all infirmaries to medical students and the appointment of assistants to workhouse Medical Officers, who often had as many as 500 patients. Masters also, she pointed out, should be drawn from men of superior position and their reports made to the meetings of the Boards of Guardians. She raised one problem not touched on before—interment. Before the 'seventies the burial of paupers was scandalous. Little improvement had been achieved by 1886 when she wrote: 'the dead are laid in shells, boards unplaned inside, on a sprinkling of sawdust, perfectly naked, with a strip of calico over their body only . . .'[4]

Other reformers were also not quiescent after the 1867 Acts. Of the provinces the *Lancet* wrote that it was evident that Boards of Guardians everywhere—with the exception of a few large towns where from accidental circumstances (as for example in Liverpool and Manchester) men of unusual intelligence took an active interest in parish affairs—were utterly incompetent to the duties assigned to them.—'The hideous social ulcer is not

[1] J. H. Stallard, *London Pauperism amongst Jews and Christians*, 1867.
[2] J. H. Rhodes, Poor Law Conference, 1883.
[3] *Transactions of the Manchester Statistical Society*, 1866–67.
[4] Louisa Twining, *Recollections of Workhouse Visiting and Management*, 1880.

checked, but aggravated by the cruel, and really wasteful parsimony of the boards.' The *Lancet* therefore urged Lord Devon to move for a Royal Commission of Inquiry.[1] Florence Nightingale also advocated this for she maintained partial reform was ineffective —the *whole* Poor Law system needed reconsideration. The Workhouse Infirmary Association held a large meeting again in the spring of 1868.[2] Hart, Anstie, Stallard, and Carr were the most active speakers, and a deputation was sent to Lord Devon to urge further Poor Law Reforms. They asked him to obtain Parliamentary power to enforce a uniform code of regulations regarding hospital and sanitary matters in all Unions. Second, they desired to see an auxiliary staff of technically skilled inspectors employed in the country as they were in London. The dispensary system should also be introduced universally so that a real and effective service might replace the inefficient arrangements for out-patients. Thereby sickness could be checked before it resulted in pauperism as it was doing on an enormous scale. The *Lancet* commenting on Lord Devon's reply called it 'timid conservatism which all along had maimed the efficiency of the legislative efforts to repair the blunders of the Poor Law Act of 1834'. The alarming increase in pauperism, the article continued, sprang from the very system which was intended to be economical, and parsimony was carried to a point of inflicting hardship, and in many cases cruelty, on the helpless class of paupers. Lord Devon promised the deputation he would insist on trained and paid nurses for the sick and that he would introduce regulations for space per bed, ventilation, and windows, and that Inspectors should have new instructions. He favoured the principle of dispensaries, but doubted whether it would be practicable to introduce them into the country. He was very reticent on skilled Inspectors because he questioned whether they would work harmoniously with the Medical Officers. He also offered what the *Lancet* called 'the threadbare truism and misleading fallacy that it was wrong to pamper the pauper so as to make his condition a matter of envy to the poorer rate-payers'. This, commented the writer, was 'suicidal absurdity and an injustice' when the authorities carefully provided that 'the condition of the convict should be the natural object of envy to the unfortunates who had fallen to the level of paupers'.[3]

Throughout the period the superiority of the condition of prisoners was held up to the Poor Law Board. At an inquest on a death in a workhouse in 1867, the Medical Officer commented on the liberality with which the deceased had been treated in a prison hospital. He had been allowed four glasses of port daily, brandy, beef-tea, eggs, mutton, fish, and anything he fancied. The Coroner pointed out that he wished he could say paupers were treated as well as prisoners, but the destitute would not fare better until inquests were held on everyone who died in workhouses. The *Lancet* reporting the case, endorsed this view and recommended a jury should attend large workhouses twice a week to investigate into the circumstances of every death prior to burial.—'We would not then hear of Medical Officers being reproved for courting publicity for neglected nursing or of the attempts to

[1] *Lancet*, 1868, i, pp. 358–60.
[2] 13 March 1868.
[3] *Lancet*, 1868, i, pp. 414–15.

hush up particulars of sudden or disgraceful death.'[1] Louisa Twining also compared the prison and the workhouse. People going to prison and confessing that it was for the sake of obtaining relief had been asked why they had not applied at the workhouse. They generally replied, that 'they did not like the disgrace of doing so'. Yet these people could commit offences and enter prison without feeling any degradation. Louisa Twining believed that the general management of prisons was felt to be so superior to that of the work-houses, that it raised them in the estimation of the lower classes—'who, even the worst ... are keenly alive to justice and fair treatment'. She gave a comparison of salaries of prison and workhouse officers, showing the former to be very much higher and that far more officials were employed.[2] Also dietaries were much better and medical treatment far superior.

That poverty was a crime had been the principle established by the 1834 Act, and in the early 'sixties the Select Committees still received evidence of the strong repugnance of the poor to enter the workhouse. The director of St. Pancras workhouse commented that many of the poor half-starved in preference to applying for institutional relief. The same was said of Bethnal Green where the workhouse test was rigidly applied, and where because of this, Farnall said the best arranged workhouse in the Metropolis was to be found![3] But in con-sequence, the amount of pauper relief applied for was relatively smaller in this Union compared with the immense amount of poverty and want. William Rathbone, when he visited the slum neighbourhoods of his town in connection with his work for district nursing, found that the respectable poor preferred to endure almost any degree of neglect or misery in their homes rather than enter the workhouse—although the Liverpool institution was good.[4]

We have traced the progress of the breakaway from the application of the principle of deterrence to the sick pauper, but among some Guardians and even among central officials, this development was not complete by the 'seventies. In 1867, Hardy as President of the Poor Law Board had made the official declaration of the change in central policy:

> There is one thing ... which we must peremptorily insist on, ... the treatment of the sick in the infirmaries being conducted on an entirely separate system, because the evils complained of have mainly arisen from the workhouse management—which must to a great degree be of a deterrent character—having been applied to the sick, *who are not proper objects for such a system.*[5]

[1] *Lancet*, 1869, i, p. 651.

[2] A prison governor received on average £600 a year—a workhouse master £80 on average; a prison matron received on average £125 a year—a workhouse matron £50 on average; a prison medical officer received on average £220 a year—a workhouse medical officer £78 on average; etc.

[3] Stated to the Kensington Board of Guardians—Minutes, August 1859.

[4] Individual reformers, the Workhouse Visiting Society and the Infirmary Association completely dis-regarded the able-bodied, thereby showing the tendency of the day to regard all pauperism save that of the sick and aged as a result of dissolute living. The deterrence principle of 1834 could still be maintained regard-ing the able-bodied as long as the reformers failed to interest themselves in the economic and social causes of poverty.

[5] *Hansard*, Vol. 185, p. 163, 8 February 1867.

But a year later Sir Michael Hicks Beach, sometime Secretary of the Poor Law Board, stated, also in the House of Commons, that he did not believe in sick wards being made too comfortable; and allowing of a cynical inference, he quoted the Marylebone infirmary which afforded a most agreeable contrast with the squalid houses in which the poor lived. In 1871 Inspector Corbett wrote to the Poor Law Board:

> The incentive to provide against sickness is . . . diminished by the present lavish administering of outdoor medical relief. I would therefore encourage the Boards of Guardians to abstain far more than at present from giving outdoor relief to able-bodied men on account of their own sickness or accident. In nine cases out of ten it would be more speedily cured in the District Asylum or in the Infirmary of the workhouse, and the knowledge that relief in this form only, would be, as a rule, offered, would do much to encourage provident habits. When outdoor relief is afforded . . . it should be generally granted by way of a loan.

And at a Poor Law Conference in 1876, Inspector Holland could still say:

> I think we should keep in view that the aim of the Poor Law is to bring as few persons as possible under its scope. The ordinary way to provide for the calamity of sickness is through provident dispensaries, and our business in administering the law is not to discourage those who belong to provident dispensaries to provide for sickness in that way.[1]

The deterrence principle was implied, but the most peculiar refinement of it was applied in Birmingham. In 1888 the House of Lords Committee on Poor Relief heard that that city still retained what was fortunately a unique system. The idea of treating the sick poor merely as sick, not as paupers was so objectionable to the Birmingham Guardians, that they 'determined to make all persons who came to their infirmary pass through the gate which led to the workhouse grounds, so that they may not draw a distinction between workhouse and infirmary'.

But to the majority of the very poor the workhouse could, from necessity, not act as a deterrent. The Poor Law infirmary was, save in large towns which had special voluntary institutions, the only place which would receive such cases as venereal disease, fevers, puerperal fever, erysipelas, measles, chickenpox, and whooping cough. Even where hospitals existed their waiting lists showed early alternative relief was not available. The aged and infirm, the chronic sick, and the children also had nowhere else to go, and however repellent the conditions of the workhouses were in the middle of the century, they were definitely more attractive by the beginning of the 'seventies. We have traced in the

---

[1] After 1871 there was growing divergence between the Presidents and their Inspectors—the former were far more enlightened and friction over policy was frequent.

main the structural improvements of the institutions; equally as important was the development in the classification of the inmates. In the 'fifties the workhouses and their infirmaries in England and Wales accommodated nearly a quarter of a million people, and it was then tardily recognized that different classes of paupers needed different consideration. It was aptly said that

> each of the buildings which we so absurdly call a workhouse is in truth a general hospital, an almshouse, a foundling hospital, a lying-in hospital, a schoolhouse, a lunatic asylum, an idiot house, a blind asylum, a deaf and dumb asylum, and a workhouse . . . It is at once equally shocking to every principle of reason and every feeling of humanity, that all these varied forms of wretchedness should be thus crowded together into one common abode, that no attempt should be made by law to classify them and to provide appropriate places for the relief of each.[1]

The Poor Law administrators themselves became alive to the drawbacks of the mixture of classes, and the first move towards the provision of separate institutions was made by an attempt at classification and the segregating of the various groups within the single institution. Where this was achieved improvement in the condition of the inmates was effected. We have seen the greatest division came between the sick and able-bodied, although even this was not according to any strictly defined rule, and masters of workhouses adhered to their own definitions. For example, people subject to fits or spasmodic outbreaks of disease were in some workhouses classed as able-bodied, nursing mothers were always entered as such, if not actually ill. The sick themselves were gradually classified and the separation of infectious and contagious diseases effected. The Manchester Guardians for instance refused in 1849 to erect a detached infirmary, but converted a building for use as a Lock and Fever Hospital, and later a separate Fever Hospital was established. The Eccleshall Board of Guardians in 1866 set apart certain rooms as syphilitic, itch, and fever wards. In the following year the infirmary of the workhouse, which must have been empty, was ordered to be cleaned and renovated for its appropriation to lunatics and a better classified system of sick wards. In Kensington the Medical Officer constantly urged in the late 'sixties for the syphilitics to be taken out of the workhouse for treatment by the Sick Asylums District.

Another class of poor who were always driven to enter the Poor Law institutions were the incurables. The movement started by the Workhouse Visiting Society in the 'sixties was not only for separating them from the rest of the workhouse inmates but to get new special hospitals built for them. Louisa Twining pointed out that all people turned out of the hospitals as incurable went to the workhouses to die. No one, she said, thought of the incurably sick till very late.

> It was probably supposed that our workhouses took this class of persons under their care, for it was known that they were not maintained in hospitals. Yet it is pitiable to think of the large number of hopelessly sick and bedridden who are shut up in our

[1] Robert Pashley, *Pauperism and the Poor Laws*, 1852.

workhouses as at present constituted. Strict rules enforced in many of them as to receiving visits from friends is one of the reasons which causes them to be deemed little better than prisons!

In 1862 she asserted she knew of no instance where a ward was set apart for them. The petition to the House of Commons in 1861 of the Workhouse Visiting Society for reform in the Poor Law Medical Service, included the statement of leading physicians of the Metropolitan hospitals that there was a large number of persons inflicted with incurable diseases who were not proper objects for admission into the general hospitals, and who therefore had no alternative than to become inmates of a workhouse

> . . . general hospitals are established for the treatment of curable diseases and not as abodes for those who are permanently and incurably disabled . . . persons who are disabled whether from consumption or from cancer, . . . require and ought to have, more care and attention, and more so-called 'comforts', than the general inmates of workhouses . . . they should be placed in wards exclusively appropriated to them, in which, under proper regulation and with the sanction of Guardians, they might receive extra comforts as private benevolence might bestow.[1]

The petition was signed by ninety of the most influential doctors attached to all the London hospitals. After this the Workhouse Visiting Society in conjunction with the National Association for the Promotion of Social Science opened a National Fund to carry out the plan for furthering the accommodation of chronics in separate wards and that in these wards private charity should help to alleviate suffering. Supported by eminent doctors, proposals were sent to all Boards of Guardians in the country, but every one replied that there was no room in the workhouse for such classification of the sick, and some opposed charitable interference, while others denied the need for reform. Some Unions promised to consider the plan, but stated that new building would have to be undertaken because of the existing overcrowding. In the first year, 1861–62, seven Unions accepted the offer of grants to put the plan into operation. The most successful was Carrick in Ireland, and in 1863, after two years' trial, a brief printed statement was issued describing the nature of help given and the cost at which it had been afforded. The *Lancet* supported the scheme, and a leading article in 1861 pointed out that there were 80,000 people whom the Registrar General noted as dying of consumption, dropsy, and cancer, and that of these tens of thousands wore away the latter months of their lives in the workhouse.[2] But the objection continued to be urged that it was not legal and contrary to the spirit of the Poor Law for supplementary relief for these people to be added to the poor rates. In rural and most urban areas nothing was done to establish separate buildings or even wards. Nor was progress made in the Metropolis until after 1870, and then many of the old institutions were retained for the chronic sick, whilst new workhouses and hospitals were built elsewhere. The Fulham

[1] Louisa Twining, *Recollections of Workhouse Visiting and Management*, 1880.
[2] *Lancet*, 1861, i, pp. 119–20.

workhouse at Hammersmith, the Hackney workhouse, the St. Clement's workhouse of the City of London and the old hospital of Greenwich for example, all became Poor Law institutions for the reception of the chronic sick. The differentiation between hospital and infirmary was thereby begun—*the Poor Law hospitals were for the acute sick and the workhouse infirmary for the remainder.*

Many of the chronic sick were in the class of aged and infirm, and it was this category of the poor that flocked in overwhelming numbers to the workhouses during the administration of the Poor Law Board. The outdoor relief of 1s. or 1s. 6d. with a loaf was entirely inadequate and wages permitted no saving for independence after a life of hard labour. The injustice of these conditions had been recognized by the Poor Law of 1834—for the aged and infirm were to be offered institutional relief! But this class of poor was also to be provided with separate institutions, and had this been effected many of the activities of the reformers in the next generation would have been unnecessary. The provision of special institutions was the principle most widely departed from in the administering of relief, and the crowding of the aged and infirm into the general mixed workhouse entailed great hardship. In 1857 Mrs. W. Sheppard drew melancholy pictures of the condition of the aged sick and infirm in her *Experiences of a Workhouse Visitor* which ran into four editions and was followed by a plan for reform—'Sunshine in the Workhouse'. Mrs. Jameson, a prolific writer on women's employment and other subjects, inspected charitable and reformatory institutions at home and abroad in 1855–56. In her *Community of Labour*, 1856, she not only described the dreadful nursing system in the workhouses and commented on the treatment in jails being superior, but showed the distressing plight of the aged. She pointed out the injustice of inflicting on them the same conditions as those under which the able-bodied had to live. Quoting a chaplain she wrote:

> The inmates of our workhouses are not generally the dregs and refuse of the population, although . . . a great many of these are mixed with the rest. In our workhouse, of the 220 inmates only two come under the class of able-bodied. This is probably below the general average, but it proves the mistake of treating the entire number of inmates . . . with harshness, as if it was the invariable rule that they enter it through their own fault. A great portion of every workhouse should be regarded as appropriated to the reception of those aged or disabled persons who have spent their health and strength for the benefit of the community, and therefore have a claim on it when that health and strength are gone. If from want of friends and relations they are obliged to enter the workhouse they ought to be treated with as much kindness and consideration as is compatible with their station. Experience tells us they yearn for this more than for increased bodily comforts.

Once again improvement was gradually introduced as the separation of classes progressed. Living conditions, diet, and treatment were very different in 1871 from what they had been in the 'thirties, 'forties, and 'fifties. Amongst his many schemes for medical reform, Richard Griffin included the provision of separate almshouses for the aged. He pointed out the horror of the aged and infirm at being offered the workhouse which, he said, they regarded as a prison. He had experienced the salutary effect of an almshouse in Norwich, which already had such an institution in the 'thirties, and where he had been an honorary surgeon. The Poor Law Commissioners had disapproved of the establishment of such refuges and Norwich had a hard struggle to keep the infirmary.[1] A meeting was held by the Greenwich Guardians in 1866 to discuss the sending of the temporarily disabled, aged, and infirm to the workhouse. Inspector Farnall was present and informed the Guardians that he did not think the workhouse a fit place for this class. He implied they should have been given domiciliary relief and insinuated that the Relieving Officer and the District Medical Officer got rid of cases this way, because the outdoor sick cost an average of 6s., whilst workhouse inmates only cost 3s. 6d. He also said that as there were only forty pauper nurses and no paid ones, these were not enough to attend the sick and all the aged.[2] A clergyman spoke to the Select Committee of 1862 of the cruelty of forcing old married people to enter the workhouse because they were separated there. But although separation was general in the earlier period there were by 1862 311 Unions in England and fifteen in Wales where aged couples over 60 could live together in the institution.[3] New workhouses made provision for this also, as for example that at Brighton, which was built in 1868.[4] The hardship inflicted on the aged by offering only institutional relief was given in a moving article by a clergyman in 1870:

> By and by—the workhouse opens its doors to receive him and his wife. Home and little comforts which become necessaries of life to the aged must be given up, goods and chattels divided amongst the sons and daughters . . . Once in the Union he parts from his wife, to meet her for a short half hour each week of the brief term remaining to them before they turn to unremembered and unremembering dust. . . . She soon pines away of no particular disease and he remains a desolate old man, so far as desolation consists in the destruction of home and family kindness, but conventional kindness is contracted for and paid by the poor rate . . . His associations in the old men's wards by day and his companions in the old men's ward by night, in all the feebleness and with something of the petulance and peevishness of the aged, are men with whom he would never have been, from feeling of all self respect, familiar as long as he could help it. . . . His relations never go near the man and he can no longer walk over to the scene of his home, and he waits with such patience and resignation as religion and experience have combined to teach him, till the jest of the club day becomes sober truth, for the parish pays for the funeral after all.[5]

The clergyman spoke of a rural area, and it was probably true of the greater part of the

[1] Evidence to Select Committee, 1862.
[2] *Lancet*, 1866, i, p. 218.
[3] *Accounts and Papers*, 1863, lii.
[4] Letter from E. F. Fussell to the *Lancet*, 1868, i, pp. 673–74.
[5] The Rev. Stratton of Kent, *Royal Agricultural Society Journal*, Vol. 31, 1870. (Discussing the advantages of benefit clubs.)

country. But by 1870 much had been done to improve the lot of old people when they were forced to seek institutional relief. In the Metropolis and other large towns both wards and diet had been altered, for during the 'sixties there were over 15,000 old and infirm, sick or well, in the London workhouses out of a total number of inmates of not quite 30,000.

The composition of the inmates of a typical workhouse was given to the Select Committee of 1862 by Rogers. In the Strand there were an average number of 530 people a year, of these, 350 were old and infirm, fifty temporarily sick, eighty able-bodied, and twenty infants under two years of age. There were in addition 125 on the permanent sick list and fifty casuals. In 1859 there had been 276 aged and infirm; by the following year there were 438. This class, Rogers said, had increased so greatly that it was difficult to know how to feed them because so many could not eat the workhouse diet—chiefly pea soup, suet pudding, and boiled beef. He therefore drew up a scheme for the modification of the dietary for the aged and infirm, Table 14.3. The Strand Guardians approved of it and it was confirmed by the Poor Law Board. (It must have been exceedingly monotonous.)

TABLE 14.3
Scheme for the Modification of the Dietary of the Aged and Infirm.

	Breakfast		Dinner			Supper	
	Bread, ounces	Tea, pints	Beef or Mutton, ounces	Bread, ounces	Potatoes, ounces	Bread, ounces	Tea, pints
Sunday	4	3/4	4	4	8	4	3/4
Monday	4	3/4	4	4	8	4	3/4
Tuesday	4	3/4	4	4	8	4	3/4
Wednesday	4	3/4	4 Leg of beef soup and barley and rice, 1 pint			4	3/4
Thursday	4	3/4	4	4	8	4	3/4
Friday	4	3/4	4	4	8	4	3/4
Saturday	4	3/4	4 Leg of beef soup and barley and rice, 1 pint				

Rogers maintained the system worked well. It was a great advantage to the aged and infirm, and saved the Medical Officer a considerable amount of trouble in writing out separate dietaries for each person. The *Lancet* wrote in favour of Rogers' scheme and pointed out the unsuitability of the ordinary diet for the aged. The Strand Union was the first to admit the principle of a liberal dietary for them, and most of the London workhouses followed suit. A Return to the House of Commons in 1865 showed that separate dietaries had been introduced for the aged and infirm and the able-bodied in Mile End, Paddington, and Shoreditch; for the able-bodied, infirm, and children, in Bethnal Green, St. George's, Hanover Square, City of London, Stepney, Strand, and Whitechapel; for the able-bodied, aged and infirm, and children—with three different diets for various age groups of the latter—in St. Giles, Hampstead, Rotherhithe, and St. Saviour's. Chelsea, Clerkenwell, Islington, Kensington, East London, St. Olave's, and Wandsworth and Clapham offered all the separate diets of the latter class of Union and another special one for nursing mothers and casuals. Fulham, St. George in the East, Marylebone, Hackney, Holborn, St. Margaret's, and St. John's, Westminster, St. Martin's in the Fields, Lewisham, Bermondsey, and Newington only differentiated between able-bodied and children. St. Luke's, Middlesex, gave separate diets to the able-bodied, aged and infirm, children, and lunatics; St. Pancras only to the infirm and the insane. In Poplar, Greenwich, Camberwell, Lambeth, and Southwark only a single house diet was offered, although 'extras' were given to the aged and infirm and nursing mothers. Some amending of diets for the aged and infirm was also undertaken in the provinces. In Bakewell (Derby) for example, the Board of Guardians in 1867 appointed a committee to examine what arrangements could be made 'for the treatment of the aged and infirm inmates of the workhouse to render it more acceptable to them, and thus induce this class of paupers more willingly to avail themselves of admission to the workhouse'.[1] The report suggested a better dietary—a bowl of tea and a slice of bread in the afternoon!

An improvement in diet was accompanied by better environmental conditions. In 1852 Paddington, for example, considered providing additional room in the aged and infirm sleeping wards, because these people often entrenched on the hospital accommodation which was subversive of the classification prescribed. Plans were obtained, but the Guardians had to inform the Poor Law Board that the proposed alterations had to be postponed because greater costs would have been incurred than had been contemplated. It was not until the late 'sixties that such schemes materialized and then only in London and large industrial cities. In 1868 even the *Lancet* could report favourably on the improvement in conditions for the aged and infirm in the Marylebone workhouse. The new wards for these inmates were far superior to ordinary workhouse wards. There were six of them each 40 feet wide, 60 feet long, and 13 feet high, and every patient was allowed 780 cubic feet of space. They were heated and ventilated in what the *Lancet* described as a novel manner. The nurses' apartments, sculleries, and lavatories were conveniently placed, hot and cold water was laid on, and the walls were coloured, yet the total cost had not exceeded £27 per head. The *Lancet* commended the example set by Marylebone regarding the treatment of the aged—but regretted the amount of improvidence which was implied in the fact that nearly 1,000 of the 1,800 inmates of this workhouse were over 60 years of age![2] In the late 'sixties

[1] Minutes of the Bakewell Board of Guardians, 1867 (Webb MSS.).
[2] *Lancet*, 1868, i, p. 540.

permission was also granted to the aged and infirm to leave the workhouse to see their relatives and friends. One old pauper of Hampstead complained to the Poor Law Board that he had been detained from going out and this was causing hardship. Permission had been refused for the salutary reason that the smallpox epidemic prevailed, but the Poor Law Board requested the Clerk of the Union to report fully on the facts.[1] Visitors were still not allowed to the aged and infirm at this time, but on fine days they were taken for walks.

The workhouses, because they catered for the sick, aged and infirm, and incurables, were inevitably made responsible for a very high proportion of burials, but they also saw a great number of births. For the Poor Law institution was also the maternity hospital for women with illegitimate children. A proposition was made in the 'fifties for establishing an asylum, like a Bridewell, for women of this class in London, but the suggestion was never carried out. In the workhouses expectant mothers were the only class of paupers who were universally segregated. The labour wards were frequently terribly small and devoid of the necessary furniture. Again improvement came in the provision of an adequate water supply, more linen and rocking chairs. The so-called midwives were no better than those who attended the outdoor poor, but the attention of a doctor was granted more readily as he received no extra fee for workhouse deliveries. When workhouse Medical Officers became resident in the 'sixties they were always on call to assist in an emergency. Puerperal fever had a high rate in the early years but declined with the increase in cleanliness, better accommodation and living conditions. The introduction of a superior class of nurses and in the late 'sixties of trained midwives, were further salutary improvements. It was recognized that the maternity wards of workhouse infirmaries made very good training schools for midwives. In 1866 a return was made of the number of births in Metropolitan workhouses and the number of women who died in childbirth. The total number of births in the thirty-nine institutions was 2,728 and the number of deaths sixteen. The deaths occurred in nine workhouses, three of which were in St. Pancras, and five in Islington, so that thirty institutions had no fatal cases. Also four of the women had been consumptive before they entered the workhouses. Dr. Smith discovered in making his extensive inquiries that deaths subsequent to childbirth and puerperal fever were almost unknown. Another report on the low mortality rate in maternity wards was made in 1868. E. F. Fussell had for the previous six years studied the mortality in the maternity wards of the Brighton workhouse and found that 223 women had been confined, forty-five of whom were married and 178 single, and only one of these had died—of puerperal fever. Fussell considered only a single death remarkable because of the large preponderance of unmarried women in the number; also most of them were servant girls, a few affected with syphilis, and the majority of them primiparae. The maternity wards had been used for years without 'lying fallow' which was the usual custom, and Fussell attributed the low death rate to the professional skill and good nursing afforded, and also to the fact that the wards were completely isolated from the infirmary and attendants were forbidden to have any contact with other patients. The

[1] Minutes, Hampstead Board of Guardians, April and May 1871.

infant mortality was very different however. Of the 223 births one in six were still-born, and a large number of live babies soon died (number not given). A close inquiry into the practice of the midwife failed to give Fussell the reason for supposing she ever administered ergot. He found an ounce of laudanum but was assured that save for aperients she never dispensed any other drug.[1] Smith also commented in his reports on the high infant mortality rate, but efficient treatment of the newly-born and the decline in the administering of opiates depended not only on the increase of skilled nursing, but also on a change in the findings of medical science.—Much of the control over 'quietening mixtures' was not in the hands of the Poor Law authorities.

There was one other reform which doctors overlooked and for which the Poor Law Board to a great extent cannot be charged with negligence. This was ante-natal and post-natal care. Had this part of obstetrics been understood, the destitution authorities could still not have increased their services, for unless a woman was a permanent pauper the Poor Law legally could provide only for the emergency of childbirth. Before confinement or after discharge from the workhouse, the Poor Law authorities were necessarily and inherently incapable of exercising any supervision over a woman's health or conduct. It was a misguided principle through which the whole community suffered. From poverty, ignorance, or wilful carelessness a woman could neglect her infant to such an extent that she saddled the community with a rickety, stunted, or permanently disabled citizen. No conditions or inspection could be enforced; indeed it is doubtful whether it would have been effective, for the treatment of infants in workhouse nurseries was often as bad as the worst mother could give. The prevalence of ophthalmia neonatorum resulted in much preventable blindness, until in the late 'sixties the new or adapted wards provided the necessary light, air, and space, and the more competent nurses gave infants proper care. *To the extent that the reforms were not universal, the Poor Law authorities perpetuated pauperism where they could have prevented it.*

There was one more category of pauper which received increasing attention from the destitution authorities—the children. They and the sick, practically ignored by the new Poor Law, became the most favoured classes and illustrate most clearly the development of the supplementary policy which grew up after 1834 in poor relief. When by the mid-'fifties over 50,000 children (of whom 12,000 were orphans) out of a total number of a quarter of a million inmates, received institutional assistance this supplementary policy was imperative. In the country children relieved indoors remained in the workhouses, but in cities and particularly in London large District Schools became ever more numerous after 1847. Institutional relief for children in separate establishments was a principle of 1834, but in 1855 Guardians were permitted to grant domiciliary relief and pay for the schooling of destitute children. If one-tenth of the workhouse inmates were children, nearly one-half of the paupers in London and over one-third in the provinces received outdoor relief. The treatment of children only falls into this study in so far as it encroached on the medical services, and unfortunately it did so to a considerable extent. *The pauper schools and*

[1] Letter from E. F. Fussell to the *Lancet*, 1868, i, pp. 673–74.

children's wards of the workhouses would probably have provided the best hospitals for paediatric training in the nineteenth century. In them children's diseases were never absent. In the majority of workhouses in the country children occupied the same rooms as adults so that they were exposed to every type of illness, and when they were admitted sick they were again mixed in the general sick wards. This grave mistake was not particularly the fault of the Poor Law authorities—save that they disobeyed the advice for separate institutional accommodation which had with prescience been advocated in 1834—for the workhouses followed hospital practice where there were no separate sick wards until the 'fifties and very few before the 'seventies. Condemnation is more appropriate to the backwardness of the general hospital system, which was constantly watched by the Poor Law authorities.

Many witnesses to the Select Committee of 1862 stressed the necessity for children's sick wards. William Nassau Senior said classification in workhouses would remain very imperfect as long as these were not provided. Inspector Lambert reported them to be a necessity from his experience, and he also pointed out the deficient opportunities for exercise for convalescents. He had had courts thrown open wherever he could and had had iron railings substituted for walls so that more air could penetrate into the children's playgrounds and the environment be brightened. Inspector Walsham, however, painted a very rosy picture.

> Every day [he said] I regard with greater astonishment the extraordinary health of the children. . . . I have seen in my district in parts of Norfolk, Essex, and Kent, diphtheria and cholera sweep up to the workhouse door and carry off children of the same classes from immediately neighbouring cottages—but I have never had a case of diphtheria amongst the numerous workhouse children in my district . . . the immunity . . . is remarkable . . . They go out twice a week to play in the fields. Although they do not go out for five days a week they have yards to play in and could go out more if the Medical Officer said their health required it.

This appertained to a rural area, but even in the country and always in the town, the evidence given in the period belied this statement. The wards in the workhouses appropriated to children were often so dreadful that they caused illness when the children were healthy on entry. As Dr. Bence Jones described in his report on St. Pancras workhouse in 1856, the wards made even the nurse and the governess sick. Overcrowding and the absence of ventilation so fouled the air that the children vomited every morning. In one room four children slept in a bed and in another eight, in the former fifteen sick children were accommodated with the healthy, but the vitiated atmosphere and the undernourishment of the children soon made them ill. Children and women were also put together in two other rooms which were semi-underground and originally intended for store-rooms.

Against these conditions and from the point of view of education, the Poor Law schools sometimes provided a great contrast but often failed in their purpose. As we have seen in an earlier chapter, separate schools for pauper children were slowly provided under private management after 1834. Through the inefficiency of their administration, legislation was passed in 1844 and 1848 empowering Boards of Guardians to unite in school districts for the purpose of erecting schools to which children from all the parishes could be sent. An outbreak of cholera in 1849 in Tooting resulting in 180 deaths, and the trial for manslaughter of the master of Norwood—the two most famous of the London pauper schools—accelerated new building. A committee was appointed in 1849 by the Paddington Guardians, who sent their children to Norwood, to investigate conditions and this reported the lack of proper sleeping accommodation. The Medical Officer's official report drew attention to the bad ventilation, the overcrowding, and the harm in allowing three to sleep in a bed. The fever ward was small and scarcely ventilated and its whole condition objectionable. Children complained of the poor quality of the food and its insufficient quantity. The health of the Paddington children, the Medical Officer concluded, was far from satisfactory—there were forty-one of them at Norwood and only thirteen were at all fit. The Guardians therefore resolved on moving the children and informed the Poor Law Board of their decision.[1] Between 1849 and 1887, eighteen new Poor Law schools were built but the majority were established in the two years 1853 and 1854. The Select Committee of 1862 heard complacent evidence from Inspector Hawley on the condition of the children in the schools. Referring to the south-west region, he said they were all strong and healthy and that no more sickness occurred among them than among the children of the same class outside. A number of children were also taken into the schools to recover from disease contracted at home. He stated that he was dwelling on the health of the children in his description rather than on the educational facilities provided, because it had been found that the great problem which arose when these schools were opened was the enormous amount of sickness in them!

Born rickety and with feeble constitutions, the children of the poor contracted disease quickly once it had been imported into the establishment. Crowded together with no means of isolation, some children were ill with one disease after another for years, so that the schools were hospitals rather than centres of education. Besides the epidemic diseases, skin affections, ringworm, and ophthalmia emerged as a problem from the very beginning. Hastily planned, the new institutions only perpetuated the evil that weighed on former workhouses and the private contractors' schools. The District Schools were regularly inspected by the District Medical Officers of the Unions, who sent their children to them. They also had nurses, generally paupers however, and Shoreditch was unique in paying them—the head nurse received £4 10s. and the seven assistants £2 10s. each a year. Shoreditch was also one of the few Unions where the District Medical Officer was paid an additional fee for attending the schools—he received £10 a year. It is in the doctors' reports to the Guardians that the prevalence of disease in the schools is revealed. The Minutes of the meetings of the London Boards of Guardians have few adverse reports from the School Visiting Committees. In Poplar such a Committee reported in 1862 that great numbers of

[1] Minutes, Paddington Board of Guardians.

the children in the Forest Gate School were suffering from ophthalmia and other diseases and that such cases should be removed. They also stated that the children looked 'dull and slovenly', but all subsequent accounts were favourable.[1]

St. George in the East had sent its children to Tooting until the cholera epidemic of 1849. On that occasion the Board of Health and the Poor Law Board informed the Guardians of the extremely dangerous position of the children there because of the ill-ventilated and overcrowded rooms. Forty-five cases and twelve of the 180 deaths at the establishment affected the children of this Union. Therefore the healthy were all removed to Mitcham at an annual cost of £100, and the weekly reports of the Medical Officer on this school nearly always spoke of the 'healthy and satisfactory conditions'. In 1852 the Plashet school was opened and St. George in the East removed most of its children there. The first report of the Medical Officer (January 1853) contained an account of the maltreatment of the children, of the remarkable spread of scabies through negligence and ignorance, and it was punctuated with phrases such as 'frightful prevalence of this disorder' and that the master, matron, and nurse were quite aware of the 'shocking state of the disease'. The nurse, the doctor stated, had not diagnosed the first case properly and had failed to report it to him, therefore the child was left to mix with others and spread the disease. Another Medical Officer reported to the Guardians that there were forty cases of ophthalmia at the Plashet School and asked for the nurse to be suspended. A preparation of bark was introduced for curing eye trouble, and two months later the Medical Officer reported that there was no more scabies and only a few in the infirmary with bad eyes. The remaining children were described as in good health. In April 1853 scarlet fever attacked the school and the doctor had all the other patients removed from the infirmary wards. The Medical Officer was conscientious and the 250–300 children at Plashet were examined every Saturday morning throughout the 'fifties and 'sixties. One-sixth of the inmates were in hospital in 'normal' times in these years and the figure often rose to one-half, for fevers were never absent and infectious diseases were constantly breaking out. In January 1857, thirty-two cases of measles were reported and several deaths occurred. Ophthalmia was by then so prevalent that the Guardians applied to the Poor Law Board for permission under the 1851 Act to pay ten guineas to the London Ophthalmic Hospital.[2] In 1858 whooping cough attacked many children; the Medical Officer again ordered isolation, but pointed out that efficient treatment was impossible with pauper nursing. He had the nurses dismissed on many occasions and one girl was killed by a severe blow from one of them although at the inquest it was maintained she had died of fever. The local epidemic of whooping cough was followed by mumps, and in one week in October 1858, twenty cases were reported. The Plashet infirmary was found no longer large enough to hold its sick children and was extended in the autumn of that year. The Medical Officer also asked for an increase in salary to £70 a year for the district and the school duties.

[1] Minutes, Poplar Board of Guardians.
[2] Minutes, Board of Guardians, December 1857. The 1851 Act (14, and 15 Vic. c. 5, s. 4) allowed Unions to subscribe to hospitals.

Many references were made in the late 'fifties to the cows and pigs which were kept at Plashet being ill or dying—although no consequence was reported, the food of the children must have come from diseased animals and bovine tuberculosis was probably widespread. In the summer of 1863 scarlet and typhoid fevers were prevalent in the school and whooping cough had been dangerous in the spring. By this time there were 400 children in the institution, and Kensington and Gravesend had added their number to those of St. George in the East. In September 1865 ophthalmia was more widespread than usual, although the situation improved in November. In the first week in September there were forty-one children in the infirmary, in the second eighty, of which over fifty were ophthalmic cases. During the winter there was a great increase in scarlet fever and the mortality rate grew. In 1866 the Poor Law Board suggested to the Guardians concerned with Plashet that all their children above the age of two should be sent there and that additional provisions for the sick should be made. In the next twelve months 500 children were maintained in the school, and during February 1867 forty-nine of them had smallpox, fifteen typhoid fever, twenty-seven low fever, and fifty-one infants and twenty-one girls had skin diseases. Inflammation of the lungs and skin diseases were mentioned in every medical report. They were part of Plashet's existence! In February also, Dr. Markham, Medical Officer to the Poor Law Board, visited the school and reported that health was good on the whole, the institution well managed, and the doctor satisfactorily isolated infectious cases—there was no mention that nearly one-third of the children were ill. The School Committee began to report frequently and regularly to the Board of Guardians in the late 'sixties and nearly every account stated the prevalence of mesenteric disease and the high proportion of children in the infirmary. In 1869 the St. George in the East Guardians wished to raise the salary of the Medical Officer to £120 for his great service to the school, both in detecting and treating disease, but the Poor Law Board denied permission. The nurses were by this time receiving £15 a year—one resigned because she objected to cleaning the children's heads. By an order of 1868 the central authorities refused to allow the appointment of any more pauper nurses in Plashet and required a list of the qualifications of nurses already engaged. There is no record whether the Guardians complied, and pauper nurses were still employed in the workhouse infirmary. The reforms of the late 'sixties had no effect on disease at Plashet. In June 1867 there were forty-five cases of scarlatina, six of ophthalmia, eleven diseases of the head, as well as whooping cough, scabies, and tuberculosis. The story of the continual ravaging of Plashet school by disease ends in 1869—when it was closed and sold to Holborn.[1]

Similar accounts can be found in the Minutes of the Boards of Guardians of Stepney, St. George the Martyr, and the Strand, who removed the whole of their destitute children receiving institutional relief to District Schools. Norwood, where Lambeth maintained its charges, was like Plashet closed by the changes made in the early 'seventies, and became a children's infirmary and nursery, whilst the school was moved to Hanwell. One of the

[1] This account is collected from the Minutes of the St. George in the East Board of Guardians, 1847–70.

objects of the Metropolitan Poor Act was to secure the entire removal of children from the workhouses to separate institutions, and five School Districts were established. It was part of the policy to relieve congestion in the workhouses and also a step towards the furtherance of the new principle—the provision of separate institutions for each class of pauper. However superior the new or adapted schools appeared, disease continued to flourish in them after 1870. Medical inspection had been introduced by the central authorities in the late 'fifties and from 1870 a considerable number of reports kept the public well-informed as to the state of the schools so that means for preventing disease could be taken.

The first of these reports was made by Sir William Bowman in 1858 on Norwood. This and all subsequent accounts revealed to the central authorities the prevalence of disease and particularly of ophthalmia. They emphasized the same lesson which had been preached earlier—efficient sanitation, cleanliness, ample space, separate wards for different illnesses, and isolation of contagious cases. Dr. George Critchett, the famous ophthalmologist of Moorfields, suggested in his report of 1868 that infected children should not only be kept apart, but should also be taught separately in convalescent wards, so as to obviate the too rapid return of previously sick children to the body of the school.[1] Inspector Mouat found in 1873 that half the children in all schools were affected by ophthalmia. He maintained the disease was introduced from outside and that once it was brought into the institution the lack of sanitary arrangements and the overcrowding made it difficult to eradicate. He advocated that all new entrants to the schools should be medically examined and infected children immediately segregated, but he preferred patients to be treated in the workhouse infirmary until they were cured or convalescent. Other suggestions were a separate bed for each child, particularly when ill, a more generous diet, and better nursing to replace the incompetent pauper assistants.[2]

The schools, however, no doubt saved hundreds of young lives during the fever and smallpox epidemics of 1869–71, for whatever their defects they were superior to the workhouses. But the result of rushing so many children, both sick and the well into them during these three years increased the risk of outbreaks of contagious and infectious diseases like itch, ringworm, ophthalmia, measles, and scarlet fever. Besides the epidemics giving an impetus to the removal of children to the schools, the Metropolitan Poor Act provided a more practical reason, for the cost of maintenance was charged to the Common Fund, whereas Unions or parishes were responsible for the maintenance of children retained in the workhouses. An experiment was made in Whitechapel which was a forerunner of great consequence for the efficient treatment of sick pauper children. Since 1867 there had been a great prevalence of ophthalmia at the Anerley School and chiefly because of this Whitechapel built a new infirmary in 1868. Ophthalmia however continued and in 1870 Dr. George Critchett was asked to investigate the cause. He repeated his advice about removing affected children to a school of their own where prolonged treatment could be given. But

[1] S. Stephenson: Report on Inquiry upon Ophthalmic State of Poor Law Children in the Metropolis, London, 1897. The use of a specialist by the Poor Law authorities is an interesting development.

[2] Inspector F. J. Mouat, Third Report of the Local Government Board, 1873–74.

no action was taken until Inspector Bridges in 1872 likened Anerley to 'a great ophthalmic infirmary'. In that year a house was converted and 300 affected children were transferred to it. The improvised hospital school was maintained for a year, the experiment was successful, and ophthalmia eradicated from the Whitechapel school. Separate special schools like those for ophthalmia or mental defectives were not introduced until the Poor Law school system was radically changed at the end of the century. But a beginning was at least made under the Poor Law Board, and the Education Authorities after the 1870 Act were supplied with a precedent for providing special State institutions. The man who had done so much to awaken the Poor Law Board out of its apathetic acquiescence in the inefficiencies of the medical services was also responsible for establishing a departmental committee in 1893 to review the whole problem of the care of Metropolitan children under the Poor Law. Ernest Hart in the *Lancet* and the *British Medical Journal* continued, under the Local Government Board, to make exposures similar to those which had made the *Lancet* so influential in bringing about the Metropolitan Poor Act. It was to a great extent through his efforts that the whole Poor Law school system was revolutionized after 1897.

One of the greatest developments that was made under the administration of the Poor Law Board and on which so much of the efficiency of the Poor Law medical services depended was the establishing of a trained nursing system. The progress in nursing was linked with the evolution of the Poor Law infirmary, and the increasing improvement in the condition of children, aged and infirm, incurables, and lunatics depended in great measure on the substitution of skilled and respectable nurses for incompetent and often dissolute paupers. Much of the story of the change effected has inevitably been embodied in the foregoing survey, but the problem was in itself so vital that it demands independent analysis.

When it was realized that in the absence of adequate general relief and because of the insalubrious home conditions, a more speedy cure of patients could be achieved in the workhouse infirmary, it was also discovered that the inattention of incompetent nurses balked many of the doctors' efforts. The employment of pauper nurses was not so much due to the Guardians' parsimony as to the entire absence of a skilled nursing system in the country. The great age in hospital building in the eighteenth century had no equivalent in the rise of the standard of nursing. John Howard criticized the squalor of hospitals and the inferior body of women who staffed them. Inferior management made them the victims of bad accommodation, long hours and miserable pay, and induced them to drink. Acquiescence in the lowest standard of nursing typified the early nineteenth century attitude to medical treatment. Dickens lamented the state of nursing in hospitals in his *Martin Chuzzlewit*; his caricatures were a factor in reform, but Sairey Gamp and Betsey Prig were taken from real life. The regulations drawn up for the nurses at the Liverpool Infirmary were a clear indication that his two characters were no exaggeration:

Nurses were forbidden to conceal the effects of any patient who might die in hospital or to take from a patient any fee, reward or gratuity. Dirt, tow, and rags were not to be thrown out of the windows, nor were the clothes of patients or others to be hung out of the windows. One window in every ward was to be left open day and night. Any nurse convicted of concealing the escape of any patient from her ward was to be discharged. Finally, all nurses who disobeyed the Apothecary's, Secretary's, or matron's orders, got drunk, neglected their patients, or quarrelled with patients, or did not cautiously reveal to the officers of the House all irregularities committed by patients in their wards (such as drinking or smoking tobacco), or quarrelled with each other, destroyed medicines or stores, feigned complaints and neglected cures, were to be immediately discharged the service of the House.[1]

In 1844 the attention of the Liverpool Infirmary Committee was drawn to the inadequacy of nursing; patients were left to take their own medicines, and cleanliness was neglected. There were no night nurses so that doctors often had to ask friends to remain with patients during the night, or convalescents were used as night staff. In 1851 the Medical Board realized the desirability of appointing night nurses, but the number was not to exceed four. A doctor in 1853 called the nurses a very 'scratch lot, some with practical knowledge but others utterly untrained and mostly slovenly and frequently inattentive'. Nearly all of them were over 60 years of age and there were only four who did not get drunk habitually.[2]

The revolution in hospital nursing came with Florence Nightingale, but attempts at reform were made before the Crimean War. In Liverpool the Roman Catholic Sisters of Mercy did great work in time of epidemics and religious bodies in other towns always assisted the sick poor. In 1836 the Protestant Deaconesses Institute was founded in Kaiserswerth in the Rhineland for the training of nurses, and in 1840 Elizabeth Fry established a small society of nurses in London to work among the poor. The only training the latter were given was daily attendance at Guy's Hospital for a few months, where they had to learn what they could from the uneducated nurses there. Some members of the Church of England founded St. John's House Nursing Institute in 1848 to train nurses for hospitals, and this Society was the first to offer its services during the Crimean War. In 1856 the entire nursing of King's College Hospital was entrusted to it and the Institute remained attached to this hospital for the future. Liverpool got its first organization for training nurses in 1855, and the Royal Infirmary granted its members admission to the wards for the purpose of instruction. In the same year the famous 'Nightingale Fund' was inaugurated under Royal patronage. The new nurses' training school, opened in 1860, was affiliated to St. Thomas's Hospital and Florence Nightingale drew up the regulations, and acted as consultant. Out of this school arose the modern practice of nursing.[3] Prospective nurses received one year's training, their salaries were paid from the liberally endowed Fund, and St. Thomas's provided the facilities for work. The Medical Act of 1858 permitted women to register as doctors, but no provision was made for the registration of trained nurses

---

[1] Bickerton, *A Medical History of Liverpool*, 1936.   [2] *Ibid.*

[3] Since this work was completed Professor B. Abel-Smith has published his *History of the Nursing Profession* (1960).

however skilled. In the second half of the nineteenth century apathy was abandoned and hospital committees began to complain that they could not get enough competent and respectable women to staff their wards. Provincial towns set up their own training schools for nurses. In Liverpool the great philanthropist William Rathbone provided for a trained district nurse in the early 'sixties. Wishing to extend the experiment he found no experienced nurse available and therefore applied to Florence Nightingale who suggested the city should form a school of its own. An association was formed in January 1862 and in the following year Rathbone built the training school and home for the nurses, presenting them to the Infirmary. The objects of the association in order of priority were, first to provide nurses for the Royal Infirmary, second for poor patients in their homes, and third for wealthier patients. In 1869 Birmingham also established a Training Institution for Nurses.

Once the system of using trained nurses in voluntary hospitals had started, the enlightened public were roused to the condition of the workhouse infirmary, for the noxious effects of the old system were worst in Poor Law institutions. The evils of making pauper inmates responsible for the care of the sick claimed the energetic attention of Louisa Twining.

When we consider [she wrote in the 'fifties] the persons to whom such extensive power and responsibility are entrusted in the care of 50,000 sick persons in the London workhouses alone, we can hardly wonder at the results of the system. The nurses are only worn-out remains of lives whose strength has been spent elsewhere. Efficient nurses, who could gain a living in any hospital . . . are not likely to offer themselves for a post in which all the work is of the hardest kind, . . . [and for no payment]. . . . It is a fact when able women are by chance found as nurses, Guardians often do not choose to keep them as inmates, . . . and they are not likely to remain themselves if not more encouragement is offered to them. If even more distinction were made in their dress . . . there would be more chance of their being respected by their fellow inmates . . . Therefore they are all incapacitated in some way . . . morally or physically . . . One of these nurses boldly stated she had been in the House of Correction sixteen times and was not ashamed of it . . . she was a woman given to drink, and of violent ungovernable temper, causing great misery to the aged people under her control. Can these women be fit to attend on the sick, infirm, and dying? Of course such labour is cheap, and it is desirable if possible to employ those who must be maintained at the cost of the parish, but in no case should they be left with the sole charge and responsibility of sick wards as continually as they are at present, without any other control than an occasional visit of the matron, at most once a day and in some cases once a week. In the intervals patients are absolutely and helplessly at the mercy of these women, of whom they dare not complain, knowing what treatment would be visited on them in revenge if they did. From the complete equality of pauper nurses and their patients, no respect is felt for them, and no authority can be exercised. Obedience therefore is obtained through fear and terror, and only those who have witnessed the wrangling and abuse that but too often are carried on by patients and nurses can imagine so sad and painful a scene. Seeing how careful Boards of Guardians are in all matters of expense, it would have been well if the recommendation of the Poor Law with regard to the employment of at least one paid nurse had been a law, as it is many workhouses are without one. That such a person would always be as able as we could desire for so important a post we could hardly hope from what we know of paid nurses in hospitals, but at any rate there would be a better chance of efficiency and character than in the present plan.[1]

For fifty years Louisa Twining campaigned for the improvement of workhouse nursing and at the time of her death Sarah Tooley published the well-known *History of Nursing*, in which she described the old system: 'Pauper nurses', she wrote, 'regarded the work as a penance for being in the House, and nursed the sick with the same turbulent spirit as the inmates who picked oakum.'[2]

The incipient feminist movement was particularly interested in the reform of nursing and Mrs. Jameson described the workhouse system in her *Community of Labour*:

There are seventy paid nurses and 500 pauper nurses and assistants. Half of these nurses are above 50; a quarter over 60; many not less than 70; and some more than 80 years old. An extra allowance of tea and beer is the reward given for their services; but the propensity to drink is so strong, that it is with the utmost difficulty that they are kept from indulging it . . . The habit is encouraged rather than checked by those in authority. In many workhouses it is the custom to allow nurses a glass of gin daily besides their portion of beer. Can we wonder that the habit thus acquired grows into drunkenness when opportunity offers. . . . If nurses are so worn out by ill-health and poverty that they really require such stimulants to enable them to perform their duty—it is argument enough against their efficiency. . . . Living night and day in sick wards, ill-ventilated as they generally are, may well impair the powers both of body and mind, and nurses should not be required to do so.

It was inevitable that societies dedicated to the promotion of social and Public Health reform should interest themselves in the problem. Foremost of these was the Epidemiological Society which had Richard Holt and Edward Sieveking as honorary secretaries. In October 1854 a Nursing Scheme Committee was formed and its first move was to send questionnaires to Medical Officers of various Union workhouses in England asking for information: on how many sick were relieved in a year; whether inmates were engaged in nursing and if so what kind and how did they behave; did doctors often feel the want of nurses in times of epidemic and other sickness; did they consider any material advantage would accrue to the community at large by the organization of a system whereby nurses could be easily obtained either gratuitously or at low charge; would the labouring classes

[1] Louisa Twining, *Recollections of Workhouse Visiting and Management*, 1880.
[2] Sarah Tooley, *History of Nursing in the British Empire*, 1906.

avail themselves of nurses if the opportunity were offered; what results regarding the arrest and prevention of disease, particularly in regard to the contagious and epidemic could be anticipated if a staff of nurses were provided in every Union; would any pecuniary saving be likely to accrue to ratepayers; if able-bodied female workhouse inmates were extensively employed as outdoor nurses, how should they be controlled and supervised; could male nurses be employed in cases of insanity and delirium. In addition the doctors were asked to include in their replies any practical suggestions for the provision of nurses for paupers and the labouring population. In 1855 the Committee, which consisted of several eminent physicians, produced a scheme with which Dr. Sieveking's name became associated. It was suggested that numerous able-bodied women in the workhouses should be trained in the infirmaries and sent out as nurses of the poor. Sieveking tried to give publicity to the plan and in 1856 led a deputation from the Epidemiological Society to the Poor Law Board. Following this a draft order was sent to the central authorities to aid them in establishing the scheme. This proposed that all trustworthy women should be systematically instructed first in the preparation of sick room diets and other domestic duties and then transferred to the infirmary to be trained as nurses. The matron and the Medical Officer were to be the superintendents. Women selected for this double training were to follow each other in regular rotation, and if they wished they could continue their instruction and be eligible for first- and second-class certificates signed by the Medical Officer and the master. All those who could read and write and who had received at least two months training as well as being of good character and neat and clean in appearance could qualify for the first-class certificate, and those who had not less than one month's training for the second. The master of the workhouse was to keep a register of nurses and the date of qualification, and this 'Engagement Book' was to be open to all who required nurses. The name and address of a person engaging a nurse was to be entered also, and if he discharged her he was to write a testimonial of her conduct which was to be entered in the register for the information of future applicants.[1]

In their letter to the Inspectors on the proposals the Poor Law Board stated it would be 'impracticable and inexpedient on their part to establish authoritatively in the workhouses . . . a general system of training for nurses'. This was also communicated to Sieveking, but they thought it not 'improbable that in large workhouses where paid nurses were employed . . . it would sometimes be practicable to adopt a system under which such of the female inmates as may be trustworthy and competent be employed in the infirmary and sick wards . . . not only to assist paid nurses', but also to be trained themselves so as to enable them subsequently to earn a livelihood independently. A register of nurses trained in the institutions was to be kept. The Poor Law Board desired their Inspectors to communicate these suggestions to the Guardians and also to point out the strong sense the Board had of the evils resulting from the want of a sufficient number of trained and efficient nurses for the poor. They hoped the Guardians would be ready to concur in any plan by which,

[1] Letter to the Poor Law Board enclosing draft order from the Epidemiological Society, 6 May 1856

consistent with the sound system of Poor Law administration and laws regulating expenditure of the poor rates, their number might be increased.[1] The Poor Law Board's sanction of the plan, even if they did not order its execution, was the earliest public acknowledgement of the urgent and growing need for efficient nurses for all classes. But the scheme aroused opposition among the reformers. Rumsey drew attention to the dreadful material which pauper women presented, who in any case could not be trained in a workhouse. He maintained technical instruction must be obtained in hospitals where lectures could be given as well as practical experience.[2] Louisa Twining wrote: 'little could have been known of the real character of this class of women by those who made the suggestion, or of the fact that the greater number of them were brought to the workhouse by some loss of character, the chief cause of which was certainly intemperance'.[3] Apart from the great doubt as to the possibility of moulding the destitute women into efficient nurses, no machinery existed in the workhouses through which the plan could have been effected. No workhouse officer had the ability or power to train the women if any could have been found capable of such important an employment. The scheme was never carried out and any training of nursing assistants had to await the provision of an efficient staff of skilled superintending nurses. The Guardians also ignored the Poor Law Board's suggestion. The Epidemiological Society circularized the Unions in 1856 on the training of nurses, but replies were all like those of St. George in the East: the scheme was not adapted to their workhouse and therefore they declined to consider it. Untrained nurses continued to staff the infirmaries.

The Select Committee of 1862 heard evidence on the use of pauper nurses in the workhouses, particularly from Louisa Twining. She maintained that a strong feeling had arisen for the necessity of appointing a better class of nurses. As the institutions were becoming hospitals for incurables and for those turned out of the best hospitals, the care and attention given should be superior to that rendered by destitute women. She reiterated that pauper women had neither the capacity, physical strength, nor moral training to fit them as nurses. She commented on the way Medical Officers were handicapped and how cure was retarded. Nurses were constantly having to be changed because the able-bodied left to obtain employment or were dismissed for misconduct. Although their remuneration was generally only additional food and drink, the system was far from economical. The Workhouse Visiting Society proposed part of the Parliamentary Grant should be used for supplying Guardians with one paid nurse for the workhouse. Although the majority of Unions at this time, and even some in London, employed no paid nurses, Guardians had begun to employ one paid supervisor and she was often not a pauper. It was very unusual for Guardians to pay all their nursing staff as Bakewell did as early as the 'forties. They received 4s. a week and from 1848 5s; in 1867 when a separate infirmary was built a head nurse was appointed

[1] Letter from the Poor Law Board to Inspectors, 15 May 1856.
[2] *Essays on State Medicine*, 1856.
[3] *Recollections of Workhouse Visiting and Management*, 1880. (The classical opinion on the able-bodied died hard even with the reformers.)

at the princely sum of £28 a year with rations. (But this was a liberal Union: for example, a high dietary scale was adopted in the 'sixties, and inmates were given beef, plum pudding, ale, tobacco, and oranges on Christmas Day.[1]) Manchester adopted a strange system in 1849. Pauper nurses were no longer employed in the non-medical department but they were to continue nursing in the sick wards! In the non-medical department there were two nurses receiving £14 and £16 a year, a male nurse in the lunatic ward £20, and a female nurse in the lunatic ward £15, all with rations. In the sick wards six male pauper nurses received £2 12s. and fifteen female pauper nurses £2 12s. with maintenance. Manchester already in 1849 appointed a resident workhouse Medical Officer at the comparatively high salary of £100 with keep, and an apothecary at £90. (The master also received £250, the chaplain £200 and the clerk £500![2]) In 1852 the Marylebone and St. Pancras Guardians, on the recommendation of the Coroner, substituted paid and efficient nurses for the pauper attendants 'whose age, condition and infirmity generally render them unfit for their situation and through which the sick poor suffered so much'.[3] This was occasioned by Wakley who, as Coroner of West Middlesex, fought a constant battle to have inquests held on deaths which occurred in the workhouses through negligence. Chelsea also paid a nurse ten guineas in 1855 and she became assistant matron at £15 in the following year to supervise nursing.[4]

In 1865 the Poor Law Board asked for a return from every master of the Metropolitan workhouses as to the number of paid nurses employed, where they were trained, their ages, and the number of pauper nurses and their ages. The information conveyed was very valuable and revealed that eleven workhouses had only pauper nurses all unpaid; twenty-one paid untrained women to supervise the nursing and only six had any trained and paid nurses. The salaries of the latter ranged from £20 to £30 and St. George's, Hanover Square, paid £50; their average age was about 40. Altogether 897 pauper nurses were employed and sixty-nine skilled. In the two largest workhouses, those of Marylebone and St. Pancras, there were fourteen paid trained nurses and thirty pauper assistants in the former, and sixteen paid and trained, and 103 pauper assistants in the latter. (In Marylebone all domiciliary medical relief centred on the workhouse also, so that there were three resident Medical Officers and two dispensers, one senior resident Medical Officer, as well as honorary physicians. As over 800 patients were seen daily in the 'fifties the demand for nurses was also very high.[5]) Paid nurses were selected by the Guardians save in Marylebone where the responsibility rested with the Medical Officers. Pauper nurses were chosen by the master and the matron except in the City of London, and in Stepney, Bermondsey, St. Giles, and Richmond the Medical Officer assisted them. About half the nurses were on duty day and night. The paupers generally wore a different dress, although they shared the

[1] Minutes of the Bakewell Board of Guardians for several years (Webb MSS.).
[2] Minutes, Manchester Board of Guardians.
[3] *Lancet*, 1852, i, p. 61.
[4] Chelsea Board of Guardians, Abstract of Accounts, 1855–56.
[5] Dr. Boyd, evidence to Select Committee, 1854.

dormitories and dining tables of the other inmates—only in a few workhouses were they completely separated.[1]

Before 1863 not a single trained nurse existed in the infirmaries in the provinces. Where Guardians appointed salaried and skilled nurses they were trained by experience only and not through organized instruction. By the General Consolidated Order of 1847 the only qualification prescribed for paid nurses was that they should be able to read the written directions on medicines. Liverpool pioneered the way and once again through the benevolence of William Rathbone. He inquired in the early 'sixties into the conditions of the local workhouse infirmary, one of the largest in the country. He found it better in structure and equipment than most others. The Select Vestry had always had a reputation for being energetic and efficient, and doctors were encouraged to apply for everything they needed for invalid paupers. As we have seen in an earlier chapter, strict and comprehensive rules were formulated for the management of the infirmary and the conduct of officers. The head nurse was ordered to obey the instructions of the Medical Officers carefully, to supervise the nurses thoroughly, and to visit the sick wards frequently to ensure patients were being properly cared for. She was in charge of patients' diets and medicines, she had to see every new admission, accompany the Medical Officers through the wards, keep an admission and discharge book, and pay particular attention to the cleanliness of beds, linen, and wards. All property and clothes of patients were left in her keeping and she had to have them purified.[2] Unremunerated until 1848, she was paid £20 a year for these and many other duties subsequently. But the care of the 1,200 sick people in every stage of every disease was left to the able-bodied pauper women. These women, it was stated, were generally unreliable and of a demoralized type, attributed to Liverpool being a great seaport. At night a policeman patrolled some wards, while others in which patients were too old and infirm to create a disturbance were locked up and left unattended. The Chairman of the Select Vestry was aware of these evils, but did not think it possible that the authority would face the expense of trained nurses.

William Rathbone came to the rescue, and offered to finance for three years at £1,000 a year an experiment by which twelve trained nurses should be obtained from the Nightingale School at St. Thomas's Hospital. These were to be assisted by eighteen probationers and thirty-seven assistants drawn from the inmates. Fifteen scourers, six cooks, a house steward, a female storekeeper, and a housekeeper were also to be drawn from the inmates to complete the unit. All the pauper nurses were to receive a small salary and were not to be counted as paupers, so that increasing self-respect would encourage them ultimately to become efficient nurses. The nursing staff were to be relieved of every duty save those which fell into the medical field, and a Lady Superintendent was to control the unit. After some hesitation the Poor Law authorities accepted the proposal and the experiment was tried in the male wards which were completely isolated for the purpose. There were on 1 June 1865, 167 male medical cases, 173 surgical and 182 infirm and bedridden, and these 522

[1] Return to House of Commons by Villiers, 1865, No. 48 (abstracted).
[2] Letter, Select Vestry to Poor Law Commissioners, 1844.

patients were placed under the care of the ninety-two officers. Agnes Jones was to become one of the heroic figures in the history of pioneer nursing through her appointment as Superintendent of the Liverpool Workhouse Infirmary. Irish, deeply religious, trained at Kaiserswerth as well as at the Nightingale School, and passionately devoted to her work, she introduced a revolutionary element into the infirmary when the scheme was inaugurated in June 1865. She found herself thwarted by officials and patients. Discipline was lax and the wards so overcrowded that three were sleeping in a bed. (The cotton famine caused great distress.) The attempt to make nurses out of the paupers proved a failure, they could not be left without supervision for one moment and obtained intoxicants at the slightest opportunity. In one of her letters Agnes Jones wrote: 'I am almost distracted between sickness and anxiety and drunkenness. I have one head nurse in great danger . . . These ex-pauper women whom we are training were paid wages on Friday . . . and next day five came in tipsy. . . . How little can I do!' Yet her achievements were enormous. Two hundred idle 'patients' were discharged, the pauper nurses replaced, and Rathbone's experiment was declared immensely successful.[1]

Dr. Smith in his report on provincial workhouses alluded to Liverpool. He spoke of the new system running parallel to the old in the infirmary and how in the opinion of the master, the Medical Officers on the male side could place more dependence on the nurses, whilst on the female side it was cleaner and more pains were taken to adorn the wards. But Smith said there was not much difference in walking through the two sections, so that the issue had to rest on the quality of the individual nurses. The Poor Law Board also included a reference to the Liverpool experiment in its Eighteenth Annual Report and stated that both in the actual nursing of the sick and the general state of the hospital the benefits were already patent. A summary of the achievements of the first year of the new scheme was given in a report by the master of the workhouse to the Poor Law Board in 1866.[2] He asserted that the most casual observer could not avoid perceiving the marked improvement in every respect: 'This applies not only to the state of the wards, the care of the sick, but is particularly observable in the demeanour of patients on whom the humanizing influence of a body of women of character devotedly discharging their duties, produced evident fruits.' Great difficulty had been experienced in procuring suitable people as probationer nurses: forty had been engaged, and of these, twenty-one resigned and three had been dismissed, while the majority remaining had only recently been appointed. The experiment for training nurses had therefore not been successful, for sixty-seven pauper nurses had also been dismissed for misconduct and sixteen had resigned. The report went on to point out that the difficulty of keeping up a staff of nurses would prove no small barrier to the extension of the system. The master testified to the good care of the patients, but the returns compiled showed expectations regarding the recovery of patients had not been justified, but this was because the trial period of the first year had not been long enough. The report

[1] T. H. Bickerton, *A Medical History of Liverpool*, 1936.
[2] 'The Training of Nurses for Workhouse Hospitals', Report by George Carr, May 1866.

included a eulogy on Agnes Jones and concluded: 'The experience of the past year renders it certain that the Poor Law as existing offers no impediments to the successful working out of a most complete scheme for efficient nursing . . . in a manner advocated by the best friends of hospital nursing.' The physicians and surgeons of the infirmary also produced reports testifying to the ability, integrity, and efficiency of the new nurses. The former stated that from years of experience it was earnestly desired to see a similar system introduced into all parochial hospitals in the kingdom, and the latter urged the unqualified success of the new system. Therefore the scheme was extended to the whole infirmary and the cost was borne by the ratepayers.—In the first year expenditure on account of the trained nurses had amounted to £3,200.—Unfortunately Agnes Jones was in 1868 attacked by typhus and she was only thirty-six when she died. The spade work had been done, and the pupils from the training school she established followed her example, until gradually a skilled nursing system spread to all Union infirmaries in the country. On the pioneer, Florence Nightingale wrote:

> In less than three years she had reduced one of the most disorderly hospital populations in the world to something like Christian discipline, such as the police themselves wondered at: she had led, so as to be of one mind and heart with her, some fifty nurses and probationers. She had converted a Vestry to the conviction of the economy, as well as humanity of nursing the pauper sick by trained nurses . . . she had converted the Poor Law Board to these views . . . it was the first instance of its kind in England . . .[1]

Chorlton also established a nursing system in 1865. In that year there was a considerable outbreak of fever, and the Guardians experienced great difficulty in providing nurses for the new workhouse hospital and new infirmary. They accepted the offer of two Protestant Sisters from the All Saints' Convent, Manchester, to act as superintendent nurses. These performed their duties gratuitously but were maintained at the workhouse. They were directly responsible to the Medical Officer and had entire control of the nursing department, thereby excluding the interference of the master and the matron. Both Sisters had had considerable experience in hospitals, and they completely reorganized the Chorlton Infirmary. The Clerk of the Union informed the Poor Law Board of the great change that took place and described the arduous and often dangerous work of the nurses, for many of the assistants died of fever.[2]

In his report on provincial infirmaries in 1867, Dr. Smith stated that the feeling general in the country was that skilled paid nurses should be appointed to the care of the sick. He said a large number of paid nurses had been elected in the previous year, but none had been engaged in the numerous small rural workhouses. The reasons were that as they contained less than 100 inmates the number of sick was not great, so their care could be supervised by the matron. Second, of the 'sick' five-sixths were aged and infirm who required no

---

[1] Florence Nightingale, article 'Una and the Lion' in *Good Words*, June 1868. See also *Homes and Hospitals or Two Phases of a Woman's Work* by Amy Dutton and Agnes E. Jones, 1873.

[2] Correspondence of the Poor Law Board, 1865.

special skill, and third, in most workhouses there were women who had acted as nurses for many years—and these were quite as competent as paid nurses. Smith maintained however that there was always someone seriously ill or a maternity case which needed special care, and that therefore a skilled trained nurse should be engaged in the smaller institutions also. He suggested pauper nurses might provide the material from which efficient nurses could be provided and they should be removed from the rank of the destitute and be installed as paid officers. This had been done in many cases with a resulting increase in self-respect and competency. But such an effect had not been achieved universally and Smith advocated that every workhouse should have a responsible trained nurse to take direct charge of the sick, and where there was a sufficient number of good pauper assistants these should be promoted to nurses and become paid officers. It was discovered that large infirmaries were employing male nurses for male patients; this Smith deprecated and advised they should never be employed in hospitals as they had no quality as nurses in comparison with women. He also maintained that nurses should have no other duties than the care of the sick, for washing linen and cleaning floors occupied too much time and were therefore a distraction from efficient nursing. But he wished to see some duties extended. Nurses should have charge of all linen and medical appliances required in their department and be responsible for their proper use. This would preclude the dividing of functions with the matron. Where numerous nurses were employed, Smith stated the system obtained that either each had immediate responsibility for particular wards and the matron superintended the whole, or a chief nurse devoted her time entirely to superintendence. Only Chorlton and Liverpool, he pointed out, had a complete organization whereby the matron could not take direct action, and here the improved systems had not been established long enough to warrant any definite conclusion on the subject. In large workhouses where many paid nurses were employed, Smith believed they were conducive to efficiency and order, especially as superintendents were not burdened with extraneous worries and could devote their whole time to discharging their particular duties.

Smith also drew attention to the way in which patients were scattered about the workhouse, which made it impossible in many cases to nurse them efficiently without employing a number of staff that would otherwise have been absurdly great. Therefore the first consideration, he said, was to reorganize the wards, so that all the sick could be brought nearer to the officers' quarters. He gave an instance which was typical of very many workhouses. In Cranbrook and Battle the male and female sick were placed in wings at opposite ends of the main building, so that up to 200 yards had to be walked by a nurse, mostly in the open air, in going from one to another. The wards for different classes of sick were also widely apart, so that besides the ordinary wards for the two sexes, there were the aged and infirm wards, foul wards, itch wards, fever wards, lying-in wards, and children's wards, all in different places and nearly all having separate entrances from the yards. In a single workhouse therefore there were twenty-seven wards in ten or twelve different places. Medical opinion might have differed from Smith's recommendations that wards should all be brought together so that in a moderately sized or small workhouse one nurse could attend thirty patients. In bigger establishments where there was a separate infirmary and where wards were larger, he thought more than this number could be allotted to one nurse. The basis of improvement in the nursing of the sick in the workhouses was concentration and, if necessary, the rearrangement of the sick wards of various classes. The appointment of paid night nurses was urgently needed in larger institutions, and if more than three nurses were employed he suggested that there should be a superintendent to take direct charge and responsibility of the whole department and have all the stores for the sick under her care.—'The state of nursing in the workhouses is one of transition . . . improvements are daily effected but much remains to be done.'

Following the disclosures of the Inquiry of 1865 into workhouse nursing in the provinces in which it was revealed that only six trained nurses were employed, the Poor Law Board had in May of that year issued a Circular 'with a view to promoting a better system of nursing in the hospitals and sick wards of the workhouses throughout the country'.[1] The attention of the Guardians was called to the responsible nature of nursing and they were urged to discontinue the practice of employing pauper nurses. The Board stated that the General Consolidated Order of 1847 provided for the appointment of a nurse as a paid officer of the workhouse, and general regulations authorized the appointment of assistants who were likewise to be paid as the Guardians thought necessary. The Poor Law Board then laid down a series of rules on the duties of these workhouse nurses. They were to attend the sick and maternity wards and administer all medicines according to the doctors' directions. They were to inform the Medical Officer of any defects in arrangements, and it was their responsibility to see a light was kept at night in the sick ward. The office, the Poor Law Board wrote, was one of serious responsibility and labour, and was required to be filled by a person of experience, respectable character, and of 'diligent and decorous habit'. Assistants were to have the same qualities, therefore it was necessary to remunerate nurses adequately and appoint them only after strict investigation into their qualifications. The Poor Law Board considered the payment of nurses of the 'highest importance'. If they were remunerated the Guardians would be able to select the most suitable and they could also be held responsible for negligence or misconduct like the superior workhouse officers. There would be no incentive to exertion to assistants who remained paupers, and there could be no trial of their capacity. In recommending the discontinuance of employing destitute inmates, the Poor Law Board realized the difficulty which would be experienced in obtaining a sufficient number of competent women. The test would be if adequate payment were offered. Guardians were also asked to provide special accommodation in the workhouses, where nurses might live apart from the patients and where they would not be distracted by other inmates. The Board concluded by urging the Guardians to give the proposals their immediate attention.

A similar circular was sent to the Metropolitan Guardians.[2] In the following year there

---

[1] 5 May 1865—Official Circular to all Boards of Guardians in the Provinces.

[2] May 1865—Circular of the Poor Law Board to Metropolitan Guardians to appoint trained nurses to attend the sick in the workhouses.

were 111 paid (not necessarily skilled) nurses in London and Dr. Smith reported on the nursing system here. He stated that it was universally admitted that pauper inmates should only be employed as servants or in an entirely subordinate capacity. In his recommendations he said it was impossible to lay down any scale of numbers of paid nurses because of the separation of various buildings; in most workhouses the classification of inmates necessitated that each institution should be studied separately. Generalizing, he pointed out a greater number would be required in lunatic, maternity, and sick wards than in the aged and infirm wards. Different nurses should attend each class and there should be day and night nurses; altogether double the number of paid staff were required than existed. He pointed out that if the Metropolitan Guardians desired to obtain trustworthy and efficient nurses they would have to pay a suitable salary and provide apartments. Marylebone with its huge workhouse only paid £14 to the majority, and Rotherhithe offered terrible accommodation. A system of general superintendence would have to be devised and carefully watched with a view to improvement, and Smith admitted that there was bound to be friction between a newly-appointed superintendent and the matron. Nurses were to be given comfortable rations but no intoxicants, and as gratuities the Guardians were to offer money instead. His experience of trained nurses in hospitals convinced him, he said, that nurses were still addicted to drink and that there were many who were careless, inefficient, and dishonest. Regarding the use of inmates, Smith advocated more care in their selection and the awarding of money or a badge of honour for good conduct. Special privileges would also excite emulation and promote self-exteem.—'At present allowances appeal almost exclusively to the appetite and lead to drunkenness and little to self-respect and ambition.' As in his report on the provinces Smith saw no reason why persons found in the workhouse by this method should not after some training be removed from the ranks of paupers and be promoted to assistant nurses. But ability to read was essential and illiterate inmates should be taught. This would utilize their time and make them more valuable in the nursing department. (Mrs. Gladstone, Mrs. Tait, and Louisa Twining had suggested the education of all able-bodied inmates.) Smith further advocated that when one workhouse had produced sufficient skilled nurses for its own use, it should send the remainder to another to assist in the training there. Finally, he proposed that midwives should be resident, they should be properly trained, and occupy a position higher than the nurses and have more comfortable apartments.

As a result of the 1865 Circular many large towns and Metropolitan Unions appointed additional nurses. Dr. Smith's Report on London assisted not only the Poor Law Inspectors in enabling them to give advice, but also the Guardians, for it was distributed to every Union. Hampstead, for example, which had no paid nurse appointed one in 1865 at a salary of £20.[1] The Guardians of St. George in the East stated they would consider the replacement of pauper nurses as soon as trained nurses were available. The workhouse Medical Officer continued in the next years to complain of the nurses' illiteracy, laziness,

[1] Minutes, Board of Guardians, 1865.

and lack of cleanliness, and eventually when one of them died in 1869 a new nurse was appointed at £20 a year. She reported that she had discovered it to have been the custom for former nurses to dilute medicines with water.[1] Improvement in the Metropolis followed the Act of 1867. With the extension and classification of Poor Law institutions came also superior management and supervision. Enlarged boards of special managers learnt their duties and they tried to staff the new infirmaries with competent nurses. In 1868 the Chairman of the St. Pancras Board of Guardians asked them to devise means for securing a better and more intelligent class of person as nurses. There had been many changes among the subordinate staff and he believed the system in this respect certainly needed improvement.[2] Florence Nightingale had demanded more definite legislation on nursing in 1867, and her name was mentioned twice in the debate on the Bill as having greatly influenced it. Inspector Farnall had become her Chief of Staff for Poor Law purposes and together they had done much back-room work to press for greater reform in nursing. Farnall expressed their disappointment: 'It is intolerable to me', he said, 'to know there are some 12,000 gasping and miserable sick poor whom we might solace and perhaps in some 5,000 cases save, and yet we have to let them wait while the world gets ready to get out of bed and think about it all.' It was the work of Florence Nightingale and Louisa Twining that greatly influenced the complete prohibition of pauper nurses—although victory was delayed until 1897.

The greatest success achieved by any Poor Law institution was when in 1870 the large modern infirmary built by St. Pancras at Highgate and sold in that year to the Central London Sick Asylums District, was staffed by nurses who had trained under the Nightingale Fund at St. Thomas's Hospital. Highgate Hospital remained connected with St. Thomas's until the matron of the infirmary died, and her death interrupted the scheme for establishing a permanent nursing school at Highgate for supplying workhouse infirmaries with nurses.[3] Louisa Twining wrote that from the testimony of all who had witnessed the results at Highgate: 'as high a state of excellence was reached as we need ever look for or expect in similar institutions'. Subsequently, the nursing of the Hampstead workhouse infirmary was undertaken by the British Nursing Association, whose pupils trained at the Royal Free Hospital.

In 1869 night nurses began to be appointed generally in the Metropolis—there were only three in the entire City previously—and the training of probationers was also started. The Guardians of St. George in the East carried out the recommendation regarding a night nurse immediately, but only to receive complaints from the Medical Officer on her incapability. She neglected her duties and struck a patient who died as a result, so that after only a few weeks of employment she was asked to resign.[4] Chelsea had appointed two

[1] Minutes, Board of Guardians for several years.
[2] Letter, W. H. Wyatt, Chairman to Board of Guardians, 1868.
[3] It was not until 1884 that a training school for workhouse nurses was established and then at Marylebone Infirmary—*London County Council Hospitals—a retrospect*, 1949.
[4] Minutes, St. George in the East Board of Guardians, 1869

superintendent nurses in 1867 at a combined salary of £25 and in 1869 engaged two night nurses for a salary of £22 this being increased to £30 in 1870.[1] In December 1869 Kensington advertised in *The Times*, the *Telegraph*, the *Lancet* and local papers regarding the appointment of a head nurse. She was to be 30–40 years of age and her salary £35 with accommodation.[2] This advertisement appeared several times and illustrated the position that even when the Guardians wished to appoint skilled nurses there were either an insufficient number available, or they were unwilling to accept appointments connected with pauperism. Both conditions were probably found. The supply of trained nurses seriously lagged behind the demand, and the reputation of the institutions provided a deterrent to the most respectable and well-educated women. This antipathy diminished as the nurses' accommodation and the workhouse environment improved. Separate rooms began to be offered them and in the next decade few instances remained where the nurses lived and slept in wards with their patients. This had been inevitable in the overcrowded general workhouses. The erection of more spacious and specially designed infirmaries catered for a nursing staff, and it was fortunate, even if it was obvious, that the demand for improved institutions and for better nursing came concomitantly.

The number of paid nurses which existed in 1869 and 1870 can be obtained from the returns of the Poor Law Board on the dismissal of officers:[3]

TABLE 14.4

Number of Paid Nurses for the years 1869 and 1870.—Returns of the Poor Law Board

Year	Nurses	Voluntarily Resigned	Forced to Resign	Dismissed
1869	Male— 98	1	3	5
	Female—689	7	6	18
1870	Male— 114	35	5	7
	Female—770	11	6	20

Therefore seventy paid nurses had in two years been forced to resign or had been dismissed. This figure showed that even paid nurses were not always competent, although the number of trained and the number of ex-pauper nurses was not distinguished in any statistical enumeration. The Poor Law Board were not sufficiently interested at any earlier period to procure any other general returns on nursing for comparative purposes. But there is no doubt that the 884 paid nurses who were employed in 1870 in the country were a tremendous increase over what had existed even five years previously. The expenditure on Poor

[1] Chelsea Board of Guardians, Abstract of Accounts.
[2] Minutes, Kensington Board of Guardians, 1869.
[3] Twenty-second and Twenty-third Annual Reports.

Law officers rose by nearly £58,000 in 1867–68 above that of the previous year, and again by £35,000 in 1868–69. A considerable proportion of this the central authorities explained was due to the appointment of paid nurses—'a great improvement in Poor Law administration'.[1]

Although such a remarkable advance had been made in the development of the workhouse medical services, the new nursing system amounted to only a crack in the deep crust of inefficiency which lay heavily on the method of caring for the sick. Scandals still occurred, as for example, that at Wigan in 1868. Here the Coroner heard that an illegitimate child nine months old had been separated from its mother on her entry into the workhouse and had been placed in the nursery in charge of a 17-year old idiot. To wash it she plunged it into a pail of scalding water and then rubbed off large pieces of skin with a towel.—'This roused the dormant feelings of an old woman in the ward, who although paralyzed and of advanced age, ranked as one of the nurses.' The child died the following day. The *Lancet* reporting on the occurrence called it 'exquisite cruelty', and concluded: 'what abuse could not be possible in a workhouse which hands over the nursing of children to a batch of five nurses—two of whom are idiots, one paralytic 73 years old, the fourth a feeble old woman of 79, and the fifth a pauper of 81 years.'[2] Scandalous brutality or ignorance on the part of a male pauper nurse caused a death at the Lambeth workhouse in 1868. He gave a fatal dose of morphia with the intention of making a patient sleep at any price. The verdict at the inquest was manslaughter and the moral blame was attached to the Poor Law Board, for it was pointed out that the central authorities should have been aware of the danger to lives where pauper nurses were employed. The *Lancet* made the startling revelation that in three-quarters of the 650 workhouses in England there was no guarantee that such accidents might not occur any day, and that instances of many more similar deaths would be revealed if inquiries were held in every case to bring the scandals to light.[3]

If the new nursing system was only a crack at the end of the 'sixties—it was a crack which could grow ever wider. Like all other improvements in the Poor Law medical service, the full harvest of the arduous work of the reformers and administrators was only reaped in the succeeding generation. As with most pioneers, the tardily converted Poor Law Board did not live to see its recommendations or rules put into effect immediately, but the trend was obvious before they relinquished office. In 1869 the Chairmen and Vice-Chairmen of all the Unions in Warwickshire held a conference under the presidency of the Lord Lieutenant of the County. The meeting resolved unanimously to memorialize the Poor Law Board 'to take steps for securing to the Boards of Guardians the power to train nurses, or to contribute to some approved institution for the training of efficient nurses, with the power to employ nurses from any such institution for nursing the sick poor'. A copy of the memorial was sent to every Union in the country requesting co-operation.[4] At the same time

[1] *Ibid.*
[2] *Lancet*, 1868, i, p. 99.
[3] *Lancet*, 1868, i, pp. 540–41.
[4] *Lancet*, 1869, i, p. 134.

the *Lancet* wrote that the efforts made on behalf of the sick poor were achieving remarkable results throughout the country: 'The force of public opinion, the perception of conscious negligence, and fear of retribution . . . are awakening the Guardians to a sense of duty, especially in regard to nursing in the workhouses.'[1] (Praise indeed if it came from the *Lancet*.) Early in 1873 William Rathbone drew the attention of the Manchester Guardians to the nursing system of Liverpool and offered to have trained at his own expense a lady superintendent and six or eight nurses for the Manchester workhouse infirmary. It was soon recognized that although trained nurses only were to be employed in new large infirmaries, the rule which governed their employment—a year of service at some institution established for the care of the sick, which included the workhouse—was inadequate. The method of training therefore had to be improved.

By the late 'seventies the problem of the nursing of the sick poor had attained such importance that in 1879 the Association for Promoting Trained Nursing in Workhouse Infirmaries and Sick Asylums was formed. The President was Her Royal Highness Princess Mary, Duchess of Teck, and the General Committee included such people as Surgeon Major Bostock, C.B., Chairman for Public Health Hospitals and Dr. Sieveking; Louisa Twining was its honorary secretary. At the inaugural meeting held at the home of the Marchioness of Lothian, it was pointed out:

> we wish it to be distinctly understood that we are endeavouring to assist a movement which has already begun and has made considerable progress in the right direction—at least so far as sick asylums and separated infirmaries are concerned. These institutions, which during the last ten years have been set apart for the sick poor are treated and considered as hospitals, and the central board has the power of enforcing the rule that paupers or unpaid women, should not be employed, at least in the capacity of *nursing* the inmates. So far we thankfully acknowledge the great step in advance that has been taken; it is hardly surprising that more has not been done, when we consider it is only recently that the reform of nursing in hospitals has claimed the attention it deserves.

The admirable plans and their successful execution make interesting reading, but they fall outside this period of transition.

Those who were neglected in 1834, even by the legislation for the outcasts of society, had within a life-time had their care placed under the patronage of the mother of a future Queen of England. The inherent significance of this development provides a fitting conclusion to the strenuous exertion and prescience of the pioneers, and is a salutary example of the progress made in the Poor Law medical services.

[1] *Ibid.*

TABLE 14.2

Returns relating to each Metropolitan Workhouse: (1) Whether patients with infectious disorders are kept in separate wards; (2) Number of inmates; (3) Numbers under medical treatment; (4) Number of Medical Officers employed; (5) Number of paid nurses employed in each.—Return made to House of Commons, 1855.

Union	Whether patients with Infectious Disorders are kept in Separate Wards from Other Patients	Present Number of Inmates	Number of Inmates under Medical Treatment, 1854, in Workhouses	Number of Medical Officers employed in each Workhouse	Number of Paid Nurses
KENT					
Greenwich	Yes	1,047	1,022	1	None
Lewisham	Yes	174	202	1	1
MIDDLESEX					
Bethnal Green	Yes	1,024	1,104	1	2
Chelsea	Yes	501	508	1	None
Clerkenwell	Yes, or sent to Fever or Smallpox Hospitals	509	622	1	None
Fulham	Yes	341	567 (with cholera patients—84)	1	None
St. George in the East	(a) Workhouse: Yes (b) Plashet School—children with infectious diseases not separated—but two wards being built	460	313	1	4
St George, Hanover Square	Parish subscribe to Lock, Smallpox and Fever Hospital. No separate wards for infectious diseases, save itch. At outbreak of cholera, separate and distinct wards appropriated for this	590	1,553	3	1
St. Giles and St. George, Bloomsbury	No separation	724	1,313	3	1
Hackney	Yes	569	1,142	1	None
Hampstead	Yes	140	227	1	None
Holborn	Yes (generally)	674	2,030	1	1
Islington	Separation as far as possible, but new wards being built. Advanced fever, smallpox and severe venereal disease to respective hospitals	361	1,641 (cases not separate people)	1 resident, 2nd acts as dispenser	15 from inmates. 1s. per week + tea, sugar, and porter
St. James, Westminster	No—removed immediately to hospitals	546	693	1	None (only inmates)
Kensington	Yes—fever and smallpox to hospitals	320	195	1 for workhouse	3
London City	Yes	844	1,252	1	1
London East	Yes	602	Old workhouses discontinued, therefore no reply	1	1
London West	No	457	993 in sick wards, 3,019 received prescriptions who were in other parts of the workhouse—many cases which did not require admission to workhouse infirmary	1	None
St. Luke	Infectious in separate wards as possible, save continued fever which give best results when distributed in largest wards	572	1,550	1	1

TABLE 14.2—continued

Parish	Separate infirmary / establishments	Inmates	Numbers relieved	Medical officers	Nurses
St. Margaret and St. John, Westminster	(a) Kensington and (b) Petty France workhouses— both: Yes	(a) 543; (b) 115	(a) 4,500; (b) 1,090	(a) 2; (b) 1	(a) 3; (b) 3
St. Martin in the Fields, Westminster	Yes	522	1,712	1	1
St. Marylebone	Yes, but not invariably	1,761	200—weekly average in infirmary + 230 in workhouse	1 in workhouse / 1 in infirmary	1 superintendent, 11 nurses in infirmary + 61 others
Paddington	No	238	295	1	1
St. Pancras	Yes	1,431	4,000	2	5
Poplar	All infectious cases kept in workhouse infirmary	474	658 in workhouse; 48 in infirmary	1 for both	(a) 5; (b) 7
Shoreditch	(a) Workhouse (b) Brentwood School: Yes	(a) 683; (b) 229	(a) 243 weekly average; (b) None	(a) 1; (b) 1	2 for infectious cases of 2 workhouses, all paid
Stepney	Four establishments: Yes	together 1,222	2,308 (altogether)	1 in each of 4	None
Strand	(a) One workhouse and (b) Infant School, Edmonton: Yes	(a) 493; (b) 167	(a) 2,256; (b) 117	1	
Whitechapel	Two workhouses and Industrial School: Yes	(a) 454; (b) 194 (c) 306	(a) 1,700; (b) 701; (c) 739	1 in each	1; 0; 3 for sick only
SURREY Bermondsey	Yes. Fever and Smallpox cases to hospital	602	65 daily average	1	0 (till recently)
Camberwell	Yes	321	910	1	1 paid pauper + 1 assistant to every 15 patients
St. George the Martyr	(a) Workhouse; (b) another in Lewisham: Yes	(a) 519; (b) 126	(a) 182; (b) 6 weekly average	(a) 1; (b) 1	1 head nurse, rest paupers
Lambeth	(a) Workhouse; (b) Norwood School: Yes	(a) 962; (b) 469	(a) + (b)—222 weekly	(a) 1; (b) 1	
Newington	Yes	598	1,274	1	
St. Olave	Yes	350	492	1	None
Rotherhithe	Yes	236	162	1	None
Wandsworth and Clapham	Yes	551	1,019	1	1

CHAPTER 15

Provision for Lunatics

THE one class of poor to whom institutional relief was generally given and against whom the deterrence principle could not be enforced was the insane. Over 4 per cent of pauperism was caused by insanity after 1860. (Up to this time it had been 1 per cent, but no doubt improvement in classification contributed much to the sharp rise in the statistics given by the Poor Law Board in the 'sixties.) And never less than 75 per cent of all persons of unsound mind came under the Poor Law authorities. The story of the treatment of the insane in the second half of the nineteenth century is one of increasing, if slow, improvement.

This falls into three broad categories—the segregation of the insane from the rest of the workhouse, the separation of the dangerous lunatic from the harmless imbecile and the consequent removal of the former into an asylum, and third, more humane treatment. The separation of lunatics from other workhouse inmates was suggested in the report of the Royal Commission in 1834, and in the following thirteen years, persons of unsound mind became recognized as a distinct class and were exempt from the outdoor prohibitory relief orders. In this period also, there was an increase in statutory powers for compulsory removal to asylums or licensed houses of persons certified to be dangerous. But the recognition of the difference between dangerous and harmless cases only came at the end of the 'forties and no real differentiating definition was made until 1875. However inadequate the distinctions remained, it became the recognized policy to send the dangerous away and retain the harmless in the workhouse.

Developments were fostered by the previous public apathy undergoing a complete reversal. Scandals in the 'fifties and 'sixties roused widespread indignation and often led to important official inquiries. Public awareness and interest in the problems involved in the care of the mentally unsound was awakened by the active intervention and inspection of the Lunacy Commissioners, although they provided the natural target for popular indignation. The Poor Law Board and the Commissioners in Lunacy were close associates in this field, and continual prodding by the latter induced the destitution authorities to keep close watch on the condition of lunatics in regard to the provision of separate wards, dietaries, nursing, and treatment. From the inception of the Poor Law Board, the Commissioners in Lunacy made reports to them on the treatment of lunatic inmates of workhouses, and already in 1849 Guardians were called on to remedy the evils. No Inspector from the Poor Law Commissioners or the Poor Law Board had ever visited the wealthy parish of St.

George's, Hanover Square, London, until a Lunacy Inspector called in 1854, and impressed on the Guardians—peers, baronets, and clergymen—the need for better accommodation and treatment of lunatic inmates of the workhouse. Very efficient reports on this parish were made for the next three years until at last Poor Law Inspector Farnall went to the workhouse, and his first visit was in connection with the insane ward.[1]

The penetrating annual reports made by the Commissioners in Lunacy to the Lord Chancellor revealed the conditions and the improvements necessary in the workhouses. In 1854 they stated that St. Peter's Hospital, Bristol (a Poor Law institution), was unfit for insane patients, that the defects of the lunatic wards were irremediable, and that casualties occurred among the patients because of the inadequate building. Further, there was no classification and no open grounds for exercise. The defects in Hull were pointed out, and also those in Norwich. Here, it was reported, dangerous lunatics were still in the infirmary, where overcrowding and drainage were very bad. The Commissioners had complained every year and desired compulsion be applied to force Norwich to make adequate provision for the insane.[2]

In one respect pauper lunatics were in a superior position to the more wealthy, for the Commissioners in Lunacy agitated to get all the former into County Asylums, which were subject to constant inspection, but great difficulty was experienced in introducing improvements in the several lunatic hospitals or charitable institutions which were chiefly for the upper and middle classes. For this reason all insane paupers were gradually withdrawn from London hospitals. Cases of extreme cruelty were also brought to light, perpetrated by the more affluent who locked up an insane member of the family at home. The Select Committee on Lunacy in 1859 found little fault with public asylums, but it heard Shaftesbury's outspoken condemnation of private asylums. The argument in favour of public institutions was well illustrated when the cholera epidemic came in 1853. On that occasion, the Commissioners in Lunacy had the power to direct officers to guard against the spread of the disease. The following Circular was issued to Superintendents and Medical Officers of Lunatic Asylums: dietaries were to be liberal, nutritious, and of good quality, there were to be more solids, well cooked and well served; the institutions were to assure themselves of a good water supply; personal cleanliness was to be strictly attended to; there was to be an abundant supply of warm, dry clothing and bedding, and frequent changes; sufficient exercise was to be given out of doors; the failing strength of the emaciated, the aged and infirm, was to be supported by placing them in warm, airy rooms, suitably furnished and with comforts; all cases of physical exhaustion and exposure to dampness were to be avoided; exposure to noxious effluvia or exhalations was to be prevented; the physical condition of all patients was to be vigilantly watched and every case of diarrhoea, cramp, or vomiting was to be instantly reported to the Medical Officer; cleanliness, dryness, warmth, and ventilation of rooms were to be objects of constant attention, any damp-

---

[1] Minutes of the Directors of the Poor, St. George's, Hanover Square, 1854–57.
[2] Eighth Annual Report of the Commissioners in Lunacy.

ness was to be remedied, and floors were to be cleansed by dry scrubbing—if water were used, fires were to be lit to dry them; overcrowding was to be prevented as far as possible; waterclosets, sinks, sloprooms, and lavatories were to be examined daily; there was to be frequent limewashing and no rubbish was to be left to decay; and finally—one room was to be set apart as a probationary ward in case a patient was brought from an area where cholera was prevalent. At the time there were over 11,000 pauper lunatics in asylums, 211 in hospitals, 1,310 in Metropolitan licensed houses, and 1,162 in provincial licensed houses. Some 14,000 pauper lunatics therefore came under the salutary attention of the Commissioners in Lunacy, whilst a great proportion of the remaining 4,500 insane, which included workhouse inmates and the wealthier patients in private institutions, were left to the mercy of Guardians and Keepers to protect them against cholera as they would. For the fifty-six years that Shaftesbury was Chairman of the Lunacy Commission he carried on an untiring campaign for the transfer of lunatics to public asylums.

One of the predominant activities of the Lunacy Commissioners was, therefore, to try and get lunatics removed from the workhouses. The Commissioners constantly complained that they had no power to enforce the proposals they made regarding the improvement of conditions, and that because the Poor Law Board also had insufficient authority, recommendations were ignored. They therefore demanded legislation. They pointed out in 1859 that workhouses had not been built for accommodating lunatics, and there was no room to allow efficient classification or exercise. As workhouses were conducted by officers for ordinary paupers, there was no one to give specialized care or discipline to the lunatics. Punishment for violence or excitement was severe, when these were really the symptoms of disease requiring medical care.[1]

Conditions and treatment in licensed houses were no better; for example, a scandal was revealed in 1853 in Gateshead. Here a pauper lunatic patient bit the arm of a licensed proprietor; for this he was put in a strait-jacket and flogged with a riding whip by the Licensor, the Medical Officer then removed two front teeth, and a long-term confinement was ordered. At the inquiry it was stated that the lunatic was dangerous and was in the habit of biting, but evidence revealed that he had not bitten anyone before, and on this occasion had not drawn blood.

The proportion of lunatics in workhouses differed greatly throughout the country. It was larger in rural areas where there were also more congenital idiots and imbeciles, whereas in towns epilepsy and paralysis were more frequent. Overcrowding of the insane in workhouses was particularly great in the Metropolis where they were often housed in an attic or basement, and their miseries were increased because there were no facilities for exercise. Where lunatics were not confined indoors permanently, the nature of the workhouse buildings circumscribed the place for obtaining fresh air. In Bolton, Blackburn, Manchester, Whitehaven, and Wolverhampton, as in most other large towns, tiny yards were provided for hundreds of people. In 1852 and 1853 the Commissioners in Lunacy

[1] Twelfth Annual Report of the Commissioners in Lunacy, 1859.

visited 323 workhouses in the provinces and here also they discovered a vast number of insane crowded into the workhouses. Clifton, near Bristol had 81 insane inmates, Manchester 57, Bolton 50, Oldham 49, Liverpool 34—Lancashire had the most—Stockport had 46, Nottingham 64, Portsea, Southampton, 62, Birmingham 38, and Halifax 39. Of the 655 workhouses in England and Wales, one-tenth in 1859 provided separate lunatic and insane wards.[1] A return made to the House of Commons in 1862 gave 195 workhouses in England and six in Wales as providing separate accommodation for the insane. But half the Unions who recorded no segregation stated that only the harmless inbeciles were mixed with the sane. By this year only three Unions in Wales—Cardiff, Corwen, and Pwllhelli—provided special lunatic wards, and only 113 Unions in England. Most of these were in the Metropolis and there were none at all in Bedford, Berkshire, Buckingham or Essex.[2] Therefore the majority of the insane were mixed with ordinary inmates, and where they were separated they had the worst rooms, dirty, dark, overcrowded, with little ventilation.

In 1847 the Poor Law Commissioners had sent a letter to the Commissioners in Lunacy to the effect that the insane wards of Plymouth workhouse were small, low, ill-ventilated, and in confusion and disorder. In 1854 the District Auditor's report showed that pauper lunatics were kept in rooms 3 feet wide and 7 feet long—mere cupboards. The attendants were paupers, some of whom were paid an extra 1s. a week. The Commissioners in Lunacy had objected to these wards being occupied by any one, but in vain. In 1856 the Poor Law Board wrote to the Guardians concerning the Reports of the Lunacy Commissioners and at last the local authorities resolved to send their lunatics to the asylum at Exminster, giving those who remained more comfortable accommodation. A new workhouse was built in the late 'fifties, but again the Commissioners in Lunacy reported the bad construction of the separate wards and cells intended for lunatics. Also because of the new building, patients had not been removed to the asylum. The deficiency in attendants, means of exercise, comforts and decent quarters, were typical of the arrangements in all other large towns. In St. George in the East (Stepney) the female imbecile ward had no windows until July 1862.[3] Dr. Bence Jones in his famous report on the St. Pancras workhouse in 1856, gave a horrible description of the insane wards. Some were underground and were made even more objectionable because of their contact with an offensive drain from the burial ground. Another had only a grating to permit ventilation and this opened into a privy. All the lunatic wards, he stated, were ill-adapted for the insane; they were not only unwholesome but also unsafe.[4] It was general for insane wards to be deficient in furniture and eating utensils. The bedding was dirty and insufficient, and some workhouses slept two lunatics in one bed—a scandalous example of which was given by the Lunacy Commissioners in 1859. Little water was provided for washing, and clothing was scanty, often no underclothing being supplied at all. Food was always poor and inadequate.

[1] Twelfth Annual Report of the Commissioners in Lunacy.
[2] *Accounts and Papers*, 1863, LII.
[3] Minutes, St. George in the East Board of Guardians.
[4] Report on Accommodation in St. Pancras Workhouse, Henry Bence Jones, M.D., F.R.S.

The Commissioners in Lunacy objected to the erection of separate wards and the conversion of old ones, because this induced Guardians to regard them as lunatic asylums and to refuse sending patients to proper institutions. In Oldham, Nottingham, and Blackburn, lunatic inmates even had their own matron and staff, who were separated from the remaining workhouse officers. The Commissioners also pointed out that attendants in these establishments were never adequately remunerated and supervision was defective. The want of trained nurses and kind superintendence was as much felt in the insane wards as in the workhouse infirmary. In most workhouses, pauper inmates, who were given an extra allowance of beer, were entrusted with the sole charge of lunatics. For example, in Stepney Union, the pauper nurse received extra food and 2 pints of beer daily. Her unkindness led to an inquiry in which it was revealed that she could not tell what the lunatics' diet was, nor could she read the names of her patients. In St. Albans workhouse the nurse in charge of the insane women was herself of unsound mind. She was allowed half a pint of beer daily as a reward. The Visiting Commissioner in 1859 suggested to the Guardians that a more competent person should be employed, but they did not comply with the request. In 1857 in St. Martin's in the Fields a violent lunatic was supervised by an old pauper of 70 and killed him with a poker. The Lunacy authorities found a great number of similar instances and reported: 'we may confidently state . . . the attendance and nursing in workhouses is totally inadequate'.

Experienced nurses were too expensive for the Guardians, and old and feeble paupers were quite incompetent. An old woman worn out with her own hard and troubled life was not likely to act gently or skilfully in such an arduous post, and the inability of the patients to speak for themselves and complain of their grievances provided a terrible temptation to tyranny and harshness on the part of their attendants. It was to the ignorance of these people that the use of strait-waistcoats, straps and shackles, and other means of restraint were often entrusted, and punishment could be meted out at any time. In 1848 a Poor Law Inspector visited Bradford workhouse unexpectedly and found two lunatics in manacles. He asked for a return of the number of insane, and after some evasion the Medical Officer gave only six. It was not until 1855 that the Bradford Guardians considered the propriety of providing separate wards for the reception of lunatics. Mechanical restraints were widely used in the 'fifties—chains and handcuffs were the most usual.[1] In 1859 cases came to light in Dewsbury of lunatics being chained to their beds or against tables. In Bury shackles and chains were used. Women were also chained, as was revealed in Llanelly and in St. George the Martyr, Southwark, where women were chained up day and night. Mortuaries and cells ('dog-holes') were also used for secluding lunatics. The Medical Officer of Colney Hatch lunatic asylum, where a great proportion of London patients went, charged the Clerkenwell workhouse authorities in 1852 with gross neglect and cruelty. Two pauper lunatics sent from the workhouse to the asylum were dressed in strait-jackets, a third had bed sores and other sores, and a fourth had been so cowed that he

[1] John Conolly's pioneering of more humane methods at Hanwell has been noted in the earlier chapter on lunatics.

could only be induced to enter the establishment with difficulty. In 1860 Hanwell complained to the Kensington Guardians against lunatics being sent in strait-jackets.[1] The Commissioners in Lunacy in the following year accused the Bristol authorities of cruelty and negligence in their new workhouse asylum which had been built for pauper lunatics. The Guardians complained against the Commissioners forbidding the use of mechanical restraints, for they could see no other way of preventing patients from doing extensive damage to clothes and other materials. This had to be stopped because the expenditure on the pauper asylum was high and a considerable debt had been incurred.[2] Because of the growing interest in the study of insanity, the Commissioners had in 1853 collected material from all Medical Officers and asylum proprietors on their methods of treatment and the decline in the use of mechanical restraint. Long and efficient reports had been sent from all over the country. The misappropriation of mechanical devices led to their use being forbidden by the Lunacy Authorities, and because the workhouse staffs could not manage without them, a further incentive was given to the Commissioners to try and get all pauper lunatics removed to County Asylums, where proper treatment, care, supervision, and accommodation were available.—'The defects radically incident to the workhouse system carry with them the almost necessary large adherence to mechanical coercion, in itself a sure and certain test of utter neglect or of the most inadequate means of treatment.'[3]

The insane were also still punished as criminals. In the late 'fifties for example, lunatics from Sheppey, Epping, East Grinstead, Hitchin, and Downham were imprisoned. These were often epileptics who caused some damage when they were in convulsions. In St. Margaret's and St. John's, Westminster, two men and a woman, classed as of unsound mind, were committed to prison, two for tearing their clothes and the third for refusing to work. The Lunacy Commissioners complained to the Poor Law Board. Three idiots from Southampton were also imprisoned because they ran away from the workhouse. A similar case occurred at Oundle Union. Here a Medical Officer had had a woman restrained and secluded, and on three occasions sent her to prison because she suffered from violent epileptic fits. The Medical Officer considered her unfit for retention either in the workhouse or in prison and had ordered her removal to an asylum. The vicar however refused to sign the order, and therefore she was treated as a refractory and sent to prison.[4] The *Lancet* in 1859 wrote that the system of the treatment of lunatics in workhouses was so reprehensible as to surpass all belief:

> The rules in force to check disorderly conduct in common paupers are most improperly extended to the insane, who are in effect, prisoners in the 'Bastilles' for life, incapable of asserting their own rights, yet amenable to as much punishment as if they were quite sane.[5]

[1] Minutes, Kensington Board of Guardians.
[2] *Bristol Gazette*, 24 January 1861 and 1863 (Webb MSS.).
[3] Twelfth Annual Report of the Commissioners in Lunacy, 1859.
[4] Twelfth Annual Report of the Commissioners in Lunacy, 1859.
[5] *Lancet*, 1859, i, p. 497.

There was an entire absence of written records on lunatic inmates of workhouses, as were required of Asylums and Licensed Houses, so no means existed of ascertaining treatment. By the Lunacy Act of 1853[1] the duty of visiting and reporting on the state of pauper lunatics was imposed on the Medical Officer. A Circular was issued by the Poor Law Board to Guardians (19 October 1853) requesting the Medical Officer to pay quarterly visits to insane inmates of workhouses, and also to attend any outdoor pauper lunatic for which he was to be paid 2s. 6d. per visit. His reports had to state whether he thought the lunatics were well cared for and whether they were fit to remain outside an asylum. A penalty of £2 to £20 could be imposed on him for non-compliance and he was also punishable if he failed to report any suspected lunatic within three days to the Relieving Officer. The restriction of the 1845 Act which prevented a Union doctor from certifying to the insanity of a pauper brought before a Justice of the Peace was repealed by the new Act, and Medical Officers were to receive a fee for this service.

But information remained scanty. There was no register by which accident, misusage, wound or fracture, or death could be ascertained. If lunatics were deprived of food or otherwise ill-treated, no one could discover it save by chance. There was no efficient or authoritative official inspection. Visiting magistrates never inspected lunatic wards of workhouses, and the visits of Lunacy Commissioners were useless, save for enabling them to detect evils which existed at the time, and which after they left they had no power to remove. In the Bath workhouse, the frauds and thefts of some of the attendants had for a long time systematically deprived the patients of half their allowance of food. Yet the only complaint made by the workhouse Visiting Committee was on the wan and wasted look of the inmates. In Bristol a dangerous lunatic committed suicide by cutting her throat in the water-closet. No inquest was demanded. The Commissioners in Lunacy heard of the case and had an inquiry held. It was found that neither of the two pauper wardens was on duty at the time of the accident, and that dangerous and imbecile were kept together in one ward. The Commissioner stated that on previous visits to the workhouse he had drawn attention to the evil of retaining lunatics instead of sending them to the asylum. The husband of the dead woman had allowed 5s. a week for her maintenance and wanted her removal to an asylum. The Guardians however crawled out of their predicament by maintaining she was not a lunatic and had only suffered from religious melancholia, and had therefore been kept in a sick ward. A great deal of correspondence took place over the incident between the Poor Law Board, the Guardians and the Lunacy Commissioners— little was achieved.[2] In 1859 the lunacy authorities recommended that Medical Officers of workhouses should keep a list of all people of unsound mind, which should be accessible to Visiting Commissioners. The latter and the Poor Law Inspector, they further proposed, should be empowered to order and direct the Relieving Officer to take any insane inmate before a magistrate who, under the Lunacy Act of 1853 might order removal to an asylum.

[1] 16, 17 Vict. c. 97, s. 66.
[2] Correspondence between the Poor Law Board and the Guardians of Bristol Union regarding the death of a pauper, 1856.

In 1862 the Commissioners in Lunacy were granted the power to order the transfer of lunatics from workhouses to an asylum if they thought the person not a proper object for retention in the workhouse.

The Poor Law institutions were entirely unsuited to minister to the special wants of the mentally unstable, and some inmates were totally unfit to be retained there. Many could have been trained in an asylum to perform useful work, whereas in the workhouses they were just neglected and kept quiet, without means of amusement or occupation. There was also until the late 'sixties no competent officer independent of the parish with the authority to prevent detention when it was no longer necessary, or to exercise a salutary control over patients who would be likely to suffer injury if they discharged themselves. The Lunacy Commissioners in the 'fifties and early 'sixties said that the difficult class on the borderline of imbecility should be left entirely to the Medical Officer's care, without the interference of the workhouse master or Guardians. He should have full power regarding classification, diet, employment, and medical and ordinary treatment. They demanded that there should be no discharge of this class—especially of women without the doctor's sanction, because cases occurred frequently of their returning to the workhouse pregnant. The Commissioners reported this as happening at Monmouth, Calne, Walsall, Newark, Tamworth, and Martley workhouses. In each instance there were several imbecile women with many illegitimate children, who should never have been allowed out of the workhouse after each childbirth, for they only returned again pregnant, with each successive child weak-minded. In such cases disease itself was promoted and perpetuated and the amount not only of lunacy but also pauperism was greatly enlarged. The Lunacy Act of 1862[1] shortened and simplified the legal procedure whereby people could prove their sanity, but litigation was impossible for paupers. Only in 1867 by the Poor Law Amendment Act, were destitute lunatics allowed to be removed from the workhouse to an asylum, registered hospital, or home—if certified sane, if relatives so wished it and undertook to provide for the removal and maintenance of the person. With regard to the converse case, the same Act provided that no person was to be allowed to leave the workhouse without a Medical Officer's certificate.

Medical attention offered to lunatic paupers was also condemned by the Commissioners in Lunacy.[2] No better instance of its total inadequacy existed than that presented by the Leicester Union where the Medical Officer only visited the workhouse insane every three months. This, as we have seen, was all that was required by the 1853 Act, and no rule was ever laid down that the ordinary attendance of the Medical Officer should invariably be extended to the lunatic wards. In Winchcombe workhouse, Gloucester, the Medical Officer only visited the infirmary once a fortnight and then did not always go to see the insane. But

[1] 25, 26 Vic. c. 8, 1862.
[2] Shaftesbury doubted the efficacy of treatment In 1862 he confessed that his long experience as a Lunacy Commissioner had convinced him that 'medical men, who had not made the subject a special study, were as ignorant of mental disease as anyone who observed it for the first time'. But he also distrusted the specialist for 'they will shut up people by the score' (1877). Quoted by J. S. and B. Hammond, *Lord Shaftesbury*, 1923.

from the Medical Officers' reports to the Metropolitan Guardians in the 'sixties, it does appear that the practice there was becoming more frequent of including lunatics among the sick patients, who were seen at least twice weekly.

Inadequate medical attention was another factor influencing the Lunacy Commissioners' demand for the removal of pauper lunatics to public asylums. In the establishment of County and Borough Lunatic Asylums provision was made for the accommodation of insane patients at the commencement of their disease, and where under skilful supervision and treatment they might have a chance of ultimate cure.[1] To effect the execution of the duties imposed on the parish and the Union officers, not only for the good of the patients but also for the ratepayers, was difficult, and serious evils sprang from the evasion of such duties. The neglect of the law directing lunatics to be taken to asylums was most frequent where there were larger workhouses and where insane wards were provided. In Birmingham, Manchester, Salford, Liverpool, Nottingham, Plymouth, Oldham, Sheffield, and in many Metropolitan districts, especially Marylebone and St. Pancras, this practice was increased in the early 'sixties, and was in direct contravention of all provisions of the law applicable to the efficient administration of asylums. The excuse when a Commissioner in Lunacy inspected the workhouse was that the lunatic was only being retained temporarily, but very often lunatics found they were not removed after the maximum time allowed of fourteen days. In 1862 Inspector Lambert told the Select Committee on Poor Relief, that all dangerous lunatics were invariably sent to an asylum, yet six years later the new Guardians of Mile End (London) found a very dangerous lunatic living in the workhouse. In the same year, 1868, an inquest was held in Yeovil (Somerset) because an aged inmate of the workhouse had been attacked and killed by a lunatic kept in the infirmary wards. The Medical Officer had repeatedly called the attention of the Guardians to the fact that the lunatic was dangerous and should have been removed. But the Guardians 'with a revolting mixture of parsimony and self-conceited obstinacy, neglected to comply with these requests of the Medical Officer'. The Coroner expressed strong indignation at the neglect of the Guardians, and the jury passed a similar verdict. In the following month an inquiry was held by the Poor Law authorities.[2]

The Kensington Board of Guardians repeatedly received letters from the workhouse Medical Officer asking for violent lunatics to be removed.[3] In 1862 a Lunacy Commissioner asked for several to be removed to the asylum. This was done, and when the manager of Colney Hatch wrote that they could accept any lunatic Kensington wished to

[1] The advocacy of early treatment for curing a patient may be considered a pious hope. According to Hooper's Medical Dictionary the recognized treatment for 'mania' included blood-letting (a powerful means of lessening excitement), purging, calomel (it may evacuate bile more freely), application of cold to the head, emetics, digitalis (for its sedative powers), narcotics, camphor and blistering. For the melancholic patient a generous diet, alcohol, tonics, attention to bowels, and exercise was recommended. Insane patients were considered to be capable of 'resisting the usual morbid effects of cold, hunger and watching and being likewise less susceptible of other diseases than before'.

[2] *Lancet*, 1868, i, 633.

[3] Minutes, Kensington Board of Guardians, 1855 et seq.

send, sixteen were taken from a house where they were boarded out and transferred to the asylum. By 1863 this Union had sixty-seven lunatics[1] in asylums. Most of the Metropolitan Unions were sending some, if not all, of their insane away—the differentiation between imbecile and dangerous lunatics had become more clearly defined and it was the former which were being retained, and amongst whom the violent were often concealed. The motive which lay behind the retention of lunatics was economy. The Metropolitan (County) Asylums of Hanwell and Colney Hatch charged nearly 10s. a week per head, and Bethnal Green 17s. 6d. The accounts of Shoreditch showed that nearly £230 a quarter was spent in 1857 on the maintenance of lunatics in County Asylums, and £1,166 a quarter in 1861: a hundred and thirty of its lunatic paupers were by then in these asylums at 10s., and 38 at other asylums, at 13s. a week.[2]

Where Guardians wished to co-operate in having their insane paupers removed they were often hindered by the insufficient number of County Asylums. In the 'fifties the Northern counties of Cumberland, Westmorland, Northumberland and Durham, the Welsh counties of Cardigan, Carmarthen, Glamorgan, and Pembroke, still had no County Asylum. Nor had Sussex or Cambridge. New asylums were erected in the early 'fifties in Gloucester, Middlesex, Surrey, Norfolk, Shropshire, and Montgomeryshire, but the demand always exceeded the supply. Although the provision of accommodation in asylums increased continuously so that Guardians were enabled to withdraw paupers from workhouses and licensed houses, another serious obstacle prevented the diminution of lunatic pauper inmates. This was the congregation and detention of large numbers of chronic cases in the County Asylums, converting them into refuges for incurables, instead of hospitals for the treatment of disease. (For the majority of patients, then as now, asylums were custodian rather than therapeutic.)

No remedy for obviating the enormous evils, which the *Lancet* had called 'disgraceful to a civilized and professedly Christian country'[3] was possible as long as insane patients were detained in the workhouse. Stringent measures were absolutely necessary. It was imperative to add to the accommodation of existing asylums and build new ones. The bad effect of crowding people into asylums was reported by Dr. Boyd, Superintendent of Wells Asylum and Inspector of Somerset Lunatic Asylums, to the Select Committee of Poor Law Medical Relief in 1854. He said that although his asylum had been built in a healthy locality there had been an increase in the rate of mortality from pulmonary consumption. He thought it better, in all cases where it was possible, to relieve people in their own homes and to use the money that was usually spent in building hospitals in making those homes more salubrious! The Lunacy Commissioners suggested the building of auxiliary asylums, which were to be intermediate with the Union workhouse and the curative asylums. These should house those mental defectives who should really not have been admitted to asylums—the idiot, the chronic, and the harmless. The buildings, it was

[1] Minutes, Kensington Board of Guardians, 1862, 1863 et seq.
[2] Shoreditch Board of Guardians, Quarterly Estimates for Poor Rates.
[3] *Lancet*, 1859, i, p. 497.

suggested, should be inexpensive and in direct connection with, or at a convenient distance from, the existing institutions. The difficulty which would have arisen if this scheme had been effected would have been classification, for chronic dementia, melancholia, and epilepsy comprise many who are idiot or imbecile, and include none who are able to take care of themselves. The fall in the number of lunatic pauper inmates of workhouses in the late 'forties and their gradual disproportionate rise in the late 'fifties was no doubt to a great extent caused by the considerable emptying of workhouses when the asylums were first built, and then, because they were filled, the workhouses had to receive back many of their chronic patients. Although the asylums were full of chronic patients too, the stipulation was made that these cases should be maintained in workhouses—and this was by far the largest category of the mentally unsound. In 1859 Inspector Farnall attended a Board of Guardians' meeting in Kensington and suggested that safe lunatic incurables might be taken back from the County Asylums and kept in the workhouse where they would be able to be maintained at half the cost.[1] The effect on the patient was often bad, because diet and environment were so different. The diet of lunatics in workhouses was far inferior to what was offered in the asylums and to what was given in gaols. The Commissioners in Lunacy pointed out that Medical Officers severely neglected their duty if they did not exercise the powers given to them to afford a more nutritious diet to pauper inmates of this class.

The Lunacy Act of 1862[2] not only granted the Commissioners the authority of ordering the transfer of lunatics from the workhouse to an asylum, but also made it legal for visitors of any asylum, and Guardians of Unions in districts where an asylum had been provided, to make arrangements for the reception and care of a limited number of chronic lunatics in the workhouses. The Poor Law Board sent an explanatory circular to the Guardians in which they pointed out that:

> the crowded state of some of the County Asylums may render it expedient that when proper accommodation is provided in the workhouse for cases of imbecile and harmless chronic lunatics . . . they should be removed from the asylum to the workhouse . . . to make room for acute cases in which the treatment provided in the lunatic asylum is more important and necessary.

Much care, the Board warned, would be required in putting this measure into operation, and arrangements were receiving their earnest attention. The proposals, it was stressed, did not authorize the detention in the insane wards of a workhouse of any dangerous or violent lunatic, and these wards were not to constitute asylums within the meaning of the Act of 1861.[3] Therefore the cost of lunatics maintained in them would not be chargeable under that provision on the common fund of the Union but to the parish to which the paupers respectively belonged. (The Act of 1861 had stated that the cost of lunatics maintained in

[1] Minutes, Kensington Board of Guardians, August 1859.
[2] 25, 26 Vict. c. 11.
[3] 24, 25 Vict. c. 55.

recognized asylums was to be charged to the Union, causing Inspector Lambert to complain to the Select Committee of 1862 of the heavy additional burden entailed on the common fund of the Unions.) Several applications were made to the Poor Law Board and the Commissioners in Lunacy for sanction to remove chronic lunatics from the asylums to wards adapted for their reception in the workhouse, under the provision of section 8 of the 1862 Act.

In 1863 an amending Act was passed, and the Poor Law Board pointed out to the Guardians that it had not been contemplated by the previous Act that chronic patients should be generally received into workhouses, thereby constituting them all small lunatic establishments. The principle involved was the selection by Visitors of one or more workhouses in which adequate accommodation, care, and attendance were provided. Therefore all applications for the approval of the Commissioners had to originate with Asylum Visitors, and 'no such application received from Boards of Guardians can be entertained'. The Poor Law Board stressed that the indispensable conditions were: separate wards, properly constructed, arranged and furnished for the patients; dormitories distinct from day-rooms, the former to allow 500 cubic feet of space per patient and the latter 400; single bedrooms to measure at least 600 cubic feet; a liberal dietary, analogous to that in asylums; ample means of exercise and recreation; due medical visits, properly qualified attendants; and medical registers and other registers were to provide records similar to those of licensed institutions.—Many Guardians began the alteration of wards in workhouses, because maintenance of lunatics in their own institution was far cheaper than the payments to an asylum. Several Unions, where this was impossible, erected small new buildings or converted old houses near the workhouse. As separate institutional relief was preferred by the Commissioners in Lunacy, they tried to foster the latter schemes. For example, in Devon, the magistrates were influenced in 1863 to contemplate the building of an asylum solely for idiots. This met with opposition, and the Devonport Board of Guardians reported that they were very concerned at the attempt made at the Quarter Sessions to commit the County to such large expenditure on the erection of an asylum. They said it was their

> decided opinion that such an establishment is altogether unnecessary, and the unfortunate persons alluded to [idiots] are quite well cared for in the workhouse, as they could be in an asylum erected for the purpose. . . . the Board believes, as they are perfectly harmless, they will be far happier in being allowed to remain in the workhouse and mix occasionally with other inmates whose minds are not affected, than to be shut in any asylum with a large body of the same class.[1]

The chronic imbeciles who remained in the workhouse helped to swell the enormous proportion of the category of inmates designated as 'aged and infirm', and it was as much for them as for the other sick that the reforms of the late 'sixties were demanded. Nearly every workhouse, and all the larger urban institutions, had by this time their separate insane

[1] Minutes, Devonport Board of Guardians, January 1863 (Webb MSS.).

586

wards, though again classification between the imbecile and those of inherently low mentality was difficult. Some of the workhouse insane wards were passed as good by the Lunacy Visitors, as for example those at Kensington, where the Guardians at the instigation of Inspector Farnall also provided a padded room at a cost of £18 for the temporary confinement of dangerous lunatics until they could be removed to an asylum.[1] But the majority were terrible. The Medical Officer of St. George in the East workhouse told the Guardians in 1865, that the female imbecile wards were totally unfit, and that they could not be satisfactorily altered.[2] A letter from the Poor Law Board in the following year suggested a separate building should be erected for sick inmates and that the old workhouse should only be retained for female imbeciles, nursing mothers, and infants. In 1869 the Commissioners in Lunacy visited the new lunatic wards and pronounced them satisfactory. Joseph Rogers described in his *Reminiscences of a Workhouse Medical Officer* the frightful condition under which imbeciles and some dangerous lunatics were kept in the Strand workhouse, and Dr. Anstie in his preliminary general report of the *Lancet* inquiry in July 1865, confirmed the state of lunatic inmates of workhouses in the Metropolis. He gave a more detailed account after he had made a special study of this department of workhouse management, in the *Journal of Mental Science* in October 1865. After the *Lancet* Commissioners had completed their investigations in 1867, the removal of all lunatics from 'their highly improper surroundings in the workhouses'[3] was demanded.

The Metropolitan Poor Act of 1867 ensured that the removal of imbecile and chronic cases from the London workhouses could be effected. The establishment by the Metropolitan Asylums Board of two new asylums at Leavesden and Caterham, each accommodating 1,500 patients meant that not only would the overcrowding of workhouses be alleviated, but also that this class of pauper would enjoy better living conditions. One result of the Act was not contemplated. Because the cost of lunatics not retained in workhouses was to be paid out of the Common Poor Fund, Guardians removed every lunatic for whom they could get a Medical Officer to certify, without thought of expense or propriety. Hanwell and Colney Hatch were soon filled, so that accommodation was sought elsewhere. Thirteen lunatics were sent each week at the end of 1868 from St. George the Martyr, Southwark, to Lichfield, and they had had a comfortable home in Mitcham. Holborn sent its patients to Salisbury, and other Metropolitan paupers were scattered far afield. The expense of removal was great and maintenance at County Asylums was 10s. and at private asylums 12s. to 15s. a week. Injustice was inflicted on Guardians who had made special accommodation for imbeciles and were keeping them at their own expense. Real supervision was out of the question. Some sane paupers were detained at Salisbury, and this was only discovered by the occasional visits of two Holborn Guardians and the Medical Officer. On the other hand, dangerous lunatics were improperly detained in the workhouse because no

[1] Minutes, Kensington Board of Guardians.
[2] Minutes, St. George in the East Board of Guardians, October 1865.
[3] *Lancet*, 1867, i, p. 215.

room was left in a good asylum. Chelsea, for example, could not move anyone out of its overcrowded imbecile wards because there was nowhere for inmates to go.[1]

In their Twenty-third Annual Report the Poor Law Board wrote that many Metropolitan lunatics had been sent from workhouses to asylums in other counties, even at considerable distances. This practice was allowed, they said, under the Lunacy Acts, and the Poor Law Board could neither control nor prohibit it. They hoped that the completion of the two new asylums would enable lunatics to be brought back to the London neighbourhood, so that they would be more accessible to their relations and friends, and a reduction in the cost of maintenance be effected. In May 1871 there were 1,600 patients at Leavesden and nearly 1,400 at Caterham. Not only did this ease the strain on workhouse accommodation but a great number of incurable and harmless cases were being removed from Hanwell and Colney Hatch. The County Asylums round the Metropolis were also overcrowded, and at the end of 1868 the Home Secretary had written to the Middlesex magistrates of the complete inadequacy of the existing lunatic asylums for the accommodation of pauper lunatics.[2] He said he was compelled to call on them to take proper steps for remedying the evil by the building of another County Asylum, and that in default of their doing so it was his duty to use compulsion.[3] After the 'temporary' Metropolitan District Asylum at Hampstead had served its purpose for the fever and smallpox epidemics which ravaged the Metropolis in 1869–71, it was appropriated to harmless imbeciles, but Dr. Bridges, a Poor Law Inspector, found that the female infirmary ward had been filled with cases of bedridden patients and those suffering from senile decay. Similar cases were found in the male ward. Dr. Bridges had to point out that the asylum was not intended for the chronic bedridden or the helpless infirm.[4]—It was an illustration of Guardians trying to rid themselves of the aged and infirm who lingered indefinitely at the workhouses, overcrowding them and causing protracted expenditure.

By the time their term of office came to a close the Poor Law Board was recognizing the pauper lunatic not only as a distinct class requiring special consideration, but also, because destitution was no fault of his own and deterrent principles were inapplicable, kinder treatment could and had to be afforded him. In 1862 Inspector Lambert had attributed the increase in the lunatic poor to the dissolute and intemperate habits of parents. Venereal disease and alcoholism produced mental infirmity, but low mental ability was also the result of generations of malnutrition and the sordid squalor amongst which the poor lived. The workhouse itself starved the will and blunted the intelligence of its inmates. Social reformers had by the 'sixties and 'seventies convinced the central authorities of this, and many regulations were issued by the Poor Law Board which made the condition of lunatics in workhouses superior to those which obtained in their homes. For example, the

[1] *Lancet*, 1869, i, p. 169.
[2] Hanwell and Colney Hatch, which were the two Middlesex County Asylums.
[3] *Lancet*, 1869, i, p. 168.
[4] Minutes, Hampstead Board of Guardians, 1873: regarding letter from Dr. Bridges to the Local Government Board.

Lunacy Commissioners had directed the attention of the Poor Law Board to the subject of the arrangements in workhouses for the bathing of idiots or other persons of unsound mind. Several instances had occurred of insane paupers being placed in baths without any attention being paid to the rules and regulations which had to be observed. The Commissioners therefore desired the Poor Law Board to adopt some definite system and issue rules for the guidance of workhouse officers. The Lunacy authorities framed the Order which the Poor Law Board circularized to all the Guardians. The rules were extremely long and contained such points as that the patient should be bathed immediately after admission to the workhouse, and once a week afterwards. The Medical Officer had to be referred to if there was sickness, enfeeblement, or excitement. In preparing a bath, cold water had always to be turned on first, and before the patient entered it the temperature had to be ascertained—it was to be between 88° and 98°. If the thermometer was out of order, all bathing operations had to be suspended. Only one patient was to be bathed in the same water, and under *no circumstances whatever* were two patients to occupy the bath at the same time. No patient had to be put under water. They were to be cleansed well with soap, dried properly, and clothed as rapidly as possible. Bruises, sores, and anything else worthy of the Medical Officer's notice had to be reported, etc.[1]

A Circular, issued in 1867, stipulated that magistrates were to visit homes or the workhouse to examine lunatics for the order of removal, instead of the sufferer having to go to an open police court, because it was believed this increased the malady and caused unnecessary hardship. Great care was also to be taken to obtain proper medical assistance.[2] Another Circular ordered that no female patient was to be sent from the workhouse to an asylum without a companion of her own sex. Before 1867 it frequently occurred that lunatics were removed from the workhouse whilst they were too ill for a journey, or also sick with some other disease. The Poor Law Amendment Act of 1867 (section 27), provided that if there were any poor in the workhouse suffering from mental disease, or bodily disease of an infectious or contagious character, and the Medical Officer on examining the patient found the person was not in a fit condition to be moved without danger, discharge had to be delayed until the Medical Officer certified that it was safe. In 1857 the Poor Law Board had circularized the Guardians of the country that they were responsible for providing vehicles at public expense for any future removals. This came in reply to a complaint from a Medical Superintendent of the Wiltshire County Lunatic Asylum against the method of removing pauper lunatics.

This period also saw attention being paid to another category of defectives—the blind, deaf, and dumb. It was a new class for the Poor Law authorities, which was only just mentioned in the Report and Act of 1834. The new Poor Law had implicitly sanctioned the granting of outdoor relief to such of these physically defective as were either wives or children, by regarding such relief as not made to husbands or fathers, even if they were able-bodied and in employment. In 1842 the central authorities issued an instructional

[1] Poor Law Board Circular, 21 March 1870.
[2] 26 November 1867.

letter that institutional treatment was to be offered them where such existed, even if it were outside the Union.—This was the only class of 'sick' which was specifically recognized in the early period as needing institutional treatment.—Little more was heard of these people until the Poor Law Amendment Act of 1867 (section 21), which authorized Guardians to provide for the reception, maintenance, and instruction of any adult pauper, being blind, deaf, or dumb, in any hospital or institution for such purposes. (The Act of 1862, 25, 26 Vic. c. 43, had provided similarly for children.) The development of this category of relief falls into the period of the Local Government Board, however, and although the Poor Law Board initiated so many supplementary policies, nothing was done for diseased or incapacitated children, who, unable to earn a living, spent all their lives in the workhouse.

The history of the mentally defective under the Poor Law Board can be told statistically. In 1850 there were 14,294 insane pauper lunatics, in 1860—31,543, and in 1870 46,548.[1] In 1852 there were 12,000 pauper lunatics in asylums and in 1868–69 27,000, whilst the number of those not in recognized institutions increased only slightly.[2] There were just over 4,000 lunatics not in licensed places or asylums in 1852, and then in the 'sixties the agitation for their removal was earnestly begun. In 1860 there were 16,000 in County Asylums, 8,210 in workhouses, and 5,204 with relatives. Table 15.1 illustrates the trend in the 'sixties.

TABLE 15.1

Disposition of the Mentally Defective under the Poor Law Board for the years 1861, 1867, and 1869.—Twenty-second Annual Report of the Poor Law Board, 1870.

	1861	1867 (probably an approximation)	1869
In County Asylums	17,373	23,000	25,460
In Registered Hospitals	889	1,200	1,541
In Workhouses	8,543	10,300	11,103
Lodged or Boarded Out	758	1,000	938
Residing with Relatives	5,357	5,000	6,631
	32,920	40,500	45,673

Between 1859 and 1869 expenditure rose from £482,425 to £722,613, an increase of 47 per cent, whilst over the last seventeen years it had increased by more than 100 per cent

[1] Third Annual Report of the Poor Law Board, 1851; Thirteenth Annual Report of the Poor Law Board, 1860; Twenty-second Annual Report of the Poor Law Board, 1870.
[2] Twenty-second Annual Report of the Poor Law Board, 1869–70

as expenditure was £322,000 in 1852.[1] The Poor Law Board explained the great increase as being due to 'the anxiety in late years to afford the protection and scientific treatment of asylums to poor persons of this [lunatic] class, who would formerly have been kept in workhouses or left in the care of relatives as outdoor paupers'.[2] This had therefore become a heavy item in Poor Law expenditure, 'an expense which stands on a different footing altogether from other items of Poor Law expenditure'.—It also showed the development possible under the Poor Law and the ever-widening range of interests with which it was concerned.

[1] *Ibid.*
[2] Some of the increase in expenditure was accounted for by the rise in the cost of maintenance, e.g., the average cost per head per week in a County Asylum was 8s. 4½d., in licensed Houses 10s. 4½d., and elsewhere 2s. 10d. in 1854. These prices had all risen by 2s. by 1870, therefore the additional cost was not only due to increase in numbers.

CHAPTER 16

Auxiliaries to the Poor Law Medical Service,
1847–71

(1) THE VOLUNTARY HOSPITAL

THE Poor Law authorities after 1847 developed the former tendency of Guardians to use the voluntary hospital as an auxiliary service to the medical relief system. This was legalized by a clause of the Poor Law Continuation Act of 1851.[1] In the 'forties the Poor Law Commissioners had sanctioned Guardians' contributions to hospitals, but doubt remained as to the power of local authorities for subscribing from the poor rates to voluntary institutions situated beyond the limits of a Union. The Poor Law Board, in their Circular covering the Act, drew the attention of Guardians to the fact that in many cases of disease or accident hospitals and infirmaries offered advantages greater than those which could be secured to the poor in any other way, and further, these could be obtained for them in the most economical manner, by a moderate annual subscription to hospital funds. From communications which the central authorities had received, they realized that the Guardians were likely to avail themselves of this power, but the consent of the Poor Law Board had always to be obtained first. Seventeen years later the Board reported that the practice had become general on the part of the Guardians to subscribe annually under the provisions of the 1851 Act, to hospitals and infirmaries in their neighbourhood with a view to sending to them the most serious cases of accident or illness, so that 'paupers suffering under dangerous and difficult diseases may have the benefit of combined skill and complete appliances for medical and surgical treatment which is afforded by those institutions'.[2]

Subscriptions varied from Union to Union. Kensington for example contributed £5 a year to St. Mary's Hospital, Paddington, and the Guardians gave evidence in the 'sixties of the benefit secured to the poor who lived in the north of the Union. Paddington Board of Guardians also subscribed 10 guineas a year to St. Mary's.[3] Poplar subscribed 10 guineas to the Poplar Hospital which was doubled in 1864;[4] patients were not frequently sent, the Guardians stated, but the Union had the advantage of the contribution because accident

---

[1] 14, 15 Vic. c. 105, s. 4.
[2] Twentieth Annual Report, 1868.
[3] Minutes, Paddington Board of Guardians, 1852.
[4] Minutes, Poplar Board of Guardians, 1864.

cases could receive immediate attention, which prevented families falling on the rates.[1] The Liverpool Vestry, however, subscribed over £150 to the Northern and Southern Hospitals there. Formerly 500 guineas had been subscribed a year to dispensaries, but this had been disallowed by the Poor Law Commissioners. This liberal scheme was undertaken because the Poor Law authorities wished to discontinue the payment of additional fees to the Medical Officers, who were to receive a fixed inclusive salary. Therefore all surgical and emergency cases were sent to the hospitals instead of being dealt with by the District Medical Officers. Three lying-in institutions were also subscribed to. A considerable increase in medical relief resulted, and the Poor Law Board offered no objection to Liverpool's policy of sending the sick poor to hospital in cases of accident without reducing the patient to a pauper. It was maintained that the charitable institutions and the liberal system of medical relief saved the poor rate. One hospital spent £8,000, another £4,000–£5,000 a year, the Central Infirmary £7,500, and the Northern and Southern £2,500 and £3,400, chiefly on the poor.[2] The Poor Law Board probably had the prevention of pauperism in mind when they authorized the Guardians' subscriptions. The recognition of the inadequacy of the State medical service can also be seen in this move to facilitate provision for the poor by non-pauper institutions, as well as the saving of expenditure on medical relief for the destitute.

The voluntary hospitals at this time however did not provide such salutary treatment as was believed. They attracted the best physicians and surgeons, but medical science was still in its infancy and environmental conditions were often little superior to those of the workhouse infirmaries. In 1861 Farr drew attention to the mortality rate in general hospitals in England and Wales, Table 16.1.

Griffin maintained to the Select Committee of 1862 that people operated on in their homes, even if they were hovels, recovered more quickly and more generally than those taken to hospital. Formerly, he said, hospital treatment had been necessary, because early Poor Law Medical Officers were incompetent, but they had become a highly educated class of the profession, capable of performing their duties. Therefore environmental factors only were comparable, and here the hospitals offered the worst conditions.

The terrible ventilation and the overcrowded and insanitary state of old hospitals were conducive to the spread of disease. At one time hospital gangrene and erysipelas had infested all medical institutions, puerperal fever had depopulated lying-in hospitals, and infants had died in their hundreds in foundling hospitals. Even in the mid-nineteenth century hospital pyaemia and other diseases contracted through cross-infection, frustrated the hopes of the most skilful surgeons and physicians. An unparalleled ferment in the hospital world had however begun. Sir James Young Simpson[3] pointed out the 'decreasing

---

[1] Correspondence with Poor Law Board, 1864: MS. Minutes.

[2] Edward Grey, Assistant Overseer and Superintendent of Relief, Liverpool, in evidence to Select Committee on Medical Relief, 1854.

[3] The celebrated Edinburgh physician who by advocating the use of chloroform in childbirth provoked a national controversy. He also made studies of cholera, leprosy, homoeopathy, and archaeology.

TABLE 16.1

Mortality Rate in General Hospitals in England and Wales.—Twenty-fourth Annual Report of the Registrar-General, 1861.

	Number of Hospitals	Inmates	Average Number of Inmates in each	Deaths	Mortality per cent
Total—hospitals	80	8,535	107	6,220	72·88
Hospitals containing:					
300 inmates and upwards	5	2,090	418	2,101	100·53
200–300 inmates	4	916	239	838	91·78
100–200 inmates	22	2,898	132	2,041	70·43
Under 100	49	2,634	54	1,240	47·08

N.B. The greater the hospital the higher the mortality rate.

health rate and the increasing death rate' in a paper on 'Hospitals'. In an address to the Public Health Section of the National Association for the Promotion of Social Science in 1867 he asked: 'To what extent are hospitals, as in general at present constituted, banes or blessings? And how can they be changed so as to convert them from the former to the latter?' Simpson had revolutionized surgery by his introduction of chloroform in 1847, Lister[1] aided him in his 'invention' of antisepsis in 1865. From this time war was waged on hospital gangrene, erysipelas, puerperal fever, septicaemia, and tetanus.

As the spread of infection was little understood and was generally attributed to pollution of air, many of the greatest hospital doctors still gave evidence to the Select Committee of 1878 (inquiring into fever hospitals) in favour of mixing fever cases in general wards. Early in the nineteenth century the ratio of one fever case to six other had been regarded as safe. G. J. Guthrie, an ex-President of the Royal College of Surgeons, said in 1854 that in London hospitals fever cases were mixed in general wards, and maintained that fever never spread, only erysipelas, and this through the insufficient ventilation.[2] A Member of Parliament interested in Metropolitan hospitals stated that he had received several letters, and one from a doctor of St. George's Hospital for thirty years, which pointed out that fever had never been communicated to other patients.[3] A physician who had had twenty years experience in the Middlesex Hospital affirmed that fever cases should be spread as much as possible throughout the medical wards. Similar cases, he said, should never be collected

[1] English surgeon and scientist—one of the greatest surgeons of his time. Professor of surgery, Glasgow, Edinburgh, and London.

[2] Select Committee on Dublin hospitals, 1854.

[3] Select Committee on Dublin hospitals, 1854. The Hon. Josceline William Percy, M.P.

together or be put in neighbouring beds; he had never had any spread of infection, and in 1845 during the typhus epidemic, not a single case occurred amongst the patients in the medical wards. In 1849 sixty-two cases of cholera were admitted, which were mixed with other patients in the medical ward, none of whom contracted the disease. St. Bartholomew's and the Westminster Hospitals also believed that the concentration of the 'fever poison' by placing patients in fever wards, retarded their convalescence, and the same system obtained as at the Middlesex. The Middlesex Hospital doctor maintained that the spread of fever among ordinary patients was a common occurrence at hospitals where there were detached fever wards. Guthrie also stated that all Metropolitan hospitals took in fevers but not smallpox. If a case of smallpox occurred, it was isolated, and if it appeared on the first day of admission patients were removed to the smallpox hospital, because everyone was afraid of the disease. In the London Fever Hospital a physician received a gratuity of £105 a year, and those at the Smallpox Hospital 50 guineas; they also had the privilege of taking pupils, but no applicants presented themselves at either institution. From this it may be inferred that doctors regarded isolation hospitals as highly prejudicial to their own interests and this provided another reason for the retarding of progress.

But there were prophets who in the early nineteenth century advocated rigid isolation. The London Smallpox Hospital had been established in 1745 (the mortality rate was 18 per cent in 1830 and 25 per cent in 1870) and a Lock Hospital in 1746. The London Fever Hospital had been opened in 1802 and it remained the only one of its kind in London until 1867 and the coming of the Metropolitan Asylums Board. Even here all forms of fever were mixed together, as there was no classification until 1861, and Southwood Smith had revealed in the 'thirties and 'forties that the mortality of fever patients between the ages of 15 and 60 increased every year at a constant rate of 1·03.[1] In 1860 answers to a circular issued by the Fever Hospital eliciting information on the reception of fever into hospitals, revealed that eight London general hospitals admitted a limited number of fever cases among ordinary patients, and of the twenty hospitals questioned in the provinces nine refused to admit fever cases, six admitted them into separate wards, and only five distributed them among their general patients. Replies showed further that conditions in the provinces were better than in London, in that general hospitals provided separate accommodation to a greater extent for infectious diseases.

The Sanitary Act of 1866 stipulated that the nuisance removal authorities should provide and maintain hospitals for infectious diseases, but little notice was taken, and the only places generally available for infectious cases were the workhouse sick wards. During epidemics hospitals always refused to admit fever cases, and temporary accommodation was provided, occasionally in the Metropolis and other large towns, and always in Liverpool. The Poor Law authorities pioneered the way in rate-aided isolation hospitals, and the establishments of the Metropolitan Asylums Board at Stockwell, Homerton, and Hampstead, secured separate institutional treatment at first for paupers, and later for all

---

[1] Mr. Edmond's deductions from Smith's figures, requoted in Farr MSS., Vol. II.

classes suffering from fevers and smallpox. The opposition of the air-borne infection theorists tried but failed to influence the Poor Law authorities, *who under the inevitable pressure of circumstances, were compelled to afford segregation to the poor in their institutions, whilst the voluntary hospitals lagged behind.* Even in Liverpool, which had a parochial fever hospital from 1806, the Medical Officer of Health in 1871 stated the provision of isolated hospitals for those above the pauper class would not only be a waste of funds but might have injurious effects. Although so many other hospitals had been established, it was not until 1872 that the first attempt was made here to meet the needs of the non–destitute suffering from infectious fevers.

But the Poor Law Board itself did not face the responsibility of providing hospital accommodation up to 1868. In 1863 at the time of the smallpox epidemic, an anxious letter was sent to the Boards of Guardians at the instigation of Dr. Buchanan, a medical inspector of the Privy Council, permitting them to adapt temporary premises for the 'destitute poor attacked by contagious or infectious disease'.[1] The recommendation was ignored. In 1866 when cholera was imminent the increase of outdoor relief and the supply of disinfectants and clothing was advised, but there was no mention of temporary hospitals. Boards of Guardians were however to prevent as far as possible the admission of cholera patients to the workhouses.[2] The central authorities had therefore realized the danger of admitting infectious diseases into the workhouses yet neglected to authorize or command the building of separate institutions. They therefore looked to the existing isolation hospitals to supply the defect till the late 'sixties. The Poor Law Board several times during their period of office circularized Boards of Guardians on the advisability of sending infectious cases to hospitals. In 1857 the London Fever Hospital drew the attention of the central authorities to the benefit which would result to the poorer classes from the more general use of the hospital by Metropolitan Unions. Inspector Farnall reported that after a careful survey of the workhouses, he had come to the conclusion that no material change had been made for providing adequate accommodation for infectious cases since the special report to the Home Secretary in 1847, and that the deficiency could be supplied by the London Fever Hospital, both in regard to situation, construction, and ventilation, and the particular requirements of such diseases. The Poor Law Board therefore sent Circulars to Guardians pointing out that the Fever Hospital was designed to be the central receptacle for the fever cases of the Metropolis, and that it was able with the aid of private subscriptions to receive indigent sufferers at so low a rate that this would not exceed the expense incurred by treating them in the workhouses, i.e., 1s. a day. Guardians were asked to take note of the 'purity of atmosphere, the constant attendance of resident Medical Officers, good nursing and appropriate nourishment' and were recommended to make general use of the institution.[3] Kensington, for example, sent its fever patients to the hospital and always received reports on patients, the numbers retained, their progress, and mortality rates. The cost was

[1] Circular, 30 April 1863.
[2] Circular, 27 July 1866.
[2] Circular, 1 August 1857 (the Fever Hospital was in St. Pancras Road).

generally 7s. a week and patients remained in the hospital about three weeks. The fever cases in Kensington cost the Union from 20s. to 25s. and the Guardians spent a further £3 a year on cabs for transporting them, besides making a small annual donation.[1] St. George in the East, Stepney, subscribed 5 guineas a year to the Fever Hospital and in the 'fifties paid about £50 a year for the treatment and maintenance of patients.[2]

The fever and smallpox hospitals were the first of the specialized institutions, but isolation hospitals were only the preliminary step in the great progress made in the latter half of the nineteenth century towards the establishment of special hospitals. Save for maternity, few towns outside London and Liverpool possessed other than general hospitals. But the rapid advances in medical knowledge and the great growth of the industrial population necessitated the provision of more hospital accommodation, as well as the widening of the scope of the medical profession in particular branches. These hospitals usually arose through one or two doctors acquiring, with the aid of philanthropists, convenient premises to start a clinic, which later, under wealthy patronage, became special institutions catering for interesting cases or those neglected by the general hospitals. For example, the Royal London Ophthalmia Hospital, Moorfields, dated back to the early nineteenth century and the National Orthopaedic Hospital had been founded in 1839; Liverpool as we have seen had an Ophthalmic Hospital, a Lock Hospital, and an Eye and Ear Infirmary and another for tuberculosis and chest diseases. In 1851 Dr. William Marsden established the Cancer Hospital in London; in 1852 Dr. Charles West the Hospital for Sick Children, Great Ormond Street, and in 1854 Dr. Andrew Reed the Royal Hospital for Incurables at Putney. Liverpool had in 1842 been the first town to set apart special wards for children in a hospital, and in 1857 erected an infirmary for children, which was rebuilt four times before 1866. (By 1880 30,000 cases were treated a year.) A dental hospital was also established for the poor in 1860 and a hospital for Cancer and Skin Diseases in 1862. In the following year the Hospital for Consumption of the Chest was opened; it was greatly extended after only a few years and included a vast out-patients' dispensary. Another Skin Hospital was erected in 1863, and in 1867 the Stanley Hospital for the treatment of diseases of the chest and diseases of women and children was established. Like all the other hospitals it was to be a 'convenient building in town in which the suffering poor might obtain relief', and nearly 11,000 patients were attended in the first year, so that larger buildings were quickly required. In 1869 Earl Derby provided a valuable site and the Stanley Hospital became a general hospital. In 1871 another Eye and Ear Hospital was opened. All these institutions were started by doctors or on their initiative, and expansion was necessary in every case within a few years. In a single generation the special hospital became an important part of the hospital system throughout the country, and cottage hospitals also arose. The first was founded in Cranleigh, Surrey, by Albert Napper, F.R.C.S., in 1859. Before this the sick poor in the country remained in their cottages, were removed to the work-

---

[1] Minutes, Kensington Board of Guardians, for several years.
[2] Minutes, St. George in the East Board of Guardians, for several years.

house infirmary, or were transported to distant county hospitals in unsprung and dangerous carts. Acute cases only, which could not wait for admission to a hospital, were taken in these new institutions, but again within a life-time they had grown in dimension and scope, and had become an integral part of the hospital system.

In rural areas Boards of Guardians subscribed to these local hospitals as they were doing to the country or neighbouring town institutions, and in urban areas it was to the special hospital that Guardians contributed most readily. Kensington, for example, subscribed 2 guineas a year to the Ophthalmic Hospital, and St. George in the East £10.[1] Most London Unions gave 5 guineas to the Lock Hospital and to asylums like the Deaf and Dumb Asylum in Upper Clapton. Donations were also made to societies, like the Truss Society.[2] In the provinces the Poor Law Board was not as anxious to sanction payments from the rates to non-hospital institutions. For example the Plymouth Guardians in 1862 applied for permission to subscribe 2 guineas to the Deaf and Dumb Asylum, but this was refused as the Poor Law Board did not regard it as constituting a hospital.[3] The Bakewell (Derby) Guardians were also forbidden to send adults to the Blind, Deaf and Dumb Asylum, but they were allowed to subscribe for the children.[4]

The increase in hospital treatment for the poor and pauper was therefore concomitant with the revolution in medical science and nursing, the development of special hospitals, and the improvement of environmental conditions within the institutions—chiefly due to the great work of Florence Nightingale, Dr. Sutherland, Timothy Holmes, and the Report of the Select Committee of 1861. New hospitals made adequate provision for ventilation, sanitation, accommodation, and cleanliness, and the older hospitals, like St. Thomas's and St. Bartholomew's in London, adapted their buildings to allow 1,000 cubic feet per bed and made new wards even larger.[5] But the reforms in hospitals, particularly those relating to accommodation, failed to keep pace with demand, and for this the inadequacy of the State medical service was much to blame.

Closely allied to this situation was the increasing financial strain on the voluntary institutions. In 1856, Rumsey in his *Essays on State Medicine* wrote that the

> munificent provisions for the accommodation and treatment of disease and injury among the working-classes, made in the hospitals and infirmaries of England, taken as a whole, are probably not surpassed in any country.

[1] Minutes, Kensington Board of Guardians, 1857; St. George in the East Board of Guardians, 1855.
[2] Accounts and Abstracts, Chelsea Board of Guardians—8 guineas a year.
[3] Minutes, Plymouth Board of Guardians, 1862 (Webb MSS.).
[4] Minutes, Bakewell (Derby) Board of Guardians, 1867 (Webb MSS.).
[5] In Liverpool in 1856 the Hospital Board of the Infirmary recommended to the Hospital Committee that 'Medical Officers should have the privilege of sending for a short time to the Bathing Establishments at Southport and New Brighton such cases as would benefit by such a change ... and the Medical Board is of the opinion this would prove beneficial to many (otherwise hopeless) cases, and would ultimately effect the saving of the funds of the charity'. The Committee also approved the suggestion but unfortunately did not have the power to appropriate funds to such a purpose. It did, however, initiate and invite subscriptions to the Southport Charity Fund which was to provide financial assistance to patients convalescing.—T. H. Bickerton, *A Medical History of Liverpool*, 1936.

He pointed out that since these institutions had been called on by the Act of 1851 to give assistance in reducing the supply of Poor Law medical relief, Boards of Guardians had taken advantage of their position and made use of their hospital subscriptions to appropriate an undue share of the privileges secured to the poor by the founders and philanthropic supporters of the institutions. The endowed charities had great difficulty, Rumsey maintained, in resisting the pressure of legally constituted representative bodies and of checking 'the tendency of the present system to shift the burden of sickness among the poor from public to charitably disposed individuals.' In 1844 he had recommended public or compulsory support of voluntary hospitals.

The Select Committee of 1854 was told by one of the administrators of the South Staffordshire General Hospital that 'Boards of Guardians subscribe and take from us [the governors] something which is in fact in aid of the general fund for the relief of the poor'. He gave the instance of the Wolverhampton Union which contributed 10 guineas a year to the hospital for which it was entitled to send five in-patients and twenty out-patients. The cost of maintaining a patient for the average duration of an illness of thirty days was £3 12s., and the cost of an out-patient 3s., so that Wolverhampton received £21 worth of treatment for its 10 guineas. Not only did the hospital lose, but this, it was evinced, was unjust to the subscribers, who were generally not among the most affluent ratepayers. The Union gained financially and the poor rates were saved because the Medical Officers did not receive extra fees. Further, the poor were given treatment far superior to what the Guardians could provide. Although this was pointed out, six years later the Wolverhampton Guardians were still subscribing only 10 guineas a year.[1] Griffin also maintained at the inquiry of 1861 that Guardians sent cases to hospital to get round the payment of additional fees and that the hospitals were taxed heavily by them. In his own Union of Weymouth for example, £5 a year was subscribed for five patients, and as these were always the very worst cases, often remaining in the local hospital for two months, they cost considerably more than the subscription. He remarked cynically on the Poor Law Board advocating the system on the grounds of providing the best treatment at the most economical rate.

In 1854 Sir Benjamin Brodie, one of the most eminent doctors of his day and long connected with St. George's Hospital, London, was asked whether he thought it advisable for Metropolitan hospitals to be placed under the guidance of the Poor Law Board. He replied in the negative not only on grounds of efficient management, but also because medical relief would not be so liberally given—'the governors have more bowels of compassion'. He did not complain of the increasing number of cases being sent to hospital, but advocated a more constructive policy—the giving of Parliamentary grants to assist them.[2] Another doctor pointed out that all countries in Europe provided Government grants to teaching hospitals. Guthrie also complained of the absence of public support and that not even a site was provided. In teaching hospitals Medical Officers were required to

[1] Dr. Fowler in evidence to Select Committee, 1862.
[2] Select Committee on Dublin Hospitals, 1854.

pay a fee for employment and so they could take pupils. Wakley had at the outset of his career revealed and fought against the abuses which existed in London owing to the institutions being private monopolies closed to public inspection. The contra-distinction of the high character of the Dublin teaching hospitals was pointed out in the Report of the Committee inquiring into them in 1854. Seven were supported by a Parliamentary grant, and not only did these provide good training schools for students, but they afforded a larger and more efficient system of medical relief for the sick poor. A specially-aided venereal disease hospital and a similar lying-in hospital had also been established, and the latter was the only institution in Ireland, save for another very small one, where instruction in midwifery was given. Many witnesses, besides those already mentioned, had advocated grants in aid of Metropolitan hospitals and especially for the impecunious Lock Hospital. As the other London institutions did not generally admit venereal disease, the financial strain imposed on this hospital with its reformatory was tremendous, and it barely had sufficient means to continue. People were loathe to endow a hospital dedicated to this purpose and the great majority of cases as it was had to receive grudging attention at the workhouse. Brodie particularly advocated a Parliamentary grant for the Lock Hospital. In 1863 the governors of the institution told the Guardians that they were in debt for £1,100, and that in future they would not be able to admit more patients than the Guardians were subscribing for, and that they would only receive those venereal disease cases whose constitutions had not already broken down. Kensington Board of Guardians, for example, were informed that as they subscribed 5 guineas a year, only five patients, one at a time, could be taken from that Union in a year.[1] Other Metropolitan hospitals were in similarly straitened circumstances. At the end of the 'fifties the Royal Free Hospital asked for increased subscriptions to relieve what was hoped to be a temporary pressure and because the hospital desired to make improvements for extending its usefulness.

The reliance placed on the voluntary hospital by the Poor Law authorities was revealed in November 1869 when the Poor Law Board addressed a communication to the administrators of the seventeen largest hospitals in London inquiring whether they had any spare accommodation which they would be willing to appropriate to pauper patients. This move was taken because of the crowded state of the workhouse infirmaries, and the powers conferred on Boards of Guardians by section 16 of the Metropolitan Poor Law Amendment Act to enter into arrangements with public hospitals for the treatment of paupers, on terms to be agreed upon by the Guardians and the hospital authorities, with the sanction of the Poor Law Board. In their letter, the Board wished to know what class or classes of cases it would be convenient for the hospital to receive, the number of destitute patients which could be accommodated, and the payment required. Guy's Hospital reported that the average number of pauper patients received was fifteen and that fifteen additional beds might be appropriated during the winter months. Charing Cross Hospital offered to receive twenty pauper patients for the payment of 10s. 6d. weekly so long as the number of

---

[1] Minutes, Kensington Board of Guardians, 1863.

persons the institution was entitled to admit permitted it. King's College Hospital would take thirty pauper patients suffering from non-contagious diseases for periods of six months as 12s. a week per bed, and the Westminster Hospital stated that two surgical wards each of nine beds could be made available for pauper patients at £50 a year per bed or 20s. a week for each pauper.[1] All other hospitals like the University College, St. Mary's, St. George's, and St. Thomas's had no spare accommodation for the reception of the destitute sick. The Poor Law Board therefore had to conclude that hospital accommodation (exclusive of that at the Fever and Smallpox Hospitals) available for paupers in the Metropolis was limited to ninety-eight beds, and so offered but small additional resource to the 12,000 beds occupied in workhouse infirmaries by sick paupers.[2] The London Hospital in the winter of 1869 asked Guardians to remove pauper patients as soon as they were convalescent because of the insufficient accommodation.[3] This was because Guardians often left patients indefinitely in hospital so as to be relieved of the responsibility for them as long as possible.

Although the number of actual paupers treated as in-patients was small, the overwhelming majority of cases in the voluntary hospitals consisted of that class which the Poor Law medical reformers maintained should have been entitled to gratuituous medical relief, and who should have been provided for under a State medical service. In Bristol, for example, the Infirmary had about 20,000 cases a year, and it was asserted that the destitution authorities would not have been able to carry out their assistance to the poor as they did, had it not been for the voluntary institution which materially diminished the number of applicants for parochial medical relief.[4] Every year the medical press, particularly the *Lancet* and the *British Medical Journal* included numerous letters and articles on voluntary hospitals relating to their accounts, method of admission, and individual circumstances which proved similar assertions.

It was not the lying-in patients however which caused the greatest concern to the voluntary hospitals at the end of the 'sixties and for the next decades, but the out-patients' departments. Not only the indigent working-class, but also paupers attended hospitals as out-patients. This was evinced by the disallowing of the practice, save with the Medical Officer's permission, by the Kensington Board of Guardians.[5] The 'abuse' of the out-patients' department was severely criticized by the medical profession and the movement for reform was assisted most by the Charity Organization Society. In 1870 a meeting of 156 doctors was held under the Chairmanship of Sir William Fergusson.[6] A resolution was passed on the 'great abuse of outdoor medical relief in hospitals and dispensaries'. And another

---

[1] The average cost per bed in 1850 had been £34 12s. a year in London (Select Committee on Dublin Hospitals, 1854). Therefore the cost had risen by one-third over twenty years.

[2] Twenty-second Annual Report, 1869–70.

[3] Minutes, St. George in the East Board of Guardians.

[4] T. F. Gilbert, Town Councillor and Registrar, Bristol, evidence to Select Committee, 1854.

[5] Minutes, 1868.

[6] William Fergusson, M.D., F.R.S.E., Inspector General of Army Hospitals. In 1839 he had written a pamphlet on 'Pauperism, Poor Law, emigration, medical relief and crime'. One of the most famous surgeons of his day, he was President of the Royal College of Surgeons, a surgeon to royalty and author on surgery.

suggested that 'the evils inseparable from the system of gratuitous medical relief administration at the out-patients departments of hospitals and free dispensaries can be met only by the establishment on a large scale of provident dispensaries in England, and by improved administration of Poor Law medical relief'. At a subsequent meeting the doctors resolved that improved administration of Poor Law medical relief in accordance with the Metropolitan Poor Act of 1867 (regarding the establishment of dispensaries) was essential to the reform of out-patients' departments. Second, in furtherance of this result and 'to limit the pauperizing tendency of the present system of gratuitous relief at hospitals and dispensaries, all free dispensaries should be under the control of the Poor Law authorities, so that a proper system of inquiry can be instituted previous to the administering of gratuitous medical relief'. Third, the doctors recommended the curtailing of hospital relief to cases which were of clinical interest and those which presented social hardships.[1]

But the movement was only beginning in the late 'sixties. It gathered momentum in the 'seventies and 'eighties, by which time articles and pamphlets revealed that the Poor Law infirmaries were not only a part of the general hospital system, but were also regarded as one of the most important types of medical institution.[2] Therefore the reform of the institutional medical services of the Poor Law were included in the demand for the establishment of provident dispensaries.

(2) MEDICAL CLUBS

The new institution had its roots in the sick club and self-supporting dispensary. The old medical club established by Guardians, philanthropists, or doctors had either been purely for domiciliary medical treatment, or had combined this with an assurance policy for giving money payments in times of illness. Occasionally the club had its own dispensary—although the self-supporting dispensary had been established—but apart from these independent institutions the provision of a central station was rare. Success only

---

[1] Notes and extracts from papers and articles bearing on the subject later contained in a memorandum of the Charity Organization Society to a special Inquiry of the House of Lords, 1889, into Charities of the Metropolis—voluntary hospitals and dispensaries, and Poor Law hospitals and dispensaries. Both Sieveking and Timothy Holmes were in this movement and wrote that out-patients' departments had no clinical value for professional training because they were too overcrowded and no real attention could be given to patients.

[2] By the 1880s the Metropolitan Asylums Board establishments had become municipal isolation hospitals as seen in the *Report on Hospitals, 1882*. This stated that as so many classes of persons would be liable to removal to them, it was of paramount importance that they should be made as tolerable as possible: 'The pauper character which now attaches to the hospitals of the Asylums Board, and renders them repulsive to all but the indigent, would disappear if the distinction between paupers and non-paupers were abolished ... The consequent mixture of different classes entails hardship of a different kind ... [and could] be obviated by separate wards ... A payment made by one class for accommodation which is afforded without payment to another places the latter on the footing of paupers which it is desirable to avoid. . . . The Royal Commission further recommended: 'no distinction between rich and poor, pauper and non-pauper'—regarding the removal of infectious cases to an isolation hospital—and desired compulsory powers. (The widespread use of the Metropolitan Asylums Board's isolation hospitals led to the abolition of constituting a person who entered them a pauper unless he were in receipt of general relief as well.)

attended the self-help of the working-classes where their means were augmented by philanthropy, and this was recognized by the advocates of the provident dispensary, which was generally founded by doctors, the local gentry, or businessmen, who also discarded sickness benefits.

Some of the early medical clubs (for treatment only) continued in the 'sixties, like those at Bethnal Green for example, one of which was Dr. Moore's, the Poor Law medical reformer. As late as 1850 the Guardians of Bradfield (Yorks.) established a sick club, each member being asked to pay 3s. a year or threepence a month; 5s. covered a whole family, and 1 guinea secured a woman attendant in a confinement. But such clubs generally belonged to the 'thirties and 'forties, and had always been short-lived. Inspector Cane pointed out to the Select Committee of 1862 that the clubs had never flourished nor were they ever likely to because the facilities for obtaining parochial relief were too great. The poor, he said, would not subscribe if medical treatment could be obtained gratuitously and if in addition necessaries were given, which a club never provided. The Barham Downs medical club was said by Rumsey to have been the only reasonably successful society of this type.[1] In this rural district of Kent, one-sixth of the population subscribed over £300 a year and £60 was given voluntarily; this was divided among five Medical Officers and the club spent £100 for every £66 of the Guardians. It was therefore doing more for the poor than the Guardians.[2] But even this club was included by Rumsey in his condemnation of the system, in which he stated the only justification for such clubs was that the poor could choose their own doctor.

The inadequacy of medical attention was generally complained of, although this did not apply to the extensive clubs which existed in large towns, particularly Coventry and Derby. One of the benefits of the medical club claimed by a Guardian of Dewsbury was that they relieved the pressure on poor rates. In his town only those already destitute were attended by the Poor Law Medical Officer, whereas in the absence of the club, the members, he maintained, would definitely have fallen to the care of the Union.[3] The Poor Law Inspectors however denied this advantage. Austin in 1854 stated that the clubs which still existed in manufacturing districts did not affect pauperism. Weale said the clubs were very troublesome to Medical Officers, who were inadequately paid, and to the poor, because they had to apply for general relief in any case, and that therefore there were very few left by the 'fifties. He maintained that sick clubs injured benefit clubs, for Guardians in their attempt to foster the former did not cut down a man's general relief in sickness if he were subscribing to a club, and thereby failed to foster independence. The Select Committee of 1854, however, reported that the purely medical club encouraged provident habits among the working-classes, and through maintaining them by their own contributions, the value attached to prompt medical attendance and the honest desire to maintain their independence was proved.

[1] *Essays on State Medicine*, 1856.
[2] Evidence to Select Committee, 1854, by its founder the Rev. C. Oxenden.
[3] J. Ellison, Select Committee, 1854.

The combined sickness and benefit societies were also discussed at the Inquiry of 1854. Formerly these clubs were continually broken up and rearranged to get rid of old members. People who had subscribed many years were suddenly, on account of age, refused membership and were paid only a proportion of the surplus funds before the club was reorganized. They therefore lost a great deal of their subscription and the clubs failed in their purpose of preventing destitution because they did not provide for age. As Dr. Wood, Secretary to the Convention of Poor Law Medical Officers, pointed out, many people who had been club members for many years came on to the parish or into the workhouse through age, because they were debarred from further membership by chronic infirmity, or because they could no longer keep up their contributions. These clubs were also financially unsound and often failed because members drew more than the society could afford to pay. Abortive health insurance Bills had been introduced in 1773 and 1789 and in the nineteenth century it was Farr who appreciated the importance of the policy both from a social and political standpoint. *He strongly urged the establishment of a government system of health insurance*. This revolutionary measure he advocated partly on the ground of the unsatisfactory financial condition of the friendly societies, which tended to check the thrift of the working-classes in this form, whilst if it had been fully developed it would have materially reduced expenditure on poor relief. On the other hand his statistical information had revealed that there were 750,000 sick annually in England alone and 1,250,000 in the United Kingdom in the late 'thirties; therefore some general overall provision for the emergency of illness was necessary. He suggested the working-classes should contribute 1s. a week for five years (which would in all probability have been far too high for labourers) for which they should be entitled to 9s. 1d. a week for every week of sickness in the following forty years after the fifth year. Up till then they were to receive 1s. 10d. a week in the first year, 3s. 8d. in the second, 5s. 6d. in the third, 7s. 3d. in the fourth, and then 9s. 1d. No more premiums were to be paid after the fifth year.[1]

Although Farr's schemes were not heeded, insurance had since 1834 (chiefly because of the principles of the new Poor Law), been placed on firmer foundations. An example was set by the Oddfellows and the Foresters.[2] Not only were prospective members medically

---

[1] Farr, chapter on 'Vital Statistics' in McCulloch for health figures; the other material in Farr MSS.

[2] The inauguration of the Prudential Assurance Company is interesting. The Rev. James Gillman, the son of the Highgate doctor with whom Coleridge lived to be cured of his opium addiction, did tremendous work amongst the poor of Lambeth during the cholera epidemic of 1848. His experience amongst the poor showed him how much distress often occurred on the death of the breadwinner or a member of a family through the funeral expenses. He therefore thought of providing a fund for this on a principle similar to life insurance. In conjunction with Henry Harben, the Secretary of a small and struggling insurance company (Prudential) he evolved a scheme for the insurance of the whole family. By the payment of one penny a week and without medical examination, a certain sum, depending on the age of the insured person and the number of contributions was to be remitted by return of post to the family of the deceased, for funeral and other expenses. Gillman developed and superintended the new scheme and became chairman of the company in 1850. It was so successful, that what had begun as a great philanthropic work had by 1877, on Gillman's death, become a national institution with £2 million capital.—from *The Gillman's of Highgate and S. T. Coleridge*, by Alexander W. Gillman, 1895.

examined on entry to a society but after 1858 a medical certificate was required on the cause of death. This was especially for children and aimed against infanticide. If a child had not been medically attended before death the Poor Law Medical Officer had to furnish the certificate and received 1s. for it. Local societies also became financially solvent and tended gradually to throw off the provision of medical treatment. But sickness benefit continued to be given, and societies were particularly strong in the industrial North, although rural districts like Norfolk also had many benefit societies providing assistance in sickness to labourers. (The growth of penny banks also encouraged providence.) A new society in Kent, for example, had as its objects provision for sick members, superannuated members, and for families in which a death had occurred; and the encouragement of 'a spirit of self-reliance, and independence from parochial relief'. Almost every man, woman, and child in the labouring class in this particular village were members and contributed a farthing for every 1s. a week of sick pay they were entitled to—or just over 8s. a year. The Club had £600 credited to it in the Savings Bank in 1870 for a population of 500. By this time its functions had grown and it had branches for obtaining allotments, coal, and clothing. Maternity and dangerous illnesses received extra benefits, and payment on death was £2 for men and £1 for women. A penny savings bank for children was also connected with the society and by 1870 full sick pay was allowed for twenty-six weeks and half pay for thirteen further weeks—it was usually 8s. For an extra payment of 10s. a year an old age pension was given at 70. Applicants for membership were carefully scrutinized and great care was taken to enrol only healthy people. The poor, it was maintained, benefited greatly, but so did the ratepayer. When certain insurances could be effected at the Post Office by the Act of 1864, the Kent Friendly Society urged on the Postmaster-General the proposal that the 'system might be established as would allow labourers to secure by a single policy of insurance to be obtained from the Post Office, sums in sickness from 6s. a week upwards, as well as burial money from £5 upwards'. Contributions were to be made it was suggested, monthly or bi-monthly to the Post Office.[1]

Members of such benefit clubs where no medical treatment was given generally contained people who refrained from applying to the Poor Law Medical Officer, but many subscribers were not deterred by the stigma of pauperization. Guardians as in the case of purely medical clubs tried to foster the movement and did not deny parochial medical advice. In one Union, for example, the Poor Law authorities encouraged a society to such an extent that a single man receiving 7s. a week from a benefit club was given free treatment. They asserted that they had no right to take advantage of a man's providence and offered him general relief as well.[2] Inspector Weale said the system which tended to place a sick member of a club, who received benefits as well as parochial treatment, in a better position than when at work, required careful watching. One steward, he stated, complained to the local Guardian that the existing system would break any club in the country, for the

---

[1] *Royal Agricultural Society Journal*, 1870: article on 'Farm Labourer, Friendly Societies, and the Poor Law', by the Rev. Stratton. (The Society was established in Wicken, Kent, in 1838.)
[2] Evidence to Select Committee, 1854, the Rev. Howman of Norfolk.

independent Medical Officer, generally the Poor Law doctor, often failed to detect diseases quickly and so kept people dependent on the club for a very long time.[1]

In the 'fifties and 'sixties the old combined societies of benefit and medical club having their own Medical Officers still existed. The Rev. Oxenden said in 1854 that his knowledge of the Canterbury club led him to believe members received far superior treatment to the poor who were afforded Poor Law medical relief. Medical Officers gave adequate attention and drugs because of the rivalry which existed between them in canvassing for club patients. Griffin commended the privilege given to members to choose their own physicians from the panel, because those doctors regarded as giving the most skilful treatment indirectly received the greatest proportion of payment from the funds. It was the Poor Law Inspectors who pointed out that medical attendance was insufficient and that the Union was often applied to for additional medical treatment. Weale revealed that he had seen records showing club patients who received nothing like the attendance that paupers obtained from Union Medical Officers. This was partly due to the dual purpose of the clubs which rendered funds insufficient for the adequate remuneration of doctors. The position was worst in the clubs where Medical Officers did not receive a share of the funds according to the number of tickets held at the end of a year, but were paid sixpence to 1s. a head of the membership a quarter. Protracted illness therefore caused great financial loss to a doctor, or often induced him to shift his burden to some public institution to save himself the cost of drugs.

A Dewsbury Guardian admitted to the Select Committee of 1854 that satisfactory attendance and medicines were not obtained in these clubs, and that paupers were in a superior position. Salaries were too low, he maintained, but the remedy lay in the clubs' own hands for they should improve their management. If such societies were to be encouraged to provide their own medical aid, another Guardian, Wooldridge, suggested medicines would have to be provided at public cost. Adequate public subscription might also make possible the reduction of contributions and thereby increase membership. He advocated Guardians should supply medicines at a dispensary whilst subscriptions should pay for the Medical Officer's advice. No stigma whatever should be attached to the receipt of free medicines, but all non-subscribers were to be constituted paupers if they did not contribute to clubs for medical treatment. His object, however, was to prevent an applicant for medical relief becoming pauperized, therefore the option of subscription to a club was to be made as attractive as possible by a low rate. In his own Union of Fareham, nearly 1,500 poor belonged to the sick club in a population of 14,000, and 600 medical orders were given in a year. If Guardians were to supply drugs for such a large proportion of people, he suggested an independent club inspector might be appointed, but the Boards of Guardians were not to be permitted to interfere. Wooldridge later elaborated his plan and suggested club subscriptions should be made to Guardians. Charles Kingsley agreed with the possibility of making the distinction that members of clubs, whose proceeds were paid to the Union, should be entitled to medical relief (from the Union) without becoming paupers.

[1] These new benefit societies were generally only for the adult male population.

Kingsley, who throughout his evidence to the Select Committee of 1854 always spoke from personal experience on all questions of medical relief, threw light on the reason for the unpopularity and decline of the old system of combined medical and benefit club. He asserted that the labouring class in rural districts were not as a body capable of supplying their own medical aid, and that only young unmarried men could afford to subscribe to benefit clubs. In his village of Eversley (Hants) a man was provided with medical relief and 8s. a week while sick and with 4s. when convalescent. The author of *Yeast* shrewdly pointed out the mysterious connections of the clubs with the great brewers, and the atrocious frauds practised on the older infirm members by the junior majorities. (Other clergymen also powerfully exposed this.) A considerable portion of funds were annually spent on festivals and dinners. The brewers' association with the establishment of a club was ill-defined but on every club night, once a month, threepence had to be spent on beer, and this resulted in a far greater consumption. Kingsley therefore objected to the constitution and management of the clubs, though not to the system itself. He also pointed out that the poor were required to pay out of their own pockets in club subscriptions, for illness brought on them by the neglect of others, such as those connected with bad drainage and building. When many of their diseases like typhus, ague, rheumatic fever, chronic rheumatism, and especially lung affections were preventable, the poor paid for the fraud of others. As in *Yeast*, *Alton Locke*, and *Two Years Ago*, Kingsley informed the Select Committee that the large majority of the labouring poor, even if they were long-lived, were consumptive, not only through their work, but through the shocking state of their cottages and houses. Capitalists, property owners, and public bodies shirked their moral responsibility. The effect of the benefit club, he maintained, was to divert the attention of both poor and rich from getting rid of preventible disease to treating the mere symptoms of it. He spoke as a Public Health reformer when he advocated that rigorous sanitary measures would lighten the burden of the Poor Law authorities and medical clubs, for such improvements would so curtail sickness that the labouring population would be enabled to pay for its own medical relief through reformed clubs.

The most outspoken criticism of the old medical-benefit society came from the doctors and they sealed the decline of the system. In 1854 Dr. Lord said the operation of these societies was very beneficial to mechanics and labourers, but many people were included in the schemes who could afford to pay far more for the benefits they received, so that the medical profession was frequently injured. By the late 'sixties grievances had reached such dimensions that a virtual 'strike' of club doctors threatened. The local committees of the British Medical Association led the agitation, and the campaign was actively carried on through the medium of the *British Medical Journal* and the *Lancet*. In 1867[1] the latter reported that the club system had grown up without any forethought on the part of the profession as to the principles by which they should be governed, and without any semblance of equity in the rules. A few months later[2] a leading article appeared

[1] *Lancet*, 1867, ii, pp. 161–2.
[2] *Lancet*, 1868, i, pp. 16–17.

urging that it was 'high time definite action was taken to amend the present plan of the remuneration of the Medical Officer of the Sick Assurance Societies'. By this time the ground had been broken for discussion by the Birmingham and Midland Counties Branch of the British Medical Association. Four main grievances were pointed out in the British Medical Association's report:—the clubs included many persons whose social position was above that of the class for whose benefits they were intended; the amount of services in illness demanded of a doctor was frequently out of all proportion to the real necessities of the case; the wages of labourers had increased rapidly in the past years without any corresponding rise in the remuneration of club doctors; and no arrangement was made for protracted cases of illness or those requiring special and constant attention. The report was adopted unanimously. The Birmingham Committee demanded not less than 5s. per head a year, 2s. 6d. for medical certificates of admission and a scale of fees for special cases similar to that adopted by the Poor Law authorities. The *Lancet* added: no plan was applicable to all districts alike and that therefore a sliding-scale of payment should be instituted to suit varying conditions and sections of the community. Rural areas, it was maintained, should be allowed lower rates of contribution than in manufacturing areas. Further, practitioners should be empowered to possess the means of excluding tradesmen and small farmers from membership, for not only had they the means for procuring private medical advice, but they were the most exacting patients. Medical Officers wrote to the *Lancet* pointing out that sick clubs should be confined to those for whom they were intended, i.e. the working classes. One doctor argued that if the agricultural labourer could pay 3s. a head a year, surely a mechanic who earned 20s. to 63s. a week could pay a far higher sum in contributions. It was also suggested that Medical Officers should not be expected to travel more than 3 miles in the country and $1\frac{1}{2}$ miles in towns, and that they should be paid an examination fee.[1]

Appended to the report of the Birmingham Committee of the British Medical Association was a plan of reform submitted by the Hon. and Rev. Samuel Best, a clergyman of enlightened views and interested in the problem of medical relief for the poor.[2] He discountenanced payment per head and based his scheme on encouraging labourers to take care of themselves in cases of slight illness. Each medical visit, he suggested, should be paid in part by the patient and in part out of the common fund of the society. The sick should purchase tickets which were to be given to the Medical Officer to be exchanged for monetary payment after a certain time. Three types of tickets were suggested, each representing the members' and the clubs' contribution. Red ones were for the doctor's attendance at a patient's home, and were to afford payment of 2s.; blue, if patients visited the surgery, valued at 1s. 6d., if the member was not claiming over 2s. a day in sickness benefit; and white for an extra supply of medicines to be worth ninepence. The payments of members were to increase by sixpence for every additional sixpence of daily sick allowance. Further,

[1] *Lancet*, 1868, i, p. 640; see also p. 646.
[2] He had also been associated with the Dean of Hereford in introducing the development of education in rural villages.

Medical Officers were to receive sixpence a mile if patients resided over 3 miles away. Additional fees ranged from £3 to £5, but consultation with other doctors had always to precede an operation as in the Poor Law medical service. This system was actually in operation in Andover where Best lived.

Practical measures were being taken by doctors meanwhile. In January 1868 the Friendly Society and Sick Club Committee of the British Medical Association resolved that, having considered the correspondence between the Medical Officers of the Cannon Street Male Adult Provident Institution of Birmingham and the Committee of that Society relating to remuneration and the Medical Officers' decision not to continue their duties at the old salaries—no member of the profession should become a candidate for the vacant offices pending the discussions between the Society and the profession. The local press such as the *Birmingham Post* and *Gazette* supported the Medical Officers' cause. The club retained only two out of its twelve doctors, and these were satisfied with 2s. 6d. a year per head. The Committee of the Society obviously calculated on the divided action of the Medical Officers, so the medical press contained many lengthy articles urging the boycott to be rigidly adhered to. Another local benefit and medical club quickly acknowledged the inadequacy of salaries and raised the remuneration of its doctors from 3s. 6d. to 5s. The *Lancet* thereupon wrote that as inducements were being offered, it was even more imperative that there should be no wavering on the part of the medical practitioners in Birmingham. In February 1868 letters were printed in the *British Medical Journal* and the *Lancet* from doctors from all parts of the country showing their support. Dr. Heslop of Birmingham proposed professional combination because of the doctors' 'curious incapacity for organization . . . they live in the midst of a storm of sterile jabber'.[1] From Cornwall a practitioner wrote that the Mutual Benefit Clubs were chiefly composed of small farmers and tradesmen, who, he said, did not sell their wares as cheaply as they expected the Medical Officer to sell his services. Doctors in his village received 1s. 6d. a year per head and he and others had resolved, on Heslop's suggestion, not to give any further assistance on those terms.[2]

A large meeting held at the instigation of the British Medical Association Friendly Society Committee in Birmingham resolved that *all* Medical Officers of friendly societies and clubs should decline to give any further treatment for less than 5s. per head a year. The 170 Birmingham and District Medical Officers had already assented and the Committee now desired the action to spread over the whole country.[3] In April the entire staff of the Birmingham General Dispensary resigned in sympathy. In South Yorkshire a Medico-Ethical Society was formed and demanded 6s. a year per head. The Wolverhampton practitioners decided at a meeting not to work for less than 5s. and actually wanted more. In Wednesbury, doctors also refused to resume their duties until they were granted 5s., and 2s. 6d. for entrance examinations. The Great Yarmouth and Southampton practitioners

[1] T. P. Heslop, M.D., Physician to Birmingham Children's Hospital: *Lancet*, 1868, i, pp. 229–31.
[2] Dr. Wm. Moorman, St. Columb, Cornwall: *Lancet*, 1868, i, p. 304.
[3] *British Medical Journal* and *Lancet*, March 1868.

acted similarly. Griffin, the old Poor Law campaigner, was Honorary Secretary to the movement of the British Medical Association.[1] Rogers and the Workhouse Medical Officers' Association only gave lukewarm support, probably because the British Medical Association had opposed Roger's agitation and the *British Medical Journal* had rigorously upheld the Strand Guardians over the long dispute about his dismissal. The British Medical Association's campaign however spread to smaller towns; for example, the club in Whitby (Yorks.) refused to augment the Medical Officers' salaries from 2s. 6d. to 4s. and they therefore resigned, writing to the *Lancet* to urge no one to come forward to fill the vacancies. By this time success had rewarded the pioneers, and in Birmingham most club doctors were being paid 5s. a year per head, and many more of the best societies in other areas were contemplating an increase in salary. The victory of the doctors was not universal, however, because where resident doctors boycotted the clubs, strangers entered the district to take up their appointments, despite the fact that the medical press constantly appealed for loyalty in the profession.[2]

(3) PUBLIC DISPENSARIES

The conflict between doctors and clubs was of critical moment at the end of the 'sixties for it coincided with the movement for the development of the provident dispensary system. Some of the doctors were already attached to a dispensary, for such institutions had been established by the societies to facilitate the provision of medical treatment. Self-supporting dispensaries attached to or independent of the sickness benefit principle had been established in the first years after the enactment of the new Poor Law. As we have seen in an early chapter they were another improved version of the old medical club, and provided professional advice for those whom the Poor Law ignored and who were yet too poor to engage a private practitioner. Medical self-help, however, whatever form it took, was never able to compete with charitable institutions in numbers relieved, or enjoy successful existence. The slow progress of both affords the proof that the only efficient medical system for the poor, as the most enlightened of the profession so frequently pointed out, was an adequate State service.

The continued growth of charitable dispensaries to which the poor paid no contribution, evinced the same need. Rumsey in 1856 maintained that the public dispensaries were only auxiliaries in a good work, and they could not be safely relied upon as substitutes for a national provision. They provided no excuse for the neglect of a public duty; even in 1844 he had pointed out that the poor who ought to have been 'attended at the expense of the Union were perpetually applying for assistance to charitable institutions'. In most communities, he said, a deserving class of poor existed for whom it was found advisable to supply medical aid apart from the State provision, although this class would be quite inconsiderable if the State provision were not a 'pauper' one. Sound measures of public

---

[1] See accounts, *British Medical Journal* and *Lancet*, March, April, May, June, 1868, *passim*.
[2] For example, see *Lancet*, 1869, i, p. 354; i, p. 355.

hygiene and of special preventive house to house visiting would also have immensely diminished the demands made on the charitable dispensaries, and perhaps, Rumsey suggested, have made them wholly unnecessary. He acknowledged the valuable service rendered by the honorary physicians and surgeons who attended the dispensaries at fixed times to give advice to those who normally would not be visited in their homes. But he pointed to the want of unity of purpose and action among the several sources of medical aid, which was detrimental to the sick, and inflicted needless expense on the community. 'In the attempts, however heartless and supine, of the poor to obtain orders and tickets for medical aid it has been shown that they suffer additional uncertainty, perplexity and delay from the circumstances that the various provisions of aid are not only separate but conflicting . . . their interests are opposed.' Charitable dispensaries like the hospitals tried to limit their services to non-paupers, yet the Poor Law Medical Officer was compelled to remove some of his pauper patients to dispensaries and infirmaries. Instead of co-operating cordially, each medical relief institution constantly sought to rid itself of a portion of its liabilities by throwing them on the others, and the poor were the victims in the struggle. Rumsey therefore advocated existing dispensaries should become part of the national provision of medical relief. Many public dispensaries, he maintained, would readily co-operate with a national system because they would save the cost of new establishments, and further, as their financial position was generally precarious, they would not refuse regular contributions from local authorities for medicines even if a more methodical coalition were inpracticable.

The number of patients given treatment by the charitable dispensaries and the expenditure on drugs was quite extensive. The medical press always published the lengthy accounts of these institutions, which revealed their circumstances. For example, the Royal South London Dispensary had over 3,000 patients in 1849 and the annual expenditure of the charity was about £680, £220 of which was for drugs.[1] The Surrey Dispensary had 6,000 patients in 1852, its income had been £1,200 and its expenditure £1,260—the deficit was however made up from £700 obtained from its festival, held annually for funds.[2] Bloomsbury Dispensary had over 2,100 patients in 1852.[3] Outside London the Bristol Dispensary admitted 2,700 patients, and even more relief could have been afforded had not the supply of subscribers' tickets always been exhausted before the end of a year. This dispensary was not well supported by donations and only sevenpence a head was spent on medicines.[4] Dr. Wallis however commended this low expenditure and accused former Medical Officers, who had brought the cost up to 1s. per case, of extravagance. The Bristol Infirmary which was complementary to the dispensary and had the worst cases and incurables from a 20-mile radius, admitted nearly 20,000 patients a year and spent £825 on medicines, chiefly for out-patients. Here also only tenpence a case was expended, although elsewhere the cost was

[1] *Lancet*, 1851, i, p. 60.
[2] *Lancet*, 1853, i, p. 419.
[3] *Lancet*, 1853, i, p. 45.
[4] T. F. Gilbert, Select Committee, 1854.

much higher. In Gloucester, for example, it was 5s. 6d. a case over a ten-yearly average, and this was far higher than what the poor could have afforded. Statistics reveal that a great amount of home visiting was also undertaken, and that a high percentage of chronic or fatal cases must have been attended, for only two-thirds at the most were entered in the accounts as 'Dismissed—cured'.

The burden taken from the Poor Law authorities can be deduced from the large number of public dispensaries which existed or were established during this period. The Medical Directories of the 'fifties and 'sixties reveal that almost every town had such an institution either independent of, or attached to a hospital. But the system was much abused by the non-indigent taking advantage of gratuitous relief. Discrimination between deserving and undeserving cases for free medical aid was difficult.

> Charities do not wish to spurn the needy, so a great proportion of funds are wasted on imposters . . . Medical Officers are defrauded of time and skill, loose morality is encouraged which impairs the sense of independence and integrity amongst the middle and working classes and the feeling of justice to the medical profession. . . . Thousands who would shrink from applying to the workhouse as the last degradation, present themselves at the charitable institutions . . . without apparent consciousness of humiliation . . . It has come to be considered that the time and skill of the Medical Officer . . . is public property.

This statement was included in a leading article of the *Lancet* in 1856 in which a meeting of the medical profession at Birkenhead was reported. The doctors at this meeting unanimously denounced the prevailing system of gratuitous medical advice to all comers, and expressed their determination to resist any further calls on their time, attention, and abilities on behalf of a new institution then being established. The *Lancet* concluded that if the profession throughout the country united to assert their just claims, in a spirit similar to that which animated the doctors of Birkenhead, much of the evil of indiscriminate gratuitous medical advice could be promptly ended.[1]

(4) PROVIDENT DISPENSARIES

The abuse of charity in the public dispensary and the voluntary hospital on the one hand and the desire to increase the providence of the working-class so as to prevent pauperization on the other, conduced to the formation of more provident dispensaries. The early self-supporting dispensaries were solicited by the governing classes in the spirit of the new Poor Law. Kay (Shuttleworth) had typically explained his advocacy of the movement:

> We must make it evident [he wrote] that by the exercise of moral restraint, and by individual sobriety and a far sighted provision for the day of calamity from which few are exempt, they [the working-class] may escape the misery into which imprudent marriages, insobriety and irregularity, turbulence, infrugality and improvidence plunge men gifted by nature with every quality necessary to procure happiness.

[1] *Lancet*, 1856, i, pp. 548–49.

The influence of Malthus was strong, for Kay continued:

> the reliance of the poor on charitable aid increases as fast as assistance is provided and outstrips the natural growth of population, so that it may be inferred that this loss in independence results in great degree from the provision made to supply the wants of infrugal and improvident people.[1]

In 1850 a doctor who was a great public health reformer still wrote that charities were the 'forcing beds of pauperism', where the poor learnt improvidence and dependence because they were given medical relief gratuitously; he made this the argument for advocating provident dispensaries.[2]

But Henry Lilley Smith gave provident dispensaries a more constructive and positive aim. As we have seen, he had from 1817 advocated the institution of self-supporting dispensaries, and in the middle of the century he was still the leader of the movement. In 1850 he wrote an article on the social importance of provident dispensaries and their advantage to the medical profession.[3] The benefits attendant on the adoption of the scheme, he said, were first, each person who received relief had paid some contribution and therefore would not feel he was receiving pure charity, and, second, material aid was offered to those who were able and willing to maintain themselves by their own labour, but whose resources were not sufficient for the expenses incurred by illness. To such people the provident dispensaries offered ready means of obviating the evils either of the degradation they felt by receiving Union relief, or incurring bills which they could never pay, or resort to quacks. In addition practical habits of forethought and economy, Smith claimed, would result, for once the advantages of the provident dispensaries were experienced, those who benefited would enter combinations for the provision of other necessities of life such as old age or clothing. Further great advantages afforded the poor were choice of Medical Officers; the absence of discrimination as existed in hospitals and charities regarding the granting of tickets, for all members were automatically entitled to one ticket; and finally, that the poor were induced to apply early for medical relief so that the worsening of disease could be prevented. Guardians would gain from diminished poor rates, and the medical profession from being secured against unpaid doctors' bills. In addition, medical knowledge would be improved because practitioners would be brought in closer contact with one another.

Smith took his rules for the formation of provident dispensaries from the Royal Victoria Dispensary of Northampton. Funds were to be obtained from subscriptions and donations of honorary members, and the weekly payments of 'free' members. The latter

---

[1] Report on Suffolk and Norfolk, App. B. No. 1, Second Annual Report of the Poor Law Commissioners, 1836. See also Kay's evidence to the Select Committee, 1838, as well as his lengthy proposals and rules for establishing a Medical Benefit Society, Appendix, Select Committee, 1838.

[2] A. P. Stewart, M.D., Physician to the St. Pancras Royal General Dispensary, in *Sanitary Economics*, 1850.

[3] H. L. Smith, M.D., Surgeon to Eye and Ear Hospital, Southam, Warwickshire: article in the *London Journal of Medicine*, 1850, Vol. II.

were to consist of working-people and servants and their wives and children not in receipt of Poor Law relief, all of whom were to prove inability to pay for private medical advice. One penny a week subscription was to be requested or twopence for a family. Payment was to be made in advance and fines incurred for arrears. If the Committee deemed a person's circumstances improved so that he was no longer eligible, they were to strike him off the membership list. The free members' fund was to defray the cost of drugs, and any surplus was with the honorary donations, to be divided among the Medical Officers according to the proportion of patients severally attended. The institution was to be managed by a Committee elected from honorary members, and Medical Officers were to attend daily in rotation. All legally qualified doctors practising in the neighbourhood were to be invited to join the panel. Choice of physician was to be guaranteed to patients and they were to be given tickets to be presented on the receipt of treatment for accounting purposes. The Northants Dispensary attracted attention. And the *Lancet* in this year printed its long account sheet which showed that one doctor had attended nearly 3,000 patients at the Dispensary, in their own homes, or as an obstetrician, and had received over £130. Another attended a total of 1,400 and received £55, a third saw over 300 and received £14, a fourth 200 for £13 10s., and the fifth 120 for £4 16s. The total remuneration of £220 had been the sum left over after all other expenses had been paid out of the contributions. The *Lancet* however concluded that as payment was less than eightpence a case, were the Committee quite certain that the people attended were really poor, or were Medical Officers being robbed? The journal desired an inquiry before support for the scheme was offered.

Twenty years later the *Lancet* itself undertook this investigation. In 1870 working-class contributions amounted to nearly £1,900, of this £400 was appropriated for drugs and other expenses and £1,500 was divided amongst the three Medical Officers in proportion to the number of patients attended. Over 50,000 cases had been seen of which 17,000 had been in the homes of the poor, and more than 62,000 prescriptions had been made. The *Lancet* commended the work of the Dispensary, but called on this and all similar institutions to employ more doctors. To this suggestion the Secretary of the Dispensary replied that although Smith had advocated all Medical Officers should be appointed, this would lead to a great division of responsibility. Northampton had tried engaging six doctors but three of them had done four-fifths of the work and the other three remained discontented. Free members had increased by 10 per cent a year yet on an average not one complaint had been made in a year. The assertions of the Secretary were disputed by an ex-committee member and an honorary subscriber. He revealed that Medical Officers were chosen by the Secretary and his brother because these two held the majority of votes as they were the largest subscribers. He also pointed out that the Dispensary admitted a class of people far superior to those regarded as eligible, for many families which were members had over £3 a week income. The system therefore was detrimental to the private practitioners of the town and excluded any progress which young doctors hoped to make. One old Medical Officer said before he died that he had been ruined by the Dispensary which had taken his patients who were tradesmen and house-owners. Gradually, it was concluded, the entire town was being swamped by a great monopoly.[1]

During the 'fifties and 'sixties while these developments were taking place in Northampton, the dispensary movement was comparatively quiescent elsewhere in the country. In 1858 an Association for the Encouragement of Dispensaries was formed in Leamington, but few provident dispensaries were established elsewhere until the late 'sixties. In 1869 Plymouth, after much difficulty regarding Medical Officers, opened a dispensary. It invited the co-operation of all medical practitioners—the only basis, according to the *Lancet*, on which such an institution could be successfully or fairly conducted. Devonport also had just established a successful provident dispensary with 200–300 members, for whom £80 was divided among the Medical Officers, a similar sum being paid for hospital donations and other expenses.[2] The reason for the flagging interest was illustrated by the mistakes made by the Leicester Provident Dispensary. Here, the working-class had always been well organized, and self-supporting dispensaries had been established in 1826 and 1833, which became a single provident dispensary in 1862. The objects of the institution were to

> place medical assistance within reach of the working-classes of the town and neighbourhood by means of their own small periodical payments . . . Members shall consist of servants, working people and wives and children . . . unable to pay for medical service . . . and such sick benefit societies as the Board of Governors may admit.

Monthly subscriptions were fourpence, or 1s. for a whole family. Each Medical Officer received every week a list of new candidates and he determined eligibility. This was quite impossible in such a large community and therefore many people were admitted to the dispensary who could well afford to engage a doctor privately. (The abuse was less likely in rural areas where people were all known to one another.) It was said that some members leaving £1,000 on death received free medical attention for 4s. 4d. a year, of which a Medical Officer received only 1s. 9d. No examination as to the health of a member was made prior to admission, so that chronic cases entailed large expenditure on the dispensary and heavy duties on the doctors. The latter were dependent on the managers and governors who could overrule their complaints on such matters as the supply of inferior drugs.

> Clergymen, benevolent old ladies, rich manufacturers, all sorts and conditions of persons, who are moved either by high motives of charity or by meaner love of ostentation and patronage, dole out guineas and become governors of the Leicester Provident Dispensary. On their vote depends the fate of the Medical Officer, and they may be called to decide purely medical and pharmaceutical questions . . . though they have no technical knowledge.

---

[1] *Lancet*, 1870, i, p. 638; 1871, i, pp. 169, 256, 327.
[2] *Lancet*, 1869, i, p. 793; see also 1870, i, p. 145.

Many grievances arose out of the Club's practice and it was maintained that some doctors gave superior treatment to their private patients.[1]

It had been hoped in many quarters that the self-help schemes would be able to supersede the Poor Law medical service, but in practice the provident dispensaries, like the other forms of medical club and medical assurance, proved to be inimical to public health and the medical profession. The movement for provident dispensaries was revived in London in 1870, largely because of the efforts of Sir Charles Trevelyan, the Charity Organization Society, and as part of the agitation for the reform of Metropolitan poor relief and charitable medical relief. In May 1870 the *Lancet* had a leading article on the Poor Law and charitable institutions. Hitherto, this said, the Poor Law medical system had been so extremely bad that had it not been for dispensaries and hospitals supported by voluntary contributions, and carried on by voluntary service, the gravest scandals would have occurred. Little hope of a genuine improvement of the Poor Law system was entertained unless the 'profession firmly and practically repudiates the claim of mere destitution to gratuitous medical relief. The fundamental remedy for the abuses which so extensively prevail consists in the introduction of an effective Poor Law service, since by that alone will be taken away the last excuse for indiscriminate medical charity.' The article continued by speaking of the charitable dispensaries and the many hours poor and hardworked young doctors put in there gratuitously.—'It is altogether unreasonable to expect young persons in active practice to give up 5–6 hours two or three times a week to the work of seeing a crowd of out-patients, many of whom have the most trifling ailments.' Most of the poor and destitute had claims on the State; and the dispensaries, the *Lancet* maintained, ought to insist on the fair admission of those claims. But no voluntary payment could be expected whilst scores of charitable hospitals and dispensaries opened their doors gratuitously to all-comers having the semblance of poverty. The public had also to be convinced that medical charities existed for special cases only, and for affording the most skilful assistance to those unable to provide it for themselves. A vast number of institutions should be closed and their incomes devoted to

> that form of real medical charity which encourages the poor to help themselves. . . .
> When an agricultural labourer joins a sick club and spares threepence or fourpence
> monthly for the privilege of obtaining medical attendance, he exhibits, . . . an illustra-
> tion of all the advantages of a fee system—the noble example of self-sacrifice.

Society, if not the Government, with its supreme responsibility for the health of the people should agree to assist without demoralizing, a man who was able to do something, but not everything, towards obtaining medical assistance.[2] The *Lancet* therefore maintained that although it recognized abuses still existed, such as those injurious particularly to the Medical

---

[1] Report of Special Commission set up by the *Lancet* to inquire into medical association and the profession, 1895. Reprinted as 'The Battle of the Clubs'; this is an excellent survey, dealing also with France, Belgium, and Ireland, as well as the whole of Great Britain, *Lancet*, 1895, ii, *passim*.

[2] *Lancet*, 1870, i, p. 775.

Officer, and the using of the provident dispensaries by honorary subscribers as means of vulgar personal advertisement, there was something in the principle and it should therefore be tried in the interest of the working-classes and the medical profession. In another article the journal urged that provident dispensaries be entirely unconnected with any charitable organization. They should be charities in so far as benefits exceeded subscriptions but these should be paid for according to the means of the recipient. At this time the British Medical Association was also converted to the provident dispensary movement. Dr. Timothy Holmes, the hospital reformer, and Dr. J. F. Anderson both read papers to the Metropolitan branch of the British Medical Association on the advantages and activity of provident dispensaries. The latter was a Medical Officer at such an institution and spoke with some authority. He outlined the practical working of the Metropolitan dispensaries, which differed little from those we have already studied. Hampstead and Wandsworth, however, allowed 'free' members a share in the management. He also suggested a 30s. wage constituted a suitable member.[1]

At the beginning of 1871 there were twenty-six charitable (public) dispensaries in the Metropolis, some dating back to the 1770s, and thirteen part-paying dispensaries.[2] Fourteen provident dispensaries existed at the time[3] which increased to thirty-four in twenty years, ten of which by then belonged to a new society, the Metropolitan Provident Medical Association. Many of the dispensaries had governors or supporters who were famous noblemen and ladies or eminent philanthropists.

One of the objects of the Charity Organization Society[4] was the co-operation between charities and the Poor Law, and in March 1871 a medical committee was appointed to advise on all medical matters and to inquire into the subject of the admission of out-patients to hospitals. This reported on the advisability of establishing provident dispensaries and submitted model rules (a slightly amended version of those existing) for management. From then onwards, particularly in the late 'seventies and 'eighties, the Charity Organization Society worked for the development of the movement. Its weekly *Reporter* always contained an article advocating the establishment of dispensaries. Sir Charles Trevelyan, J. Stansfeld, W. H. Smith, Dr. Acland, Timothy Holmes, the British Medical Association, and the most noted of the medical profession contributed to the hundreds of tracts which were published. These reiterated the reasons for the new movement and the developments which it was hoped would follow. The failure of the general medical system was pointed out. Hospitals which had been established for serious and difficult cases had turned through

---

[1] *British Medical Journal*, 1870, i, p. 517.

[2] Charity Organization Society Memorandum to the Select Committee of the House of Lords, 1889.

[3] *Lancet*, 1870, i, pp. 497-99. The fourteen Provident Dispensaries in 1871 were at: Camberwell, Hampstead, Haverstock Hill, Westbourne, Hendon, Chelmsford, Islington, Paddington, Portland-town, Marylebone, Wandsworth, Rugeley, Pimlico and Dulwich.

[4] The development of the Charity Organization Society is interesting, i.e., from negative to positive policy—from crime and pauperism to family welfare. This is illustrated by the change in title. It began as the Association for the Prevention of Pauperism and Crime, then became the Charity Organization Society and latterly the Family Welfare Association.

their out-patients' departments into institutions dealing with trivial illnesses, because people were too poor to pay for domiciliary treatment. 'But the task of providing for the entire wants of the mass of the people is beyond the power of even the most liberal charity, and out-patients' treatment has become not only a mockery and a scandal, but owing to over-crowding and the vitiation of air, even the primary object for which the hospital was established is seriously threatened.' Only by the principle of mutual assurance, it was maintained, could the medical profession be placed in a satisfactory relation to the working-class. If payments were required by the provident dispensaries, they could be fixed at so low a rate that all might afford them who were not entirely destitute, and for these sums the poorest could obtain advantages equal to those possessed by the richest. A family doctor could be elected from the Medical Officers of the dispensary, and in 1878 home nurses were provided. The Charity Organization Society desired to see all charitable dispensaries placed on the principle of mutual assurance. Later it was realized that medical relief must be accompanied by general relief, for the new institutions like the former clubs never provided 'extras' or 'necessaries'. The Secretary stated that drugs were of no benefit if people lacked necessary food, therefore 'assessors' were appointed to inquire into this need and to follow up the convalescence of patients. These were the almoners of the future, and they had already been established in hospitals to prevent abuse of free treatment by people who had the means for making private provision for medical advice.[1]

The Poor Law authorities placed much reliance on the self-supporting forms of medical treatment and insurance, as well as on charitable assistance. They provided the argument for the objection to an increase in the scope of Poor Law medical relief. As Inspector Farnall stated in 1870, a national system of meeting the medical requirements of the people would eventually destroy the valuable societies which existed—'the abandonment of which would incalculably increase pauperism'.[2] But the benefits of the deliberately organized arrange-ments for aiding the working class were to a great extent an illusion. Many illnesses the dispensary and club doctors could never attempt to treat. Infectious diseases, lunacy, chronic infirmity, and the great mass of people suffering from tuberculosis were provided for in the rate-supported institution, and acute surgical cases were treated in the voluntary hospitals. Unhygienic habits and living conditions, poverty, and all the ramifications of the Public Health movement were ignored by provident dispensaries, when attention to these was more important than the bottle of medicine. Home environment and nourishment were not supervised, and although the free choice of doctor was a salutary innovation, this often led to physicians canvassing for popularity not by giving outspoken advice on bad habits and cleanliness, but by a liberal supply of drugs. Neither working-class self-help nor charit-

[1] See particularly the pamphlet on 'Extension of Provident Dispensaries throughout London and its Environs', also 'Ten years Work for the Reform of Metropolitan Medical Relief', an article in the Charity Organization Society's *Reporter*, March 1879.
[2] Farnall's Report on Outdoor Relief, 1870.

able organizations could ever become a substitute for the Poor Law medical service, for they were not intended to include membership of those for whom the latter was provided. As auxiliaries they were important. But as their functions overlapped because the demarcation between poor and destitute was so slender in the emergency of sickness, both the Poor Law medical service and the charitable and self-help organizations were inadequate. Integration in a State medical system for the poor with comprehensive Public Health provisions, could alone have made medical relief efficient.

CHAPTER 17

The Poor Law and its Influence on the Rise of the Public Health Service

THE social pathology of disease was a new study during the years of early industrialism. One of its major fields was defined in the day-to-day administration of poor relief, and it developed with the growth of the Poor Law medical system. Inherent in that was the implication of a preventive Public Health service, for the social cost of sickness among the indigent and the necessity of diminishing its economic cost became evident. These factors were perforce the foundation of the two movements, which were sometimes parallel, at others inevitably intertwined, and which together paved the way for the establishment of a regular medical system both preventive and curative.—They were the progenitors of the Twentieth-Century Welfare State.

In our survey of the Poor Law medical services we have partially ignored the environment from which the paupers came to seek medical relief, and which was to a great extent the causative factor of their destitution. The study of this background is necessary to a comprehensive survey, and therefore it is inevitable that the history of Public Health must be encroached upon. Without the Industrial Revolution and its wider ramifications in politics, economics, and philosophy, it is probable that neither the Poor Law medical service nor the Public Health service would have arisen. It is certain that they would not have assumed the forms they did, for industrial expansion was the agent of social dislocation. Concomitant with industrialization was the planless town, without regulation or supervision. Great masses of people were herded together without regard to health, decency, or comfort; and soil, air, and water were polluted without restraint. The new towns were the environment and often the appendages of factories; diseases threatened whole communities. Rapid demographic expansion could not afford to tolerate urban inefficiency. Already in the 'forties the high social cost was evident, and it could be demonstrated that urban populations were thinning.

Changes in the economic system demanded constant departure from the crude simplicity of the creed of competitive individualism; new expendients and controls were necessary until the system of social police developed into a system of social security. Edwin Chadwick began as a conspicuous party to the deterrent principles of the Poor Law, but it was also his work which initiated the transition to the establishing of minima for effective citizenship and personal well-being to cover the insecurities which the economic system produced. With the Poor Law and Public Health movements as nuclei, the whole conception of public obligations altered, and in Chadwick's change from Poor Law administrator to Public Health reformer, the substitution of prevention for the framework of repression and deterrence can be traced. The Poor Law medical service was allowed only to cure sickness, and then was limited to the pauper; the Public Health movement tried to prevent it and thereby to forestall destitution. To the nineteenth-century working class the worn adage 'prevention is better than cure' was of utmost significance.

To apply the prevention principle to the new social problems necessitated a new type of activity. Departure from *laissez-faire* was inevitable. Scientific investigation, the use of statistics, strong centralization, and control over the obscurantism of the effete and corrupt municipal and parochial government were required. The service of the expert became necessary, and great advances had to be made in medical science and sanitary engineering. Chadwick's claim to be one of the greatest social reformers of all times lies in the fact that he understood such changes were of the utmost importance. He was a new man, with new ideas and new methods. He heralded the twentieth-century administrator, and in his methods it is illuminating to contrast him with his some-time colleague Lord Shaftesbury, the 'eighteenth-century' humanitarian. By early training Chadwick was a Utilitarian. The first re-emergence of the Sanitary Idea appeared in the *Westminster Review* in 1825, in an article by the Benthamite radical, Dr. Southwood Smith, later Chadwick's lieutenant, and in Chadwick's own study 'Sickness, decreptitude, and mortality', in which he advocated the collection of complete information by the Government on the causes of death and sickness. Bentham had in the 'twenties demanded a Minister of Health and a Minister of Preventive Service, so that by the 'thirties when Chadwick had for some time been his secretary, the 'Sanitary Idea' was embodied in a scientific formula with Chadwick as its custodian. Bentham and Robert Owen laid the foundation of national health and constructive social evolution. The 'Father of English Radicalism' had desired to be a doctor, but without medical knowledge he attempted to provide the social England in which medical practice could find scope as a popular ameliorative agency.

Chadwick's conversion and the direction taken by social legislation were therefore neither capricious nor accidental. As an influential member of the Royal Commission in 1833, and then as Secretary to the Poor Law Commissioners, he was in part to blame for the inadequacy and irrelevancy of the new Poor Law, but he quickly recognized that poverty was also a problem of public health. In 1837 reporting to Lord John Russell on the Irish Poor Law, he wrote: 'In London and other towns there are whole districts inhabited by the Irish where fever is never absent. So also with many classes of English operatives in receipt of high wages.'[1] The Sanitary Reports of Drs. Arnott, Kay, and Southwood Smith in 1838, and that by Southwood Smith in 1839, were made at Chadwick's instigation—he was using

---

[1] Home Office Papers, 20 June 1837.

the expert for a particular work.[1] Only four years of office provided the Poor Law Commissioners with enough experience and actual observation to force on them the fact that a vast amount of pauperism was the direct and immediate results of ill-health. The three doctors were asked to try to discover what made certain areas in the Metropolis so unhealthy and so poor.

The joint report of Drs. Arnott and Kay gave a terrible picture of the ravages inflicted by infectious disease in London. Life was shortened because 'certain poisons are disseminated in the air. Most noted are matters of smallpox, measles, whooping cough, and that called malaria, the chief subject of this report, which is generated wherever animal and vegetable substances are undergoing putrefactive decomposition, and which produces a great variety of fevers.'[2] Dr. Kay from his own experience told of the field behind Euston Square upon which sewers drained in an open ditch, and which often overflowed forming a large lake of the most 'odious filth'. In this neighbourhood fevers were frequent, and the girls in a school nearby contracted many diseases. In one year thirty of the children suffered from violent convulsions, in another typhoid fever affected an equal number, and ophthalmia and mesenteric diseases were never absent. Dr. Arnott had seen analogous effects produced by foul obstructed drains in private houses where one family after another contracted a fever. He also related how on several occasions people were suffocated by descending into cesspools and old wells. Together the two doctors visited the East End of London and investigated conditions in Wapping, Stepney, and districts which from the records of the London Fever Hospital were known to be permanent seats of fevers:

> We found, as we were expected to find, wherever fever had appeared, one or more of the causes now noticed: (1) Homes and courts and alleys without privies, without covered drains, and with only open surface gutters, so ill-made that fluid in many places was stagnant. (2) Large open ditches containing stagnant liquid filth. (3) Houses dirty beyond description . . . and extremely crowded with inhabitants, who had no means of separation in case of disease arising among them. (4) Pigs kept in backyards, with styes very filthy, and masses of half putrid food . . . around. In one instance they were in the back room of a house with an open door to the front room, in which was

---

[1] ARNOTT was Physician Extraordinary to the Queen, a Fellow of the Royal Society, a member of the London University Senate, and a consultant of the Poor Law Commissioners in the 1840s. He has many inventions to his credit and was a sanitary pioneer. KAY was a private and dispensary physician in Manchester. He became Secretary to the Manchester Board of Health in 1832 and in the same year wrote a book on *The Moral and Physical Condition of the Working Class of Manchester*. Appointed Assistant Poor Law Commissioner and First Secretary to the Education Committee of the Privy Council in 1839. He was active in organising relief during the distress in Lancashire in the cotton famine. SOUTHWOOD SMITH was first a clergyman and then a doctor in East London. He became chief physician to the London Fever Hospital in 1820. From this dates his career as a sanitary reformer. He published articles in the *Westminster Review*. From 1835 to 1854 he was employed intermittently in health inquiries for official commissions and the General Board of Health.

[2] The bacteriological causes of disease were not understood and it was believed that bad air—malaria—was the actual source; however, the suggestion for combating the infectious diseases was correct. Also there was little distinction between fevers, which were all regarded as springing from the same source.

lying a man in the last stages of fever. (5) Heaps of refuse and rubbish, vegetable and animal remains, at the bottom of close courts and in corners.

Not only did the two physicians visit several areas but they also conferred with many Boards of Guardians, and with some of the doctors. The greatest amount of information was obtained however from the reports of the Poor Law Medical Officers, made in reply to a Circular from the Poor Law Commissioners inquiring into the causes of fever which might be remediable if Boards of Guardians possessed the authority to enforce measures of sanitary police.

The reports of the Medical Officers gave two classes of causes of fever: first, those arising independently of the habits of the poor—bad sewerage and sanitation, the presence of abattoirs in densely populated districts, the state of burial grounds, and the want of ventilation in narrow alleys and courts; second, those originating to a considerable extent in their own habits—the state of lodging houses, the overcrowded dwellings, the great want of cleanliness, the prevalence of intemperance, the keeping of pigs in houses, the indisposition to be removed to hospital when infected with contagious diseases, and last, the neglect of vaccination. In the first category, Medical Officers reported such conditions as rivers of filth on the edge of which the poor lived, as for example, near Blackfriars Bridge, where fever was never absent and where the workhouse fever ward was always full with sixty patients. Here the Medical Officer recommended the pulling down of all the old houses arching the sewer, and the building of new streets. Hackney was also never without cases of fever and the Medical Officer had repeatedly endeavoured to impress on the poor the importance of cleanliness for their own welfare. The Medical Officer of Stanmore urged the draining of the marshland there by a public authority because of the prevalence of typhoid fever. He had had the filth from the privies removed, but feared fever would prevail if all ditches were not kept clean. Several Poor Law doctors wrote on the accumulation of refuse and some had had scavenging undertaken by the Guardians. Removal of nuisances by public means could alone produce efficient cleansing of slum neighbourhoods. In Hammersmith drainage had been improved, save in poverty-stricken areas!—and here 104 cases of fever had occurred in six months, independent of smallpox, all of which the Medical Officer said could have been avoided by better drainage and cleanliness. A Peckham District Medical Officer suggested that 'landlords of the wretched, filthy tenements should be held responsible for their being habitable and clean, and this could be enforced by rent not being made payable in cases of negligence'. Other Medical Officers stressed the need for ventilation in densely crowded courts, and the removal of infectious cases to hospital immediately on the outbreak of disease, both for the good of the family, the patient, and the prevention of an epidemic.

A District Medical Officer of the West London Union described his district as

the poorest and most dirty, lowest and worst ventilated parts of the City of London, chiefly inhabited by the humblest classes of Irish, and the most abandoned of both sexes . . . with numberless intricate labyrinths and courts, the haunts of prostitutes, pickpockets, and thieves of every description, in which fever seems to have taken a permanent abode; I have known it to exist there through heat and cold, through wet and through drought, through every variety of weather. . . . The absence of cleanliness, the crowded state of the rooms, six or seven inmates sleeping in one small room, intemperance, the accumulations of filth and dirt . . . all constitute to feed disease and *to futilize the efforts of the Medical Officer to eradicate it*. In addition to this [there are] the number of slaughterhouses . . . in the neighbourhood . . . and the Fleet Ditch, the reservoir of all contagious sewers run underneath these places, above the bed of which many of the houses in the back alley of Field Lane are only a few feet elevated —all of these circumstances constitute the source of contagion. . . . The last six or seven weeks we have been called on to attend many cases of typhus fever, of a very malignant character, chiefly attacking the labouring classes. . . . Upwards of twenty cases have occurred in the last three weeks, three of which terminated fatally, two were taken into the workhouse . . . and the other was an outdoor casual for whom we had no room. The majority attacked were those who were unable to procure adequate nutriment from want of employment during the last inclement winter, which predisposed them to the attack of the contagion, and deprived them of the power to resist its ravages . . .[1]

A Medical Officer of Cripplegate called attention to the cheap burial grounds in the Metropolis which were generally situated in poor neighbourhoods. Graves were dug and left open from one Sunday to another until they were filled, only sufficient earth being used to cover the sides of the coffins. The grounds were divided into three or four different areas according to price. Graves were also so close together that the heads and feet of coffins in adjoining graves touched. 'Those long dead as well as the recent, give forth the mephitical effluvia of death . . . one of the reasons why pestilence attacks the poor first is by their visiting these pest-houses as mourners.' In the densely populated area of Cripplegate there were four burial grounds within 200 yards of each other and close to the walls of the houses. One of the adjoining courts was attacked by fever in 1837, and so dreadful were the effects that it was ordered to be closed unless it was thoroughly repaired. A Medical Officer advocated the use of absorbents in the burial grounds and a thorough system of inspection for which beadles should be paid a few pounds a year. Another Poor Law doctor recommended a rigid system of medical police should be instituted, without which he maintained the existing evils could never be removed. He also suggested regular purification of courts, limewashing of houses and rooms, some restraint on the numbers admitted into the lowest class of lodging houses, and a wider distribution of the densely-crowded inhabitants.

The second category of the causes of fever given by Kay and Arnott could however scarcely be distinguished from the first. Yet the instances where fevers were said to have arisen to a great extent through the personal habits of the poor were very numerous. A district Medical Officer of Deptford stated that between thirty and forty people sometimes lodged for the night in one small lodging house, and at the time of the cholera epidemic

[1] J. R. Lynch, M.D., Medical Officer of the West London Union, 1 May 1838.

there were more cases here than in any part of Deptford. In Highgate, the Medical Officer said scarlet fever and other eruptive fevers were prevalent in lodging-houses, particularly where the Irish beggars slept three or four in a bed with four or five beds in a small room. The Irish generally occupied the worst dwellings in London. In Shadwell, for example, the houses were built of wood and were 'in external appearance and internal decency, inferior to common cattle sheds, yet because they had not been pulled down, they were inhabited by Irish families who could not afford to live elsewhere, and were the prolific foci of scarlet fever to the surrounding neighbourhood'.

A Whitechapel Medical Officer reported he scarcely knew which portion of the district to describe as the worst—all were equally prolific of fever cases and the common lodging houses were the constant abodes of disease. He also demonstrated the fearful fact that in every instance when a patient died from fever or was removed to a hospital or workhouse, the rooms in the dwellings were immediately re-let to new tenants without any precautions being taken. He could not particularize on drainage and sanitation because all courts and streets were hot-beds of fever. Outside the workhouse this Medical Officer alone had attended 600 cases of fever in his district, a large proportion of which he said were clearly ascribable to the evils generally mentioned. He did not see advantage in the erection of a local fever house as this would have encouraged the influx of casual poor. He did however recommend the building of wide and extended roads to sweep away the districts which were morally and medically objectionable. The local authorities would not be backward in combating the evils, but they possessed no authority to do so.—'A general and complete power of enforcing sanitary precautions is needed, as also an extensive improvement in the sewerage of the whole district.'

Kay and Arnott in summarizing the Medical Officers' reports said that the evils complained of had caused occasional and irregular efforts for their removal by the local authorities, but because they required in most cases legal sanction, and were dependent on the general concurrence of the inhabitants for the authorization of expenses incurred, they had necessarily been inadequate. Frequently the cost of improvement had been charged to the poor rates, but this was illegal, and therefore auditors were unable to sanction it, so that even the irregular and insufficient efforts would cease. The two doctors pointed out that the cholera epidemic of the early 'thirties and the special Boards of Health then formed, had roused public attention to the extent of the existing evils. Sanitary measures had ceased with the dissolution of the Boards and the disappearance of the epidemic, but, it was maintained, the impression produced on the public remained, so that the more intelligent members of the middle class would welcome any efforts which the Government might make to procure legal sanction for their efforts. Kay and Arnott desired all authority for health measures to be vested in the Boards of Guardians, because their paid officers already provided the means of inspection for detecting and preventing the sanitary nuisances. Further, they were a representative body, in constant communication with the inhabitants, who were interested alike in the removal of the evils and in the right application of the funds contributed by them, as ratepayers. The third reason given for wishing to make

Boards of Guardians the Public Health authorities, was that the improvements contemplated especially affected the health of the poorer classes and their fitness to work, the deterioration of which led them to seek parochial relief. The Boards of Guardians would therefore be able to witness the effect of the evils complained of on the health of the poor and would also be in a position to ascertain the results of the interference.

The powers which Kay and Arnott recommended conferring on the Guardians were that they should at public expense have open drains emptied and cleansed, dangerous marshes drained, piggeries, cowsheds, and stables removed, lodging-houses inspected periodically and their rooms whitewashed twice a year at the owner's expense. The Boards should also be empowered to order the cleaning and whitewashing by the owner of any houses in which three or more families lived, and also to direct two public surveyors to examine any house reported as so dilapidated and insecure as to threaten the safety of the inmates. An owner of such property should, on penalties to be summarily recovered, make it safe, and during these operations tenants should be removed. Finally, Guardians were to be empowered to prevent the inhabiting of houses which had been deserted because they were unsafe, and which might be opened by the poor because no rent was chargeable for them. Arnott and Kay ended their report by stressing that 'the extirpation of the evils arising from these defects in the sanitary police of large cities cannot be effected unless powers are conferred to some authority selected by the legislative for the prevention of those grievous defects to which our attention has been drawn'. They pointed out that it was not only in the old towns that bad conditions existed but also in the most recently erected suburbs of the great cities. That all obvious precautions had been ignored they attributed to the rapid increase of population which allowed property owners to procure tenants despite the absence of all essential amenities. The investigators did not hope for immediate improvement, but they urged the Government to place the problem in the hands of some competent body who would supervise the entire programme, and who would enforce certain necessary conditions. Thus, a Central Board should be entrusted with precautionary measures and regulation, whose duty it would be, for example, to see no buildings were commenced until plans of the intended streets were prepared, and who could watch that no further buildings were erected on the site other than those delineated in the plans. The Board should have powers to stipulate the minimum width of streets and to prevent the formation of closed courts. It should also be authorized to forbid cellar dwellings after a certain period, and finally, it should enforce the drainage of building sites and the provision of an efficient sewerage system.

> We have no doubt [the doctors concluded] that by proper sanitary police regulations, such as a Board of Health might decide upon, the typhoid fevers of London and other places might be made to disappear, and we think the remedial measures would cost less than it now costs to parishes and public charities to take care of the sick, and to provide for the helpless widows or orphans of those who die!

While Kay and Arnott were making their investigations, Southwood Smith was deputed to make a separate report on Bethnal Green and Whitechapel. The records of the London Fever Hospital from its foundation in 1802 demonstrated that not only was fever particularly prevalent in these districts, but the worst forms of the disease always abounded in them. Southwood Smith, as chief physician of the Fever Hospital and a former physician of the Eastern Dispensary in Whitechapel, knew his districts well. 'Fever' of a malignant or fatal character was never absent; in some streets it had by the late 'thirties invaded every house, and in some instances every room of every house. Cases were recorded in which each member of a family had been attacked in succession, of whom several died, and frequently whole families were swept away. Smith himself saw six people in one small room ill with fever, four in one bed, and two in another. With such a concentration of infectious disease the danger to the neighbourhood was frightfully increased. In 1837 there were 2,084 cases of fever in Bethnal Green Union, and 2,557 in Whitechapel Union, so that the Poor Law Medical Officers in these two areas had to attend 4,641 cases of fever alone in a single year. These figures included only those who sought parochial relief, but Smith drew attention to the high incidence of fever amongst people above the rank of pauper, and in numerous instances it affected the families of the wealthy.—'There is no strength of constitution, no conservative power in wealth, capable of resisting constant exposure to the exhalations which are always [generated] from these collections of filth.' In Bethnal Green it was almost universally the handloom weavers who were exposed to the most wretched conditions, but Smith maintained that even the constitutions of the wealthy of Grosvenor Square could not have saved them. In addition the houses in Bethnal Green were permanently damp because a large part of the district was a swamp, so that in rainy weather entire streets were under water. Winter and summer, stagnant pools covered considerable areas. Similar conditions of the worst type reported by Kay and Arnott existed here, and Smith offered two illustrations of the improvement in health which had followed drainage in one place, and a new sewerage system in another where abattoirs were situated. He, like the preceding investigators, urged that the prevention of fevers and disease by the removal of the source of poisons would be cheaper than the expense incurred by sickness. The latter expenditure would never cease whilst the cost of protective measures would be liable only once. The expediency of sanitary measures was therefore highly commendable as a matter of economy alone, and further, whole populations would be affected, whilst money spent on cure touched only a few individuals. The improvement of Bethnal Green and Whitechapel seemed a hopeless task, but Smith warned that if the opportunity were not taken quickly it would never be regained, for the ratepayers of Bethnal Green were contemplating taking a few progressive steps and had presented a petition to Parliament for the district to be incorporated in the proposed Metropolitan Improvements Bill. Permission was sought for the widening and draining of streets—very necessary to the 700,000 people, and the memorialists seemed well aware of the 'causes' of infectious disease, for they wrote: 'When cholera raged in a frightfully appalling degree ... adequate sewers and drainage might probably have assuaged the scourge and saved the lives of many individuals.'

Smith desired to see a local fever hospital built for isolation purposes, because Medical Officers were unwilling to admit fever cases into the workhouses, with the result that the majority of sufferers were left in their wretched hovels to spread the infection. He also urged the enforcing of efficient sanitary regulations and that the Poor Law authorities should interest themselves in the problem.

> Seeing that the evil as it exists at present is so vast in extent and so unceasing in its operation, and seeing that it brings such deplorable consequences on that class of population, more especially which is least able to guard against and to resist them, this subject is one which deserves the serious attention of those who labour for the improvement of the physical condition of the poor, and who are charged with providing in the most effectual and economical manner for their maintenance, when, by the prevalence of epidemic or other diseases they are rendered unable to support themselves.

He admitted some conditions of poverty were attributable to the consequences of improvidence, but stressed that no prudence or forethought, no exertion on the part of the poor, could remove the gravest and yet most remediable of all evils connected with physical environment. It was not fever alone that that was perpetuated by insanitary conditions, but also a general weakening of the constitutions of the poor.

> This poison acts as a powerful predisposing cause of some of the most common and fatal maladies to which the human body is subject . . . The deaths occasioned in this country by diseases of the digestive organs, for example, by the inflammation of the air passages and lungs, and by consumption, form a large proportion of the annual mortality. No one who lives long in, or near, a malarial district, is ever for a single hour free from some disease of the digestive system.[1]

The reports of the three doctors therefore gave a glaring example of social conditions in the Metropolis, some areas of which were constant seats of fever. If London was chosen for investigation, infectious diseases also rioted uncontrolled over great areas in the provinces. The economic loss occasioned by ill-health was great and could not be restricted to the poor. Therefore the most successful argument used by reformers was that the indigent lived under circumstances which endangered the lives and incomes of the affluent.

So the initial impulse to Public Health action stemmed from a Poor Law problem, the chief aim being to save expenditure from the rates. In their Annual Report of 1838 the Poor Law Commissioners gave priority to the prevention of pauperism by health measures. They recommended that legislative sanction should be given to the application of rates to a number of objects where the charge would be inconsiderable, but where the inconvenience and evil occasioned to the public by their disallowance would be

[1] Report on Prevalence of Certain Physical Causes of Fever in the Metropolis which might be removed by Proper Sanitary Measures', Neil Arnott, M.D., and James P. Kay, M.D., to Poor Law Commissioners, 12 May 1838. 'Report on Some of the Physical Causes of Sickness and Mortality to which the Poor are particularly Exposed, and which are capable of removal by Sanitary Regulations . . . in Bethnal Green and Whitechapel', Southwood Smith, M.D., May 1838.

severe and excessive. They therefore hoped that the reports of the three doctors on the suggested means of removing the indirect source of disease and death, of destitution of the survivors, and of the consequent burdens on the poor rate, as well as on the savings of the working class in sick clubs and benefit societies, would be found deserving of Parliamentary consideration. All evidence, the Poor Law Commissioners continued, strongly expressed the need for immediate legislation. The Guardians themselves admitted that efficient drainage was essential but that they had insufficient funds and power; and the working classes, 'although aware of the surrounding causes of evil, have few or no means of avoiding them and little or no choice in their dwellings'. As a temporary measure the Poor Law Commissioners desired powers of nuisance removal to be conferred on the Guardians because they possessed an efficient body of officers including experienced doctors to guide them. In a letter to the Home Secretary, the central authorities pointed to the overburdening of the poor rates by disease, the desirability of making provision for the prevention of nuisances, and that Guardians should be empowered to indict parties responsible for sanitary offences. The most prominent and pressing measures necessary were those for averting charges on the poor rates,

> which are caused by nuisances by which contagion is generated and persons are reduced to destitution. . . . All epidemics and all infectious diseases are attended with charges immediate and ultimate on the poor rates. Labourers are suddenly thrown by infectious disease into a state of destitution, for which immediate relief must be given. In the case of death, the widows and children are thrown as paupers on the parish. The amount of burdens thus produced is frequently so great, as to render it good economy on the part of the administrator of the Poor Laws, to incur the charge for preventing the evils which are ascribable to physical causes, which there are no other means of removing.[1]

This letter was memorable because it was the first time that a government department had taken direct responsibility for the state of public health. *A new type of Government duty had arisen—medical inquiry*, and a century later the activity of the Poor Law Commissioners in 1838 was described as 'the first step in the modern utilization of medicine by the State'.[2] In 1839 Southwood Smith was commissioned to report on 'The Prevalence of Fever in Twenty Metropolitan Unions and Parishes'. The inquiries of the previous year had dealt only with certain districts and it was felt desirable to obtain knowledge on the whole population of London. From the returns of Poor Law Medical Officers to him, Smith found that in 1837–38 there were over 77,000 paupers in a total population of 850,000; of these 14,000 had contracted the four most prevalent types of fever—intermittent, synochus, typhus and scarlatina, and 1,300 had died.[3] He discovered that the existence of fever in several districts

[1] Poor Law Commissioners to the Home Secretary, Lord J. Russell, 14 May 1838. Home Office Papers.
[2] Sir G. Newman, *Building of a Nation's Health*, 1939.
[3] We must here, as throughout this study, remember that mid-nineteenth-century diagnoses and definitions are being used.

bore less relation to the number of paupers than the number of paupers to the general population. For example, Bermondsey had 3,000 paupers and 593 fever cases; Bethnal Green, 3,632 paupers and 1,209 fever cases; St. George in the East, 6,869 paupers and 672 fever cases. Therefore, there were twice as many paupers in the latter as in Bethnal Green, yet only half the number of fever cases. In Hackney and Holborn the number of paupers were almost the same, yet Holborn had double the amount of fever. Stepney also had half the fever cases of Bethnal Green. In St. George the Martyr, Southwark, there were 1,467 paupers and 1,276 fever patients, so that almost the entire population was affected. Camberwell, Wandsworth, Clapham, and the Strand had practically the same proportion of destitute as St. George the Martyr, yet the fever cases in each were just over 200. Smith therefore had striking proof of the localization of the disease—seven Unions had nearly 10,000 cases between them and these areas also had the severest forms. Over half the deaths from scarlatina occurred in Lambeth, Stepney, and Whitechapel. Fever was less prevalent but more fatal amongst men, and the mortality rate increased with steady and rapid progress as age advanced—two-thirds of the deaths occurred between the ages of 20 and 50. The disease most commonly attacked the heads of families, on whose labour they depended for their maintenance. Over one-fifth of London pauperism was a consequence of fever; in Bethnal Green it was one-third, in Whitechapel one-half, and in Southwark nearly all. Setting aside the great suffering of the individual and the distress brought to a family, Smith concluded:

> It is plain this disease is one of the main causes of the pressure on the poor rates. This pressure must continue and the same large amount of money spent year after year for the support of families afflicted with fever, as long as the dreadful *sources* of fever which encompass the habitations of the poor are allowed to remain. . . . They would not be allowed to remain if their nature were really understood, and if the ease with which the most urgent of them might be removed were known.

He compared how much had been done in wealthy districts with the utter neglect of the poor ones, and pointed out how dangerous the duties of the Relieving Officers and the Medical Officers were in the latter. Many doctors lost their lives after only residing among and attending to the poor for a short while. He described conditions and recommended improvements similar to those of the 1838 Reports, and closed with the admonition: 'the prevention of evil, rather than the mitigation of the consequences of it, are not only the most beneficent, but the most economical course'.

From this time Chadwick never ceased to agitate for Public Health measures as the most effectual means of reducing pauperism. The instigation of the Inquiries was the first public act by which he secured his place as founder of the English Public Health services. In 1839 he induced Bishop Blomfield to move in the House of Lords for an investigation into the causes of ill health in the country. Characteristically, Lord John Russell entrusted this to the Poor Law Commissioners for the problems were regarded as entirely of Poor Law concern.[1] The whole Inquiry was undertaken by the Assistant Commissioners, Boards of Guardians, and Poor Law staff, but Chadwick was responsible for the General Report which was issued in 1842:—'Chadwick has been writing a long report on the means of preventing disease by drainage, cleansing, etc. It contains a good deal of good matter, and on the whole, I prefer it to anything else he has written. We shall present it as his report without making ourselves responsible.'[2] The report revealed that the annual slaughter in England and Wales from preventable causes of fever which attacked poor people in the prime of life, was twice that suffered by the allied armies at Waterloo. Deaths caused during one year in England and Wales by epidemic, endemic, and contagious diseases were 56,471, at least a quarter of which were avoidable. 'The number of persons who die are an indication of a much greater number of persons who fall sick, although they escape, they are subjected to suffering and loss because of the disease.' The 1838 Metropolitan Inquiries had shown that deaths from fever were one in ten of the number attacked; if this had held true throughout the country, a quarter of a million would have died. But where the proportion of deaths were less, the reports had indicated the intensity of distress from protracted illness generally increased. Some 16,000 people were killed in a year by smallpox, and 80,000 suffered directly or indirectly from its ravages, and in this had to be included loss of employment and continued debility, permanent disfigurement, and occasionally loss of sight.

It was inevitable that attention was primarily directed to the physical or mechanical side, to the accumulation of filth and stenches, to water supply and drainage, and to the non-human environment.—'Such is the absence of civil economy in some towns that the condition in respect of cleanliness is almost as bad as that of an encamped horde or undisciplined soldiery.' Chadwick explained his dwelling on the external side of the problem to the fact that the defects came most immediately within practical, legislative, and administrative control. His remedies included simple means of drainage for marshy areas and the removal of refuse from houses and streets by adequate sewerage. He described methods of sewage disposal and the value for agricultural purposes—cheaper food was also conducive to health.—Liebig had already outlined the economy of an efficient sewage system by making refuse available to agriculture.—Chadwick also pointed out the need for supplying pure water to houses, for long hours of work indisposed the labouring class to collect water from pumps so that habits of cleanliness deteriorated. He next turned his attention to bad ventilation and overcrowding, and included a description of insalubrious working conditions, as for example, in the tailoring trade, where the incidence of tuberculosis was high and premature deaths drove wives and children to the parish. In 1839 only twenty-nine of the 233 deaths in this trade had been credited to age. In London 53 per cent of the deaths were due to diseases of the respiratory organs, but only 39 per cent in the rural districts. In the Metropolis 5 per cent died of typhus but only 1 per cent in the country. These facts Chadwick maintained demonstrated the ill effects of defective ventilation. But medical

[1] Letter from Home Secretary to the Poor Law Commissioners requesting Inquiry, August 1839. Home Office Papers.
[2] G. C. Lewis to Sir E. Head, 13 March 1842, in *Letters from Sir G. C. Lewis*, 1870.

science itself was only just recognizing the results of this evil and Chadwick believed nothing would be done until the public as a whole were made aware of it. Overcrowding was usual in the country as well as in the towns, however, and two sets of effects resulted from the polluted atmosphere—one, indulgence in drink, general improvidence and the waste of food because it decayed quickly, thus increasing the cost of living, and second, the depressing effect on the minds of people and on their nervous system. All overcrowded places investigated, said Chadwick, presented a proportionate amount of severe cases of destitute orphanage and widowhood, and in some instances they were marked by the excessive recklessness of the working population.

The pecuniary cost of 'noxious agencies' Chadwick continued, was high, and the cost should include much of the public charge for vice and crime. Productive power lost through insanitary conditions had become a truism, as had the burden of maintaining the dependants of the prematurely aged and dying. Pauperism occasioned by the sickness of one man might entail destitution on a family for generations. In 1840 there were 112,000 orphans receiving poor relief and 43,000 widows. Prisons, said Chadwick, were once distinguished for their filth and bad ventilation, but Howard's worst descriptions were exceeded in every wynd in Edinburgh and Glasgow inspected by Arnott and himself and accompanying municipal officers. Conditions were most pernicious among the cellar dwellers of Liverpool, Manchester, Leeds, and London. Doctors vouched for the fact that the health of prisoners was superior to that of the independent population surrounding them, although the criminals came from the worst neighbourhoods and lodging-houses. In Glasgow, prisoners were weighed on their entrance to and departure from the Bridewell, and it was always found they had gained in weight. In Edinburgh, instances were related where the sick poor were committed to prison from motives of humanity. Sanitary measures, Chadwick demonstrated, could prevent one-third of the sickness, and he produced statistics showing how a penny or twopence a family per week could achieve these objects. The cost of one dram of gin consumed by every poor person who frequented the gin palaces would defray the expense of installing drainage, by which some of the strongest provocations to habitual drunkenness could be removed, and which would add eight to ten years to the working life of a man.

Finally, Chadwick drew attention to the work of the Poor Law Medical Officer, without whom the conditions described in all the reports could not have been ascertained. From a consideration of the practical evidence it was seen that the ordinary duties of the Relieving Officer and the Medical Officer ensured domiciliary inspection of large areas to an extent and degree of certainty that could scarcely be ensured by, or expected of any agents or member of a board of health, unconnected with positive administration. As a preliminary general arrangement Chadwick suggested a Medical Officer should be given the additional duty, for which he should be remunerated, of examining patients' dwellings for physical and removable causes which may have indirectly or directly produced the disease. Statements should be forwarded to the Relieving Officer who should then take measures for getting rid of the 'morbific' agencies at the expense of the owner of the tenement. No delay was to be brooked. The occasional visits of the doctor would eventually require the establishing of a permanent local medical service under a superior medical practitioner, who should supervise a wider local district than did an ordinary Medical Officer. A District Medical Officer independent of private practice should therefore be employed with special qualifications and the responsibility to initiate sanitary measures and have them put into effect legally.—Chadwick wished to see the institution of a comprehensive medical service:

> Money now spent in a comparatively fragmentitious and unsystematized local medical service for the public, would if combined . . . afford advantages at each step of combination. We have in some towns public Medical Officers as inspectors of prisons, inspectors of lunatic asylums, and inspectors of recruits.

There were also the Poor Law Medical Officers and doctors granting certificates for children under the provision of the Factory Act whilst other doctors undertook post-mortem examinations for Coroners' inquests (11,000–12,000 a year). . . . 'The multiplication . . . of such fragmentitious professional services is injurious to the public and the profession. . . . It is injurious to the profession by multiplying the poor, ill-paid and ill-conditioned medical men.' Remuneration was inadequate for the maintenance of a doctor without the aid of private practice; it only sufficed to sustain competitors for practice. From such competition the public derived no improvements from medical knowledge—*for the rest of his life Chadwick agitated for the whole-time service of doctors engaged in Poor Law and Public Health duties.* As a long-term policy, therefore, a single, well-qualified and securely appointed responsible local officer should be engaged, who would consider the whole town as one sick person and regard every part of it as an organ in the wide fields of public health. These health officers should also be ably assisted by well-qualified responsible scientists and skilled engineers.[1]

Chadwick's report was really the starting-point of Public Health organization in the country. An abortive House of Commons Committee on the Health of Towns in 1840 (Slaney's) and another report on Interment in Large Towns had prepared the public for the disclosures of 1842. The former had reported in favour of a General Building Act, a General Sewerage Act, and the setting up of a Board of Health in every town. Southwood Smith had been the first witness and he gave evidence of absorbing interest. In a finely sympathetic passage he pointed out that people living in the worst conditions were the least inclined to complain, they succumbed to wretchedness, and dullness and apathy indicated their mental as well as physical paralysis.—'Wretchedness is greater than humanity can bear and annihilates mental faculties.' His main theme was that unhealthy conditions wasted life unnecessarily and that the poor were left to die in their homes instead of being put to death forcibly—the effect was the same. In 1843 Chadwick added a second report on the 'System of Interment in Large Towns' in which he pointed out the high cost of death to the poor in

---

[1] Report on the Sanitary Condition of the Labouring Population of Great Britain, 1842.

funerals. Liverpool had one burial per annum to every thirty of the inhabitants, Hereford one to every fifty-five. After describing the dreadful conditions of the cemeteries and the consequences, he advocated the abolition of intra-mural interment and the establishing of public mortuaries for the sake of decency as well as health. He also recommended the municipalization of funerals, with a reduction of expense to the poor and greater simplicity of arrangements.

In 1841 Lord Normanby had succeeded in getting a Drainage of Buildings Bill passed in the Lords, but it was not introduced in the Commons. (He had been taken over the slums of Bethnal Green and Whitechapel by Smith.) The year following he made a second attempt and tried to obtain the abolition of back-to-back dwellings, but was defeated. The Government, however, had been convinced of the necessity for action, and in 1844 Sir Robert Peel appointed a Royal Commission on the Health of Large Towns. Throughout, assistance and inspiration were given by Chadwick, although he was not a Commissioner. The report revealed that out of fifty towns studied, scarcely one had an efficient drainage system, and in forty-two it was decidedly bad. It was recommended that the Government should supervise and inspect the administration of sanitary laws in large towns and well populated districts, and that the local authorities entrusted with the execution of these laws should receive wider powers of control. Further, water supply and drainage, as well as paving and lighting of streets, etc. should be concentrated in the hands of one and the same authority in each district. The Commission also emphasized the necessity of giving the central department powers of compulsion against local authorities convicted of negligence.

Various schemes for drainage and cleaning had been adopted locally in the late 'thirties and early 'forties, as for example those in Bristol, Birkenhead, Ramsgate, and the City of London. Private Acts had been obtained for 'better paving, cleansing, lighting, watching, and otherwise improving' the towns, and Commissioners had been appointed empowered to purchase land and buildings for the purpose of general improvement and rates might be levied for the undertakings. Manchester, the Potteries, and Bradford-on-Avon had Acts in 1839; Stamford, Lincoln, Weston-super-Mare, and Middlesbrough had followed in 1840–41. The earliest local Act for compelling houses to be drained into sewers had been obtained by Leeds in 1842, followed by Rochdale, Manchester, and Southampton in 1844.[1] But the Acts were only permissive and no municipal enterprise was undertaken, public utilities remained in private hands and competition among the companies increased the existing evils. Private bill legislation was also rendered nugatory or useless because of the lack of co-ordination among the chaos of competing authorities, which had been appointed *ad hoc*. In London there were 300 such bodies. The development of municipal health reforms was seriously retarded by the absence of a properly constituted governing organization. Reform in municipalities came slowly after the 1835 Benthamite Act, but regarding Public Health the municipal corporations long remained hopelessly corrupt, obscurantist,

[1] F. Clifford, *A History of Private Bill Legislation*, 1885–87, Vol. III.

and demonstrably inadequate for the purpose of local government. Liverpool in 1842 however established a Health Committee from members of the Town Council. The local Act laid down the width of streets, forbade the building of closed courts and the occupation of cellar dwellings of certain types, stipulated the size of rooms and windows, regulated conditions as to privies and ashpits, and ordered houses which were filthy and unwholesome to be cleaned to the satisfaction of the Medical Officers.

In 1847 came the Nuisances Removal Act. The Privy Council was to be the central authority, and the local administrators were to be the corporations of towns; if there was no Council, the Improvement Commissioners were to be responsible, and ultimately if no other body existed, the Boards of Guardians were to constitute the Public Health authority. Draining, cleansing, whitewashing, and the removal of nuisances were to be undertaken on complaints made to two Justices of the Peace. Where property owners defaulted the health authority might undertake the operation and recover the cost summarily. The Act only applied however to cities and places threatened or affected by formidable contagious or epidemic disease. In 1848 a second Nuisances Removal and Diseases Prevention Act was passed which amplified the sanitary measures of the first and stipulated that the Privy Council would issue orders when the provisions were to be put into operation, i.e., when disease or epidemics threatened. In addition local authorities were to supply drugs and medical attention in emergencies—all expenses being defrayed out of the poor rates.

By these Acts the Boards of Guardians were really the sanitary authorities and only in large towns were Poor Law and Public Health administration separated. Referring to the new legislation Sir George Nicholls wrote: 'The execution of sanitary measures ... appears to come within the province of Poor Law administration, since disease in any shape tends to create destitution, the relief and prevention of which are the especial object of every Poor Law.' But permanent legal separation between the two social services was begun by the Public Health Act of 1848. The Nuisances Removal Acts were occasioned by fear of impending cholera and especially the fear of the existing spread of fever, but by 1848 the additional influence of the overwhelming evidence of earlier reports and the agitation of reformers, played an important part in securing the legislation.

Most significant had been the activity of the Health of Towns Association. Established in 1844 it had continued the investigations made between 1838 and 1842. An active campaign had been initiated which included lectures and publications. The objects were defined as the

> diffusion of information on physical and moral evils arising from existing insanitary conditions and a correction of the misconception as to expense, ... [We] would substitute Health for disease, cleanliness for filth, order for disorder, economy for waste, prevention for palliation, justice for charity, enlightened self-interest for ignorant selfishness, and to bring to the poorest and meanest—AIR, WATER, LIGHT.

Weekly sheets of facts and figures were published and in its first year the Association sent a petition to the House of Commons describing the glaring abuses and their results, such as that working ability was reduced by twelve years. In 1845 the Association had reported that in Manchester alone nearly 14,000 children had perished in eleven years over and above the normal mortality rate. It had also stated that while the average age of the gentry and professional people was over 44 the average age attained by the working-class was only 22. Southwood Smith, a prominent member of the Association, had in 1847 urged the people to rouse themselves:

> Let your voice . . . startle the ear of the public and command the attention of the legislature, petition Parliament to give you sewers, petition Parliament to secure a constant and abundant water supply . . . petition Parliament to remove—for it is in the power of Parliament universally and completely to remove—the sources of poison that surround your dwellings and that carry disease, suffering, and death into your homes. Tell them of the parish of St. Margaret, Leicester, where in a population of 22,000, almost all of whom are artisans . . . the average age of the whole parish in 1846 was 18 years . . . in some streets only $13\frac{1}{2}$.

Dr. Hector Gavin, another well known Public Health reformer and member of the Committee of the Association, wrote a book exposing the conditions in Bethnal Green and the terrible consequences. He had made a detailed survey of every street and produced statistics on sickness, disease and mortality.[1] Many other publications were made by members of the Association to further the demand for legislation, and the success of the campaign could not be prevented.

But there had been general public awakening in the middle 'forties, the Hungry 'Forties, when the working classes themselves were growing self-conscious and demanded reforms not alone connected with Chartism. The middle-class had established such societies as the Metropolitan Association for Improving the Dwellings of the Industrious Classes, and the Society for Improving the Conditions of the Labouring Classes. Newspapers at the time had also devoted much space to the discussion of health problems and thereby excited widespread interest. The books of Mrs. Gaskell, Dickens, Kingsley, and Engels had made great contributions by advertising conditions in a popular form, though Engels' dissertation on sanitary evils and consequent sickness and crime was a long and serious analysis, and Dickens had been deeply influenced by his friend Southwood Smith. The appeal was not only to humanitarian sentiment, for the severe economic loss was demonstrated of avoidable disease and premature death and of unemployment caused by unnecessary disability. This had been Chadwick's chief argument for overcoming the prejudices of the middle classes. Both ignorance and vested interests had had to be combated by statistical propaganda. The Royal Statistical Society and the Manchester and Liverpool Statistical Societies had proved valuable sources of information, but it was the work of William Farr which proved one of the most potent influences in Public Health reform,

---

[1] *Sanitary Ramblings—Sketches and Illustrations of Bethnal Green, a type of the condition of the Metropolis and Other Large Towns*, Hector Gavin, M.D., F.R.C.S.E., Physician and Lecturer at Charing Cross Hospital, 1848.

both before and after 1848. His investigations into vital statistics went far beyond what was embodied in the Registrar-General's Reports. Hygiene and medical statistics were his chief subjects and he was a qualified doctor.[1] Chadwick had been the dominant influence in the institution of Registration of births and deaths, but an equally great service was rendered to Public Health by his discovery of Farr, for, over a period of forty years, Farr turned the searchlight of publicity on the evils which could not be neglected indefinitely. In the 'forties he showed that thirty-eight people were destroyed every day in London by local causes and gave a graphic description of how the Poor Law Medical Officers should lead the Lord Mayor and the Corporation of the City of London in procession through the alleys and courts which were the fatal fields of fever, and where they would see 'disease gleaming in the eye of children, wasting the bodies of women, prostrating the strength of men'. . . . Enlightened members of the medical profession had also given one answer to the social problem and had asserted that the question of disease-ridden people could not be solved by Ricardian philosophic and economic principles. Lastly, fear had been a great ally of the reformers, for the upper classes had been given sufficient evidence that their Improvement Commissioners were useless in preventing outbreaks of cholera and fevers, especially when they were attached to corrupt and inefficient local authorities.

Therefore the Public Health Act of 1848 was passed. With the institution of the Medical Officers of Health the growth of the English State medical service, begun with the Poor Law Medical Officer, was assured. But the Act had to secure the division between Poor Law and Public Health. The Poor Law was a deterrent aimed at reducing costs, and the Public Health movement by its obvious insistence on prevention, entailing large expenditure, was incompatible with Poor Law principles.

The Poor Law Commissioners, a nucleus of the modern Civil Service, had aroused animosity by their adamant adherence to centralization. Chadwick had long since detached himself from them, and his influence was paramount in the Public Health sphere by 1848. Therefore the Act created a central board on the Poor Law model, for in his eyes strong centralization was the only means to efficiency. The inquiries of the Poor Law Commissioners had confirmed that individuals were helpless and collective action imperative. The Government had originally intended the General Board of Health to be composed of five Members of Parliament, a person gifted with administrative talent, and two medical men. But at the first opposition the three paid members of the Board had been dropped, and the country had only been saved from having the Act administered by two unpaid members

---

[1] To supplement his precarious income Farr in the 'thirties wrote for various medical journals mainly on the subject of vital statistics. He attempted to establish a course of lectures on 'Hygiology'—but he was ahead of his time and no medical body recognized the desirability of Public Health lectures. Therefore the subject matter was embodied in a series of articles to the *Lancet* (1835-36)—Wakley was first to recognize the talent of Farr. He also contributed to the *British Journal of Medicine*. When he was appointed Compiler of Abstracts to the General Registry Office, 1837, he ended his career as a doctor and for the next forty years he created and developed a national system of Vital Statistics. He settled the question of nosology.—*Vital Statistics* is the collection of Farr's works made by the Sanitary Institute.

through the firmness of Joseph Hume,[1] who had protested against the absurdity of unpaid and consequently irresponsible commissioners. One paid member was voted by the House of Commons, and the 'able and indefatigable Chadwick was appointed to the office. Medical members, the only men practically and thoroughly cognizant with the subject of Public Health, were voted to be useless, and not one voice in Parliament was raised against the folly'.[2] Chadwick himself probably did not desire to see a medical specialist on the Board as he regarded doctors as 'necessary evils not likely to last' to be made redundant through the results of the contemplated sanitary improvements. The other two members of the General Board of Health—The 'Board of Sanitary Works'[3]—were Lord Morpeth and Lord Ashley; therefore there was no representative in the House of Commons. (Southwood Smith was later added as a medical adviser.)

The most important section of the Act excited the strongest controversy and opposition. This was the provision empowering the central board to create local health districts and local boards, either on a petition from 10 per cent of the ratepayers or in an area where the annual mortality reached a specified figure, without the cumbrous procedure and expense of a Private Act. Where the Act was applied in municipal boroughs, town councils became the local sanitary authority, but elsewhere the creation of new bodies was involved designated Local Boards of Health. In some cases they were to be empowered and in others compelled, to execute a number of special functions, not only in regard to sanitation, sewerage, and drainage, but also in the more general requirements of water supply, street management, burial, and the provision of parks. The regulations were extremely detailed and numerous, but the Act suffered from the gravest defect—it was only permissive! It had however to contend with a mass of prejudice, and had it applied universally and compulsorily to the whole country, it would probably not have been passed at all. A leading article in the *Observer* described the opposition which the measure had faced. After referring to the hopelessness of securing sanitary reform by local legislation and the previous apathy of the wealthy, it voiced its disapproval of the exclusion of large towns from the provisions of the Act.

> Great towns are now affecting to be the unbending tyrannical few who are to dictate to the Government what is to be done with their less powerful brethren. London, Manchester, Birmingham, Leeds, Exeter are the haughty nobility—that will brook no control over themselves . . . Incapable of patriotic views, regardless of miseries of their own populations, not designing to acknowledge the existence of other interests than theirs, they would fain bully the Government out of paying any regard to the condition of a great body of Her Majesty's subjects. Until the narrow ends of their dominant cliques are fully consulted, they will not allow the Government to move a single step if

[1] Member of Parliament and a great 'Free Trader'. Active in Sir Robert Peel's Government (1841–46) for the Repeal of the Corn Laws. Called the 'apostle of retrenchment' by C. R. Fay, *Great Britain from Adam Smith to the Present Day*, 1937, p. 65.

[2] *Digest of Several Reports on Sanitary Reform*, Wm. Sampson Low, 1849.

[3] *Observer*, 3 December 1848.

they can prevent it—and a high and urgent duty is now laid on the representatives of smaller towns, and such representatives of larger towns as are identified with the great mass of their inhabitants. The newly-formed despotism and dictatorship, which is set upon maintaining the system that annually wastes more human lives than the most sanguinary wars, has to be resisted with becoming resolution . . . A combination of Messrs. Hudson, Urquhart, and Divett, influencing Parliament to decree there should be no cleansing of towns would leave far less to local self-government than Lord Morpeth and his Health Commissioners. . . .

Referring to Cobden's idea of paying for improvements by cutting the Civil List, the article continued that he should read Dr. Lyon Playfair's Report on the Sanitary Condition of Lancashire (1844) which demonstrated that the excess of preventable sickness cost that county nearly £1 million.[1] Wakley gave a penetrating answer to the Free Traders when he said he obtained no support from them while he was seeking to limit the power of the Poor Law Commissioners over the lives of the poor, but they now cried out because a new set of Commissioners were to be given very limited powers over property. The movement hostile to the formation of local Boards of Health was led by Toulmin Smith, who strongly attacked centralization and defended the system of Common Law. In the latter he saw all remedies necessary for the redress of sanitary evils, yet for a man in his position he should have recognized that the absolute neglect of Public Health services was due to the inadequacies inherent in Common Law.[2] Although the Act was generally welcomed throughout the country, it provoked the jealousy of the Royal Medical Colleges. The College of Physicians, instead of welcoming the measures, informed the Lord Mayor of London that they were ready to resolve any questions which might be put to them affecting Public Health. In this animosity, wrote the *Observer*,

> the college will be found to be a little unreasonable, and to have assumed pretensions to a science for which they have certainly done nothing—viz. the science of prevention of disease, and of the means which in large scale are provided for in the Public Health Act —it will appear manifestly in their books that they know nothing.[3]

The Act was amended and extended in later years, particularly by the Nuisances Removal Act of 1855, the Local Government Act of 1858, and the Sanitary Act of 1866. For the poor the Lodging Houses Acts of 1848, 1851, 1853 were also of great importance, but the enactment of 1848 remained the dominant measure in the development of Public Health services for twenty-seven years. The activities of the Board of Health were tolerated just long enough to see new principles take root. Chadwick's scheme gave the central authorities the complexion rather than the substance of power; if they could force local boards on districts, they had no real control over them; if they could advise and guide, a

[1] *Observer*, 14 May 1848.
[2] 'On Principles and Practical Efficiency of Common and Statute Law of England in relation to promotion of, and removal of, causes injurious to Public Health', P. H. Toulmin Smith, Tract, March 1848.
[3] *Observer*, 3 December 1848.

town could defy their authority and remain negligent. The local authorities were themselves regarded as an inquisition rather than as leaders for building new cities. Above all, ratepayers and local boards grew to hate not only central control, but the dominant figure in the administration—Chadwick. The Board completely ignored the necessity of converting people to desire health and cleanliness, and as *The Times* remarked they would rather risk cholera than be bullied into health by Chadwick. The stormy career of the Board ended in 1854. As the only paid member Chadwick had been the target for all attacks, but as he was not a Member of Parliament he had no opportunity of speaking in his own defence. Like Shaftesbury and Southwood Smith he was entirely indifferent to the clamour of party politics and has been called the 'best abused man of his time'.[1]

But political events from 1832 to 1845 were too exciting, and obscured the movement of social reconstruction. In his particular sphere Chadwick's abilities were unrivalled, and his genius lay in his infinite capacity for taking pains. He lacked, however, the tact and patience necessary to a public administrator. He had seen for himself what slum life was, he knew the helplessness of the poor and the misery and havoc wrought by dirt and disease. He was accused of impatience when every year of delay meant thousands of preventable deaths. His theory was utilitarianism, his practice, like that of all Benthamites, was ruthless efficiency. He was ardently enthusiastic to apply scientific ideas; he believed strongly in the importance of material environment, in the paid expert, in the community rather than in the individual, and in the 'Sanitary Idea' as part of higher economics, i.e., national survival: 'The Nation's Health is the Nation's Wealth.' He had been in office only a few years, yet for thirty-six years more he wrote papers on social and sanitary subjects and took part in the work of many learned societies. In 1861 he became President of the Economic Section of the British Association; in 1870 President of the Public Health section of the National Association for the Promotion of Social Science for which he wrote many papers and took an active part in the discussions, not only on Public Health but also on the Poor Law. In 1878 he became President of the Sanitary Institute. His life was spent partly in blue books—and much of his important work is buried in them, and partly on Boards and Commissions, studying drains, sewers, slums, and fevers. At the age of 87 he was still publishing pamphlets, and it is interesting that he did not receive a knighthood until a year before his death—his work was not officially recognized before.

Not only Chadwick's reforming activity, but also his personal character aroused opposition. Harsh, dogmatic, unsympathetic, he brooked no opposition. He neither listened to, nor would he submit to alternatives, giving no thought to the consequences on his career. Critics accused him of having a passion for administrative efficiency and of lacking a similar passion for humanity. He hated waste, dirt, misery, and stupidity which he saw

[1] Chadwick remained an enigmatic figure for nearly a century. Apart from B. W. Richardson's biographical work *The Health of Nations*, published in 1887, he received little attention from social historians until the publication of *The Life and Times of Sir Edwin Chadwick*, by S. E. Finer, London, 1952, and *Edwin Chadwick and the Public Health Movement 1832–54*, by R. A. Lewis, London, 1952. This chapter was already complete when these books appeared.

was poisoning the lives of the poor. His great faith in central government, in statistical research, heightened by his foresight and great constructive powers, made him the prophet of much that was to come in the twentieth century. He gave Public Health administration a series of clear objectives by showing how the census and bills of mortality could be used to diagnose public evils, which necessitated Public Health legislation. He wished to build hospitals, asylums, and separate institutions for different classes of poor. His research led him to demand such things as wood blocks for paving streets, water-carriage for refuse disposal, employers' liability for accidents, and the provision of public parks. The modern system of pensions was outlined in one of his papers, as was the twentieth-century scheme of trade and technical instruction to Service men. Chadwick's ideas formed a watershed as the deterrent police policy of the State gave way to positive prophylaxis against social evils. He was the first link between Poor Law and Public Health and watched the development of each. Born in 1800 just four years after the pioneer Manchester Board of Health was founded, he lived until 1890 to see the emergence of Chamberlain's 'High Rates and a Healthy City', and 'Gas and Water' Socialism. To trace the transition from *laissez-faire* to collectivism is to trace the development of nineteenth-century social history and also Chadwick's career. To give him a predominate place in that history is to show that he was a pioneer of the Welfare State.

Of Chadwick's fellow members on the Board of Health, Lord Morpeth had only an ex-officio seat and was little heard of, but Lord Ashley gave Chadwick full support. He had been chosen because his public spirit and his capacity for hard, unpaid, and disagreeable work was already known. He had also supported Normanby's Bills and had taken part in housing and sanitary reform, but he was an individualist and failed when forced to co-operate with others or use methods of popular action. His similarities to Chadwick were that he favoured bureaucracy and strong authority; together they made the central board the most unpopular public body the nineteenth century produced. Parliament and people continued to regard centralization as a great danger, for local and central government were only slowly acquiring new functions, administrative habits, and trained personnel. Therefore in 1854 no one mourned the overthrow of what was regarded as a new monster. The *Observer* wrote an article on its fall, showing that no government department had ever been inaugurated under more favourable auspices, for the whole of England had been roused by the agitation for sanitary reform and the Bill had been passed with a great majority.— 'Everything was expected from the new Public Health Act, cholera was to be stayed, towns to be drained, nuisances were to be abolished, and in fact the whole nation was to be thoroughly purified.'[1] The Board of Health had however achieved some improvement— 200–300 towns applied for the introduction of the measures, but as preliminary investigations had always to be made, retrenchers and the Treasury looked askance at the increased expenditure. As only a few men understood the new problems the Board naturally confided the undertakings to their own officials. This raised a host of enemies especially among the civil engineers. An engineer who was Secretary of the Private Enterprise Society

[1] *Observer*, 26 July 1857.

informed Palmerston that all the best technicians opposed the principles of the authorities. He scoffed at the 'self-cleansing pipes' as opposed to 'sewers of deposition' and objected to the expense of all the 'piping' that was laid. He also quoted the general feeling against interference with cemeteries and interment, but fortunately the question of intramural burial had been finally settled.[1] The Board of Health had also attempted to secure a better water supply for the Metropolis and abolish the Sewers Commissions, although these were not effected until the following years. But in many respects the Board had failed. Manchester, for example, although it had a mortality rate of above 23 in 1,000—which was the limit fixed for compulsory interference—was never ordered to establish a health board. Resistance in the city was too great, and having successfully ignored the proposals of the first Board of Health, subsequent Health Acts and central authorities were also opposed. Chadwick had tried to dispose of narrow local initiative, but the Board of Health failed to find adequate or efficient central officials. The Board had been aided by scientific inventors like Doulton, who made cheap drainage possible, and Liebig who demonstrated the advantage of sewage for agriculture, but it had been handicapped by the two invasions of cholera of 1849 and 1853. These had provided a certain stimulus to local authorities and made pressure from the central board possible, but people pointed to the 58,000 deaths. In their final report, however, the Board made it clear that had it not been for their exertions the death rate would have equalled that of the Continent and 600,000 victims would have been claimed.

After the dissolution of the Board, Shaftesbury, with the public health reformer Dr. Hector Gavin, was responsible for the investigations into sickness in the Crimea. He maintained his interest in the housing problem and offered continuous and generous help to the voluntary associations promoting the building of model dwellings for the poor. The Housing Bills of 1867 and 1875 had his support and he was the first witness to the Royal Commission on Housing in 1884. Chadwick, who had been appointed to the Board of Health partly because the Poor Law Commissioners wished to be rid of his interference, was dropped by the Public Health authorities without even a word of thanks. His work did not die with his dismissal. His mantle fell on Sir John Simon whose reports were worthy successors to Chadwick's investigations of 1842. Until 1871 he piled up statistics with the aid of Farr[2] and became the first State organizer of medical research. But his story is long and is ably described in his comprehensive work on English Sanitary Institutes published in 1890.[3] In a chapter aptly entitled 'Politics of Poverty', he urged that while the law left

[1] Letter to Palmerston on Report of General Board of Health by George R. Barnall, C.E., London, 1854.

[2] Dr. W. A. Guy, Professor of Forensic Medicine and Public Health reformer for many decades was also an important advocate of the use of statistics. He had in 1844 given evidence on the value of statistics in medical and sanitary questions and lectured on the subject on behalf of the Health of Towns Association. See *Unhealthiness of Towns*, 1845 and important arguments for new methods in his *On the Value of Numerical Methods as applied to Science, but especially to Physiology and Medicine*, 1844.

[3] For the most comprehensive and recent study on Simon see Royston Lambert, *Sir John Simon (1816–1904) and English Social Administration*, London, 1963. This work was not published until after this chapter was completed.

wages to find their own level through the strength of unrestricted competition there ought to be strong safeguards for the poor against deterioration of food and against industrial and environmental conditions, which involved risk and danger to the employed. Like Smith and Chadwick he became impressed with the utter impossibility of the working-class doing anything for themselves in the matter of sanitary improvement.

He was the first scientific official and the prototype of professional advisers. Under him the Medical Department of the Privy Council made of Public Health problems an exact and precise study, and in his reports Simon tried to produce sufficient evidence for political and public appreciation and use. In the first decade inquiries were based on 'excesses of disease in particular districts or particular groups of the population', and new epidemiological facts were elicited. In 1859 Simon and his new staff investigated into the fatality of diarrhoea, in 1860–61 into pulmonary diseases, and Dr. Greenhow studied the environment of many branches of industrial, mining, and factory employment. In 1861–63 the high infantile mortality was investigated, and the quantity and severity of ague (a poverty fever) in marshy districts. The causes and preventibility of consumption was inquired into in 1867, and the severe epidemic of scarlatina in 1869 occasioned a renewed collection of evidence. General questions like common nuisances, water-supply, housing, food, were also comprehensively studied, and adequate medical and pharmaceutical services were demanded for the public welfare. A spate of statistics were produced in an appeal for more adequate sanitary laws. Dr. Bristowe and Timothy Holmes made a report in 1863 to the Medical Department of the Privy Council on 'The Hospitals of the United Kingdom'. Although health became an issue of practical politics, much of the success of the department was due however to the peaceful contrast it offered to the first Board of Health, for the actual scientific work was unaffected by political considerations. From 1865 Simon induced his superiors to permit the undertaking of medical research and in 1870 the first State grant of £2,000 was made for this purpose.—'The laboratory worker came to the aid of preventive medicine.' By 1871 it was clear the Medical Department of the Privy Council ought to be greatly extended. As the inquiries into the prevention of disease needed systematizing, Simon desired a large body of Inspectors to be available for every sphere of Public Health work.—'The Medical Department had left behind the hostilities and suspicions' of the early years which had been roused by the demand for sanitary progress, it had become interested in problems of medical science and therefore the goodwill and interest of the public had increased. This activity was an important reason for the progressive separation of the Poor Law and the Public Health movements between 1854 and 1871. Administratively, Public Health passed on the dissolution of the General Board of Health under the official guidance of a new Board of Ministers with a paid President. In 1857 the duties of the President were transferred to the Education Committee of the Privy Council, in 1858 they were divided between the Privy Council and Home Office, until in 1871 the Local Government Board once again united Poor Law and Public Health.

Between 1854 and 1871 the paths of reform in the two services diverged. One reason why they ran together until the first Board of Health was dissolved was because Chadwick and Shaftesbury had placed great confidence in the Poor Law Medical Officer. As Shaftesbury wrote: 'The Poor Law Medical Officer knew more than all the flash and fashionable doctors in London.' Also the Boards of Guardians had come in for much of their criticism: —'we exposed their selfishness, their cruelty, their reluctance to meet and relieve the suffering poor in the days of epidemic'.[1] Criticism of the Guardians in the late 'forties and early 'fifties was rare because the French Revolution and Louis Blanc's experiments had scared the English public from the 'Right to Relief' and from increasing the welfare policy of the State. In 1848 the former Poor Law Commissioner G. Cornewall Lewis could write that the English Poor Law had ceased to occupy public attention as a national question.[2] The development of the Poor Law medical service however continued, and spread into Public Health fields. The Medical Officer was a completely separate functionary from the new Medical Officer of Health, and although they sometimes conferred together they were only indirectly and unconsciously close allies. But if movements diverged the actual work was inevitably closely linked.

In their last report the Poor Law Board stated that the 'duties which were unexpectedly imposed on the Guardians by the epidemic [1869–71] bore a greater analogy to those of strictly sanitary description than the duties connected with the ordinary administration of the Poor Law'. This applied to a part of the work of the Boards of Guardians throughout, for by the Nuisances Removal and Diseases Prevention Acts and their operation in time of epidemic, the local Poor Law administrators were brought strictly into Public Health activity. The Poor Law Commissioners and the Poor Law Board themselves were also forced, by the fear of epidemics, to keep in close contact with the new movement, for as the diseases were chiefly connected with poverty, correspondence between central and local authorities on the problems raised took place every year. Right from the initiation of the Poor Law Commission, Guardians reported to them the prevalence of some epidemic disease in their Unions, and from the correspondence information can be obtained on the measures the Poor Law authorities took to combat outbreaks of infectious illnesses. In 1837 Assistant Commissioner Mott reported on Stepney that the cholera outbreak of that year had occurred in exactly the same place as the 1832 epidemic. The Clerk to the Guardians had to report daily to them any new cases or fresh facts connected with the disorder for it was attracting universal public attention. The Guardians, Mott said, acted promptly and communicated the result of their inquiry to Lord Russell at the Home Office, who however showed no desire to make the facts public. One of the Medical Officers converted a house for the reception of fever and other infectious cases. In a letter from Chadwick to the Poor Law Commissioners it was shown that in Limehouse the Stepney Guardians proposed to use the workhouse as a cholera hospital as it had been appropriated to this purpose in the previous outbreak, but the Commissioners refused permission for the institution to be used for what they termed 'such objectionable pur-

[1] Shaftesbury's Diary, 9 August 1853: Hodder II, p. 443.
[2] Letters of the Rt. Hon. Sir G. C. Lewis to his friends. Edited by Sir G. F. Lewis, 1870.

poses'.[1] From his survey of Limehouse, Mott informed the Poor Law Commissioners that cholera was infectious to a dangerous degree in districts where constitutions were 'predisposed to receive the infection' and that it was generally succeeded by low fever 'such as the medical profession described as being produced by a filthy stagnant atmosphere'. He believed more deaths occurred from fever following immediately on cholera than from attacks of cholera themselves. Mott was in every sphere the most enlightened of the Assistant Commissioners, and was the only one of the Poor Law administrators (save Kay who was a doctor) who pointed out the possibilities of prevention to which the reports of 1838–39 drew attention. He described to the Poor Law Commissioners the insanitary state of districts and the overcrowding in houses in Bethnal Green, Spitalfields, Lambeth, Mile End, and Limehouse, saying that in some areas disease was never absent. In evidence to Chadwick when he was a member of the Royal Commission of 1833, Mott had stated that bad conditions were the great source of pauperism and that property owners should be compelled to keep dwellings in a fit state for habitation. In his report to the Poor Law Commissioners in 1837 he maintained:

> An independent labourer may be industrious and provident, and yet both he and his family may be subjected to a fever or other disease and thrown upon the Parish in consequence of the want of drainage, and filth and other causes which he has no means of removing ... so that looking at the poor rates, it would be a good economy to pay attention to the drainage and enforcement of sanitary regulations.

Some neighbourhoods were so constantly the seats of particular diseases and the sources of pauperism from that cause, that it would be quite simple for Guardians who were acquainted with districts to go out and return immediately with two coachloads full of 'the most deplorable objects, the victims of frightful disease'.—'I believe', he concluded, 'that no greater benefit could be conferred on those districts than the enforcement of Regulations by which the inhabitants might be protected from the frightful consequences of the present filthy state of the dwellings of the lower classes.'[2]

But according to the Poor Law, cure and not prevention of sickness fell into the province of the Poor Law Commissioners. They could not authorize or order Guardians to undertake sanitary improvement even if they had been as enlightened as Mott. When cholera broke out in 1837 they did however empower Guardians in the affected areas to call on the best medical aid. For example, instructions were sent to Bristol that the most eminent doctors whom the district could furnish should be employed, and if difficulty were experienced the Poor Law Commissioners would send an Assistant Commissioner with great experience to give advice.[3] (As a medical commissioner did not exist it is hard to imagine what help the Poor Law Commissioners could have afforded.) From rural areas Assistant Commissioners reported that the Poor Law Medical Officers were actively and

[1] Chadwick letter, 30 December 1837.
[2] Report of Assistant Commissioner Mott on Stepney Union, Limehouse Area, November 1837.
[3] Letter, 30 October 1837.

efficiently combating the disease, and few instances were given of workhouse inmates being affected; generally it was the poor, just above the class of paupers, and here additional food and clothing were provided. Houses were cleansed and whitewashed at the instigation of the Guardians, who, although not responsible for the non-destitute poor, had in 1837–38 realized that they could by these means prevent an increase in the burden of providing relief.

By the New Police Act of 1839,[1] Metropolitan Guardians were made responsible for the cleansing of houses reported to be in an unfit state. The Poor Law Commissioners issued a Circular[2] summarizing the findings of the 1838–39 sanitary investigations and drawing attention to the large proportion of destitution which arose from sickness attributed to the defective 'internal and external economy of the dwellings of the labouring classes, and to the want of proper cleanliness in them'. By the new Act, Guardians and Poor Law Medical Officers were empowered to report insanitary dwellings to magistrates, who could order cleansing and repairs to be undertaken within seven days. In cases of refusal, Guardians were to undertake the necessary operations at the owner's expense. The Poor Law Commissioners urged the Guardians to use their powers immediately, especially in areas where relief figures demonstrated that disease and poverty were most prevalent. The Poor Law Medical Officers were particularly asked to co-operate because they were the only people who really knew the districts well. The Commissioners pointed out that the findings of the 1838–39 investigations had greatly surprised most of the middle and upper classes of London; therefore, Medical Officers were required to publicize the conditions they discovered. Further, Guardians and Medical Officers were not to wait until life was actually threatened, but were to take steps to prevent the danger to the health of the poor by interfering in houses which were likely to become dangerous. Guardians were to put up public notices stating the names of streets, the numbers of houses regarded as insalubrious, and the action to be taken by the owners. Whitewashing and cleansing of houses and courts, and draining of cesspools were however the only fields which Guardians could touch—the general drainage system of an area did not fall within the scope of the Act. The Act and the Circular only applied to London, but the Sanitary Act of 1846 affected the whole country. The Poor Law Commissioners, as on every piece of legislation, issued an explanatory Circular pointing out the nuisance removal provisions and the powers conferred on Guardians thereby. On the receipt of a certificate signed by two doctors stating the filthy and unwholesome conditions of any dwelling-house or other building, the accumulation of any offensive refuse, or the existence of offensive drains, privies, or cesspools, the Guardians or other local authorities were to lay the complaint before two Justices of the Peace, who were then to order cleansing and removal of the nuisances. On default of the owner's compliance, Guardians were to undertake the cleansing and recover the cost—£2 to £10—for wilful obstruction. The Poor Law Commissioners again urged them to exercise their powers and concluded the Circular:

[1] 2, 3 Vic. c. 71, s. 41.
[2] 11 November 1840.

The improvement of the sanitary conditions of the poorer classes tends so greatly to remove many of the causes of destitution and pauperism, that money judiciously expended on such an object now sanctioned by the legislature . . . will be found to be most profitably laid out even in reference to the more direct object of the duties of Guardians.[1]

After the passing of the Nuisances Removal and Prevention of Contagious Diseases Act in 1847, the Poor Law Board forwarded a letter to all Boards of Guardians in the country pointing out not only the provisions of the Act, but also preparing them for the directions which were about to be issued by the Board of Health, because a formidable epidemic of cholera was approaching England from Europe. The Circular of the Poor Law Board stated that Guardians could take the usual steps for preventing disease after notices had been received from only two householders as to noxious drains, privies and cesspools or filthy houses. The keeping of pigs and cattle on any premises, and the accumulation of manure and refuse was also defined as a nuisance. Guardians could enter premises after twenty-four hours to investigate, with or without a Medical Officer. If an owner refused to carry out the suggestions, a fine of 10s. for each day of default could be charged by the Guardians, and the manure removed by them could be sold, the proceeds going to augment the poor rates. Drainage by open ditches of new houses after 4 September 1848 evoked a penalty of £5 per day as long as the offence continued, and an owner could also be indicted for a misdemeanour. The Poor Law Commissioners pointed out to the Guardians that this Act differed from former ones in that notification by two householders sufficed for instigating action, whereas previously two Medical Officers had had to give written certificates. Further, the new legislation made it imperative on Guardians to act when notice was given, and distinct duties were assigned to them as well as to Medical Officers and surveyors. The second part of the Act applied to the prevention of contagious and epidemic diseases, and the provisions did not take effect until called into operation by an order from the Privy Council. This part of the enactment, the Poor Law Board pointed out, charged the Board of Health with the duty of preparing regulations which Union and parochial officers were required to enforce in the event of the country being invaded by epidemic, endemic, or contagious disease. As the Act itself had been passed because of the fear of cholera, an Order in Council had already been issued.[2]

At the same time the Poor Law Board communicated with their Inspectors on the prevention of epidemic diseases. They stated that when Asiatic cholera had come in 1832, it had been found necessary in larger towns—because of the inadequacy of local administrative machinery—to form new bodies as Boards of Health expressly for the purpose. But in 1848, the Poor Law Board said that the legislature deemed the local authorities adequate in the form of Boards of Guardians with regularly appointed Medical Officers and Relieving Officers and new workhouses containing suitable wards for the reception of

[1] Circular, 8 October 1846.
[2] Circular, Poor Law Board, 6 October 1848.

fever cases, and so they would in many cases render unnecessary the creation of new and separate authorities for the special emergency. But as the Boards of Guardians in densely populated towns already had heavy duties, the Act provided that they could appoint additional officers for the superintendence and execution of the new regulations. The General Board of Health desired house to house visiting in poor insanitary districts, and could authorize extensive limewashing and the complete cleansing of such places. Additional labourers were to be employed for the operations. Attacks of cholera were preceded by premonitory symptoms, and if these were promptly attended to and properly treated, there would be little danger of a fatal outcome of the disease. Therefore the Poor Law Board requested the Inspectors to confer with the Guardians and suggest Orders where necessary. The Inspectors were also asked to ensure that the medical assistance required for the additional local examinations and the treatment of actual attacks would be adequate. Extra Medical Officers were to be engaged where circumstances warranted it. The requisite medicines were to be dispensed at the houses of the doctors and also at special places which it might be found necessary to establish. Packets of drugs were to be made up to be carried about by the Medical Officers so that they could be used immediately on the discovery of any premonitory symptoms. The Inspectors were to note any special local regulations required for towns in their districts, and were to impress upon the Guardians that the new arrangements were to take precedence over all ordinary services. For measures of more permanent relief and complete prevention, the Guardians' attention was to be directed to the provisions of the Public Health Act.[1]

When the Board of Health issued its directions and regulations for Boards of Guardians, the Poor Law Board forwarded copies to all Unions in the country. The recommendations fell into two groups; first, those for prevention where cholera had not appeared, such as drainage, sewerage, cleansing, and removal of animals and poultry from houses, ventilation, and the lighting of fires in homes to get rid of dampness; and second, measures of relief where cholera existed, such as immediate house to house visiting by Medical Officers to ascertain the most dangerous areas and to afford relief to those suffering from premonitory symptoms, and also inspection of all large premises and schools by employers, proprietors, and masters.[2] The Board urged collective and individual action should be taken immediately on both sets of recommendations. Where cholera appeared they sent forms to Medical Officers of Unions for making returns to them—minutest details of cases were required and of the method of treatment adopted. In the First Annual Report the Poor Law Board stated they were in frequent communication with Guardians as to procedure under the Nuisances Removal Act: 'which in the present state of Public Health requires earnest attention'. Information they received from all parts of the country led them to conclude that the Act was being zealously carried into effect:—'The urgency of the occasion is sensibly felt and actively met by Guardians and their officers, on whom the law has cast the obligation of

---

[1] Letter from the Poor Law Board to Inspectors, 6 October 1848.

[2] Chadwick always urged regular inspection for sanitary purposes of all schools, Poor Law and primary, and inspection of places of employment.

carrying out its provisions.' In this year there was no mention of the Poor Law medical services as such; all medical questions were in the Public Health field.

A large amount of Public Health work was undertaken by the Poor Law Medical Officers. In Kensington, for example, they made constant reports to the Guardians in the 'forties regarding the want of cleanliness in certain districts, and pointed out the necessity for the Guardians to seek legal powers for covering open sewers and building new ones. They enumerated the houses which were in a filthy state and where sanitation was defective.[1] In Chorlton, the Medical Officer wrote to his Guardians that he conceived it his duty to point out anything which might be advantageous or injurious to the poor under his care. He laid stress on the state of back streets where manure was kept in front of doors and where no sewerage system existed at all. He desired the Guardians to interfere because his remonstrations with the tenants had met with nothing but abuse, and he prophesied frightful consequences if any infectious disease were to break out. Finally, he led a deputation to the Guardians to request intervention.[2] But while the Medical Officers were elected annually they were generally deterred from reporting nuisances from fear of losing their posts, especially as many Guardians were small householders. When permanency of office was introduced in 1842 and made a General Order in 1847, the restraint on the Medical Officers was lifted, and the cholera epidemic, with the activity of the Poor Law Board and Board of Health, made it imperative on them to point out 'morbific agencies', and most Guardians furthered their efforts.

In 1849 the expected epidemic of cholera broke out virulently. Mortality was high in certain places, but many rural areas and some manufacturing towns were scarcely touched. Nicholls, formerly a Poor Law Commissioner and then Secretary to the Poor Law Board reported that very few cases occurred in the workhouses. He also maintained that the Union machinery proved its efficiency for other objects besides the administration of relief under the Poor Law. Poor Law expenditure in this year reached the high figure of over £6 million, but the results of the epidemic belied Nicholls' assertion. Chadwick wrote that local authorities were inept and dilatory, that action during the intervals between Boards of Guardians' meetings was slow, and there were too few skilled and responsible officers. Much was done however, he admitted, in the worst districts of the Metropolis and elsewhere in surface cleansing. The parish fire-engines were turned out and courts and alleys thoroughly washed down. For covering refuse, sodden pavements and the surfaces of close courts, fresh mould was obtained. Where this was done, he said people declared they felt themselves in a new atmosphere. Pigs were also evicted and styes were cleansed, as were stagnant ditches. Some people, where conditions were irremediably bad, were tented out, but when they returned to town they always succumbed to a slight attack of cholera so that they had to be sent back to the camps. House to house visiting was undertaken, but difficulty was experienced in finding properly qualified inspectors and in getting them into action. Chadwick maintained that the default of local authorities in organizing this

[1] Minutes, Kensington Board of Guardians for several years.
[2] Minutes, Chorlton (near Manchester) Board of Guardians, 1838.

scheme was due to the fact that Public Health service was still combined with private medical practice. He continually remonstrated against this, especially during periods of epidemics, when, he pointed out, pressure was acute for public service yet the private interests of the doctor had to predominate, and on these occasions the wealthier classes also demanded greater attention.

The activity of the Boards of Guardians and the Poor Law Medical Officers during the epidemic is best illustrated from local records. In Kensington, for example, the Medical Officers reported in January 1849 that cholera had broken out, they had previously been inspecting premises and the Guardians had purchased two horses and carts for cleansing streets and houses. Men had also been employed as scavengers at 1s. 6d. a day. The Medical Officers were asked to draw up a report when cholera came and include directions for combating its spread; this was printed and circulated among the poor (the majority of whom were probably illiterate). The Guardians appeared keenly interested in their Public Health duties, for the Medical Officers had to keep them constantly informed on progress made and they always attended Board meetings to give sanitary reports. Summonses on house-owners were frequent and individuals also furnished the Guardians with lists of unsuitable and filthy premises. Reports on the doctors' house to house inspections were forwarded to the Poor Law Board and the Board of Health, and the Guardians asked the latter for permission to drain an area, but received the reply that this was outside their powers. The three Poor Law Medical Officers on one occasion made a joint report inform-ing the Guardians of their activity in a certain court which was very densely populated, chiefly by the Irish. These, the Medical Officers said, were of filthy dissipated habits, and many had no ostensible means of subsistence save parochial relief. The court was sur-rounded by a high wall which prevented ventilation, drains were foul and offensive. As many as eight to ten people lived in one room, lying on straw or heaps of shavings, and almost destitute of food and clothing. As the Medical Officers had been authorized to take any action necessary, they had appointed a man to inspect every house to examine carefully into the state of drains, etc. so that steps could be taken to compel the owners to undertake improvements. The Medical Officers had also ordered the whole place to be flushed by the parish fire-engine and every accumulation of filth removed once every twenty-four hours because of the state of the overcrowded rooms. They had also given instructions for a ward to be appropriated at the workhouse to which people could be removed from the rooms where cholera already prevailed. Subsequently an assistant Medical Officer was employed especially for cholera patients in this court. His labours were reported to have been in-defatigable for he had to be nurse as well, as nurses were unobtainable and neighbours were apathetic. He, like all the other Medical Officers, had to supply his own medicines.

A Board of Health Inspector was also sent to Kensington to make investigations with the Medical Officers, and on his suggestion another assistant doctor was appointed in addition to health visitors. In February 1849 the epidemic was still not virulent but the Guardians looked for additional premises to which able-bodied inmates of the workhouse could be removed in case the old and new institutions had to be appropriated solely to the sick. The Poor Law Board however informed them that this was quite unnecessary if all children (sick and well presumably) were sent to a school. Unfortunately, later in the year the workhouse accommodation was needed for cholera patients, and the Board of Guardians complained to the Board of Health of the overcrowding, and therefore the danger, that existed. The local hospital—St. George's—refused to take cholera patients so that all cases entered the workhouse. The reply from the Health authorities was that its own powers were inadequate to enforce a remedy, but they communicated with the Poor Law Board on the problem and temporary premises were acquired. (Several Unions had to provide temporary accommodation; for example, in the Whitechapel Union, a warehouse in Spitalfields was converted into a cholera hospital.) The Medical Officer of Kensington workhouse ordered meat to be given four times a week, mutton broth instead of pea soup, and cocoa instead of gruel, in an effort to provide some nourishment for his patients. The Board of Health also ordered drier and more solid food should be given in the institution. Here as well as in the districts, the Medical Officer could not obtain the assistance of nurses, but the Guardians authorized him to engage women that might offer their services.

In the spring the Medical Officers sent another report on the worst district in the Kensington Union, known as the Potteries. This area had already been described in the 1838 Report of Kay and Arnott. Cottages, chiefly inhabited by the Irish, had been built over stagnant pools of water which could be seen through the cracks in the floors. In some cases the floors had given way so that parts of rooms were under water; the remainder then held the beds or straw on which families slept. It was in this district where the abattoirs were situated, and offal, blood, filth, and refuse of every description was left to decompose, for people refused to carry it away. Fevers and cholera raged here, but the Medical Officers were told that drainage and sewerage could only be remedied by the Commissioner of Sewers, to whom application was then made. To have removed the pigs would have deprived the poor of their livelihood, but the Guardians attempted it. The mortality exceeded that of St. George in the East, reported as the most unhealthy part of London. Eighty per cent of the children under fifteen died in the Potteries; one-fifth of the poor of Kensington Union lived there, yet it was responsible for half the deaths. An additional Medical Officer was employed for the district who received £3 15s. for every ten cases of cholera. In October, the Guardians suspended their action against the keeping of pigs in the Potteries because a petition had been sent by the inhabitants. The Medical Officers however remonstrated as sickness and death were still increasing, and the magistrates were implored to intervene. They pointed out that fifty-six out of sixty-one children had died and that the average age in the Potteries was 12, whereas in other working-class areas in Kensington it was 24. Pigs had been removed from one street and no case of cholera had occurred; the death rate had also declined. Even if the Potteries were drained, the Medical Officers pointed out there were so many pigs to the population and so much stench from decaying refuse, that disease would still continue and entail considerable expense on the parish. Dr. Grainger, the General Medical Inspector of the Board of Health, attended the meeting of the Board of Guardians when the Medical Officers put their case forward, and agreed with them, pointing out again that in all areas where sanitary regulations were disregarded poor rates rose steeply. In June, the Guardians wished to abolish the post of Inspector of Nuisances as cholera was abating, but the Medical Officers effectively intervened and the Inspector offered his service gratuitously. In September a fresh outbreak of the epidemic was imminent, and house to house inspection was again undertaken by the doctors and Health Visitors. Once more filthy and dangerous streets were reported, and the Guardians had them cleansed, distributed hand-bills, and ordered pigs to be removed from some mews and courts. The Medical Officers then asked for an increase in salaries because of their additional Public Health duties. During the summer quarter one Medical Officer had attended forty-two cases of cholera and 1,120 of dysentery, another Medical Officer, 740 cases of cholera, and a third 575—all over and above their normal medical duties. Salaries were £60 a year; one of them was raised to £85 but the other applications were refused. At the end of the year £30 was given as a gratuity to one doctor because he so forcefully described his harassing day and night duties as well as the heavy cost of medicines.[1]

In St. George in the East, similar provisions were made during the epidemic. One of the Coroners for Middlesex (Baker) in December 1848 drew the attention of the Guardians to the occurrence of two cases of cholera and suggested additional Medical Officers and nurses should be appointed. A committee was formed to consider future arrangements. This recommended the establishing of a temporary cholera hospital next to the workhouse with its own nurses and a Medical Officer at £30 a year, because the London hospital refused admission to cholera patients. Four hot air baths were also to be provided, one at each of the Medical Officer's surgeries, and the other at the workhouse. A scandal occurred almost immediately and Wakley held an inquiry into the 180 deaths at Tooting School. Dr. Grainger on behalf of the Board of Health described the insanitary conditions of the institution to Wakley, and his account contrasted strangely with the facts given by the Poor Law Inspector, who only pointed out that the school was subject to half-yearly inspection. Following the inquiry, the Board of Health reported on the scandal, stating that the school at the time of the epidemic held 1,400 children, and that they had on earlier occasions represented to the Guardians the necessity of removing all healthy children. They had stressed urgent and prompt action as every day of delay had added to the number of children dying. The provision of separate rooms or houses had also been recommended and that on no account should the children be transferred to the already overcrowded and dangerous workhouses. Two of the Boards of Guardians had persisted in refusing to remove the children and the daily deaths had produced no impression on them until 180 had been recorded. Then the majority of children had been removed to work-houses where over 300 had become infected with diarrhoea or cholera. After the Board's inquiry the District Medical Officer of Tooting prohibited further interment of children in the school's churchyard, and Dr. Grainger also advised bodies should not be taken through the Metropolis. St. George in the East Guardians meanwhile removed their healthy children

[1] Minutes, Kensington Board of Guardians, 1849 (whole year).

to Mitcham, but refused extra remuneration to the Medical Officer for his work among the sick who remained in Tooting.

Cholera also broke out in the workhouse in St. George, and eighteen cases were re-corded in the first week in March. Ratepayers complained to the Poor Law Board of the nuisances which existed in the front and at the back of the institution and that because of these, cholera was raging in the streets around.[1] The Guardians denied the charge, but the Board of Health intervened and asked for reports and statistics on cholera cases to be given daily. In July the Guardians, on the recommendation of Dr. Grainger, appointed two additional Medical Officers for a few weeks to supply medicines day and night to those with premonitory symptoms of cholera—they were to be paid £3 13s. 6d. each a week. The cholera hospital was at the same time ordered to be kept exclusively for cholera patients and three additional hot air baths were also provided. The chief nurse, hitherto un-remunerated, was offered 10s. a week and rations. In August the Medical Officers were requested to supply anyone who had diarrhoea with free medicine without requiring them to obtain orders for relief first. The following month the Board of Health ordered the Guardians to appoint three more doctors, and if these were not available three advanced medical students, to devote their whole time to house to house visiting, especially in the cholera infected areas. The Guardians replied that this order was unnecessary and inexpedi-ent because their arrangements were adequate, as the permanent Medical Officers made inquiries regarding symptoms of cholera. At the end of the year when the epidemic was over the three permanent doctors received gratuities of £40, £30, and £15 and the Inspector of Nuisances £10 10s.[2]

Additional Medical Officers were generally appointed during the epidemic especially in London, and from this time the practice grew up of allowing extra remuneration during periods of emergency. In Paddington the Workhouse Visiting Committee assumed the authority in 1849 of circularizing every doctor living in the district to give assistance, but the Guardians informed them all that as the appointments were so irregularly made they were not confirmed by the Board. The Visiting Committee had engaged eleven additional doctors—the Guardians appointed two.[3] In Poplar also, two temporary Medical Officers were employed, and this Union adopted the Poor Law Board's recommendation of a more solid diet. But as the Visiting Committee and the Guardians could not agree on the amended dietary, changes were constantly made and eventually the Poor Law Board asked for information on the quantity of the ingredients which were included in soup, gruel, and puddings.[4] The Guardians of St. James, Westminster, were ordered by the Board of Health to appoint three additional Medical Officers who were to devote their whole time to regular house inspection and carry medicines with them to administer on the spot to all

---

[1] People in houses neighbouring workhouses complained in several Unions on the danger of infection spreading from the institutions. Where temporary accommodation was provided in houses for infectious cases those living next to them demanded compensation.

[2] Minutes, St. George in the East Board of Guardians, 1849.

[3] Minutes, Paddington Board of Guardians, 1849.

[4] Minutes, Poplar Board of Guardians, 1849.

attacked by cholera. Further, the parochial authorities had to provide a House of Refuge for poor families who had contracted the disease.[1] Many other letters were sent by the Board of Health to Unions, and Medical Officers made long reports to them on the epidemic. In December 1849 the Metropolitan Poor Law Medical Officers estimated the number of their outdoor cases had been 4,800.

In large towns similar action was taken by the Boards of Guardians. In Bradford a Sanitary Committee was appointed to take any steps they deemed advisable for the prevention of cholera. The Relieving Officers were also authorized to select a number of women suitable as nurses to attend cholera patients.[2] Eccleshall in Yorkshire employed a team of paupers to go round removing cholera victims.[3] In Bristol the Poor Law authorities, alarmed at the prevalence of the disease, asked the Board of Health to institute an inquiry into the system of burial with a view to the abolition of intra-mural interment. They also divided the city into districts and established a cholera dispensary in each. Any person, not only poor or pauper, was at liberty to attend, and thousands of diarrhoea cases were supplied there with medicines. In the workhouse hospital four or five doctors attended cholera patients every day including Sundays. The system was said to have been far more efficient than the ordinary procedure of giving medical relief. Save where cholera attacked every member of a family, very few people sought additional assistance. An overseer pointed out that prompt intervention during the epidemic, by the affording of free medical attention to everyone, greatly curtailed the incidence of the disease, and he advocated that medical relief in times of emergency should always be given without requiring a sick person to obtain an order from a Relieving Officer first.[4] Doctors generally urged that parochial medical relief should be given to everyone in times of epidemic, for it was still the practice for Relieving Officers to visit a patient's home to inquire into his means, and all those whom the Poor Law Medical Officer attended, even if they were only temporarily assisted, were counted as paupers.

Dr. Grainger in his report on cholera made to the Board of Health in 1850, stated that the provisions laid down by legislation were for common protection against impending dangers to *all* classes, for individual means were quite inadequate. The general functions of the Guardians however, he said, related exclusively to one class—the paupers, and therefore they had at first to confine 'measures of prevention to the destitute and administer them according to the settled practice as respects the relief of paupers—which is to do nothing except on application, and then only on proof given of the urgency of the case'. (This warning to the Government and Boards of Guardians was left unheeded and in 1854 the epidemic again took its course.) The Board of Health stated that in many instances they were unable to carry into effect the beneficial intentions of the Government because of the inappropriate and inadequate machinery provided by the Public Health Act for its

[1] Minutes, St. James Board of Guardians, 1849.
[2] Minutes, Bradford Board of Guardians (Webb MSS.).
[3] Minutes, Eccleshall (Yorks.) Board of Guardians.
[4] S. Gilbert in evidence to Select Committee, 1854.

local administration. Medical Inspectors of the Board such as Drs. Sutherland and Greenhow complained that there were no real searchers in London for many disease-ridden areas. Dr. Glover revealed there were no Health Visitors in Greenwich or Deptford even when cholera was at its peak. He also pointed out that although some of the poor had been removed to the workhouse, most objected to removal even if it was for their own safety. Dr. Greenhow was told by one woman that she would rather drown herself and her children than become a pauper. No Houses of Refuge had been provided for families despite the recommendations of the Board of Health, and it was obvious that the advice of the Poor Law Board—that 'unnecessary outlay should be prevented'—had been taken. Dr. Gavin reported to the Board of Health that the Chairman of the Bethnal Green Guardians, a magistrate, had told him that the Board was 'quite sick of having charge of medical arrangements for the relief of the poor and that they would be heartily glad to get rid of it'. Gavin said the statement was made deliberately and appeared to be the unanimous feeling of the Guardians, and although it was expressed in consequence of the additional responsibility imposed on them by the prevalence of cholera, he believed the opinion to be the same with reference to the ordinary superintendence of medical relief.

The Inspectors generally reported the 'paltry pecuniary considerations' of the Guardians, and also frequently gave evidence of their incompetence. Some were not only negligent but also obstinate, and refused to execute the recommendations of the Board of Health. In Whitechapel for example, when the mortality rate was already high, the Guardians resolved that the orders of the Board of Health did not need to be acted upon by that Union. In November 1849, the Clerk of the Union laid before the Guardians the returns from four Medical Officers to the Registrars of the districts where the disease was most prevalent. In reply the Guardians resolved that the particulars could be forwarded to the various parishes, but that 'Medical Officers be *not* called upon to visit the places in question'. This move attracted the attention of Baker, one of the Middlesex Coroners, and he strongly denounced the Guardians' patent neglect. In the following months he again addressed them, saying that his attention as Coroner had been called to several cases of sudden death of the most awful and appalling character. He stated that he felt heavy responsibility lay not only on his shoulders but also on those of the Guardians. He had visited the worst affected districts and seen the suffering and death, as well as the filth, overcrowding, and bad drainage. Many lives that had been lost could have been saved if the Guardians had carried into immediate effect the Orders and Regulations of the Board of Health. After a long investigation into the circumstances of the several deaths he brought in a verdict against the Guardians of 'very great neglect'.[1]

In contrast to the inefficiency of some Boards of Guardians there was universal praise for the Poor Law Medical Officer. The report of the Board of Health in 1850 on the outbreak of cholera in the previous year was concluded with the eulogy:

[1] As Thomas Wakley was the other Middlesex Coroner (succeeded by his son Henry in 1852), Baker was probably greatly influenced by him. See Chapter 7 of *Battling Surgeon*, by Charles Brook, Glasgow, 1945.

We would call attention to the unanimous testimony borne by all classes to the exemplary manner in which Medical Officers of parishes and Unions, and medical visitors specially appointed for this service, have performed their difficult and dangerous duties. . . . Regarding the medical service of the Metropolis, Mr. Grainger writes, 'at a time when all who were able, quitted even the healthiest parts of London, the Medical Officers often debilitated by their incessant labours, and even suffering under unmistakable symptoms of the disease, never quitted their post. One surgeon did not change his clothes for eight or nine days, sleeping at intervals on a sofa, another had for eighteen days not two hours consecutive sleep . . . Their services were performed in the obscurity of dark alleys and pestilential dwellings, unseen by the public eye, frequently undervalued, always underpaid . . .'[1]

Some of the larger towns did not trust the inadequate machinery supplied under the Poor Law to combat cholera. Liverpool and Manchester, for example, set up special Medical Relief Committees. Liverpool had just recovered from a widespread outbreak of fever. General hospitals had refused admission to cases and several additional fever hospitals had been established apart from that attached to the workhouse. Besides the expenditure on hospital buildings the attack had cost £20,000 to the city in outdoor relief to the Irish alone. On this occasion, as on previous outbreaks of epidemics, the city had been taught how to cope with an unusual amount of disease. Many of its Medical Officers were engaged wholly in Poor Law work and in addition to the nine public Medical Officers twenty more were employed in 1849. These temporary doctors had the duty of visiting daily every house in their respective districts, to inquire into the existence of untreated premonitory diarrhoea or cholera, to give advice, and to transfer to hospital cases requiring institutional treatment. The local Board of Health which had been voluntarily established under the Public Health Act of 1848 provided the materials for the limewashing of courts, and the work was executed by gangs of paupers. In 1849 the Board of Health empowered the efficient Medical Officer of Health to remove either the sick or the healthy from rooms occupied by one or more families where cholera appeared. But 6,400 deaths from cholera occurred in Liverpool—outside the Metropolis the highest rate in the country. The fearful conditions which Dr. Duncan had described and was to describe in his comprehensive reports, could not be remedied in so short a time, even if vested interests had been submissive. Chadwick called the city the least healthy in Great Britain. Even in 1866, despite Duncan's work and all the improvements undertaken, he still referred to it as at the very top of the list of towns notorious for their mortality.[2] Manchester also took relief activity out of the hands of the Board of Guardians, but it was not until Dr. Sutherland was sent by the Board of Health that the city took really active measures. In October 1849 all doctors were appointed house to house visitors, and dispensaries were established under superintending Medical Officers. A table of the daily incidence of cholera showed that the rapid decline of the epidemic was

[1] Quoted by H. W. Rumsey, *Essays on State Medicine*, 1856.
[2] T. H. Bickerton, *A Medical History of Liverpool*, 1936.

exactly coincident with the new medical arrangements—but in fact the epidemic was peter-ing out all over the country by this time. In a population of 164,000, Manchester recorded a comparatively low death rate of 828 between June and November.[1] In London 14,590 died of cholera in 1849, in Bristol 1,154, in Leeds 2,323; Hull, Merthyr Tydfil and many other towns reported over 1,000 deaths. During the epidemic 53,000 died in England and Wales. Allowing for the increase in population and the defective statistics in 1832 (voluntary), not much could be said in favour of the efficiency of the new health measures. Farr compared the two epidemics, and demonstrated that the 1849 outbreak had attacked the same places as in 1832, although it had been more fatal in some and less fatal in others.[2] What had been made clear by the last epidemic was the urgent need for drastic intervention in areas where it had recurred. Dr. Sutherland showed that only 2·2 per cent of the cholera victims in the Metropolis had belonged to the gentry, 13·6 per cent to tradesmen, and 60·8 per cent to the working-class—the remainder were 'undescribed'.[3]

But once the extraordinary epidemic had disappeared the special organization and powers of prevention of the Poor Law authorities were allowed to lapse. In two years Poor Law expenditure had been reduced by £7,500,000 and much of this amount must have been due to the Guardians ceasing to take an interest in sanitary measures. No more was heard of Public Health in their meetings for the next few years. But for this legislation was in part to blame, for the Nuisances Removal Acts ceased to operate at the end of 1849. Yet what could be achieved by sanitary improvement was pointed out by Southwood Smith. In 1852 the mortality in model dwellings built through the Metropolitan Associa-tion for the Improvement of Dwellings was seven in 1,000; in the rest of London it was twenty-two per 1,000. Infant mortality was ten per 1,000 in the former and forty-six per 1,000 in the latter. He compared the health of children with those of the Potteries of Kensington, where by 1852 there was still no drainage, sanitation, or water supply. Cholera and typhus were similarly absent from the model dwellings; not a single case of cholera had appeared there in 1849, nor was there one in 1854, although there were as many as six deaths per house in the neighbourhood. Since the Lodging Houses Acts, improve-ments meant that in 1853, 25,000 people living in the 1,308 Metropolitan houses had not a single case of fever among them, whilst previously there had been as many as twenty cases in a few weeks in a single house. In Wolverhampton there were 200 lodging-houses through which over half a million people passed in a year, yet not a single case of fever had occurred since the 1852 enactment, and the police reported a similar return from Wigan.[4] A contrast to this was provided when Southwood Smith inquired with Dr. Sutherland in 1853 into an epidemic of fever in Croydon. The usual story of high mortality rates from zymotic diseases and their prevention through sanitary improvement was told, and it was also revealed that between 1845 and 1850 the death rate had risen far above what it had been

[1] *Sanitary Economics*, A. P. Stewart, 1850.
[2] W. Farr, *Report on the Mortality from Cholera in England 1848–49*, London, 1852.
[3] Sutherland's Report to the Board of Health, 1854.
[4] T. Southwood Smith, M.D., *Results of Sanitary Improvement*, London, 1854.

from 1840 to 1845.[1] Another Inspector of the Board of Health wrote a good digest of reports on forty towns in 1851 and tried to convince the authorities of the urgent need for further action:

> Is sanitary reform a thing to be accepted or rejected at will by individuals, or even by communities? Is it a subject for a show of hands, when the persons whose lives depend on the decision are mostly either ignorant, misled, or coerced? Can it be left to the ordinary principles of supply and demand? . . . By the constitution of this country no man is allowed to injure or take the life of another, or even his own life, without being branded as a felon; and therefore excessive mortality ought to be prevented, by measures compulsory on all parties without exception.[2]

The chief importance of epidemics from the Public Health point of view was that they gave impetus to sanitary reform, for real panics made an ineffaceable impression. But after 1849 the reformers were aided by the medical profession because the epidemic of that year stimulated research, and an increase in medical knowledge was an invaluable ally to combating the infectious diseases. Chadwick and the Public Health reformers believed sanitary improvements would eventually abolish all diseases—and the need for doctors—and this dictated the form of legislation and administration. Their view that zymotic disease was propagated by the filth and insanitary condition of towns was correct, and doctors corroborated the opinion. It was believed that fevers were actually caused by *mal-aria*, when in fact the poisons engendered by the organic filth were only the contributory cause. For example, Southwood Smith in his report of 1839 stated:

> the poison generated is so intense and deadly that a single inspiration is capable of producing instantaneous death, there are others in which a few inspirations are capable of destroying life in two to twelve hours,

. . . and again . . .

> in the crowded, filthy, unventilated, damp, undrained habitations of the poor . . . the poison generated, although not so immediately fatal, is still too potent to be breathed long, even by the most healthy and robust without producing fevers of a highly dangerous and mortal kind.

All fevers were also considered to have a common origin, and there was little differentiation between the various types. It was not until 1843 that William Budd differentiated between typhus and typhoid fever (independent of an American who had reached the same conclusion in 1837). Sir William Jenner's research published between 1849 and 1857 confirmed the separate identity of the two diseases and showed that typhus corresponded to the rapid malignant variety of fever and typhoid to the slow abdominal type. Twenty years elapsed,

[1] Inquiry by T. Southwood Smith and J. Sutherland on Epidemic at Croydon and Report by R. D. Grainger and Henry Austin for General Board of Health, Croydon, 1853.
[2] W. Lee, *Summary of Experience on Disease and Comparative Rates of Mortality*, 1851.

however, by which time the former was rapidly declining, before deaths from the two diseases were shown separately in the Registrar-General's Reports. Typhoid rose steadily from 1865; and from 1869, when it first appeared in the Reports, it held a steady figure for the following ten years. At the end of the 'sixties the third and smaller constituent of the group—relapsing fever, the conditions of which were known under the name of famine or seven day fever, was clearly defined. (The disease is believed to be carried by bed bugs or lice.) Diphtheria was not identified from scarlatina until the middle of the nineteenth century and in 1855 appeared for the first time in the Registrar-General's Report. The whole country was affected by an epidemic in 1856 and it was a novel condition for the medical profession. (Subsequently it has been an endemic disease.)

Budd was the first to show that typhoid was conveyed by water, and his investigations in Bristol led him to demand a pure water supply. In the teeth of medical opposition he also advocated isolation, for hospital doctors believed the spreading of infectious cases in the general wards would lessen the intensity of air contamination. In 1868 when scarlet fever was prevalent, Budd as consulting physician to the Bristol Royal Infirmary, published a document on precautions for preventing the increase of the disease in the town. As the epidemic spread the attention of Health Officers throughout the country was drawn to the memorandum. Farr however commented that although the minutest directions were given, their execution was unfortunately beyond the power of the poor, and only zealous administrators could effect adequate measures of public hygiene. He agreed that the 'soap and water' referred to was generally within the reach of the poorest.[1] Dr. Taylor of Penrith in 1858 traced the outbreak of typhoid to infected milk, and in 1870 showed scarlet fever could be spread in the same way. Dr. John Snow was acclaimed as the first to discover that cholera was a water-borne infection after his researches into the epidemics of 1849 and 1854. But the Board of Health in charge of investigating the view opposed the theory. The true method of infection was therefore suspected but it was not till the 'eighties that the cholera bacillus was identified. The long study of Pettenkofer in Munich throughout the latter half of the nineteenth century on ventilation, clothing, and soil affecting cholera and typhoid, and his views on the relation of ground water to disease, had great weight in biasing the opinions of sanitarians. The revelations of Snow, Budd, and Taylor also aided the reformers in their demands for preventive measures. Their discoveries were remarkable in that they preceded the revolution in bacteriology which scientifically demonstrated the causal organisms of cholera, typhoid and other infectious diseases.

Medical progress had therefore been made when another outbreak of cholera threatened. It appeared during the summer of 1853 in Newcastle, and the Nuisances Removal Act was—a little tardily—put into operation throughout Great Britain. The Poor Law authorities were again called into action in the Public Health field. The Poor Law Board had several interviews with the Board of Health and communication was frequent. Once again the former circulated Orders to all Unions and parishes and urged the Guardians to take

[1] Part of MSS. for 'History of the Medical Profession and its Influence on Public Health in England', Farr MSS., Vol. III.

immediate steps. The directions which they were requested to follow (signed by Chadwick and Smith) were similar to those recommended during the previous epidemic. They were to draw up a list from the Medical Officers' books of places in the Union where cases of cholera, diarrhoea, typhus, or any epidemic or endemic disease had recently been frequent. Medical Officers were to visit all places mentioned in the lists to examine houses as to cleanliness and sickness. In addition they were to inquire into the health of children in schools, of workers in their places of employment, and of inmates in common lodging-houses. Where any premonitory stage of an epidemic disease existed, they were to give or direct immediate treatment. The Medical Officers were also to certify in writing to the Guardians all places they thought dangerous to health or which required cleansing and draining. Town councils or local authorities were then to see that the scouring of streets and alleys was effected. To ensure efficient treatment to the poorer classes, the Guardians were desired to provide, on the recommendation of the Medical Officer, suitable rooms to which people attacked by cholera could be removed. Houses were to be cleansed and purified by the order of the Guardians while these people were away. Many other Orders were given and additional Medical Officers were to be employed where necessary. The Poor Law Inspectors were also directed by the Poor Law Board to communicate with, or visit Unions, to give advice on the regulations, and to co-operate personally with Guardians. They were further requested to report periodically to the central authorities. In London every workhouse was to be specially visited with a view to a reconsideration of the numbers of inmates each should accommodate.

After the first few months the Poor Law Board reported: 'We have reason to believe the Boards of Guardians generally exhibited much energy and promptitude in the adoption of necessary measures precautionary and remedial.'[1] Some Guardians undertook preventive action immediately. St. George the Martyr, Southwark, for example asked the Board of Health for permission to appoint Inspectors of Nuisances, and Paddington also engaged six additional doctors. Little was recorded in this year of the cholera itself as the attack was only slight.[2] In April 1854, however, the Board of Health sent a long notice to Guardians warning them to beware of placing too much optimism in the disappearance of cholera. A lull had been experienced in every previous epidemic and therefore they urged increased vigilance and quick action in the cleansing of houses and in improving sanitary arrangements in the Unions. The Poor Law Board also issued a Circular, again directing the Guardians to their powers and duties under the Nuisances Removal Acts, and to the importance of preventing overcrowding in the workhouses.—'*You cannot be too careful* in guarding against the slightest overcrowding.' Workhouse dietaries were also to be amended, and the drainage, cleanliness, ventilation, state of repair, and general condition of the institution were to be attended to. Guardians were, in addition, to examine the weekly returns on the state of health of the inmates and of the poor in the districts; in every case where it was necessary, they were to increase the amount of medical assistance and

---

[1] Sixth Annual Report, 1853.
[2] Minutes of several Boards of Guardians in the London area, 1853.

establish depots for dispensing medicines. On these matters immediate steps were to be taken and general precautionary sanitary measures were to be introduced also.[1]

The prophecy of the Board of Health was correct, but it had not been acted upon before the epidemic broke out again in the summer of 1854. Twenty thousand people died of cholera and half of them in London. Here there were four death rates, graded according to the foul water supply. (Simon in this year stated that the general death rate among those using the foulest water in London was 130, whilst it was thirty-seven where it had been improved.) The *Lancet* described the negligence of the Metropolitan Guardians. In Lambeth, for example, they had taken measures for sanitary improvement very inefficiently although incidence of cholera was high. They had refused to adopt the suggestions of the Board of Health regarding house to house visiting and had only had a few houses cleansed. Only two pounds of chloride of lime had been used as a disinfectant over the entire parish. During the whole period of the epidemic one solitary man had been appointed to assist each Inspector. For nearly six months there had been no dust collectors, so refuse had not been removed, and the streets were described as disgraceful. Many lives, the *Lancet* said, had been unnecessarily sacrificed, not through ignorance but parsimony.[2] Dr. Hassall, a Board of Health Inspector, reported that the Lambeth Guardians had done less in 1854 than in 1849. At the height of the epidemic there were no day or night dispensaries and no Houses of Refuge. The sole accommodation for cholera patients was two wards in the workhouse. For 140,000 inhabitants there were only nine Medical Officers and two assistants. Hassall had recommended that a dispensary be opened and nine house visitors appointed to act under the District Medical Officers, but the Lambeth Guardians had declined the suggestions. He concluded: 'The efforts of the Guardians were directed to one end—how best to evade the directions of the Central Board,' and they frequently showed direct opposition and extreme discourtesy. On Stepney, Dr. Sutherland reported the Guardians were often owners of slum property or engaged in noxious trades, so that they were interested in the perpetuation of particular nuisances.[3]

Writing on the epidemic in the *Lancet*, Rumsey pointed out the social peril of trusting any longer to 'so inadequate, so fallacious a public provision of medical care, and especially at such a time'. In his *Essays on State Medicine*, he asserted that Guardians were utterly incompetent to direct the execution of comprehensive measures of palliation and prevention during times of unusual sickness, and such times were the only sure test of their competency in ordinary circumstances. What was really required was uniform machinery, so that the multiplicity of local authorities might be abolished. The Nuisances Removal Act of 1855 again provided for eight health authorities—Local Boards of Health, Town Councils, Town Improvement Commissioners, Highway Boards, Nuisances Removal Commissioners, Boards of Lighting and Watch, and Boards of Guardians. The chief authority was the first named in this list, which existed in a town or village,

[1] Circular, Poor Law Board, 21 August 1854.
[2] *Lancet*, 1854, ii, p. 303.
[3] Reports to the General Board of Health, 1854.

but in practice all had some share in Public Health arrangements. Over a great part of the country only the Boards of Guardians existed, and everywhere the work carried out under the Nuisances Removal Acts was chargeable to the poor rate. Chadwick wrote strongly on this 'Local Mismanagement'—which still existed in the 'eighties:

> Of every two deaths from typhus one at least is due to that same government, . . . of the scourge of rheumatism more than half is now due to it, one of the results of insanitary conditions, especially diseases in childhood is due to the conditions of local misgovernment.

Rumsey in 1856 outlined a scheme for reform. He suggested new local administrative bodies should be formed with larger jurisdiction than any of the existing bodies. Sanitary districts should comprise 60,000–80,000 inhabitants—'by this means alone can Boards of Guardians be equitably dealt with'. A Civil Medico-Sanitary Service should be organized, to undertake all Poor Law medical services and Public Health duties, inspect workhouses, hospitals, and asylums. But the Government and Poor Law Board entertained no new schemes, and the new Board of Health continued the policy of its predecessors.

In 1855 a Circular was sent by the Poor Law Board to all workhouse Medical Officers enclosing a questionnaire prepared by the Board of Health. A close check was going to be kept on cholera, and Medical Officers were asked to state the number of cases of cholera occurring in the workhouses, their percentage to the inmates, the particular times of the year, whether strangers introduced it or whether it broke out in the institution, whether it existed in towns nearby, and whether it had occurred in the workhouse in 1849—stating the numbers attacked and the mortality. Similar information was required regarding typhus. Medical Officers were also asked to give particulars on the changes in sanitary arrangements which had been made between 1849 and 1855.[1]

In this year the Registrar-General reported that the population had a mortality rate above the average. In the South-East scarlatina, fevers, cholera, and smallpox were predominant and in some areas deaths exceeded births. Smallpox, scarlatina, and measles prevailed in the Midlands and the great majority of deaths in the South Midlands were occasioned by zymotic diseases which occurred in the worst drained and most densely populated localities. The North-West had cholera and typhus but no smallpox, and it was reported that the death rate had decreased in Lancashire, Cheshire, and part of Yorkshire because of the sanitary improvements. An influenza epidemic[2] attacked the Eastern Counties, and typhus the South-Western—Plymouth particularly suffered, and was described as very insanitary. Scarlatina was epidemic in the mining areas of Cornwall and this was attributed to the bad sanitary conditions and filthy lodging-houses. In the North, where vaccination was neglected, smallpox caused great suffering, and typhus, cholera, and scarlatina also occurred. In 1855 zymotic and tubercular diseases accounted for half the total

---

[1] Circular, 26 April 1855.

[2] Influenza was epidemic in 1855 and 1870 and pandemics occurred in 1843, 1847–48, and 1853, after which it declined till the end of the century, when the incidence arose again.

deaths in England—and both groups were diseases of the poor.[1] The following year saw far fewer deaths from zymotic diseases—they formed 20 per cent of the total, and tubercular diseases 21 per cent.[2] The Registrar-General's Reports demonstrated that epidemic diseases were always present in the country and occurred in severe or spasmodic form, although the public was generally ignorant of the fact.

It was for this reason that the Board of Health instituted an Inquiry into the incidence and fatality of zymotic diseases in 1857. The investigation was undertaken by Dr. Green-how, and Simon wrote the long introduction for the report. He pointed out that the accounts of the Registrar-General proved a quarter of the deaths in the country were preventable, and these resulted from the filth diseases. Between 1848 and 1856 there had been over 17,000 deaths a year from typhus: 'It is from hovel to hovel, from crowded lodging-house to crowded lodging-house that the infection of fever spreads' and Simon drew attention to its unexplained (in the 'fifties) connection with extremes of poverty and destitution, and its spread into workhouses and hospitals. Besides the 17,000 deaths there were thousands more who suffered through it or whose families were impoverished. Another quarter of the deaths per year were due to pulmonary affections—diseases, Simon said, which were tending to produce a progressive degeneration of the race because they were congenital. (The diseases were not but the weak constitutions were.) Childhood diseases between 1848 and 1855 had destroyed 300,000 children, of whom three-quarters were under five years of age. These illnesses were particularly prevalent in the Northern industrial towns and illustrated 'the very terrible possibility of an increasing weakness of life in the population of the great centres of industry'. . . . 'Other influences essentially connected with poverty tend to make all diseases more fatal in places which are thronged with a poor labouring population.' Smallpox killed nearly 5,000 a year between 1848 and 1856, and occurred most frequently in areas where mortality was highest from endemic or epidemic diseases. Simon continued that rheumatism and scurvy were not very fatal maladies, but they could also be prevented by sanitary precautions and an adequate diet. Puerperal fever was the cause of 1,500 maternal deaths in a year, out of a total number from childbirth of 3,000. This was an infectious illness against which, Simon stressed, it was criminal not to guard women by adequate ventilation and sanitation. Much insanity he argued was caused by the privation and exhaustion of disease. Health deteriorated progressively through the insalubrious conditions of homes and places of employment, and people then succumbed to mental disease. Simon believed that if adequate statistics could be produced, the greatest number of mental sufferers would have been found in areas where the largest amount of preventable disease occurred.

Crime was also closely connected with poverty-stricken and insanitary districts: 'Local circumstances which are hostile to health are likewise hostile to moral and intellectual education', and 'vice, ignorance, and brutality are among the active causes of disease'. Simon concluded that a high death rate should interest ratepayers. Sanitary neglect was

[1] Eighteenth Annual Report of the Registrar-General, 1855.
[2] Nineteenth Annual Report of the Registrar-General, 1856.

mistaken parsimony, and fever and cholera were costly items to count against the cheapness of filthy environment and ditch-drawn drinking water. Widowhood and orphanage made it 'expensive to sanction unventilated work places and needlessly fatal occupations'. The question was also important to economists, for the physical strength of the nation was no mean part of national prosperity. Greenhow's report paid great attention to occupational disease, because, he said, this was generally neglected by sanitary reformers. He allied it to housing conditions and destitution over selected districts. Actual pauperism, he maintained, was an imperfect measure of poverty, for people in receipt of parochial relief did not give a correct indication of the amount of that form of poverty which most affected Public Health. All those who were diseased, had bad food and terrible lodgings, were poverty-stricken in its real sense, for the privations of the independent poor were often worse than those of the technically destitute.[1]

Farr aided the Public Health reformers throughout the 'fifties and 'sixties by his writings and explanatory notes to the Registrar-General's Annual Returns. He pointed out that there were 712,000 deaths in thirty large towns between 1851 and 1860, exactly double the mortality of 'Healthy Districts', so that over 30,000 people died unnecessarily every year. His descriptions of the unhealthiness of towns were the same as those that had been given in the 'forties. He constantly alluded to the offensive condition of the Thames, which, he said, played a decisive part in the outbreaks of fevers and other diseases in London. In 1861 the Thames drinking water was analysed and improvements made, but in 1869 Farr was still able to give a terrible description. It was he, who gave the warning that cholera was imminent in London in 1866, because the foul water supply would not permit of the prevention of its outbreak after it had reached the country via Southampton.

Smallpox was epidemic in the Metropolis in 1863–64. Simon in a letter from the Medical Department of the Privy Council drew the attention of all Guardians to the necessity for taking special measures.[2] He suggested a close perusal of the register of successful vaccinations and the register of births, and that an inquiry should be undertaken into elementary schools and Poor Law establishments to discover the unvaccinated children. Every facility was to be provided for immediate vaccination by the Guardians, and public notices were to be put up throughout the Unions. Legal proceedings were to be taken against parents or Guardians for non-vaccination. Most Unions took precautionary measures, but the Smallpox Hospital was quickly filled, for hundreds of cases occurred every week and additional accommodation had to be provided in the workhouses. Lambeth, for example, which had done so little in earlier cholera epidemics immediately set apart two wards of the institution for isolation purposes and house to house visiting was undertaken to discover the unvaccinated.[3] St. George in the East, however, did not

[1] 'Results of Inquiry into the Different Proportions of Death produced by Certain Diseases in Different Districts in England' to the Board of Health, by E. H. Greenhow, M.D., Lecturer in Public Health at St. Thomas's Hospital and Physician to the Western General Dispensary. Introduction by J. Simon, Medical Officer of the Board of Health.

[2] April 1863.

[3] Minutes, Lambeth Board of Guardians, 1863.

even provide a temporary ward in the workhouse although smallpox was very prevalent.[1] Kensington had always had a great number of smallpox cases. In 1855 the Guardians had provided a special carriage to convey patients with infectious disease to the hospitals. This had been done at the request of the Smallpox Hospital, for the danger to the community of transporting patients in ordinary open vehicles was pointed out. During the severe outbreak of diphtheria in 1859 the Guardians had authorized Medical Officers to keep a close watch on its spread. In the late 'fifties and early 'sixties the Medical Officers had constantly urged the Guardians to have nuisances removed, and the interment hastened of those who died from infectious diseases. The new epidemic saw no undue increase in smallpox in this Union, but the Medical Officers and Public Vaccinator were requested to carry out the recommendations of the Privy Council.[2] A further letter from the Public Health authorities re-emphasized the duties of Guardians and Medical Officers, and asked for separate smallpox establishments to be provided. This was because the Smallpox Hospital and other hospitals were only able to offer beds to one-tenth of the number who should have received institutional treatment. The remainder of the smallpox patients were left in their overcrowded homes or were sent to the workhouse infirmary where they could only be imperfectly separated from other inmates. The Medical Department of the Privy Council urgently recommended Unions, especially in the East End where the epidemic was worst, to combine for the provision of a separate isolation hospital with its own staff of doctors and nurses. Dr. Buchanan, the Inspector of Public Vaccination in London, made a report on the epidemic and this was circulated by the Poor Law Board to all Metropolitan Boards of Guardians. He drew attention to the inadequate hospital accommodation, for the Smallpox Hospital would only receive thirty-two patients a week, and the result of admitting cases to other hospitals, in violation of the express rule for their exclusion, was disastrous. Over thirty deaths per week from smallpox occurred in London during the first quarter of 1863; by the end of April this doubled, and Buchanan pointed out that as the disease gathered in intensity, the vaccinated were attacked as frequently as the unvaccinated.

Typhus also broke out in the Metropolis in 1863–64. The Lambeth Guardians explained its prevalence in their Union by the great overcrowding, which had been accentuated by the demolition of houses for the building of a railway.[3] Great reluctance was expressed by Guardians to admit patients into the workhouses, and all tried to obtain beds in hospitals for their cases. St. George in the East fitted up the oakum room in the stoneyard of the workhouse as a fever ward for twenty-two typhus victims![4] But the epidemic was more virulent in the North. Liverpool for example lost 1,165 people in 1836 from typhus, 1,174 in 1864, and 2,336 in 1865. In Newcastle nearly £1,700 was spent on account of the typhus epidemic between 1863 and 1866. The *Lancet* pointed out the economic aspect. In 1863 twenty-seven males over the age of 20 died, in 1864 thirty-six, in 1865 seventy-four, and in

[1] Minutes, St. George in the East, 1863–64.
[2] Minutes, Kensington Board of Guardians, 1863–64.
[3] Minutes, Lambeth Board of Guardians, 1864.
[4] Minutes, St. George in the East.

1866 eighty-seven. For every death there were five cases of illness, so that there were 1,120 men not working for six to twelve weeks at an average wage of 20s. a week. Therefore the loss in weekly earnings equalled £10,000. The number of orphans and widows rendered permanently chargeable to the poor rate, owing to the death of fathers or husbands were 474 and cost nearly £1,900 a year, so that over five years, poor relief on this account was more than £9,000. From these data the *Lancet* deduced typhus cost Newcastle £20,000. Yet in this great commercial centre of the North-East, a singular reluctance was shown to adopting remedial measures, and the apathy towards sanitary reform was hardly equalled anywhere.[1]

Distress and disease were particularly widespread in the North in the early 'sixties because of the cotton famine. In 1863, Inspector Farnall was detailed as Special Commissioner of the Poor Law Board to make an inquiry into the twenty-seven Unions comprising the cotton manufacturing districts and report on the health of the operatives.[2] Reports were received from 117 Poor Law Medical Officers. Scarlatina of a virulent nature prevailed in some districts, and smallpox was epidemic in others, such as Stockport, Manchester, Burnley, Ashton, and Warrington. On the whole, Medical Officers stated that their districts were 'healthy' but that people were debilitated, recuperated slowly, and that there was a gradual physical degeneration. Additional medical fees for extra duties in these Unions amounted to £1,250 above the normal rate. Robert Rawlinson, who was Consultant Engineer to the Poor Law Board and keenly interested in the Poor Law medical service (see papers to the Social Science Association), reported in 1866 on the public works instituted in the cotton manufacturing districts.[3] The Public Works (Manufacturing Districts) Act of 1863 had offered legal powers specially designed to meet the requirements of towns.—It had a dual object, public utility and sanitary improvement, and employment for indigent factory operatives. Where it had been put into force results were good—roads were paved or built, land was drained and rivers cleared. But much remained to be done, for the scheme had progressed but slowly. More relief was paid in the worst districts in a year than it would have cost to erect new houses and completely remodel districts. Rawlinson described the defective nature of the local Improvement Acts, and the 'general filth produced by apathy and occasionally dissipation and despair'. Consumption, he said, prevailed in excess, and epidemic diseases reduced entire families to pauperism for life.— 'This round of sanitary neglect, producing filth, misery, drunkenness, disease, pauperism, and sometimes crime, is as consequent and certain as any other form of cause and effect.'

The general mortality rate had risen throughout the whole country in the early 'sixties, and fevers had been endemic. In 1865 cholera broke out again and the 1860 Nuisances Removal and Diseases Prevention Act was put into operation. Fewer Boards of Guardians were by this time in charge of palliative and preventive measures, but where none of the new local authorities existed, they were still the Public Health bodies, and costs were

---

[1] *Lancet*, 1867, i, p. 499.
[2] 4 November 1863.
[3] Report to the Poor Law Board, January 1866.

defrayed out of the poor rates. The new Act added powers to those given to health authorities by earlier measures. A carriage was to be provided for conveying sufferers from infectious disease to the workhouse or hospital, and a doctor had to be engaged to make inquiries and report on sanitary conditions, for which he was to be remunerated. In many areas therefore the duties of a Medical Officer of Health and a Poor Law Medical Officer overlapped. When the Act was put into force the Poor Law Board issued instructions to the Metropolitan Guardians to undertake cleansing and the removal of nuisances on the recommendations of Medical Officers. Additional clothing and food were also to be given to the sick poor. Copies of the regulations were sent to all Unions in the country so that they could be acted upon immediately if the epidemic spread. (They were to wait until the epidemic was upon them before preventive steps were taken!) A further Circular forbade the admission of cholera cases into workhouses—but there was no mention of the provision of temporary accommodation. The Guardians were to engage additional Medical Officers where the emergency made it necessary and the Poor Law Board sanctioned additional payment to doctors for extra duties.

The Kensington Guardians in conjunction with the Vestry set up a Committee of Health to take over the work previously done during epidemics by the Guardians. Before the appearance of cholera three Poor Law doctors were appointed as Medical Visitors and were paid £2 a day. Arrangements were made for the provision of gratuitous advice and medicine at two hospitals, and three temporary stations were established. Public notices were issued giving full directions as to how and where to apply in case of need. Workmen were employed to cleanse privies, sinks, and gullies, to sweep roads, and cart away the accumulations of refuse. Some 620 notices were served and forty-three summonses, with the result that houses were whitewashed and cleansed, rubbish dumps removed, drains and cesspools purified, and various other nuisances abolished. This was all done prior to the appearance of cholera![1] St. George in the East converted the Wapping workhouse, which had been rented from Limehouse, into a cholera hospital to which patients might be transferred if the infirmary wards of the workhouse were filled. This also was arranged before the actual outbreak of the epidemic. But in the summer of 1866 cholera and diarrhoea raged and the workhouse Medical Officer had to ask for an assistant. Cholera nurses were employed at 15s. a week because there were not enough pauper nurses. The vagrant ward was appropriated to provide additional room for cholera patients. Dozens of new cases appeared every week and Medical Officers were urged to issue free medicines without orders being required from the Relieving Officer first. There were so many deaths that not enough coffins could be obtained. The Guardians were however very active and by the end of the year the epidemic was over in St. George in the East.[2] Throughout the Metropolis precautionary and palliative measures had increased in efficiency, so that the epidemic

[1] Minutes, Kensington Board of Guardians, 1866.

[2] Minutes, St. George in the East, Board of Guardians, 1866. On one occasion thirteen corpses were conveyed in an open cart through the Parish from the workhouse to the cemetery—for which the Guardians severely reprimanded the undertaker.

was short-lived. An additional salutary factor had been the increase in the competence and the number of nurses. Besides adding to the workhouse staff, many Unions had empowered their Medical Officers to employ 'district nurses' and the Guardians paid for them.

Although cholera spread into the country it was far less virulent than on former occasions. Fourteen thousand people succumbed, but in large towns the new local health authorities or town councils were undertaking improvements under the influence of the Medical Officers of Health. In these areas greater efficiency was shown in combating cholera and other infectious diseases than in places where Guardians remained the Nuisances Removal authorities. In Leeds, although a Nuisances Committee existed, the Guardians performed their duties, and they had been extremely efficient in the early 'sixties in attending to defects pointed out by the Medical Officers. During the cholera epidemic they constituted themselves into a Committee for carrying out the Diseases Prevention Act. Two Inspectors were advertised for at 28s. a week each, four Medical Officers were appointed as Medical Superintendents in their respective Poor Law districts at 6 guineas a week plus 8s. for cab fares, and the old workhouse was adapted as a hospital. The Guardians also appointed a Sub-Committee to confer with the nuisance authority of the Town Council. The Poor Law officials naturally felt flattered and pleased that they had been called upon to take action because they had expected the whole work to devolve on the Town Council.[1]

This was the last epidemic of cholera, although it remained endemic for some decades. In 1869 scarlet fever broke out in the Metropolis, but the provisions made by the Metropolitan Asylums Board both in their two permanent fever hospitals and in the temporary accommodation, curtailed what would have been a serious epidemic. The large industrial towns suffered also. In Liverpool, cases of fever rose from 138 a week in June 1870 to 1,375 a week by October, when the epidemic began to decline. A large fever hospital was provided next to the workhouse into which nearly 100 cases a week were admitted in 1869. In 1870 twenty other fever hospitals were established and a school was also converted for the emergency. Added to this, nearly 2,000 paupers were given medical relief every week in their homes.[2] Inspector Cane reported the arduous work imposed on the Guardians in the northern industrial towns and the satisfactory way in which duties were performed. Everywhere additional accommodation for the poor was provided where it was urgently required. Farr, however, pointed out the excessive mortality in certain towns, like Bristol and Northampton, and that 'by some culpable negligence deaths have been allowed to exceed births, and measles, diarrhoea, and scarlet fever, among other diseases, have raised mortality to an annual rate of forty-three in 1,000'.[3]

No sooner had the fever epidemic abated when smallpox reappeared, first in London and then in various parts of the country. (The spread of epidemics was swift in an age of rapidly increasing mobility.) Dr. Bridges, a Poor Law Inspector, maintained great value would

---

[1] *Leeds Intelligencer*, August 1856, January 1863; *Leeds Mercury* 28 July 1866.
[2] Report of Inspector Cane to the Poor Law Board, 1870, on the North-West Region.
[3] Annual Report of the Registrar-General, 1869.

have accrued from a systematic registration of contagious diseases if this had been under-taken by the Poor Law Medical Officers under the supervision of the Poor Law administra-tion, for many weeks would have been gained for preventive measures. Once again during the epidemic Poor Law Medical Officers made house to house visits to discover the un-vaccinated, and they found a tremendous number.—The nine Medical Officers appointed in St. George in the East for example, found 800, despite the fact that the Vaccination Act had been passed in 1867 to consolidate the provisions of 1840 and 1853, and to establish special machinery for enforcing compulsory vaccination. A great deal of outdoor medical advice had to be given but everywhere attempts were made to provide institutional relief. In London, the Metropolitan Asylums Board used its two hospitals at Stockwell and Homerton, but despite these and the temporary accommodation provided, the incidence of the disease and the mortality was high—nearly 8,000 people died. In the provinces, additional isolation facilities were obtained by the Poor Law authorities as well as by the local Health Boards. But Inspector Cane pointed out that 'the establishment of hospital accommodation and measures for preventing the spread of infection, except regarding pauper patients are matters which more properly come under the jurisdiction of the authorities appointed for the purpose of the sanitary Acts'.[1]

By this time it was realized that the overlapping of the Poor Law and Public Health services in sanitary and medical fields was not conducive to maximum efficiency. Not only were the numerous local health authorities sometimes responsible to a chief organizing body, but often they were each in charge of a particular department, upon which none of the others could encroach. Administrative chaos existed everywhere. In the central administration, not only was the Public Health authority in an anomalous position, but its functions integrated with those of the Poor Law Board. For example, by the Act of 1858 the Privy Council was to undertake vaccination duties supplementary to those of the destitution authorities. Whilst the Poor Law Board had formal control over vaccination contracts, the Privy Council was to give medical advice, and regulate and supervise the service. (This dual government was not found to work well, especially as the Medical Department of the Privy Council introduced Vaccination Inspectors to report on the work of the Poor Law Medical Officers who were generally the vaccinators.) The activities of the two administrations were necessarily closely interrelated as one was interested in preventive medicine, the other in curative, and their duties for the greater part affected the same classes of people, those of the former the poor and those of the latter the pauper. On the efficiency of the Medical Officer of Health to a great extent, depended the amount of work the Poor Law Medical Officer was required to perform. As one-sixth of the annual deaths came under the destitutes' doctor although only one-twenty-fifth of the popula-tion were paupers, he was, as we have seen, keenly interested in Public Health as well as in the reform of the system to which he was attached. Sometimes the views of the two public servants clashed, as in Manchester where the very capable Medical Officer of Health Dr.

[1] Report to Poor Law Board on the North-West Region, 1870.

Leigh, who had himself throughout the 'forties and 'fifties been a Poor Law Medical Officer, attempted to have all infectious cases removed to hospital. Such powers of transfer were not enjoyed by the Guardians, and Leigh suggested Simon should be approached. The Poor Law doctors disagreed with the scheme and the Privy Council declined the petition of the Town Council.[1] On the need for sanitary and housing reforms however, Public Health and Poor Law views coincided, especially as Manchester still had 60,000 open cesspools in 1885 and one-sixth of the mortality in the late 'sixties was caused by five infectious diseases. The environment of both Medical Officer of Health and Poor Law Medical Officer was the same; they covered the same garbage laden streets, saw the same overcrowded and filthy houses, and one wrote of, and the other dealt with, the consequences of bad drainage, polluted water, and inadequate sewerage.[2]

It was for this reason and because the specialization in the functions of the Poor Law officers was too big for single classification under the Poor Law Board, that from the 'fifties onwards some of the pioneers of social medicine agitated for the fusion of the Public Health service and the Poor Law medical service, and the combination of the duties of Medical Officer of Health and Poor Law Medical Officer. Foremost in this movement was Rumsey, who for forty years advocated medical poor relief should be dissociated from the administration of the Poor Law and merged into a general Public Health system. He tried to impress on the Select Committee of 1844 that Boards of Guardians were utterly incompetent to direct the execution of comprehensive preventive and curative measures. He wished to see a national provision of medical relief, the cost of which, he said, would amount to only a minute fraction of what the country paid annually for the loss of life and general health arising from the insufficient care of the working-classes. But he also mentioned the moral issues—that health was the basis of social virtues. He therefore advocated the establishing of a National Board of Health (reserving certain powers to the Poor Law authorities) and local boards, which should combine the administration of medical aid with the sanitary care of the population. The duties of a District Medical Officer would be the prevention as much as the cure of disease. He should constantly represent to the new health authority the removable sources of disease, and should be responsible for the adoption of measures to combat the spread of epidemics. He should also be the district vaccinator and should visit the houses of the working-classes and report periodically on their condition. It would be both his duty and in his interest to advise the poor on their physical management such as clothing, bedding, food, cleanliness, and care of the sick and to suggest such domestic improvements as they could effect themselves. Engineers, architects, and surveyors were necessary assistants, but Rumsey maintained that the great reform which was needed had to be directed by the doctor. The new District Medical Officer should also

[1] Long report of Medical Officer of Health to Manchester City Council Health Committee, 1870. Leigh was the first Medical Officer of Health and was not appointed until 1868. His scheme for compulsory isolation of every case of infectious disease was in later years widely discussed and acted upon.

[2] Salaries were however very different: a Medical Officer of Health generally received more than £100 a year—£300 in large cities; few Poor Law Medical Officers received £100.

superintend the public dispensary which he hoped would be established. Medicines should be supplied to the poor at public expense, and where this was impracticable, the Medical Officer should be paid separately for them. When sick, the poor should be provided freely and promptly with medical aid without any official investigation or stigma of pauperization.

The general duties of the Guardians were incompatible with the reforms Rumsey advocated, their policy also had to be based on retrenchment of expenditure, and they had enough work in their own sphere without medical and sanitary responsibilities being added. Further, the majority of Guardians lacked the information (and often the education and intelligence) which would be required, for they were a body elected from the ratepayers. Rumsey's local authority was to consist of persons of educated and enlightened views—magistrates, clergymen, chairmen of Boards of Guardians, architects, engineers, lawyers, and doctors from the locality. They were to have compulsory powers, and control all sanitary and medical matters. One paid medical referee was to be appointed who should be a leading practitioner of the area and whose duty it would be to attend the meetings of the Board, give advice and assistance in the execution of sanitary improvement, and form the medium of communication between the District Medical Officers and the Health Board. The Medical Officers were to be selected, and in greater numbers, by the Board and not by the Guardians—a reform, Rumsey maintained, which would be hailed with delight not only because they had a strong repugnance to being controlled by an unprofessional body, but also because they were afraid of pointing out the sanitary and medical improvements necessary, as these touched the Guardians' own, or the Union's finances. A Board might also appoint a civil engineer or surveyor to be present at the meetings in an advisory capacity. Rumsey also urged the provision by his proposed new authorities of public baths and a supply of well-trained nurses and properly educated midwives for the poor. The Boards should examine Registrars' reports and direct the vaccination of children, and should receive reports from local charities and hospitals. He recommended that the authorities should be co-extensive in their sphere of action with Boards of Guardians, the two bodies should co-operate for the benefit of the poor, but all medical and sanitary work should be vested in the Boards of Health. Funds for the health services should be raised by a separate rate and expenditure controlled entirely by the local Board under the control of a central authority.

The Provincial Medical and Surgical Association of which Rumsey had been a leading member, had in its 1841 Report urged the necessity for instituting sanitary boards especially in large towns. But the strongest objection was expressed, not only against the delegation of functions to Boards of Guardians, but also to the subjection of any officers responsible for Public Health to the control and authority of the Poor Law Commissioners. The report suggested that a Board of Health be formed in each town consisting of all medical practitioners and well-educated people. Ceely, also a member of the Provincial Medical and Surgical Association, had given evidence to the Select Committee of 1838 on the desirability of giving Medical Officers the power of inspecting for nuisances and the authority to report on the sanitary state of the neighbourhood. A Medical Officer of

Whitechapel impressed on the Select Committee of 1844 the necessity of making the Poor Law Medical Officer a Public Health officer, and that he should be engaged full-time in Union duties. He should also be the District Registrar and see every deceased person before registering him so that correct returns on the cause of death could be made. (At this time tradesmen were often Registrars and made very inaccurate returns.) In 1848 Lord Ashley included sanitary duties in his motion in the House of Commons for the appointment of Poor Law Medical Inspectors.[1] Dr. Leigh, the future Medical Officer of Health of Manchester, suggested a similar scheme to the Select Committee of 1854 and added that Medico-Sanitary Inspectors should be itinerant and should occasionally examine houses. Further, he recommended local Inspectors be drawn from resident Poor Law Medical Officers. Charles Kingsley, who all his life was devoted to improving the health of the people, and who as we have seen, keenly interested himself in the Poor Law medical services, also wished to see Poor Law doctors become Public Health officers, as they understood the dangers which threatened health better than any Nuisance Inspector or Improvement Committee.[2]

By the mid 'fifties the Poor Law–Public Health movement had grown. The Convention of Poor Law Medical Officers proposed a medical department should be established to conduct medical relief for the poor and Public Health work under a Minister of Health responsible to Parliament. This Minister was not required to be a medical man but was to be chosen for his wide and comprehensive views on preventive and curative medicine. The officers of the central department would have complete responsibility over State medicine for the poor, sanitation, vaccination, and registration, and the Poor Law Medical Officer would be fused with the Sanitary Inspector. Dr. Wallis who propounded a new medical relief scheme to the Select Committee of 1854, also wished to see the creation of a Central Medical Board which should be the Public Health Board as well. Rumsey had by this time elaborated his schemes. His research had revealed that half the Poor Law medical relief could be reduced by improved sanitary management. He pointed out in his *Health and Sickness of Town Populations* and to the Select Committee of 1854, that Guardians had not shown themselves ardent promoters of sanitary improvement, and had only acted partially on the recommendations of the Board of Health during the epidemic of 1849. The Board had admitted in one of its reports that Guardians were not the best possible auxiliaries, but had inferred that as the community became more intelligent the Guardians would fulfil their duties more efficiently. Therefore Rumsey again deprecated local Poor Law authorities being responsible for Public Health matters, and he now advocated that his new Boards of Health should no longer be co-extensive with Unions, but should embrace far wider areas, which in their turn should be integrated by a regional supervising Board with Medical Inspectors appointed as representatives of the district Boards. Rumsey drew attention to

[1] House of Commons, 16 March 1848.

[2] In Ireland the Poor Law Commissioners were the Board of Health, and the Medical Officers of Health were the legislative offspring of the Inquiries of the Select Committee of the House of Commons of 1819 on 'The State of Disease and Condition of the Labouring Poor in Ireland'. A Medical Officer of Health had been established in Dublin at that time.

the Poor Law Medical Officers having become sanitary officers under the Nuisances Removal Acts, which proved that Public Health and sickness could not be ultimately separated. Local dispensary boards had also been established, and he advocated that the Central Board of Health should control these and all medical relief. For as long as they were provided by the Boards of Guardians under the direction of the Poor Law Board so would pauperism be promoted in the country. But the Central Board should be reformed, for he accused the existing authority of neglecting and imperfectly managing the medical matters for which they were already responsible. Medical inspection should be instituted and this was to include sanitary as well as purely medical duties, so that prevention and cure could be supervised together. Expenditure should be increased, parsimony would not diminish pauperism caused by sickness, whilst enlarged and comprehensive measures would protect and maintain the health of the poor, thereby enriching the community. The Medical Officers should have special qualifications regarding their new sanitary duties, and should intervene early in disease, giving treatment if possible at the symptomatic stage. Also morbific agencies should be removed before illness actually ensued. The salaries of the Poor Law Medical Officers at the time made it impossible, Rumsey admitted, to call on them to perform any further duty, but as health improved through increased Public Health arrangements, so medical duties would diminish. It would therefore be in the interest of every public doctor to improve the sanitary condition of his district. Salaries should be raised, however, and the size of a Medical Officer's area reduced. He did not advocate what Chadwick urged for fifty years, that the Poor Law Medical Officer should be wholly engaged in public duties so that he might attend to Public Health problems as well.

The ideas of Chadwick and Rumsey collided at this time. Chadwick had first pointed out the advantage of employing Poor Law Medical Officers in sanitary duties, Rumsey desired them to be more than common informers and advocated they should inquire into clothing, nursing, occupational disease, and adulteration and decay of food of the poor. Rumsey's criticism of Chadwick was that he was responsible for introducing into the administration of Public Health the deterrent policy of the Poor Law. A Medical Officer he said, 'should be not merely a public informer, but . . . in a peculiar sense a Missionary of Health in his own district . . . instructing classes in personal and domestic hygiene and practically proving to the helpless and debased, the disheartened and the disaffected, that the State cares for them—a fact which until of late, they have seen but little evidence'.[1] Rumsey earnestly recommended public lectures should be given and libraries opened for the purpose of instructing people on such matters as home nursing and cleanliness.[2] His more positive policy desired to carry Public Health to its logical conclusion of embracing many social services for producing healthy and useful citizens in the widest sense.

[1] *Essays on State Medicine* and Letter sent to the Manchester Statistical Society, 1865. A great number of papers were read or sent to this Society at this time on Public Health and many eminent physicians collaborated —see *Transactions* from 1853 to 1875: there were forty-five Public Health and Poor Law papers.
[2] *Ibid.*

To Simon also, sanitary laws and administration meant not only the saving, but the strengthening of life. He was not involved however in the movement for Poor Law–Public Health reform, save that in 1849 he had urged on the Metropolitan authorities that Poor Law Medical Officers could be advantageously employed in sanitary duties. He elaborated the point in 1854 in his *Sanitary Condition of the City of London*, for he realized that 'although disease and destitution are treated under different headings in the statute-book, their reciprocal relations, their relations as cause and effect to each other are among the important facts which a student of Sanitary Science has to remember'.

In 1858 Rumsey criticized the new Health Bill as he had criticized the Nuisances Removal Act of 1855. He opposed the existence and continuation of the seven alternative local health authorities,[1] and agreed with the evidence given on the Bill by Hawkesley, the engineer and Public Health reformer, when he suggested that Boards of Guardians were better local health bodies than the other six.

> Town Councils [Hawkesley said] do not come into communication constantly with the poor, or rather the working class, for whose benefit . . . this bill is principally promoted . . . The Medical Officers of the Boards of Guardians constantly visit the poorer classes and altogether are in my opinion much fitter bodies for the initiation of proceedings of this kind than Town Councils; and inasmuch as these councils do not exist everywhere, and as Boards of Guardians, as nearly as possible, do exist everywhere, and as it is desirable to have one single form of proceeding, and one well-known body all over the Kingdom, to carry out purposes of this kind, I think it very much better that Boards of Guardians should have the powers rather than Town Councils.[2]

The Nuisances Removal Act of 1860 virtually converted the District Medical Officer into a Medical Officer of Health. The *Lancet* expressed great objection. A leading article maintained this would mean a Poor Law doctor coming into collision at every move with his employers, and would also constitute the creation of a monopoly.[3] The Poor Law Medical Officers' Association agreed with the provisions of the Act, and Griffin, giving evidence on their behalf in 1862, deprecated the negligence of local authorities in putting it into practice.[4] Only London and a few other towns had complied because the clauses were permissory, and expense acted as a deterrent.—'Let the Poor Law Medical Officers be made

[1] The seven bodies set up by the Act as sanitary authorities were:
  1. Local Boards under the 1848 Act.
  2. Town Councils.
  3 Improvement Commissions.
  4. Highway Boards.
  5. New local authorities—Nuisances Removal Committees to be appointed by Vestries.
  6. Boards for Lighting and Watching
  7. Guardians and Overseers in single parishes.
The first on the list that happened to exist in each place was to constitute the sanitary authority.
  [2] Quoted by Rumsey in his *Sanitary Legislation and Administration in England*, 1858.
  [3] *Lancet*, 1860, i, p. 473.
  [4] Select Committee on Poor Relief, 1862.

sanitary officers', he said, and 'in a short time the mass of information collected will cause the public to do its duty and remove the causes of disease.' He described the back alleys and courts, drains and cesspools which still existed everywhere and indirectly kept the poor rates high. He repeated that preventive medicine was cheaper than curative, and urged that no man was better suited to be a sanitary officer than the Poor Law Medical Officer, for he alone was conversant with every corner of his district. The doctors did comment on the state of their areas, he asserted, but Guardians ignored them. Every case book demonstrated where disease increased or death ensued through insanitary dwellings, but Guardians had done nothing. He therefore suggested Poor Law Medical Officers should make half-yearly statistical reports of diseases and forward these for classification to a proposed Medical Secretary of the Poor Law Board. Half-yearly accounts were already given to the Poor Law Board by each Union of the numbers receiving medical relief, but these were never published, nor did they classify diseases. In 1857, for example, 136,000 sick were attended by Poor Law Medical Officers, but the nature of the complaints were not revealed. The Registrar-General had done much, to lessen the mortality rate, but no individual record was given of the diseases affecting the poor, so that no public intervention was possible to prevent disease and reduce mortality. Griffin therefore desired his proposed Medical Inspector to present the Poor Law Medical-Sanitary Officers' reports to Parliament, after classification, so that public attention could be attracted to the subject.

Rumsey had advocated the registration of disease in his *Essays on State Medicine* in 1856. He desired records to cover sporadic attacks of infectious diseases as well as epidemics, and they should include all local and physical circumstances connected with sickness. Machinery was at hand, he said, in the District Medical Officer, who could be of great value to medical science. As the poor were always the first victims of a prevailing disease, their medical advisers were the obvious people to report the facts, as well as to carry out the preventive measures, The Epidemiological Society, which had been formed in 1851 for investigating into epidemic disease as to cause, prevention, and mitigation, estimated in 1864 that there were twenty to thirty cases of sickness for every death, but pointed out that no reliable data were at hand to determine the truth of this statement. Machinery for the purpose existed in the Army and the Navy, and the Society recommended that what had been done with such good results for the armed forces, was equally applicable to the pauper population, and would be productive of similar beneficial results. Further, the material in Medical Officers' books only required collection and arrangement to render them the most instructive registers on a large scale. The Secretary prepared a simple scheme for Union doctors and the Poor Law Board whereby monthly returns could be made giving tables of diseases, sex, age groups, and the number of new and old cases.[1]

But the Poor Law Amendment Acts of 1866 and 1867, and the Sanitary Act of 1866, as all previous legislation, ignored the advice of reformers on the Poor Law–Public Health question. The latter reiterated and added to previous Nuisances Removal Acts—temporary

[1] Select Committee, 1864: Letter from President and Secretary of the Epidemiological Society to the Select Committee on 'Statistics of Disease among the Pauper Population in England and Wales'.

hospitals could be provided, and magistrates could order the removal to such an institution of any person suffering from dangerous infectious disease if lodgings were unsuitable or overcrowded. It was also the first Act to apply compulsion to Public Health provisions: '*The grammar of common sanitary legislation acquired the novel virtue of an imperative mood.*'[1] The work of Simon, Chadwick, Shaftesbury—and Florence Nightingale—had to a large extent been rewarded, but the chaos of local authorities remained. At the end of the 'sixties there were more than 114 bodies of Improvement Commissioners and 670 local Boards of Health.—'No exact line can be drawn between bodies established for paving, cleansing, lighting, and watching, and those for maintaining turnpike roads, constructing bridges, erecting markets, effecting street improvement, improving harbours, or draining land.' Even at this time Improvement Commissioners were inextricably confused with municipal corporations or vestries, Poor Law authorities or church building trustees.[2] After another nuisance authority was created in rural parishes in 1868, Simon said privies were under one authority and pigsties under another.

The complication of statutes and authorities had become intolerable. The first public remonstrance came from the medical profession and once again it was Rumsey who was the leading voice. It was at his instigation that in May 1868 a joint Committee of the British Medical Association and the Social Science Association memorialized the Government for a Royal Commission. They proposed an inquiry should be made into the compilation of Public Health statistics, coroners' inquests, the operation and administration of sanitary laws, sanitary organization, and the revision and consolidation of the laws.[3] The Royal Commission desired to appoint Assistant Commissioners to carry out extensive research, but Gladstone's Government quickly succeeded Disraeli's and the Treasury refused to grant additional money for such purposes. It was therefore said that the 'Sanitary Commission . . . reported in the dark, they had no means of knowing how far the existing organizations of the country were fitted for the work they had to do'.[3] The Report of the Committee (1871) was however the first account of English local government and disclosed the chaos of authorities, rates, and areas, and also the complete confusion at the centre. It recommended consolidation, universal and uniform under a Minister, a composite

[1] J. Simon, *English Sanitary Institution*, 1890, p. 300.

[2] *Laws relating to Sewers and Drains*. Alex Macmorran and W. A. Willis, 1904. Speaking regarding the late 'sixties and early 'seventies.

[3] The following points were in the late 'sixties put forward as the Social Science Association's demands for reform. (1) Repeal of existing laws and re-enactment in one statute of compulsory application. (2) Division of whole country into health districts. (3) Local Boards of Health be elected like Town Councils. (4) New Union Board for each county: chosen representatives of each Health Board in area. (5) Ministry of Health—general control, attached to it general Medical Officer of Health and staff of legal, medical, and engineering inspectors. (6) Medical Officer of Health, clerk, and surveyor, whole time to duties of areas. (7) Rearrangement of rating and borrowing. (8) Registration of sickness, births, and deaths—duty of new Medical Officer of Health. Central Office of Registration appended to Health Ministry. (9) Ample powers for water-supply, sewers, control of building, vested in new local authority.—See Sessional Proceedings of the National Association for the Promotion of Social Science, 1870–71. Paper read by W. H. Michael, 29 March 1871. This body was generally referred to as the 'Social Science Association'.

[3] Poor Law Conference, 1876—in discussion.

inspectorate, a Chief Medical Officer with an expert staff, and a local Medical Officer of Health. The network of 3,000 District Medical Officers with which the Poor Law Board had covered the country were for the most part to become the Medical Officers of Health for their respective districts. Both the Poor Law medical service and the Public Health Service were thereby to be united into a single rate-supported medical service with sanitary and preventive objects.

The report was received with almost unanimous approval and was accepted by the Government—but instead of a Ministry of Health for which Simon and others agitated, the country in 1871 got the Local Government Board. This absorbed all other boards which had previously acted autonomously and the Poor Law Board. The fear of the propertied classes stripped the Public Health Act of all but its organization features, and the omitted clauses were not enforced until 1875. From the Public Health side the Act showed the same negative qualities as previous enactments. Supply was trying to catch up with demand racing ahead, and which only a really new and constructive policy could satisfy. Environmental hygiene had not developed supplementary policies and Public Health work was to remain an engineering job. Therefore personal medical care was sorely neglected and the fusion between the Poor Law medical services and Public Health remained nominal.

Divergent opinions on the relation between the two services were voiced by all the leaders of the movement for the development of social medicine. Some criticized the union of the health authorities with the Poor Law Board: 'the functions seem to be essentially different. In one case judicious restraint appears to be the principal factor, in the other judicious enlargement and development of action.'[1] Simon considered Poor Law medical questions should have been taken out of the hands of the destitution authorities because of their rigid control over finance and the reliance of the Boards of Guardians on non-medical officers in these problems.[2] A meeting of the Social Science Association, at which Shaftesbury presided, heard the opinion that Guardians had been completely incompetent to deal with Public Health matters, and that medical relief for the poor could not be mixed with measures necessary for disease prevention. It was maintained that the degradation of the whole Public Health system would result from a President of the destitution authorities being the Health Minister, as the influence of the Poor Law would lead to under-estimation and the relegation of vital problems to the status of mere appendages to poor relief.[3] Rumsey approved of the new measures relating to Public Health improvement, the definition of areas, the appointment of Medical Officers of Health, and the complementary compilation of vital statistics by Poor Law and Public Health authorities. He also welcomed the stipulation that highly qualified experts were to be appointed and believed an improved organization of medical poor relief would ensue.[4] Dr. Child advocated a

[1] Sir A. Helps, *Social Pressure*, 1878.
[2] *English Sanitary Institutions*, 1890.
[3] Sessional Proceedings of the National Association for the Promotion of Social Science, 1870–71. Paper read by W. H. Michael, 29 March 1871.
[4] *Summary of Principle of Comprehensive measure for improvement of Sanitary Laws*, 1872.

closer fusion between sanitary and Poor Law services, and the union of Medical Officer of Health, public vaccinator, certifying factory surgeon, District Registrar and Poor Law Medical Officer to make this doctor essentially a public servant with an adequate salary enabling him to be independent of private practice:

> The poor would benefit most because the care of them would become the main business of competent and fairly paid functionaries, instead of receiving shreds and scraps of time fully occupied by other and more profitable work.[1]

Although a single inspectorate was established for Poor Law and Public Health purposes, there was no combination of Medical Officers and Medical Officers of Health. (In some localities this was later effected.) Farr, Dr. Fowler, Ernest Hart, Dr. Lord, Dr. Edward Smith, Dr. Stallard, and Robert Rawlinson all desired to see closer harmony between them,[2] and Chadwick stated that the duties of the Poor Law Medical Officers carried them into the houses of the most wretched, 'yet their services are of comparatively little avail for the want of preventive functions'. He therefore again urged that the Poor Law doctor should be given Public Health duties.[3] Rogers however maintained that Union Medical Officers could not undertake Public Health functions as well, for preventive and curative work had to be divided. He called Stansfeld's Act a 'disastrous and ludicrous failure' because the medical department of the Privy Council was absorbed in the Poor Law Board. In his opinion the central health authorities had done their work well and now they were subordinated to the discredited section of the Poor Law Board who had always obstructed reform. Under the Poor Law authorities, 'those who understood the subject were ignored, and those were consulted who had never done anything well'. He greatly objected to the recommendation that District Medical Officers should be health officers and that reports on insanitary conditions should be made to the Guardians. To the permanent Secretary of the Local Government Board he wrote: 'Medical Officers would hesitate in effronting Boards of Guardians, many members of which are the worst offenders against the Act, and in the few cases where parish officers would faithfully carry out the requirements and thereby offend the respective Boards—they would be sacrificed to the resentment of members, and if an appeal were made for support to the central department, such honest men would be called on to resign for not exhibiting sufficient courtesy, etc., and not working with the Boards.'[4] The British Medical Association and the Social Science Association sent deputations to the Local Government Board, for they desired to see a reversal of the arrangements, so that the medical services would be removed from the Poor Law and merged with an independent Public Health administration. The Poor Law Medical Officers' Association backed their leader and thereby demonstrated the impossibility of uniting the two streams of work.

[1] Dr. Child, 'Sanitary Legislation and its relation to Poor Law medical relief and medical science and local sanitary legislation'. A paper read at the Poor Law Conference, 1876.
[2] Meeting, Social Science Association, 25 March 1871.
[3] Paper to Social Science Association, 30 May 1872. He had given similar views in a paper in 1869.
[4] Rogers, *Reminiscences of a Workhouse Medical Officer*.

The creation of a new consolidated department could have brought together and harmonized the sanitary and preventive service with the developments of the Poor Law in transforming workhouses into hospitals, and in the provision of medical relief to all the poor, not only the destitute, which had been under consideration. But Poor Law and Public Health continued side by side, each according to its own principles and ignoring the effect on the other. The Public Health attitude objected to Medical Officers of Health consisting of private practitioners who had no knowledge of, and were alleged to be not interested in, sewage and drainage.—Public Health had not passed the 'Sanitary Idea'. But it admitted whole-time adequately remunerated Medical Officers of Health had to have the assistance of District Medical Officers for economy and efficiency. From the Poor Law side, fusion was opposed because it meant the development of the medical services in the direction of Public Health, and therefore in outdoor medical relief, when it was interested chiefly in hospitalization. After 1871 leading Poor Law officials crusaded against outdoor relief. Goschen's idea of free medical aid to *all* the poor, which would necessarily have included positive reform of environmental conditions, was heard of no more. Therefore the gulf between Poor Law and Public Health Medical Officers widened, and the local authorities pursued policies each ignoring the other.

CHAPTER 18

Conclusion

THE medical service of the Poor Law was an orphan. It grew up in a *laissez-faire*[1] State. Its childhood and adolescence were hard. In an economic system which began to change rapidly after the mid-'thirties, society too was in a state of flux, and the mobility of labour assumed significant dimensions. Upheaval both in town and country added to a rapidly increasing population entailed social dislocation—and this spelt insanitary towns and dwellings, poverty, crime, and ill-health.

A new Poor Law was inevitable, but politicians lacked prescience. A piece of anachronistic legislation, with deterrence as its key word, could not foresee new classification in the realm of social services as the great need of the future. *Laissez-faire* and state provision for the many requirements of the working-class were antipathies. So the unwelcome orphan, whose birth was registered only by the briefest allusion in the 1834 Act—that magistrates could order medical relief in cases of sudden or urgent illness—spent his childhood groping in all directions to find means for growth to a comprehensible, efficient maturity.

He had not generated from sound and well-established stock. No previous Poor Laws had specifically provided medical services, but relief had been given to the sick and infirm so far as the paucity of medical knowledge and practitioners had allowed. Under Common Law, courts had decided that overseers of parishes should provide medical aid, and charges could be recovered by a doctor if he acted spontaneously when the overseer neglected his duty. Many former parish surgeons tended the sick poor well, and by 1834 about half the parishes in England appointed a Medical Officer. An Act which did not think the subject sufficiently important to provide new rules, or worthy of establishing it as a new national system, left the Poor Law Commissioners free to issue their formulae on the same lines as the old precedents. The new ideas infiltrated into orders and regulations very slowly and often painfully, and developments came not from the small 'expert' administration as it had been hoped, but through pressure from below.

For a new social service the principle of centralization was admirable, although its success would have entailed a too rigid uniformity and would have caused hardship to local divergencies. To effect the optimistic creed of Bentham by State omnipotence and scientific centralization was impossible when no experts were at hand, and his principles were

---

[1] The actual experiences of nineteenth-century welfare achievements make this term a misnomer, although it remained a predominant 'principle'.

compromised with Spencer's who desired to solve problems by appropriate development through the interaction of individual character and voluntary enterprise. Also the powers of the central authorities were always throughout the period circumscribed by a legislature which feared State action, respected economic liberalism, showed timidity before the size of the problem, and worst of all failed to understand what their action meant. But even if the Poor Law Commissioners had been accorded wider powers more could not have been done, for an authority consisting of a country gentleman (Frankland Lewis, later succeeded by his son), a business man (Shaw Lefevre), and a retired sea captain and bank manager (Nicholls) could understand little of the new problems, and the Poor Law Board similarly consisted of 'inexpert' Presidents. Chadwick was the only individual who could have entered office with comprehensive plans and the knowledge of where to find his subordinates. He was disappointed at being relegated to the secretaryship and his disobedient and unorthodox service soon led to his dismissal. It is remarkable therefore that so much was accomplished towards establishing a medical system before 1847.

This year was the watershed, and the following decades saw the fulfilment of most of the ideas of the early period and the execution of the regulations which were consolidated just before the Poor Law Commissioners relinquished office. The Poor Law Board under a single responsible President, were for the first ten years unspeakably dull, and were satisfied with carrying out mechanically their predecessors' orders, exercising a minutely regulative influence and showing precise insistence on duties to increase uniformity in the country. (Nearly 1,000 individual Orders were issued in 1850 alone.) Very little reference was made to medical relief in the Annual Reports during the 'fifties. But in the 'sixties began the great era of reform in the medical services. There were a few active and efficient Presidents, who while not able to keep pace with demands, were able by 1871 to alter completely the structure of the medical system and so of the Poor Law itself. After 1871 enlightened Presidents, often of Cabinet rank, and the new legislative liberalism together desired a more positive policy, and discovered the fault which had lain in the system of centralization. A rift ensued between the inspectorate and their superiors. An effective central administration, it was realized, depended on efficient Inspectors and capable local authorities. The Poor Law pioneered the way to the development of the modern Civil Service. For the institution of medical services, the Poor Law Inspectors were completely incompetent. Only Charles Mott and Kay-Shuttleworth in the early days had any medical knowledge or insight into the urgent requirements. In the latter period Farnall was the only enlightened Inspector, until the Poor Law Board recognized the need for medical advice and belatedly appointed doctors as Inspectors at the end of the 'sixties. Real medical supervision on a national scale was ignored and proved the greatest handicap to the efficient development of the Poor Law medical system.

The central administration also was never strong enough to dominate the local authorities, and legislation in accordance with popular political ideas had indeed never intended this to be effected. But at the time when local government was in a chaotic state regarding authorities, rating, and areas, the Boards of Guardians and the Unions were the only universal, and therefore the outstanding, local authorities in the country. Through them as a medium, the early development of the social services took place. Although the Poor Law was a pioneer in this field also, the activity of the central administration was curtailed because many areas only gradually came under its jurisdiction. But by 1871 a national system was virtually complete—an important development because it was the only means of ensuring an efficient system of relief. Local divergencies were however throughout this period of progress too much respected by the central authorities, and uniformity only existed in broad outline. Yet in some areas the Guardians were ahead of the Poor Law Board, and so filled in the gaps left by their sluggishness. In the 'fifties the Poor Law Board only used persuasion and advice, which were ignored; when in the 'sixties orders were given, they were generally only tardily and perfunctorily executed, out of habit, and for this reason there was an increasing demand for legislation by the central administration and by the reformers.

For the effective implementation of principles, strong centralization imperatively needed an incorruptible legal system to supplant the old industrialist or land-owning magistrates, so that transgressors of policy could be punished. Throughout nearly the whole of this period Inspectors, Guardians, and the law were of the same mind, until in the 'sixties the work of Wakley, who in his office as Coroner had settled on behalf of justice for the poor, saw some reward in that verdicts on the death of sick paupers came to be attributed to the negligence of Poor Law officers.

Little help came from the Government regarding the legal aspect of the medical services. Between 1834 and 1870, eighteen Poor Law Acts were passed, yet only one, the Metropolitan Poor Act (and its successor applying it to the country) was devoted to medical aspects. It provided the landmark in the history of the development of the Poor Law medical services, and in founding the Metropolitan Asylums Board established the first organized hospital system in the country. 'The sorry spectacle of ruin and decay' which the Poor Law presented to the Royal Commission of 1905 needs modification for the medical services of 1871. If they were the 'outcome of practice rather than the creation of law', they proved that administration on central and local levels had made great strides between 1834 and 1871. When the most outstanding development within the Poor Law was in connection with medical relief, and when this was accompanied by a singular paucity of legislative reference to the care and treatment of the sick, the gradual enlightenment of the authorities was also demonstrated. For the growth of administrative efficiency depended on outside agencies being given scope to elucidate requirements.

The infant social service found guidance from the outset. This came from the Poor Law Medical Officers, who, growing yearly in numbers and importance until they became a collective and well organized body, were really responsible for development and reform. Their struggle against obscurantism and obstruction was hard and relentless. Their most revolutionary aims were never achieved, because they had to contend with the apathy and opposition of those who pointed to Victorian economic prosperity as a justification for *laissez-faire* in social legislation. For their own interests, they had by 1871 secured permanency of office, fixed salaries which were also higher, additional fees for surgery, midwifery, and extraneous duties, and better qualifications. Medical districts had been reduced and Guardians were supplying drugs. These reforms were not complete or universal, and the Medical Officers were still responsible to lay supervision, but their position was vastly different from what it had been in 1834, which the increase in their status in social and medical spheres proved. The Medical Officers were fortunately never completely absorbed in the Poor Law administration; even those workhouse doctors whose whole time was engaged in public service remained aloof in spirit from its cramping and restrictive influence. It was in the development towards a Poor Law medical system that the doctor and the State first worked together, but the relationship was far from amicable. For this reason and because the Poor Law Medical Officer always retained his professional ties, other doctors came to his aid. Therefore in the breakdown of *laissez-faire* principles the whole medical profession in the nineteenth century played a dominant part. Their own standards rose progressively, so that illumination came to them first that the conditions and ramifications of the social polity needed drastic alteration. Assistance in drawing attention to the growing evils came from the incipient unorthodox social and political philosophy, and from orthodox Benthamite philosophy as to the methods of securing remedies. The doctors as one of the new bodies of experts, were from the middle decades of the century increasingly called on to supply facts for every branch of the nascent Welfare State and to play their part in its evolution. From intermittent contributions to improvements, they became organized specialists, and were the first scientific individualists to co-operate with State collectivism. Although the Royal Medical Colleges offered only spasmodic support to the work of the Poor Law Medical Officer, many eminent physicians concurred in the reforms suggested or made recommendations themselves. The British Medical Association and local medical societies followed developments assiduously, and the *British Medical Journal* and particularly the *Lancet*, afforded a means of articulation on a national scale for medical improvements in the Poor Law and Public Health fields.

In addition to the professional impetus given to the progress of the Poor Law medical services, there came also the direct or indirect influences, both practical and theoretical, of Public Health, housing, and education reformers, for the integration of the growing social services began after the middle of the century. Reform in all spheres was induced and assisted not only by the interplay of conditions, but also by the association of the pioneers with more than a single movement. They gathered information on what was required for their own social service which incidentally was of help to others, and in turn could adapt the progressive ideas from other movements to suit their own special needs. Kay-Shuttleworth for example was a doctor, an Assistant Poor Law Commissioner, and leading educationist. As a Manchester man and having practised there, he knew and wrote about the conditions of the poor. He was closely connected with the Public Health movement and had been secretary of the Local Board of Health in 1831 as well as undertaking dispensary and hospital duties. E. C. Tufnell was an Assistant Poor Law Commissioner and interested in factory conditions and education. Robert Rawlinson was attached to the Poor Law Board as a civil engineer and was keenly interested in housing and Public Health reform, as well as in the general questions relating to poverty. Shaftesbury was connected with reforms relating to lunatics, chimney-sweeps, and the industrial and agricultural worker; and the Poor Law, Public Health, mining and factory movements, found a staunch advocate in him. Chadwick and Southwood Smith retained life-long interests in every sphere of Public Health and the Poor Law. Wakley was not only a 'battling surgeon' interested in medical and hospital reforms, but campaigned against slavery, adulterated food, the corrupt legal system, and the Poor Law, as well as on behalf of improvement in the medical relief system. Rumsey, one of the greatest reformers of the Poor Law medical service, was a member of the Social Science Association and the Manchester Statistical Society. From both, he learnt much of the views of the other professions and public opinion; to both, by speeches, papers, and lectures, he pointed out the evils of the medical system and solicited their support.[1] As a member of the Health of Towns Association, he, like so many Poor Law Medical Officers, was connected with the Public Health movement. The contribution of Farr, doctor and statistician with a passion for hygiene, to the Poor Law medical service and the Public Health movement was inestimable. His influence was greatest as a public servant, but as an independent writer and member of the Social Science Association, he gave individual help to many movements by his particular knowledge of vital statistics and his research into their meaning.

The work of societies was also of enormous importance for the development of the Poor Law medical services. The Workhouse Visiting Society, the Workhouse Infirmary Association, the Epidemiological Society, the Social Science Association and the Charity Organization Society made the demands of the reformers in the 'sixties irresistible, and it was through these societies that the late 'sixties were the high-water mark of progress in the Poor Law medical services. Again, leaders like Sieveking, Rogers, Ernest Hart, Dr. Anstie, and Chadwick were members of more than one society. Between twenty and thirty of the most interesting figures in the Poor Law or Public Health fields were found in the Social Science Association and on the committees. No movement for the growth of the social services after the middle of the century was without its women supporters, and some like Louisa Twining, F. P. Cobbe, Mrs. Jameson, and Florence Nightingale were interested in workhouse nursing, public health, general poverty, workhouses, and education simultaneously. Interaction fostered development, and the sum total of the activities of various organizations and people forced the incipient Social Service State on the community. The single Poor Law authorities central and local were likewise unable to withstand the onslaught. When maturity was reached by the 'seventies the Poor Law medical system was therefore no longer an orphan, and had itself grown so much and had become so important that it was reported to be making its foster parents, to whom it should never have been attached, superfluous.

Twice, long Inquiries were held solely on medical relief, and other Select Com-

---

[1] See *Transactions* and *Sessional Proceedings* of the two societies.

mittees on general Poor Law questions delved deeply into the medical problem. They erroneously reported all was well, but when tentative recommendations were made these were effected. The importance of the investigations lay not only in the fact that they revealed the growing interest in the new service, but that they gave reformers opportunity for articulation, and some even succeeded in becoming examiners. The pertinent questions posed by Wakley, Shaftesbury (Chairman, 1844), Palmer, Miles, and Slaney were invaluable. Conservative and unsympathetic interrogators predominated however; they failed to draw essential information and so biased the findings of the Select Committees. But through official and unofficial channels the difficult but successful campaign continued unabated. Positive progress was marked not only by the increase in the quantity of medical relief, but also in improved quality, which in turn led to an explicit disavowal of any application to the sick pauper of the principle of less-eligibility. The new departure by 1871 ensured to the destitute a standard of medical relief superior to that obtained by the poorest independent labourer or even the generally 'poor'. Tufnell's report on education in 1841 urged the provision of the most efficient education possible for a child so that it was less likely to descend to pauperism. The advice was also taken by the Poor Law authorities, for they gradually appreciated the intimate relation between the shortcomings of the medical service and the excess of destitution.

This causal connection also came to be realized by the population. Not only did the comprehensive General Consolidated Order and the change in central administration make 1847 a watershed, but about this time the 'principles of 1834' began to be discarded. The cold officialdom of Victorian legislation continued, but feelings of humanity crept into the minds of the thinking public. Standards rose, the growing sensitiveness of articulate opinion was made evident, and the sick, aged, children, and insane became the favoured poor. Their poverty, it was realized, was not self induced; they were often the victims of social conditions they had not created and over which they had no control. A Poor Law conceived for reforming the able-bodied and for deterring 'rogues and vagabonds' was not applicable to them, and depauperization by the affording of adequate medical relief was the marked feature of the 'sixties and 'seventies. The *Lancet* gave adequate proof of the change in public opinion, for it offered this as the reason for embarking on its far-reaching and consequential investigations.

> Society in England [wrote Dr. Anstie] had undergone important changes, in no respect more remarkably modified than regarding 'the exchange of sympathy and kindly feeling between the higher and middle-classes and the poor' ... and ... 'in this changed state of public feeling the medical profession has borne an active part.'

Therefore the *Lancet* had only to follow the tradition which had always belonged to the profession. The weighty questions of Poor Law administration had for years past, Anstie continued, excited a deep and lively interest in all classes of society, and the medical profession had peculiar opportunities and a duty to guide this sympathy into correct and useful channels.

The claims of the poor upon medical men and of medical men on the poor are reciprocal . . . it is on the wide field . . . far wider than that afforded even by our noble voluntary hospitals, which is presented by the great infirmaries of our workhouses, that many a problem of deep and vital importance to the health and happiness of society must be worked out: with what incalculable benefit to all the interests including even the mere pecuniary well-doing of society, only those can tell who have intimate knowledge of the diseases of the poor, and that practical acquaintance with hospital management and economy, which enable them to forecast in some measure the course which reforms to be successful must ultimately take.

The old aphorism was still true—'work badly done, though ever so cheaply, can never in the end be economical'. Therefore the *Lancet* felt its task to convince its readers, that 'the great problem involved in the management of thousands of sick inmates of the workhouses has been far too little understood for it to be possible as yet to secure a satisfactory return for national expenditure—our knowledge has been too limited and our processes too rough'.[1]

Therefore the most remarkable change in attitude related to the institutional treatment of the sick. By 1871 the hospitals branch of the Poor Law had been firmly established and had assumed overwhelming dimensions, so that workhouse infirmaries were generally far larger than voluntary hospitals. Improvements were coincident with the alteration which had occurred in the classes of inmates. The workhouse test, introduced as a deterrent against the great proportion of able-bodied, was no longer applicable when institutions found themselves largely peopled by aged and infirm, chronic sick, and even sufferers from acute diseases. Therefore the central authorities pressed for the most efficient treatment that could be obtained. As a future President of the Poor Law Board stated in 1865[2]:

there is one thing we must peremptorily insist on, namely the treatment of the sick in workhouses being conducted on an entirely different system; because the evils complained of have mainly arisen from workhouse management, which must to a great extent be of deterrent character, having been applied to the sick who are not proper objects of such a system.

There was great local variation in the period of transition, but there was one uniform feature common to the whole country: large or small, good or bad, alterations were made to existing institutions to enable them to house and treat the sick. Progress was demonstrated by the capital expenditure. Up to 1865 the total sum authorized for new buildings and the altering and enlarging of workhouses and schools was £6 million, by 1871 it had risen to £8½ million (half of the increase was in the Metropolis and a quarter in Lancashire). In the early years special provision was not made for the sick and only occasionally for infectious diseases. The incidental sick-wards of the workhouses had the same forbidding

[1] *Lancet*, 1865, ii, p. 14.
[2] Gathorne Hardy, House of Commons, 1865; *Hansard*, Vol. clxxxv.

quality as the rest of the institution, and they were only a small part of the whole. As the occupation of sick-rooms was to be temporary and the occupants few—for only inmates who fell ill were catered for—scarcely any attention was paid to providing suitable bedding, baths, kitchens, or conveniences. But as the number of able-bodied dwindled through the increasing economic prosperity and the affording of outdoor relief (so that there were often too few to perform the menial work of the institution) and as the number of sick grew with the change in policy towards institutional relief for them—not only more space was provided in the nature of separate wards for classification purposes, but arrangements were made for furnishing special amenities. Great changes in circumstances demanded equally great changes in construction and organization, yet the fabric of a 'work-house' was not of itself changeable, so that remodelling was difficult. At first old wards were converted into sick wards; when these proved inadequate and detrimental to health, new wards were erected until the main building of the institution was the infirmary and the 'workhouse' was comparatively superfluous—and the designation became a misnomer. Finally, the Poor Law hospital emerged, at first a general hospital, and then for special diseases as workhouse infirmaries of various Unions were converted for the use of one type of case only. Insufficient space for the 'special' categories of pauper led to specialization, so that the policy of 1834 was forced to be executed, on a far wider scale, thirty years later. The complete change was however only necessary and practicable in London and the revolution was well under way by 1871.

The Metropolitan Poor Act of 1867 was the high-water mark of reform. It was introduced to counteract the evils of institutional conditions and the system of management, by applying principles which had been urged over the past decades—the classification and separation of the various heterogeneous populations of the workhouses. But the Act only gave legal impetus to what had already been begun under the pressure of circumstances over a large part of the country. Children were removed from workhouses and placed in separate or district schools. Noisy and dangerous lunatics were transferred to county and private asylums; imbeciles and the chronic insane, where they existed in considerable numbers, were segregated in wards of their own or in a separate building, and in 1870 the Metropolitan Asylums Board established two large lunatic asylums for the poor. Cases of infectious disease were by 1871 being removed from their homes to the workhouse where they were isolated as far as possible in detached wards or separate buildings. Here again the Metropolitan Asylums Board built two large institutions consisting of four hospitals. In the Metropolis and other well populated towns temporary isolation hospitals were also provided in the late 'sixties, but permanent municipal institutions of this nature originated in the Poor Law medical service. If the London destitution authorities pioneered the way in providing special hospitals, Manchester, Birmingham, Leeds, and Liverpool followed quickly.

Where the general mixed workhouses continued, an attempt was made in the 'sixties not only to segregate the sick from other inmates, but also, where space permitted, to classify them. For the workhouses were generally the only institutions which would admit such infectious diseases as erysipelas, puerperal fever, venereal diseases, measles, whooping-cough, and chicken-pox, irrespective of whether sufferers were technically destitute or not. They also received a great proportion of accident and urgent cases from the streets, as well as maternity cases, and in their provision for these compared favourably with that of the voluntary hospitals. Generally the diet, treatment, and environmental condition of patients, also made great strides forward when it was realized deterrence could not be applied to the casualty of sickness. In 1868 the Poor Law Board issued several Circulars giving minute details of comforts and amenities both personal and general which were to be provided, and stipu-lating the minor structural adaptations which were to be made. Some Guardians subscribed to libraries for the supply of books in the late 'sixties, and Villiers had told the House of Commons in 1860 that the Poor Law Board readily consented to the establishing of a library for workhouse inmates.[1] (No order had been given to this effect.) Even flowers, and tablecloths were permitted to the sick in some Unions.

These improvements were rarely found in a single workhouse in their entirety. In the absence of any embodiment of the new policy in a General Order, arrangements were left to the dilatory and capricious discretion of the Guardians, who carried out recommenda-tions as they desired. The period of transition was not over by 1871 for the impetus to reform really started only in the late 'sixties, and the time was too short for demands to penetrate universally. The trend definitely existed however, even if the innovations gener-ally applied only to the extensive industrial slum towns, which had the advantage and disadvantage of a large pauper population. The advantage was that they were more liable to criticism and inspection, and public opinion was more easily stirred; they also had sufficient poor to make classification and separate institutional provision practicable. The disadvantage was that infirmary accommodation could never keep pace with demand. It was the greatest unsolved problem in 1871. Improvements came more slowly in small rural workhouses, but were of vital importance to the local population, for people suffering from chronic rheumatism, asthma, and all other diseases, the sick children, the expectant mothers, the village idiots, and the senile had no other hospital. Here, as in the urban infirmaries, the great boon to all sufferers which the Poor Law had just begun to provide, was competent nursing. The revolution in nursing was as salutary as the development of the infirmaries themselves.

Much remained to be done in 1871 in improving environmental conditions and in treatment. Convalescent homes or sanatoria did not come into the vision of the authorities, for the Poor Law medical service began and ended with actual disease. The medical staff still waited to be placed under the supervision and inspection of professional experts. The Poor Law infirmaries would have made good medical schools, but students were admitted for only one year, in 1868. Medical treatment was therefore divorced from clinical research, as it was from Public Health experiments. The infirmaries remained comparatively closed institutions with few contacts in outside medical practice, and visitors were generally only

[1] *Hansard*, Vol. clviii, 4 May 1860.

admitted through the Relieving Officer. For efficiency, specialists and private practitioners should have been encouraged to take an interest in the work. The publication of comprehensive and valuable statistics and information also remained absent. But as a broad generalization the spirit of Malthus and the descriptions of Dickens no longer applied to institutional medical relief in 1871.

The historians who have condemned failed to take into account comparative institutional conditions. Bad ventilation and overcrowding, for example, were general in all public establishments. Architects were by 1870 only just beginning to pay attention to ventilation and access of light.—So many workhouse problems waited for technical innovation. It must also be remembered that hospitals harboured similar conditions to the infirmaries, and reforms came simultaneously. The Poor Law authorities adopted the general practice and frequently looked to the voluntary institutions for guidance. Competent nursing and the classification of the sick, for example, were not introduced till after the middle of the century, and in the separation of children the destitution authorities made swifter progress than their counterparts. Further, the workhouse infirmary had to admit everyone who was destitute, hospitals had freedom of choice—and often sent unwanted cases to the Poor Law establishment, so that classification and accommodation problems in the hospitals were not as acute. A projection into nineteenth-century conditions is therefore of vital importance before a just criticism can be made. The State hospitals[1] were in the workhouse wards, and the State by the 'seventies had awakened to its responsibilities.

In 1873 the Local Government Board could report that workhouses (in London) had become 'attractive to paupers' and contained 'many persons who could maintain themselves out of doors. In short, the workhouse furnishes no test of destitution.' But the memory of the old deterrent character of the workhouse died hard. Although institutional relief became more popular, many poor, suffering from incipient disease and requiring hospital treatment, refused to enter the infirmary, until they were driven in by actual destitution caused by the worsening of their condition. The stigma of pauperism rather than infirmary conditions now provided the deterrent. Throughout the 'seventies and 'eighties the Poor Law Inspectors zealously carried out a campaign for institutional relief. The improvement in medical practice provided a useful auxiliary, if not the logical complement, for this crusade from which domiciliary treatment was not excepted:

> The granting of outdoor relief in case of temporary sickness . . . this I would sweep away on the ground that experience has shown that the infirmary is the proper place for cases of temporary sickness . . . where the sick applicant is made to enter the infirmary,

---

[1] Dr. Ernest Hart read a long paper to a meeting of the National Association for the Promotion of Social Science on 18 December 1867 entitled 'On a National Scheme for the better organization and management of workhouse infirmaries'. (Chadwick was in the Chair.) He revealed that during the famous *Lancet* inquiries, which for the first time showed that the inmates of London and provincial workhouses were the sick, infirm, and children, he himself had named the Poor Law institutions 'State Hospitals', and that this term had been accepted and generally adopted since that time.

he gets well in half the time. The infirmary . . . should be the only state relief given in case of sickness . . .[1]

But the movement was still in its infancy and, the largest proportion of sick paupers were still in 1871 receiving domiciliary treatment. Here improvement had not been as thorough or as far reaching, because inspection of outdoor relief was difficult and patients were scattered. Also so much depended on circumstances beyond the control of the Poor Law authorities. Progress had been made however, both in increasing the scope and the efficiency of the service, either through Orders from the Poor Law Board or more generally through the unconscious pressure of circumstances. The latter made uniformity impossible, but the general trend throughout the country from 1834 to 1871 was unmistakable, and permits of broad generalization on developments. After 1847 earlier policy was put into practice, so that in the next generation medical districts were reduced and the number of Medical Officers increased. The sick poor were given general relief, without they or their families being offered the workhouse, and medical extras were generally given liberally and without question. Guardians began to supply drugs, and the sick were no longer required to be technically destitute before receiving treatment. Many people above the ordinary class of pauper were by the end of the period coming to the Guardians for medicines. They were those who could just maintain their independence but could not meet the emergency of sickness wholly or partly, and who came between the permanent pauper and the thrifty club member. Such cases were common among agricultural labourers and among the casual workers of the industrial towns. These people received medical relief when ordinary assistance was denied them, because it was realized that there was greater economy in affording treatment and in the incipient stages of disease, than to have an entire family pauperized through protracted or chronic illness. District relief was far from adequate in 1871, but a remedy had been tardily found. After a long campaign by the doctors, the dispensary system was inaugurated in the Metropolis, and other large towns quickly followed.

By this elaborate systematization of outdoor medical relief, the Central Authorities, not only put within reach of sick paupers medical attendance far superior to that accessible to the lowest grade of independent labourers, but even placed sick paupers in the Metropolis, without loss of liberty, in a position equal to that of the superior artisan subscribing to a good provident dispensary.[2]

But Poor Law domiciliary medical relief could never be adequate without embracing Public Health measures. Yet administrators had been installed to *cure*. The Guardians had neither the power, inclination, nor aptitude to *prevent* sickness. At the beginning, awareness of the close connection between health and positive precautions was absent also, save among the doctors. A generation later a Poor Law official giving his reason for the new

---

[1] Poor Law Conference, 1876: Mr. Holland speaking on 'out-relief'.
[2] B. and S. Webb, *Poor Law Policy*, 1910—Praise indeed!

crusade for institutional relief, stated that 'because of the overcrowded and insanitary quarters where the poor live in great towns, it is of highest public importance that the sick should be removed from conditions where cure is prevented and delayed'.[1] In their campaign, the Poor Law Inspectors were inevitably hostile however, to the progressive movement which had begun for combining domiciliary medical relief with Public Health measures. Public Health began as a Poor Law problem, and at a time when the connection between poverty and disease, and their mutual aggravation, became understood. The industrial slum and its consequences have been aptly described as a 'hell of depression and misery and hopeless degradation. Foul odors, vermin, vile food, drunkenness and promiscuity were the chief by-products of its depauperate and crowded existence: crime and disease were but the inevitable psychological and physiological responses.'[2]

Fear and economic considerations were the best allies of the reformers against the prejudice and ignorance of vested interests and obscurantist legislators. The new era of Public Health reform was heralded when the Poor Law Commissioners instituted their investigations in 1838. And while the infant movement dwelt on environmental and negative provisions it was constantly connected with the Poor Law medical service. The Union Medical Officers were a mine of information on social conditions, and before and often after the institution of the Medical Officer of Health, they were the health officer under the nuisance authority. Many doctors and reformers advocated the combination of the two offices, by the merging of Poor Law duties into the Public Health service, so that all medical problems should be divorced from their connection with destitution. But the Royal Commission of 1868–71 began the separation of Poor Law and Public Health, for the grand inventory on the latter closed one epoch and opened another. The 'Sanitary Idea' which concentrated on the removal of environmental evils, and which was chiefly concerned with minimum conditions necessary to ward off disease and preserve health, gave way to an enlightened positive programme with emphasis on optima and an 'inclusive' outlook for the enhancement of health, and the cultivation of physically, mentally, and morally fit citizens. When it was realized that conditions for Public Health were to a great extent purchaseable, and when the State appreciated that it could not afford to do without them, in contrast to that it could not afford them, the Poor Law medical services lost their direct place in the Public Health movement. The Poor Law had provided its share towards Public Health improvement and in return had been amply rewarded. The problem of epidemics, like the poor, had always existed, but the Public Health service had done much to prevent an increase in poverty by its fight against morbific agencies. Epidemics had provided the link between the two services and they had often overlapped. Both had been aided by the progress of education, which alone made an understanding of the elementary principles of hygiene possible; by the Factory Acts; by increased knowledge on how to improve housing and streets; by technical innovations; by the cheapening of materials for constructional purposes; by a cheap press and the easing of communication; by Victorian

[1] Poor Law Conference 1883: Mr Bousfield, speaking on medical relief.
[2] Lewis Mumford, *Culture of Cities*, 1940, p. [12].

economic prosperity; by the growth of the expert, particularly the engineer and the statistician; by the combating of vested interests so that a cheap and abundant pure water supply, and efficient and adequate sewerage were possible; by the institution of parks, libraries, baths, and wash-houses; and by the great revolution which had begun in medical science. The ramifications of the Poor Law medical service and the Public Health movement were endless, like the associations connected with them, ranging from a Street Cleaning Association[1] and a Soup Kitchen Association,[2] to a Ladies Sanitary Association.[3]

Although they were aided by the same agencies and assisted each other, close integration between the two services was impossible. Public Health was the favoured child, because it was so loudly acclaimed that the nation's material wealth depended much on a healthy people, and that to increase the latter, the State had to curtail individual opportunities for making profit out of public nuisances. It performed no similar duty for the parent, so that the medical services had on the whole to develop and battle on without legislative guidance, although social pathology had become a study in higher circles by 1870. The differential incidence of disease and death among the various classes, so ably pointed out by Farr and Simon, gave a lead on the one hand to what ought to have been done. On the other hand, doctors demonstrated prophylaxis and therapeutics were inseparably associated in practically every disease. Yet preventive and curative medicine were kept apart. It was cheaper to prevent pauperism, and ultimately reduce expenditure on Poor Law medical relief by Public Health measures for increasing health and national efficiency than to relieve existing distress. But because the Public Health schemes depended on increasing cost, whilst the Poor Law was conceived as a means to reduce them, the two principles were incompatible, However, the description of the Webbs in 1910, that 'good administration of medical relief meant not the curing of the sick or the preventing of ill-health, but the cutting down of medical orders', needs stringent modification. It was not part of a Poor Law Medical Officer's duty to inculcate personal health habits nor to exercise sanitary supervision in the homes of patients—functions which Rumsey had so ardently advocated. The institution of dispensaries and the consequent abandonment of domiciliary visiting save for the bedridden minimized the consideration of environment. The prevention of disease, either recurring in the same patient or in its spread to others, was not regarded as falling into the category of 'relief' to which the Poor Law medical service was dedicated. And legally it was no duty of the District Medical Officer to reduce the incidence of sickness in his district. But this interpretation of legislation which the Webbs took as a general practice must be greatly modified on examination of the actual work of the doctors.

In the therapeutic field the Medical Officer's intervention was also limited, but in parentheses one might ask what was the value of medical treatment where it was given? The period of transition in the Poor Law medical services coincided with upheaval in the

[1] Established in Metropolis, 1845: 2s. 6d. a day was paid to the poor engaged in the operation.
[2] Several were established in the 'forties.
[3] Established 1860: had Health Visitors in 1862 for working in the homes of the poor; and published 44,000 tracts by 1861, edited by Farr, Southwood Smith, Sutherland, Lancaster, and Sieveking.

medical world and ferment in medical science. The cheapening of drugs, the discovery of new ones and the campaign against their adulteration, were of particular importance to the poor, but their efficacy is doubtful. Cod liver oil introduced in the 'forties was invaluable for the debilitated. But the Medical Officer was probably right in ordering food instead of medicine, and not only for cases of malnutrition. Great reliance was placed on spirits and beer until Benjamin Ward Richardson, Chadwick's biographer and coiner of the phrase 'the Nation's Health is the Nation's Wealth', upset pharmacology by his advocacy of abstinence from alcohol from the physiological point of view. He was unpopular for undermining the faith in one of the basic medicines of his day, for he pointed out that bodily temperature should not be raised, and that an intoxicant was a drug and narcotic rather than a food and stimulant. Reform also came in this period with antiseptic surgery. In 1864–66 Lister's statistics revealed a 45 per cent mortality rate from amputations. Through his discovery they fell to 15 per cent in the next three years. Antiseptics and anaesthetics were still in their infancy; by the 'seventies however their effect was becoming self-evident. Ophthalmology, otology, and orthopaedics became medical specialties in the 'fifties. Bacteriology only developed in the late nineteenth century, but empirical treatment was becoming increasingly effective.

But whatever the advances in medical knowledge, the treatment afforded by doctors could not offset the narrow scope of Poor Law medical relief. Convalescence could rarely be supervised, although some Unions granted orders for a few months. Graver consequences ensued from a Medical Officer not receiving a case until treatment was impossible. When intervention was denied a young worker with symptoms of tuberculosis (of whom there were very many) and when he was left unattended until cure was too late, he and perhaps his family whom he had infected, were admitted to the sick-wards of the workhouse infirmary never to leave it. (But regarding many diseases condemnation must be restricted, for medical science had not developed far enough for early and effectual diagnoses.) Besides the unnecessary suffering of the patient and the frustration of the doctor, incipient disease left to become serious entailed far greater expense on the poor rate, and the percentage of incurables in workhouses was very high in this period. Every case of neglected sickness was not only an economic loss to the community but also a potential cause of future destitution, and the danger was particularly great with regard to infants and children.

Therefore the inability of the Poor Law authorities, first to alter environment, and second, to search out disease, put the medical service in a cruel dilemma, just at the time when the policy of attempting to reduce destitution by efficient relief had evolved. The beneficial effects of elaborate rules for improving infirmary treatment and for producing professional competence were to a large extent counterbalanced by the two principles of confining medical advice to the actual period of sickness and to its 'pauperizing' result. Although by 1871 the former principle of deterrence had disappeared from the bestowing of medical relief, in so far as help was not given in such a form as to prevent a person from coming again, the stigma of being designated a pauper even for a short period of illness, discouraged many deserving and urgent cases from applying for gratuitous treatment. The Webbs condemned Poor Law medical relief for the reason that it was confined to the destitute: 'The Poor Law fails with regard to the sick in town and country alike because it has to wait until destitution has set in.'[1] This statement is only partially correct, for although the question of eligibility was never successfully solved, by 1871 medical relief was generally given to those who could not afford private advice, not necessarily the technically destitute. They were classified as paupers only while treatment was being provided, although for some this dependence was elemental in the breakdown of their personal character and they ceased to strive for independent maintenance afterwards.

To divorce the medical service from the Poor Law was the dominant theme of the reformers in the 'fifties and 'sixties—first, because no level of administration contained an authoritative medical voice so that the system was in the care of laymen; second, because positive Public Health provisions could not be undertaken; and third, because of its associaton with destitution. 'So long as you connect medical relief to the poor with the Poor Law, so long will you continue to maintain and increase the pauperism of the country.'[2] The crusade against non-pauperization linked to the campaign for combining preventive and curative medical functions failed with the inadequate Act of 1871, when instead of comprehensive Local Boards of Health under a central Health Department, reformers received the Local Government Board and the authorization that a Poor Law Medical Officer might undertake the duties of a Medical Officer of Health.

But by this time the inadequacy and the pauperizing quality of the Poor Law medical service had taught many of the poor the advantages of self-help for the contingency of sickness. Indeed, in so far as the system leaned on the crutches of the voluntary hospital and charitable dispensary on one side, and the provident dispensary and medical club on the other, it was itself a cripple. In 1909[3] it was said that without external support the Poor Law medical system would have broken down.—This would not have been the case. The Poor Law made national and systematic provisions, whilst the efforts of the working-class and philanthropists were incomplete and insufficient. Without the overlapping or supplementary medical aid, the legislature would probably have been compelled to add to the national service with its greater potentiality for efficiency. This some reformers demanded in the 'fifties and 'sixties. By 1871 whatever the reported situation in the early twentieth century, the Poor Law medical service was efficient as far as its scope extended. There was still an insufficiency of staff both of doctors and nurses, and too few well-constructed and suitably managed infirmaries. The aged, the children, and the mentally deficient were still to be found in some general mixed workhouses—where starvation of intellect and paralysis of will continued, and for which no remedy was ever found. The dispensary system also was only in its infancy—but reforms were too many and were too well launched for progress to be retarded, and uniformity of standards was growing. Our survey unfortunately closes

[1] Pamphlet, 1909, 'Failure of the Poor Law' (Propaganda for their 'cause').
[2] Rumsey, Evidence to the Select Committee, 1854.
[3] Report of the Royal Commission on Poor Laws and the Relief of Distress, 1909-10.

with the period of the successful pioneers who heralded the modern era of medical treatment, which lasted until the final break-up of the Poor Law eighty years later.

The 1909 Report showed how much had still to be done at the end of the century, but unqualified condemnation was unjust, for in great sections of the country the Poor Law provided medical aid far superior to what the poor could procure for themselves. In so far as good treatment, the supply of 'extras', and general relief could cure disease, destitution was prevented and the spread of disease curtailed. Important supplementary functions had been produced for the benefit of the entire population, such as vaccination, provision for various infectious diseases, and Public Health measures in time of epidemics. Expenditure and numbers relieved had increased steadily and more quickly than pauperism, and this had been facilitated by increased prosperity affording the means to Guardians. Regarding the medical services no retrogressive step was taken, and if slow and exiguous, development was constantly in the right direction. Occasionally it was possible for a sick person receiving public relief to be treated as well as a sick person of affluent means. The Act of 1834 conceived for the welfare of the wealthy, had by 1871 been adapted to supply the wants of the poor. Engels' dictum that the Malthusian Poor Law regarded poverty as a crime was answered by a leading Victorian economist pointing out in 1870, that

> a poor rate is an insurance of the labourer's life and health. It maintains him in old age, assists him in sickness and protects him when labouring under mental disease, and supplies him with the services of a highly skilled person in the shape of a medical officer . . . At the existing rate of agricultural wages a farm labourer and to some extent the artisan . . . could hardly supply these services for himself.[1]

From the statement of Engels to that of Thorold Rogers was spanning the development of the whole field of Poor Law activity from a deterrent police system based on the misconception of the causes of poverty, to the pioneering of the social services. In 1834 there existed no efficient public sanitary, education, prison, lunacy, or police authority. There was no pension system for the aged, disabled, or unemployed. The absence of these provisions made direct action by the Poor Law administrators imperative, for they were the only single central and local bodies dedicated to welfare duties, and existing on a national scale. The Poor Law was at the beginning the all-embracing social service to whose offspring, development, and mistakes the Twentieth Century Welfare State must give recognition. Its own internal growth overwhelmed it. By 1871, it was obvious that it was quite impossible for the central authorities and the inspectorate to supervise adequately the various functions which came under the single denomination of 'relief for the destitute'. However efficient they might have been, Bentham's small body of experts could not have been specialists on all the services together. Nor could they keep a grip on local administration, which also suffered from having responsibility for a too varied and too large a collection of duties.

The Poor Law authorities had by 1871 made a limited success of the medical service,

[1] Thorold Rogers, 'Incidence of local taxation', *Journal of the Royal Statistical Society*, Vol. 33, p. 250.

but paradoxically it was bound to be a failure, because the whole system was faulty. Specialization of functions, because they had become too big for single classification, was advocated by the Poor Law medical reformers before the 'seventies, when they demanded the divorce of medicine from the general relief of destitution. They then added the most prescient of all reforms—the granting of gratuitous medical treatment to the whole of the poor. The narrowness of the scope of the medical services was their greatest failing, and one which had by far the gravest consequences. When Goschen as the last President of the Poor Law Board recommended the extension of public medical assistance to the wide class of poor, he made the most enlightened speech that had ever come from a Poor Law administrator, and the one most pregnant with future developments. It affords the best proof of the tremendous change in attitude of the central authorities, and modifies the unalleviated condemnation and scorn of early twentieth-century reformers for the Poor Law administrators. For the failure to investigate and embark upon the proposal must be ascribed chiefly to the legislature.

Many of the enactments of the Twentieth Century Welfare State grew out of the omissions of the Poor Law. Its famous critics afforded little grateful recognition to the pioneer who had had to struggle against very different social and economic philosophies. Through the Poor Law, the politics of poverty with its tremendous ramifications was learnt. One of the results was the evolution of the medical services out of piecemeal rules, regulations, and experiences into a comprehensive system. This system had become efficient when the original principles to which it still had to adhere had become effete. Its potentiality and the overthrow of those principles, together indicated that collectivist measures for social services were both possible and imperative.

In our contemporary medical provisions the sectional supply of gratuitous relief for sickness has found its logical conclusion. In the popular insurance with the State, the early efforts of self-help for the contingency of sickness have also reached complete development. The prescient doctors who were able to function within the Poor Law are forgotten, but the reforms they outlined in the 'forties, 'fifties, and 'sixties of the nineteenth century are incorporated in the policy of the Welfare State of the mid-twentieth century. The National Health Service has its direct roots in the medical services of the Poor Law.

Bibliography

PRIMARY SOURCES

(a) ORIGINAL MANUSCRIPTS

Minutes and Correspondence of the Poor Law Commissioners (Public Records Office).

Boards of Guardians' (or Local Vestries) Minutes, Account Books, and Workhouse Visiting Books —some provincial and these are included in the text, but most important are those in the Archives of the Greater London Council at The County Hall. Poor Law Medical Officers' records are not extant.

Sidney and Beatrice Webb MSS. at the British Library of Political and Economic Science.

William Farr MSS. at the British Library of Political and Economic Science.

(b) GOVERNMENT PUBLICATIONS

(The detailed titles of the following are contained in the text or footnotes)

Annual Reports of the Poor Law Commissioners, 1835–47.

Annual Reports of the Poor Law Board, 1847–71.

Official Circulars and Orders of the Poor Law Commissioners and Poor Law Board.

Reports of the Poor Law Commissioners and Poor Law Board to the Home Secretary on particular problems.

Reports to the Poor Law Commissioners and Poor Law Board on charges against the system or on abuses.

Reports on Inquiries instigated by the Poor Law Commissioners and the Poor Law Board.

Accounts and Papers of the House of Commons. Detailed returns of the Inspectors. Statistical data.

Hansard.

Report of the Select Committee into the operation of the Poor Law, 1838—especially the section on Medical Relief.

Four Reports, 1838–39, on Fever and Health Problems in London by Drs. Arnott, Kay, and Southwood Smith.

Report of the Poor Law Commissioners on the Continuance of the Poor Law Commission, with replies to questionnaire by Assistant Commissioners, 1839–40.

Report of the Select Committee on Poor Law Medical Relief, 1844.

Report of the Select Committee on Poor Law Medical Relief, to ascertain whether any additional facilities might be afforded the poor in obtaining medical aid, 1854.

Reports of the Select Committee on the Administration of Relief to the Poor under the Poor Law Commission and Poor Law Board, 1861–64.

Annual Returns and Reports of the Registrar-General.

Annual Reports of the Commissioners in Lunacy.

Annual Reports of the General Board of Health 1849–54, 1855–58, and Reports of the Medical Officer to the Privy Council, 1859–71.

Report of Dr. Edward Smith on Metropolitan Workhouses, 1866.

Report of Dr. Edward Smith on forty-eight Provincial Workhouses, 1867.

(c) OTHER PUBLICATIONS
(Details are included in the footnotes)

The *Lancet*, 1834–71.

The *Lancet* Reports on Workhouse Infirmaries, 1865–66, 1867–68 and the 'Battle of the Clubs', 1895–96.

The *British Medical Journal*, 1856–71.

Other shortlived, medical journals of the mid-nineteenth century, listed in the text.

Reports of the Poor Law Committee of the Provincial Medical and Surgical Association, 1835, 1840, 1841, 1842.

Sessional Proceedings of the National Association for the Promotion of Social Science, 1866–72. Several papers of the Social Science Association of the 1850s.

Publications of the many societies devoted to various causes such as Public Health, Workhouse Reform, Nursing, Provident Associations.

The Works of Edwin Chadwick.

SECONDARY SOURCES
(Details are included in the text or footnotes)

(a) GOVERNMENT PUBLICATIONS

Report on the Sanitary Condition of the Labouring Population of Great Britain, 1842.

Report of the Select Committee on the Health of Towns, 1842.

Report of the Royal Commission on the State of Large Towns, 1843.

Report of the Metropolitan Sanitary Commission, 1847.

Report of the Select Committee on Dublin Hospitals, 1854.

Report of the Commissioners for Improving the Sanitary Condition of Barracks and Hospitals, 1861 (Hardy and Nightingale).

Report to the Medical Department of the Privy Council on Hospitals in the United Kingdom, 1863 (Bristowe and Holmes).

Report on the Royal Sanitary Commission, 1870.

Report of the Committee and Sub-Committee on Out-patients' admission to Hospitals in the Metropolis, 1871.

Reports on Medical Acts, 1838, 1878–79, 1880.

Supplementary Reports to the Annual Reports of the Registrar-General, by William Farr, 1851–60, 1861–70, published 1874.

Annual Reports of the Local Government Board, 1872–74.

Reports of the Conferences of the Poor Law Officers, for the early seventies.

(b) OTHER PUBLICATIONS

Transactions of the Manchester Statistical Society.

Publications of the Charity Organization Society.

Publications of the Sanitary Inspectors' Association.

Journal of the Workhouse Visiting Society, 1859–65 and the pamphlets published by this society.

The Medical Directory.

Hooper, Robert, *Medical Dictionary*, London 1831.

Press—particularly *The Times*, local papers for Leeds, Bradford, and Manchester.

Baernreither, J. M., *English Associations of Working Men*, translated by Alice Taylor, London, 1893.

Baxter, G. R. Wytham, *The Book of the Bastilles. History of the New Poor Law*, London, 1841.

Bowen, John, *The National Debt and the New Poor Law dissected*, London, 1850.

Dutton, Amy and Jones, Agnes E., *Homes and Hospitals or Two phases of a Woman's Work*, Boston, 1873.

Engels, F., *The Condition of the Working Class in England*, London, 1844.

Farr, W., *Memorial Volume of Selection from Reports and Writings*, edited for the Sanitary Institute of Great Britain by N. A. Humphreys, London, 1885.

Fergusson, W., *Thoughts and Observations on pauperism, emigration, medical relief and the prevention of crime*, London, 1839.

Kay-Shuttleworth, J., *The Moral and Physical Condition of the working class of Manchester*, London, 1832.

Low, S., *The Charities of London in 1861*, London, 1862.

Martineau, Harriet, *Poor Laws and Paupers* (4 vols.), London, 1833–34.

Mayhew, H., *London Labour and London Poor* (4 vols.), London, 1851–61.

Pashley, R., *Pauperism and the Poor Laws*, London, 1852.

Richardson, B. W., *Hygieia*, London, 1876.

——— . *Health of Nations*, London, 1887.

Rogers, J., *Reminiscences of a Workhouse Medical Officer*, London, 1889.

Rumsey, H. W., *Medical Relief for the Labouring Classes on the Principles of Mutual Insurance*, London, 1837.

——— . *Essays on State Medicine*, London, 1856.

——— . *Essays and Papers*, London, 1875.

Simon, Sir J., *Public Health Reports*, ed. for the Sanitary Institute of Great Britain by E. Seaton, 2 vols., London, 1887.

——— . *English Sanitary Institutions*, London, 1890.

Sorsby, A., *The Origin and Development of White Oak Hospital*, Reprinted from the Annual Report of the London County Council, Vol. IV, Pt. III, 1935. Medical Supplement.

Sprigg, S. S., *The Life and Times of Sir Thomas Wakley*, London, 1889.

Stallard, J. S., *Workhouse Hospitals*, London, 1865.

——— . *London Pauperism amongst Jews and Christians, an inquiry into the practice of outdoor relief in the Metropolis*, London, 1867.

——— . *Pauperism, Charity and the Poor Laws*, London, 1869.

Stewart, A. P., *Sanitary Economy, Principles and Practice*, London, 1850.

Tooley, Sarah, *History of Nursing in the British Empire*, London, 1906.

Trevelyan, C., *Metropolitan Medical Relief*, London, 1877. (paper to C.O.S.)

Twining, Louisa, *Recollections of Workhouse Visiting and Management during twenty-five years*, London, 1880.

Webb, S. and B., *Poor Law Policy*, London, 1910.

——— . *English Poor Law History, in the last hundred years*, London, 1929.

——— . *The State and the Doctor*, London, 1908.

The writings of Doctors Henry Lilley Smith, J. Sutherland, Southwood Smith, W. H. Duncan, Hector Gavin and others have been very instructive, as well as the works of Professor Lyon Playfair and the novels of such authors as Charles Dickens, Charles Kingsley and Mrs. Gaskell. A prolific amount of nineteenth-century material exists in the many fields allied to this study but little bearing directly on the subject. Scarcely any modern work touches the problems described. The above bibliography includes only the most useful works. Many more references are contained in the footnotes. The total number of nineteenth- and twentieth-century books consulted would amount to a small library and in order to avoid making the work even more voluminous, the list has been omitted. The subject catalogues of libraries should be consulted for more general reading on the social, economic and medical history of the nineteenth century.

Index